SIERRA NEVADA ROSY FINCH

ANIMAL LIFE IN THE YOSEMITE

AN ACCOUNT OF THE MAMMALS, BIRDS, REPTILES, AND AMPHIBIANS IN A CROSS-SECTION OF THE SIERRA NEVADA

BY

JOSEPH GRINNELL

AND

TRACY IRWIN STORER

CONTRIBUTION FROM THE MUSEUM OF VERTEBRATE ZOOLOGY
UNIVERSITY OF CALIFORNIA

UNIVERSITY OF CALIFORNIA PRESS
BERKELEY, CALIFORNIA
1924

6316

PREFACE

The national parks of America render as their most important service a full free opportunity to all who will to find in them a complete recreation, physical, mental, esthetic. In performing this service the animal life existing within their borders constitutes a valuable asset. For the best recreative forces in nature are those which serve most quickly to call into play latent or seldom used faculties of mind and body whose exercise tends to restore to normal balance the human mechanism that has been disturbed by special or artificial conditions of living. Foremost among these forces are the living things that move and utter sounds, exhibit color and changing form, and by these qualities readily attract and fix our interest. To seek acquaintance with those primal objects of interest is to know the joy of vigorous muscular activity; better still, it is to realize the possession of the generally neglected senses of far-seeing and far-hearing, and to invite an esthetic appeal of the highest type and an intellectual stimulus of infinite resource.

Of the thousands who each year visit the Yosemite Valley and its environs, a certain proportion are already interested in natural history; and anyone who leaves the region without gathering some definite knowledge of its natural history has failed to get adequate gain from his opportunities. The geology, topography, and botany of the Yosemite have been studied with some care; and there are instructive and stimulating manuals available dealing with these subjects. But heretofore only a few brief accounts have appeared in print concerning the bird life of the region, and practically nothing has been made available regarding its mammals, reptiles, and amphibians. It was in an effort to supply this deficiency that a survey of the vertebrate natural history of the Yosemite region was undertaken by the California Museum of Vertebrate Zoology. The present volume deals with the results of that survey.

The principal objects in view in undertaking the survey were: To find out what species of mammals, birds, reptiles, and amphibians exist, or have within modern times existed, in the circumscribed area selected for study; to learn as much as possible concerning the local distribution of each of these species, and to map out the general life areas within the region; to learn as much as time permitted of the food relations, the breeding habits, and the behavior, individually, of each of the species; and finally to put all this information on permanent record, in a form accessible to, and generally assimilable by, the public, both lay and scientific.

In attempting the achievement of this last aim the authors have brought together their materials with every precaution to insure accuracy of fact and correctness of inference. No sacrifice of precision has been made consciously with the end merely of affording 'attractive reading.' At the same time, technical terms, where the same ideas could be expressed in words familiar to every reader of fair education, have been avoided. Ideally, we have tried to present our science, perfectly good science, in straightforward, readable form.

JOSEPH GRINNELL.
TRACY IRWIN STORER.

BERKELEY, July 6, 1922.

[v]

ACKNOWLEDGMENTS

The Museum of Vertebrate Zoology is under obligation to numerous persons and organizations for support and assistance in the prosecution of the Yosemite survey. The greatest aid from any one source has come from Miss Annie M. Alexander, who made the enterprise possible through her unstinted financial support of the Museum during the several years in which the field and office work has been under way. Her unswerving faith in the worthiness of the undertaking served continually to encourage and energize those who were concerned with its conduct.

When the plan was first outlined it was put before Dr. William F. Badè, then President of the Sierra Club. Its merits and feasibility were enthusiastically endorsed by him and subsequently by the Sierra Club formally. This endorsement went far toward bringing the enterprise to the favorable attention of the people in Washington and in Yosemite Valley, to whom we later found it needful to appeal for material help of various kinds.

Mr. Stephen T. Mather, Director of National Parks, besides personally contributing to the fund for field work, has rendered aid in other ways. Financial help, at a time when this was most needed, was received also from Mr. George W. Marston of San Diego and from Mr. James D. Phelan of San Francisco.

The National Park Service of the Federal Government granted the special permits necessary for the taking of specimens within the boundaries of the Yosemite National Park. Many of the local employees of the same Service rendered valuable aid. To Mr. Gabriel Souvelewsky, then Supervisor of Yosemite Park, we owe grateful acknowledgment for immediate and practically expressed interest in our program of field work in the winter of 1914–15. Among others in the Valley who have helped us materially we may mention in particular Messrs. W. B. Lewis, E. P. Leavitt, Forest S. Townsley, Ansel F. Hall, Charles C. Bull, Charles W. Michael, N. L. Guiberson, and the late George W. Bell. Information on specific and general questions has been freely furnished by these men, and many valuable specimens have been secured through them for the Museum of Vertebrate Zoology. Many of the organizations engaged in business connected with Yosemite Valley aided our enterprise by granting special privileges. Among these are to be named the Yosemite Valley Railroad Company, The Yosemite Transportation Company, The Sentinel Hotel, and The Curry Camping Company. The Sierra Club, during the field season of 1915, gave us the use of their pack train.

The colored and wash drawings used for illustrating the present volume were executed by Major Allan Brooks upon the basis of Yosemite materials. The skill of Mrs. Frieda L. Abernathy was very helpful in preparing the line drawings. The photographs used were taken in course of our regular field work except four whose outside sources are acknowledged in their respective captions. To Professor Oliver M. Washburn, Manager of the University of California Press, we are indebted for important help in assembling the illustrations that appear in this book. And to Mr. Joseph W. Flinn, Superintendent of the University Printing Office, we hereby express our appreciation of his personal interest in guiding the work through the press.

The United States Bureau of Plant Industry and the University of California Division of Forestry aided in the determination of seeds found in the cheek pouches of chipmunks. The United States Bureau of Biological Survey determined the crop and gizzard contents of a number of birds. Dr. Harvey M. Hall identified numerous plants submitted to him.

Much information and many vertebrate specimens have been obtained from Mr. Donald D. McLean, whose home is at Dudley, on Smith Creek, six miles (airline) east of the town of Coulterville. Mr. McLean's parents and uncle, Mr. and Mrs. John L. McLean and Mr. Walter Dudley, also aided us in many ways while field work was going on in their neighborhood.

CONTENTS

PAGE

List of plates, colored.. xv
List of plates, half-tone... xvi
List of text figures.. xvii
Introduction.. 1
Distribution of animal life in the Yosemite section...................................... 4
Table of occurrence, according to life zone, of the mammals, breeding birds, reptiles,
    and amphibians of the Yosemite section... 14
Censuses of birds in the Yosemite section.. 22
The interrelations of living things... 36
Scope of the species accounts... 40

THE MAMMALS.. 43
Moles, Scapanus latimanus.. 43
    Yosemite Mole, Scapanus latimanus sericatus
    San Joaquin Mole, Scapanus latimanus campi
    Mono Mole, Scapanus latimanus monoensis
Shrews, Genus Sorex... 47
    Dusky Shrew, Sorex obscurus obscurus
    Adorned Shrew, Sorex ornatus
    Yosemite Shrew, Sorex montereyensis mariposae
    Sierra Nevada Shrew, Sorex vagrans amoenus
    Lyell Shrew, Sorex lyelli
Navigator Shrew, Neosorex palustris navigator... 50
Little California Bat, Myotis californicus californicus................................... 51
High Sierra Bat, Myotis lucifugus altipetens... 55
Long-legged Bat, Myotis longicrus longicrus.. 56
Fringed Bat, Myotis thysanodes... 57
Merriam Bat, Pipistrellus hesperus merriami... 57
Large Brown Bat, Eptesicus fuscus... 58
Hoary Bat, Nycteris cinerea... 59
Pacific Pallid Bat, Antrozous pacificus.. 60
Mexican Free-tailed Bat, Nyctinomus mexicanus... 61
American Black Bear, Ursus americanus.. 63
Grizzly Bear, Ursus henshawi... 68
Mountain Coyote, Canis latrans lestes... 71
Cascade Red Fox, Vulpes cascadensis... 77
San Joaquin Kit Fox, Vulpes macrotis mutica... 77
California Gray Fox, Urocyon cinereoargenteus californicus......................... 78
California Ring-tailed Cat, Bassariscus astutus raptor.................................. 81
California Coon, Procyon lotor psora... 81
Sierra Pine Marten, Martes caurina sierrae.. 82
Pacific Fisher, Martes pennanti pacifica.. 83
Sierra Nevada Wolverine, Gulo luscus luteus... 85
Mountain Weasel, Mustela arizonensis.. 86
Sierra Least Weasel, Mustela muricus... 89
Pacific Mink, Mustela vison energumenos... 89

California Spotted Skunk, Spilogale phenax phenax.. 90
Striped Skunk, Mephitis occidentalis.. 91
California Badger, Taxidea taxus neglecta.. 92
Northwestern Mountain Lion, Felis oregonensis oregonensis.................................... 95
California Wildcat, Lynx eremicus californicus... 99
House Mouse, Mus musculus.. 101
Alexandrine Rat, Rattus rattus alexandrinus.. 103
Common White-footed Mice, Peromyscus maniculatus.. 104
      Gambel White-footed Mouse, Peromyscus maniculatus gambeli
      Sonora White-footed Mouse, Peromyscus maniculatus sonoriensis
Boyle White-footed Mouse, Peromyscus boylii boylii.. 110
Big-eared White-footed Mice, Peromyscus truei... 111
      Gilbert White-footed Mouse, Peromyscus truei gilberti
      True White-footed Mouse, Peromyscus truei truei
Parasitic White-footed Mouse, Peromyscus californicus californicus........................ 112
Short-tailed Grasshopper Mouse, Onychomys leucogaster brevicaudus.................... 113
Long-tailed Harvest Mouse, Reithrodontomys megalotis longicauda......................... 114
Streator Wood Rat, Neotoma fuscipes streatori... 116
Gray Bushy-tailed Wood Rat, Neotoma cinerea cinerea.. 120
Yosemite Meadow Mouse, Microtus montanus yosemite... 122
California Meadow Mice, Microtus californicus.. 126
      Tule Meadow Mouse, Microtus californicus aestuarinus
      Mariposa Meadow Mouse, Microtus californicus mariposae
Sierra Cantankerous Meadow Mouse, Microtus mordax sierrae................................ 129
Short-tailed Meadow Mouse, Lagurus curtatus.. 133
Mountain Lemming Mouse, Phenacomys orophilus.. 133
Pocket Gophers, Genus Thomomys... 134
      Fresno Pocket Gopher, Thomomys bottae pascalis
      Digger Pine Pocket Gopher, Thomomys bottae mewa
      Yosemite Pocket Gopher, Thomomys alpinus awahnee
      Sierra Nevada Pocket Gopher, Thomomys monticola monticola
      Fisher Pocket Gopher, Thomomys quadratus fisheri
Pocket Mice, Genus Perognathus.. 144
      California Pocket Mouse, Perognathus californicus californicus
      San Joaquin Pocket Mouse, Perognathus inornatus inornatus
      Great Basin Pocket Mouse, Perognathus parvus olivaceus
Kangaroo Rats, Genus Dipodomys.. 146
      Heermann Kangaroo Rat, Dipodomys heermanni heermanni
      Merced Kangaroo Rat, Dipodomys heermanni dixoni
      Pale-faced Kangaroo Rat, Dipodomys leucogenys
Mono Kangaroo Mouse, Microdipodops polionotus.. 149
Allen Jumping Mouse, Zapus pacificus alleni... 149
Yellow-haired Porcupine, Erethizon epixanthum epixanthum.................................... 151
Sierra Mountain Beaver, Aplodontia rufa californica... 155
Southern Sierra Marmot, Marmota flaviventer sierrae.. 158
California Ground Squirrel, Citellus beecheyi beecheyi.. 162
Belding Ground Squirrel, Citellus beldingi... 168
Stephens Soft-haired Ground Squirrel, Citellus mollis stephensi.............................. 173
Sierra Nevada Golden-mantled Ground Squirrel, Callospermophilus chrysodeirus
      chrysodeirus.. 173
Tahoe Chipmunk, Eutamias speciosus frater.. 176
Allen Chipmunk, Eutamias senex... 183
Mariposa Chipmunk, Eutamias merriami mariposae... 185
Long-eared Chipmunk, Eutamias quadrimaculatus.. 187

Alpine Chipmunk, Eutamias alpinus.. 190
Mono Chipmunk, Eutamias amoenus monoensis.. 194
Sagebrush Chipmunk, Eutamias pictus.. 195
California Gray Squirrel, Sciurus griseus griseus.. 196
Sierra Chickaree, Sciurus douglasii albolimbatus.. 203
Sierra Flying Squirrel, Glaucomys sabrinus lascivus.. 211
Golden Beaver, Castor canadensis subauratus... 215
Yosemite Cony, Ochotona schisticeps muiri.. 218
Black-tailed Jack Rabbits, Lepus californicus.. 221
      California Jack Rabbit, Lepus californicus californicus
      Desert Jack Rabbit, Lepus californicus deserticola
Sierra White-tailed Jack Rabbit, Lepus townsendii sierrae.. 224
Sacramento Cottontail, Sylvilagus audubonii audubonii.. 227
Washington Cottontail, Sylvilagus nuttallii nuttallii.. 227
Mariposa Brush Rabbit, Sylvilagus bachmani mariposae... 228
Mule Deer, Odocoileus hemionus hemionus... 231
Dwarf Elk, Cervus nannodes... 241
Pronghorn Antelope, Antilocapra americana americana.. 242
Sierra Nevada Mountain Sheep, Ovis canadensis sierrae.. 243
THE BIRDS... 247
American Eared Grebe, Colymbus nigricollis californicus... 247
Pied-billed Grebe, Podilymbus podiceps.. 248
California Gull, Larus californicus... 248
Forster Tern, Sterna forsteri.. 251
Black Tern, Hydrochelidon nigra surinamensis.. 251
Farallon Cormorant, Phalacrocorax auritus albociliatus... 251
White Pelican, Pelecanus erythrorhynchos.. 252
American Merganser, Mergus americanus.. 252
Mallard, Anas platyrhynchos... 253
Baldpate, Mareca americana... 253
Cinnamon Teal, Querquedula cyanoptera.. 253
Shoveller, Spatula clypeata... 254
Pintail, Dafila acuta... 254
Harlequin Duck, Histrionicus histrionicus.. 255
American Bittern, Botaurus lentiginosus.. 256
Least Bittern, Ixobrychus exilis exilis... 256
Great Blue Herons, Ardea herodias.. 256
      California Great Blue Heron, Ardea herodias hyperonca
      Pallid Great Blue Heron, Ardea herodias treganzai
Anthony Green Heron, Butorides virescens anthonyi.. 258
Black-crowned Night Heron, Nycticorax nycticorax naevius....................................... 259
Virginia Rail, Rallus virginianus... 260
Mud-hen, Fulica americana... 261
Northern Phalarope, Lobipes lobatus.. 261
Wilson Phalarope, Steganopus tricolor.. 262
Wilson Snipe, Gallinago delicata.. 263
Least Sandpiper, Pisobia minutilla... 263
Spotted Sandpiper, Actitis macularia.. 263
Killdeer, Oxyechus vociferus vociferus.. 265
Mountain Quail, Oreortyx picta plumifera.. 267
Valley Quail, Lophortyx californica vallicola... 270
Sierra Grouse, Dendragapus obscurus sierrae... 272
Sage-hen, Centrocercus urophasianus.. 274
Band-tailed Pigeon, Columba fasciata fasciata... 275

Western Mourning Dove, Zenaidura macroura marginella................................ 278
Turkey Vulture, Cathartes aura septentrionalis.......................... 279
White-tailed Kite, Elanus leucurus.................................. 281
Marsh Hawk, Circus hudsonius.................................... 281
Sharp-shinned Hawk, Accipiter velox............................. 282
Cooper Hawk, Accipiter cooperi.................................. 284
Western Goshawk, Astur atricapillus striatulus...................... 286
Western Red-tailed Hawk, Buteo borealis calurus.................... 287
Red-bellied Hawk, Buteo lineatus elegans.......................... 289
Swainson Hawk, Buteo swainsoni................................. 290
Ferruginous Rough-legged Hawk, Archibuteo ferrugineus............. 291
Golden Eagle, Aquila chrysaetos................................. 292
Prairie Falcon, Falco mexicanus................................. 294
Duck Hawk, Falco peregrinus anatum............................ 294
Northern Pigeon Hawk, Falco columbarius columbarius.............. 295
American Sparrow Hawk, Falco sparverius sparverius............... 296
American Osprey, Pandion haliaetus carolinensis................... 297
Barn Owl, Tyto pratincola....................................... 298
Long-eared Owl, Asio wilsonianus............................... 300
California Spotted Owl, Strix occidentalis occidentalis.............. 304
Great Gray Owl, Scotiaptex nebulosa nebulosa.................... 305
Saw-whet Owl, Cryptoglaux acadica.............................. 307
Southern California Screech Owl, Otus asio quercinus.............. 308
Pacific Horned Owl, Bubo virginianus pacificus................... 309
Burrowing Owl, Speotyto cunicularia hypogaea................... 310
California Pigmy Owl, Glaucidium gnoma californicum............. 311
Road-runner, Geococcyx californianus............................ 313
Western Belted Kingfisher, Ceryle alcyon caurina................. 313
Modoc Woodpecker, Dryobates villosus orius..................... 315
Willow Woodpecker, Dryobates pubescens turati.................. 317
Nuttall Woodpecker, Dryobates nuttalli.......................... 319
Northern White-headed Woodpecker, Xenopicus albolarvatus albolarvatus............ 320
Arctic Three-toed Woodpecker, Picoides arcticus.................. 326
Sierra Red-breasted Sapsucker, Sphyrapicus varius daggetti......... 327
Red-naped Sapsucker, Sphyrapicus varius nuchalis................ 330
Williamson Sapsucker, Sphyrapicus thyroideus thyroideus........... 331
Northern Pileated Woodpecker, Phloeotomus pileatus abieticola....... 334
California Woodpecker, Melanerpes formicivorus bairdi.............. 337
Lewis Woodpecker, Asyndesmus lewisi............................ 341
Red-shafted Flicker, Colaptes cafer collaris...................... 342
Poor-wills, Phalaenoptilus nuttalli............................... 343
          Dusky Poor-will, Phalaenoptilus nuttalli californicus
          Nuttall Poor-will, Phalaenoptilus nuttalli nuttalli
Pacific Nighthawk, Chordeiles virginianus hesperis................ 346
Texas Nighthawk, Chordeiles acutipennis texensis................. 347
Northern Black Swift, Cypseloides niger borealis.................. 349
Vaux Swift, Chaetura vauxi...................................... 350
White-throated Swift, Aeronautes melanoleucus.................... 351
Black-chinned Hummingbird, Archilochus alexandri................ 352
Anna Hummingbird, Calypte anna................................ 353
Rufous Hummingbird, Selasphorus rufus.......................... 354
Allen Hummingbird, Selasphorus alleni........................... 355
Calliope Hummingbird, Stellula calliope.......................... 356
Western Kingbird, Tyrannus verticalis............................ 359

[xi]

PAGE

Ash-throated Flycatcher, Myiarchus cinerascens cinerascens..................................... 360
Say Phoebe, Sayornis sayus... 362
Black Phoebe, Sayornis nigricans.. 362
Olive-sided Flycatcher, Nuttallornis borealis.. 364
Western Wood Pewee, Myiochanes richardsoni richardsoni... 365
Wright Flycatcher, Empidonax wrighti.. 367
Hammond Flycatcher, Empidonax hammondi.. 370
Traill Flycatcher, Empidonax trailli trailli.. 371
Western Flycatcher, Empidonax difficilis difficilis... 372
Gray Flycatcher, Empidonax griseus... 373
Horned Larks, Otocoris alpestris... 374
    California Horned Lark, Otocoris alpestris actia
    Dusky Horned Lark, Otocoris alpestris merrilli
Black-billed Magpie, Pica pica hudsonia.. 376
Blue-fronted Jay, Cyanocitta stelleri frontalis.. 379
Interior California Jay, Aphelocoma californica immanis.. 387
Woodhouse Jay, Aphelocoma woodhousei... 392
Western Raven, Corvus corax sinuatus.. 392
Western Crow, Corvus brachyrhynchos hesperis.. 392
Clark Nutcracker, Nucifraga columbiana... 393
Piñon Jay, Cyanocephalus cyanocephalus... 397
Cowbirds, Molothrus ater.. 398
    Dwarf Cowbird, Molothrus ater obscurus
    Nevada Cowbird, Molothrus ater artemisiae
Yellow-headed Blackbird, Xanthocephalus xanthocephalus.. 399
Red-winged Blackbirds, Agelaius phoeniceus.. 400
    Bi-colored Red-winged Blackbird, Agelaius phoeniceus californicus
    Nevada Red-winged Blackbird, Agelaius phoeniceus nevadensis
    Kern Red-winged Blackbird, Agelaius phoeniceus aciculatus
Tri-colored Blackbird, Agelaius tricolor... 407
Western Meadowlark, Sturnella neglecta.. 409
Bullock Oriole, Icterus bullocki.. 411
Brewer Blackbird, Euphagus cyanocephalus.. 413
California Evening Grosbeak, Hesperiphona vespertina californica............................... 417
California Pine Grosbeak, Pinicola enucleator californica... 419
California Purple Finch, Carpodacus purpureus californicus.. 420
Cassin Purple Finch, Carpodacus cassini.. 423
California Linnet, Carpodacus mexicanus frontalis... 425
Sierra Crossbill, Loxia curvirostra bendirei.. 428
Sierra Nevada Rosy Finch, Leucosticte tephrocotis dawsoni.. 430
Willow Goldfinch, Astragalinus tristis salicamans... 434
Green-backed Goldfinch, Astragalinus psaltria hesperophilus...................................... 435
Lawrence Goldfinch, Astragalinus lawrencei... 437
Pine Siskin, Spinus pinus pinus.. 438
English Sparrow, Passer domesticus.. 439
Vesper Sparrows, Pooecetes gramineus.. 440
    Western Vesper Sparrow, Pooecetes gramineus confinis
    Oregon Vesper Sparrow, Pooecetes gramineus affinis
Savannah Sparrows, Passerculus sandwichensis.. 442
    Aleutian Savannah Sparrow, Passerculus sandwichensis sandwichensis
    Western Savannah Sparrow, Passerculus sandwichensis alaudinus
    Nevada Savannah Sparrow, Passerculus sandwichensis nevadensis
Western Grasshopper Sparrow, Ammodramus savannarum bimaculatus........................ 443
Western Lark Sparrow, Chondestes grammacus strigatus.. 444

White-crowned Sparrows, Zonotrichia leucophrys.. 446
     Hudsonian White-crowned Sparrow, Zonotrichia leucophrys leucophrys
     Intermediate White-crowned Sparrow, Zonotrichia leucophrys gambeli
Golden-crowned Sparrow, Zonotrichia coronata.. 450
Western Chipping Sparrow, Spizella passerina arizonae........................... 452
Brewer Sparrow, Spizella breweri.. 456
Black-chinned Sparrow, Spizella atrogularis.. 458
Slate-colored Junco, Junco hyemalis hyemalis.. 458
Sierra Junco, Junco oreganus thurberi.. 459
     Shufeldt Junco, Junco oreganus shufeldti
Bell Sparrow, Amphispiza belli.. 464
Nevada Sage Sparrow, Amphispiza nevadensis nevadensis...................... 466
Rufous-crowned Sparrow, Aimophila ruficeps ruficeps............................. 467
Song Sparrows, Melospiza melodia.. 468
     Modoc Song Sparrow, Melospiza melodia fisherella
     Rusty Song Sparrow, Melospiza melodia rufina
     Heermann Song Sparrow, Melospiza melodia heermanni
     Merrill Song Sparrow, Melospiza melodia merrilli
Lincoln Sparrows, Melospiza lincolni.. 470
     Northeastern Lincoln Sparrow, Melospiza lincolni lincolni
     Northwestern Lincoln Sparrow, Melospiza lincolni gracilis
Fox Sparrows, Passerella iliaca.. 472
     Shumagin Fox Sparrow, Passerella iliaca unalaschcensis
     Kadiak Fox Sparrow, Passerella iliaca insularis
     Valdez Fox Sparrow, Passerella iliaca sinuosa
     Alberta Fox Sparrow, Passerella iliaca altivagans
     Slate-colored Fox Sparrow, Passerella iliaca schistacea
     Mariposa Fox Sparrow, Passerella iliaca mariposae
     Mono Fox Sparrow, Passerella iliaca monoensis
     Thick-billed Fox Sparrow, Passerella iliaca megarhyncha
Spurred Towhees, Pipilo maculatus.. 477
     Sacramento Spurred Towhee, Pipilo maculatus falcinellus
     Nevada Spurred Towhee, Pipilo maculatus curtatus
Northern Brown Towhee, Pipilo crissalis carolae...................................... 480
Green-tailed Towhee, Oberholseria chlorura.. 482
Pacific Black-headed Grosbeak, Zamelodia melanocephala capitalis......... 484
California Blue Grosbeak, Guiraca caerulea salicarius.............................. 490
Lazuli Bunting, Passerina amoena... 491
Western Tanager, Piranga ludoviciana... 493
Western Martin, Progne subis hesperia.. 497
Cliff Swallow, Petrochelidon lunifrons lunifrons...................................... 497
Barn Swallow, Hirundo erythrogaster erythrogaster................................ 499
Tree Swallow, Iridoprocne bicolor.. 500
Northern Violet-green Swallow, Tachycineta thalassina lepida................. 501
Rough-winged Swallow, Stelgidopteryx serripennis................................. 503
Bohemian Waxwing, Bombycilla garrula... 504
Cedar Waxwing, Bombycilla cedrorum... 504
Phainopepla, Phainopepla nitens... 505
Shrikes, Lanius ludovicianus... 506
     California Shrike, Lanius ludovicianus gambeli
     White-rumped Shrike, Lanius ludovicianus excubitorides
Western Warbling Vireo, Vireosylva gilva swainsoni................................ 508
Cassin Vireo, Lanivireo solitarius cassini... 511
Hutton Vireo, Vireo huttoni huttoni... 513

PAGE

California Least Vireo, Vireo belli pusillus.. 514
Calaveras Warbler, Vermivora ruficapilla gutturalis............................ 516
Orange-crowned Warblers, Vermivora celata...................................... 519
    Lutescent Warbler, Vermivora celata lutescens
    Rocky Mountain Orange-crowned Warbler, Vermivora celata orestera
California Yellow Warbler, Dendroica aestiva brewsteri....................... 521
Alaska Myrtle Warbler, Dendroica coronata hooveri........................... 523
Audubon Warbler, Dendroica auduboni auduboni............................... 524
Black-throated Gray Warbler, Dendroica nigrescens............................ 529
Townsend Warbler, Dendroica townsendi.. 531
Hermit Warbler, Dendroica occidentalis.. 532
Tolmie Warbler, Oporornis tolmiei... 534
Yellowthroats, Geothlypis trichas.. 538
    Western Yellowthroat, Geothlypis trichas occidentalis
    Tule Yellowthroat, Geothlypis trichas scirpicola
Long-tailed Chat, Icteria virens longicauda... 539
Pileolated Warblers, Wilsonia pusilla.. 540
    Golden Pileolated Warbler, Wilsonia pusilla chryseola
    Alaska Pileoated Warbler, Wilsonia pusilla pileolata
American Pipit, Anthus rubescens... 542
American Dipper, Cinclus mexicanus unicolor...................................... 543
Sage Thrasher, Oreoscoptes montanus.. 546
Western Mockingbird, Mimus polyglottos leucopterus........................... 547
California Thrasher, Toxostoma redivivum redivivum............................ 548
Rock Wren, Salpinctes obsoletus obsoletus.. 550
Dotted Cañon Wren, Catherpes mexicanus punctulatus......................... 552
San Joaquin Bewick Wren, Thryomanes bewicki drymoecus.................... 555
Western House Wren, Troglodytes aedon parkmani............................... 556
Western Winter Wren, Nannus hiemalis pacificus................................. 558
Western Marsh Wren, Telmatodytes palustris plesius............................ 560
Sierra Creeper, Certhia familiaris zelotes.. 561
Slender-billed Nuthatch, Sitta carolinensis aculeata............................. 564
Red-breasted Nuthatch, Sitta canadensis... 568
Pigmy Nuthatch, Sitta pygmaea pygmaea.. 571
Plain Titmouse, Baeolophus inornatus inornatus.................................. 572
Short-tailed Mountain Chickadee, Penthestes gambeli abbreviatus.......... 574
California Bush-tit, Psaltriparus minimus californicus.......................... 579
Lead-colored Bush-tit, Psaltriparus plumbeus...................................... 582
Pallid Wren-tit, Chamaea fasciata henshawi.. 582
Western Golden-crowned Kinglet, Regulus satrapa olivaceus................. 586
Western Ruby-crowned Kinglet, Regulus calendula cineraceus................ 589
Western Gnatcatcher, Polioptila caerulea obscura................................. 593
Townsend Solitaire, Myadestes townsendi.. 595
Russet-backed Thrush, Hylocichla ustulata ustulata............................. 600
Hermit Thrushes, Hylocichla guttata... 602
    Sierra Hermit Thrush, Hylocichla guttata sequoiensis
    Alaska Hermit Thrush, Hylocichla guttata guttata
    Dwarf Hermit Thrush, Hylocichla guttata nanus
Western Robin, Planesticus migratorius propinquus.............................. 605
Northern Varied Thrush, Ixoreus naevius meruloides............................ 614
Western Bluebird, Sialia mexicana occidentalis.................................... 615
Mountain Bluebird, Sialia currucoides... 622

PAGE

THE REPTILES.. 626
Blue-bellied Lizards, Sceloporus occidentalis.. 626
    Western Fence Lizard, Sceloporus occidentalis occidentalis
    Pacific Blue-bellied Lizard, Sceloporus occidentalis bi-seriatus
    Tenaya Blue-bellied Lizard, Sceloporus occidentalis taylori
Mountain Lizard, Sceloporus graciosus graciosus.................................. 628
California Horned Toad, Phrynosoma blainvillii frontale...................... 630
Alligator Lizards, Genus Gerrhonotus.. 630
    San Diego Alligator Lizard, Gerrhonotus scincicauda webbii
    Sierra Alligator Lizard, Gerrhonotus palmeri
California Whip-tailed Lizard, Cnemidophorus tigris mundus................ 632
Western Skink, Plestiodon skiltonianus.. 633
Rubber Snake, Charina bottae.. 635
Garter Snakes, Genus Thamnophis.. 636
    Pacific Garter Snake, Thamnophis sirtalis infernalis
    Giant Garter Snake, Thamnophis ordinoides couchii
    Mountain Garter Snake, Thamnophis ordinoides elegans
    Wandering Garter Snake, Thamnophis ordinoides vagrans
Western Ring-necked Snake, Diadophis amabilis amabilis...................... 639
Coral King Snake, Lampropeltis multicincta... 640
Boyle King Snake, Lampropeltis getulus boylii...................................... 640
California Striped Racer, Coluber lateralis.. 641
Western Yellow-bellied Racer, Coluber constrictor flaviventris.............. 643
Valley Gopher Snake, Pituophis catenifer heermanni........................... 643
Pacific Rattlesnake, Crotalus oreganus.. 645
Pacific Mud Turtle, Clemmys marmorata... 650

THE AMPHIBIANS... 651
Pacific Coast Newt, Notophthalmus torosus... 651
Mount Lyell Salamander, Eurycea platycephala.................................... 652
Arboreal Salamander, Aneides lugubris lugubris.................................... 653
Slender Salamander, Batrachoseps attenuatus...................................... 654
Western Spade-foot Toad, Scaphiopus hammondii hammondii.............. 654
California Toad, Bufo boreas halophilus... 655
    Northwestern Toad, Bufo boreas boreas
Yosemite Toad, Bufo canorus.. 657
Pacific Tree-toad, Hyla regilla.. 661
Yellow-legged Frogs, Rana boylii.. 663
    California Yellow-legged Frog, Rana boylii boylii
    Sierra Yellow-legged Frog, Rana boylii sierrae
California Red-legged Frog, Rana aurora draytonii................................ 666

BIBLIOGRAPHY: Articles relating chiefly or importantly to the vertebrate animals of the
    Yosemite section, published up to the end of 1920................................ 667

INDEX.. 743

PLATES, COLORED
(scattered through the text)

PLATE
1. Sierra Nevada Rosy Finch..frontispiece
OPPOSITE PAGE
2. Sierra Golden-mantled and Belding ground squirrels; Marmot.................. 158
3. Chipmunks of the Yosemite section... 182
4. Band-tailed Pigeon... 278
5. Woodpeckers of the Yosemite section.. 326
6. Family group of Williamson Sapsuckers... 334

PLATE   OPPOSITE PAGE

7. Cassin and California purple finches and California Linnet.................................... 422
8. Some sparrows of the Yosemite section... 454
9. Warblers of the Yosemite section.. 518
10. Some small birds of the Yosemite forests... 566
11. Townsend Solitaire and Russet-backed and Sierra Hermit thrushes...................... 598
12. Coral King Snake; Western Skink, young and adult....................................... 630

PLATES, HALF-TONE

(in signatures at end of text)

PAGE

13. Merced River bottom near Snelling; blue oak in winter, with mistletoe................... 671
14. Digger pine association near Pleasant Valley; edge of yellow pine association three
    miles east of Coulterville.. 673
15. Golden oak association near Rocky Point; south bank of Merced River near El
    Portal... 675
16. Yosemite Valley from Big Oak Flat road, with golden-oak talus in foreground;
    meadow and cottonwood associations in Yosemite Valley................................ 677
17. Jeffrey pine and huckleberry oak associations east of Half Dome; white fir associa-
    tion near Chinquapin... 679
18. Vogelsang Lake and Pass; Tuolumne Meadows.. 681
19. Mounts Gibbs and Dana from the east; Williams Butte near Mono Lake................... 683
20. Navigator, Yosemite and Dusky shrews... 685
21. Bats of the Yosemite Valley and higher Sierra Nevada.................................. 687
22. Tracks of Black Bear in Yosemite Valley... 689
23. Pacific Fisher, Sierra Pine Marten and Sierra Nevada Wolverine....................... 690
24. California Badger and its work.. 691
25. Boyle and Common white-footed mice and House Mouse.................................... 692
26. Some "leaping" rodents of the Yosemite section.. 693
27. Yosemite Pocket Gopher and Yosemite Mole.. 695
28. Surface workings of mole and pocket gopher.. 697
29. Yosemite Pocket Gopher in action.. 699
30. Winter earth cores made by pocket gophers.. 701
31. Sierra Mountain Beaver and its burrow... 702
32. Southern Sierra Marmot.. 703
33. Long-eared Chipmunk and California Gray Squirrel...................................... 704
34. California Gray Squirrel.. 705
35. Cones of white fir exhumed from caches made by Sierra Chickaree; twig tips of
    lodgepole pine cut by Sierra Chickaree... 707
36. Granite talus at head of Lyell Cañon, home of Yosemite Cony; kitchen middens on
    log where Sierra Chickaree had been dissecting red fir cones......................... 709
37. Work of Yellow-haired Porcupine; work of Golden Beaver................................ 711
38. Yosemite Cony and its lookout station... 712
39. Mountain Coyote; Mule Deer.. 713
40. Records in the road... 715
41. California Gulls on Paoha Island, Mono Lake... 717
42. Long-eared Owls... 718
43. Band-tailed Pigeons; Nuttall Poorwill; Great Gray Owl................................ 719
44. Principal diurnal birds of prey in the Yosemite region............................... 720
45. Nests and eggs of Swainson Hawk and Texas Nighthawk.................................. 721
46. Hummingbirds, Swallows, and White-throated Swift..................................... 723
47. Nests of Cliff Swallow and California Linnet.. 724
48. Mariposa Fox Sparrow, Green-tailed Towhee, and Sacramento Spurred Towhee.. 725
49. Nests of Green-tailed Towhee and Northeastern Lincoln Sparrow........................ 726
50. Vireos of the Yosemite region... 727

PLATE   PAGE

51. Nests of California Least Vireo and Tolmie Warbler................................ 728
52. American Dipper.................... 729
53. Western Mockingbird and California Shrike; Dotted Cañon Wren and San Joaquin Bewick Wren.................... 731
54. Western House Wren and nest sites.................... 733
55. Nests of Western Robin and Townsend Solitaire.................... 734
56. Black-billed Magpie and Mountain Bluebird.................... 735
57. Mountain Lizard, Western Fence Lizard and California Whip-tailed Lizard........ 736
58. Western Skink and alligator lizards.................... 737
59. Valley Gopher Snake and Pacific Rattlesnake.................... 739
60. Some amphibians of the Yosemite region.................... 741

MAPS, COLORED

(at end of half-tone plates)

61. Profile of Yosemite section showing relation of life-zones to altitude and slope
62. Map showing life-zones of Yosemite section

FIGURES IN TEXT

FIGURE   PAGE

1. Zonal restriction of certain mammals.................... 5
2. Zonal restriction of certain breeding birds.................... 7
3. Sample census sheet.................... 23
4. Snout of Yosemite Mole.................... 43
5. Fore foot of Yosemite Mole and of Sierra Nevada Pocket Gopher.................... 44
6. Zonal distribution of shrews.................... 48
7. Pacific Pallid Bat.................... 61
8. Mexican Free-tailed Bat.................... 62
9. Sierra Least Weasel, Mountain Weasel and Pacific Mink.................... 87
10. Heads of white-footed mice.................... 105
11. Zonal distribution of white-footed mice.................... 107
12. Tails of Alexandrine Roof Rat, and of Streator and Gray Bushy-tailed wood rats 116
13. Streator Wood Rat.................... 117
14. Nesting quarters of Streator Wood Rat in log.................... 119
15. Gray Bushy-tailed Wood Rat.................... 121
16. Tails of Yosemite Meadow Mouse and Sierra Cantankerous Meadow Mouse........ 123
17. Burrow-system of Mariposa Meadow Mouse.................... 128
18. Enlarged section through part of preceding.................... 129
19. Zonal distribution of meadow mice.................... 130
20. Sierra Cantankerous and Yosemite meadow mice and Mountain Lemming Mouse 131
21. Willow association at head of Lyell Cañon.................... 132
22. Method of work of mole.................... 136
23. Method of work of pocket gopher.................... 137
24. Zonal distribution of pocket gophers.................... 139
25. Cartoon suggesting relation of pocket gopher work in high mountains to accumulation of fertile sediments in lowlands.................... 143
26. Quill of Yellow-haired Porcupine.................... 152
27. Zonal distribution of squirrels and marmot.................... 163
28. Zonal distribution of chipmunks.................... 178
29. Sierra Chickaree.................... 205
30. Sugar pine cones as worked upon by Sierra Chickaree.................... 206
31. Kitchen middens: remains of cones of Jeffrey pine.................... 207
32. Sierra Flying Squirrel.................... 212
33. Head of California Jack Rabbit.................... 223

[xvii]

FIGURE   PAGE

34. Head of Sierra White-tailed Jack Rabbit.. 225
35. Heads of Mariposa Brush Rabbit and Sacramento Cottontail Rabbit.................... 229
36. Skulls and horns of Sierra Nevada Mountain Sheep and Domestic Sheep 245
37. Harlequin Ducks.. 255
38. Debris from beneath Cooper Hawk's nest.. 285
39. Owls of the Yosemite region... 299
40. Debris from beneath Long-eared Owl's nest... 303
41. Work of Willow Woodpecker on apple tree... 319
42. Feet of Northern White-headed Woodpecker and Arctic Three-toed Woodpecker 326
43. Diagram of workings of Sierra Red-breasted Sapsucker...................................... 328
44. Fresh work of Williamson Sapsucker.. 332
45. Scars on trunk of lodgepole pine, result of work of Williamson Sapsucker.............. 333
46. Head of Northern Pileated Woodpecker.. 335
47. Head and tongue of California Woodpecker.. 339
48. Drillings of California Woodpecker and nest site of Lewis Woodpecker.................. 340
49. Head of Clark Nutcracker... 395
50. Tails of California Purple Finch and California Linnet.. 421
51. Bill of Sierra Crossbill and cone and seeds of lodgepole pine.............................. 430
52. Bills of Cassin Purple Finch, California Evening Grosbeak, and Sierra Nevada
       Rosy Finch.. 431
53. Tails of Willow, Green-backed, and Lawrence goldfinches, and Pine Siskin............ 436
54. Tails of Western Lark Sparrow and Western Vesper Sparrow............................... 444
55. Young of Mariposa Fox Sparrow and Pacific Black-headed Grosbeak.................... 489
56. Forage niches of warblers in Yosemite Valley... 517
57. Tails of Alaska Myrtle Warbler and Audubon Warbler....................................... 527
58. Tails of Sierra Creeper and Red-breasted Nuthatch... 562
59. Heads of Sierra Hermit Thrush and Cassin Purple Finch................................... 604
60. Young Western Robin.. 607
61. Zonal distribution of certain reptiles and amphibians....................................... 627
62. Western Yellow-bellied Racer and Giant Garter Snake...................................... 637
63. Boyle King Snake and California Striped Racer... 641
64. Rattle of Pacific Rattlesnake... 647
65. Poison apparatus of Pacific Rattlesnake... 649

INTRODUCTION

THE AREA CONSIDERED

The region studied is designated in this report as the 'Yosemite region,' or, more precisely, as the 'Yosemite section.' It involves, as shown on the accompanying map (pl. 62), a narrow rectangular area, 89¼ miles in length by 17⅓ miles in width. It reaches from the eastern margin of the San Joaquin Valley eastward across the mountains to include the western margin of the Great Basin, around Mono Lake, and thus constitutes a typical cross-section of the central Sierra Nevada. The altitudes range from 250 feet, at Snelling, to slightly over 13,000 feet, on Mount Lyell. The total 'map' area is 1547 square miles. Yosemite Valley is included in its entirety; the Valley ends of the Wawona and Big Oak Flat roads are within the 'section,' as are the greater parts of the Coulterville and Tioga roads. But neither the Mariposa Grove of Big Trees nor Hetch Hetchy Valley is included.

Within the limits of this 'section,' the members of our field party traveled over most of the regular trails (routes are shown on the map); in addition they sought out high points from which practically every square mile of territory could be seen and mapped as to life zone. All together, 40 collecting stations were occupied by different members of our party. The number of persons working at any one station at one time varied from one to five. Certain camps such as those in Yosemite Valley, at Porcupine Flat, on Tuolumne Meadows, and at the Farrington ranch were 'base camps,' from which short trips were taken in different directions. At all the places marked on the map as collecting stations, trapping for mammals was done on one or more nights.

STATISTICS OF FIELD WORK

The first regular field work of the Yosemite Survey was a reconnaissance trip by the senior author in the autumn of 1914. (Both authors were already familiar with the lay of the land from previous visits to Yosemite Valley and its environs.) Formal field work was instituted on November 19, 1914, and continued until January 9, 1915; it was commenced again on May 15, 1915, and continued until July 31; it was again taken up on August 16 and carried on until November 23 (1915). In 1916 continuous work was carried on in the neighborhood of Mono Lake from

April 26 until July 6. That same year, two brief trips were made into Yosemite Valley, at the end of February and at the end of April. In 1919 work in the western part of the region was carried on from May 5 to 27; and in 1920 work was in progress there from June 20 until August 11.

Nine hundred and fifty-seven 'man-days' (one man in the field one day) were put in. The field notes written occupy 2001 pages, and the specimens secured by our regular field men number 4354. The photographs obtained number 700. In addition, as indicated elsewhere, much valuable information and many important specimens were secured from residents in the Yosemite region.

All the materials upon which this report is based, including specimens, maps, notebooks, and photographs, are now contained in the Museum of Vertebrate Zoology of the University of California and are the property of the State of California.

FIELD PERSONNEL

Eight different persons participated at one time or another in the field work of the Yosemite Survey; 248 days were put in by Joseph Grinnell, 170 days by Tracy I. Storer, 111 days by Walter P. Taylor, 110 days by Joseph Dixon, 103 days by Charles L. Camp, 92 days by Gordon F. Ferris, 91 days by Charles D. Holliger, and 32 days by Donald D. McLean. It should be understood that whatever degree of accuracy and fullness the present report may possess rests upon the diligence, as field collectors and observers, of each and every one of these persons.

FIELD METHODS

The general plan of work was much the same at all the collecting stations. It was of course essential, in the interests of truth and scientific accuracy, that many specimens be obtained in order that correct identification of the species might be insured. Hence, each member of the party kept out a line of mouse and rat traps for the capture of the various species of small mammals. These were set in 'likely' places: along stream banks for shrews; in runways of meadow mice; about brush heaps or downed logs for white-footed mice, and so on. Special traps were set for moles, for pocket gophers, and for carnivorous species. These traps were baited the last thing each evening and were visited early the next morning so as to collect the animals caught before they might be harmed by sunshine or by insects. Where chipmunks abounded, or ground dwelling birds were numerous, traps were often visited during the day to recover such animals as were caught; or else the traps were purposely sprung in the morning and reset again in the evening in order to avoid capturing mammals or birds not needed for specimens. Birds were obtained, when necessary, by shooting selected individuals. Many reptiles were captured by hand, although some of the swifter ones could be obtained only by shooting.

But the taking of specimens was only one of several lines of activity. The morning of each day was usually spent away from camp observing and making notes upon the various species to be seen—their local distribution, forage habits, nesting behavior, and all the other observable features connected with their life histories. Each member of the party carried a notebook (journal) in which the observations of each day were recorded. Notes on the behavior of individual animals were written down usually while observation was in progress, to insure the entry of details with accuracy. When nests, burrows, or other 'workings' were examined, the measurements and diagrams were entered directly in the journal. Censuses were gathered as they were taken, the individuals pencil-checked one by one according to the method described fully elsewhere (p. 22). Photographs were taken of 'associations,' workings, tracks, and nests, and these materially supplemented the written data.

LIMITATION OF TIME

It became necessary, as in all such undertakings as this, arbitrarily to fix upon a date beyond which no further matter would be incorporated into this report. This date was set as December 31, 1920. Even though important new facts have been reported from the Yosemite region by competent observers since that date, we have forborne inclusion thereof. Inevitably, such additions will continue to be made so long as people with an interest in natural history visit the Yosemite region. The natural history resources will never become exhausted; and that is one fascinating feature of this field of inquiry. Our efforts, then, have been to assemble all the available information concerning the vertebrate animals of the Yosemite region up to and including December, 1920.

DISTRIBUTION OF ANIMAL LIFE IN THE YOSEMITE SECTION

Probably the primary stimulus which leads people to visit our national parks is the *change* that is experienced from familiar surroundings to those which are emphatically different. This change involves 'air' (that is, climate), and 'scene' (topography and vegetation). An entirely new set of conditions is encountered, and the new reactions set up mean recreation in the physiological sense—the exercise of faculties, both mental and physical, in kind or degree, that are more or less dormant during the ordinary routine of the year's program. Quick transportation between the lowlands of the San Joaquin Valley and the upper altitudes of the Sierras carries the traveler in either direction from one set of surroundings into a totally different one where he is thrilled because of the great changes which he encounters.

Let us now discuss, then, these *differences* in environment and their correlation with the continuous or discontinuous occurrence of vertebrate animals in the region. The section of the Sierra Nevada selected for faunal study is of such extent transversally to the Sierran axis that it takes in almost as great extremes of conditions as are to be encountered anywhere in California. Analysis of the changes to be observed as a person traverses the section from the west will soon show that he has witnessed not one single change, evenly and progressively from one set of conditions to just one other set, but that, having reached the highest altitudes, he has witnessed *several steps.* There has not been a uniform and continual gradient but he has passed through several *belts,* parallel roughly to the axis of the Sierra Nevada, each characterized by a considerable degree of uniformity as regards the plant and animal life.

A total of 231 kinds of birds are now (December 31, 1920) authentically known from the Yosemite section; there are 97 kinds of mammals, 22 kinds of snakes and lizards, and 12 kinds of frogs, toads, and salamanders. This makes a grand total, for the vertebrate fauna outside of fishes, of 362 forms. This seeming richness in number of kinds, be it emphasized, is apparent only when one takes into account the full extent of the Yosemite section. As a matter of fact, but a small proportion of the total number of species occur together at any one level. And here is the remarkable thing: They are more or less assorted and delimited in occurrence so that they help to constitute the belts, or 'life zones,' just referred to.

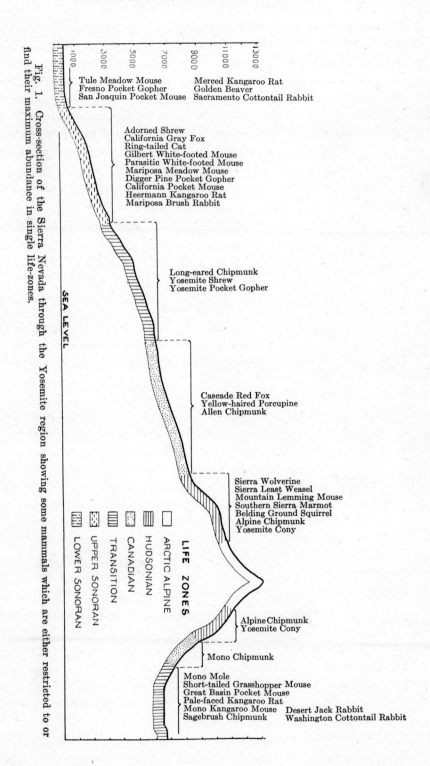

Fig. 1. Cross-section of the Sierra Nevada, through the Yosemite region showing some mammals which are either restricted to or find their maximum abundance in single life-zones.

We may express the facts in another way. The large number of kinds of animals present in the entire Yosemite section is due to the great range of physical conditions (temperature, moisture, soil, light, and perhaps others) with the accompanying diversity of vegetational features. Man is able to traverse the whole gamut of these conditions, even with benefit to himself by reason of the stimulus change produces, adjusting his mode of dress and behavior to them and carrying his food with him. But animals and plants are more or less directly in contact with the conditions around them; they are, as a rule, far less adaptable; and they are vitally affected by differences in temperature, in moisture, in food supply, and so on. The interesting thing is that in many species the degree of sensitiveness is so great that they can maintain existence only within a relatively narrow range of the critical conditions.

Such underlying reasons as those just suggested help to explain what impresses the traveler in ascending the west slope of the Sierras, namely, the correlation, roughly, with respect both to animals and plants, of zonation with altitude and, therefore, temperature. And it is because of this inter-correlation that the student is led to the conclusion that it is the factor of temperature which has most to do with the causation of life zones.

Reference to our map and cross-section diagram (pls. 61, 62) will show the application, to the Yosemite section, of the system of recognizing these belts of animal and plant life as some naturalists have worked them out and named them. Each life zone is a belt of relatively uniform constitution with respect to species. At the same time, we must emphasize that there is rarely an abrupt line of demarcation between any two adjoining zones. There is, as a rule, along the meeting ground more or less mixing or overlapping of the specific elements. This is especially true where the slope is very gentle, broad, and all facing in one direction. The steeper the slope, or the more abrupt the change of exposure (say from west to north), the sharper will be the boundary between the two adjacent zones.

To enter here into a further discussion of the life-zone concept is not necessary. We will simply refer the inquiring reader to some of the literature relating to the subject[1] and confine the present treatise to the

---

[1] C. Hart Merriam, Life Zones and Crop Zones of the United States (U. S. Dept. Agric., Div. Biol. Surv., Bull. no. 10, 1898), 79 pp., 1 colored map. C. Hart Merriam, Results of a Biological Survey of Mount Shasta, California (U. S. Dept. Agric., Div. Biol. Surv., N. Am. Fauna, no. 16, 1899), 179 pp., 5 pls., 46 figs. in text. H. M. Hall, A Botanical Survey of San Jacinto Mountain (Univ. Calif. Publ. Bot., vol. 1, 1902), pp. 1–140, pls. 1–14. J. Grinnell, An Account of the Mammals and Birds of the Lower Colorado Valley, with Especial Reference to the Distributional Problems Presented (Univ. Calif. Publ. Zool., vol. 12, 1914), pp. 51–294, pls. 3–13, 9 figs. in text. J. Grinnell, A Distributional List of the Birds of California (Pac. Coast Avifauna, no. 11, 1915), 217 pp., 3 maps. H. M. Hall and J. Grinnell, Life-Zone Indicators in California (Proc. Calif. Acad. Sci., ser. 4, vol. 9, 1919), pp. 37–67.

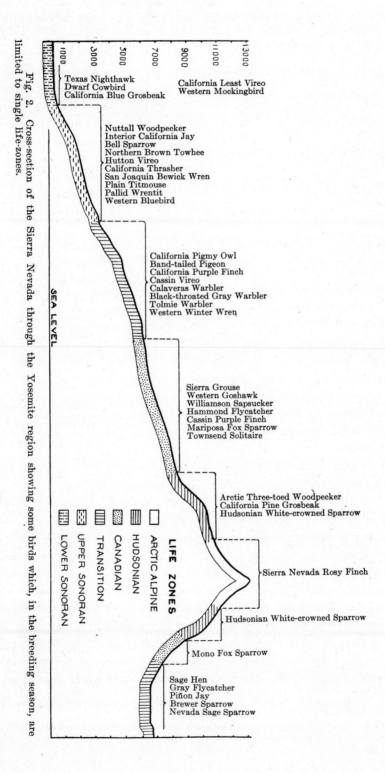

Fig. 2. Cross-section of the Sierra Nevada through the Yosemite region showing some birds which, in the breeding season, are limited to single life-zones.

particular state of affairs found in the Yosemite region. Since all animal
life is more or less directly dependent upon plant life for its existence, the
zoologist who seeks to explain the distribution of animals must concern
himself attentively also with the botany of the region he is studying. A
very useful essay on the distribution of plant life on the upper western
slope of the Yosemite section is contained in Professor and Mrs. Hall's
Yosemite Flora[2]; and further valuable data on the distribution of plants
in the Sierras will be found in a report by Dr. Smiley.[3]

All of the six life zones in the Yosemite region are represented in full
measure on the western slope of the section. There the distance involved
in the slope is so great, over seventy miles, that there is plenty of room
for the development of a separate representation of species, both plant
and animal, in each zone. But on the eastern slope the situation is somewhat different; and we find the zonation there obscure. Indeed, in our
field work below the Hudsonian Zone we met with much trouble in
diagnosing many of the localities; for instance, whether to call the upper
meadows on the Farrington ranch (pl. 19a), Canadian or Transition; the
south face of Williams Butte (pl. 19b), Transition or Upper Sonoran.

On the basis of the facts obtained within the eastern boundary of our
Yosemite section alone, the situation would be exceedingly difficult, even
impossible, of explanation. But when we take into account the east-Sierran
region generally, especially toward the southern end of the Sierran ridge
in the vicinity of Walker and Tehachapi passes, it becomes fairly easy to
see why conditions are as we find them between Mono Lake and Mono and
Tioga passes.

Base-level in the Mono Basin is high, averaging 7000 feet in altitude.
Furthermore, the distance between Mono Lake and the high Sierran crest,
which is 10,000 to 13,000 feet in altitude, is short. In other words, this
slope is abrupt; in fact, close to the divide, a declivity. The life zones,
in so far as characteristic representatives of them are to be found, are
crowded together—telescoped, as it were. There is a well established law
that a sequestered faunal area can be too small to support a permanent,
distinctive fauna of its own, even though conditions be otherwise wholly
propitious. The Sierra Nevada, which by area is of mainly western slope,
supports a large mass of 'boreal' plant and animal life; the Great Basin
area to the east is the metropolis of a highly developed 'austral' assemblage
of species. These two major areas adjoin one another at the steep eastern
declivity of the Sierras. On the long western slope where austral adjoins

  [2] H. M. Hall and C. C. Hall, A Yosemite Flora (Paul Elder, San Francisco, 1912),
pp. viii + 282, 170 text figs., 11 pls.

  [3] F. J. Smiley, A Report upon the Boreal Flora of the Sierra Nevada of California
(Univ. Calif. Publ. Bot., vol. 9, 1921), pp. 1–423, pls. 1–7.

boreal there is not only a well-marked belt of overlapping (comprising the Transition Zone) but in this belt there are numerous species closely restricted to it. On the eastern slope, however, Canadian and Upper Sonoran are jammed so closely together by reason of the steepness that the belt of intermingling of elements is very narrow or at best indistinct; there is scarcely if any room for the existence of restrictedly Transition Zone species.

Although presenting a strongly Great Basin aspect, the Mono basin, doubtless because of its high altitude, does not show a pure representation of austral life. It does contain a number of elements (that is, species) which from a study of their entire ranges we know to belong predominantly to the upper division of the austral, namely Upper Sonoran. But there are also present about as many, or as dominant, boreal elements.

Frankly, we found difficulty in assigning some parts of the Mono portion of the Yosemite section to one life zone rather than to another. This was particularly true of the south, sun-facing slope of Williams Butte (pl. 19b), which is clothed with piñon. This tree to the southward along the Sierras forms a belt which through Walker Pass is continuous with the digger pine belt of the west slope of the Sierras; and as a rule we can safely diagnose this belt by reason of this one plant indicator as Upper Sonoran. But on Williams Butte the piñons are mixed with western junipers, Jeffrey pines, mountain mahogany, and certain shrubby plants which are accepted as diagnostic of Transition, Canadian, or even Hudsonian. We found in this anomalous assemblage of plants such 'good' Upper Sonoran birds as bush-tits and Woodhouse jays in close association with mountain chickadees and Clark nutcrackers. This was after the breeding season; and, of course, there was a chance that in the case of the last-named species, at least, the individuals observed had moved down from the higher altitudes but a very few miles to the westward. In the case of small mammals, which are incapable of quickly traversing considerable stretches of territory, we found, on Williams Butte, True white-footed mice, which are typically Upper Sonoran, in the same trap-line with Mono chipmunks, which find their metropolis in the Canadian life zone.

Another tract in the Mono country which was for similar reasons perplexing occupies the lower slope down toward the lake shore from Mono Mills. There, pale-faced kangaroo rats, Stephens soft-haired ground squirrels, and desert jack rabbits were found, species which belong to groups whose habitats lie chiefly within the Upper Sonoran Zone, but here were found in company with animals and plants of more northern, Transition or even Canadian, predilections. The sage-hen, to cite one of these latter, is a 'good' Transition bird.

In the nature of the case, as regards these exceptional localities, we trust that the reader will understand why it is impossible for us to make positive statements with regard to their zonal complexion. Two persons, with some difference in perspective—that is, with a different understanding of the 'importance' of indicators—would very probably weight their findings differently. Our conclusion, as shown on our map and in our life-zone table, namely, to call the western part of the Mono Lake basin, that part included within the Yosemite 'section,' Transition, is therefore presented tentatively. The margin of determination is so small, with regard especially to Williams Butte and the tract immediately south of Mono Lake, that someone else, working the territory more intensively and listing the critical species statistically (by *individual* composition, which we did not), might find adequate grounds for mapping it as Upper Sonoran.

Returning to the Sierran divide: The Hudsonian Zone is found to be well characterized on the east slope down to an average of about the 9500-foot contour. This zone simply mantles the Sierras, save for the Arctic-Alpine 'islands' which rise above timber line. Below the Hudsonian, good Canadian is represented, with marked resemblance florally to that on the western slope, in the lower part of Bloody Cañon. Moisture conditions are there more exactly as they are on the west flank of the Sierras. Elsewhere, Canadian is rather different in aspect from what it looks like on the western slope, because of the prevailing aridity. Jeffrey pines and mountain mahogany predominate in the place of red firs and aspens. The steepest declivities, close to the Sierran divide, involve a lowering of altitude to about the 8000-foot contour; thence east to Mono Lake the slopes involved in the long, lateral moraines are gentle, and the blending of Canadian through Transition with 'austral' takes place gradually over several miles of territory. Here is where most trouble was experienced in fixing upon a boundary between Canadian and Transition—and for the same reasons as given above with respect to the Transition-Upper-Sonoran boundary. Good Canadian extends east along the cold streams, where it is marked conspicuously by thickets of aspen, well down toward the shores of Mono Lake—to as low as 7000 feet; Transition extends west up toward the foot of the east Sierran face, especially along the south-facing slopes of glacial ridges, to 9000 feet. Thus at Walker Lake one finds the interesting situation of the Canadian Zone occupying the cool, shaded bed of the glacial groove, with Transition on the south, sun-facing wall *above* it: the usual zonal relationship is reversed. Facts such as this strengthen our belief that the prime physical factor accounting for zonation is not altitude, or moisture, or soil, per se, but temperature.

As is clearly set forth in some of the literature we here cite for perusal by the inquiring reader, the limitation of species on the basis of the life-zone concept is not the only sort of segregation which occurs. Indeed, locally, as in Yosemite Valley proper, often a far more conspicuous manner of delimitation is manifest, the delimitation which takes place on the basis of 'associations.' These minor units involve each a certain type of environment within one zone; furthermore, closely similar or even identical associations may recur, or be continuous, in two or more adjacent zones. Not rarely, associational restriction seems to be transcendent over zonal restriction, as in the case of the badger, western chipping sparrow, and rock wren. Appropriate discussion of these cases will be found in the chapters (pp. 92, 452, 550) treating of these species.

Some of the more important associations of animal with plant or substratum conditions that it has proved useful to recognize in the Yosemite section are as follows, classified by zones. The names chosen are those of some predominating feature, usually of the vegetation. (Consult plates 13 to 19, 36a, and figure 21.)

ASSOCIATIONS WITHIN THE LOWER SONORAN ZONE

Open-water (two types, River and Slough)
Riparian (Willow–cottonwood)
Marsh
Meadow
Rose-thicket
Valley-oak
Hog-wallow prairie
Rock outcrop

ASSOCIATIONS WITHIN THE UPPER SONORAN ZONE

Stream
Riparian (Willow)
Meadow
Live-oak
Chaparral (two types, Adenostoma and Ceanothus cuneatus)
Digger-pine
Blue-oak
Dry grassland
Rocky-slope

ASSOCIATIONS WITHIN THE TRANSITION ZONE

Swift-stream
Riparian (two types, Willow–cotton-wood and Alder)
Meadow
Dry grassland
Chaparral (two types, Sticky-manzanita and Buckthorn)
Black-oak
Golden-oak
Yellow-pine
Silver-fir
Boulder-talus
Cliff

ASSOCIATIONS ON THE ARID EAST SIDE OF THE SIERRA, IN THE GREAT BASIN FAUNAL DIVISION OF THE TRANSITION ZONE

Alkali-lake
Riparian (Willow)
Rose-thicket
Shepherdia
Sagebrush
Piñon-juniper
Cercocarpus

ASSOCIATIONS WITHIN THE CANADIAN ZONE

Swift-stream

Riparian (two types, Willow and Cornus pubescens)

Aspen

Meadow

Chaparral (three types, Red-cherry, Arctostaphylos patula, and Huckleberry-oak)

Red-fir

Lodgepole-pine

Jeffrey-pine

Granite outcrop

Cliff

ASSOCIATIONS WITHIN THE HUDSONIAN ZONE

Lake

Shore

Swift-stream

Riparian (Willow)

Meadow

Heather

Lodgepole-pine

Hemlock

Whitebark-pine

Talus (or Rock-slide)

Cliff

ASSOCIATIONS WITHIN THE ARCTIC–ALPINE ZONE

Swift-stream

Willow-thicket

Meadow

Dry grassland

Talus (Rock-slide)

Cliff

Within each general association there is often plainly to be seen still further restriction in the habitat preferences of species. For example, in the major association, "coniferous forest," in its minor division (within the Canadian Zone) known as the red-fir association, we find several species of birds and of mammals, each adhering closely to a yet smaller division of the general environment. The Sierra Creeper keeps to the larger tree trunks, the Short-tailed Mountain Chickadee to the smaller twiggery, the Western Golden-crowned Kinglet to the terminal leafage, and the Hammond Flycatcher to the most prominent twig-ends and the air-spaces between branches and between trees. The Tahoe Chipmunk is largely arboreal, the Allen Chipmunk terrestrial.

In final analysis, no two species well established in a region occupy precisely the same ecologic space; each has its own peculiar places for foraging, and for securing safety for itself and for its eggs or young. These ultimate units of occurrence are called "ecologic niches." If two species of the same ecologic predilections are thrown into the same environment, one or the other will quickly disappear through the drastic process we call competitive replacement. Thus it comes to pass that the amplitude of the general environment—the number and extent of distinct ecologic niches it compasses—determines the richness of the fauna, both as regards number of species, and the number of the individuals to the unit of area representing each species. This principle may be abundantly verified by any student who will carry on active field observations a season or two over even a small part of the Yosemite section.

TABLE OF OCCURRENCE, ACCORDING TO LIFE ZONE, OF THE MAMMALS, BREEDING BIRDS, REPTILES, AND AMPHIBIANS OF THE YOSEMITE SECTION

NOTE.—It is intended, in the using of this table, that comparison be made with the life-zone map and profile, plates 61, 62. Width of bar indicates relative abundance of the species concerned; in other words, the widest place in the bar indicates the place, zonally, where the population is believed to be densest. In case there is some reason to suppose that a species ranges beyond what is shown by the actual facts at hand, such extension is indicated by a broken line. Some of the species which are listed in the present work are omitted from the table because they are non-native, extinct, or of unknown or doubtful status. Water birds are omitted entirely, as are also non-breeding land birds.

It must be distinctly understood that this table of zonal distribution is based on our findings in the Yosemite region only; it must not be interpreted as setting forth the distributional situation in the Sierra Nevada generally, or in the State at large, though this may approximately be true in the great majority of cases. The zonal diagnoses of species apply primarily to the long, western slope of the Sierra Nevada; many of the species occur only on that side. Exclusively east-side species are so indicated by foot-note reference; and where these latter are known to extend into the Transition Zone from the Upper Sonoran Zone (hence beyond the limits of our section) this fact is indicated by cutting off the bar squarely at the vertical line of demarcation between these two zones.

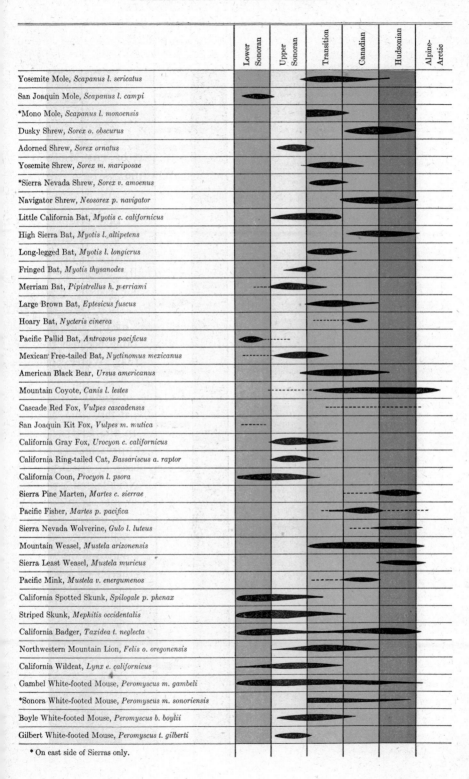

	Lower Sonoran	Upper Sonoran	Transition	Canadian	Hudsonian	Alpine-Arctic
Yosemite Mole, *Scapanus l. sericatus*						
San Joaquin Mole, *Scapanus l. campi*						
*Mono Mole, *Scapanus l. monoensis*						
Dusky Shrew, *Sorex o. obscurus*						
Adorned Shrew, *Sorex ornatus*						
Yosemite Shrew, *Sorex m. mariposae*						
*Sierra Nevada Shrew, *Sorex v. amoenus*						
Navigator Shrew, *Neosorex p. navigator*						
Little California Bat, *Myotis c. californicus*						
High Sierra Bat, *Myotis l. altipetens*						
Long-legged Bat, *Myotis l. longicrus*						
Fringed Bat, *Myotis thysanodes*						
Merriam Bat, *Pipistrellus h. merriami*						
Large Brown Bat, *Eptesicus fuscus*						
Hoary Bat, *Nycteris cinerea*						
Pacific Pallid Bat, *Antrozous pacificus*						
Mexican Free-tailed Bat, *Nyctinomus mexicanus*						
American Black Bear, *Ursus americanus*						
Mountain Coyote, *Canis l. lestes*						
Cascade Red Fox, *Vulpes cascadensis*						
San Joaquin Kit Fox, *Vulpes m. mutica*						
California Gray Fox, *Urocyon c. californicus*						
California Ring-tailed Cat, *Bassariscus a. raptor*						
California Coon, *Procyon l. psora*						
Sierra Pine Marten, *Martes c. sierrae*						
Pacific Fisher, *Martes p. pacifica*						
Sierra Nevada Wolverine, *Gulo l. luteus*						
Mountain Weasel, *Mustela arizonensis*						
Sierra Least Weasel, *Mustela muricus*						
Pacific Mink, *Mustela v. energumenos*						
California Spotted Skunk, *Spilogale p. phenax*						
Striped Skunk, *Mephitis occidentalis*						
California Badger, *Taxidea t. neglecta*						
Northwestern Mountain Lion, *Felis o. oregonensis*						
California Wildcat, *Lynx e. californicus*						
Gambel White-footed Mouse, *Peromyscus m. gambeli*						
*Sonora White-footed Mouse, *Peromyscus m. sonoriensis*						
Boyle White-footed Mouse, *Peromyscus b. boylii*						
Gilbert White-footed Mouse, *Peromyscus t. gilberti*						

* On east side of Sierras only.

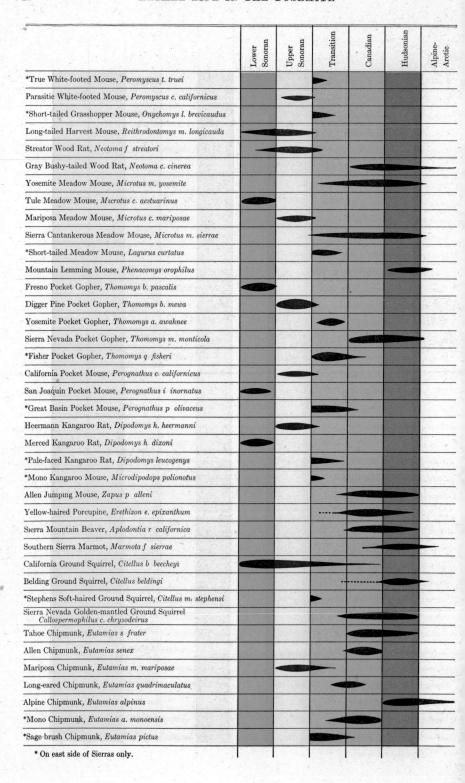

	Lower Sonoran	Upper Sonoran	Transition	Canadian	Hudsonian	Alpine-Arctic
*True White-footed Mouse, *Peromyscus t. truei*			▬			
Parasitic White-footed Mouse, *Peromyscus c. californicus*		▬				
*Short-tailed Grasshopper Mouse, *Onychomys l. brevicaudus*			▬			
Long-tailed Harvest Mouse, *Reithrodontomys m. longicauda*	▬	▬				
Streator Wood Rat, *Neotoma f streatori*		▬				
Gray Bushy-tailed Wood Rat, *Neotoma c. cinerea*				▬	▬	
Yosemite Meadow Mouse, *Microtus m. yosemite*			▬	▬		
Tule Meadow Mouse, *Microtus c. aestuarinus*	▬					
Mariposa Meadow Mouse, *Microtus c. mariposae*		▬				
Sierra Cantankerous Meadow Mouse, *Microtus m. sierrae*				▬	▬	
*Short-tailed Meadow Mouse, *Lagurus curtatus*			▬			
Mountain Lemming Mouse, *Phenacomys orophilus*					▬	
Fresno Pocket Gopher, *Thomomys b. pascalis*	▬					
Digger Pine Pocket Gopher, *Thomomys b. mewa*		▬				
Yosemite Pocket Gopher, *Thomomys a. awahnee*			▬			
Sierra Nevada Pocket Gopher, *Thomomys m. monticola*				▬	▬	
*Fisher Pocket Gopher, *Thomomys q fisheri*			▬			
California Pocket Mouse, *Perognathus c. californicus*		▬				
San Joaquin Pocket Mouse, *Perognathus i inornatus*	▬					
*Great Basin Pocket Mouse, *Perognathus p olivaceus*			▬			
Heermann Kangaroo Rat, *Dipodomys h. heermanni*		▬				
Merced Kangaroo Rat, *Dipodomys h dixoni*	▬					
*Pale-faced Kangaroo Rat, *Dipodomys leucogenys*			▬			
*Mono Kangaroo Mouse, *Microdipodops polionotus*			▬			
Allen Jumping Mouse, *Zapus p alleni*				▬	▬	
Yellow-haired Porcupine, *Erethizon e. epixanthum*			----	▬	▬	
Sierra Mountain Beaver, *Aplodontia r californica*				▬		
Southern Sierra Marmot, *Marmota f sierrae*				▬	▬	
California Ground Squirrel, *Citellus b beecheyi*	▬	▬				
Belding Ground Squirrel, *Citellus beldingi*			-----------			
*Stephens Soft-haired Ground Squirrel, *Citellus m. stephensi*			▬			
Sierra Nevada Golden-mantled Ground Squirrel *Callospermophilus c. chrysodeirus*				▬	▬	
Tahoe Chipmunk, *Eutamias s frater*				▬		
Allen Chipmunk, *Eutamias senex*				▬		
Mariposa Chipmunk, *Eutamias m. mariposae*		▬				
Long-eared Chipmunk, *Eutamias quadrimaculatus*			▬			
Alpine Chipmunk, *Eutamias alpinus*					▬	
*Mono Chipmunk, *Eutamias a. monoensis*				▬		
*Sage-brush Chipmunk, *Eutamias pictus*			▬			

* On east side of Sierras only.

	Lower Sonoran	Upper Sonoran	Transition	Canadian	Hudsonian	Alpine-Arctic
California Gray Squirrel, *Sciurus g. griseus*		■	■			
Sierra Chickaree, *Sciurus d. albolimbatus*				■	■	
Sierra Flying Squirrel, *Glaucomys s. lascivus*			■	■		
Golden Beaver, *Castor c. subauratus*	■					
Yosemite Cony, *Ochotona s. muiri*					■	■
California Jack Rabbit, *Lepus c. californicus*	■	■				
*Desert Jack Rabbit, *Lepus c. deserticola*			■			
Sierra White-tailed Jack Rabbit, *Lepus t. sierrae*				■	■	
Sacramento Cottontail, *Sylvilagus a. audubonii*	■					
Washington Cottontail, *Sylvilagus n. nuttallii*			■			
Mariposa Brush Rabbit, *Sylvilagus b. mariposae*		■				
Mule Deer, *Odocoileus h. hemionus*			■	■		
Mountain Quail, *Oreortyx p. plumifera*			■	■		
Valley Quail, *Lophortyx c. vallicola*	■					
Sierra Grouse, *Dendragapus o. sierrae*				■		
*Sage-hen, *Centrocercus urophasianus*			■			
Band-tailed Pigeon, *Columba f. fasciata*			■			
Western Mourning Dove, *Zenaidura m. marginella*	■	■				
Turkey Vulture, *Cathartes a. septentrionalis*	■					
Sharp-shinned Hawk, *Accipiter velox*				■		
Cooper Hawk, *Accipiter cooperi*		■				
Western Goshawk, *Astur a. striatulus*				■		
Western Red-tailed Hawk, *Buteo b. calurus*	■	■				
Red-bellied Hawk, *Buteo l. elegans*	■					
Swainson Hawk, *Buteo swainsoni*		■				
Golden Eagle, *Aquila chrysaetos*	■	■	■			
American Sparrow Hawk, *Falco s. sparverius*	■	■				
Barn Owl, *Tyto pratincola*	■					
Long-eared Owl, *Asio wilsonianus*			■			
California Spotted Owl, *Strix o. occidentalis*			■			
Great Gray Owl, *Scotiaptex n. nebulosa*				■		
Saw-whet Owl, *Cryptoglaux acadica*			■			
Southern California Screech Owl, *Otus a. quercinus*		■				
Pacific Horned Owl, *Bubo v. pacificus*	■	■				
Burrowing Owl, *Speotyto c. hypogaea*	■					
California Pigmy Owl, *Glaucidium g. californicum*			■			
Road-runner, *Geococcyx californianus*	■					
Western Belted Kingfisher, *Ceryle a. caurina*		■	■			
Modoc Woodpecker, *Dryobates v. orius*			■			

* On east side of Sierras only.

	Lower Sonoran	Upper Sonoran	Transition	Canadian	Hudsonian	Alpine-Arctic
Willow Woodpecker, *Dryobates p. turati*		●	●			
Nuttall Woodpecker, *Dryobates nuttalli*	●	●				
Northern White-headed Woodpecker, *Xenopicus a. albolarvatus*			●			
Arctic Three-toed Woodpecker, *Picoides arcticus*				●	●	
Sierra Red-breasted Sapsucker, *Sphyrapicus v. daggetti*			●			
Williamson Sapsucker, *Sphyrapicus t. thyroideus*				●		
Northern Pileated Woodpecker, *Phloeotomus p. abieticola*			●			
California Woodpecker, *Melanerpes f. bairdi*	●	●				
Red-shafted Flicker, *Colaptes c collaris*	●	●	●			
Dusky Poor-will, *Phalaenoptilus n. californicus*	●	●				
*Nuttall Poor-will, *Phalaenoptilus n. nuttalli*						
Pacific Nighthawk, *Chordeiles v. hesperis*			●	●		
Texas Nighthawk, *Chordeiles a. texensis*	●					
Northern Black Swift, *Cypseloides n. borealis*			●			
White-throated Swift, *Aeronautes melanoleucus*		●	●			
Black-chinned Hummingbird, *Archilochus alexandri*		●	●			
Anna Hummingbird, *Calypte anna*		●				
Calliope Hummingbird, *Stellula calliope*				●		
Western Kingbird, *Tyrannus verticalis*	●	●				
Ash-throated Flycatcher, *Myiarchus c. cinerascens*	●	●	●			
Black Phoebe, *Sayornis nigricans*	●	●				
Olive-sided Flycatcher, *Nuttallornis borealis*				●		
Western Wood Pewee, *Myiochanes r. richardsoni*			●	●		
Wright Flycatcher, *Empidonax wrighti*			●	●		
Hammond Flycatcher, *Empidonax hammondi*				●		
Traill Flycatcher, *Empidonax t. traïlli*	●	●	●			
Western Flycatcher, *Empidonax d. difficilis*			●			
*Gray Flycatcher, *Empidonax griseus*			●			
California Horned Lark, *Otocoris a. actia*	●					
*Black-billed Magpie, *Pica p. hudsonia*			●			
Blue-fronted Jay, *Cyanocitta s. frontalis*			●	●		
Interior California Jay, *Aphelocoma c. immanis*		●	●			
*Woodhouse Jay, *Aphelocoma woodhousei*			●			
Clark Nutcracker, *Nucifraga columbiana*				●	●	
*Piñon Jay, *Cyanocephalus cyanocephalus*			●			
Dwarf Cowbird, *Molothrus a. obscurus*	●					
*Nevada Cowbird, *Molothrus a. artemisiae*			●			
Bi-colored Red-winged Blackbird, *Agelaius p. californicus*	●					
*Nevada Red-winged Blackbird, *Agelaius p. nevadensis*			●			

* On east side of Sierras only.

	Lower Sonoran	Upper Sonoran	Transition	Canadian	Hudsonian	Alpine-Arctic
Kern Red-winged Blackbird, *Agelaius p. aciculatus*			●			
Tri-colored Blackbird, *Agelaius tricolor*	●					
Western Meadowlark, *Sturnella neglecta*	●─────	─────	───			
Bullock Oriole, *Icterus bullocki*	●─────	───				
Brewer Blackbird, *Euphagus cyanocephalus*	●─────	─────	──			
California Evening Grosbeak, *Hesperiphona v. californica*				●		
California Pine Grosbeak, *Pinicola e. californica*					●	
California Purple Finch, *Carpodacus p. californicus*			●			
Cassin Purple Finch, *Carpodacus cassini*				●─────		
California Linnet, *Carpodacus m. frontalis*	●─────	──				
Sierra Nevada Rosy Finch, *Leucosticte t. dawsoni*						●
Willow Goldfinch, *Astragalinus t. salicamans*	●					
Green-backed Goldfinch, *Astragalinus p. hesperophilus*	●─────	──				
Lawrence Goldfinch, *Astragalinus lawrencei*		●				
Pine Siskin, *Spinus p. pinus*			●─────	──		
*Western Vesper Sparrow, *Pooecetes g. confinis*			●			
*Nevada Savannah Sparrow, *Passerculus s. nevadensis*			●			
Western Grasshopper Sparrow, *Ammodramus s. bimaculatus*		●				
Western Lark Sparrow, *Chondestes g strigatus*	●─────	──				
Hudsonian White-crowned Sparrow, *Zonotrichia l. leucophrys*			------	────	●	
Western Chipping Sparrow, *Spizella p arizonae*	●─────	─────	─────	──		
*Brewer Sparrow, *Spizella breweri*			●─────	──		
Sierra Junco, *Junco o. thurberi*			●─────	─────	──	
Bell Sparrow, *Amphispiza belli*		●				
*Nevada Sage Sparrow, *Amphispiza n. nevadensis*			●			
Rufous-crowned Sparrow, *Aimophila r. ruficeps*		●				
*Modoc Song Sparrow, *Melospiza m. fisherella*			●			
Northeastern Lincoln Sparrow, *Melospiza l. lincolni*				●		
Mariposa Fox Sparrow, *Passerella i. mariposae*				●		
*Mono Fox Sparrow, *Passerella i. monoensis*				●		
Sacramento Spurred Towhee, *Pipilo m. falcinellus*	●─────	─────	──			
*Nevada Spurred Towhee, *Pipilo m. curtatus*			●			
Northern Brown Towhee, *Pipilo c. carolae*	●─────	──				
Green-tailed Towhee, *Oberholseria chlorura*			●─────	──		
Pacific Black-headed Grosbeak, *Zamelodia m. capitalis*		●─────	──			
California Blue Grosbeak, *Guiraca c. salicarius*	●					
Lazuli Bunting, *Passerina amoena*	●─────	──				
Western Tanager, *Piranga ludoviciana*			●─────	──		
Cliff Swallow, *Petrochelidon l. lunifrons*	●─────	──				

* On east side of Sierras only.

	Lower Sonoran	Upper Sonoran	Transition	Canadian	Hudsonian	Alpine-Arctic
Barn Swallow, *Hirundo e erythrogaster*						
Tree Swallow, *Iridoprocne bicolor*						
Northern Violet-green Swallow, *Tachycineta t. lepida*						
Rough-winged Swallow, *Stelgidopteryx serripennis*						
Phainopepla, *Phainopepla nitens*						
California Shrike, *Lanius l. gambeli*						
*White-rumped Shrike, *Lanius l. excubitorides*						
Western Warbling Vireo, *Vireosylva g. swainsoni*						
Cassin Vireo, *Lanivireo s. cassini*						
Hutton Vireo, *Vireo h. huttoni*						
California Least Vireo, *Vireo b. pusillus*						
Calaveras Warbler, *Vermivora r gutturalis*						
Lutescent Warbler, *Vermivora c. lutescens*						
*Rocky Mountain Orange-crowned Warbler, *Vermivora c. orestera*						
California Yellow Warbler, *Dendroica a. brewsteri*						
Audubon Warbler, *Dendroica a. auduboni*						
Black-throated Gray Warbler, *Dendroica nigrescens*						
Hermit Warbler, *Dendroica occidentalis*						
Tolmie Warbler, *Oporornis tolmiei*						
Tule Yellowthroat, *Geothlypis t. scirpicola*						
Long-tailed Chat, *Icteria v. longicauda*						
Golden Pileolated Warbler, *Wilsonia p. chryseola*						
American Dipper, *Cinclus m. unicolor*						
*Sage Thrasher, *Oreoscoptes montanus*						
Western Mockingbird, *Mimus p. leucopterus*						
California Thrasher, *Toxostoma r redivivum*						
Rock Wren, *Salpinctes o obsoletus*						
Dotted Cañon Wren, *Catherpes m. punctulatus*						
San Joaquin Bewick Wren, *Thryomanes b drymoecus*						
Western House Wren, *Troglodytes a. parkmani*						
Western Winter Wren, *Nannus h. pacificus*						
Sierra Creeper, *Certhia f. zelotes*						
Slender-billed Nuthatch, *Sitta c. aculeata*						
Red-breasted Nuthatch, *Sitta canadensis*						
Pigmy Nuthatch, *Sitta p. pygmaea*						
Plain Titmouse, *Baeolophus i. inornatus*						
Short-tailed Mountain Chickadee, *Penthestes g. abbreviatus*						
California Bush-tit, *Psaltriparus m. californicus*						
Pallid Wren-tit, *Chamaea f. henshawi*						

* On east side of Sierras only.

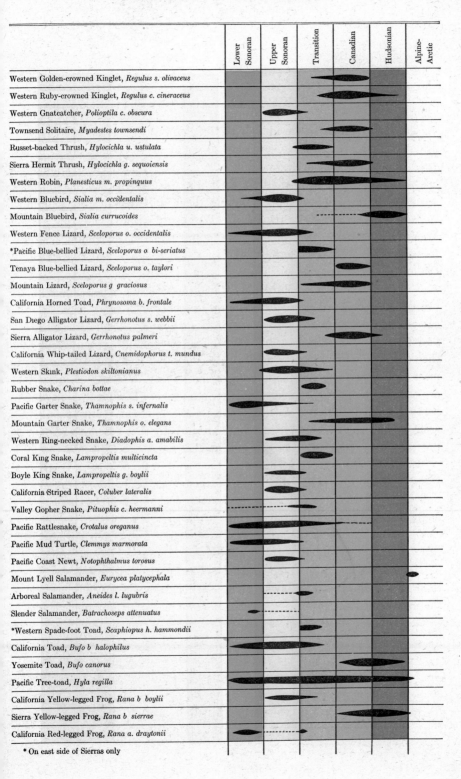

	Lower Sonoran	Upper Sonoran	Transition	Canadian	Hudsonian	Alpine-Arctic
Western Golden-crowned Kinglet, *Regulus s. olivaceus*						
Western Ruby-crowned Kinglet, *Regulus c. cineraceus*						
Western Gnatcatcher, *Polioptila c. obscura*						
Townsend Solitaire, *Myadestes townsendi*						
Russet-backed Thrush, *Hylocichla u. ustulata*						
Sierra Hermit Thrush, *Hylocichla g. sequoiensis*						
Western Robin, *Planesticus m. propinquus*						
Western Bluebird, *Sialia m. occidentalis*						
Mountain Bluebird, *Sialia currucoides*						
Western Fence Lizard, *Sceloporus o. occidentalis*						
*Pacific Blue-bellied Lizard, *Sceloporus o. bi-seriatus*						
Tenaya Blue-bellied Lizard, *Sceloporus o. taylori*						
Mountain Lizard, *Sceloporus g. graciosus*						
California Horned Toad, *Phrynosoma b. frontale*						
San Diego Alligator Lizard, *Gerrhonotus s. webbii*						
Sierra Alligator Lizard, *Gerrhonotus palmeri*						
California Whip-tailed Lizard, *Cnemidophorus t. mundus*						
Western Skink, *Plestiodon skiltonianus*						
Rubber Snake, *Charina bottae*						
Pacific Garter Snake, *Thamnophis s. infernalis*						
Mountain Garter Snake, *Thamnophis o. elegans*						
Western Ring-necked Snake, *Diadophis a. amabilis*						
Coral King Snake, *Lampropeltis multicincta*						
Boyle King Snake, *Lampropeltis g. boylii*						
California Striped Racer, *Coluber lateralis*						
Valley Gopher Snake, *Pituophis c. heermanni*						
Pacific Rattlesnake, *Crotalus oreganus*						
Pacific Mud Turtle, *Clemmys marmorata*						
Pacific Coast Newt, *Notophthalmus torosus*						
Mount Lyell Salamander, *Eurycea platycephala*						
Arboreal Salamander, *Aneides l. lugubris*						
Slender Salamander, *Batrachoseps attenuatus*						
*Western Spade-foot Toad, *Scaphiopus h. hammondii*						
California Toad, *Bufo b. halophilus*						
Yosemite Toad, *Bufo canorus*						
Pacific Tree-toad, *Hyla regilla*						
California Yellow-legged Frog, *Rana b. boylii*						
Sierra Yellow-legged Frog, *Rana b. sierrae*						
California Red-legged Frog, *Rana a. draytonii*						

* On east side of Sierras only

CENSUSES OF BIRDS IN THE YOSEMITE SECTION

To convey an adequate idea of the bird life of any given area, enumerations of *species* are not alone sufficient; the numbers of *individuals* of each species must also in some way be indicated. The usual terms "abundant," "common," "rare," and the like, are unsatisfactory in that their meaning varies both with the person employing them and with the kinds of birds considered. In the latter regard, the Western Chipping Sparrow and the Western Red-tailed Hawk might both be put down as "common," whereas the sparrow may have been observed in actual numbers ten times those of the hawk.

Counts of individual birds are fairly practicable when made in the breeding season on the basis of some unit of area such as an acre. At that season each adult pair is settled within a particular circumscribed locality, and the male is in song. But as soon as the young are out, and from then on throughout the year until the beginning of the next nesting season, most species of birds are moving about incessantly. Counts of individuals are then very difficult to make and furthermore are likely to be misleading because of their great variation in any small area from hour to hour and from day to day. And so, in our field work in the Yosemite region, we put into effect the following *different* method.

Instead of using a unit of area, we used a unit of time. Birds were listed, as to species and individuals, per hour of observation. In a general way this record involved area, too. Our censuses were practically all made on foot, and the distance to the right or left at which the observer could see or hear birds did not differ, materially, in different regions. The rate of the observer's travel did, of course, vary some; for example, when climbing a steep trail, or going through chaparral, progress was slower than when hiking straightaway along open ridges. Also, in some places, the greater density of the vegetational cover acted to limit the range of sight. But for each of these adverse features of the method there were certain compensations.

For recording a census, a piece of cardboard and a pencil were carried, the names of the various species of birds jotted down, and their numbers checked, as they came to notice. The presence of no species was assumed; but probabilities were given consideration in making identifications. In cases where birds were seen or heard, but their identity was not established with certainty, provisional names were entered, each followed by a question

MUSEUM OF VERTEBRATE ZOOLOGY   **CENSUS SHEET**

Locality *Yosemite Valley, Calif.* Nature of route (zone, fauna, associations) *Transition*

Date *April 28, 1916* .... *Zone, Sierra Nevada fauna, riparian and open*

Observer *Tracy I. Storer* .... *forest assoc. — route: village to Happy Isles,*

Time in field *3 hours* .... *to n. side Road, Kenneyville, to village*

Approximate no. miles *5* .... Weather *clear, warm, sunny, slight west wind*

Species	Hours ➤➤➤	12⁵⁵-2	2-2³⁰ 3¹⁵-3⁴⁵	3⁴⁵-4⁴⁵	p.m.		Totals
Blue-fronted Jay		1					1
Sierra Junco		5	2	6			13
Audubon Warbler		10		3			13
Ruby-crowned Kinglet		6		1			7
Western Robin		2	4				6
Hermit Warbler		4	7	3			14
Western Chipping Sparrow		1	2	2			5
Pine Siskin		2	1	1			4
Calaveras Warbler		2±	1				3±
Mountain Chickadee		1	1				2
Sierra Creeper		2	2	1			5
Golden-crowned Kinglet		2	3	1			6
West. Warbling Vireo		3	2	2			7
Cassin Vireo		3	2	3			8
Calif. Yellow Warbler		3	1	1			5
Water Ouzel		1					1
Belted Kingfisher			1				1
Brewer Blackbird			3				3
Black-headed Grosbeak				1			1
Willow Woodpecker				1			1
Red-shafted Flicker				1			1
Band-tailed Pigeon				100+			100+
?Parkman Wren				1?			1?
TOTALS (hourly and grand)		**48**	**32**	**128+**			**208+**

Fig. 3. A sample census sheet.

mark. Occasionally the bird could be identified only as to its general grouping, as "hawk." Species of very close resemblance were sometimes grouped together in a joint entry; for example, the crowned sparrows (*Zonotrichia*). The plus sign indicated that more were present than the actual number entered: the birds could not be counted with certainty; flocking birds, for instance, frequently could not be counted accurately.

At the close of the day or of the period of observation, we were accustomed to transfer our censuses from the field sheet (more or less scribbled, in lead pencil) to our permanent notebooks. If but few species of birds had been seen, these were entered seriatim with numbers of each observed, and comments; if a goodly census had been secured we entered the results in more formal, tabular style, on special sheets printed for this purpose (fig. 3). In either case, record was kept of exact time involved, approximate distance covered, nature of territory traversed, and weather conditions.

Totals were computed, both of species and individuals. Comparisons of these totals for different parts of the Yosemite region and for different seasons have brought forth some interesting conclusions. Outstanding among these generalizations are the following: The greatest bird population, both summer and winter, is found in the Upper Sonoran Zone. Next come the Lower Sonoran and Canadian zones. The Transition Zone has a fairly large population in summer, but its population drops far down in winter. The Hudsonian has the sparsest summer population, except, of course, for the Alpine-Arctic. The winter population below the snow line consists more largely of seed and berry eaters than of insect feeders; the summer population everywhere contains a predominating proportion of insect-eating birds.

We present below a series of censuses, selected from the more than 250 in our notebooks. The censuses given are chosen to illustrate, first, the nature of the avifauna in various representative parts of the Yosemite section, and, second, the marked changes in bird life taking place in Yosemite Valley from season to season through the year.

The series of censuses given for Yosemite Valley is more complete than for any other station in the section. It begins at the height of the nesting season with two censuses on separate days in two different parts of the Valley, embracing widely different sorts of habitats (associations) and consequently unlike assemblages of birds. The decline of song and general activity at the end of the nesting season is indicated in the census of July 30. That for October 25 shows replacement of the summer visitants by winter invaders. The censuses of December 10 and February 29 show how completely the Valley is deserted by birds with the advent of the midwinter snows; there are scarcely one-fourth as many birds present there in midwinter as in early summer. Return of summer species is already much in evidence in the list made on April 29.

In the census at Mono Lake Post Office on May 31 a 'wave' of migration is indicated in the numbers of species and individuals of warblers seen, which are in excess of what would be present there a month later, in the height of the nesting season. The census on the Big Oak Flat Road in December exhibits the congregation, in a favorable situation, of berry-eating species such as the Townsend Solitaire and Western Bluebird. Had it not been for the berry-laden mistletoe in the golden oaks on the talus slope (pl. 16*a*) this census in all likelihood would have been no larger than the one taken at the same season on the floor of the Valley.

The census-taker is struck by the variation in his records from hour to hour during the day, irrespective of kind of territory covered and of his own degree of alertness. This fluctuation is due in large part to the fact that there are two daily periods of marked activity on the part of birds, namely, in the early morning, within an hour or so after sunrise, and in the late afternoon, about two hours before sunset. Of these two periods, that in the morning is the most impressive; in other words the observer, by selecting the earlier hours for his census-walk, will make the highest score and also the most representative one. It is quickly apparent that in comparing the enumerations for different days and for different localities, allowance should be made for this daily double fluctuation in the visibility and audibility of birds.

It is the earnest recommendation of the authors that observers in a position to do so will get into the habit of taking bird censuses. The method here advocated is a practicable one; we believe it can be adopted to advantage by anyone possessed of a fair acquaintance with bird species. A 'collection' of census records will afford basis for much future satisfaction. On the one hand, is the pleasure of recalling to mind pleasant days afield spent among the most attractive things in nature; and on the other hand is the intellectual enjoyment derived from comparing bird populations in kind and size from place to place and season to season, and from endeavoring to account for the fluctuations which are shown, on the basis of all the factors known to control the birds' existence.

SNELLING, altitude 250 feet, Lower Sonoran Zone, riparian association; January 6, 1915, 9:30 A.M.–12:00 M.; rain the night previous, the morning somewhat cloudy; distance covered about 3 miles, within a mile east of the town.

Pied-billed Grebe	1	Song Sparrows (2 subsp.)	12+
California Great Blue Heron	4	Northwestern Lincoln Sparrow	2
Mud-hen	1	Sacramento Spurred Towhee	8
American Sparrow Hawk	2	Northern Brown Towhee	4
Black Phoebe	6	California Shrike	2
Interior California Jay	8	Orange-crowned Warbler	2
Brewer Blackbird	100+	Tule Yellowthroat	10
California Linnet	10+	Western Mockingbird	6
Willow Goldfinch	6+	San Joaquin Bewick Wren	1
Green-backed Goldfinch	4	Western House Wren	1
Intermediate White-crowned Sparrow	10	California Bush-tit	15+
Golden-crowned Sparrow	10+	Western Ruby-crowned Kinglet	12

Total: species 24, individuals 237+.

SNELLING, 250 feet, Lower Sonoran Zone, riparian association; May 26, 1915, 6:00–9:00 A.M.; warm, sunny; distance covered about 3 miles, close to Merced River, within a mile east of the town.

California Great Blue Heron	3	Brewer Blackbird	8
Black-crowned Night Heron	1	California Linnet	50+
Killdeer	2	Willow Goldfinch	40+
Valley Quail	4	Green-backed Goldfinch	6
Western Mourning Dove	40+	Western Lark Sparrow	1
Turkey Vulture	1	Western Chipping Sparrow	1
Red-bellied Hawk	1	Sacramento Spurred Towhee	10+
American Sparrow Hawk	2+	Northern Brown Towhee	7
California Woodpecker	2	Pacific Black-headed Grosbeak	10
Lewis Woodpecker	1	California Blue Grosbeak	6
Red-shafted Flicker	12+	Lazuli Bunting	10+
Western Kingbird	10	Barn Swallow	4
Ash-throated Flycatcher	6+	Western Warbling Vireo	1
Black Phoebe	6	California Least Vireo	4
Western Wood Pewee	12+	California Yellow Warbler	8+
Traill Flycatcher	10+	Tule Yellowthroat	8+
Interior California Jay	4	Long-tailed Chat	6+
Western Crow	2	Western Mockingbird	1
Bi-colored Red-winged Blackbird	87+	San Joaquin Bewick Wren	6
Western Meadowlark	12+	Russet-backed Thrush	2
Bullock Oriole	20		

Total: species 41, individuals 427+.

PLEASANT VALLEY westward toward Forty-nine Gap and return, 600 to 1100 feet, Upper Sonoran Zone, blue-oak, chaparral and grassland associations; February 27, 1916, 7:30–9:30 A.M., and 10:30 A.M.–12:00 M. (actual census time 3 hours 30 minutes); cloudy, with rain 9:30–11:30; distance covered about 6 miles, all on foot, chiefly along roadways.

Valley Quail	1	Sierra Junco	50
Turkey Vulture	5	Sacramento Spurred Towhee	8
Western Red-tailed Hawk	1	Northern Brown Towhee	15
Nuttall Woodpecker	1	California Shrike	3
California Woodpecker	11	Hutton Vireo	1
Red-shafted Flicker	4	Audubon Warbler	2
Black Phoebe	2	California Thrasher	1
California Horned Lark	33	San Joaquin Bewick Wren	10
Blue-fronted Jay	1	Plain Titmouse	9
Interior California Jay	15	Pallid Wren-tit	2
Western Meadowlark	37	California Bush-tit	11
Brewer Blackbird	2	Slender-billed Nuthatch	7
California Linnet	7	Western Ruby-crowned Kinglet	1
English Sparrow	2	Western Robin	5
Western Lark Sparrow	10	Western Bluebird	42
Golden-crowned and Intermediate sparrows	87		

Total: species 31, individuals 386.

PLEASANT VALLEY westward to high hill near Forty-nine Gap and return, 600 to 1700 feet, Upper Sonoran Zone, blue-oak, chaparral and grassland associations; May 24, 1915, 7:30 A.M.–12:30 P.M.; the day cloudy, considerable rain the night previous; distance covered about 8 miles.

Killdeer	4	Pacific Black-headed Grosbeak	6
Valley Quail	4	Lazuli Bunting	6
Western Mourning Dove	30+	Western Tanager	10+
Turkey Vulture	20+	Cliff Swallow	10
Cooper Hawk	1	Barn Swallow	4
Western Red-tailed Hawk	1	Northern Violet-green Swallow	20+
Nuttall Woodpecker	12+	Phainopepla	8+
California Woodpecker	10+	California Shrike	1
Lewis Woodpecker	8+	Cassin Vireo	4
Red-shafted Flicker	2	California Least Vireo	1
Anna Hummingbird	1	California Yellow Warbler	2
Western Kingbird	6	Townsend Warbler	4
Ash-throated Flycatcher	25+	Warblers (species?)	10+
Olive-sided Flycatcher	1	Long-tailed Chat	3
Western Wood Pewee	20+	California Thrasher	1
Wright (?) Flycatcher	6+	Rock Wren	2
Interior California Jay	8+	Dotted Cañon Wren	2
Western Meadowlark	20+	San Joaquin Bewick Wren	6+
Bullock Oriole	25+	Plain Titmouse	30+
Brewer Blackbird	20+	California Bush-tit	8+
California Linnet	40+	Pallid Wren-tit	6
Green-backed Goldfinch	10	Western Gnatcatcher	16+
Western Lark Sparrow	20+	Russet-backed Thrush	2
Western Chipping Sparrow	8	Western Bluebird	20+
Northern Brown Towhee	4		

Total: species 48, individuals 488+.

Smith Creek (Dudley), 3000 feet, Transition Zone, riparian, grassland and forest associations; July 21, 1920, 8:10–11:10 A.M.; the day clear, hot; distance travelled about 6 miles, on foot, from Dudley northeast over ridge, thence down a cañon to Smith Creek and back up to Dudley.

Mountain Quail	11+	Western Lark Sparrow	2
Western Mourning Dove	3	Sierra Junco	1
Modoc Woodpecker	1	Sacramento Spurred Towhee	4
Willow Woodpecker	1	Northern Brown Towhee	7
Northern White-headed Woodpecker	1	Pacific Black-headed Grosbeak	6
California Woodpecker	5	Western Tanager	8
Red-shafted Flicker	6	Western Warbling Vireo	5
Anna Hummingbird	2	Cassin Vireo	1
Black Phoebe	3	Hutton Vireo	1
Western Wood Pewee	13	Black-throated Gray Warbler	1
Traill Flycatcher	5	Sierra Creeper	1
Blue-fronted Jay	8	Slender-billed Nuthatch	5
Interior California Jay	13	Red-breasted Nuthatch	1
Western Meadowlark	1	California Bush-tit	8
California Purple Finch	4	Western Gnatcatcher	2
California Linnet	9	Western Robin	5
Green-backed Goldfinch	8	Western Bluebird	15

Total: species 34, individuals 167+.

El Portal and vicinity, 2000 feet, Upper Sonoran Zone with few Transition Zone elements, riparian, chaparral, and blue-oak and golden-oak associations; April 27, 1916, 7:00–11:40 A.M. (actual census time 4 hours); clear, hot day, little or no wind; distance covered about 5 miles, all on foot, within 2 miles of the settlement.

Valley Quail	1	Lazuli Bunting	10
Willow (?) Woodpecker	3	Northern Violet-green Swallow	5
California Woodpecker	6	Western Warbling Vireo	5
Red-shafted Flicker	2	Cassin Vireo	3
White-throated Swift	14	California Yellow Warbler	3
Ash-throated Flycatcher	12	Black-throated Gray Warbler	3
Blue-fronted Jay	1	Dotted Cañon Wren	2
Interior California Jay	17	San Joaquin Bewick Wren	3
Bullock Oriole	4	Western House Wren	5
California Linnet	1	Plain Titmouse	4
Green-backed Goldfinch	23	California Bush-tit	7
Western Chipping Sparrow	10	Pallid Wren-tit	4
Sacramento Spurred Towhee	13	Western Gnatcatcher	18
Northern Brown Towhee	14	Western Robin	4
Pacific Black-headed Grosbeak	5		

Total: species 29, individuals 202.

YOSEMITE VALLEY, altitude 4000 feet, Transition Zone, chaparral, meadow, forest and riparian associations, May 31, 1915, 2:00–6:00 P.M.; from Sentinel Hotel to LeConte Lodge, then across Stoneman Bridge and along Sequoia Lane, with many zig-zags to likely looking brush clumps or trees, or to run down doubtful songs.

Sharp-shinned Hawk	1	Pacific Black-headed Grosbeak	12+
Western Belted Kingfisher	2	Lazuli Bunting	3
Modoc Woodpecker	1	Western Tanager	8
California Woodpecker	4	Northern Violet-green Swallow	6+
Red-shafted Flicker	2	Western Warbling Vireo	15+
White-throated Swift	2	Cassin Vireo	15+
Calliope Hummingbird	2	California Yellow Warbler	20+
Western Wood Pewee	18+	Audubon Warbler	10+
Wright Flycatcher	1	Hermit Warbler	6+
Traill Flycatcher	6	Tolmie Warbler	3
Blue-fronted Jay	4	Sierra Creeper	1
Brewer Blackbird	1	Short-tailed Mountain Chickadee	2
California Purple Finch	6	Western Ruby-crowned Kinglet	4
Pine Siskin	12+	Russet-backed Thrush	2
Western Chipping Sparrow	16+	Sierra Hermit Thrush	1
Sacramento Spurred Towhee	4	Western Robin	30+

Total: species 32, individuals 220+.

YOSEMITE VALLEY, 4000–4500 feet, Transition Zone, forest, golden-oak and boulder-talus associations; June 3, 1915, 7:00–11:00 A.M.; clear day, windy; distance traveled about 8 miles, all on foot, from old Presidio down nearly to base of El Capitan and return, on Valley floor and up talus to base of cliff.

Band-tailed Pigeon	10	Western Warbling Vireo	12
California Woodpecker	4	Cassin Vireo	12
White-throated Swift	2	Calaveras Warbler	8
Western Wood Pewee	12	California Yellow Warbler	10
Traill Flycatcher	3	Audubon Warbler	2
Western Flycatcher	1	Hermit Warbler	2
Blue-fronted Jay	10	Black-throated Gray Warbler	4
California Purple Finch	4	Tolmie Warbler	1
Pine Siskin	12	Dotted Cañon Wren	2
Western Chipping Sparrow	24	Sierra Creeper	1
Sierra Junco	4	Red-breasted Nuthatch	1
Sacramento Spurred Towhee	2	Short-tailed Mountain Chickadee	2
Pacific Black-headed Grosbeak	8	Russet-backed Thrush	1
Lazuli Bunting	2	Sierra Hermit Thrush	2
Western Tanager	10	Western Robin	18

Total: species 30, individuals 186.

YOSEMITE VALLEY, 4000 feet, Transition Zone, forest, golden-oak, talus and chaparral associations; July 30, 1915, 7:30–10:00 A.M.; along north side of Valley from old Presidio to vicinity of Rocky Point and return; distance traveled about 4 miles.

Band-tailed Pigeon	4	Western Tanager	2
Red-shafted Flicker	1	Western Warbling Vireo	3
Western Wood Pewee	8	Cassin Vireo	2
Western Flycatcher	1	Black-throated Gray Warbler	5
Blue-fronted Jay	2	Dotted Cañon Wren	3
California Purple Finch	1	Sierra Creeper	2
Western Chipping Sparrow	12	Short-tailed Mountain Chickadee	4
Sacramento Spurred Towhee	2	Pallid Wren-tit	2
Pacific Black-headed Grosbeak	2		

Total: species 17, individuals 56.

YOSEMITE VALLEY, 4000 feet, Transition Zone, forest, chaparral and riparian associations; October 25, 1915, 2:35–5:35 P.M.; afternoon to late dusk of evening; weather clear; distance traveled about 6 miles, from old Presidio along north road to Kenneyville, to Camp Curry, to village, to Presidio, then to Ahwahnee footbridge and return.

American Sparrow Hawk	1	Audubon Warbler	6
California Pigmy Owl	3	American Dipper	2
Western Belted Kingfisher	2	Sierra Creeper	2
Willow Woodpecker	1	Short-tailed Mountain Chickadee	1
California Woodpecker	6	Western Golden-crowned Kinglet	11
Red-shafted Flicker	4	Western Ruby-crowned Kinglet	1
Blue-fronted Jay	12	Hermit Thrush (Alaska?)	2
Golden-crowned Sparrow	1	Western Robin	10
Sierra Junco	12	Western Bluebird	23

Total: species 18, individuals 100.

YOSEMITE VALLEY, 4000 feet, Transition Zone, chiefly in forest association; December 10, 1914, 7:50 A.M.–12:10 P.M.; eight inches of fresh snow on ground, and snow falling off and on during the morning; trees heavily laden with snow; from village via Camp Curry and Clark Bridge to Mirror Lake and up lower zigzags on Tenaya Lake trail, returning by same route.

California Pigmy Owl	1	Sierra Creeper	4
Modoc Woodpecker	4+	Short-tailed Mountain Chickadee	2
Red-shafted Flicker	1	Hermit Thrush (Alaska?)	1
Blue-fronted Jay	1	Western Robin	2
Dotted Cañon Wren	1	Western Bluebird	9+

Total: species 10, individuals 26+.

YOSEMITE VALLEY, 4000 feet, Transition Zone, forest and riparian associations; February 29, 1916, 1:30–3:00 P.M.; about 3 feet of snow on ground; distance covered about 2 miles, west of village in vicinity of Camp Ahwahnee.

Duck	1	Red-breasted Nuthatch	3
Western Belted Kingfisher	1	Short-tailed Mountain Chickadee	2
Sierra Junco	15+	Western Golden-crowned Kinglet	25+
American Dipper	1	Townsend Solitaire (?)	1
Sierra Creeper	3		

Total: species 9, individuals 52+.

YOSEMITE VALLEY, 4000 feet, Transition Zone, forest, meadow, chaparral and riparian associations; April 29, 1916, 7:10–10:55 A.M. (actual census time 3 hours 30 minutes); a bright day with few thin clouds and slight wind; distance covered 8 miles, from village to Yosemite Falls Camp, to El Capitan bridge, and return to village.

Mountain Quail	1	Western Warbling Vireo	33
Red-shafted Flicker	4	Cassin Vireo	29
White-throated Swift	1	Calaveras Warbler	3
Calliope Hummingbird	1	California Yellow Warbler	13
Wright (?) Flycatcher	5	Audubon Warbler	13
Blue-fronted Jay	10	Hermit Warbler	31
California Purple Finch	7	Golden Pileolated Warbler	1
Sierra Crossbill (?)	2	Sierra Creeper	7
Pine Siskin	22	Red-breasted Nuthatch	3
Western Chipping Sparrow	35	Short-tailed Mountain Chickadee	2
Sierra Junco	25	Western Golden-crowned Kinglet	3
Sacramento Spurred Towhee	6	Western Ruby-crowned Kinglet	6
Pacific Black-headed Grosbeak	11	Western Robin	20

Total: species 26, individuals 294.

CRANE FLAT TO MERCED GROVE BIG TREES, 6000–5500 feet, Canadian and Transition zones, coniferous and oak forest, meadow and riparian associations; June 15, 1915, 7:30–11:00 A.M.; the day clear and hot; distance traveled about 4 miles, in more or less direct course between the two stations but with many short side trips to examine 'unknowns' or to study rare species.

Mountain Quail	4	Western Warbling Vireo	6
Sierra Grouse	1	Cassin Vireo	1
Sierra Red-breasted Sapsucker	1	California Yellow Warbler	8
Red-shafted Flicker	1	Audubon Warbler	3
Calliope Hummingbird	3	Black-throated Gray Warbler	5
Olive-sided Flycatcher	5	Hermit Warbler	3
Western Wood Pewee	5	Golden Pileolated Warbler	1
Hammond (?) Flycatcher	5	Western Winter Wren	1
Western Flycatcher	1	Sierra Creeper	8
Blue-fronted Jay	3	Red-breasted Nuthatch	4
California Evening Grosbeak	2	Pigmy Nuthatch (?)	flock
Pine Siskin	3+	Short-tailed Mountain Chickadee	8
Western Chipping Sparrow	10+	Western Ruby-crowned Kinglet	5+
Sierra Junco	20+	Russet-backed Thrush	1
Mariposa Fox Sparrow	8	Sierra Hermit Thrush	2
Green-tailed Towhee	5	Western Robin	10+
Western Tanager	6		

Total: species 33, individuals 149+.

BIG OAK FLAT ROAD below Gentrys, 4500–5700 feet, Transition Zone, golden-oak, talus, yellow-pine, and chaparral associations; December 28, 1914, 9:40 A.M.–1:30 P.M.; the day clear, crackling cold, trees covered with frost, snow on ground; distance traveled about 4 miles.

Golden Eagle	2	Western Ruby-crowned Kinglet	1
Blue-fronted Jay	1	Townsend Solitaire	42+
Sierra Junco	14+	Hermit Thrush (Alaska?)	2
Hutton Vireo	2	Northern Varied Thrush	8+
Dotted Cañon Wren	3	Western Bluebird	143+

Total: species 10, individuals 218+.

CHINQUAPIN and below, along Indian Creek, 6200 to 4500 feet, Canadian and Transition zones, forest association chiefly; June 11, 1915, 7:30–11:30 A.M.; distance covered about 7 miles, going and returning along different routes.

Mountain Quail	6	Western Tanager	6
Sharp-shinned Hawk	1	Western Warbling Vireo	8+
Northern White-headed Woodpecker	1	Cassin Vireo	1
Calliope Hummingbird	1	Calaveras Warbler	10+
Olive-sided Flycatcher	2	Audubon Warbler	2
Western Wood Pewee	4	Hermit Warbler	5
Wright Flycatcher	10+	Golden Pileolated Warbler	2
Blue-fronted Jay	4+	Sierra Creeper	8+
Purple Finch (species?)	2	Red-breasted Nuthatch	8+
Sierra Junco	18	Sierra Hermit Thrush	2
Mariposa Fox Sparrow	12+	Townsend Solitaire	1
Pacific Black-headed Grosbeak	2		

Total: species 23, individuals 116+.

CHINQUAPIN to MONO MEADOW along ''Glacier Point road,'' 6200–7700 feet, Canadian Zone, forest, riparian and chaparral associations; June 18, 1915, 7:20–10:30 A.M.; distance covered about 8 miles.

Mountain Quail	2	Green-tailed Towhee	2
Northern White-headed Woodpecker	2	Pacific Black-headed Grosbeak	1
Northern Pileated Woodpecker	2	Western Tanager	6
Olive-sided Flycatcher	3	Western Warbling Vireo	4
Wright Flycatcher	10	Audubon Warbler	6
Blue-fronted Jay	6	Tolmie Warbler	2
Cassin Purple Finch	4	Golden Pileolated Warbler	7
Pine Siskin	1	Sierra Creeper	2
Western Chipping Sparrow	8	Red-breasted Nuthatch	4
Sierra Junco	30	Short-tailed Mountain Chickadee	6
Northeastern Lincoln Sparrow	8	Western Ruby-crowned Kinglet	10
Mariposa Fox Sparrow	10	Western Robin	12

Total: species 24, individuals 148.

Above YOSEMITE FALLS, 6600–7300 feet, Canadian Zone, chaparral and forest associations; October 30, 1915, 10:20 A.M.–4:20 P.M.; distance traveled about 5 miles, from top of zigzags, along old Snow Flat trail to west branch of Indian Cañon, and return.

Cooper Hawk	1	Kadiak Fox Sparrow	5
Western Red-tailed Hawk	2	Sacramento Spurred Towhee	1
Modoc Woodpecker	1	Red-breasted Nuthatch	14
Northern Pileated Woodpecker	1	Slender-billed Nuthatch	2
Red-shafted Flicker	2	Short-tailed Mountain Chickadee	20
Blue-fronted Jay	22	Western Golden-crowned Kinglet	3
Clark Nutcracker	1	Townsend Solitaire	13
California Evening Grosbeak	4	Western Robin	4
Cassin Purple Finch	4	Northern Varied Thrush	3
Golden-crowned Sparrow	1	Western Bluebird	2

Total: species 20, individuals 106.

TIOGA ROAD between Porcupine Flat and Snow Flat, and return, 8100 to 8700 feet, across Canadian-Hudsonian Zone boundary, forest and meadow associations; June 28, 1915, 6:55 A.M. to 1:45 P.M. (actual census time 5 hours 45 minutes); clear, moderately warm, much snow about, covering road in places; distance covered about 6 miles, by two observers jointly.

Mountain Quail	4	Mariposa Fox Sparrow	5
Sierra Grouse	2	Green-tailed Towhee	2
Modoc Woodpecker	1	Western Tanager	6
Williamson Sapsucker	4	Western Warbling Vireo	7
Red-shafted Flicker	1	Audubon Warbler	9
Olive-sided Flycatcher	3	Golden Pileolated Warbler	3
Western Wood Pewee	8	Sierra Creeper	3
Blue-fronted Jay	5	Red-breasted Nuthatch	8
Clark Nutcracker	4	Short-tailed Mountain Chickadee	9
Cassin Purple Finch	3	Western Golden-crowned Kinglet	7
Pine Siskin	18	Western Ruby-crowned Kinglet	14
Western Chipping Sparrow	9	Townsend Solitaire	1
Sierra Junco	12	Sierra Hermit Thrush	9
Northeastern Lincoln Sparrow	1	Western Robin	6

Total: species 28, individuals 164.

MERCED LAKE, 7500 feet, Canadian Zone, forest and riparian associations; August 20, 1915, 8:00–10:30 A.M.; distance traveled about 2 miles, all within one mile of upper end of lake.

Red-shafted Flicker	1	Cassin Vireo	2
Hammond Flycatcher	2	Calaveras Warbler	2
Blue-fronted Jay	2	Audubon Warbler	2
Sierra Junco	8+	Red-breasted Nuthatch	2
Mariposa Fox Sparrow	1	Short-tailed Mountain Chickadee	4
Western Warbling Vireo	2	Western Ruby-crowned Kinglet	2

Total: species 12, individuals 30+.

VOGELSANG LAKE to Evelyn Lake and return, via Fletcher Creek, 10,350 feet, Hudsonian Zone, rock-slide, riparian and white-bark pine associations; September 4, 1915, 7:30 A.M.–12:30 P.M. (but actual census time 4 hours); heavy frost in morning, ice on quiet pools; distance traveled about 5 miles.

Western Mourning Dove	1	Lutescent Warbler	1
Prairie Falcon	1	Audubon Warbler	14
Blue-fronted Jay	1	American Dipper	3
Clark Nutcracker	7	Short-tailed Mountain Chickadee	4
Hudsonian White-crowned Sparrow	7+	Western Gnatcatcher	1
Sierra Junco	10		

Total: species 11, individuals 50+.

GLEN AULIN, 7700 feet, Hudsonian-Canadian Zone boundary, riparian and forest associations; September 30, 1915, 9:15 A.M.–12:15 P.M.; clear, moderately warm in sunlight, west wind; distance covered about 4 miles, in territory northeast of the Glen.

Western Belted Kingfisher	1	Audubon Warbler	8
Red-shafted Flicker	4	American Dipper	1
Blue-fronted Jay	3	Short-tailed Mountain Chickadee	24
Clark Nutcracker	5	Townsend Solitaire	23
Sierra Junco	15+	Western Robin	2

Total: species 10, individuals 86+.

TUOLUMNE MEADOWS, 8600 feet, Hudsonian Zone, forest, riparian and meadow associations; July 7, 1915, 8:00–10:00, 11:00–11:45 A.M.; clear, sunny, warm; distance traveled about 4 miles, chiefly along road on south side of meadows.

Spotted Sandpiper	3	Sierra Junco	11
Killdeer	2	Green-tailed Towhee (?)	1
Pacific Nighthawk	2	Audubon Warbler	3
Western Wood Pewee	8	Short-tailed Mountain Chickadee	2
Cassin Purple Finch	4	Western Ruby-crowned Kinglet	3
Pine Siskin	11	Sierra Hermit Thrush	1
Hudsonian White-crowned Sparrow	11	Western Robin	12
Western Chipping Sparrow	2	Mountain Bluebird	4

Total: species 16, individuals 80.

YOUNG LAKE (near Conness Mountain) to Tuolumne Meadows, 10,000–8600 feet, Hudsonian Zone, forest, meadow and rock-slide associations; 8:30 A.M.–12:30 P.M., July 9, 1915; clear, hot, slight westerly wind; distance covered about 7 miles.

Golden Eagle	1	Sierra Junco	18
Western Wood Pewee	4	Audubon Warbler	4
Wright (?) Flycatcher	1	Rock Wren	4
Clark Nutcracker	7	Short-tailed Mountain Chickadee	8
Cassin Purple Finch	12	Western Ruby-crowned Kinglet	3
Pine Siskin	10	Sierra Hermit Thrush	4
Hudsonian White-crowned Sparrow	1	Western Robin	4
Western Chipping Sparrow	1	Mountain Bluebird	5

Total: species 16, individuals 87.

WARREN FORK OF LEEVINING CREEK, 9200–11,000 feet, upper part of Hudsonian Zone, open forest and cliff associations, chiefly; September 26, 1915, 7:10 A.M.–2:30 P.M.; after slight snowstorm on September 25, partially clear day; distance covered about 10 miles, from camp in cañon up onto Tioga Crest, thence around head of cañon to southwest slope of Warren Mountain, and return.

Sierra Grouse	8+	Cassin Purple Finch	11+
Hawk (unidentified)	1	Sierra Nevada Rosy Finch	16
Owl (probably Horned)	1	Sierra Junco	59+
Modoc Woodpecker	1	American Pipit	2
Williamson Sapsucker	2	American Dipper	2
Red-shafted Flicker	3	Short-tailed Mountain Chickadee	21+
Clark Nutcracker	45+	Mountain Bluebird	11

Total: species 14, individuals 183+.

FARRINGTON RANCH to Walker Lake and return, 6600–8000 feet, Transition and Canadian zones, meadow, riparian and sagebrush associations; May 9, 1916, 2:00–7:00 P.M.; strong west wind; distance traveled about 12 miles, returning through sagebrush on ridge adjacent to Williams Butte.

California Gull	1	Western Vesper Sparrow	2
Mountain Quail	1	Nevada Savannah Sparrow	8
Sierra Grouse	3	Hudsonian White-crowned Sparrow	5
Western Mourning Dove	16	Brewer Sparrow	2
American Sparrow Hawk	1	Sierra Junco	4
Long-eared Owl	1	Modoc Song Sparrow	2
Red-shafted Flicker	3	Mono Fox Sparrow	1
Lewis Woodpecker	2	Green-tailed Towhee	1
Traill (?) Flycatcher	1	Western Tanager	1
Black-billed Magpie	2	Audubon Warbler	4
Blue-fronted Jay	1	Alaska Pileolated Warbler	1
Clark Nutcracker	6	Western House Wren	1
Nevada Red-winged Blackbird	25	Western Robin	13
Western Meadowlark	7	Mountain Bluebird	4

Total: species 28, individuals 119.

FARRINGTON RANCH (near Mono Lake) to MONO CRATERS and June Lake, and return; Transition and Canadian zones, sagebrush, Jeffrey-pine and meadow associations; September 17, 1915, 7:50 A.M.–6:50 P.M.; distance covered about 25 miles, on horseback.

Mud-hen	100+	Intermediate White-crowned Sparrow	3+
Marsh Hawk	1	Brewer Sparrow	107+
Large Hawk (Red-tailed?)	1	Small sparrows (*Spizella*)	3
American Sparrow Hawk	1	Nevada Sage Sparrow	10
Red-shafted Flicker	1	Green-tailed Towhee	12
Say Phoebe	1	Audubon Warbler	4
Dusky Horned Lark	14+	Sage Thrasher	7
Clark Nutcracker	18+	Sierra Creeper	1
Piñon Jay	51+	Slender-billed Nuthatch	9+
Western Meadowlark	1	Pigmy Nuthatch	1+
Brewer Blackbird	106+	Short-tailed Mountain Chickadee	11+
California Linnet	6	Mountain Bluebird	1
Western Vesper Sparrow	8+		

Total: species 25, individuals 478+.

MONO LAKE POST OFFICE and vicinity, Transition Zone, willow-cottonwood, meadow and sagebrush associations; May 31, 1916, 7:00 A.M.–12:00 M.; weather bright and warm; distance traveled about 2½ miles, chiefly along lake shore.

American Eared Grebe	50	Modoc Song Sparrow	13
California Gull	13	Green-tailed Towhee	2
Black-chinned Hummingbird	1	Pacific Black-headed Grosbeak	3
Western Kingbird	2	Lazuli Bunting	1
Western Wood Pewee	14	Rocky Mountain Orange-crowned	
Traill Flycatcher	14	Warbler	4
Nevada Cowbird	3	Yellow Warbler	34
Nevada Red-winged Blackbird	22	Townsend Warbler	2
Western Meadowlark	6	Tolmie Warbler	4
Brewer Blackbird	16	Western Yellowthroat	3
Nevada Savannah Sparrow	1	Pileolated Warbler	57
Western Lark Sparrow	1	Western House Wren	3
Hudsonian White-crowned Sparrow	4	Western Robin	13
Brewer Sparrow	2	Mountain Bluebird	5

Total: species 27, individuals 293.

THE INTERRELATIONS OF LIVING THINGS

That forests afford the means of existence for a great number of animals, with reference to both species and individuals, is a trite statement which no one is likely to question. We would offer, however—albeit with some caution—a second statement: Forests depend, for their maintenance in the condition in which we observe them in this age of the world, upon the activities, severally and combined, of the animals which inhabit them.

Beginning at the root of the matter, in a double sense, as we have emphasized beyond in the chapter on the pocket gophers, mammals which burrow are of importance to forests. The pocket gophers, the ground squirrels, the moles and the badgers, are natural cultivators of the soil (see p. 142), and it is, in considerable degree, the result of their presence down through long series of years that the ground has been rendered suitable for the growth of grasses and herbs, and even of bushes and trees, particularly in their seedling stages. A host of insects, also, which live in the ground at least part of their lives, contribute to rendering the soil more productive of vegetable life.

Vegetable materials, leaves, twigs and trunks of trees as well, contribute to soil accretion by reason of their being torn to pieces by animals (see p. 322), their particles scattered by animals, and these finally overlaid by the earth brought up by animals from deeper substrata. The animals which figure conspicuously in this process are the woodpeckers, chickadees, and nuthatches, the tree squirrels, chipmunks, and porcupines, the burrowing beetles, the termites, and the ants, and then the burrowing and burying mammals already referred to. This process of incorporating humus into the soil, accomplished in large measure by animals, is of direct and lasting importance to the forests.

We do not make any claim that *all* animal life is directly beneficial to the forests. For many insects may be *seen* to feed upon the foliage, the bark, and even the live wood of individual trees, and in so doing such insects shorten the lives of these trees, or even sometimes kill them outright within a single season. It is obvious that a sudden overabundance of such destructive insects would bring serious injury to the forests.

But observation has led us to recognize, in certain groups of *birds*, natural checks to undue increase of forest-infesting insects. Insects of one category inhabit the bark of a tree or the layers of wood immediately beneath; others pursue their existence among the smaller twigs; still others live amid the foliage of the tree. In all these cases the substance of the tree is levied upon by the insects for food, and if levied upon unduly, the trees suffer commensurately. But, as counteracting factors, we find corresponding categories of birds, each specially equipped to make use of one of these categories of insects. The woodpeckers, nuthatches, and creepers search the tree trunks and larger limbs; the chickadees comb the finer twigs; while the kinglets and warblers go over the foliage leaf by leaf. The great value of the bird to the tree comes when the harmful insects have begun to multiply abnormally; for birds are well known to turn from other food sources and concentrate upon the one suddenly offering in generous measure.

It is to the interest of the forest at large that a reserve nucleus of birds be maintained constantly, as a form of insurance, to be ready at just such a critical time. Incursions of insects from neighboring areas, as well as eruptions of endemic species, have probably occurred again and again from remote times. In other words, as we see the situation, it is an advantage to the forest that a continual moderate supply of insects be maintained for the support of a standing army of insectivorous birds, which army will turn its attention to whatever insect plague happens suddenly to manifest itself.

We would claim, then, a nice interdependence, an adjustment, by which the insect and the bird, the bird and the tree, the tree and the insect, all are, under average circumstances, mutually benefited. Such a balance is to be found in the primeval forest, where thoroughly 'natural' conditions obtain as a result of long ages of evolution on the part of all the animate things there touching upon one another's lives. These relations may, of course, be entirely upset where man has interfered, directly or indirectly; as, for instance, when he brings in insects or plants alien to the original fauna and flora. Then an entirely new program, one of readjustment, begins.

After a good deal of study, and contemplation of the modes of life of various kinds of animals, naturalists have come to recognize as essential *three* factors which seem inseparably bound up with the successful existence of any one species of vertebrate animal. These factors are: (1) presence of safe breeding places, adapted to the varying needs of the animal; in other words, depending upon the inherent powers of construction, defense, and concealment in the species concerned. (2) Presence of places of temporary refuge for individuals, during daytime or night-time, or while foraging, when hard pressed by predatory enemies, again correlated with the inherent powers of defense and concealment of the species involved. (3) Kind of food supply afforded, with regard, of course, to the inherent structural powers in the animal concerned to make it available.

To say all this a bit more simply, not alone food is necessary to the bird life or the mammal life in our forests, but also safe places for rearing young, and places of refuge when needed, for the grown-up individuals themselves. Referring again to the relationships borne between certain insects, birds, and trees: The White-headed Woodpecker (see p. 320) is a species which does practically all of its foraging on trees which are living, gleaning from them a variety of bark-inhabiting insects. But the White-headed Woodpecker lacks an effective equipment for digging into *hard* wood. It must have dead and *decaying* tree trunks in which to excavate its nesting holes. If, by any means, the standing *dead* trees in the forests were all removed at one time, the White-headed Woodpecker could not continue to exist past the present generation, because no broods could be reared according to the inherent habits and structural limitations of the species. Within a woodpecker generation, the forests would be deprived of the beneficent presence of this bird. The same, we believe, is true of certain nuthatches and of the chickadees—industrious gleaners of insect life from living trees. They must have dead tree trunks in which to establish nesting and roosting places, safe for and accessible to birds of their limited powers of construction and defense.

We would go so far, even, as to urge that *down* timber, fallen and decaying logs, are essential factors in upholding the balance of animal life in forests. Certain kinds of chipmunks, and rats and mice of various kinds, find only in fallen logs homes adapted for their particular ways of living. And these chipmunks and other rodents have to do with seed scattering, with seed planting, and with humus building, again directly affecting the interests of the chaparral, of the young trees, and even of the older trees of the forest.

It is true that there are some kinds of birds and mammals which at times directly injure trees to an appreciable extent. The birds of the genus of woodpeckers called sapsuckers (see p. 327) drain the vitality of the trees they attack. An overabundance of these birds would bring disaster to the forest at large. An overabundance, likewise, of tree squirrels (see pp. 202, 208) would probably play havoc with certain trees, beyond the powers of these trees to meet the crisis.

Just as in the case of the leaf-eating insects and of the kinglets in the arboreal foliage, these birds and mammals of the sapsucker and tree-squirrel category are kept in check by other, predatory birds and mammals. In the Sierran woods are Great Gray Owls and Spotted Owls, Cooper Hawks, Martens, and Weasels, levying upon the vertebrate life about them, and each equipped by size, degree of alertness, or time of foraging, to make use of some certain sort of prey. The longer we study the problem the clearer it becomes that in the natural forests, which, happily, are being preserved to us in our National Parks, a finely adjusted interrelation exists, amounting to a mutual interdependence, by which all the animal and plant species are within them able to pursue their careers down through time successfully.

The opportunity here to moralize is tempting. If the above course of reasoning be well founded, then, to realize, esthetically and scientifically, the greatest benefit to ourselves from the plant and animal life in Yosemite Park, its original balance must be maintained. No trees, whether living or dead, should be cut down beyond what it may be necessary to remove in building roads or for practical elimination of danger, locally, from fire. Dead trees are in many respects as useful in the plan of nature as living ones, and should be just as rigorously conserved. When they fall, it should be only through the natural processes of decay. The brilliant-hued woodpeckers that render effective service in protecting the living trees from recurrent scourges of destructive insects, in other words, in keeping up the healthy tone of the forest, depend in part on the dead and even the fallen trees for their livelihood.

No more undergrowth should be destroyed anywhere in the Park than is absolutely necessary for specific purposes. To many birds and mammals, thickets are protective havens which their enemies find it difficult or impossible to penetrate. Moreover, the majority of the chaparral plants are berry-producing and give sustenance to mountain quail, to wild pigeons, to robins and thrushes, to chipmunks and squirrels, and this, too, at the most critical times of the year when other foods for these animals are scarce or wanting. The removal of any of these elements would inevitably reduce the native complement of animal life. Nor do we approve, as a rule, of the destruction of carnivorous animals—hawks, owls, foxes, coyotes, fur-bearers in general—within the Park. Each species occupies a niche of its own, where normally it carries on its existence in perfect harmony on the whole with the larger scheme of living nature.

ACCOUNTS OF THE SPECIES

Scope

In the chapters to follow, dealing with the three hundred and fifty-five kinds of terrestrial vertebrate animals in the Yosemite section, general uniformity of treatment has been one aim. For each species there is given, first, the accepted or approved vernacular name; then the scientific name, chosen with regard to the best technical usage. The order in which the chapters follow one another is essentially that in which the species are classified in the standard lists of North American vertebrates; namely, for mammals, Miller's List of North American Land Mammals in the United States National Museum, 1911; for birds, the American Ornithologists' Union Check-list of North American Birds, edition 3, 1910; and for reptiles and amphibians, Stejneger and Barbour's Check List of North American Amphibians and Reptiles, 1917. Departures from these authorities, either in sequence or in names employed, have been made occasionally by us, but only when justified by special study.

The present volume is not a systematic treatise in the sense of relating primarily to descriptive zoology or to classification. Hence, technicalities along these lines are reduced to a minimum, being mentioned briefly, or restricted to small-type footnotes. *The* theme of the present book is *natural history*—that which relates to the *living* animal.

The "field characters" are intended to include the chief features by which each species may be recognized out of doors. They do not have to do with the scientific 'specimen,' such as constitutes the basis of the usual descriptive account. Ideally, our "field characters" are such as are discernible in the living animal at the ordinary eye-range into which a person can approach the animal under normal conditions. The great majority of these characterizations have been derived from our own observations in the Yosemite region, as recorded in our notebooks. Exceptionally, we have drawn upon our experience elsewhere; or, in the few cases where experience was lacking altogether, we have drawn upon specimens for characters inferred to be useful in the field.

In small mammals and in reptiles and amphibians, the field characterization has been amplified to cover their appearance and proportions when in hand; for opportunity to capture these animals often presents itself to an out-of-doors observer. Even in these cases, however, it is exclusively the external, macroscopic features of the animal that are set forth in the paragraph on "field characters."

Field characters may consist in relative size, in proportions of parts, in general color tone, in pattern of contrasted markings, in peculiarities of movement (flight, gait, mannerisms), in voice, and, with many mammals, in 'sign' (foot-prints, tooth-marks, droppings). Measurements are given, more especially with mammals, and are stated as a rule in both inches and millimeters. Otherwise, size is indicated by comparison with some animal commonly familiar. Since size impressions in the field are likely to associate themselves in memory with the best known animals, comparisons among birds are most often made with the robin; among mammals, with the house mouse, house rat, or house cat.

Our paragraph on "occurrence" relates explicitly to the Yosemite section. The status we give of each species is as based on actual findings *in* the Yosemite section, not upon inference from conditions in the surrounding territory. It must not be supposed to apply to the Sierras generally or to any larger area. "Occurrence" is intended to cover concisely the concepts: season, relative abundance, and distribution by geography, life zones, and vegetational tracts.

In the general, large-type account next following, there will often be found one or more paragraphs discussing some or all of the field characters, especially in comparison with similar species with which confusion in the field might occur. In some cases, characters are discussed with relation to the distinctive habits of the species in question; in other words, correlation of structure and function may be dealt with.

But, let it be emphasized by repetition that, save for only occasional general statements, each account is limited to what was found out by us in the Yosemite region. This will explain the very uneven magnitude of the accounts. Their relative degree of comprehensiveness merely reflects our own varying opportunities of observation. A number of well-known species of the Sierras at large are given but meager attention here because opportunity did not present itself for studying them adequately in the Yosemite 'section.'

Each general account, where the facts have been fully available, has been drawn up, with regard to its subject-matter, on a more or less definite plan of presentation. An introductory paragraph gives local names, other than the accepted vernacular, and an epitome of the leading facts about the species. Comparisons with related species are then made. There follows a discussion of its distribution in the Yosemite region and the special nature of its habitat preferences. Then comes a description of the animal's behavior; its voice; nests, or dens; eggs, or young; care of young; and its feeding habits. We give as much as we have learned with respect to the food of the species, and its relation to plant life in general; also, its relation to other animals, as predator or victim. And, finally, though not appearing at any definite point in the account, we attempt to point out where general biological principles are illustrated.

The facts observed have been gathered together in orderly sequence, and every effort has been made to secure accuracy of expression. Where these facts, thus assembled, point toward some generalization, we have felt free to set it forth. At the same time, we have tried to refrain from idle speculation.

The study of natural history should develop the power of insight—keenness, not only in seeing what animals do, but in determining why those things are done. The interrelations existing between any animal and its environment are exceedingly manifold and vital. To understand these, even in some small degree, brings into play a superior type of intellectual activity, and, we believe, leads to enhanced powers of perceiving and solving human problems. We therefore recommend to the reader that he take advantage of his opportunities to observe and infer without limit beyond whatever we may have set forth herein, to the end that he find both pleasure and profit.

THE MAMMALS

Moles. **Scapanus latimanus** (Bachman)[1]

Field characters.—Total length 6 to 6¾ inches (150–170 mm.), tail about 1½ inches (38 mm.); body short and cylindrical; snout long and pointed (fig. 4); forefeet with greatly expanded and flattened palms and long heavy claws (fig. 5a); tail scantily and coarsely haired; no eyes or ears visible. Pelage short, soft, plush-like in texture; coloration uniform, dark brown, gray, or blackish (according to subspecies), appearing silvery when smoothed down. *Habits:* Strictly subterranean; live in tunnels formed by the animals themselves in the ground. *Workings:* Low raised ridges (containing runways) along the surface of ground; also, less commonly, mounds of earth with irregular surface, erupted from underground tunnels, and with no indication left of any opening to burrow (fig. 22).

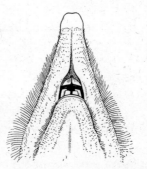

Fig. 4. Snout of Yosemite mole, from below, showing elongate tip beyond mouth, short front (incisor) teeth, and heavy covering of hairs on sides of face. Twice natural size.

Occurrence.—Present in small to moderate numbers locally across the Yosemite region; noted from Snelling eastward to Mono Mills and up to an altitude of 9500 feet (in Lyell Cañon); especially common in meadows of Yosemite Valley.[1] Individuals live and work independently.

The mole and the pocket gopher, and the respective workings of the two, are often confused in the popular mind. The two animals, and their workings, however, are entirely distinct in practically all respects save that both inhabit the ground. In most places in California, and this includes the Yosemite region, moles are much less common than gophers. This fact probably accounts for some of the misunderstanding which has arisen. By careful searching we found some evidence of moles at almost every locality which we visited in the section (below the 9500 foot contour) from the San Joaquin Valley eastward across the mountains to Mono Lake. On the floor

---

[1] Three slightly differing subspecies of moles occur in the Yosemite section. These, with their principal external characters, and ranges, are as follows:

YOSEMITE MOLE, *Scapanus latimanus sericatus* Jackson, distinguished by relatively large size and blackish coloration, is found in the Transition and Canadian zones, sparingly in the Hudsonian, from 3 miles east of Coulterville eastward to Tuolumne Meadows. It is abundant in Yosemite Valley.

SAN JOAQUIN MOLE, *Scapanus latimanus campi* Grinnell and Storer, a smaller, paler and more brownish colored form, occurs in the Lower Sonoran Zone, at Snelling.

MONO MOLE, *Scapanus latimanus monoensis* Grinnell, a still smaller and grayish-toned subspecies, was found near Williams Butte; its workings were noted at Mono Mills.

The workings of these three races are alike in all respects, save for differences conditioned by the various sorts of ground in which they occur. Thus the forage runways of *monoensis* in the dry sandy soil of the Mono Lake region are more likely to be caved in than are those of *sericatus* on the damp forest floor in the mountains.

[43]

of Yosemite Valley there is an unusually large mole population, and, as gophers are present also in considerable numbers, the habits of the two may there be studied and compared to good advantage.

The mole is rather more strictly subterranean than the gopher. The latter animal is not infrequently seen at the mouth of its burrow, and occasionally it comes clear out on the top of the ground. The mole, however, habitually stays below the surface. All of its foraging is done in the ground; even when excavating a burrow, the animal itself is not exposed to view from above. Moles are said to run about on the surface of the ground at mating time, but of this we have no direct knowledge.

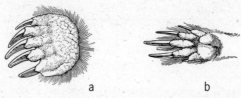

a   b

Fig. 5. Forefoot of (*a*) Yosemite Mole and of (*b*) Sierra Nevada Pocket Gopher. The Mole's palm is greatly expanded and the claws are relatively huge, which features together with powerful arm and shoulder muscles make it possible for the animal almost literally to swim through the earth; the Gopher's foot is less extreme, yet with elongated claws for special service in digging and with hairs between the toes which serve to increase the area of the foot when loose earth is being pushed out of or along the burrow. Natural size.

In physical configuration the mole is admirably suited for life underground (pl. 27*c*). Its nose is long and pointed and equipped with numerous fine sensory bristles. The mouth opens on the under side of the head where dirt is less likely to enter when the animal is burrowing. The head joins directly onto the firm stout cylindrical body without any constriction at the neck region. The body as a whole is an 'entering wedge.' The forelegs are extremely short so that the feet lie close alongside the head. The front feet are highly modified to form 'spades,' the palms being enlarged into thickened discs and turned outward, and the nails or claws being elongated and very stout. By means of these broad strong members the mole literally swims through the loose surface soil. The hind feet are much smaller and quite normal in shape and function. The body ends behind abruptly, and there is a short tail but scantily haired. The whole body of the mole is densely covered with short hairs of remarkably uniform length and texture which give a silky plush-like effect to the pelage. This sort of coat enables the animal to pass through the ground with a minimum of resistance; in other words, it acts as a lubricant.

The mole makes and uses two distinct sorts of underground passageways. One of these is the 'surface' runway, actually a subsurface run or subway, an inch or less below the top of the ground. The mole 'swims' along by strokes of the forefeet; its feet and body push the soil up in a low ridge, leaving numerous small lengthwise cracks showing on the outside (pl. 28*a*). These runs go here and there along the ground, between rocks and beside logs; they are made when the mole is searching for the worms and ground-dwelling insects which it uses as food. The second type of shelter, formed by actual excavation as in a gopher's burrow, is a regular underground tunnel, circular in section, and situated at a greater depth in the ground. The mole's tunnels are not so extensive and are of less diameter than those of any of the gophers of the region. To make these deep burrows the mole must force the loosened earth out onto the surface of the ground. This it does through laterals constructed at short intervals. Earth is loosened below ground (by the use of the forefeet?), then is forced along the existing tunnel way presumably by the joint use of forefeet and chin (though the actual method of operation has yet to be seen), and it is then forced up a lateral. As we stated before, there is never any direct opening to the exterior. Each fresh lot of earth is forced into the vertical or nearly vertical lateral, pushing the earth already there out on top of the ground to topple over in one direction or another (see pl. 28*b* and fig. 22). Because of this method of digging, there are usually six inches or so of earth between the mole and the outside world. The freshest earth forms a central 'core' in the molehill. This core, of whose position there is seldom any external indication, can often be distinguished if the mound be sectioned in a vertical plane.

Practically all of our specimens of moles were taken in special mole traps designed to be set over a surface runway, and the use of such traps gave some information concerning the use of these runways. Sometimes a trap set over a newly made runway would catch a mole within a few hours; in other instances the trap remained several days before being disturbed. These facts indicate that there is considerable variation in the frequency with which the surface runways, once made, are traversed. On still other occasions no reoccupation of the run was noted. After one mole was caught in a runway, another individual sometimes appropriated the vacated system to its own use. On November 18, for example, a mole was taken in a run on the forest floor of Yosemite Valley. On the nineteenth the trap was sprung again, and being reset, caught a second mole on the twenty-first. It is believed that ordinarily but one individual inhabits a particular system of runways and tunnels at any one time.

Evidence of the activity of moles was found below the 5000-foot contour during every month of the year. In the summer and the fall months both surface runs and molehills indicative of deeper excavations were observed in Yosemite Valley; and at the end of December new runways were noted in places in the Valley where the ground was not frozen. During the height of winter in the high mountains when the ground is frozen to a considerable depth, conditions would certainly seem unfavorable for active existence of moles. But whether or not those animals become dormant, as do the chipmunks, we do not know.

Though there is no one kind of territory save solid rock where moles are absent, more of their work is to be found in dryish meadowlands than elsewhere. One runway was found in the gravelly ground beneath the boulder talus along the base of the north wall of Yosemite Valley. The dry needle- and leaf-strewn ground of the forest floor is often extensively marked by surface runways. The concentration of moles in these places is undoubtedly due to the greater abundance and accessibility there of suitable food.

The breeding season of moles generally, in California, is in the early spring. A male captured at Snelling January 9, 1915, was in breeding condition; a nearly grown young male was collected at the same place on May 29, 1915. Two individuals collected on June 2, 1915, 3 miles east of Coulterville and in Yosemite Valley, respectively, were, to judge by the unworn condition of their teeth, animals born during the current season. Another juvenal mole was obtained 3 miles east of Coulterville on June 6. These data suggest that the breeding season at the levels indicated is early, probably just at the end of the winter months.

As already intimated the mole's diet consists almost exclusively of animal matter. In lowland districts, earthworms probably constitute a large portion of its fare. For example, the stomach of a mole trapped by one of our party at Snelling, January 9, 1915, contained ''long sections of earthworms'' together with some ''dirt.'' As earthworms are relatively scarce or absent in the higher mountains the moles there must feed on other sorts of 'worms.' Elsewhere it is known that they eat the larvae of certain insects, such as cutworms (moth larvae), and it is probable that, in the higher mountains, too, such larvae form part of the mole's bill of fare.

A ''Macabee'' gopher trap set in a surface runway of a mole on the sandy 'second bottom' at El Portal on November 27, 1914, caught a mole during the night. When the trap was examined on the following morning the trapped mole had been completely defleshed, the skull was almost clean save for ligaments, and the skin was turned inside out leaving an almost perfect skeleton. This probably was the work of another mole, though there is the possibility that a shrew, following the mole's run, was responsible.

The mole, it will be seen from the above account, occupies a very different niche from that of the gopher. Yet the two inhabit the ground; and in their regular existence both promote in various ways the development of soil and, consequently, conditions that are favorable to plant growth. This principle has been set forth in detail in the chapter on the gopher. (See p. 141.)

Shrews. Genus **Sorex**[2]

Field characters.—Size varying, but always less than half that of House Mouse. Head and body not over 3 inches (75 mm.) long, tail 2 inches (50 mm.) or less. Snout long and pointed (pl. 20); eyes and ears inconspicuous; pelage short, dense and smooth-appearing. Forefeet like hind feet, not specialized for digging. Coloration uniform, brown above (varying in tone according to the species), lighter, sometimes whitish, on under surface.

Occurrence.—Common from upper margin of Upper Sonoran Zone up to upper edge of Hudsonian Zone; recorded from Dudley, on Smith Creek (east of Coulterville), eastward to vicinity of Mono Lake.[2] (See fig. 6.) Live chiefly in damp situations along stream banks or in meadows, but sometimes found in protected situations at considerable distances from water.

Shrews are present in the Yosemite region in large numbers, yet because of their small size and secretive habits they are much less well known than are the majority of other small mammals, such as meadow mice. The shrews leave little or no visible evidence of their activity, and it takes much

[2] Five species of true shrews (Genus *Sorex*) occur in the Yosemite region. The general appearance and the habits are much the same in all of these, though but little information other than that gained by trapping is available regarding their life histories. The species, their ranges, and their chief characters are as follows:

DUSKY SHREW, *Sorex obscurus obscurus* Merriam, a wide-ranging species found both in the Rocky Mountains and in the Sierra Nevada south to Tulare County, is common in the Canadian and Hudsonian zones of the Yosemite region from Mono Meadow (near Glacier Point) and from East Fork of Indian Cañon eastward to Warren Fork of Leevining Creek and to Williams Butte. Extreme altitudes of capture were 6900 and 10,800 feet. It lives not only along streams and in marshy places but also about logs on the forest floor. Total length about 4 to 4½ inches, tail 1¾ inches, hind foot ½ inch (12.2–13.0 mm.); coloration dull sepia brown above, ashy on under surface. (See pl. 20c.)

ADORNED SHREW, *Sorex ornatus* Merriam, is found in mountainous parts of southern California and on the lower west slope of the Sierra Nevada, from the Mexican boundary north to the Yosemite region. Locally it is common at El Portal, and one individual was taken at Dudley, 6 miles east of Coulterville. Lives both along streams and on hillsides covered with live oaks and brush. Total length 4 inches, tail 1¾ inches, hind foot about ½ inch (12–13.5 mm.). Coloration dull brown above, whitish beneath.

YOSEMITE SHREW, *Sorex montereyensis mariposae* Grinnell, lives in the Transition Zone and lower part of the Canadian Zone on the west flank of the Sierra Nevada. It was found from Sweetwater Creek and Merced Grove Big Trees eastward to East Fork of Indian Cañon and to Merced Lake; it is the only shrew recorded for the floor of Yosemite Valley. Extreme altitudes of occurrence, 3800 and 7500 feet. It inhabits almost exclusively damp places near streams. Total length 4½ to 5 inches, tail 2 inches, hind foot somewhat more than ½ inch (14–15 mm.). Largest local shrew of the genus *Sorex*. Coloration mixed hair brown and drab gray above, drab gray below with a silvery sheen. (See pl. 20b.)

SIERRA NEVADA SHREW, *Sorex vagrans amoenus* Merriam, of wide distribution along the northern Sierra Nevada, was found by us only at Williams Butte and Mono Lake Post Office. Lives near streams or in meadows. Total length about 4 inches, tail usually less than 1½ inches, hind foot about ½ inch (11.5–13 mm.). Pelage sooty brown, grizzled with lighter brown above; under surface buffy white. The relatively short tail as compared with the tail of other shrews is a fairly good distinguishing feature.

LYELL SHREW, *Sorex lyelli* Merriam, is a rare species, known at present only from the general neighborhood of the peak for which it is named. Single specimens were taken by our party at Vogelsang Lake, 10,350 feet altitude, September 1, 1915, head of Lyell Cañon (= slopes of Mount Lyell) at 9800 feet, July 24, 1915, and near Williams Butte, at 6900 feet, September 20, 1915. Inhabits moist situations, near streams, in grass or under willows. Total length about 4 inches, tail 1½ inches or more, hind foot less than ½ inch (11–12 mm.). Light hair brown above, paler on under surface.

observation, and usually trapping, to demonstrate their presence. Shrews and moles have many features of structure and behavior in common and are classed together in an order known as Insectivora, a term which indicates their principal food. The two groups are quite distinct, however; the shrews exhibit none of the peculiar specializations for digging possessed by moles, being in general much like small mice.

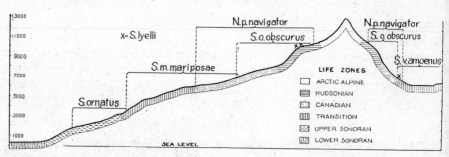

Fig. 6. Cross-section of the Sierra Nevada through the Yosemite region showing general zonal and altitudinal distribution of the shrews (genera *Sorex* and *Neosorex*).

The shrews live and do most of their foraging above ground, yet they keep beneath cover of varying kinds such as is afforded by matted vegetation and prostrate logs. Sometimes when foraging they invade the runways and even the burrows of other mammals—meadow mice, for instance—but none of our local species of shrews are known to make runs of their own or to put up mounds as do moles. Most kinds of shrews regularly patrol the sides of streams where often there are little beaten paths close under the overhanging banks. The Dusky Shrew, and to a less degree, the Adorned Shrew, are to be found away from water, sometimes a hundred yards or more, on hill slopes covered with trees and rocks. But none is known to inhabit the dry foothill chaparral, or the sagebrush tracts.

The nose of a shrew (pl. 20) is long and slender and equipped with numerous sensory hairs or vibrissae. The snout with its equipment is in almost constant motion when the animal is active. The eyes, while discernible, are small and do not seem to be of much use to the animal. The external ear also is small though the sense of hearing of shrews is said to be acute. The body of the shrew is cylindrical as in the mole, but the forefeet are normal in appearance like the hind feet. The tail, though varying somewhat according to the species, usually occupies slightly less than half the total length; it is thinly haired and has a constriction or narrowing at the extreme base where it joins with the body. This latter feature is not possessed by any of the mice. The teeth of shrews are sharply pointed and serve well in holding and killing insects or tearing the flesh of other sorts of prey.

The shrews, though of small bodily size as individuals, constitute, by reason of their numbers and their great activity, an important biological group in the fauna of the Yosemite region. They are actually "micro-carnivores" and exhibit an even greater degree of voracity than do the larger and better known flesh-eating species such as weasels, martens, and wildcats. Shrews kept in captivity have been known to eat more than their own weight of flesh in twenty-four hours. If they do this while in confinement there is no reason to suppose that their capacity would be any less (but rather more) when they are traveling about with full freedom in the wild. It is a common experience among naturalists who are trapping to find each morning one or more of the specimens in the traps mutilated to a greater or less degree. Numerous cases of this kind came to notice while we were engaged in field work in the Yosemite region. A part at least of this work may fairly be attributed to shrews, though various species of small rodents are known to eat maimed, trapped, or dead individuals of their own kind. Where only a beginning on the feast has been made, it is usually the brain of the trapped animal that is eaten. But not infre-quently the work is done so completely that only a few fragments remain—scarcely enough to identify the victim. Not only rodents but even trapped shrews suffer from attacks of this sort. And this cannibalistic tendency has been reported by observers who have kept shews in captivity. When any of the large carnivorous mammals, such as a coyote or a fox, raids a trapped specimen, the trap and all frequently disappear; if carnivorous beetles go after such prey, they accomplish but little in a single night; but if the shrews find the victim, they are apt to make short work of it, and without disturbing the trap in any way.

Evidence of several kinds shows that shrews forage to some extent by day as well as during the hours of darkness. It is likely that they depend less upon sight in searching for prey than upon the senses of smell, touch, and hearing.

As an indication of the density of population among the small mammals in a favorable location, and also of the extent to which shrews (in this case the Dusky Shrew) 'police' the ground in search of food, a record of trapping near Porcupine Flat may be cited. A line of traps set in a small meadow there from June 27 to July 3, 1915, produced the following mammals: Meadow Mouse, 3; Allen Jumping Mouse, 3; Sierra Nevada Pocket Gopher, 4; Dusky Shrew, 6; total, 16, in six nights of trapping. And the traps were still catching specimens when the line was taken up. This particular meadow had a total area of about 7350 square feet—the size of a large city lot (50 × 147). The vegetation consisted of grasses, lupines, and a species of orchid. It is possible that so large a number of shrews did not live and forage exclusively within so limited a tract. Only two or three may have been resident in the meadow; the others may have wandered in from adjacent territory.

The bodies of shrews have a distinctive odor, similar to that possessed by moles. This odor is currently presumed to be disagreeable to the flesh-eating birds and larger mammals, and so is of value to the shrews in saving them from attack. Examination of the stomach contents of hawks and owls elsewhere has shown that but few 'insectivores' are taken by predatory birds. As an exception, however, a Sparrow Hawk collected by us in Yosemite Valley on October 25, 1915, had the remains of a shrew in its stomach along with parts of a meadow mouse and some insects. Perhaps each individual carnivore has to make one trial in order to learn that a shrew is an undesirable article of food.

We learned nothing with regard to the breeding places of shrews. As to season of birth and the numbers of young in a litter, only the following records can be offered: (1) Sierra Nevada Shrew, Mono Lake Post Office, May 21, 1916: 6 embryos. (2) Yosemite Shrew, Chinquapin, June 13, 1915: 4 small embryos. (3) Dusky Shrew, Mount Hoffmann, June 27, 1915: 6 large embryos; Porcupine Flat, June 29, 1915: 4 large embryos; Tuolumne Meadows, July 7, 1915: 5 large embryos; Merced Lake, August 24, 1915: 2 embryos.

NAVIGATOR SHREW. **Neosorex palustris navigator** (Baird)

Field characters.—Size about that of House Mouse; total length 6 to 6½ inches (150–165 mm.), tail about 3 inches (75 mm.) long. Snout pointed; fore and hind feet of about same size and structure; ear inconspicuous. Pelage short, fine in texture; hind toes fringed with short close-set hairs (pl. 20a). Coloration black or hoary black above, often with a distinct sheen; whitish on under surface.

Occurrence.—Common in Canadian Zone and parts of Hudsonian Zone, on both slopes of Sierra Nevada. Recorded from Merced Grove Big Trees (5500 feet altitude) and Chinquapin, eastward to Mono Lake Post Office and Walker Lake. Highest station, 10,350 feet altitude at Vogelsang Lake. Lives in and near swift-flowing streams. Solitary.

The Navigator Shrew is larger than any of the other shrews in the Yosemite section and is more strictly an inhabitant of aquatic situations. We did not find even one of the animals that was more than four feet from running or standing water, and most of our specimens were taken immediately at the water's edge.

In structure the Navigator Shrew exhibits marked adaptations for existence in and near streams. The feet are large (pl. 20a); the toes of the hind foot are obliquely placed and margined with close-set fringes of hairs which serve like webbing to increase the surface of the foot. Furthermore, the pelage is of a rather distinctive type, like that found in aquatic or semi-aquatic animals; it does not soak up water, but holds air within its surface. An animal swimming beneath the water presents a shining silvery appearance because of this 'envelope' of air.

This is the species which fishermen, patrolling the banks of Sierran trout streams, often see swimming in the water. The fact that this shrew is active during the daytime is thus attested.

The breeding season of this shrew occupies the summer months. In 1915, suckling females were captured at Merced Grove on June 11, in Indian Cañon on June 20, and at Porcupine Flat on June 26 (this latter individual contained 6 small embryos). A female containing 7 embryos nearly large enough to be born was taken on June 23, 1915, in East Fork of Indian Cañon. Since none of the individuals collected in the fall months was sufficiently small to be classed on superficial inspection as young-of-the-year, the adult size must be attained rapidly.

At Mono Lake Post Office two specimens of Navigator Shrew were collected, on June 30 and July 2, 1916. These were taken in grass along a stream through a poplar grove, while in the sagebrush not over 100 feet away, specimens of the Great Basin Pocket Mouse were captured. The capture of this species of shrew at such a low station on the east side of the central Sierras was unusual and also furnished a striking example of how species of animals with totally different habitat preferences may occur in close proximity because of the juxtaposition of their respective niches.

LITTLE CALIFORNIA BAT

Myotis californicus californicus (Audubon and Bachman)

Field characters.—Size small, much smaller than House Mouse (slightly larger than Merriam Bat, about ⅓ size of Large Brown Bat). (See pl. 21c.) Total length about 3 inches (75–80 mm.), tail about 1½ inches (30–39 mm.), hind foot ¼ inch (6–7 mm.), spread of wings about 8½ inches (220 mm.). Coloration dark brown above, slightly paler on under surface; flight membranes, ears, lips, and muzzle brownish black. Flies with rapid fluttering of wings and marked indirection of course.

Occurrence.—Common in Upper Sonoran and Transition zones on west slope of Sierra Nevada. Recorded from Pleasant Valley eastward to Yosemite Valley. Extreme altitudes, 600 and 4500 feet. Forages about foliage of oaks and other trees, and around larger brush plants; keeps usually less than 25 feet from the ground. Not colonial.

The Little California Bat is probably the most common of the bats in the Yosemite region. It is relatively abundant on the floor of Yosemite Valley and so is likely to come to the attention of summer visitors there who go walking beneath the oaks and pines at twilight. This species does its foraging close about the foliage of the trees and larger shrubs, and ordinarily it stays within a few feet of the ground. It is seemingly oblivious to human presence, so that its actions may be watched at close range.

Often this is the first species of bat to appear abroad in the evening, though it is sometimes preceded by the Merriam Pipistrelle. At El Portal on November 22, 1914, a Little California Bat was out at 5:10 P.M. At Pleasant Valley, late in May (24th to 27th) of the year following, the species was still among the first to appear, though at that season individuals did not come out until much later, 7:25 to 7:45 P.M. The strength of the light was about the same at the two hours mentioned. The bats evidently stayed in their retreats for some 2½ hours longer in summer than in winter.

Little California Bats are to be found in the Yosemite region throughout the year. Our records include nine of the twelve months and are so distributed as to indicate continued residence by the species, at least below the 3500-foot contour. But whether the same individuals are present at all seasons or whether, like the fox sparrows, the summer population moves out and is replaced by another contingent which comes in from the north and winters here, is a point still to be determined. In Yosemite Valley bats believed to be of this species have been seen out as late as October 27. At Pleasant Valley the species was recorded abroad definitely on December 5 (1915), and a dead individual was picked up on Smith Creek, 6 miles east of Coulterville, on February 7, 1916.

These bats find shelter in a variety of situations. In Yosemite Valley, at 6 P.M. on August 10, 1915, a Little California Bat, after circling over and drinking at a pool near the foot of Yosemite Falls, was seen to take refuge in a crevice between boulders. On May 30, 1911, the smoke of a fire built in a rocky cavern near the foot of Illilouette Falls routed out a Little California Bat which had been hanging in a crevice overhead. A number of these bats have been found on or in the walls of old wooden buildings and a few have been discovered in crevices in pine trees. Under original conditions as well as at the present time the species was probably very adaptable in its choice of shelter.

Bats are active only at twilight and after dark. Their daytime retreats are often difficult of access or unknown and their capture is neither easy nor sure. It is therefore more difficult to gather information concerning them than concerning birds and most other mammals. For these reasons the body of accurate knowledge accumulated by naturalists is much less complete for bats than it is for many other forms of animal life, despite the fact that, in many cases, a disproportionately large amount of time has been devoted to their study. While our parties were engaged in field work in the Yosemite region one or more members would be out almost every evening attempting to shoot the bats seen coursing over lakes or ponds, or across openings in the forest; and every clue concerning the location of ''roosts'' was eagerly followed up. Yet our total collection of bats from the Yosemite region numbers only 80 specimens, most of these being of 2 of the 9 species represented.

The wing of a bat is a thin elastic double membrane or skin which stretches between the greatly elongated 'fingers' of the forelimb and between the fifth of these and the body of the animal. The hind limbs and tail are included in this flight membrane so that the total expanse when extended is many times that of the body alone. By moving the forelimbs the bat is able to fly, and its passage through the air seems much better controlled than in the case of most birds. Most birds must dart through the air at a relatively high rate of speed in order to maintain themselves aloft, and even the swallows, which like bats feed on flying insects, must perform long sweeps through the air. The bat is able to fly fast or slowly, to turn sharply, and to check its flight abruptly, if occasion demands. It can thus control its passage through the air with greater precision. When not in flight a bat clings, head downward, to some upright surface, using for this purpose the slender, curved, and sharply pointed claws of the hind feet.

The wings of a bat are provided with numerous sensory hairs which upon being struck by air waves apprize the animal of the location of objects in its vicinity; and this fine sense of touch, if such it may be called, is the basis of the bat's ability to course about in twilight or even in pitch darkness without striking objects as would a mammal or a bird which is dependent solely upon sight. The ears of bats are proportionately large (see pl. 21 and text figs. 7, 8), and these big external conchs probably catch sound waves made by flying insects and thus the bat becomes aware of the direction of objects of prey.

Bats spend the day in some sort of retreat, the location chosen being more or less different for each of the different species. But such retreat is never dug or modified; nor is any bat known to make a nest as do so many other nocturnal mammals. Some species such as the Free-tailed and Pallid bats are characteristically colonial; others, such as the Little California Bat, are usually, but not always, solitary; while the Hoary Bat seems to be strictly solitary. Each species issues forth when the light of day has reached a certain degree of weakness—a different degree for each species—and once abroad, each hunts its prey in a rather definite niche. The pursuit of prey usually occupies only a short period at and after dusk, though additional foraging may be done just before daybreak. The daytime hours and, with most species, the middle of the night are spent in rest. Bats are therefore abroad and active less than almost any other sort of animal; this is likely made possible, in part at least, by the concentrated nature of the food upon which they subsist.

The method used in collecting bats may be illustrated by giving the circumstances under which a Little California Bat was taken at El Portal on November 20, 1914. Well before twilight the collector had taken up a station in the open where a clear view was obtainable. The first bat seen abroad on that evening was a Hoary Bat, noted at 5:10 p.m. Up to 5:35 four more bats, all small, the size of the Little California Bat, were seen. Twice, as these small ones crossed low places in the horizon line, and so could be seen against the sky, loads of dust-shot were fired at them. In the case of the one bat obtained, the collector fired his gun in the general direction taken by the bat after it passed the clearing; it just happened that the animal had continued its flight in a straight line. A soft thump told that the bat had been dropped. The collector lined it up with a distant object, dragged the toe of his shoe to leave a location mark, walked forward, and then at the judged distance began working over the ground in concentric circles, picking up every dark object—until his fingers encountered the soft body of the bat.

All our bats are strictly insectivorous. The food of the Little California Bat, so far as we know, consists solely of flying insects. Because of their crepuscular habits bats are able to feed upon an entirely different category of insects than are the day foraging insectivores, the swallows, swifts, fly-catchers, etc. Their forage comprises to a considerable extent beetles and moths, and since the larvae of these are often destructive forest pests, the bats are thus of material service to the trees. In truth the bats constitute one big arm of the "night patrol."

A rather unique departure in forage range was noted in the case of a Little California Bat at Pleasant Valley early in December, 1915. The house in which a member of our party was quartered there had on one side a large shed-room in which were unusually large numbers of house flies. At dusk, when the flies were buzzing about slowly and seeking warm resting places in which to spend the night, a Little California Bat would come forth from its daytime retreat and course back and forth in the room, where it found easy forage in the logy flies. All too soon, to the naturalist's way of thinking, the bat had captured enough flies for its evening meal and retired.

During the late summer and autumn months bats, as a rule, become very fat. In all probability this storage of excess nutriment is an adjustment to provide against winter and early spring when forage is scarce or when the weather is such that bats cannot venture out to feed. When collecting specimens during October or November, it is a rather common experience to find bats so fat that when they are shot the 'oil' begins at once to ooze out of the shot holes and, by the time the collector has retrieved his specimen, the fur of the bat will be matted with the grease. During periods of unfavorable weather some species of bats go into dormancy, a condition of reduced animation resembling that of hibernating chipmunks. But we learned nothing in this regard concerning the bats of the Yosemite.

The young of the Little California Bat are born during the early summer months. A female taken at Pleasant Valley May 21, 1915, contained one large embryo; and in a group of these bats secured on July 13, 1920, there were five females each accompanied by a single youngster one-third to two-thirds grown. With this bat, young are borne but once each year, and there is only one young at a birth. These facts indicate that the existence of the species is relatively a very safe one—assuming of course that the birth rate has been adjusted to the maximum 'expectation' of casualty.

On July 13, 1920, an examination of the deserted, windowless buildings at the McLaughlin mine south of Dudley revealed the presence of eleven Little California Bats. Those mentioned in the preceding paragraph were of this lot. These bats were found by systematically ripping off the muslin-mounted wall paper. They were on the west side of the building where the wall was shaded on the outside by trees. Much previous pounding on the walls of other parts of the building had not disturbed them in the least. The bats were not clustered together, as is typical of colonial species, but were clinging individually to the rough boards beneath the loosened wall paper, within a circle 2 feet in diameter and only about 30 inches from the floor. There were five adult females (all in nursing condition) and five young (three females and two males). The young were clinging to the walls independent of, but close to, their mothers. Off to one side was a female without any young one. Later, when confined together in a box, two of the adults were found each with a young one attached to a nipple. The young ranged in weight from 1.6 to 3.0 grams, while the weight of the adult females averaged 4.3 grams.

HIGH SIERRA BAT. **Myotis lucifugus altipetens** H. W. Grinnell

Field characters.—Size medium (larger than Little California Bat, smaller than Large Brown Bat). (See pl. 21e.) Total length 3½ inches (91–93 mm.); lower leg (tibia) well under ¾ inch (15.3–16.4 mm.); hind foot ⅖ inch (10–11 mm.); ear ½ inch or over (13–15 mm.). Coloration light brown above, buffy beneath. Distinguished in hand by relatively large hind foot, more than half length of tibia.

Occurrence.—Inhabits Canadian and Hudsonian zones on Sierra Nevada. Altitudes, 7500 to 10,350 feet. Recorded at Merced Lake and Vogelsang Lake. Flies over and about tops of forest trees, and over lakes.

Bats inhabit the entire extent of the forested regions of the Sierra Nevada but each species occurring there occupies a definite part of this general range. The territory of the present species involves two high zones, the Canadian and Hudsonian. Vogelsang Lake, altitude 10,350 feet, where we obtained specimens, is next to the highest recorded station of occurrence for any bat in the United States.

Small bats, presumably of the present species, were observed occasionally about our camps at Tuolumne Meadows in July; but they came out so late that it did not prove possible to shoot specimens. But at Merced and Vogelsang lakes, in late August, three individuals were secured.

At Vogelsang Lake the bats were seen close over the water, but whether they came to drink or to capture the little insects seen 'spinning' on the surface of the lake could not be learned definitely. The continued skimming of the bats over the water suggested that they were actually gathering insects.

On August 19 and 30, 1915, pairs of bats were seen with one individual in rapid pursuit of another. In one instance the pursued individual was shot and was found to be a female. The actual mating of bats is believed, on fairly good evidence, to occur in the fall; but the young do not develop until spring. These pursuits may therefore have been of females by males. Between August 19 and September 6, in 1915, the High Sierra Bats made their first appearance from 6:58 to 7:10, on different evenings, the earliest appearance being on a quiet sultry evening.

LONG-LEGGED BAT. **Myotis longicrus longicrus** (True)

Field characters.—Size medium (noticeably larger than Little California Bat, smaller than Large Brown Bat); total length 3½–4 inches (90–102 mm.), lower leg (tibia) ¾ inch (18 mm.), hind foot ⅓ inch (8 mm.), ear ⅖ inch (9–11 mm.). Coloration brown.

Occurrence.—In Transition Zone on west slope of Sierra Nevada, where recorded definitely at Dudley, 6 miles east of Coulterville. Also taken once at Walker Lake, on east slope. Forages chiefly about trees at 6 to 25 feet from ground, occasionally higher.

The Long-legged Bat is a species of medium size which is likely to be observed flitting across the spaces between trees in the yellow pine forest of the Transition Zone. Our own definite records of the species are confined to two localities; but further work between altitudes of 3000 and 5000 feet on the west slope of the Sierras would doubtless show it to be of general occurrence there.

At Dudley, 6 miles east of Coulterville, three specimens were taken on the evenings of July 13 and 16 and August 1, 1920, respectively, as they alighted on the vertical boards beneath the gable of a barn. It was found that the bats sought this perching place repeatedly in order to devour at leisure the insect prey which they had captured while in flight. This habit of perching to eat, though it is a well-known trait of the Pallid Bat, does not seem to have been recorded hitherto for the present species. Other ndividuals of the Long-legged Bat were taken during the daytime from heir resting places on a pine tree. At Walker Lake a bat of this species vas shot on the evening of September 11, 1915, at 6:52 P.M., from among several which were flying down the cañon high over the aspens and sage-brush. These bats were probably going from their daytime resting places n the forest to some especially productive forage area farther down the valley.

A female Long-legged Bat taken at Dudley on July 16, 1920, gave evidence of having recently suckled young; and on August 1, a young ndividual, nearly full-grown, was taken there. This young animal was clothed in hair of somewhat softer texture and more grayish color than that of the adults.

Fringed Bat. **Myotis thysanodes** Miller

Field characters.—Slightly larger than Little California Bat, much smaller than Large Brown Bat. Total length 3½ inches (80–87 mm.), tail about 1½ inches (37–40 mm.), hind foot ⅓ inch (8–9 mm.), ear ⅝ inch (14–16 mm.). Coloration dull yellowish brown above, paler on under surface, flight membranes, ears, and muzzle blackish. A fringe of fine hairs along edge of membrane on each side of tail toward tip is distinctive.

Occurrence.—Taken only near Dudley, 6 miles east of Coulterville; altitude 3000 feet.

The Fringed Bat has been taken but a few times in California, and it is not yet possible to give its range, forage habits, or other characteristics with any degree of satisfaction. In the Yosemite region this bat was found only in the neighborhood of Dudley, which is near the western margin of the yellow pine belt. One immature specimen was shot at dusk at a deer lick a little north of Dudley. Another was routed out of the deserted building at the McLaughlin mine where the group of Little California Bats was found. This specimen was started from its retreat by our pounding on the walls. A third individual was jarred out of a loose shake roof in an old building at the Red Cloud Mine. The first example mentioned was taken on July 21, 1920, the other two on July 13 of the same year; all three were males.

Merriam Bat. **Pipistrellus hesperus merriami** (Dobson)

Field characters.—Smallest bat in the Yosemite region (about three-fourths size of Little California Bat). Total length 2½–2¾ inches (67–72 mm.), tail 1¼ inches (29–30 mm.), hind foot about ⅕ inch (5 mm.), ear ⅓ inch (9 mm.), spread about 7¾ inches (197 mm.). Coloration warm buff above, paler beneath; flight membranes, ears, lips, and muzzle black. (See pl. 21*b*.)

Occurrence.—Common in Upper Sonoran and lower part of Transition zone on west slope of Sierra Nevada. Recorded from Pleasant Valley eastward to floor of Yosemite Valley. Forages in the open, well above the smaller trees.

The Merriam Bat, smallest of the local bats, is a species likely to be seen by anyone who visits Yosemite Valley or the neighboring country to the west. It appears early in the evening, being usually the first species to be seen abroad, and flies high, in the open air, well above the horizon line. Its flight is notably irregular, even for a bat, and this feature alone often serves to identify a solitary individual when comparisons of size cannot be made. The pipistrelle finds shelter in crevices among the rocks and of such retreats it has a wide range for choice in the Yosemite.

On the evening of July 24, 1915, one of our party went bat hunting near Rocky Point, on the north side of Yosemite Valley. The first bat seen, at 7:18, was shot and proved to be a "pipistrelle." It was flying high in the open among the yellow pines and black oaks, but well away from the foliage of these trees. No other bats were seen that evening until 7:30 when the Large Brown and the Free-tailed appeared simultaneously.

This bat is evidently resident in the foothill districts throughout the year, as a specimen was shot at El Portal on the evening of January 1, 1915. Its continuance in the Yosemite Valley during the winter season seems doubtful; no bats, of any species, were noted there after the end of October.

At Pleasant Valley on May 22, 1915, a female Merriam Bat was obtained which contained 2 embryos.

LARGE BROWN BAT. **Eptesicus fuscus** (Peale and Beauvois)

Field characters.—Size large, about 3 times that of Little California Bat, and only slightly smaller than Hoary Bat. (See pl. 21*d*.) Total length 4¼–5 inches (110–124 mm.), tail 1¾–2 inches (47–52 mm.), hind foot ⅖ inch (10 mm.), ear ½ inch (12–13 mm.), spread of wings 13¼ inches (337 mm.). Coloration rich brown above, pale brown beneath; flight membranes, ears, and muzzle blackish.

Occurrence.—Common in summer in Transition and Canadian zones on west slope of Sierra Nevada. Recorded from Smith Creek, 6 miles east of Coulterville (3000 feet), eastward to Merced Lake (7500 feet). Forages in open spaces between trees at 20 to 50 feet above ground.

The Large Brown Bat merits its name both as to size and color, as it is several times as large as the other 'brown' bats (genus *Myotis*) of the region, and its coloration is a rich brown. Since it is common in practically all parts of the Yosemite region between altitudes of 3000 and 7500 feet, it is likely to come to the attention of visitors in most of the well-known stopping places on the west slope of the mountains. It has not yet been recorded on the east side of the Sierras in the Yosemite section.

The Large Brown Bat does not come out until some time after the Little California and Merriam bats have begun to fly. In Yosemite during June of 1915 this bat appeared from 7:40 to 7:50 P.M., while toward the end of July the days had shortened so that *Eptesicus* was abroad at 7:30. In late August, at Merced Lake, it was out at 7:15 P.M.; and on October 2 that same year, in Yosemite Valley, a bat of this species was seen over Sentinel Meadow at 5:46 P.M., when Half Dome was still pink-tinged with direct sunlight.

When foraging, this bat courses about in clear places in the forest or over open cañons; usually it keeps well up, anywhere from 25 to 50 feet above the ground. Each individual seems to have a definite forage route or beat. If the collector misses a shot, he is sure to have another chance at the same bat if he but holds his post until the animal swings around over its course again. The flight is relatively slow, and its course is maintained in a direct line for longer periods than is that of most other bats. These features, together with its larger size, render the Large Brown Bat an easier target for both the eye and the gun than are most other species.

The electric lights in the 'streets' of Yosemite's tent cities serve to attract multitudes of native moths and other night-flying insects and these in turn draw the bats. One evening in July there were fully 20, mostly of the present species, to be seen about the lights in one of the camps, where they seemed to be faring exceedingly well.

Our records for this bat, based upon specimens taken, end with August 28 (1915) at Merced Lake; but bats believed to be of this species were seen until late in October. No Large Brown Bats have been observed in the region during the winter months. The species seems not to have been found anywhere in California during that season; in all probability, like many of the birds, it retires to some more southerly locality to spend the period when flying insects are scarce or wanting in our latitudes.

HOARY BAT. **Nycteris cinerea** (Peale and Beauvois)

Field characters.—Largest bat in the Yosemite region, slighly larger than either Large Brown Bat or Pallid Bat. Total length 5½ inches (135 mm.), tail 2½ inches (60 mm.), hind foot ⅖ inch (11 mm.), ear ⅓ inch (9 mm.), stretch 15½ inches (398 mm.). Coloration 'hoary,' the hairs being brown at base and extensively tipped with white; wing membranes blackish. Tail membrane furred like back. (See pl. 21*a*.)

Occurrence.—Recorded definitely twice in Yosemite region; probably rather common. Individual specimens taken at Snelling, April 15, 1916, and at Merced Lake, August 20, 1915. Inhabits wooded localities and finds daytime refuge in trees. Solitary.

The Hoary Bat, one of the most distinctive of our Californian bats, is included in the fauna of the Yosemite region on the basis of two specimens captured. On several other occasions, however, individual bats which we believed to be of this species were seen in flight.

Compared even with the Large Brown Bat the present species stands out as of very large size. As additional characters, it has long and pointed wings and a swift and irregular flight. Usually it flies low among the trees but sometimes courses up 25 to 30 feet above the ground. It appears at about the same time in the evening as does the Large Brown Bat. One Hoary Bat was shot at 7:12 P.M., August 20, 1915, at Merced Lake.

The Hoary Bat is known to be a definitely migratory species. In winter it occupies the hills and valleys of California; in summer it goes to the higher mountains or to more northern latitudes. Its seasonal movements thus parallel those of some of our birds, the Audubon Warbler, for instance.

This bat is strictly solitary in its habits, and spends the day hanging amid the foliage of some tree. Its heavy coat of fur, which extends out onto the upper surface of the wings and clear over the tail membrane, is an evident adaptation to the relatively low temperature of its alpine and northern habitat, and to its solitary and open manner of 'roosting.'

PACIFIC PALLID BAT. **Antrozous pacificus** Merriam

Field characters.—Size large among the local bats; slightly smaller than Hoary Bat, several times size of Little California and Merriam bats. (See text fig. 7 and pl. 21.) Total length 4–4½ inches (103–118 mm.), tail 1½–1¾ inches (36–46 mm.), hind foot ½ inch or over (12–14 mm.), ear 1–1⅓ inches (26–32 mm.), spread about 13–14 inches. Coloration pale brown above, light buff beneath; flight membranes dark brown, ears and muzzle light brown.

Occurrence.—Common in Lower Sonoran Zone, at Snelling. Lives in buildings during daytime, foraging abroad at late dusk. Hunts near the ground. Colonial.

The Pacific Pallid Bat is a rather large-bodied bat with extremely large ears. Its coloration as compared with that of the other local species is very pale. It was found at only one station, Snelling, but may possibly occur in portions of the adjacent foothill country, for it has been found in the Upper Sonoran Zone in other parts of central California. This bat appeared abroad in late May at about 7:45 P.M. Some were seen to forage on the leeward side of a row of cottonwoods near the Merced River.

On the evening of May 27, 1915, some boys were found making an effort to rid the village church in Snelling of a colony of pallid bats which had taken possession of the wall of a gable. One of our party lent his assistance in order to obtain some specimens. A trap of wire screen was set up in front of the opening. At 6:30 P.M. the bats had become active within the walls and could be heard squeaking. The first individual emerged at 7:30, escaped the net and flew away. Another coming out soon afterward likewise went free of the net, but then circled and alighted on the side of the building. No more came out until 7:40; then they began to emerge and drop into the net at the rate of about four per minute. As darkness came on the animals came out faster and faster. The net was taken down at 8:00 o'clock after which still more were seen to emerge from the wall, circle about a bit, and then fly away. The gable of the church which harbored the bats also housed a swarm of bees and a Red-shafted Flicker.

Fig. 7. Pacific Pallid Bat; from freshly collected specimen, natural size. Snelling, May 26, 1915.

Of the bats captured, 1 male and 19 females were saved as specimens. The male was not in breeding condition. Fifteen of the females contained 2 embryos each, 3 had 1 embryo and 1 none. Many of the embryos were of such large size as to indicate that they would have been born very soon.

MEXICAN FREE-TAILED BAT. **Nyctinomus mexicanus** (Saussure)

Field characters.—Size medium, more than twice size of Little California Bat, decidedly smaller than Large Brown Bat. (See fig. 8 and pl. 21.) Total length about 4 inches (97–103 mm.), tail about 1½ inches (32–40 mm.), hind foot less than ½ inch (7–12 mm.), ear about ½ inch (13–14 mm.), spread of wings 11½ to 12 inches. Coloration dull dark brown above, paler on under surface; flight membrane, ears, and muzzle blackish. The terminal half of the tail projects behind the edge of the flight membrane (fig. 8), a character not shared with any other species of bat in the Yosemite region. Musty odor characteristic.

Occurrence.—Resident in Upper Sonoran Zone and lower part of Transition Zone on west slope of Sierra Nevada, where recorded at Coulterville, on Smith Creek (6 miles east of Coulterville), at El Portal, and in Yosemite Valley. One record for Walker Lake, east of Sierra Nevada. Forages high in open air apart from trees or other vegetation. 'Roosts' in buildings. Colonial.

The Free-tailed Bat is a bat of the open places, and in its route of forage and manner of flight more nearly resembles the swallows than does

any one of the other local bats. It is to be looked for over fields, or else well above the level of the tree tops or brush. A distinctive feature of this species is the narrowness of its wings, a shape which is perhaps more useful to an animal flying swiftly in the open.

This bat is highly colonial, sometimes being found in gatherings which include hundreds of individuals. It seeks by preference the attics of buildings rather than natural abodes in crevices in trees or cliffs.

In time of appearance the Free-tailed Bat resembles the Large Brown Bat. Thus, the two species appeared simultaneously at 7:30 P.M. in Yosemite Valley on July 24, 1920. At El Portal, January 1, 1915,

Fig. 8.   Mexican Free-tailed Bat; from specimen, about 9/10 natural size. Dudley (six miles east of Coulterville), June 24, 1922.

a Free-tail was shot shortly after 5:14 P.M. This latter occurrence indicates not only that this species winters in the region, but also that individuals forage abroad in midwinter when weather conditions are favorable.

The single example from the east side of the mountains was picked up dead on September 12, 1915, at Walker Lake.

At Coulterville, on June 7, 1915, two members of our party visited several buildings in the town which were reported to be inhabited by bats. The specimens obtained in one of these places were all Free-tailed Bats, but whether all the buildings had been tenanted by this species could not be ascertained. The attic over the local drug store was a large affair open under the eaves so that bats could easily gain entrance. Only four individuals were seen there at the time of our visit; but on the floor of the place there was bat guano to the depth of 4 inches or more, indicating that a large colony had tenanted the place in previous years. Mr. W. J. McCarthy, who was a druggist there for many years, told us that he once burned some sulphur in this attic and killed "hundreds of bats." We found the village assembly hall to contain a few Free-tailed Bats crowded into a space about $2 \times 4 \times 36$ inches beside a door casing, and others had evidently roosted along the ridge pole.

The Masonic Temple had suffered more extensively from the bats. In the low attic of this building were found only a very few individuals. But at some previous time there had been a large population, for guano lay in considerable heaps over the ceiling laths, and bat urine had stained the walls of the room beneath. We were told that "thousands" of bats had lived in this attic and that it had taken "an hour and a half for them to come out in the evening," but these multitudes were not present at the time of our visit. Guano left in the attic of such a building, sheltered from moisture, retains its characteristic odor for many years, therefore it does not give a wholly satisfactory clue as to the recency of bat occupation.

The two bats taken at Coulterville were both females and each contained one large embryo.

AMERICAN BLACK BEAR. Ursus americanus Pallas

Field characters.—Size large (adults, total length up to 60 inches, height at shoulder up to 40 inches); forefoot squarish (size, up to about 6½ by 4 inches), hind foot triangular in outline (total length from heel, up to about 9 inches, width to 4½ inches); all five toes and claws showing in track of each foot (pl. 22b); tail very short, 6 inches or less. Pelage long and heavy, in color either glossy black, or cinnamon brown of varying shades. *Voice:* Commonly only sniffs or snorts; when badly frightened or wounded, a loud growl or bawl.

Occurrence.—Resident on west slope of Sierra Nevada, chiefly in Transition and Canadian zones. Recorded, or reported on good authority, from 3 miles east of Coulterville, from near Bagby, and from Bullion Mountain, eastward to Tuolumne River at 8000 feet, to McGee Lake, and to Tenaya Lake. Lives on forest floor or about brush thickets, taking shelter in caves, under rock piles, or in hollow trees. Cubs run with mother through first year.

The Black Bear is the largest carnivorous animal now to be found in the Yosemite region, and, strangely enough, also the one most often seen by visitors to the Park. Indications of its presence, in the form of footprints, claw marks on tree trunks, and droppings, are to be seen in many places during the summer and fall months, so that persons who do not succeed in catching sight of the animals themselves are apt to find plain evidence of their presence. In former years the Grizzly Bear, a much larger and more ferocious animal than the subject of the present account, was found in the western part of the Yosemite region; but as told in the chapter on that species, it became extinct there, at the hand of man, many years ago.

Our Yosemite Black Bear exhibits two color phases. That is to say, there are both 'black' and 'cinnamon' bears; but these two phases seem to hold somewhat the same relation to one another as do brunettes and blonds in the human species. A cinnamon-colored mother bear has been seen with 2 coal-black cubs, and several cases have been reported in which a female has had one black and one cinnamon-colored cub in the same litter. The proportion of cinnamon and black bears in the Yosemite region is not known. One resident stated that it was 10 to 1; but our experience points exactly in the opposite direction—we happened to see no cinnamon-colored bears at all while in the region!

The Black Bear is an animal of the Transition and Canadian zones and only rarely ranges above or below the limits of those two zones. So far as known it occurs only on the western flank of the Sierra Nevada, and in this region seldom goes above 9000 feet or below 2000 feet altitude. On the west it was probably restricted in range in former times by the presence of the bellicose Grizzly and it does not seem to have taken much advantage of the disappearance of its larger congenor to increase its range, while in the higher zones conditions are evidently not suitable for its existence.

The density of the bear population of the Yosemite National Park varies widely from place to place. It has been estimated that at times there have been 15 or 20 bears living in Yosemite Valley, the greater percentage of these being about the lower part of the Valley. On the trail between Aspen Valley and Gentrys, a distance of 8 or 9 miles, the junior author saw tracks of 5 or 6 different Black Bears in one day, October 19, 1915. But in other likely-looking places the animals are much scarcer, or absent altogether. Perhaps there are, at the present time, somewhere in the neighborhood of 125 bears in the 1124 square miles of territory included within the Park, or about one individual for every 9 square miles of territory. The mecca of the bears in the Yosemite region is the north-central part of the Park, in Tiltill and Pleasant valleys, Kerrick Cañon, and on the slopes of Rancheria Mountain. Bears are said to be abundant in each of these localities. In Pleasant Valley (north of the Tuolumne River) the brushy slopes are said to be traversed in many directions by their deeply worn trails.

Most carnivorous animals are abroad and active throughout the year, and if, in winter, the presence of heavy snow either directly or indirectly restricts or cuts off their food supply they descend to lower altitudes. Such is the case with the Mountain Coyote and the Mountain Lion. But the Black Bear, depending as it does on plant life for so much of its food, is a striking exception to this general rule and meets the situation in an entirely different way. It hibernates, after the manner of some of the rodents. With the arrival of the first heavy storm of the winter (usually in December or January) it seeks a warm and sheltered cave among the rocks or some other similar situation and there sleeps during the time that heavy snow covers the ground outside. It remains in hibernation until the middle or end of April, when the bulk of the snow at middle altitudes has melted. In 1920 the first bear tracks noted in the lower part of Yosemite Valley were seen on March 18. Those individuals which live below the limit of heavy snow (about 3500 feet in this latitude) are prone to come out and forage actively abroad from time to time throughout the winter. Some residents of the region have suggested to us that the bears living in the higher mountains perform a limited altitudinal migration, but we have no definite information on this point.

The dens used by the bears in the Yosemite region are chiefly such as are found in the heaps of talus and slide rock which abound in various parts of the Park. The bears which feed at the garbage pits in the Yosemite Valley are thought to have their dens in the rock slides under Cathedral Spires, for in this vicinity a trail leads from the pits toward the wall of the Valley.

When the Black Bears go into hibernation in the early winter they are very fat, but most of this excess fat is used up during the long winter sleep. When they first emerge in the spring they are not very active and little is to be seen of them for some time. Soon, however, they begin to eat again, sparingly at first, and then more greedily, until in summer and fall they amply justify the oft-made remark, "hungry as a bear." As the summer wanes their search for food leads them farther and farther afield, their tracks and sign become more and more in evidence, and they themselves are more frequently seen by visitors. During the autumn they must eat not only to sustain their bodies from day to day, but enough in addition to provide another supply of fat to carry them through the following winter. This fat is especially important in the case of the females, as their cubs are born in midwinter and the only source of nourishment for the young until they emerge in the spring is the milk elaborated in the bodies of the mothers from this reserve of fat.

Under original conditions of life the Black Bear is active in the daytime as well as at night, but most of the depredations which it commits in the vicinity of camps and buildings are done under the cover of darkness. The Black Bear is an adept at climbing, from the day that it first emerges from the den, a young cub in the care of its mother, on throughout its entire life. When frightened it often seeks safety by ascending the nearest tree strong enough to support it. When trailed by dogs it finally evades them in this manner.

The tracks of a bear are not likely to be mistaken for those of any other animal. The toes and claws, of which there are five on each foot, all leave distinct impressions in the soft earth of roads and trails, while the square pad of the forefoot and the triangular-shaped heel pad of the hind foot are both of distinctive character (pl. 22*b*). The track of the rear foot resembles in appearance the print of a human foot. We have measured hind-foot tracks which were 9 inches long, but the average length is considerably less.

Bears are adaptable creatures and profit by the presence of man in several ways. They make much use of man-made trails, especially when going up or down hill, and when doing so follow each turn and zig-zag with remarkable fidelity. Their own trails are as distinctive in character as are their footprints. Through tracts of dense brush the openings left are low—so low in fact that a man in traversing one of them must stoop or crawl on his hands and knees. Then, too, each bear steps in exactly the same place as the one which preceded him, literally "walking in the footsteps of his predecessors," and if a bear comes into a trail of this sort at some point along its course he adapts his tread to that of the main trail. These traits are well shown in a trail through light snow, where the tread of the animals crushes down and melts the snow where they step, yet leaves the snow between the footprints undisturbed (pl. 22*a*).

Black Bears usually have 2 cubs at a birth, but on June 19, 1910, the junior author saw a black female with 3 black cubs near Camp Curry on the floor of Yosemite Valley. In the account of the Grizzly killed by R. S. Wellman there is mention of 3 Black Bear cubs with their dam, these being actively abroad as late in the season as October 17. Sometimes a litter consists of but a single cub. The earliest report of young out of the den is that by Mr. O. R. Prien who, during the week of April 29, 1916, saw a female with 2 black cubs less than 18 inches long. The cubs of one litter travel with the mother until she dens up for the following winter. Mr. Gabriel Souvelewsky saw tracks of an old bear and two "good-sized" cubs near Mirror Lake, on December 14, 1914.

As regards food the Black Bear will eat anything and everything it can lay its paws on. It is an omnivorous feeder in every sense of that word, departing widely from the customs of most carnivorous animals in this respect. In its natural environment our Yosemite bear eats various kinds of seeds, fruits, and berries, including those of the coffee berry (*Rhamnus californicus*), green manzanita (*Arctostaphylos patula*), wild cherry (*Prunus demissa*), and poison oak (*Rhus diversiloba*). Grasses, liliaceous plants, and seed heads of various annuals are consumed. Carpenter ants and other insects are taken in considerable numbers. In the vicinity of human habitations it finds a wide choice of fare. It visits isolated or unguarded camps and purloins hams, bacon, canned goods and fruits, raids garbage cans, and digs up heaps of tin cans and other kitchen refuse buried by campers. A considerable number of the bears living in Yosemite Valley regularly forage at the garbage pits and incinerators in the vicinity of Cathedral Spires, as many as 10 and even 15 having been seen there by attendants, usually at late dusk. Tin cans are nosed over and thoroughly cleaned of any remaining particles of their original contents, and melon rinds and other vegetable materials are readily devoured. Peach, plum, and olive pits, watermelon, muskmelon, and apple seeds, lemon rinds, eggshells, bones of chickens, mammal hair, and bones from various cuts of meat are among the objects we found to have been devoured by these bears. Even papers which have been wrapped around butter and cured meats are eaten for the grease and salt which they have absorbed. At the storehouse of the construction camp in Hetch Hetchy Valley, in the winter of 1915–16, bears ripped 2-by-12-inch planks off the window openings, clambered in, and made way with hams, bacon, and canned goods, even while lights were burning in the house and persons were present in other portions of the building.

As regards the relation of Black Bears to stock, Mr. George Smith of Jamestown, Tuolumne County, has told us that in the seventies it was necessary to 'thin out' the bear population before sheep could be run with safety in the mountains. At that time almost every meadow had its bear trap or pen, a small log house of stout construction with a heavy door so arranged that when a bear entered and seized the bait the door would fall and the animal would be imprisoned. Some of these traps may still be seen on meadows in the northern part of the Park. Horses readily take fright at the sight of a bear, although we know of no case in which a bear has actually attacked a horse. In Hetch Hetchy Valley Mr. C. C. Bull has told us of bears visiting hog pens and feeding in the troughs alongside of the rightful partakers without molesting or disturbing the latter. Mr. John L. McLean has told us that bears come down around his ranch on Smith Creek (6 miles east of Coulterville) to feed on acorns, but that they have never molested either poultry or stock. However, he knew of one occasion when some pigs were taken by Black Bears on Bullion Mountain.

Finally in regard to persons: We know of but two instances in which a Black Bear has even attempted to molest any human being in the Park. One case, of a mother bear resenting disturbance of her young, is recounted in the chapter on the Grizzly Bear. The second instance is as follows. Mr. George Smith states that while cruising timber in the Tuolumne basin a number of years ago he was chased down-hill by a she-bear. He distracted the attention of the animal by picking up stones and pieces of wood and throwing them to one side or another as he ran. Finally he jumped upon and ran along a fallen tree trunk and dropped into a willow thicket at the base of the log. The bear, evidently losing the trail, thereupon gave up the chase. Mr. Gabriel Souvelewsky relates that while traveling along the south wall of the Tuolumne Cañon late one afternoon he came to a rock ledge occupied by two cinnamon bears. One of these growled and made threatening advances so that Mr. Souvelewsky thought it best not to continue farther in their direction. But he was not actually pursued. The female mentioned above as being seen by the junior author near Camp Curry in June, 1910, even though accompanied by her cubs, was not unduly resentful of human intrusion. Several persons were taking pictures of her while she had her cubs in sight, and later, when she had hidden them, she came down and fed at a garbage heap while some forty people looked on and snapped pictures at as short a distance as twenty feet.

GRIZZLY BEAR. **Ursus henshawi** Merriam

The history of the Grizzly Bear in the Yosemite region and indeed throughout California is evidently a closed chapter in the book of nature. In the "days of '49" numbers of the big fellows roamed over the hills and valleys of California, and the Yosemite region doubtless had its full quota of them. But the presence of the Grizzlies was incompatible with the interests of the white man, and so they were killed off rapidly, until now it seems likely that they are entirely gone. So sudden was their extermination that no complete specimens were secured to be preserved in our museums. And reliable accounts, published or in manuscript, of the California grizzlies are meager at best.

The word Yosemite[3] is derived from a word in the tribal dialect of the southern Miwok Indians who inhabited the Valley when it was discovered by white men. This word, Uzumati, or Uzhumati, means grizzly bear, a full-grown animal rather than a cub. The use of this name in association with the Valley might be taken as an indication that Grizzly Bears originally inhabited the Yosemite Valley. But we have no precise evidence to show that such was the case. Early visitors to the Yosemite often mention "grizzlies" and "bears" in their narratives, but with an ambiguity that leaves the reader uncertain as to whether a veritable Grizzly was encountered anywhere in the Valley proper.

The names Bear Valley, Bear Creek, Big Grizzly Flat, and Little Grizzly attest the former wide occurrence of Grizzly Bears in the foothill district of the region.

---

[3] For the circumstances surrounding the choice of the name consult L. H. Bunnell, *Discovery of the Yosemite;* for discussion of the meaning of the word see paper by A. L. Kroeber, California Place Names of Indian Origin (Univ. Calif. Publ. Am. Arch. Ethn., vol. 12 [1916], p. 68).

The Grizzly Bears as a group (including several species and races) are quite distinct from the Black Bears. The size of adults was generally much larger, though the species which occurred in the Yosemite region was one of the smaller of the grizzlies. No weights or detailed measurements of locally captured grizzles are preserved. The ''nose to tail'' measurement of ''nearly 10 feet'' given by its captor for the Wellman specimen referred to below, applied to a skin as pegged out fresh. It is well known that considerable stretching results from such procedure, and that when the skin is relaxed and tanned it shrinks somewhat. The length of the Wellman grizzly skin is now 7½ feet and its width at the middle is 5 feet. Judging from the dimensions of bears before skinning, in known cases, as compared with those of the tanned skins measured subsequently, the Wellman bear in the flesh probably measured between 6½ and 7 feet in length, tip of nose to tip of tail. The Washburn skin mentioned later measures 6 feet 7 inches in length, somewhat smaller; and the living animal was therefore probably close to 6 feet long.

The foreclaws of the Grizzly are much less sharply curved and somewhat longer than those of the Black Bear; this is an absolutely distinctive character. The longest claws on the Wellman skin are 3 inches (measuring the chord of the claw from tip to upper base), while the middle foreclaw of a large California-taken Black Bear is only 2 inches in the same dimension. The track of an old Grizzly, either front or hind foot, was much larger than that of a Black Bear. Wellman's figures, 10 by 13 inches, and McLean's, 9 by 17 inches (even allowing for considerable sliding of the foot, especially in the latter case) are 50 per cent larger in each dimension than the track of a good-sized Black Bear. These measurements of course refer to the hind foot, which is decidedly longer than the forefoot. The latter (if the 'wrist' does not touch) leaves an imprint that is more nearly square in outline. In coloration the Grizzly was dark brown, and some individuals had grayish or whitish ends to the longer guard-hairs on the back, which gave rise to the name ''silver-tip.''

The Grizzly differed from the Black Bear in habits as well as in structure. It was, particularly in the case of the Henshaw Grizzly, a frequenter of chaparral (and hence essentially an inhabitant of the foothill districts), and it never (or rarely) climbed trees. Its food, as with the Black Bear, was quite varied, including berries, fruits, and insects, as well as flesh; but the Grizzly worked much more havoc among large game, and in later years, stock, than does its smaller relative.

During our work in the western part of the Yosemite section we questioned numerous old residents concerning the former occurrence of Grizzly Bears, but rarely obtained definite information. Mr. J. B. Varain, of Pleasant Valley (= Varain), told us that there were no Grizzlies there when he arrived in 1867, but that they were then still to be found in the territory to the east. The various gold rushes to Tioga and Mammoth, together with the running of sheep and other stock in the region, served to clear the Yosemite country of its Grizzlies at a relatively early date. The occurrence of the one taken in 1887, by Wellman, was by that year considered an unusual event.

We were unable to get track of even a fragment of a specimen of the Grizzly in the narrow section which we worked across the Sierras; but since our field work was completed, there have come to light two skins of Grizzlies killed elsewhere within the present boundaries of Yosemite National Park. Both of these skins are now in the Museum of Vertebrate Zoology of the University of California. One of these bears (obtained from Mrs. John S. Washburn) is the last known to have been killed in the region. It was shot "about 1895" at Crescent Lake, which lies some ten miles air-line east of Wawona at an altitude of 8500 feet.

It is possible that a few individuals persisted in the same region until a considerably later date. This surmise is strengthened by the following account. Mr. John L. McLean and his son Donald have told us that during the fall and winter months from 1908 until 1911 a very large bear lived on Bullion Mountain. The tracks, which were examined on two or more occasions in two successive years, "were 9 by 17 inches (or a little more) by actual measurement." The animal had long claws, as shown by the tracks. The bear had five separate trails leading up the side of the mountain from the heavy chaparral (composed of *Adenostoma* and scrub or "vine" oak) on the lower slopes, to the black and blue oaks on the top. The dung indicated that the bear was living principally upon acorns. There were wild hogs on the mountain and these may have been an attraction to the big bear. The smaller (Black) bears seemingly had little or nothing to do with the big fellow, avoiding his trails and staying off in another cañon. A trap was once set for the big bear, and caught him; but he pulled loose "at one jump." Finally a party of men with dogs got after the big bear and it "left the country," without being injured, and was not seen again. Small bears are still present in the region.

The circumstances surrounding the killing of the "Wellman bear" have been set down at considerable length in a letter written by one of the principals, Mr. Robert S. Wellman, under date of April 20, 1918. This letter is now on file at the Museum of Vertebrate Zoology, and from it we take the following.

Mr. Wellman's headquarters were, at that time, at Buck Camp, some 16 miles east of Wawona, near the South Fork of the Merced River. On the evening of October 17, 1887, at the head of a small valley about a mile away from the camp, he discovered the carcass of a cow on which bears had already commenced to feed. A search of the vicinity disclosed the presence of a female Black Bear and three cubs.

The next morning Mr. Wellman visited the place again and found that during the night a larger bear had come and dragged the carcass several yards from where it first lay. Being certain that this new arrival was a veritable Grizzly he rode over to the camp of his friend Jim Duncan,[4] now long deceased, and got him to come over to help in the hunt. The two men built a scaffold, or platform, 10 feet above the ground and some 60 feet from the dead cow. And on this platform watch was kept for the succeeding three nights. One or more black bears and a coyote came to feed, but it was not until the third night that the big bear put in its appearance again. When it did, it happened that three small bears were at the carcass; but these quickly quit the vicinity when the large bear appeared. Finally, the Grizzly caught sight of the scaffold, and made toward it. The two men fired simultaneously and the bear fell to earth with a series of 'bawls,' evidently wounded. The men did not come down until daylight, when the animal was found in some bushes and killed by a shot behind the ear.

The skin of this bear was sold by Mr. Wellman to the artist, Thomas Hill, and, through the latter's son-in-law, was procured in 1918 for the University of California.

MOUNTAIN COYOTE. **Canis latrans lestes** Merriam[5]

Field characters.—General appearance that of a large collie dog (pl. 39*a*); head and body about 30 to 33 inches long, tail with hairs 12 to 15 inches; ears pointed, about 4½ inches (114 mm.) high, habitually carried erect. General coloration gray, or grayish

---

4 This is in all probability the same Duncan mentioned by John Muir in the chapter on ''The Animals of the Yosemite'' in his book, Our National Parks (see Bibliography, p. 667). Muir relates that Duncan, who had quite a reputation locally as a bear hunter, had a cabin on the shore of Crescent Lake. In nine years he had killed no less than 49 bears [probably both Black and Grizzly]. He kept count of his killings by ''notches cut on one of the timbers of his cabin.'' Crescent Lake is but a short distance from Buck Camp, and Duncan was doubtless living there in 1887 when Wellman went to get his assistance.

5 Our series of specimens, skins and skulls, from the Yosemite region, serve to demonstrate beyond much doubt that two races of 'mountain' coyote are represented, a high mountain and Great Basin form, and a foothill form. The Park rangers, and trappers generally, recognize the two, often distinguishing the larger, stouter, and more grayish colored animal under the name ''gray wolf.'' This is certainly the *Canis latrans lestes* Merriam. The foothill animal, ranging down the west slope of the Sierras from about the 6000-foot contour nearly to the edge of the San Joaquin Valley, differs from *lestes* proper, in being of smaller average size, in having brighter color (more reddish) and a lighter built skull, and in certain other cranial characters. The relationship of this foothill form is clearly close to *lestes*, under which name we place it. Some of the specimens at hand from both El Portal and Yosemite Valley are intermediate in character, indicating that there had been free interbreeding of the animals at about the level where their respective ranges meet. There is likelihood that a third kind, the Valley Coyote, *Canis ochropus ochropus* Eschscholtz, also occurs in the Yosemite section, at its extreme western end, about Snelling. Unfortunately, we obtained no specimens of coyote out on the plains. This coyote of the open San Joaquin Valley is sharply distinct from either of the races of the Mountain Coyote by reason of its coarser, less furry coat, which is of a light reddish rather than either deep reddish or grayish cast of color. It has much larger ears, a longer slenderer snout, and smaller teeth.

brown, with black along back, and with reddish brown of varying tone on nose, ears, back, and legs. Tail very bushy, 4 or more inches in diameter, black tipped. *Tracks:* Dog-like, longer than wide, in a large animal 2¼ by 2¾ inches (6 by 7 cm.); impression of heel pad but little larger than that of any individual toe; claw marks not always showing. *Droppings:* Dog-like, about ¾ inch in diameter. *Voice:* A loud, moderately high-pitched barking, interspersed with shrill wailings, usually continued for several seconds; rarely heard except during the night.

Occurrence.—Moderately common almost throughout the Yosemite section, from the westernmost foothills eastward across the Sierran crest to the Mono Lake district. In winter some of the high mountain individuals descend to lower altitudes, and range down on the west slope to at least the 3500 foot contour, as at Cascades. In Yosemite Valley the animal is most often seen or heard in fall and winter. Frequents various sorts of country; often seen in the open. Usually seen singly.

In spite of the great amount of trapping and hunting carried on against them for many years, coyotes remain fairly common in the Yosemite section. Summer travelers, especially in the territory above the level of Yosemite Valley, are likely to catch sight of the animals or, if not so fortunate, at least to see their tracks or hear their howling. At almost every camp which we made in the region we ourselves were apprized of the presence of the animals in one or another of these ways.

The coyote is not easily to be confused with any other wild mammal. It resembles in general appearance some of the domestic breeds of dogs, especially the collie and the 'wolf dogs,' yet offers decided points of difference. The body of the coyote is high and narrow (compressed), the face and snout long and tapering (pl. 39a), the ears high (4 inches or more in an adult) and habitually carried erect, the tail moderately long, round, and bushy, the feet smaller than in a dog of the same bulk, and the legs slenderer and relatively long, the body being carried well above the ground. From all of the foxes the coyote differs in its much larger size and in its relatively longer legs. From the California Valley Coyote, which lives on the San Joaquin plains, the Mountain Coyote is distinguished by larger size, stouter build, greater weight of body, and heavier fur. In tone of color some of the high mountain individuals are so much paler than the foothill and valley animals as to give rise to the local term "gray wolf."

An average adult Mountain Coyote measures about 45 inches from tip of nose to tip of tail. The tail is about 13 inches long. The height of the animal at the shoulder is about 20 inches. The weight of a male is in the neighborhood of 25 pounds. Some will exceed this weight, while many of the animals which are trapped in late fall, that is, the young of the year, will weigh considerably less. Females are somewhat smaller and of lighter weight than males of a corresponding age.

The pelage of the Mountain Coyote is heavy all through the year, being always denser and 'woollier' than that of the Valley species at the same season. In the coat of the Mountain Coyote there are relatively few of the coarse overhairs or 'guard hairs' while there is proportionately more of the fine under-fur. The reverse is the case in the Valley Coyote. In other words, the Mountain Coyote is a 'woolly' animal; while the Valley species is 'hairy.' A thick coat of fur to protect it from cold is of course essential for an animal which dwells during the winter months in snow-covered mountains. The coat of the Mountain Coyote is probably subjected to relatively slight wear, because the animal lives more in the open and has its den among rocks rather than in a burrow in the ground. Its tail never loses its rounded 'bottle-brush' form. One molt occurs each year, in the fall, taking place some time between September and December. The transition from the old hair and fur to the new does not bring about nearly so great a change in appearance in this species as it does in the Valley Coyote. Just after the molt is completed, when all the old hair has fallen out and all of the new is fully grown in, the fur is prime, from the standpoint of the trapper and fur dealer. The wear which does occur in the Mountain Coyote, even though slight, results in lightening the coat color; some of the black hair tippings are lost and at the same time the reddish tones pale out, so that the general gray tone becomes even more pronounced.

With the coming of autumn, many of the small mammals at the higher elevations go into hibernation and, with the arrival of the snow, the retreats and forage grounds of others are covered over. The Mountain Coyotes, which have lived well all summer, are now forced to hunt more assiduously for food. The migratory tendency which results in the appearance of some of the big gray coyotes at the lower altitudes on the west side of the mountains may well be a result of this stress. In October, the numbers of coyotes in Yosemite Valley are augmented, and from then on the animals are more or less common in the environs of the Valley between the altitudes of 3500 and 7000 feet. The high-zone animals probably never go lower than is necessary to find an adequate supply of food. In Yosemite they keep to the north side of the Valley about Mirror Lake and in the taluses near Rocky Point, Yosemite Falls, and Indian Cañon, where favorable den sites abound, and whence they can sally forth at night to search the meadows for mice and gophers, the houseyards for chickens, or the garbage pits for table scraps.

The Mountain Coyote ranges upward regularly to above timber line. On July 17, 1915, tracks of a Mountain Coyote were seen in Donohue Pass, altitude 11,100 feet, near Mount Lyell. This is our highest station for the occurrence of the species. This animal had crossed the 'pot-marked' snowfield, stepping carefully on the edges of the 'riffles,' seldom dropping into the holes.

The track of a coyote cannot be distinguished surely from that of a large dog, but as dogs are not allowed in Yosemite National Park, save when they are occasionally used by rangers, little chance of confusion on that score is likely to arise. The four toes and one heel pad each make an impression, that of the heel being only slightly the larger. On soft ground or snow, into which the feet can sink, the claws, also, leave imprints. The foot impression as a whole is longer than broad, that of a large animal in soft snow measuring 80 by 70 millimeters. The Mountain Lion track is much larger, and proportionately wider, the heel imprint is much wider, and no claw marks ever show. The wolverine's track shows five unequal toes and a very large triangular heel pad. The tracks of all the other mountain carnivores (bears of course excepted) are much smaller than those of the Mountain Coyote.

The coyote's foot is so constructed as to give the animal, in spite of its weight and size, a decided advantage when traveling over snow. The toes spread somewhat, thus giving an expanded area of support. The coyote is thereby enabled to run over relatively soft and deep snow, where a deer would break through and make, at best, only slow progress.

The gait of a Mountain Coyote resembles in certain respects that of a dog. Undisturbed, the animal walks or trots. When stalking prey, such as a mouse or gopher, in the open, it proceeds very slowly and with caution. Its best gait for making distance is a gallop, which is easier than the gallop of most dogs. The speed at which a frightened coyote can lope away is surprising to anybody observing one for the first time. The animal now and then casts a crafty glance to one side or the other but this in no degree lessens the rate of its departure. We did not ourselves catch sight of more than a single coyote at any one time. Ranger Townsley reports seeing two together on one occasion. We have no definite knowledge of the animals occurring in larger groups at any time, in spite of rumors that they sometimes "hunt in packs."

The Mountain Coyote as compared with the Valley species is thought to be of bolder disposition; and it is much more of a hunter of the larger active sorts of prey. The Mountain Coyote seems to prefer to get its prey through capture in the open or by digging it out. It is less of a carrion feeder. It is not at all averse, however, to eating carrion. It will feed on the carcass of a deer long dead; and we have captured coyotes in traps baited with the partly decayed bodies of small mammals and birds discarded days before in the preparation of specimens.

On July 25, 1920, at the Dudley ranch, 6 miles east of Coulterville, Mr. Donald D. McLean had an exceptional opportunity to see a coyote in action. Mr. McLean had taken his position at daylight on top of one of the barns. Considerably before sunrise a coyote suddenly appeared close to the house and snapped up one of a flock of chickens that had just started out to forage. The coyote nabbed the chicken so quickly that the bird gave but one frightened squawk. Seemingly the coyote held the head and breast of the bird both at once in its jaws; also he so held it that it could not flap its wings; and he quickly and quietly bore it out of sight.

The majority of the Mountain Coyotes trapped are relatively young, for it is of course the younger, less experienced individuals that most easily fall victims to the trapper's skill. Some individuals may be trapped yet escape, and these probably carefully shun traps and bait thereafter. Removal of even a small number of the younger coyotes, however, gives the others a greater chance for survival since there are fewer to use up the available food supply. Those Mountain Coyotes who, made wise ('educated') through experience, survive their various enemies, grow to unusually large size and probably attain to ages far above the average for the species. These particularly old, large, and crafty individuals sometimes live in a locality for years and become well known to the residents of the region. One such animal was reported to us in 1915 to be living in the vicinity of Sweetwater Creek. These large individuals of the Mountain Coyote are the present day "wolves" of the Yosemite region. No true wolf is known to have occurred anywhere in middle California since about 1870.

The most usual utterance to be heard from coyotes is a rapid series of rather high pitched barking notes, interspersed with shrill wails, the whole continued for several seconds at a time. Trapped animals have been heard to give low growls and snarls, and we may infer that these weaker notes are used by the coyotes when in the wild, either toward others of their kind, or when alone and pursuing prey. The voice of the Mountain Coyote, as usually heard, is deeper toned than that of the Valley species, and so much more voluminous that to one observer it suggested comparison with a steam whistle. There is less of the high-pitched wailing, or squealing, in the voice of the Mountain Coyote, and its howling is therefore more like that of a large domestic dog. The barking choruses are most often heard in early morning or late evening; sometimes they are given during the night, especially when it is moonlight, but they are rarely heard during the middle of the day. Often, when one animal, or a pair, calls, others in the vicinity will answer. Thus, at Williams Butte, on September 18, 1915, at 5:40 A.M., one or more coyotes off to the south began baying. These were answered by others nearby, and then the animals called back and forth for some time. At 9:30 A.M. the same day, in broad sunlight, others were heard, and at 7:15 P.M. there was another chorus. Loud noises sometimes start coyotes barking. On the night of July 28, 1915, at Tenaya Lake, two burros brayed, whereupon coyotes in the neighborhood set up a succession of calls.

The chorus may, in reality, be the product of but one individual, whose intonations are such as to give the effect of two or even more voices heard simultaneously. We are unable to give any conclusive statement in this regard.

The food of the Mountain Coyote includes a wide variety of items, some of which have been alluded to in the preceding paragraphs. Usually, little knowledge of the coyote's food habits can be obtained by direct observation, as the animals do much of their hunting and feeding during the night. Even persons whose business keeps them out of doors much of the time in good coyote country do not often see a coyote actually eating. Our evidence, therefore, is, much of it, indirect. By far the greatest amount of data now at hand has been obtained by examining faeces (droppings). The hair and bones of mammals, the feathers of birds, and the seeds of plants are often recognizable in the droppings of the animal, and in many instances they may be identified even as to the species.

The droppings of a Mountain Coyote found in a trail at the head of Yosemite Creek basin on October 9, 1915, contained the forepaws of a Sierra Nevada Pocket Gopher (*Thomomys monticola monticola*), jaws, other bones, and hair of an adult and an immature Gambel White-footed Mouse (*Peromyscus maniculatus gambeli*), hair of the California Ground Squirrel (*Citellus beecheyi beecheyi*), and hair of the Rocky Mountain Mule Deer (*Odocoileus hemionus hemionus*). Another lot contained what appeared to be hair of the Golden-mantled Ground Squirrel. A third lot of faeces, collected near Dudley on August 9, 1920, consisted almost entirely of seeds from manzanita berries (*Arctostaphylos mariposa*).

Deer hair is commonly found in the droppings of the Mountain Coyote, but this fact does not necessarily mean that coyotes themselves regularly kill deer. On the contrary, it is likely that much of the coyote's venison comes from carcasses of deer killed and left cached by the Mountain Lion. Ranger Townsley has told us that on April 11, 1916, near Grouse Creek, he came upon two Mountain Coyotes circling the carcass of a deer which had been killed by a Mountain Lion, and that they were evidently about to feed on the deer when frightened off by shots. However, the coyote is known to have pursued and killed deer. Young does and fawns are probably the ones most often obtained in this way. When, in early winter, the deer are overtaken by a fall of snow more than a foot in depth, progress for them becomes difficult; they may be more easily and successfully run down by coyotes then than in the summer.

Cascade Red Fox. **Vulpes cascadensis** Merriam

Field characters.—General appearance that of a collie dog, but size smaller; tail extremely large and bushy; ears prominent; head and body about 26 inches, tail (excluding hairs at end) 16 inches, ear (about 4 inches?). Coloration (red phase) rich yellowish brown above, becoming white on belly and throat; feet and tips of ears black; inside of ears and end of tail white.

Occurrence.—Rare resident in higher zones on Sierra Nevada. Recorded definitely only at Big Meadows (4500 feet altitude), northeast of El Portal, about February 10, 1916; but to be expected anywhere from this level up to timber line. Lives chiefly in forest.

The Cascade Red Fox in the Yosemite region proved to be a notably elusive creature. We, ourselves, were not able to gain any direct information concerning it. On a number of occasions we saw tracks or sign which were believed to be those of this species, but we neither saw nor trapped the foxes. They must be present in only limited numbers, as even experienced trappers in the region, who have made good catches of other fur-bearers, have rarely taken the Red Fox. Inclusion of the species in the fauna of the Yosemite rests definitely upon a single imperfect specimen obtained through Mr. F. S. Townsley of the Park Ranger Service.

This specimen was taken at a locality, Big Meadows, which lies well within the Transition Zone and hence inside the range of the California Gray Fox. And it may be that the captured fox was driven to this low level by the extreme severity which marked the winter of 1915–16.

The Red Fox is quite different in appearance from its foothill relative, the Gray Fox. While exhibiting the dog-like appearance of foxes in general, the present species has proportionately larger ears, a softer and heavier coat of fur, and a more cylindrically bushy tail which looms large in proportion to the size of the animal's body. An occasional individual of the Red Fox departs from the regular color scheme and becomes a "cross" fox or even a "black" fox. The general darkening in tone results from replacement of the red in the pelage by black. One of our local informants told of seeing a "black" fox in the vicinity of Tioga Pass in September, 1915.

San Joaquin Kit Fox. **Vulpes macrotis mutica** Merriam

Field characters.—Similar to Red Fox in general appearance, but size smaller; head and body 19 to 21 inches (480–540 mm.); tail 10 to 12 inches (260–310 mm.); ear 3 to 3½ inches (80–93 mm.); weight 4 to 6 pounds (1800–2700 g.).[6] Upper surface light grayish brown, grizzled with white; tail bushy, with end conspicuously black; under surface of body pale yellowish to white; inside of ears white.

---

[6] Measurements from specimens taken elsewhere in San Joaquin Valley.

Occurrence.—Reported from Dry Creek, north of Snelling. No specimen obtained by us in Yosemite section. Inhabits dry uncultivated prairie, living in burrows in the ground.

The San Joaquin Kit Fox, or "swift," is an animal of the broad, open San Joaquin Valley, and it reaches the limit of its range at the beginning of the foothills. Only a narrow strip of territory typical of its range was included in our Yosemite section, and we did not succeed in trapping any specimens within it, but residents at both Snelling and Lagrange told us that the animals were formerly to be found in the open country lying between these two towns. Kit Foxes may still exist on parts of the dry rolling lands just below the foothills, for the country there, which has not yet been brought under cultivation, seems specially suited to their requirements. In other parts of the San Joaquin Valley, which like the Dry Creek region are pastured to cattle but otherwise unchanged by man, Kit Foxes are still to be found. Their requirements are met by the loose sandy soil in which they can make their burrows, and by the abundance of small game such as kangaroo rats, which affect similar situations.

The Kit Fox is more nearly related to the Red Fox than to the Gray Fox. It has the general form and scheme of marking observed in the former species, but the tip of its bushy tail is black instead of white as is that of the Red Fox, and its coloration generally is paler, more ashy, in tone, in keeping with the general color tone of its chosen environment.

CALIFORNIA GRAY FOX. **Urocyon cinereoargenteus californicus** Mearns

Field characters.—Form and size suggestive of a small collie dog; tail bushy; head and body 22 to 27 inches (549–690 mm.), tail (without hairs at end) 13 to 16 inches (330–410 mm.), height of ear 2¾ to 3⅛ inches (68–78 mm.); weight 7 to 10 pounds (3.2–4.5 kilograms). Coloration of body and tail chiefly iron gray; stripe down middle of back and along tail to tip, black; breast, sides of body, and much of legs, rich yellowish brown; chin and middle of belly white. *Voice:* A sharp bark; captive individuals sometimes make growling sounds. *Droppings:* Doglike, but smaller, ½ inch in diameter.

Occurrence.—Common resident in Upper Sonoran and Transition zones on west slope of Sierra Nevada. Recorded from Pleasant Valley eastward to floor of Yosemite Valley. Lives chiefly in chaparral. Solitary.

The California Gray Fox is the predominant carnivorous mammal in the great tracts of chaparral which clothe the western flanks of the Sierra Nevada. While it ranges somewhat outside the brushland, it is as characteristic a member of the fauna there as is the wren-tit or the California Thrasher among birds.

Indications of the presence of Gray Foxes were observed at every camp which we made in the foothills. Tracks in the dust of roadways, droppings in the trails through the chaparral, accumulations of feathers in clearings where birds had been eaten, and even momentary glimpses of the foxes themselves, all testified to the abundance of the species. In fact we were led to suspect that the paucity of small mammals in certain places might be due in part to the relatively large numbers of Gray Foxes present. Estimates as to the actual population of foxes are difficult to make, but there must be, in favorable situations, at least two pairs to a square mile.

The Gray Fox is often active during the daytime; the members of our party saw at least three individuals at large during the midday hours. Two explanations may be suggested for this peculiarity of behavior: (1) In the chaparral a fox would usually be as well screened from view as though it were operating under cover of darkness. (2) At certain seasons vegetable materials predominate in the diet of this fox, and it is quite as easy to forage for such food during the daylight hours.

When moving about, a Gray Fox usually travels at a rapid trot, a gait which carries it over the ground with considerable speed, but without obvious effort. To judge from the tracks seen in some places, individuals do considerable scouting. In Yosemite Valley on the snowy day of December 10, 1914, the tracks of at least three foxes were observed between Mirror Lake and the foot of the Tenaya trail. They had covered a great deal of ground, mostly off the trail, going over and under boulders and through the brush thickets in their search for prey.

In general outline, the track of the Gray Fox resembles a dog's, but it is much smaller, being about an inch in each dimension. In the soft dust of roadways imprints of the claws are often made in addition to those of the four toes and the foot pad.

In silhouette the Gray Fox presents a slender body, relatively large ears, and a bushy tail, though that member is not quite so large proportionately as it is in the Red Fox. The presence of much steel-gray or iron-gray in the body coloration readily distinguishes the Gray Fox from the Red Fox, which is of similar general size but has larger ears, and from the coyote, which is much larger.

The most common note heard from the fox is a sharp bark, dog-like in character, and never prolonged like the wail of a coyote. A trapped fox sometimes makes growling sounds when a person approaches. It is probable that in the wild a fox gives voice just about as a dog would do under similar circumstances.

The Gray Fox is classed as a carnivore (flesh-eater) by reason of its structure and relationship, yet it partakes extensively of food that is vegetable in nature. During the fall and early winter months we saw many fox droppings along the trails which consisted largely and often exclusively of the hulls and seeds from manzanita berries (*Arctostaphylos mariposa*). These berries when ripe are notably sweet to the human taste and must be highly nutritious. This easily gotten food is also abundant and the berries are available over a long season, from the first of August to at least December. On the brushy slopes of the hills a fox would need to do much skilful hunting to get a sufficient supply of meat daily from cottontail rabbits, wood rats, mice and small birds; plenty of berries are to be had, however, simply for the eating. As to other vegetable food, we may note that in the stomach of a fox trapped at El Portal we found, among other items, some blades of grass; another stomach contained some finely chewed material which looked like oak-mast.

As to animal food, we are able to definitely report that one stomach contained the remains of a pocket gopher; another had claws of some carnivore (which, however, may have been used as bait for traps). One lot of droppings included ribs and vertebrae of a small rodent, probably a white-footed mouse. Local trappers told us that Gray Foxes would come readily to traps baited with 'cracklings,' even though this material was buried in the ground. The members of our field party used successfully, in addition to bacon scraps, the bodies of small birds and mammals whose skins had been removed for specimens. In only one instance were we able to affirm that a fox had devoured a quail. In Yosemite Valley on the morning of December 24, 1914, one trap in a setting put out for foxes contained the leg of a Mountain Quail. Beside the trap were fox droppings and quail feathers. The bird had accidentally gotten into the trap; then the fox had come along and feasted.

Foxes evidently prey upon small birds to some extent, though our evidence on this point is rather inferential in character. For example, while the senior author was walking along a road through the chaparral near Pleasant Valley, on May 25, 1915, there came to his ears, from a nearby cañon bottom, the remonstrant chirping of a pair of Rufous-crowned Sparrows concerned over some marauder near their nest. A Bell Sparrow and a male Lazuli Bunting nearby lent voice to the demonstration. The observer approached cautiously and soon a Gray Fox was jumped in the ravine bottom. At Blacks Creek, near Coulterville, in May, 1919, a fox crossed the creek near our camp. At the instant the fox appeared a male Valley Quail, standing guard nearby, uttered a series of explosive sputtering notes indicative of great concern.

Judging from specimens obtained in the foothill country, the breeding season of the Gray Fox occurs in the spring months. No data were obtained locally as to the number of young, but elsewhere it has been ascertained to average four in a litter.

California Ring-tailed Cat. **Bassariscus astutus raptor** (Baird)

Field characters.—Body slender and tail long, the two of about equal length; general bulk that of house cat; ears broad, scantily haired; head and body 13½ to 15½ inches (346–396 mm.), tail 13¾–15½ inches (350–392 mm.), ear about 1¾ inches (45–47 mm.); weight 28–39 ounces (0.8–1.1 kg.). Body coloration drab brown, shaded with black on back; under surface white; tail full-haired, with alternate rings of black and white; a narrow black ring around eye, this nearly surrounded by white.

Occurrence.—Moderately common resident in Upper Sonoran Zone on west slope of Sierra Nevada. Recorded from Pleasant Valley eastward to El Portal; also taken in one verified instance on floor of Yosemite Valley. Inhabits rocky and brushy places, usually near streams.

The California Ring-tailed Cat, as might be inferred from its general scheme of coloration and particularly from its zoned tail, is a relative of the raccoon. In early days it was known commonly as 'miner's cat,' because many of the gold-seekers in the Sierras kept the animal as a free-roaming pet to rid their cabins of native mice. It has less often been called 'civet cat,' a doubly unfortunate choice of name, first, because the ring-tail is in no wise related to the Old World civets; second, because this particular name is locally applied by trappers to our Spotted Skunk. The ring-tail is not at all nearly related in either structure or habits to the cat family.

In the fall and early winter of 1914 trappers in the vicinity of El Portal captured a number of Ring-tailed Cats; the species seemed to be common in the nearby cañons. One specimen was taken by our party at Pleasant Valley on May 27, 1915; and in early February of 1920 Mr. F. S. Townsley obtained an individual in Yosemite Valley.

The California Ring-tailed Cat is of rather gentle demeanor, and hence a desirable animal to keep as a pet. In the wild it seldom causes any concern to people resident in the territory where it occurs, for its prey is almost entirely the smaller native animals. Occasionally in dusty places the small, somewhat cat-like tracks of the Ring-tailed Cat may be seen in the early morning, showing where it has been hunting abroad at night in search of wood rats, white-footed mice, and similar game. It spends the daytime in small caves among rocks or in the hollows of logs or trees.

California Coon. **Procyon lotor psora** Gray

Field characters.—Body size that of dachshund; legs and tail both short; toes of all feet long. Head and body 18 to 23 inches (460–585 mm.), tail 10½ to 12 inches (264–308 mm.), ear 2 to 2½ inches (52–65 mm.), weight 9 to 15½ pounds (4.1–7 kg.) [these figures from specimens taken elsewhere in California]. Body coloration grayish brown, hairs on back tipped with black; tail with alternating rings of black and pale ashy brown; face crossed by a conspicuous black band. *Track:* 'hand-like'; impressions of all five toes and of 'palm' showing distinctly.

Occurrence.—Common resident in Lower and Upper Sonoran zones, less common in lower part of Transition Zone, on west side of Sierra Nevada. Recorded from Snelling and Lagrange eastward to El Portal and Hazel Green. Lives chiefly in vicinity of streams, foraging on ground but taking shelter in hollow trees. Solitary; nocturnal.

The California Coon, or ''raccoon'' in the book terminology, is abundant in the lowland and foothill districts of the Yosemite region. It is essentially an inhabitant of the stream-side and seldom ventures any great distance away from the banks of rivers or creeks. Yet its requirements with regard to water are rather simple and it will often be found in cañon bottoms where in summer there is little more than a trickle of water or a series of disconnected seepage pools.

Hand-like tracks in the mud of creek banks, in evidence of a coon's presence, are much more likely to be seen than the animal itself. For coons are exclusively night prowlers and spend the daytime in hollow trees or other similar retreats. In the Yosemite region we found tracks in the neighborhood of every camp below 4000 feet altitude, and on one occasion tracks were noted along a creek near Hazel Green, altitude 5665 feet. In the latter case the animal had probably wandered up the creek from some lower station to the south. At Snelling the species seemed to be of maximum abundance; one trapper had 25 skins which had been obtained from his headquarters at a ranch a mile west of the town.

Throughout much of their local range coons must depend upon natural food, rather than that obtainable around human habitations. This food is no doubt varied, and includes both animal and vegetable materials. At Smith Creek, according to Mr. Donald D. McLean, coons live, in some part, on frogs. On Sweetwater Creek in late October the coons had been visiting a garden where grapes and other fruits were growing.

SIERRA PINE MARTEN. **Martes caurina sierrae** Grinnell and Storer

Field characters.—Size of small domestic cat, but form more slender (pl. 23*b*); tail somewhat bushy, about one-half length of head and body. Head and body 15 to 16½ inches (374–420 mm.), tail (without end hairs) 6¾ to 7½ inches (170–194 mm.), ear 1¼–1¾ inches (29–43 mm.), weight 26 to 33 ounces (746–929 grams). Coloration plain brown above; paler on under surface with an area of buff or orange on throat, varying in extent in different individuals; tail brown, becoming blackish toward tip.

Occurrence.—Common in Hudsonian Zone on Sierra Nevada, where recorded from near Glen Aulin and Vogelsang Lake eastward to Lyell Cañon. Inhabits rock slides chiefly.

The Pine Marten, or American Sable as this animal is sometimes called in books by reason of its relationship to the sable of the Old World, is rather common in the higher parts of the Sierra Nevada. We found the species only in the Hudsonian Zone, between altitudes of 8000 and 10,350 feet; it seems to remain there throughout the year.

The common name of this animal would suggest that it is an inhabitant of the forest, and so it is in Canada and Alaska; but the race inhabiting the Yosemite region seems to have departed from its ancestral predilections in some measure, for it here lives about the rock slides. Our knowledge of the marten locally was all gained during the summer season when its addiction to the talus rocks is marked; but it may be that, in winter when the rock slides are buried in snow, the animals live in the adjacent forest. Only winter observatoins in the high mountains can determine this particular point.

None of our party happened to see any Pine Martens except those trapped for specimens; but a group of campers located on Fletcher Creek in September of 1915 reported seeing four or five in a rock slide opposite their camp. It is not unlikely that watchful visitors in the Hudsonian Zone may, with some frequency, catch sight of martens, as well as other interesting but elusive denizens of the rocks.

In general form, especially in its relatively slender body, the Pine Marten resembles the weasel. But the tail is much more heavily haired and the tip is not abruptly black. The facial expression, with pointed features, recalls strongly that of the weasel. The marten never gets white in winter, but retains its brown color throughout the year.

It might be expected that the marten would pursue game of a size proportionate to its own bulk; but its constant residence in the rock slides makes it seem likely that the decidedly smaller conies and Bushy-tailed Wood Rats are the most important items of its food. Our specimens were caught in traps baited with the bodies of small mammals and birds; in one case fish was used.

Pacific Fisher. **Martes pennanti pacifica** (Rhoads)

Field characters.—Size twice that of a large domestic cat; body rather slender (pl. 23a), tail bushy, more than half length of head and body; ears short and rounded. Head and body 20 to 25 inches (520–625 mm.), tail (without end hairs) 15 inches (375–380 mm.), ear 1½ inches (35–40 mm.); weight (from specimens taken elsewhere in California) 8 to 10 pounds for males, 4 to 5½ pounds for females. Coloration black on tip of nose, legs and feet, hind part of body and whole of tail; rest of body drab brown (many of the hairs black-ended), becoming grayish on head and shoulders; occasionally white spots on chest and belly.

Occurrence.—Moderately common resident in boreal region of Sierra Nevada. Winter specimens taken from Big Meadows and Tuolumne Grove Big Trees eastward to Chinquapin and floor of Yosemite Valley at Pohono Bridge. Seen in head of Lyell Cañon at about 11,000 feet altitude, July 18, 1915. Mostly inhabits forest. Solitary.

Information concerning the Pacific Fisher in the Sierras, save for that obtained through trapping, is slow in accumulating. In fact, except for the specimens obtained from trappers in the western part of the Yosemite

National Park during the winter months, we have only a single observation to record. The species seems to be even more retiring in its habits than is the Pine Marten.

The Pacific Fisher is a considerably larger animal than the Pine Marten, the weights of the two being in a ratio of about 3½ to 1. Both exhibit the comparatively slender form of body which characterizes so many members of the Mustelidae, the chief family of the fur-bearers. The fisher is somewhat longer legged and its tail is decidedly longer proportionately than the marten's. In coloration the fisher is more varied than the majority of its relatives, and its fur is long as well as dense. Naturally, therefore, it is a species especially sought for the fur trade.

All of the winter records of the fisher in the Yosemite region are from a narrow belt of country in the western part of the Park because it is only or chiefly in that area that trappers have plied their trade. To judge from the habits of the fisher in other parts of its wide range, some individuals of the species probably remain during the winter months in the Canadian and even in the Hudsonian Zone of the Yosemite section. So far as we know no trapping or observation has been carried on in the heart of the high Sierras during the winter months; consequently, there is an almost total lack of information concerning the distribution and habits of the mammals which winter there. The one definite record for the fisher on the floor of the Yosemite Valley was made in the middle of winter, February 14, 1920, when an individual was obtained near the Pohono Bridge. The species does not stray onto the Valley floor very frequently, else, with the numerous campaigns of trapping (for coyotes) carried on there during the winters of different years, it would have been captured more often.

The fisher, to judge from its structure, especially from the sharp and curved claws, is an animal well fitted to climb trees. Its feet, at least during the winter months, are well furred between the toe and foot pads. This fact suggests that it also travels about to a considerable extent on the snow. The habits of the fisher in the woods of Canada show it to be a truly carnivorous species, for it there destroys many of the fur animals caught in traps.

While four members of our party were ascending Mount Lyell on the morning of July 18, 1915, a good view was obtained of a Pacific Fisher. As we crossed a little depression at about 11,000 feet altitude, we scared the animal up and it bounded lightly away over the rocks and snow with the agility of a cat. The snow was 'pocketed' at this season and the animal had to leap deftly from one narrow ridge to another as it made off across the snow field. As it ran we noted the slender legs, slim body, and long tail, the light patch on the forehead and another on the back. The animal resembled a marten somewhat, but was larger. It made leaps of about 2 feet, and finally disappeared from sight behind the very last patch of stunted white-bark pines on the north side of Mount Lyell. When first seen, the fisher was about 200 yards off; as it ran it paused occasionally to look back in our direction. Its whole demeanor suggested that of a house cat making its way over a rough surface at a rather good rate of speed.

SIERRA NEVADA WOLVERINE. **Gulo luscus luteus** Elliot

Field characters.—Size and proportions of heavily built dog; body stout (pl. 23c), rather broad; legs short, feet big; tail quite short. Head and body 27–29 inches (682–742 mm.), tail about 10 inches (250–260 mm.), ear about 2 inches (50–55 mm.); weight 17 to 25 pounds (7.6–11.3 kg.). Coloration above, yellowish brown, dark on lower back; head (except crown), feet, under surface of body, and end of tail, blackish.

Occurrence.—Sparse resident of Hudsonian Zone along crest of Sierra Nevada. Recorded definitely in head of Lyell Cañon at altitudes of 10,100 and 11,000 feet, July 26 and 25, 1915. Probably inhabits sparse forest. Solitary.

The wolverine is a rare animal anywhere on the Sierra Nevada, and it dwells only in the highest parts of these mountains. In consequence there is but scant information concerning it locally and much of that is hearsay. Only one of the local trappers in the Yosemite section had anything to relate concerning the species and he merely reported one killed in the region prior to 1914. Inclusion of the species here is based upon the capture of two individuals at the upper end of Lyell Cañon, late in July of 1915, by Mr. Charles L. Camp of our party.

Our station at the head of Lyell Cañon was at 9800 feet, but trapping was carried on up to timber line toward Mount Lyell in an effort to obtain various desirable species. For nearly a week a certain setting of steel traps was visited daily and baited with marmot bodies and other similar material. These traps were placed on bare rocky ground at the side of a thicket of white-bark pines at timber line (11,000 feet) on a rocky ridge between the McClure and Lyell forks. The snow was 4 feet deep in places near by. On July 25, a female wolverine was captured in this setting, and the day following an adult male was taken in another 'set' not far off, at 10,100 feet.

The first individual was held securely in all three traps. Nevertheless, it struggled violently, and from time to time uttered grunting sounds. When the observer placed his gun within reach, the animal quickly and easily bit off a piece of the black walnut stock.

The second wolverine captured was held by one hind foot in a steel trap, but this did not hinder it from going through a variety of motions limited only by the length of the trap chain. It climbed readily into a nearby wind-distorted lodgepole pine about three feet in diameter, using the claws in holding on to the trunk. Several times while being watched the animal started to dig into the ground, throwing up the earth at a lively rate; it would then turn over on its back and wallow in the cool earth, putting its feet into the air while doing so. Twice the wolverine sat up on its haunches with the forefeet against its breast after the manner of a bear. When approached very closely it made a lunge at the aggressor, uttering hoarse growls somewhat like those of a badger, and wrinkled up its nose, exhibiting its blunt teeth. The iris of this wolverine looked black; but when the pupil was dilated, the aqueous humor of the eyeball made the eye look green at certain angles.

In several other places, as at Vogelsang Lake and Fletcher Lake, tracks were seen which, chiefly through a process of elimination, were ascribed to the wolverine. The only other large carnivore in the high mountains is the Mountain Coyote. But the wolverine's track is not dog-like; the sole pad on the forefoot is divided up into small units, whereas the sole pad of the coyote is a single unit. The badger, which also has a relatively large track, has an elongated triangular foot pad.

Mountain Weasel. Mustela arizonensis (Mearns) [7]

Field characters.—Body about as long as that of California Ground Squirrel, but much more slender (fig. 9b); tail about half length of head and body. Head and body 8⅓–10½ inches (211–269 mm.), tail 5¼–6⅓ inches (132–160 mm.), ear ⅘–1 inch (21–26 mm.), weight 7½–12¼ ounces (212–345 grams); among adults, males are larger than females. Coloration in summer uniform brown above, under surface rich creamy yellow; in winter, solidly white above and below; end of tail black at all seasons.

Occurrence.—Moderately common in Transition, Canadian, and Hudsonian zones on both slopes of Sierra Nevada. Recorded from Merced Grove Big Trees and Chinquapin eastward to Walker Lake and Mono Lake Post Office. Common on floor of Yosemite Valley. Lives around rock piles and old logs and under buildings. Solitary.

The weasel is a fearless animal, and active at all seasons of the year. Visitors to the Yosemite region therefore frequently see it, sometimes at very close range, both in the Valley and in the higher mountains.

The weasel is one of the most bloodthirsty of all of its tribe; the wild birds and mammals know this as thoroughly as do naturalists, for the presence of a weasel in any locality is immediately announced by cries of alarm from the native denizens. The weasel's body is extremely slender (fig. 9b); so small is the girth that it can easily make its way into the retreat of a ground squirrel or even into the burrow of a pocket gopher; and it readily enters the nests of those rodents which live among rocks or

---

[7] Another species, the California or Yellow-cheeked Weasel, with whitish patches on the nose and cheeks, common in the Lower and Upper Sonoran zones of southern and central California, probably occurs in the lowland and foothill districts of the Yosemite region, though we obtained no specimens. We were told of a weasel having been seen at Snelling; presumably it was of this lowland species, *Mustela xanthogenys* Gray.

in hollow logs or trees. Furthermore, the weasel is an adept climber and can run up or down the trunks of the smaller trees as readily almost as a tree squirrel. By reason of its structure and capabilities, it is therefore able to prey upon a much larger variety of animals than any other species of carnivore.

Fig. 9. (*a*) Sierra Least Weasel; Vogelsang Lake, August 31, 1915. See p. 89. (*b*) Mountain Weasel; Ten Lakes, October 8, 1915. See p. 86. (*c*) Pacific Mink; Merced Lake, August 23, 1915. See p. 89.
All photographed from freshly taken animals; reproduced about ⅓ natural size.

The body coloration of the weasel is unique among our predatory mammals. It changes abruptly with the seasons, being solidly white in the winter months and brown and yellow in the summer season. The weasel is thus able to hunt the year round, well concealed in its protective coloration be the season that of blanketing snow or of brown logs on the bare ground.

In the summer months we found weasels at practically all of our camps in the territory from the 4000-foot contour up to the head of Lyell Cañon, at 9800 feet altitude. In Yosemite Valley, in both the winter and summer months, weasels are observed commonly. On December 20, 1914, a 'white' weasel was reported near Sentinel Hotel. December 9, 1914, tracks were seen in the snow on the Yosemite Falls Trail, and December 23, the same year, tracks were seen on the Vernal and Nevada Falls trail. In the latter case runways crossed the trail in many places, but these did not extend very far out on the unbroken snow. The weasels were then evidently living among the rocks which bordered the trails, for the short runs often led into holes about 1½ inches in diameter burrowed in the snow covering the rocks and adjacent bushes and small trees.

During the rather brief stops which our party made at the various camps occupied in the Yosemite country, we saw many of these animals. At Chinquapin, on June 19, 1915, one of our party came upon a weasel in a small pile of old logs near a clearing. The weasel disappeared. The observer waited ten minutes and then went cautiously around to the other side of the pile where he found the animal peeking out at him curiously. When we stopped near the Tuolumne Meadows camp of the Sierra Club in late July of 1915, one weasel was shot right in camp as it made its appearance under a log beside a small rocky eminence. Another individual was seen close by, at the base of the same rock heap, where it was traveling in long bounds along the boulders. These two individuals caused particular concern to a number of White-crowned Sparrows which had their broods in the near vicinity; the birds evinced their anxiety over the presence of the enemy with many sharp notes of alarm. In Yosemite Valley on June 25, 1920, a Mountain Weasel was discovered through the excited calling of a pair of Spurred Towhees in a cascara thicket. This weasel took refuge from our pursuit up in an apple tree; there he dodged about among the branches and repeatedly looked down at us, monkey fashion. The black-appearing head, big round ears, and beady eyes had a strikingly alert expression.

In Yosemite Valley domestic cats were kept by the local residents until about 1908 when they were banished by order of the park authorities. The following year mice swarmed; then weasels began to be noted and they have been observed there in numbers ever since. We were told by Mr. C. W. Baker that on July 25, 1915, there was a brood of young to be seen playing about an occupied tent. The same informant stated that weasels were common about the horse barns and that they came out and watched like cats when bales and sacks were moved about and mice were likely to appear. Twice, we were told, weasels in the Valley had been seen carrying pocket gophers. At Tuolumne Meadows a packer told us that he saw one kill a 'picket-pin' (Belding Ground Squirrel); the weasel had the squirrel by the back of the neck.

At Walker Lake on September 12, 1915, a Red Squirrel was caught in one of the traps in a setting placed between the butts of two logs. Later, a Mountain Weasel happened along and nearly consumed the squirrel before it in turn was caught in another of the traps in the same set. On the same day the greater portion of another weasel caught elsewhere had been eaten, but there was nothing to indicate the identity of the animal which had attacked the victim of the trap. It is evident from the first mentioned case and from other trapping experiences not specifically cited that weasels will eat dead flesh, even when not fresh.

A Mountain Weasel three-fourths grown, living in a den under a willow clump at the edge of the lake, was taken at Mono Lake Post Office on June 30, 1916. There were many droppings at the entrance to the den.

SIERRA LEAST WEASEL. **Mustela muricus** Bangs

Field characters.—Size small and form slender; our smallest carnivore (fig. 9*a*); body about as large as that of Tahoe Chipmunk; tail small, round, about ⅓ length of head and body. Head and body 6½ inches (159–161 mm.), tail 2⅓ inches (59 mm.), ear ⅓ inch (8 mm.), weight about 2 ounces (56–62 grams.). Coloration in summer season chocolate brown above, under surface white; end of tail blackish.

Occurrence.—Sparse resident in Hudsonian Zone along Sierra Nevada. Recorded at Ten Lakes (9200 feet altitude), October 10, 1915, and at Vogelsang Lake (10,350 feet), August 31, 1915. Lives in or about rock slides. Solitary.

The Sierra Least Weasel, as its name suggests, is much smaller than its better known relative, the Mountain Weasel. We obtained two specimens, as recorded above, and no others were seen; it would seem from our experience both in the Yosemite region and elsewhere that the species is decidedly less numerous than is the Mountain Weasel. The Least Weasel is a member of a rather wide ranging group which fills some small corner in the economy of nature not occupied by the larger species. So far as our local information indicates, the Least Weasel is an associate of the Pine Marten, Yosemite Cony, and Bushy-tailed Wood Rat.

At Vogelsang Lake on August 31, 1915, the senior author, while making the rounds of his traps before sunrise, heard two conies across the lake basin (pl. 18*a*) 'screeping' vociferously. Upon going to the rock slide, he saw these animals running excitedly in and out of the crevices between the rocks. Presently a Least Weasel appeared, crossing between two rocks. Soon, it put its head out from under a flat rock within 30 feet of the observer, who shot it. The inference that this weasel is a regular enemy of the conies and is so recognized by them seems justified.

PACIFIC MINK. **Mustela vison energumenos** (Bangs)

Field characters.—Body size about that of California Ground Squirrel, but tail short, about half head and body (fig. 9*c*); head and body 11¾–13¼ inches (297–337 mm.); til 6–6¾ inches (150–170 mm.); ear about ½ inch (11–14 mm.); weight 13¼–18¾ ounces (377–530 grams). Coloration deep, dark brown, only a little paler on under surface; end of tail blackish.

Occurrence.—Recorded definitely only at Merced Lake (altitude 7500 feet), but likely to be found on any of the streams up to this altitude. Inhabits streams and ponds and their margins.

The Pacific Mink was collected in only one place in the Yosemite region; but, to judge from other information at hand, it is certainly of more widespread occurrence than this record would indicate. In Yosemite Valley above the Pohono bridge an animal which was believed to be a mink was seen swimming in the river November 26, 1914. The species was reported to us as occurring in the neighborhood of Mount Bullion and on the South Fork of the Merced River. On one occasion while at the Farrington Ranch east of the Sierras, near Williams Butte, Mr. Dixon saw tracks of a mink along a creek, and a few days later a resident of the vicinity saw one of the animals in a pasture.

The mink has a moderately slender body and uniform general coloration, both of which features indicate its relationship to the weasels and the marten. It is, however, closely restricted to the vicinity of water. As may be expected from such a choice of habitat, its diet consists largely, if not exclusively, of fish. Were it abundant in the Sierra Nevada we might look upon it with concern as an enemy of the trout, but the species is present in such small numbers that no fear need be felt on this score. The animal is evidently nocturnal in its habits, else we should have more frequent reports of it from the many fishermen who patrol the banks of the Sierran waters where trout abound.

At Merced Lake three specimens of mink were taken on August 23, 25, and 28, 1915, all being obtained within 20 feet of running water. The bait in each case included heads and entrails of trout. One individual, probably just caught, when approached in the trap was very lively. It gave a series of loud, shrill, rasping cries, and when threatened showed its teeth and grinned cat-like.

CALIFORNIA SPOTTED SKUNK. **Spilogale phenax phenax** Merriam

Field characters.—Size slightly less than that of California Ground Squirrel; tail slightly over half the length of head and body. Head and body 9 to 12 inches (232–300 mm.), tail 5¼ to 6¼ inches (135–160 mm.), ear about ¾ inch (15–26 mm.), weight 10 to 21 ounces (276–600 grams). Coloration of body black, with spots and irregular short stripes of white; end of tail white. 'Skunky' odor, same as that of Striped Skunk.

Occurrence.—Common resident in Lower and Upper Sonoran zones, and sparingly in Transition Zone, on western slope of Sierra Nevada. Recorded from Snelling and Lagrange eastward to floor of Yosemite Valley. Seeks shelter in burrows of other mammals and under piles of logs or rocks; forages in open at dusk and during the night.

The Little Spotted Skunk, not infrequently referred to as "hydrophobia skunk," and known to most trappers as "civet cat," is a common resident of the lower western portion of the Yosemite region, and, in small numbers, reaches the floor of Yosemite Valley. Locally it was found very commonly at Snelling; probably its maximum abundance is in that direction.

In Yosemite Valley the species came to our notice only along the warm north side. One was trapped December 29, 1914, in the talus at the foot of Indian Cañon, where it had a retreat beneath a granite boulder. Another was taken June 25, 1915, beneath a boulder pile near the lower end of the Yosemite Falls trail.

The Spotted Skunk makes use of natural retreats and of the burrows of other mammals. Our records indicate that specimens were taken not only near crevices or holes under rocks, but at the mouths of ground squirrel burrows, and near old badger holes.

The food of this skunk, as of its larger relative, is quite varied, including small mammals, insects, and vegetable materials of several sorts.

The Spotted Skunk is provided with glands near the base of the tail which, when the animal is provoked, emit a malodorous secretion. To our nostrils this odor does not differ in strength or quality from that of the Striped Skunk.

Striped Skunk. **Mephitis occidentalis** Baird

Field characters.—Size of adult about that of domestic cat; tail nearly as long as head and body and very bushy. Head and body 12½ to 17¼ inches (318–440 mm.), tail 11 to 13½ inches (280–345 mm.), ear about ¾ inch (15–20 mm.), weight 3⅓ to 8⅓ pounds (1.5–3.8 kg.). Coloration black except for a narrow line of white up middle of forehead, and a white area beginning on hind neck and continuing backwards, dividing into two stripes which extend to rump and usually run out on either side of tail; more or less white also on bases of tail hairs. 'Skunky' odor characteristic.

Occurrence.—Common resident at lower altitudes on both slopes of Sierra Nevada. Recorded on west slope from Snelling and Lagrange eastward to Sweetwater Creek, Yosemite Valley, and Chinquapin; east of mountains in vicinity of Williams Butte. Lives in holes in ground and in culverts and under rocks and buildings; forages far and wide at dusk and during night.

The Striped Skunk needs no introduction. It has long been sought after because of its valuable fur, and it is also well known in the environment of farms even in settled portions of the country. Persons who walk abroad in the early evening along the country roads of the Yosemite foothills are likely to encounter this animal as it starts out on its nightly forays; for the skunk, unlike most other wild animals, does not take to cover at the approach of a human being.

The Striped Skunk is nearly twice the length of, and from 4 to 6 times as heavy as, the Little Spotted Skunk. Its body is heavy and the fur is relatively long. The hairs on the tail are often as much as 5 inches in length, and give to this member a plume-like appearance. Indeed, when held aloft, as it is when the skunk is disturbed, the tail constitutes its most conspicuous feature.

In the lower portion of the Yosemite region skunks make extensive use of ground squirrel burrows as dens, appropriating those which are deserted or possibly, even, holes from which the rightful owners have been evicted. It likewise uses deserted badger holes to a considerable extent. On the mesa-prairie near Snelling, Striped Skunks were trapped fully three-fourths of a mile from the nearest bluff of the foothills; and it seemed as though the animals must have been foraging abroad fully this distance, as no burrows were found short of the bluffs.

Relatively large numbers of Striped Skunks are trapped by the residents of the region both for their fur and because of the depredations which they commit about poultry houses. But despite this draft on the population the species has maintained itself in goodly numbers. The tracks are to be seen commonly in the morning along dusty roads through the foothills.

As one of us was motoring up the Coulterville Road not far above Lagrange one moonless night in August, a Striped Skunk was sighted in the road ahead. The beast was traveling up-grade in the right-hand wheel rut, ambling along at the regulation matter-of-fact rate characteristic of the species. As the machine approached, going in 'low,' the skunk accelerated its pace in no perceptible degree; neither did it leave the rut. In order to avoid the consequences of a rear-end collision, the driver, the last instant it was yet possible, simply *had* to turn out to the left, leaving the skunk still pursing its own course when the shadow-limit from the lights cut it from view.

California Badger. **Taxidea taxus neglecta** Mearns

Field characters.—Up to twice size of domestic cat; body flat, depressed (pl. 24*b* and *c*); legs short; tail short, one-fourth head and body; feet large and claws stout and long. Head and body 20½–24 inches (520–610 mm.), tail 5–6¾ inches (125–170 mm.), ear 1⅕–2 inches (30–50 mm.); weight 9½–17 pounds (4.3–7.7 kg.) [extralimital specimens included in these measurements]. General coloration yellowish brown, grizzled with white; feet and top of head black; a prominent streak of white from nose over middle of crown to between shoulders (pl. 24*c*); side of head white with a large patch of black on cheek. *Voice:* Low grunting and puffing noises.

Occurrence.—Resident in certain parts of the Yosemite region, irrespective of altitude. Recorded from Snelling, Lagrange, Pleasant Valley, Smith Creek (6 miles east of Coulterville), Vogelsang Lake, Tuolumne Meadows, Lyell Cañon, and near Williams Butte. Lives in open country; makes burrows in ground. Sometimes abroad in daytime. Usually solitary.

The California Badger is found at numerous localities in the Yosemite region, from the San Joaquin Valley on the west to Mono Valley on the east, and it ranges upward to an altitude of 10,350 feet. Yet it does not occur continuously over our Yosemite section as do several other wide-ranging species like the Gambel White-footed Mouse and Red-shafted Flicker. Its distribution is controlled by the presence or absence of flat clear areas of soil, rather than by temperature or any of the other factors which limit the ranges of most animals. Thus, on the uncultivated level lands of the San Joaquin Valley, the badger is, or was originally, common; in the foothill districts where there are but few meadows or other level open spaces, it is scarce or wanting; in the main forest belt it is altogether absent; while on the high meadows near the crest of the Sierras and on the floor of the Great Basin, east of the mountains, it is again to be found in numbers.

In settled portions of the San Joaquin Valley the badger has been reduced or exterminated by man, chiefly because the large holes (pl. 24a) which it digs in the ground are a menace to horsemen riding over the country. On the whole, however, the badger is a beneficial species, for its habitual food consists of rodents, like the ground squirrels and pocket gophers, most of which happen to be harmful to agriculture. In the high Sierras, where the relation between rodents and carnivores is still almost in its original condition, the badger is a relatively common animal. On Tuolumne Meadows in the summer of 1915 it was judged to be the most abundant carnivore present, with one exception, the Mountain Weasel.

The badger's whole being is organized for digging. The body, especially the trunk region, is thickset and muscular (pl. 24b). The legs are stout and short so that they can get an effective purchase. Both pairs of feet are disproportionately large, as compared, for example, with those of a Sierra Marmot. The claws on all the feet are large, those of the forefeet being especially long and heavy.

In addition, the badger is curiously flattened horizontally in the general configuration of its head and body; this 'pancake' effect is emphasized by the greater length of the overhairs along the sides of the body. The ears are short (pl. 24c), the eyes rather small, and the head is joined directly onto the body, with no definite neck region.

When hunting, the badger specializes in a method rarely used by any of the other carnivores of the region. The other predators hunt chiefly by stealth; the badger uses its prodigious strength and special equipment for the purpose and *digs* its victims out of their retreats. Nature has provided the badger with some means for locating accurately the underground nests of pocket gophers, ground squirrels, and rabbits. Whether smell or hearing or both function in this, we do not know. But once an occupied burrow is located, the badger quickly digs out and feasts upon the luckless inhabitants.

During the summer of 1915, the work of the California Badger was much in evidence on Tuolumne Meadows and the floor of Lyell Cañon.

The gophers had moved up to occupy the margins of the meadows, and the badgers had concentrated their activities in these areas, which had a maximum gopher population. Time after time we saw places where we inferred that gophers had been dug out. In the midst of an area showing new surface mounds and perhaps some winter earth-cores, there would be a hole 8 to 12 inches in diameter, with the torn remains of a gopher's nest at the bottom and signs of badger on the ground above. Three such excavations were noted by the junior author on one day in July, 1915, while traversing the floor of Lyell Cañon. Belding Ground Squirrels are probably captured to some extent by the badger in the mountains, as are California Ground Squirrels, in the lowlands.

On Tuolumne Meadows, July 11, 1915, a trap set in a locality where gophers and evidences of badger work were common caught a badger. The remarkable strength and energy of this individual, as an example of the species, were illustrated in a striking way. The animal had been caught by one hind foot. With its forefeet it had scraped up the earth within a circle of 3 to 4 feet diameter, the limit of its reach, and this earth had been accumulated in a flat-crowned mound. Its intention had been, presumably, to escape by digging, and it had stopped only when the accumulating earth had made further work impossible. On top of this mound the badger was squatting (pl. 24b).

On two occasions while our party was at Tuolumne Meadows, badgers were found at work during the afternoon. One animal was discovered digging in a hole in the ground. It was already below the surface, "kicking up the dirt at a lively rate," and when come upon, it quickly plugged the entrance so that further observation of it was impossible. The other animal was out on the surface of the ground near the border of a meadow. It ran quickly up a sidehill, and, in spite of its seeming clumsiness, outdid the observer in his attempt to follow. This badger also went into a hole, the opening of which it soon blocked with earth from within.

At Pleasant Valley Mr. J. B. Varain told us that he once opened a badger den on a neighboring hill and found at the bottom two young which were "nearly pure white." There was no nest of any sort.

Near the Farrington Ranch, southwest of Mono Lake, a half-grown badger was captured in late June, 1916 (pl. 24c). On one occasion it was let go free on the ground so that something of its habits might be observed. True to its kind it immediately commenced to dig, but continued only long enough to make a shallow excavation barely deep enough to hide in. A gopher or mole under similar circumstances would not only have tunneled out of sight, but would have kept on going. At any unusual noise the young badger would put his head out of the hole and look about.

Its general behavior was like that of adult badgers seen elsewhere, but it displayed little or none of the combativeness which characterizes the full-grown animals.

Northwestern Mountain Lion

Felis oregonensis oregonensis Rafinesque

Field characters.—Appearance cat-like; size of a mastiff dog; tail long and slender; head and body about 4 feet, tail about 2½ feet; ear about 3½ inches; weight, adult males about 135 pounds, adult females about 100 pounds. Coloration rich reddish brown above; chin and throat and middle of under surface white; outer sides of ears, nose, feet, and end of tail blackish. There is also a 'gray' phase where the pelage is grayish brown rather than reddish brown. *Tracks:* cat-like, usually wider than long, 3 to 4½ inches across; heel pad wide.

Occurrence.—Resident in moderate numbers on west slope of Sierra Nevada, chiefly in Upper Sonoran, Transition and Canadian zones. Lives in both brushy and forested country. Usually solitary.

The Northwestern Mountain Lion, which is also known as cougar, panther, and puma, is the second largest carnivorous mammal in the Yosemite region, being exceeded in size only by the bears. The Mountain Lion is large and strong enough, no doubt, to prey upon human beings if it so chose; but instead of being the terror of the country, as are lions and big cats in other parts of the world, our lion has practically never been known to attack a person, and indeed very seldom does it come to notice at all. Many persons, even woodsmen and hunters, long resident in regions where Mountain Lions occur, have never so much as caught sight of one. And in spite of the hundreds and even thousands of persons who camp each summer in the mountains, no one has been reported to have been molested by lions.

In general appearance the Mountain Lion, save for its far larger size, is much like a domestic cat. The head is short and massive, the forelegs are of heavy build, the body rather slender, and the tail long and cylindrical with an even covering of hair clear to the end, but with no 'tassel.' The Mountain Lion is several times the size of a large Mountain Coyote or a Sierra Nevada Wolverine. As to actual size we will cite, in the absence of carefully measured specimens from the Yosemite region, two typical individuals killed at a point farther north in the Sierra Nevada (Lynchburg, Placer County). The male measured 6 feet 6¼ inches from tip of nose to end of tail (excluding hairs), the tail was 2 feet 6½ inches, and the ear 3¾ inches. It measured 28½ inches in height at the shoulder and by two reliable observers was estimated to weigh about 134 pounds. The female measured 6 feet 4 inches over all, with tail 2 feet 6 inches, and ear 3½ inches. Its height at shoulder was 27½ inches, and estimates of weight were 95 to 100 pounds.

The range of the Mountain Lion in the Yosemite region is not so definitely bounded as that of many other species of mammals. In general the lions are to be found in the territory occupied by the Mule Deer, namely, the Canadian, Transition, and Upper Sonoran zones. There is to some extent, doubtless, a shifting of the lion's range in unison with the seasonal migrations of the deer. In the winter of 1915–16 Mr. Jay Bruce secured 11 lions in a rather limited tract of country near Wawona, and others were obtained by him in later years in the same region, a total of 31 being taken in the three winter seasons, 1915 to 1918. During the winter of 1915–16 at least 4 lions were obtained by other hunters in and about Hetch Hetchy Valley. Lions are noted not infrequently in the vicinity of the Dudley ranch on Smith Creek, east of Coulterville. Several individuals usually winter on Pilot Peak ridge where there are many deer. But Mountain Lions are likely to turn up at any point in the region. Thus, one was reported to have lived in the vicinity of Williams Butte, near Mono Lake, prior to 1910. And in 1920, about June 23, a lioness was shot under the road bridge across the Crocker-Hoffman canal halfway between Merced and Snelling, out in the San Joaquin Valley. Another is said to have been killed in the same locality a few days later. Lions are also said to have occurred at the "Three Buttes" on the plains south of Merced Falls.

The total population in the Yosemite section of an animal as stealthy in its habits as the Mountain Lion, is, as might be surmised, very difficult to estimate. Placing the number at one to a township (36 square miles), an average figure for an area well stocked with deer, there would be about 12 to 15 lions in our Yosemite section, and 20 to 25 in Yosemite National Park. These figures give the average population at a time when no intensive hunting has been done. With a total kill of 31 in three seasons in the Wawona district, the figures given are doubtless high. But these numbers may again be expected if efforts to destroy the animals be discontinued.

In 1918, and for some years subsequently, there was in the "zoo" in Yosemite Valley a female Mountain Lion which had been captured as a young kitten. Because of the interest which this individual excited among visitors to the Valley and because her record is the only bit of local information we have concerning the breeding of the Mountain Lion, we give her history and some notes on her habits in detail.

On April 27, 1918, Mr. Jay C. Bruce, now lion hunter for the California Fish and Game Commission, trailed and shot a female Mountain Lion in her lair in a rocky, brush-covered bluff about 3 miles north of Wawona. The den was among rocks, about 6 feet long and 2 feet wide, and was lined with pine needles. In the den were found 3 dusky spotted kittens, 2 females and a male, which were about the size of cottontail rabbits. Their eyes were just open and they were judged to be about ten days old. This is the litter mentioned in an article in *California Fish and Game* (vol. 4, 1918, pp. 152–153). The kittens were taken to Yosemite Valley where one of the females was successfully reared "on the bottle" by Mr. and Mrs. Gabriel Souvelewsky.

The authors saw this lioness in May, 1919, when she measured 30 inches from nose to base of tail and 21 inches from base to tip of tail, and weighed, by estimate, about 40 pounds. Her coloration was rich warm brown with small light tawny areas about the face. In a cage adjoining the one occupied by this native lion (*Felis o. oregonensis*) were two Rocky Mountain Lions (*Felis o. hippolestes*), from Yellowstone National Park. These were of paler, tawny yellow, coloration with whitish facial areas. They were of such a disagreeable disposition that their cage could be entered only with extreme caution. The Wawona lioness, on the other hand, was quite tame and permitted grown persons and even children to enter her cage freely. The animal was kitten-like in demeanor, romping with the children and chasing a ball in playful fashion. Whenever it struck, its claws were kept retracted so that a person would feel the impact of only the big furry paw. Once while several people were in the cage the cat jumped on the back of the junior author and the momentum, even at short range, was almost enough to cause him to lose his balance. Even in later years, we have been told, this individual still exhibited a high degree of tameness, although greater caution was exercised in entering her cage.

When the kitten sighted persons or animals at a distance it would gaze at them intently, meanwhile moving its big furry tail slowly from side to side. Children in particular seemed to hold its attention. It was surprising to note the distance at which the lioness caught sight of moving objects. This suggested a reason for the fact that Mountain Lions are seldom seen by people—the lions see the people first and quickly take themselves off.

The captive animal was most active during the morning and evening hours. The mid-day usually found her drowsy. One of our visits was at dusk when the lioness was very active and keenly alert to all that was going on. In this connection it may be recalled that Mule Deer are most active in the early and late hours of the day.

The preferred food of the Mountain Lion is deer. Whenever evidence of a reliable nature has been obtained it points to the fact that the deer contributes by far the largest portion of the lion's fare. The current estimate is at least one deer a week for each adult or sub-adult lion. The lion stealthily creeps up within a short distance of the deer, then with a few quick bounds, reaches its quarry and strikes it down. Sometimes a large portion of the deer is eaten, at others, only a small part is taken. The lion may or may not return to its kill for a subsequent meal. Sometimes only flesh is eaten, sometimes the internal organs are partly devoured. In one winter the carcasses of 20 deer killed by lions were found in a limited area near Wawona. Four were seen on one day in an area a half-mile square.

Assuming that each lion kills on the average one deer a week, a total of 1250 deer a year are killed in the Park. Does have one or two fawns at birth so that about 800 does would be required to provide the annual supply of venison for these lions. As there are deaths among the deer from other causes, the total population of breeding does in the Park must be well above the number mentioned to hold the deer population at its present numbers. The ratio between males and females in the Mule Deer we do not know. An estimate of the total deer population is not possible with the data at hand; but there is no indication of decrease during the past six or seven years. We seem safe in assuming that during this period the lions present have not levied upon the deer population in excess of the deer's recuperative powers.

Smaller game is resorted to at times by Mountain Lions. One resident near Smith Creek told of seeing a young lion killing a ground squirrel. An instance of a lion in the Yosemite section feeding upon skunk has already been reported in print by Mr. Donald D. McLean (*California Fish and Game,* vol. 3, 1917, p. 39). The circumstances of capturing this lion were later recounted to the senior author in person by Mr. John L. McLean, as follows:

On November 8, 1916, Mr. McLean, senior, was riding on horseback along the road about 8 miles east of Coulterville. His shepherd dog was scouting along the adjacent sidehill through the manzanita and ceanothus brush. At one place there was a strong odor of skunk, and shortly the dog began to bark in tones which indicated that he had treed something. Mr. McLean rode to the spot and found up in a golden oak what he at first thought was a bob-cat. Parenthetically, it may be stated that both of the cats (*Lynx* and *Felis*) in this region, when seeking safety, climb into golden oaks, probably because the dense foliage of these trees affords better shelter than does that of other trees. Presently Mr. McLean saw a long tail hanging below a limb and realized that the animal was a Mountain Lion. Promptly he shot it, the rifle ball passing through the lion's neck. The animal "smelled powerfully" of skunk, and later its stomach was found to contain flesh, skin, and black-and-white hair of a striped skunk. This item of food may have been chosen in extremity, though this lion was fat. It measured 5 feet 2 inches in length and weighed 37½ pounds.

CALIFORNIA WILDCAT. **Lynx eremicus californicus** Mearns

Field characters.—Appearance unique among our wild mammals; size much larger than that of domestic cat; legs longer, but tail much shorter. Head and body 19½ to 29 inches (493–735 mm.), tail 4¼ to 6¼ inches (107–160 mm.), ear excluding tuft 2½ to 3½ inches (66–89 mm.), weight 7¾ to 19 pounds (3.5–8.6 kg.) [some extra-limital specimens included in measurements]. The smaller extreme applies to females, the larger to males. General coloration above, light reddish brown in summer, gray in winter; under surface of body and inner sides of legs white, spotted or barred with black; ears black-tufted, black at end and base, white on middle. *Tracks:* Round, about 2 inches in diameter; sole pad doubly notched behind, not triangular as in coyote.

Occurrence.—Common resident on west slope of Sierra Nevada, chiefly in Upper Sonoran and Transition zones. Recorded from Snelling eastward to Yosemite Valley; altitudinally, ranges to 6500 feet (at head of Nevada Falls). Inhabits brushland, rock slides and timber. Active somewhat by day, as well as at night. Usually solitary.

The California Wildcat is a common inhabitant of the hill and mountain country immediately to the west of the Yosemite Valley and is also present in some numbers on the floor of the Valley itself. It is by no means as reclusive an animal as is the Mountain Lion, and is abroad to a considerable extent during the daytime, so that visitors to the region are likely to catch sight of it. The name "bob-cat" is often applied to this species because of its short or bobbed tail, this member being only about one-fourth the length of the head and body. Trappers often refer to large individuals as "lynx-cats," believing that they constitute a species distinct from the ordinary bob-cat or wildcat, as "granite bucks" are sometimes compared with ordinary deer; but there is only one species of wildcat known in the region.

The 'pencil' or tuft of black hairs on the ear, often supposed to be diagnostic of a true (Canada) lynx, is just as regularly present in our wildcat. The coloration of the latter, both as to tone of color and boldness of the black markings, is variable, and, although it has only one molt (this in late summer and fall), its pelage shows considerable seasonal change. In fall and winter the coat is distinctly gray in cast, but with the wearing off of the ends of the over-hairs at the advent of summer, the underlying color, a light reddish brown, comes into view.

In Yosemite Valley, and on the trails leading out of the Valley, the tracks of wildcats can often be seen after the snow comes. In December, 1914, we saw numerous tracks on the Yosemite Falls trail, some of which were well above Columbia Point while others led down close to the buildings in the old Presidio. Likewise on the Nevada Falls trail that same season, bob-cat tracks were common in the snow, even to the top of the zig-zags. This fact suggested that the cats were using the man-made trail as a pass between Yosemite and Little Yosemite valleys. During the summer the wildcats are doubtless just as active as in the winter, but they then do more of their hunting in the brush and among the rocks where few or no tracks show.

The track of the wildcat is of a rounded shape and on soft earth measures about two inches in diameter. In snow it is somewhat larger, as the toes then tend to spread apart, a characteristic which makes it possible for the cats to hunt over rather soft snow. The hind foot is put exactly in the tread of the forefoot of the same side; therefore the footfall is more silent. On one occasion successive footprints in the snow were about ten inches apart. In some cases each of the cats which followed along the Yosemite trails had walked in the footsteps of his predecessors. In other cases the different individuals, or the same individual at different times, had taken separate courses, for as many as seven parallel lines of tracks were noted in one place. On the Yosemite Falls Trail the wildcats had done much wandering; their tracks left the trail and went out into the boulder talus, then came back, only to leave again after a few steps; the cats were obviously foraging for the small mammals which dwell in the rock heaps.

Where not molested, the wildcat probably hunts nearly as much by day as by night. On at least three occasions members of our party came upon wildcats in the daytime. On December 9, 1914, a cat was sighted on the lower part of the Yosemite Falls Trail. A second was noted December 20, 1914, about 5 P.M., below the mouth of Indian Cañon. The third individual was seen one day in October, 1915, at about 4 o'clock in the afternoon, on a roadway below El Portal.

The wildcat is a skillful hunter and levies upon a wide variety of the medium-sized birds and mammals. Because of its diurnal activity, the cat naturally includes in its menu a number of diurnal birds such as Valley Quail, which forage on the ground but roost high, out of reach, at night. We found no direct evidence of the cat eating quail in the Yosemite section. On a number of occasions, however, we saw scattered feathers which indicated that a quail had been killed and eaten by some carnivore, whether by a Gray Fox or by a wildcat we could not determine. The numbers of quail captured by cats are probably overestimated by sportsmen. At Smith Creek, east of Coulterville, the wildcats during the winter months subsist to a considerable extent upon Western Robins. Mr. Donald D. McLean has reported (1919, p. 160) the finding of the remains of no less than six robins in the stomach of one wildcat killed March 10, 1919.

As for mammals, the stomach of a wildcat taken in Yosemite Valley about March 18, 1920, contained a considerable amount of Gray Squirrel hair. The cats seen hunting on the boulder talus near Yosemite Falls Trail were presumably after Boyle White-footed Mice and Streator Wood Rats, the two rodents which are common there.

Definite information concerning the food of the wildcat is slow in accumulating. The most dependable information is that gained by examining the stomach contents of animals caught by trappers. But in many instances the stomach of a trapped animal is empty or contains nothing but the material used as bait; had the cat been able to get its regular food it would not have been drawn to the trap. Of three wildcats trapped in Yosemite Valley in March, 1920, the stomach of one was empty, that of the second held only bait, and the third contained the hair of a gray squirrel.

The California Wildcat is an adept climber and when tracked with dogs will often take to trees, golden oaks or incense cedars being preferred, probably because the dense foliage of these two affords a greater measure of concealment. Whether the wildcat makes use of its climbing ability to go after birds or mammals which nest or live in trees we do not know.

The only local information which we have relative to the breeding of this animal is a statement by Ranger F. S. Townsley to the effect that near Big Meadows about April 20, 1916, he killed a female wildcat which contained 4 embryos. Data at hand from other parts of California indicate that this is an average number.

House Mouse. **Mus musculus** Linnaeus

Field characters.—Size small; tail about equal to head and body (pl. 25c); tail nearly naked, scaly; eye small. Head and body 3 to 4 inches (75–106 mm.), tail 3 to 3⅝ inches (74–92 mm.), hind foot ⅔ to ⅘ inch (17.5–20 mm.), ear from crown ½ to ⅗ inch (11–14 mm.); weight about ½ ounce (12.7–18.8 grams). Coloration above dark grayish or yellowish brown; under surface uniformly dusky brown, buff or whitish in different individuals; feet dusky.

Occurrence.—Not native; came with the white man; now common in and around practically every town or settlement on west slope of Yosemite region, from Snelling and Lagrange eastward to Yosemite Valley. Lives about dwellings, barns, and storehouses, and also to a limited extent in grassy places away from buildings.

The same House Mouse which is found in our cities is to be found in the western part of the Yosemite region. This alien interloper, so much more aggressive than most of the local rodents, is in firm possession of territory in and about the towns and settlements from the San Joaquin Valley eastward through the foothills and even into Yosemite Valley. It was not detected about Mono Lake, though it does occur farther to the southeast, at Laws, Inyo County.

The general appearance of the House Mouse is familiar to so many people that description is scarcely necessary. It is the standard (pl. 25c) by which other small animals are judged when said to be 'mouse-like.' The tail comprises about half the total length and is scaly in appearance, there being only a very few short hairs and no 'pencil' or tuft at the end. The general coloration is the same over the entire upper surface of the body, a mixed yellowish brown or grayish brown 'ticked' with black hair endings. The under surface of the House Mouse is ordinarily but little paler than the back; many individuals here in California, however, and especially in the Yosemite region are buff or even white beneath; the latter color, when present, is never so pure as on the White-footed Mouse, and is not so sharply demarked along the sides. The feet are usually dusky-colored, sometimes pale, but never white. The eye of the House Mouse is small, about half the size of the eye of the Common White-footed Mouse.

A striking similarity in external appearance is found between the House Mouse and the Harvest Mouse, the measurements, proportions of body and tail, and even the coat color being much alike, particularly with light-bellied specimens of *Mus*. The appearance of the upper incisor teeth at once separates the two, however. In the Harvest Mouse each of these teeth is marked by a vertical groove; in the House Mouse, the surface of the tooth is perfectly smooth.

The House Mouse is now well established in the Yosemite region and doubtless has been for a great many years. It was probably quite an early arrival, as the foothill districts bordering the Yosemite were among the first areas settled by white people in California; and this mouse, in America, has closely followed the white settler. Living about houses and barns, it often makes its nest amid household effects, or in bags of grain or bales of hay. When these are carried to a new locality the mice often go also, as stowaways; their spread in this manner is thus passive so far as the mice themselves are concerned. When the goods or other articles are set down in a new location the mice, being in new territory, speedily increase and take possession of their surroundings; and, sooner or later, because of their more aggressive nature, they compel the native small rodents of the neighborhood to give way and finally altogether displace them.

But the House Mouse at the lower and middle altitudes is not only about man's habitations. At Snelling and as far into the foothills as El Portal this mouse was found living apart from buildings, in fields and grassy ravines. At the former station specimens were trapped near bluffs fully a mile away from the town. These individuals were living in a really wild state; and this was true in winter (January) as well as in the spring and summer. Their numbers were fully as great as those of the Gambel White-footed Mouse which was present amid the same general surroundings.

Besides being an aggressive and adaptable species, this mouse is also prolific. It breeds practically throughout the year, has rather large broods, and these may follow one another at relatively short intervals. Adults taken at Snelling in January showed signs of breeding activity; while young, not fully grown, were captured about the barns in Yosemite Valley at the end of December. The broods elsewhere are known to average between 5 and 6.

ALEXANDRINE RAT. **Rattus rattus alexandrinus** (Geoffroy)

Field characters.—The typical 'rat' of household notoriety; tail longer than head and body; tail scaly, with but few short hairs (fig. 12a); pelage coarse, with many long overhairs. Head and body 7¼ to 8 inches (182–205 mm.), tail 8⅓ to 10 inches (213–250 mm.), hind foot about 1½ inches (36–39 mm.), ear from crown about 1 inch (23–26 mm.); weight under ½ pound. Upper surface of body plain grayish brown or yellowish brown; under surface uniform dull yellowish; feet dusky, not white.

Occurrence.—Not native; now well established, both about settlements and on wild land nearby, at various localities on west side of Sierra Nevada. Recorded at Snelling, Lagrange, and El Portal. Lives in houses and in thickets and drift débris along banks of rivers.

The Alexandrine or 'Roof' Rat is one of the few alien species which has become well established in the Yosemite region. Its introduction was wholly unintentional on the part of man, an unwelcome incident in his occupation and settlement of the country. This rat arrived on the California coast when ships first began to visit San Francisco in numbers. From the coast it spread to the interior, aided no doubt by the active boat traffic along the Sacramento and San Joaquin rivers. At first the rat lived exclusively about human habitations, but in later years it has also taken to living in the wild, and is now so well established out-of-doors in many locations that a person unacquainted with its history would be likely to consider it a native species.

The Roof Rat is considered to be only a color variety of the Black Rat. It has the long slender tail of the latter, a character which at once distinguishes it from the Norway or Brown Rat. Specimens of the Norway Rat have not as yet been forthcoming from the Yosemite region. The Roof Rat is much more of a climber than the Norway Rat. About maritime ports the former predominates on shipboard. On shore it takes to the roofs and walls of buildings, while the Norway or 'sewer' rat lives in cellars and basements. But along the Sacramento and San Joaquin rivers and their principal tributaries the Roof Rat has taken to living in the piles of drift material and brushy thickets along the river banks. This departure from man-made shelters is made possible by the relatively mild winter of central California, which is closely similar to the winter of the original home of the Roof Rat, in the countries of Asia Minor. Along the coast in central California the Brown Rat has largely supplanted the Roof Rat, and possibly may do so eventually in the interior.

At Snelling, in January, 1915, a number of roof rats were taken in piles of drift and thickets along the Merced River. There were old deserted nests of the Streator Wood Rat in the same locality and the suggestion presented was that possibly the alien, with similar associational predilections, had driven out the native species. Along the Tuolumne River below Lagrange the roof rats had made numerous pathways which were at first mistaken for large runs of meadow mice. At El Portal two of the rats were captured November 23 and 25, 1914, in the upper stories of the large hotel building then there. The species is unknown at Coulterville, according to Mr. Donald D. McLean, though House Mice are present there. The mice are transported readily in bales of hay hauled on wagons, but the rats require larger vehicles such as river boats or railroad cars.

COMMON WHITE-FOOTED MICE.   **Peromyscus maniculatus** (Wagner)[8]

Field characters.—Size slightly greater than that of House Mouse; ear larger and tail shorter (pl. 25*b* and text fig. 10*a*); tail distinctly less than length of head and body, not scaly in appearance. (For measurements, see footnote 8.) General color above yellowish brown (blue-gray in young); below pure white, sharply set off from color of upper surface; tail bicolor, that is, white, with a dark stripe above; feet pure white.

Occurrence.—Abundant resident throughout the entire Yosemite section from the San Joaquin plains at Snelling eastward without interruption across the mountains to Mono Mills; range upward to at least 10,800 feet.[8] Inhabit every sort of cover from stream margins to the dryest slopes and most barren rock slides. Nocturnal.

The Common White-footed Mice are without any doubt the most abundant mammals in the Yosemite section. Indeed, it is not unlikely that the total population of this one species nearly or quite equals that of all the other mammals in the region together. Its numbers do vary somewhat according to place and season, but it is always present, and in some places it may be said to fairly swarm. In whatever locality we placed our traps this kind of mouse was sure to be caught. In places these mice simply have to be 'trapped out' before representatives of other species can be

---

[8] Two subspecies of these mice occur in the Yosemite section, one on the west slope, the other on the east side of the mountains, the two intergrading over the crest of the Sierras.

GAMBEL WHITE-FOOTED MOUSE, *Peromyscus maniculatus gambeli* (Baird). The form which is distributed throughout most of California west of the Sierran crest. It is found from Snelling and Lagrange eastward in more or less typical form to the vicinity of Tuolumne Meadows, and intergrades insensibly over the Sierran crest with the Sonora White-footed Mouse.

SONORA WHITE-FOOTED MOUSE, *Peromyscus maniculatus sonoriensis* (LeConte). A paler, less dusky, and slightly larger subspecies which inhabits the Great Basin and desert country to the east of the Sierran crest. It was recorded from Walker Lake eastward to Mono Mills.

Measurements.—*Gambeli:* head and body 3 to 3¾ inches (75–95 mm.), tail 2–2¾ inches (52–72 mm.), hind foot about ¾ inch (18–20 mm.), ear from crown ⅝ inch (13–16 mm.), weight about ½ ounce (12.8–21.1 grams); *sonoriensis:* head and body 3½ to 4⅛ inches (83–106 mm.), tail 2⅛–3 inches (55–75 mm.), hind foot about ⅘ inch (19–21 mm.), ear from crown ⅝ inch (15–17 mm.), weight ⅔ ounce (19.9–28.5 grams).

obtained. Yet White-footed Mice are practically never seen by daylight, for they are as strictly nocturnal as are bats.

Except for the fact that it does most of its foraging on or close to the ground there is scarcely any limitation to the range of this mouse. It frequents the very edge of running water, thickets and grass clumps on the banks of streams, the runs of meadow mice in damp grasslands, the sides of dry gullies, mixed growths of brush plants on the hill slopes, old buildings, logs and boulders in the forest, and heaps of slide rock on the mountain sides. On one occasion some mice of this species were found living in burrows on altogether open ground, a place where only kangaroo rats were expected to occur.

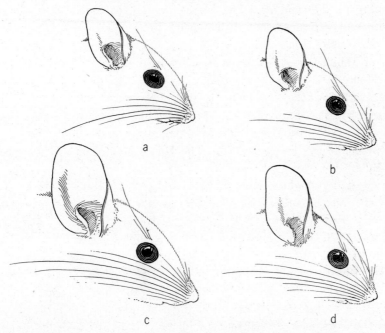

Fig. 10. Showing differences in ear between the four species of White-footed Mice found in the Yosemite section. (*a*) Gambel (Common) White-footed Mouse; (*b*) Boyle White-footed Mouse; (*c*) Parasitic White-footed Mouse; (*d*) Gilbert White-footed Mouse.

For nesting places and daytime retreats White-footed Mice make use of any available cover, such as is afforded by crevices or holes in rocks, hollows in trees or in logs, or holes in the ground. Often they use burrows made by other rodents, while in some cases it seems likely that they do a certain amount of excavating themselves.

Despite its great numbers this mouse does not leave any very obvious indications of its presence. Its small black droppings are the only regular and definite evidences to be found. Nothing distinctive pertaining to its nest, or route of travel, or choice of food, is left as a clue, as is the case with most other rodents. It seems to be the most adaptable of all the small mammals, fitting into types of habitat unused by any of the more specialized mammals and venturing into the special territory of these which may not be fully occupied. With this flexible nature it might be expected that the White-footed Mouse could and would become a pest about human habitations, but there has been no development in this direction. The species does hold the last line of defense for the wild species, living, as it does, about cabins and barns in newly settled territory; but it quickly retreats upon the arrival of that more aggressive alien, the House Mouse.

The Common White-footed Mouse is somewhat larger, differently proportioned, and differently colored than the well-known House Mouse. (Compare pl. 25*b* and *c*.) The average weight of the Gambel Mouse is 0.62 ounce (17.5 grams), and of the Sonora Mouse, 0.86 ounce (24.5 grams), while that of the House Mouse is 0.58 ounce (16.4 grams). The tail of the Common White-footed Mouse is *less* in length than its head and body; in the House Mouse it is about equal. The ear of the Common White-footed Mouse averages larger, ⅝ inch (16 mm.), compared with about ½ inch (13.5 mm.) in the House Mouse. The White-footed Mouse is conspicuously white on its under surface, this white extending to the under side of the tail and including the entire feet. The House Mouse, on the other hand, is dingy gray underneath, with no sharp line of demarcation along the sides; the tail is monochrome, not bicolor; and the feet are dusky. The tail of the White-footed is well haired (though the hairs are very short), not nearly bare and scaly, as is that of the House Mouse.

It should be stated here that there are no less than four species of white-footed mice in the Yosemite section, and in certain places on the west slope of the mountains all four are to be found in close proximity to one another. (See fig. 11.) All four of the species bear a general resemblance to each other and two of them (the Boyle and True) are enough alike to make it difficult to identify individuals. The Common White-footed Mouse (*Peromyscus maniculatus* with subspecies), the subject of the present chapter, is the smallest of the four (see fig. 10 and pl. 25). Its tail is shorter than the head and body, 3 inches or less (75 mm.), and is distinctly bicolor, that is, pure white with a dark stripe along the top. The hind foot is shortest, measuring ¾ to ⅘ of an inch (18–21 mm.); its ear is smallest, measuring ½ to ⅔ of an inch (13–17 mm.).

The Boyle White-footed Mouse (*Peromyscus boylii*) is the next in point of size, and can be recognized further by the combination of medium sized hind foot (21 to 23 mm.) and medium sized ear (from crown, 17 to 20 mm.). In this and the following two species the tail is distinctly longer than that of the Common White-footed Mouse, equaling or exceeding the combined length of the animal's head and body.

The True and Gilbert white-footed mice (which are subspecies of the one species, *Peromyscus truei*) have much larger ears, measuring 20 to 26 mm.; and the hind feet average longer, measuring 22 to 25 mm. Also the pelage is longer (hair on rump 11 mm., instead of 7 or 8 mm. as on the Boyle Mouse). The Gambel and Sonora Mice are short-haired, while the Parasitic is long-haired.

The fourth species in the series, the Parasitic White-footed Mouse (*Peromyscus californicus*), is decidedly larger than any of the other three; its hind foot is longer, measuring 25 to 28 mm., but its ear is no larger than that of the True and Gilbert, since it measures 21 to 23 mm. above crown of head. (See accounts of each of the species for detailed measurements.) The relative size of each of the four species of white-footed mice may be judged from the following weights, which are averages obtained from selected adult specimens: *Peromyscus maniculatus*, 21.0 grams; *P. boylii*, 26.5; *P. truei*, 29.5; *P. californicus*, 45.0.

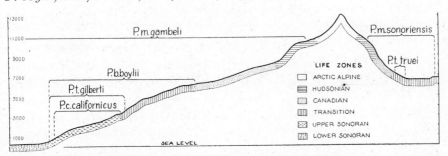

Fig. 11. Cross-section of the Sierra Nevada through the Yosemite region showing zonal and altitudinal ranges of White-footed Mice (genus *Peromyscus*).

The white-footed mice are practically all under cover through the daylight hours. Occasionally a few are trapped during the day, especially when traps are set in shaded places; but they are by no means as active then as are the meadow mice. Their 'day' comes at night. As soon as the dusk has claimed all but the nearest of objects, these mice begin to venture abroad. Most of their running about is done during the earlier hours of the night, but some are still abroad when the Wood Pewees utter their first calls shortly before the break of day.

The camper who goes early into his sleeping bag and there listens for the night sounds is likely to hear little rustlings among the leaves, indicating that the white-foots are abroad. One evening in mid-May at Hazel Green, one of us happened to put his sleeping bag close to the base of a large tree beneath which there was an accumulation of leafy débris. Soon after dark a Common White-footed Mouse began exploring the neighborhood. For some time it stayed within a radius of 6 or 8 feet, rustling among the leaves and occasionally making larger shifts of position. These were accomplished by swift runs; the rapid patter of small feet would be followed by several seconds of quiet while the mouse took account of its new surroundings. About this time the moon came up and the mouse could be seen clearly in the bright light. Whenever the observer moved, the mouse would scamper into some hiding place; but its fright was of very short duration and it would soon reappear.

That the Common White-footed Mouse does on occasion range higher than the ground is indicated by the fact that several individuals were trapped on pantry shelves up to six feet above the floor in a house in Yosemite Valley, and another individual was caught eight feet above the ground on top of a prostrate tree in a windfall at Tuolumne Meadows. Practically all our traps were set on the ground, so we are unable to state the extent to which these mice may climb. The animals sometimes venture well out from shelter; individuals were taken on open ground as much as 20 feet away from cover of any sort. Most of those trapped, however, were obtained close to or under logs, rocks, or brush, where the majority of our traps were set.

At Snelling an adult and a juvenile mouse were caught together in the same trap, this incident suggesting that young individuals may forage for a time in company with their parents. The species is not colonial, in any definite sense of the term; although it occurs locally in considerable numbers, the adult individuals are, as a rule, intolerant of one another's presence.

It is not known with certainty that the Common White-footed Mice hibernate. There is even good evidence to the contrary. In the winter months their tracks are often to be seen in Yosemite Valley, on the surface of the snow. Individuals were trapped in December in dead grass and leaves in sheltered places. Here, it seemed likely, they had been running about among the bases of grass stems beneath the snow mantle.

The breeding season is of long duration and each female very probably bears more than one litter a year. Females with embryos were taken from May 13 until October 24, and evidence, in the form of blue-pelaged juvenals or sexually active males, suggested that, in the lower altitudes at least, the species was breeding practically throughout the year. The number of young to a litter ranges from 3 to 7, averaging 5. Of 38 sets of embryos examined, in two cases there were 3, in eight cases 4, in thirteen 5, in thirteen others 6, and in two cases there were 7. The young come quickly to maturity and some of them undoubtedly breed during the same season in which they are born. Thus within one favorable season, when all of the offspring would be able to find sufficient food of a suitable nature, the numbers of these mice might increase very greatly.

A maximum concentration of Sonora White-footed Mice was encountered at Mono Mills in 1916. A line of 30 traps about one-half mile in length was set on the ground in the sagebrush among Jeffrey pines near the mill. On the night of June 6, 10 *Peromyscus m. sonoriensis* and 6 other rodents were caught in this one trap-line. During the day of the seventh 8 chipmunks and 2 Golden-mantled Ground Squirrels were obtained. The night of June 7, 21 *Peromyscus* and one pocket mouse were trapped; the night of the eighth, 20 *Peromyscus* and two pocket mice; and the night of the tenth, 15 *Peromyscus* and 1 Kangaroo Rat. Then the line was taken up. The collector's own footprints made as he visited his traps at nightfall to bait and re-set them would in places by morning be obliterated by the multitude of tiny tracks made during the night. Many of the mice in the traps were partially eaten, probably by others of their own species. Food in general seemed scarce.

The suggestion presents itself that an unusually large population had resulted from exceptionally favorable conditions, including abundant food during a preceding period; and because of the discontinuance of these favoring conditions, the mice were on the verge of starvation just at the time the member of our party started trapping. The potential powers for the expansion of mouse population, as based upon the figures for rate of breeding given above, are enormous, possibly twenty-fold in a single year. A sequence of favoring conditions may on occasion bring about the full realization of this potentiality; but eventually there will be a return to normal numbers.

Many of the Sonora White-footed Mice trapped at Williams Butte in the fall of 1915 were sorely afflicted with huge rabbit-fly bots on the back or flank. An immature male, trapped September 22, 1915, had one of these maggots imbedded beneath the skin on one flank and opening toward the ankle. The mouse weighed 14 grams, and the fly larva 1.3 grams— nearly one-tenth the weight of the host!

In Yosemite Valley when the melting snows at higher levels cause a rise of water in the Merced River, the Valley meadows are flooded and the non-aquatic animals which live there are forced, at least temporarily, to seek higher ground. The white-footed mice then move up-slope, invading, en route, the gardens and even the houses of the people living in the Valley. One householder told us that on one particular night, during such an invasion, there were fully 20 of these mice running about the rooms in her house. After a few days the white-foots leave the neighborhood of the houses and seek their more natural retreats.

BOYLE WHITE-FOOTED MOUSE. **Peromyscus boylii boylii** (Baird)

Field characters.—Size more than half again that of House Mouse, about one-third larger than Common White-footed Mouse (see pl. 25a); tail usually slightly longer than head and body; hind foot and ear (fig. 10b) both of moderate size. Head and body 3½ to 4 inches (87–100 mm.), tail 3¾ to 4⅓ inches (95–110 mm.), hind foot about ⅞ inch (21–23 mm.), ear from crown about ¾ inch (17–20 mm.); weight ¾ to 1¼ ounces (22.6–34.4 grams). General coloration above dark brown (bluish gray in juvenal), this color sharply set off along sides from pure white of under surface of body; feet white.

Occurrence.—Common resident on west flank of Sierra Nevada, chiefly in Upper Sonoran and Transition zones, but occasionally at higher stations. Recorded regularly from Pleasant Valley eastward to walls of Yosemite Valley and sparingly at Porcupine Flat and Glen Aulin. Inhabits vicinity of rocks and brush on sides of ravines and cañons, less often grassy places, but as a rule not far from water. Nocturnal.

The Boyle White-footed Mouse is second in point of size, numbers, and extent of range among the four species of white-footed mice in the Yosemite region. It is larger than the Common White-foot but smaller than the Gilbert Mouse, and it also stands between these two in relative numbers as is revealed by our extensive trapping. The range of the Boyle Mouse lies entirely on the western drainage of the Sierras; the species has no counterpart on the eastern side of the mountains in this latitude. The local range embraces much of the territory between the altitudes of 600 and 6000 feet.

A variety of situations is occupied by this mouse, though it is rather more restricted in this respect than is the Common White-foot. Some Boyle mice were captured on brushy and rocky stream banks, others (at El Portal) were in sandy 'second bottom' land under wild grapevines, still others under brush plants on hillsides, and many were obtained at El Portal and in Yosemite Valley, amid rocks on talus slopes covered with golden oaks. In Yosemite Valley this species is a regular inhabitant of the rock heaps along the Valley walls, but it seldom occurs out on the floor of the Valley. One factor which seems to be constant in its requirements is proximity to water, not necessarily very close at hand but where it can be reached during the animal's nightly foraging.

The Boyle Mouse is the best climber among the four local species of white-footed mice. One was trapped on a shelf of rock 10 feet above the bottom of a cañon; on this rock were many droppings indicating that mice had run about on it upon various occasions. Elsewhere Boyle Mice have been seen climbing about in trees.

Among the numerous specimens trapped in Yosemite Valley were many having the ears variously notched and otherwise mutilated; also individuals with tails more or less bobbed. These things point to a certain trait known to manifest itself among captive mice, namely, propensity toward violent combat between adults, especially during the periods when they are sexually active.

Definite information concerning the breeding season of the Boyle Mouse consists of records of embryos in 7 females and the capture of a number of blue-pelaged juvenal animals. The females with embryos were taken from May 19 to June 7 (1915), and held from 2 to 5 embryos, averaging about 3. But blue-pelaged young were taken as early as June 7, indicating birth about a month earlier. Even as late as December 2, blue-coated young were trapped, a fact which indicates that some litters may be born in late October or even early November.

BIG-EARED WHITE-FOOTED MICE. **Peromyscus truei** (Shufeldt)[9]

Field characters.—Size about twice that of House Mouse, and somewhat greater than Common White-footed Mouse; tail about equal to head and body; ears large (20 mm. or over). (See fig. 10*d*.) Pelage long and dense; tail well haired, with a slight 'pencil' at tip. General coloration above dark brown, sharply set off from pure white of under surface; feet white.

Occurrence.—Resident on west slope of Sierra Nevada, chiefly in Upper Sonoran Zone. Recorded from Pleasant Valley eastward to 6 miles east of Coulterville and to El Portal (subspecies *gilberti*). Also east of Sierra Nevada on Williams Butte (subspecies *truei*).[9] Lives about rocks and brush. Nocturnal.

White-footed mice of the big-eared or *truei* group are present on both slopes of the Sierra Nevada but never in as large numbers or so widely distributed as the common species (*maniculatus*). The range of this species on the west slope lies chiefly in the Upper Sonoran Zone; on the east side it was found in the belt of piñon pines. The Gilbert Mice of the west side were found on the ground in brushy places or under pines and other trees near the chaparral, and on one occasion about a deserted building. The True Mice of the east slope were mostly taken in or near rocks, though this species is not necessarily a rock dweller.

---

[9] Two slightly differing subspecies of this group occur on the opposite slopes of the Sierra Nevada. Their ranges do not touch at any point in the Yosemite region, but they do come together at other localities to the south, and intergradation takes place there. Hence the two are considered as subspecies of one species.

GILBERT WHITE-FOOTED MOUSE, *Peromyscus truei gilberti* (Allen). The form common through much of California west of the Sierra Nevada. It was found locally from Pleasant Valley eastward to Smith Creek (6 miles east of Coulterville) and to El Portal.

TRUE WHITE-FOOTED MOUSE, *Peromyscus truei truei* (Shufeldt). A slightly paler, more silky haired subspecies, which occupies a wide range of territory east of the Sierra Nevada. It was recorded by us on the south slope of Williams Butte in small numbers.

Measurements.—*Gilberti:* head and body 3½ to 4⅓ inches (88–110 mm.), tail 3¾ to 4⅓ inches (94–111 mm.), hind foot ⅞ to 1 inch (23–25 mm.), ear from crown ⅘ to 1 inch (20–26 mm.), weight ⅚ to 1⅖ ounces (23.5–41 grams). *Truei:* head and body 3⅔ to 4 inches (91–100 mm.), tail 3⅔ to 4 inches (92–100 mm.), hind foot about ⅞ inch (22.5–24 mm.), ear from crown ⅘ to 1 inch (20–24 mm.), weight ⁷⁄₁₀ to 1⅙ ounces (20.6–33.0 grams).

At Blacks Creek, west of Coulterville, on the nights of May 10 and 11, 1919, a line of 37 traps, set through a mixed stand of brush plants on a shaly hillside, produced 7 and 8 Gilbert Mice. They seemed to be the only mice of the white-footed group (*Peromyscus*) present there. They were evidently finding daytime shelter in heaps of shale at the mouths of old prospect holes, in weathered outcrops of the same rock, and in tangles of dead brush.

At El Portal and Pleasant Valley the numbers of this species were less than those of the Gambel and Boyle white-footed mice though greater than those of the Parasitic Mouse. No conspicuous differences in habitat were evident between these several species and it yet remains to work out their ecology. A postulate in animal distribution is that no two species can permanently occupy exactly the same niche in nature, and the evidence in many cases is convincing. But with the several species of white-footed mice there is still much to be explained in this connection.

One of the Gilbert Mice obtained at Blacks Creek was caught only by the tail and as it seemed uninjured it was carried to a pool in the creek bed to test its swimming abilities. The instant it touched the water the mouse began to swim, using all four feet, and soon gained the bank. It walked slowly up the rocks, but when the observer made an attempt to follow, the mouse put on speed, ran quickly up the hill, and was lost to view in the brush.

The breeding season of this mouse is not known with any certainty. Between May 25 and June 3, 1915, 5 females, each containing 3 or 4 embryos, were trapped. Blue-pelaged juvenals were obtained at about the same time, and suckling females were captured in July. These meager data point to a breeding season three months in extent, with the probability that it is of somewhat longer duration.

PARASITIC WHITE-FOOTED MOUSE
Peromyscus californicus californicus (Gambel)

Field characters.—Size more than twice that of House Mouse or of Common White-footed Mouse; ear very large (see fig. 10c); tail longer than head and body. Head and body 4 to 5 inches (99–123 mm.), tail 4⅝ to 5⅓ inches (117–136 mm.), hind foot 1 to 1⅛ inches (25–28 mm.), ear from crown ⅘ to ⅞ inch (21–23 mm.); weight 1½–1¾ ounces (41.5–48.4 grams). General coloration dusky brown on upper surface, sharply set off from pure white of under surface; feet white.

Occurrence.—Resident in Upper Sonoran Zone on west flank of Sierra Nevada where recorded at Pleasant Valley and El Portal. Lives on hillsides covered with oaks and chaparral; sometimes about deserted nests of Streator Wood Rat. Solitary.

The Parasitic White-footed Mouse is the largest of our four species of white-footed mice; indeed, in point of size it approaches an immature wood rat. The name 'parasitic' was applied to this mouse because it is often found about nests of the wood rat and for a time was believed to live habitually with that species. Now it is known that the Parasitic White-footed Mouse, while using deserted wood rat nests to some extent, is also to be found in other sorts of shelter. Its particular niche in the fauna of the foothill oak-chaparral belt is not surely known, though this species does not seem to be greatly different in habits from the Boyle and Gilbert mice.

The present species is the least common of our white-footed mice. Only 6 specimens were obtained in all the trapping which we did within its range, while at the same time the other white-footed mice were obtained literally by the score.

In one instance a trapped Parasitic Mouse was found to have its stomach enormously distended with some finely chewed material that smelled like oak mast. The stomach with contents weighed 9.7 grams, which was one-fifth the total weight of the mouse.

Short-tailed Grasshopper Mouse

Onychomys leucogaster brevicaudus Merriam

Field characters.—Size nearly twice that of House Mouse; tail very short, about one-third length of head and body, and clothed evenly and densely with very short hairs; claws on front feet long and sharp. Head and body about 4 inches (85–105 mm.), tail about 1½ inches (32–40 mm.), hind foot ¾ inch (18–22 mm.), ear ⅜ inch (13–16 mm.); weight nearly 1 ounce (23–30 grams) [measurements and weights from eastern Mono County specimens]. Coloration sharply bicolor; upper surface pale sandy brown (light gray in young); under surface of body, and legs and feet, pure white; a large white spot at forward base of each ear.

Occurrence.—Resident in Great Basin region east of Sierra Nevada. Recorded in our Yosemite section only on the Farrington Ranch near Williams Butte. Lives on ground beneath sagebrush.

Very little is known of the habits of the Short-tailed Grasshopper Mouse. Our own experience with it in the Yosemite section was limited to the capture of a single individual, September 23, 1915, in an oat-baited trap set beneath a small sagebush on the flat south of Williams Butte. This mouse was caught on exactly the same sort of ground as the plentiful Sonora White-footed Mouse, which species the Short-tailed Grasshopper Mouse resembles in a general way. There are pronounced differences, however, in that the latter species has a conspicuously shorter tail, rather smaller ears with a white spot at forward base, and front feet which are armed with longer and sharper claws.

The grasshopper mice, as the name suggests, have a well-known predilection for feeding extensively upon insects. Furthermore, examples captured alive elsewhere and introduced into a cage with Harvest Mice and White-footed Mice promptly killed and proceeded to eat those mammals.

Long-tailed Harvest Mouse

Reithrodontomys megalotis longicauda (Baird)

Field characters.—Size and general form of House Mouse; each upper incisor tooth with a single groove down its front surface; tail about equal to head and body, very scantily haired. Head and body 2⅓ to 3¼ inches (61–83 mm.), tail 2½ to 3⅛ inches (63–79 mm.), hind foot about ¾ inch (16–18 mm.), ear about ½ inch (11–15 mm.); weight about ⅓ ounce (8.5–12.5 grams). Coloration above buffy and black mixed in fine pattern, blending along sides with dull white of under surface; ear clothed with very short tawny-colored hairs.

Occurrence.—Common resident in Lower and Upper Sonoran zones on west slope of Sierra Nevada. Recorded from Snelling and Lagrange eastward to Sweetwater Creek, to El Portal, and to Smith Creek, 6 miles east of Coulterville. Lives chiefly in grassland, occasionally on brush-covered slopes, if these be shaded and damp or near water.

The Long-tailed Harvest Mouse is a small dun-colored animal, of retiring habits, that to the casual eye is simply a field mouse. It dwells in grasslands, among weeds along fences and irrigation ditches, and in similar places. Unlike the meadow mice it leaves no reliable indication of its presence and so must be specially sought for, else it will escape observation entirely.

Externally, the harvest mouse has much the appearance of the House Mouse, the size of the head and body and the relative length of the tail being about the same in the two. In the harvest mouse, the pelage is longer and silkier, and the tail is less conspicuously scaly, than in the House Mouse. The ear is clothed with short tawny hairs. Perhaps the best character for surely distinguishing these two species pertains to the upper incisor teeth. In the harvest mouse the front of each tooth has a conspicuous groove running the full length, the effect of which is to suggest that the mouse has four rather than two upper incisors. The harvest mouse is much smaller than even the smallest of the local white-footed mice and so is not likely to be confused with any of that group at all. Lack of fur-lined cheek pouches distinguishes it from the pocket mice.

For practically all of the harvest mice caught in the Yosemite section we have records of the circumstances of capture and so are able to state satisfactorily the local haunts of the species. The animals inhabit a considerable variety of situations ranging from the immediate vicinity of water to dryish rocky and brushy hillsides. By far the greater number, however, were captured in rather damp grassy places. At Snelling, cat-tails, grass, wild oats, horehound, and blackberry were growing at points of capture. Marshy places, meadow, dry ravine bottoms, rolling lands, bottoms of small gulches, grain fields, and weed growths along fences were all places which the species frequented. At Smith Creek, east of Coulterville, and at El

Portal, a few harvest mice were taken in the runways of meadow mice. And at the last-named place some harvest mice were obtained amid rocks on a steep greasewood-covered hillside which was several hundred feet higher than the grasslands bordering the river, and as far removed from any stream. In all instances our specimens were trapped on the ground. Harvest mice are said sometimes to use birds' nests above ground as foundations for their own nests, but we found no evidence on this point.

The total population of this species must be great. We have no means of stating it in relation to any given area occupied, and furthermore the density of the population varies greatly from place to place. But in favorable situations, especially amid grassy growths, our trap lines produced harvest mice as long as the lines remained in place. It was no uncommon thing to obtain along with other small rodents 5 or 6 individuals of this species in one night, from 40 to 60 traps set over a half-mile of favorable country.

At Snelling, in January and May, the males numbered 20 and the females 15, in the cases where sex was recorded. A preponderance of males in January, when breeding activity was commencing, might be expected; for males then range more widely than females and hence are likely to be caught more commonly in traps. The sexes in the Harvest Mouse are in reality probably about equal.

The breeding season for the Long-tailed Harvest Mouse is a long one. As just indicated, males began to show breeding activity during the first week of January. By May, young of nearly adult size were abroad in small numbers at Pleasant Valley, and females with embryos were common. The number of embryos ranged from 3 to 6, averaging close to 4. A female with large embryos was taken at Smith Creek on July 13, 1920. The absence of trapping records from August to October leaves doubt as to how late the breeding season continues, but it seems likely, from information gained elsewhere, that it continues until some time in the fall. At El Portal in December, where numbers were taken, no breeding individuals were noted.

A species which produces four young at a birth, and in which the young mature rapidly and probably breed late in the season in which they are born, has the potentiality of a rapid numerical increase within a single season. Despite this ability to increase its numbers, the Long-tailed Harvest Mouse has never been found to play any economic rôle, either harmful or otherwise, for it retires before cultivation and occupies marginal areas only.

STREATOR WOOD RAT. **Neotoma fuscipes streatori** Merriam

Field characters.—Form and size about those of House Rat, but tail shorter than head and body (fig. 13); tail round, closely haired, not bushy (fig. 12*b*); pelage soft and smooth; ear rather large, rounded. Head and body 7¼ to 8¼ inches (183–209 mm.), tail 6½ to 7½ inches (165–191 mm.), hind foot about 1½ inches (35–38 mm.), ear from crown 1 to 1¼ inches (24–32 mm.), weight 7¼ to 8¾ ounces (206–247 grams). Coloration brownish gray with a general overlay of black hair tippings; whole under surface of body, under side of tail, and upper surface of feet, white.

Workings.—Nests or 'houses,' 2 to 3 feet high, conical in shape, composed of twigs, leaves, chunks of wood, etc.; placed on ground beneath brush plants or trees, or, less often, on horizontal branches of oak trees at height of several feet from ground. *Droppings:* Cylindrical, about ⅜ inch long and ⅛ inch in diameter, scattered in and about nest, or at intervals along runways.

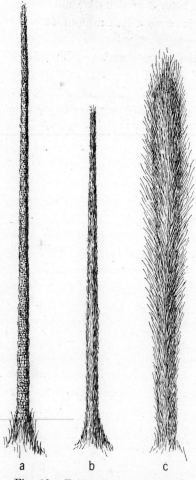

Fig. 12.   Tails of (*a*) Alexandrine Roof Rat, (*b*) Streator Wood Rat, and (*c*) Gray Bushy-tailed Wood Rat. One-half natural size.

Occurrence.—Common resident chiefly in Upper Sonoran Zone and lower part of Transition Zone, on west slope of Sierra Nevada. Recorded from Snelling and Pleasant Valley eastward to floor of Yosemite Valley. Lives in mixed stands of trees and brush, occasionally among rocks. Chiefly nocturnal.

The Streator Wood Rat is well known to residents of the foothill country of east-central California. The animal itself is seldom seen, but evidence of its presence in the form of large nests or 'houses' is to be observed in many places. This animal is often referred to as 'pack rat' or 'trade rat' by reason of its propensity for carrying articles from place to place in and about cabins or camping places.

The Streator Wood Rat is close to the house rat in size, the length of body and the weight being about the same in the two; but the wood rat's tail is shorter than its head and body, while the reverse is true of the roof rat. The pelage of the wood rat is rather short, with no conspicuous coarse over-hairs; it is dense and even, and feels soft to the touch. The coloration above varies from blue gray in the younger animals to sandy brown in adults. Very

arge males become suffused with reddish or buffy brown, particularly on
he sides of the body. On the whole under surface of the body and tail
at all ages the fur is pure white. Although *streatori* is grouped with the
prown-footed wood rats, its feet are pure white, as is also the lower half
of its tail. The tail of the Streator Wood Rat is well haired and hence
quite different in appearance from the scaly tail of the roof rat; but the
hairs on the tail of *streatori* are short and closely laid, with no long hairs
on the sides of the tail as in the Bushy-tailed Wood Rat. (See figs.
12*b*, 13.)

Fig. 13. Streator Wood Rat. Photographed from fresh specimen trapped near foot
of Yosemite Falls trail in Yosemite Valley, November 22, 1915. About ⅓ natural size.

The Streator Wood Rats are active chiefly by night, so that sight of
one is seldom obtained. Most of our information relating to the rats themselves was gained by setting traps baited with rolled oats near nests or
other places which showed signs of recent occupancy by the animals. The
individuals taken for specimens were all trapped during the night-time.
Only three of the animals were noted abroad during the daytime and on
each occasion the rat was in view for but a few seconds. At El Portal, in
early December, one was seen to run into a brush pile on the hill above
the river; near Cascades in November a wood rat appeared while one of
our party was 'squeaking' at a Winter Wren; and near Coulterville an
adult wood rat was frightened from its nest while one of our party was
dismantling the structure.

The 'round-tailed' wood rats are active throughout the year, so far
as we know; trapping at any season is likely to produce specimens. In
Yosemite Valley tracks of the Streator Wood Rat were seen in snow on
the Yosemite Falls Trail on December 9 (1914). In midwinter, when
snow covers the exterior of the rock slides on the Valley walls, the wood
rats are able to run about in comfort and safety in the spaces between and
beneath the granite blocks.

Usually the wood rats obtained for specimens were trapped close to nests, but in one instance an immature individual was taken in a trap set on the ground beneath chaparral in a place where no evidence of wood rat activity was to be seen. At El Portal there were indications that the wood rats were using the trails made by the brush rabbits through and beneath the greasewood chaparral. These rats have regular paths or trails of their own, especially along the walls of narrow ravines. These paths are kept more or less bare of leaves, evidently by the frequent passage of the animals over them. At Dudley the rail fences through dense chaparral were being used regularly as highways; the lower rails were chosen rather than the uppermost one, doubtless on the principle of "safety first." At Kinsley, droppings of wood rats were found in the farthest recesses of a cave some 50 feet from its entrance. Animals living there would have to seek territory for foraging altogether outside the cave.

The most conspicuous feature in the life history of the Streator Wood Rat is its propensity to build houses. These structures are usually conical in shape and measure from 18 inches to 3 feet in height, having the same or a slightly greater diameter at base. A majority of the houses are built on the ground, among or beside brush plants, but seldom far away from such trees as live oaks and willows. Sometimes the nests are placed on horizontal branches in oak trees at heights of as much as 15 feet above the ground. Less often the animals live among the rocks, and then the shape of the house or nest is accommodated to the crevices available between adjacent slabs or boulders. Now and then the structure is heaped around a downed tree, as described below; and in one case a nest was found in the hollow trunk of a living black oak.

The usual wood rat nest is only a pile of various sorts of material of such kinds as can be accumulated from the near vicinity of the site. Within, there is a nest chamber of varying size and proportions. The houses sometimes have underground retreats or passageways, as through a hollow tree root, so that in time of danger the wood rat can escape from the nest without appearing on the surface of the ground until it is some distance away. Entering into the composition of different houses in the Yosemite foothills we found the following materials: twigs and green cuttings of *Ceanothus cuneatus*, *C. integerrimus*, buckeye, live oak, golden oak, yellow pine, and willow, reed stalks, cones of yellow pine, chunks of decayed wood, and, in one case, stones each weighing several ounces.

On a digger-pine-covered hillside which had been burned over within a year, near the McCarthy ranch, 3 miles east of Coulterville, a house of the Streator Wood Rat was found and studied, June 2, 1915. (See fig. 14.) This structure had been built on and partly within a rotten log which lay on the ground. There was a thatch of dry sticks and pieces of bark from the digger pine, and this covering seemed to have protected the interior of the nest effectively against moisture. At one end of the log was an entrance to the interior and here was accumulated a mass of droppings and other débris which the animals had removed from within the house. Inside the house, partly or completely inside the log, were no less than four beds or nests proper; only one of these was occupied when the place was examined. The beds were composed of shredded wood, dry twigs and grass stems, and some green leaves. In one place a quantity of fresh young leaves of the golden oak was found. Three holes led out from the main interior cavity of the house, one of these going down lengthwise of the log, while the two others went into the ground.

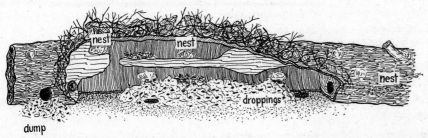

Fig. 14. Sketch showing interior arrangement of nesting quarters of a Streator Wood Rat in a hollow log. Locality, three miles east of Coulterville, June 2, 1915.

In one of the beds a very young wood rat was found; and an adult animal ran out of the same nest as the place was opened up. No other wood rats were seen nor had any been trapped adjacent to this log during the few days preceding, so it seems likely that the place was tenanted by just the two. Part of the interior of the nest contained a mouldy mass of old droppings and bits of twigs, and fresher droppings were found about the beds. The animals seem to exercise none of the precautions for cleanliness observable in some rodents, for example, pocket gophers. The damp earth beneath one nest abounded in fleas, though none of these pests were to be seen on the young wood rat which was found in this nest.

The breeding season of the Streator Wood Rat, to judge from the capture of strictly juvenile specimens, includes most of the warm months of the year. Thus, a juvenile animal trapped at Pleasant Valley on May 19 (1915) points to an early commencement of breeding activity, possibly in March; whereas an immature specimen captured on November 24 (1915) near Cascades could not have been born earlier than September. Trapping in May and June, however, gave evidence that the greatest amount of breeding activity occurred at about that season. Most of the females taken then were suckling young, and two nests examined each held a single young animal. A female collected May 24

at Pleasant Valley contained one embryo, and another obtained June 1
3 miles east of Coulterville, contained 2 small embryos. By late autumn
(November), young born during the current year weigh about 5 ounces
(150 grams), which is about three-fifths the weight of adults.

GRAY BUSHY-TAILED WOOD RAT. Neotoma cinerea cinerea (Ord)

Field characters.—Size larger than Streator Wood Rat or House Rat; tail shorter
than head and body, with long hairs on sides forming a flat brush (figs. 12c, 15); pelage
thick and soft. Head and body 7 to 9⅓ inches (180–237 mm.), tail 4¾ to 7⅖ inches
(120–188 mm.), hind foot 1⅝ to 1⅘ inches (40–46 mm.), ear from crown 1 to 1⅓
inches (26–34 mm.); weight 9½ to 16¼ ounces (271–459 grams). Coloration above
sandy brown, tail somewhat darker; feet, and under surface of body and tail, pure white.
Workings: Sparse accumulations of sticks and other débris in crevices among rocks.
Droppings: Black, cylindrical, about ½ by ⅙ inch.

Occurrence.—Resident in boreal parts of Sierra Nevada. Recorded from near Gentrys
(5900 feet) and Little Yosemite Valley eastward to Williams Butte. Life zone, upper
Canadian and whole of Hudsonian. Lives in rock slides and in and about logs. Nocturnal; partially colonial.

The Gray Bushy-tailed Wood Rat is an inhabitant of the higher and
more easterly portions of the Yosemite section and so comes only to the
attention of those visitors who spend some time in the back country. When
human beings do become aware of the presence of this rodent it is because
the animal literally forces itself upon their attention. Campers tell many
tales, some humorous, some semi-tragic, of the activities of the big 'pack-
rat' or 'trade rat' among their belongings.

The range of this species is separated from that of the foothill-inhabiting
Streator Wood Rat by a hiatus usually several miles in width and a gap
of at least 1500 feet in altitude. The nearest approach of one to the other,
according to our records, is that of *streatori* on the floor of the Yosemite
Valley to *cinerea* on the slopes close above Gentrys. The main range of
the bushy-tail involves the belt of country characterized by the alpine
hemlock, namely the Hudsonian Zone. A few of these rats live at or above
timber line, as on Mount Lyell (up to an altitude of 13,090 feet); and on
the east slope of the Sierras, as at Walker Lake and on Williams Butte,
they occur at much lower altitudes and in lower zones.

In the Yosemite region the Bushy-tailed Wood Rat is an inhabitant of
rock slides. A very few were captured away from rocks, but only enough
to emphasize the mass preference of the species for heaps of talus. There
are rock slides in the Transition and Canadian zones on the west slope
which to our eyes seem indistinguishable from those at higher levels, but
the bushy-tails do not inhabit them. Immediate competition with the other
near-related species is lacking, for the Streator Wood Rat is not found to
any large extent in the Transition Zone rocks and is entirely absent from
the Canadian.

When compared with the common round-tailed, house-building wood rat of the western foothills, the bushy-tail is found to be of the same general form, but it is larger and heavier, with longer fur. (See fig. 15.) The hair on its tail is elongated so that this member has something of the flat, brush-like appearance associated with tree squirrels and chipmunks. The dense body coat of the Bushy-tailed Wood Rat is doubtless an adaptation to life in a boreal region. The general configuration of the head and body of this species, especially if seen in a rock slide where the tail may be concealed, reminds one of a cony.

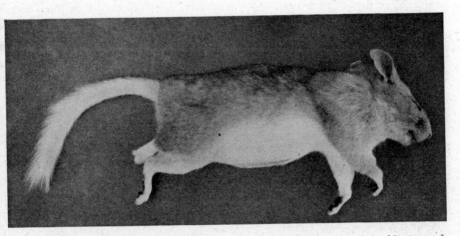

Fig. 15. Gray Bushy-tailed Wood Rat. Photographed from animal freshly trapped near Vogelsang Lake, August 31, 1915.

A feature of this wood rat is the musty odor which is associated with both the animal and its home precincts. This odor is produced by glands at the side of the anus, a condition similar to that obtaining in the skunk. Places which are continuously inhabited by the bushy-tail take on this odor, the presence of which furnishes a clue to naturalists who may be hunting for places to trap the animals.

The present species like its foothill relative is essentially a night prowler. The rat traps, baited with rolled oats, which we set in rock slides at elevations above 8000 feet trapped conies during the daytime and Bushy-tailed Wood Rats at night. On but one occasion did we see a Bushy-tailed Wood Rat abroad during the daytime. On July 18, 1915, four members of our field party had ascended to the summit of Mount Lyell, and while we were eating lunch there a bushy-tail came forth and gathered lunch scraps which we and previous visitors had dropped. Bits of hardtack scattered on the rocks were eagerly sought and devoured, though the rat retired into a crevice to chew them up. No general source of natural food was to be seen on the peak.

This species is less of a builder than its foothill cousin. Nowhere did we find the large accumulations of material that the Streator Wood Rat gathers. In a few places bushy-tails had accumulated twigs, sticks, old bones, and similar material in crevices among the rocks, much after the manner of the Streator Wood Rat in the boulder taluses of Yosemite Valley. But many of the localities inhabited by the bushy-tail were entirely devoid of building material of any sort. Since there are, in such places, many crevices within the rocks in which the animals may take shelter, they have, perhaps, no need to build elaborately. In those cases where we saw no external evidences of a nest, there may have been inhabited shelters deep down among the rocks where human beings and the larger carnivores could never penetrate.

The young of the Bushy-tailed Wood Rat are produced during the mid-summer season. One female, taken in Lyell Cañon on July 17, 1915, contained 3 embryos. The females have only four teats, which suggests that the litters are small. Several females captured between July 9 and 21, 1915, gave evidence of having recently suckled young. By the last week of August young were being trapped in considerable numbers and were then from one-fourth to one-half the weight of the parents. Their juvenal pelage is very soft and short and lacks the prominent sandy brown overcast seen on adult animals. At this age the tail is only beginning to show the lengthened hairing at the sides and end.

YOSEMITE MEADOW MOUSE. **Microtus montanus yosemite** Grinnell

Field characters.—Body size about three times that of House Mouse; tail short (fig. 16*a*), less than ½ head and body; pelage long and lax; ear nearly buried in fur. (See fig. 20*b*.) Head and body 4⅖ to 5⅖ inches (112–138 mm.), tail 1⅜ to 2⅛ inches (35–54 mm.), hind foot about ⅘ inch (20–22 mm.), ear from crown ⅖ to ⅔ inch (10–17 mm.); weight 1⅓ to 2⅝ ounces (38.0–74.8 grams). Coloration dark brown above, sometimes with a reddish tinge on back; under surface dark gray. *Workings:* Pathways or runways 1 to 1½ inches wide, cut along surface of turf and connecting with small round holes in earth, which are always open.

Occurrence.—Common resident chiefly in Canadian and Hudsonian zones on both slopes of Sierra Nevada. Recorded from Gentrys (on Big Oak Flat Road) and from Mono Meadow (south of Glacier Point) eastward across the mountains to Mono Lake Post Office and to near Williams Butte; present in numbers on floor of Yosemite Valley. Lives in meadows and grasslands, usually at no great distance from water. Active to some extent during daytime, but otherwise nocturnal.

The level or sloping grasslands of the Yosemite region are inhabited by many of the small furry-coated animals known popularly as field mice and to students of natural history as meadow mice or voles. Two distinct groups are represented, a long-tailed, free-ranging type, the Cantankerous Meadow Mouse, and several short-tailed species, the Tule, Mariposa, and

Yosemite meadow mice, which cut pathways in the grassland. Of the latter group the first two inhabit respectively the San Joaquin Valley and the western foothills. The last, the subject of the present chapter, is distributed over most of the high Sierras from the neighborhood of Yosemite Valley eastward to the plateau country on the western side of Mono Lake. (See fig. 19.)

The local meadow mice are all much alike in general outward appearance and so the Yosemite Meadow Mouse may be taken as an example for detailed treatment. (See fig. 20b.) The nose is blunt, the eyes prominent and bead-like though not so large in proportion to the head as those of white-footed mice. The ear is rather short and therefore nearly or quite buried in the copious fur. The body is rather chunky, the tail short and slender, and both front and hind pairs of feet are inconspicuous. The pelage of these mice is distinctive, being rather long, dense, and soft, and of fluffy appearance. This type of pelage is found in various other animals which like the meadow mice live about water where the pelage must perform the dual function of keeping the animals both dry and warm.

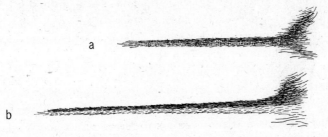

Fig. 16. Tails of (*a*) Yosemite Meadow Mouse and (*b*) Sierra Cantankerous Meadow Mouse. Natural size.

The Yosemite Meadow Mouse like the other path-cutting species has a short tail, less than half, even but a third the length of the head and body; also the tail is of nearly uniform color. These features will usually serve to distinguish any of the path-cutting species from the Cantankerous Meadow Mouse. But within the first-named group there is no good external character to separate the species. The distinctive features are found in the skulls and hence can be determined only from museum specimens. The Yosemite Meadow Mouse is generally more blackish, but old individuals have as much reddish coloration on the upper surface as does the foothill and valley species (*californicus*). In the field, distribution is the best clue for separating the short-tailed species. No specimen of *yosemite* has been found below 3800 feet (the floor of Yosemite Valley), while *mariposae* of the foothills penetrates the mountains no farther than Cascades (3600 feet).

As a group the meadow mice are grass feeders, and when green vegetation is available they will take little or nothing else. (See fig. 21.) Sometimes when the animals are unusually plentiful they gnaw the bark of trees. Since the main item of diet is grass, their whole scheme of existence is modeled for obtaining this sort of food.

In order to be close to their source of food supply and also to be able to escape if danger threatens while they are foraging, these mice carry on their whole existence right in the meadows. They dig small shallow burrows or tunnels down through the sod to a depth of several inches and place their nests in enlarged parts of these tunnels. When they venture out to forage, they follow runways which they cut through the vegetation; along these they can run readily without interference and are to some extent shielded from observation. These surface runways constitute the most obvious indication of the presence of meadow mice and are the things which a naturalist always searches for when he wishes to locate these rodents. Sometimes in making a runway the grass is merely trampled down, but usually the mice carefully cut away the stems so that the floor of the run is at or even slightly below the level of the ground. In the latter case, to the eye of a person, the runway shows as of earth color in contrast with the surrounding green vegetation. The floor of the run is kept free of obstructions by the mice, but often the growing grass arches over the top forming a canopy under which the animals may travel for long distances without much danger of being observed by a foraging hawk or owl overhead. The system of surface runways is often extensive, with many intersections; as many as five and even six different paths may radiate from a single hole. The direction and extent is probably dictated by the relative abundance and location of forage material. The usual width is from 1 to 1½ inches. The average dimensions are slightly greater in the runways of the Mariposa than in those of the Yosemite Meadow Mouse; the former mouse is on the average a slightly larger animal. In late summer on Tuolumne Meadows many small narrow runways were noted which were thought to have been made by the young of the year after they had taken up an independent existence apart from their parents.

At the end of September (in 1915), on Tuolumne Meadows, the meadow mice were exceedingly active. Extensive surface runways were seen, as well as many holes leading to underground burrows. In some places there were 4 to 6 holes per square yard of surface. There was much cut grass in the runways and in one place, under an overhanging bank, a mass aggregating about two handfuls was noted. Droppings were scattered along all the runways, and occupation of the runs for a considerable period of time was indicated.

These mice are abroad to a considerable extent during the daytime, although they are perhaps most active in the early hours of the night. The protection afforded by the runways, particularly those arched over by grass, probably promotes daytime activity. Several of the animals were seen running about by members of our party. One individual noted in Sentinel Meadow, Yosemite Valley, on October 8, 1914, darted along 20 feet or more of tunnel with amazing speed considering the turns which had to be negotiated. The sensitive 'whiskers' may be of considerable service in traversing the runs; the animal literally "feels its way." Its relatively smaller eye, as compared with that of a free-ranging animal like the white-footed mouse, may be indicative of the meadow mouse's lessened dependence upon acute sight.

Meadow mice are active during winter as well as summer even in localities above the snow line. In Yosemite Valley in late December runways were found through the snow at the margin of the Merced River, and openings to the surface were found at short distances along the runs. In other parts of the region winter nests were seen which had been built on top of the ground where, of course, they had been fully protected by the blanket of snow. Considerable activity on the part of the mice is to be observed during the fall months, evidently in preparation for the long Sierran winter. This was noted on Tuolumne Meadows in late September of 1915, and in Yosemite Valley in early October of 1914. In the latter instance excavation of underground burrows was being diligently prosecuted.

Our data relative to the breeding of the Yosemite Meadow Mouse are plentiful, chiefly because we spent much time and did a great deal of trapping within the range of this species. The evidence in the form of females with embryos or recently born young points to a breeding season extending at least from March or April until October. Thus, on May 4, 1916, a female meadow mouse taken near Williams Butte contained 6 embryos. Another captured October 22, 1915, at Gentrys, held 5 small embryos. Between these inclusive dates 30 females with embryos were obtained. The number of embryos ranged from 4 to 9, with an average of between 6 and 7 (6.3). With the long breeding season indicated, it is probable that each female rears more than one and perhaps several broods. The species thus has the ability to increase rapidly when conditions are favorable. A still further factor greatly enhancing the potentiality for increase is that the females may breed at an extremely early age. On May 22, 1916, a female containing 6 embryos was captured; this animal was still in the juvenal pelage and hardly half-grown, as it weighed only 24.5 grams, scarcely half the weight of an adult. Two other females taken May 21 and May 4, weighed 30.0 and 32.5 grams respectively, and these also contained embryos. These latter animals had molted out of the short blackish juvenal pelage but were otherwise immature. It seems safe to assume that the youngest of these mice was not much over two months of age when it began to breed, and that both had been born during February or March.

In Yosemite Valley during the fall months more than half the population of meadow mice was found to consist of obviously young animals— at least this was so indicated by our trapping records. Of 43 individuals obtained October 8 to 10, 1914, 23 were juveniles.

Over the entire northern hemisphere meadow-inhabiting mice are to be found wherever the ecologic niche of this group is represented, but under very diverse climatic conditions. The Lemmings of the Arctic regions and the Meadow Mice of the Great Basin are extreme examples. From time to time great fluctuations in the populations of these mice are to be noted. Sometimes the animals are so scarce as to be found only by diligent search; in other years they are extremely plentiful. A case of the first sort is related of the Mariposa Meadow Mice at Bean Creek east of Coulterville in 1915; on Tuolumne Meadows the same year the Yosemite Mice were so numerous that 5 or 6 holes per square yard were counted in places. Under certain favoring conditions, regarding the nature of which we still have much to learn, meadow mice may increase enormously, even far beyond the population indicated for Tuolumne Meadows. Then a 'mouse plague' results. It was a race closely related to the Yosemite Meadow Mouse which over-ran Humboldt Valley, Nevada, in 1907 and 1908 and caused great damage to agricultural interests there by destroying practically all the surface vegetation and even the roots of the alfalfa.

CALIFORNIA MEADOW MICE. **Microtus californicus** (Peale)[10]

Field characters.—Body size between that of House Mouse and House Rat; tail short, less than one-half head and body; pelage long, soft, and dense; ears short, nearly buried in the fur. (For measurements see footnote.) General coloration above dark brown, middle of back red tinged; under surface blue-gray to whitish. *Workings:* Runways 1 to 1½ inches wide through grass, connecting with round holes in earth.

----

[10] Two subspecies of California Meadow Mice occur on the west slope of the Yosemite section. These inhabit different life zones and can best be distinguished on the basis of distribution.

TULE MEADOW MOUSE, *Microtus californicus aestuarinus* Kellogg, a subspecies which inhabits the Sacramento and San Joaquin basins and other lowland districts in central California, is common in the bottom lands near Snelling and Lagrange.

MARIPOSA MEADOW MOUSE, *Microtus californicus mariposae* Kellogg, a form found in the foothills along the west side of the Sierra Nevada, has been recorded at Pleasant Valley and thence eastward to Smith Creek (6 miles east of Coulterville), to Cascades, and to Sweetwater Creek. This subspecies is distinguished from the Tule Meadow Mouse by its brighter, more reddish coloration and somewhat larger size.

Measurements: *Aestuarinus:* head and body 4 to 5½ inches (99–139 mm.), tail 1¾ to 2⅝ inches (44–67 mm.), hind foot nearly 1 inch (22–25.5 mm.), ear from crown ½ to ⅔ inch (14–17 mm.), weight 1⅓ to 1¾ ounces (38.3–49.2 grams). *Mariposae:* head and body 5 to 5¾ inches (128–145 mm.), tail 1⅞ to 2½ inches (48–64 mm.), hind foot nearly 1 inch (21–25 mm.), ear from crown about ½ inch (10–14 mm.), weight 2¼ to 2½ ounces (64.0–73.8 grams).

Occurrence.—Common resident in Lower and Upper Sonoran zones on west slope of Sierra Nevada. Recorded from Snelling (subspecies *aestuarinus*) eastward to El Portal and Cascades (subspecies *mariposae*).[10] Inhabits grassland.

The California Meadow Mouse is an inhabitant of grassy fields and marsh lands near the rivers and streams of the western part of the Yosemite region. Its range here is restricted to those rather scattered portions of the region which are open and fairly level. The species is common in the flat areas along the eastern margin of the San Joaquin Valley, but in the foothill districts it is for the most part found only in the scattered stream-side tracts which man has found to be most suitable for his own purposes.

In general appearance and habits the California Meadow Mouse is much like the Yosemite Meadow Mouse which lives in the territory from Yosemite Valley to the crest of the Sierras. It is, however, of somewhat larger size and makes slightly wider runways.

As with other meadow mice, the breeding season of this species is long. At Pleasant Valley and near Coulterville, in late May and June of 1915, young were already about in some numbers; and near El Portal in late November and even as late as December 5 (1914), half-grown individuals were trapped. On November 29, an adult female captured at El Portal was found to contain 5 large embryos. This number is probably an average.

The food of this mouse consists chiefly of grass, which is freshly cut in lengths of about 1 inch, presumably so that it can be more readily carried along the runways and burrows.

This meadow mouse, like others of its tribe, is subject to decided fluctuations in population from year to year. If one examines for a number of successive years the ground where the animals occur, one will note decided changes in the extent of their operations. In 1915, the population in the meadows adjacent to Bean Creek east of Coulterville seemed to be at a low ebb, for only by vigorous efforts in trapping could we obtain even a few individuals; whereas, as a rule, the capture of meadow mice in numbers is a relatively easy matter. Many of the burrows and runways which we examined in this place were in a state indicating disuse. The holes were frequently covered with cobwebs, and small plant growths had sprung up in the runways. Neither of these conditions is to be noted in runs which are in current use by the mice. In 1920, trapping a short distance to the east of this locality, on Smith Creek, produced a number of the animals.

At El Portal, on December 4, 1914, an adult meadow mouse was found with its hair firmly entangled on a twig in a brush pile. It had evidently made frantic efforts to escape, going round and round the twig, but this had only served to bind its hair all the tighter and being thus held the mouse perished, either from exposure or starvation.

Meadow mice, particularly those species which inhabit runways, are given to extensive travel during the daytime. The runways are, in many instances, nearly or completely covered by the adjacent grass, and would seem to afford a more complete protection than is available to many of the other small rodents. Nevertheless, meadow mice, more often than other small rodents, fall victims to hawks; and their activity at dusk likewise results in many of them being caught by owls.

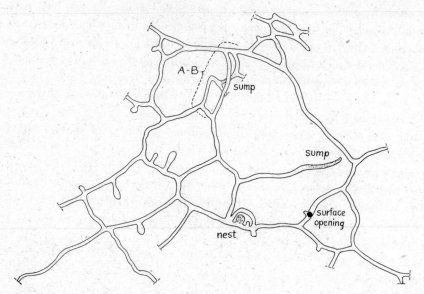

Fig. 17. Plan of the underground burrow system of a Mariposa Meadow Mouse. Excavated on meadows 3½ miles east of Coulterville, June 8, 1915. Surface scale about 1:25.

On a meadow at the head of Bean Creek east of Coulterville a series of runways and burrows of the Mariposa Meadow Mouse was opened up, studied, and mapped by two of our party on June 8, 1915. (See figs. 17, 18.) The meadow was covered with a dense growth of rush, foxtail grass, blue-eyed grass, soaproot, buttercup, wild celery, and other plants. The fine black humus through which the tunnels were dug was damp and the soil a few inches below the surface of the ground was saturated with water. Some slight depressions in adjacent parts of the meadow still held standing water. The part of the meadow where the tunnels were located was very green; while on nearby higher and rockier parts the grass was already dry and no evidences of meadow mice were to be found.

Both surface runways and underground tunnels were found in this colony, but only the tunnel system is shown on the accompanying diagram. Some of the runways led into holes which looked like abandoned gopher holes, a fact which suggested that the meadow mice had possibly made use of tunnels dug earlier by gophers.

An area approximately nine feet square was gone over in detail and the sod lifted off so as to expose the tunnel system. The ground was so soft that for the most part the work could be done with the hands, only a few of the deeper parts requiring the use of a shovel. Some of the tunnels contained evidence of recent occupation by meadow mice in the form of scattered short cuttings of grasses and composites; in a few places there were footprints of the mice in the soft earth on the tunnel floor. A reddish material covered the floor in some of the old galleries, and here the footprints showed to good advantage. Scattered along the tunnels were the droppings of the mice. Only about half the tunnels which were opened up gave any evidence that they were in use during the current season.

One recently built nest of dry grass, and part of an old one, were found in side pockets off two main tunnels. The newer nest cavity had two entrances, serviceable also as avenues of escape in time of danger, and there was also a short accessory loop leading around the nest. In various places there were 'sump' holes (fig. 18) which were dug to a lower level than

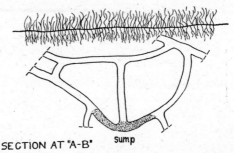

SECTION AT "A-B"   sump

Fig. 18. Enlarged section through part of burrow system shown in figure 17 in region indicated at ''A–B.''

the tunnels off from which they branched. These undoubtedly served to keep the tunnels drained, as each sump had more or less mud in its bottom. At other places there were slight side pockets or 'turn abouts' just large enough to hold a mouse. Only one hole connecting the surface runways and tunnel systems was found in the area studied. This is an unusual condition as compared with other *Microtus* runways which we have examined. Only one *Microtus*, quite a young individual, was obtained at this system of runways, though trapping was continued there for several nights.

Sierra Cantankerous Meadow Mouse

Microtus mordax sierrae Kellogg

Field characters.—Body size more than twice that of House Mouse; tail slightly more than ½ head and body; pelage soft and dense. (See figs. 16b, 20a.) Head and body 4¼ to 5 inches (108–128 mm.), tail 2 to 2⅝ inches (50–66 mm.), hind foot about ⅘ inch (20–23 mm.), ear from crown ½ to ⅔ inch (13–17 mm.); weight about 1 to 1¾ ounces (30.3–48.0 grams). Coloration above dark brown with a grayish cast; sides of body conspicuously grayish; under surface grayish white; tail distinctly darker above than below.

Occurrence.—Common resident, chiefly in Canadian and Hudsonian zones, on both slopes of Sierra Nevada. Recorded commonly from Merced Grove Big Trees and Chinquapin eastward to Warren Fork of Leevining Creek and Walker Lake; present on floor of Yosemite Valley in some numbers and taken once at El Portal. Lives chiefly along banks of swift-flowing mountain streams and in marshes but also on dry hillsides at some distance from water. Largely nocturnal.

Besides the path-cutting meadow mice (*californicus* and *montanus*) there is present in the Yosemite region a free-ranging species, the Cantankerous Meadow Mouse. It occurs in greatest numbers on the ground beneath the bushes which line the banks of mountain streams, but strangely enough is also found in some numbers on dry hillsides well away from water.

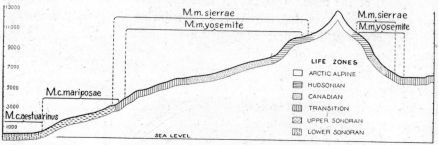

Fig. 19. Cross-section of the Sierra Nevada through the Yosemite region showing zonal and altitudinal ranges of Meadow Mice (genus *Microtus*).

The present species is a 'long-tailed' meadow mouse, but is so only by comparison with others of its own tribe (figs. 16*b*, 20*a*). The tail of *mordax* is as a rule slightly over one-third the total length (one-half head and body), whereas in the California and Yosemite voles the length of tail is somewhat under the proportions given. In other features *mordax* closely resembles other meadow mice with its blunt nose, black bead-like eyes, small ear, and soft dense pelage.

The range of the Cantankerous Meadow Mouse includes the whole of the high Sierras. Nominally it embraces the Canadian and Hudsonian zones, the 'boreal' portion of the region; but the species locally extends well below the limit of the lower of these zones. Thus on the floor of Yosemite Valley, in the little swamp near the Happy Isles power house, and again in an area near Rocky Point, some of these mice were found; and on one occasion (November 21, 1914) an individual was captured at El Portal. It is an observed fact that along the course of a river or large creek a tongue of the next higher zone will often extend down into the zone below. This is due to the fact that the colder water and greater evaporation keeps down the temperature in the neighborhood of the stream. This, in the case of the Cantankerous Vole, would operate to permit the animal to reside comfortably at lower levels as illustrated by its occurrence in Yosemite Valley. The occurrence at El Portal may, of course, have been purely fortuitous, due to an individual having wandered or been carried down-stream from some Canadian Zone location on the slopes above. Altitudinally, this mouse was recorded as high as 10,700 feet in the head of Lyell Cañon, close to timber line. The lower limit of its regular range on the west slope is between 5000 and 6000 feet.

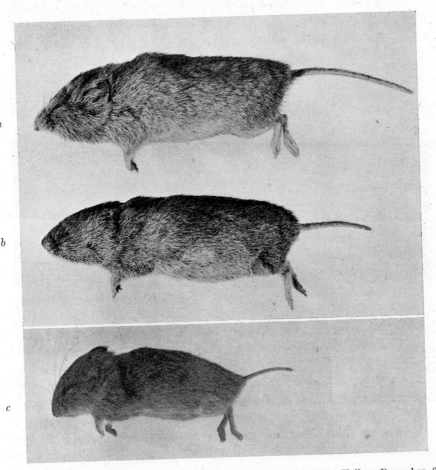

Fig. 20. (*a*) Sierra Cantankerous Meadow Mouse; Yosemite Valley, December 29, 1914. See p. 129. (*b*) Yosemite Meadow Mouse; same data. See p. 122. (*c*) Mountain Lemming Mouse; Ten Lakes, October 8, 1915. See p. 133.

All photographed from freshly trapped specimens, about ⅝ natural size.

The Cantankerous Meadow Mouse does not regularly construct runways as do the California and Yosemite meadow mice. As a rule, it merely runs about here and there on the surface of the ground. In a few places, however, notably at Glen Aulin and Vogelsang Lake, we did notice ill-defined pathways on the ground beneath the thickets of bilberry and Labrador tea bordering the streams; and along these Cantankerous Meadow Mice were caught. Extensive use of the paths was indicated by the numerous small, elongated black droppings of this species. These natural avenues of travel are used also by other small mammals such as white-footed mice and chipmunks. One of these meadow mice was captured in a trap set on top of a heap of dead branches of aspen, about 2½ feet above the ground. Foraging is carried on down close to the water's edge, as many individuals were trapped close beside streams; and occasionally one is seen swimming in the water.

Fig. 21. Willow and grass covered seepage slope in head of Lyell Cañon; altitude about 10,000 feet, Hudsonian Zone. Habitat of the Sierra Mountain Beaver or Aplodontia. In the willow thickets were Hudsonian White-crowned Sparrows. The grassy banks contained burrows and runways of the Yosemite Meadow Mouse. Photograph taken July 24, 1915.

This mouse is more restricted than its path-traveling relatives to night-time foraging. Being a free-ranging animal it might be subject to capture by day-prowling, carnivorous birds or mammals in the same way as is *Peromyscus*. For that reason, probably, it is abroad but little during the day. Only on one occasion did we see an individual of this species alive. In Glen Aulin at about 9:30 A.M. on October 1, 1915, one was seen scampering over the leaf mold on the floor of a lodgepole pine forest.

The breeding season of this mouse, as revealed by our trapping records, embraces most of the summer season; we are unable to give its exact limits. A quarter-grown youngster collected at Merced Grove Big Trees on June 13 suggests commencement of breeding activity at some time in late April or early May. When we first came into the range of the species on June 10 many of the females contained embryos; this condition obtained throughout June and July. The latest records of breeding females are for August 30 at Vogelsang Lake and September 10 at Walker Lake. Continued trapping within the range of the species during October failed to reveal further breeding; hence the warmer six months of the year seem to encompass the breeding period. The numbers of embryos ranged from 3 to 7, the average for 21 cases being close to 5 in a litter. It may well be that females bear more than one litter a year, as is known to be the case with other meadow mice. A few females gave evidence of having bred before attaining the dimensions of a fully grown animal.

Short-tailed Meadow Mouse. **Lagurus curtatus** (Cope)

Field characters.—Body size about twice that of House Mouse; tail very short, less than ¼ head and body; pelage dense and lax. Head and body 4¼ inches (110 mm.), tail 1 inch (25 mm.), hind foot ¾ inch (19 mm.), ear from crown about ⅜ inch (11 mm.); weight slightly over 1 ounce (32.5 grams) [one individual only]. Pelage light ashy gray above; paler, almost white, on under surface.

Occurrence.—Recorded only at Mono Mills, east of Sierra Nevada. Lives on and in ground beneath sagebrush.

The Short-tailed Meadow Mouse was collected in only one locality, the extreme eastern end of the Yosemite section, at Mono Mills, south of Mono Lake. Two female individuals, an adult and a half-grown youngster, presumably representatives of one family, were obtained, June 7 and 10, 1916. Both were taken in one location, under sagebrush on the edge of a dry gully. The stomach contents of the adult consisted solely of chewed-up leaves of sagebrush. There was neither water nor meadow nor grassland anywhere near the place where the two animals were caught. This species appears not to require such surroundings, but to be adapted to life in an arid situation. It is distributed throughout a considerable portion of the Great Basin sagebrush country.

Mountain Lemming Mouse. **Phenacomys orophilus** Merriam

Field characters.—Body size about twice that of House Mouse; tail short, decidedly less than one-half head and body (fig. 20c); hind foot under ⅘ inch. Head and body about 4 inches (98–108 mm.), tail 1⅛ to 1½ inches (28–40 mm.), hind foot ¾ inch (18–19 mm.), ear from crown about ⅗ inch (14–16.5 mm.); weight ¾ to 1 ounce (21.0–30.2 grams). Coloration ashy, brown-tinged on back, whitish on under surface; feet and tail pale ashy.

Occurrence.—Sparse resident chiefly in Hudsonian Zone. Recorded at Ten Lakes (9200 feet altitude), Glen Aulin (7700 feet), head of Lyell Cañon (at 9750 feet) and near Vogelsang Lake (10,100 feet); single individuals taken in each place. Lives about patches of Sierran heather and under other plants characteristic of the same altitudes. Solitary.

Our first specimen of the Mountain Lemming Mouse was captured at an altitude of about 9750 feet in the head of Lyell Cañon on July 20, 1915. Mr. Charles L. Camp of our party had spent much time examining clumps of Sierran heather (*Bryanthus breweri*) for evidence of the rodent and had set several lines of traps in likely looking situations. This individual was taken in a trap set beside a log at a small hole out of which fresh earth had recently been pushed. On the top of a nearby rock and beneath some brush was a mouse nest with a hole at the side, and a trap set there had been sprung two nights previously. About 50 feet distant from the hole, and in a patch of heather, a pile of old droppings about 6 inches in diameter lay on the ground as if they had been deposited in a cavity beneath the previous winter's snow. The general situation was in an open stand of lodgepole pines at a level place dotted with clumps of heather. A rocky cliff stood to one side, and a stream ran by about a hundred yards distant.

At higher altitudes in Lyell Cañon, even up to 10,700 feet, masses of black and greenish droppings were found which, because of their similarity to the dung-masses of a species of *Phenacomys* in the coast region of California, were believed to be those of *orophilus*. Possibly the animals had wintered here beneath the shelter of down logs or rocks. Also in various situations, usually associated with the droppings, there were found numerous cuttings of heather and other plants, these cuttings being 1½ to 3 inches in length. In one instance willow cuttings of the same nature were observed.

The four specimens of Mountain Lemming Mouse captured include 2 adult males, 1 female, and 1 male, sub-adult. In general appearance they remind one of meadow mice (see fig. 20c), to which they are certainly not distantly related. The short tail and pale gray coloration are the chief external features of difference. Obviously the population of this mouse is far below that of even the Cantankerous Meadow Mouse, else more would have stumbled into the many traps set in places similar to those in which our four specimens were taken.

POCKET GOPHERS. Genus **Thomomys**[11]

Field characters.—Size near that of House Rat, but form stout, tail short, ears and eyes very small (pls. 27, 29); length of body six inches or less; tail less than half length of body, scantily haired, bare at tip; a fur-lined cheek pouch opening outside of mouth on each side; cutting teeth (incisors) project conspicuously beyond lips which never cover them; forefoot not spade-like but provided with long slender claws (fig. 5b), longer

---

[11] The Pocket Gophers of the Yosemite section are representative of five distinct kinds, as enumerated below. Although two of these, *pascalis* and *mewa*, are indicated as subspecies of one species, *bottae* (upon the basis of conditions farther northward in California), actual intergradation between any two of them was not found by us to take place within the region studied; all the five forms in the Yosemite section behave toward one another as full species; no two were found living in exactly the same locality. The geographic habitat of each is distinct (fig. 24).

than those on hind foot; skin loose-fitting; fur short, smooth but not plush-like; coloration uniform, light to dark brown, varying according to age as well as to species. *Habits:* Fossorial; live in self-constructed burrows in ground, appearing above surface but rarely. *Workings:* Low mounds of loose earth with crescentic or moraine-like topography (pl. 28c), mouth of burrow being near one side and left plugged.

Occurrence.—Common practically without interruption throughout the Yosemite section up to timber line.[11] Most plentiful about margins of meadows and on semi-open, timbered slopes; absent only in densest forests and on bare rock formations. Individuals work independently, though often in close proximity to one another.

The characters upon which most emphasis is laid by systematists for separating the species of pocket gophers have to do with the skull and teeth, and determination of these requires preparation of materials and special technical knowledge. It does not seem desirable to deal with these internal characters here; for them the reader interested is referred to Bailey's Revision of the Pocket Gophers of the Genus Thomomys (N. Am. Fauna, no. 39, 1915, U. S. Dept. Agr., Bur. Biol. Surv.). As to external characters our pocket gophers, though much alike, do possess features of difference which are appreciable. These consist in tone of color, general size, and relative size of ear. These external features are here given. The sequence of species is from the west base of the Sierras across the mountains to Mono Lake.

FRESNO POCKET GOPHER, *Thomomys bottae pascalis* Merriam, a race occupying most of the floor of the San Joaquin Valley, was found to enter the Yosemite section only along the bottom lands of the Merced River around Snelling. There it was abundant, and troublesome in gardens and alfalfa fields. This gopher is slightly the largest of the five kinds, and it is palest in color of those on the west side of the Sierra Nevada. In summer it is bright cinnamon-buff all over, save for whitish tail and feet and dull brown around mouth; in winter, darker, snuff brown, paler underneath. Head and body 5⅛ to 6⅝ inches (130–168 mm.), hind foot 1 to 1¼ inches (25–32 mm.), ear (from crown) about ¼ inch (5–7 mm.), weight 3 to 6 ounces (82–172 grams). In this race and the next, maximum dimensions and weights are for males, minimum for females; but in the other three species, the sexes differ in size little or not at all.

DIGGER PINE POCKET GOPHER, *Thomomys bottae mewa* Merriam, a race inhabiting a long narrow north-to-south strip along the western flank of the Sierras, was found in the Yosemite section to occupy very closely the Upper Sonoran Zone. We found it from Lagrange and Pleasant Valley east to six miles east of Coulterville, El Portal, and Pinoche Peak (at 5500 feet). This gopher is smaller than *pascalis;* its color tone in summer is still brighter, more reddish, and in winter darker, almost blackish down the middle of the back. Head and body 4¾ to 6 inches (120–153 mm.), hind foot about 1 inch (24–28 mm.), ear (from crown) slightly less than ¼ inch (6–7 mm.), weight 2¼ to 4½ ounces (67–129 grams).

YOSEMITE POCKET GOPHER, *Thomomys alpinus awahnee* Merriam, occupying the Transition Zone along the west flank of the Sierras, chiefly south of the Yosemite section, was found to be the common gopher on the floor of Yosemite Valley, west to Cascades. Outside of the Valley it has been recorded only from Sequoia. This gopher is dark grayish brown both summer and winter, and nearly all the individuals examined have more or less blotching of pure white on the under surface, especially around the chin and on the chest. Head and body 5¼ to 6 inches (132–150 mm.), hind foot 1 to 1⅛ inches (26–29 mm.), ear (from crown) about ⅕ inch (5–6 mm.).

SIERRA NEVADA POCKET GOPHER, *Thomomys monticola monticola* Allen. A species whose range covers the higher parts of the central and northern Sierras. It inhabits rather strictly the Canadian and Hudsonian zones of the Yosemite region. We found it from Aspen Valley and Chinquapin eastward across much of the intervening territory below timber line to Gem Lake. Highest point of actual capture, 10,350 feet, at Vogelsang Lake. This gopher differs from all the others in its finer, longer pelage and in its larger, pointed ears; the color tone on the back is dark brown tinged with russet, with lower surface dull buffy white; a slaty patch behind ear. Head and body 5 to 6 inches (126–150 mm.), hind foot 1 to 1¼ inches (26–31 mm.), ear (from crown) about ⅓ inch (8–9 mm.), weight 3⅙ to 5½ ounces (90–158 grams).

FISHER POCKET GOPHER, *Thomomys quadratus fisheri* Merriam. Occupies the western parts of the Great Basin, and inhabits the arid east slopes of the Sierras and the territory around Mono Lake, chiefly within the Transition Zone. We took specimens from Leevining Creek (at 9200 feet), Walker Lake, and Silver Lake, east to Mono Craters. This is the smallest and palest colored of the five kinds; its ear is very small. Color a dull pinkish cinnamon above, buffy white beneath; a dusky spot at base of ear. Head and body 4⅝ to 5¾ inches (117–146 mm.), hind foot about 1 inch (25.5–27 mm.), ear (from crown) about ⅙ inch (3–5 mm.), weight 2⅓ to 3½ ounces (65–98 grams).

The Pocket Gopher is a modest, retiring animal of subterranean habits, known chiefly by his works. Indeed so rarely is one of the animals seen alive by the casual observer that the evidences of its presence are often ascribed to that totally unrelated but more widely known animal, the mole. There is close similarity in general appearance and habits between the several species of pocket gophers inhabiting the Yosemite region, and for this reason it has seemed better to combine in one account what we have learned about all of them. Brief descriptions of the five species and statements of their respective ranges are given in footnote 11.

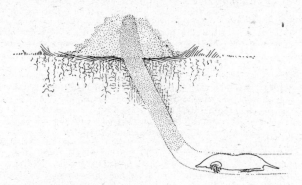

Fig. 22. Illustrates method used by Mole in putting earth up from below-ground. Successive loads of earth are forced up one after another and topple out on the surface of the ground, volcano-like, without ever leaving the mouth of the tunnel exposed or open. Compare with figure 23 illustrating work of Pocket Gopher.

Gophers live in tunnel systems which they themselves excavate at a relatively uniform depth five inches or so below the surface of the ground. They appear on the surface from time to time only when necessary to push out earth loosened in extending their tunnels or to forage in the close vicinity of the open burrow. They seem to be most active about sundown and during the early hours of the morning; for it is then that the majority of new surface mounds appear, and that the animals themselves are most often seen at the mouths of open burrows.

The presence of gophers is indicated by small mounds of loose earth which the animals push out here and there on the surface of the ground. The typical mound is of a fan shape, the opening of the burrow from which the earth was pushed, although closed, being clearly indicated at the base of the fan. (See pl. 28*b*.) The upraised surface of the fan is marked with more or less sharply indicated concentric 'moraines,' each registering the terminus of an operation from the mouth of the burrow. The rim of the mound is often irregular, the earth having been pushed farther out at some points on the periphery than at others. The mouth of the burrow is plainly outlined in a perfect circle of raised earth two or three inches in diameter, but this small circle is lower than the preponderance of the heap.

Gopher workings can easily be distinguished from those made by moles. Mole mounds never show an open tunnel at any time, even during construction; the animals themselves never come out on the surface when pushing out earth (fig. 22.)   The earth is pushed straight up from the initial opening and new earth is placed only beneath the pile already started, with the result that the pile is raised still higher.   In rising, the earth at the top separates and keeps toppling over, leaving a peculiarly porous or cleft surface (pl. 28*b*), with no indication of the location of the burrow from which the earth was extruded.   And so it is that the concentric 'moraines' which characterize the gopher workings are never to be seen on the mounds of moles.

Fig. 23.   Illustrates method used by Pocket Gopher in removing earth from burrow. Note that each load of earth is brought up from below and shoved out on top of the ground opposite the mouth of the open ''lateral.''   The pushing out of successive loads in different directions from the mouth of one lateral gives the surface mound a semicircular outline as viewed from above.   Compare with plate 28.

In addition to their characteristic mounds, pocket gophers often afford much less conspicuous evidences of their activity, especially during the dry season.   At frequent intervals circular openings in the ground are to be seen, which have been filled with loose earth nearly or quite to the level of the surrounding surface.   These burrows have been used as exits from short side branches of the main subterranean tunnels, for the purpose of exploring the immediately adjacent surface for food.   Gophers are exceedingly loath to leave shelter and ordinarily do not venture so far even as the length of their bodies from the open mouths of their burrows (pl. 29*a*). As an evident result of this timidity, each feeding exit becomes the center of a small circle, shorn of vegetation, the radius of which is less than the body length of the gopher.   The haunches of the animal remain in contact with the orifice of the burrow as a sort of anchor by means of which he can pull himself back into safety at an instant's warning.   It is well known to gardeners that a gopher will burrow underground some distance to a plant rather than risk capture by venturing forth on the surface even a short distance. Many times gophers tunnel toward the surface beneath plants and cut off roots and even the main stems, without causing any disturbance above ground until the plant begins to wither and die.

When excavating, gophers loosen the earth with their strong incisor teeth and the long claws of the forefeet (pl. 29c). The earth thus loosened is swept back underneath the body until a considerable amount has accumulated. The animal then turns around (being able to do so within the diameter of its own body), and pushes the earth along the tunnel to a surface opening where it is shoved out on top of the ground. (See pl. 29b and fig. 23.) Only the forefeet, in conjunction with the broad furry face below the level of the nose, are used in moving the earth; the outside-opening cheek pouches (pl. 27b) with which the animal is provided, and which open at either side of the mouth, are used for the sole purpose of carrying food material. After tunnel excavation has proceeded a few inches beyond one surface opening, the opening is closed and a new opening made at a more convenient position, nearer the spot where earth is being removed. Most of the surface openings are at the ends of side tunnels which are but a few inches in length. Sometimes a great quantity of earth is pushed out at one surface opening. One mound observed in the Ten Lakes basin was 25 inches (62½ cm.) in diameter at the base and 6 inches (15 cm.) high; the total earth pushed out amounted to 7825 cubic inches, or about four and one-half cubic feet (123,705 cc.).

Gophers at the higher altitudes show most activity during the late afternoon and early evening hours. It is then that most new mounds are to be seen and that trapping is most successful. In high meadows where there is a heavy frost, the surfaces of mounds made during the night are usually frozen stiff by morning, showing that the mounds were piled up before the nightly drop in temperature. However, especially in lower altitudes, gophers work a good deal in the morning and do some work at almost any hour of the day.

With regard to breeding habits in the Yosemite, we have little to report save what is shown by the specimens captured. We did not in any instance try to dig out the home burrows. A quarter-grown juvenal (*pascalis*) taken at Snelling January 5, 1915, indicates early breeding at that low altitude (250 feet). A female (*mewa*) taken at Pleasant Valley, May 21, 1915, contained four large embryos. Two young (*monticola*), one-quarter to one-third grown, were taken at Mono Meadow on June 18, 1915. Five pregnant gophers (*monticola*) were taken in 1915 at the higher altitudes: Porcupine Flat, June 28, 6 large embryos; same locality, July 1, 5 small and 7 small; same locality, July 2, 3 embryos; Tuolumne Meadows, July 11, 5 embryos.

The pocket gopher is one of several Sierran rodents which carry on active existence throughout the entire year. It does not hibernate, so far as we know, even at the highest altitudes. As described beyond, there is good evidence of their continued work beneath the snow, however deep this may become. Yet there is some variation in degree of activity with the change of seasons and at different elevations. In the foothills and lower valleys the rains seem to have much to do with the behavior of these animals. Soon after the first soaking rain of the autumn, and with the first appearance of the annual vegetation, new outpushings of moist earth become conspicuous. In the higher mountains greatest activity, save for that in winter, is shown in September and October. Least surface work is shown during the first few weeks of spring after the snow melts.

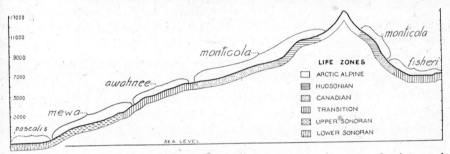

Fig. 24. Cross-section of Sierra Nevada through the Yosemite region showing zonal and altitudinal ranges of Pocket Gophers (genus *Thomomys*).

During the winter and spring in the high country, where snow lies on the ground for several months, gophers are, as just stated, continually active, but are led to adopt a somewhat different method in extending their tunnel systems than that used during the summer months. Tunnels are made in the snow some distance above and more or less parallel to the surface of the ground; these "snow tunnels" are usually greater in diameter than the subterranean ones and obviously serve the purpose of allowing the gophers to reach food plants which are imbedded in the snow. Certainly many of these snow tunnels are also used in extending the subterranean system; the earth from below ground is carried up and packed into the snow and thereby solid earth-cores are formed above the ground. When the snow melts these cores are lowered intact onto the surface of the ground, where they often remain distinguishable for several months despite the summer thunder showers. (See pl. 30.) The height to which the snow tunnels extend above the ground depends upon the depth of the snowfall; but there is reason to believe that their course is also modified by the position of the vegetation encountered. In early spring, after the snow has gone, we have found portions of earth-cores lying on top of flattened branches of snow-bushes, over fallen tree branches,

over logs and rocks, these various locations indicating that the animals
had pursued courses through the snow well above these objects, that is to
say, at least 12 inches from the top of the ground. When active right after
a light fall of snow, the gophers run their tunnels along directly upon the
surface of the ground, appropriating to their uses the stems of grass and
the other plants encountered as they go.

Very often the material composing the cores is quite different in
character from that of the top of the ground immediately underneath them.
This makes the cores very conspicuous, for they are, with reference to the
ground on which they lie, in the relation of a geological unconformity.
This kind of gopher work is carried on even after but light snow storms
in the fall when snow may lie on the ground only a few days. We noted
evidences of such work in 1915, about Tuolumne Meadows after a light
snowfall on September 24 and 25, and after another in Yosemite Valley on
November 12.

Rather than being a drawback to the interests of the pocket gopher,
snow seems to be of real benefit to them. Two factors are here involved.
We have referred to the timidity of the animals because doubtless of
relentless pursuit by certain carnivorous birds and mammals, and to the
resulting precautions evinced by the gophers in keeping out of sight. The
snow provides cover which conceals them still more effectually from their
enemies. At the same time, the vertical range of accessible food sources
is greatly increased, for the gophers are able to reach plant stems and
leaves enveloped in the snow mantle many inches and even feet above the
ground surface. All this is subject to indubitable proof through study
of winter workings uncovered at the time of the spring thaw.

Some estimates made by our field party while near Porcupine Flat
during the first week of July, 1915, will serve to indicate the amount of
work done by gophers. It was found that the average amount of earth
pushed up in the form of winter cores was, on a selected area, 1.64 pounds
per square yard (0.90 kilograms per square meter). Assuming that, on
the average, gopher workings cover 0.1 per cent of the land surface of
the Park there would be 3.675 tons of earth accumulated per square mile
or 4132 tons over the whole Park. And this in a single winter! It will be
recalled that there are many square miles of either solid rock or slide rock
in the Park, where gophers cannot work. On the other hand, in favorable
localities workings sometimes occur on every square yard of surface; the
average of 0.1 per cent is therefore believed to be conservative for the
Park as a whole. In summer the amount of material excavated is probably
at least as great as it is in winter—exactly how much has not yet been
determined. But for the year we feel safe in doubling the total figure
just given, which, to put it in another unit of measure, would be close to

60 carloads of 50 tons each. We estimate further that this great quantity
f earth is lifted by the gophers an average distance of at least 8 inches;
500 foot tons of energy is expended in excavation alone by these animals
n Yosemite Park during a single year!

The question then presents itself, what are the general effects of all
his work upon the terrane at large, upon the vegetation, and even upon
he other animal life of the region. Some of these relations borne by pocket
gophers to their environment may be enumerated as follows:

(1) The weathering of the substratum is hastened by the burrow
systems carrying the water and contained solvents as well as air to the
sub-soil particles and rock masses below.

(2) The sub-soil is further comminuted and brought to the surface
where it is exposed to increased rate of weathering.

(3) The loose earth brought up and piled on the surface of the ground
thereby becomes available for transportation by water; rain and melted
snow carry it from the slopes down to fill up glacial depressions and make
meadows of them, and when these are full the sediment is carried on still
farther by the gathering streams to contribute to the upbuilding of the
great and fertile valleys beyond the foothills.

(4) Water is conserved for the reason that snow melts more slowly
on porous ground than on hard-packed soil or bare rock so that the spring
run-off is retarded and the supply to the streams below is distributed over
a longer period of time; furthermore, the porous soil retains the water
longer than packed ground and gives it up with corresponding slowness.
Spring floods are less liable to occur, and a more regular water supply is
insured to the lowlands.

(5) A porous, moist soil produces a fuller vegetational cover—forest,
brushland, and meadow—and this again favors water conservation.

(6) The ground is rendered more fertile through the loosening of the
soil as well as through its permeation by the tunnels themselves, as thereby
both air and water are admitted to the roots of the plants; the mineral
constituents of the soil become more readily available, and the rootlets are
better able to penetrate the earth.

(7) The accumulated vegetational débris on the surface of the ground
is eventually buried by the soil brought from below by the gophers, and
becomes incorporated to form the humus content so necessary for the
successful growth of most plants.

Our readers will have been reminded by a portion of the above con-
siderations of Darwin's classical study on the relation of earthworms to
soil formation. There is undoubtedly a parallel here, the more significant
in that the earthworm is a relatively rare animal in the Sierra Nevada, and
what there are of him, are of small size, and of relative inconsequence in

cultivating the soil. The pocket gopher is wonderfully equipped to handle the refractory young soils of the semi-arid Sierran slopes, and his is the rôle here of Darwin's earthworm in England.

Now that the greatest of all agencies of erosion, the glaciers, so stressed by John Muir, have almost ceased to operate, the less obvious agencies stand ready to claim their due prominence, if we will but look for them. The element of time granted, we are able to conceive of vast accomplishments on the part of even so humble a contributor as the pocket gopher.

A real service, it seems to us, performed by burrowing animals, among which in the Sierras the pocket gopher stands foremost, is that of counteracting the packing effect of large mammals on uncultivated pasture lands. The impact of heavy feet on the soil, especially when wet, crowds the particles together and renders the earth less suitable for plant growth. Close tamping tends to exclude air and hence to suffocate the plant roots, to which oxygen is as essential as it is to animal life. One has but to observe the condition of mountain meadows outside the limits of National Parks, to appreciate the point here made. Often where the country has been overstocked with cattle or domestic sheep, the grasslands have become poor—the crop of grass is scrawny—*except* where gopher workings occur; the sites of these are marked by patches of vivid green. Indeed, on ordinary hill slopes within the Yosemite section we have repeatedly noted the rejuvenation of the plant cover here and there due directly and obviously to the activity of the gophers. Before the advent of the white man with his cattle and horses a similar service was rendered, though in lesser degree, perhaps, when the wild deer, mountain sheep, and bears frequented the same meadows.

The pocket gophers, then, are the chief natural cultivators of the soil, and upon their continued activity the maximum thrift of wild vegetation is dependent.

The question of damage by gophers to forests under natural conditions, for example, injury to young trees, has been raised by foresters. There is no doubt that gophers do girdle or cut off the stems of many seedlings and thus terminate the existence of numerous individual trees. But the great number of seedlings observable on parts of any forest floor, vastly more than could ever reach maturity, would seem to indicate that an adjustment in this direction had been reached long ages ago. Plants in general provide for a rate of replacement sufficient to meet the maximum probabilities of casualty, this involving all stages from the seed to the mature fruiting plant.

In the arable lowlands of California the pocket gopher is well-nigh universally condemned for pursuing his normal activities, while making his living, on lands that have been appropriated and cultivated by man.

There, man has disturbed the original balance of natural relations between plants and animals; he aims to make the land produce crops of selected plants in the largest measure possible, and to that end he cultivates the ground himself by very effective 'artificial' means. He resents the levy upon the land and its products by any other animal. Most of the original quota of herbivorous mammals have gone before him; but the gopher and ground squirrel have been able to persist under the changed conditions and have availed themselves of man's crops. Yet it is clear that we have here, most surely, a reversal of the relationships obtaining in the wild. In the wild, there *is* no cultivation in the artificial sense. The crops of wild plants—grasses, herbs, shrubs, and even trees—depend upon whatever favorable agencies coöperate in natural ways. The happy relation found by our pioneers was the result of eons of adjustment among all of the elements concerned. Gophers have been at work as gophers of modern type since Miocene time. We grant that the farmer must combat the gopher in his fields; we sympathize with him for yearning for the total eradication of the rodents there. But we do not agree with the policy of wholesale extermination advocated by some persons for all areas alike. We hold that the native plant life on hill and mountainside, in cañon and mountain meadow, would at once begin to decline, were the gopher population completely destroyed. Not that such a thing is at all possible; but it should not be thought of, even, by any intelligent person who seeks to interpret nature corectly. On wild land the pocket gopher, with its fellow-rodents of burrowing habits, constitutes a necessary link in the system of natural well-being.

Fig. 25. Cartoon suggesting relation between work of Pocket Gophers on the Sierra Nevada and accumulation of fertile sediments on floor of San Joaquin Valley.

POCKET MICE. Genus **Perognathus** Maximilian[12]

Field characters.—Size small, body size usually about that of House Mouse; tail long, about equal to head and body (pl. 26*b*, *c*); forelegs and feet short and small; hind feet long and relatively large (see footnote for detailed measurements); a fur lined pouch in each cheek, opening at side of mouth. Coloration yellowish brown above, white on under surface. *Workings:* Small holes about ¾ to 1¼ inches in diameter, usually in sandy soil about bases of bushes; occupied holes plugged with earth during daytime.

Occurrence.—Resident at lower altitudes on both sides of Sierra Nevada, from Snelling east to El Portal and again around Mono Lake, east of the mountains.[12] Lives chiefly in areas of sand or other easily worked soil. Nocturnal.

The pocket mice constitute but one of several groups of small nocturnally active animals which pass unnoticed, even in places where they are abundant, unless special search is made for them. The naturalist when hunting for pocket mice looks at the loose sandy or fine soil about the bases of desert, valley, or foothill bushes, and if he finds little burrows plugged with earth he sets his traps there with the expectation of capturing some of the animals when they come abroad at night. They may not, however, take the bait (usually rolled oats or cornmeal is used) and will thus refuse to disclose their specific identity. The pocket mice are diminutive relatives of the kangaroo rats, their mode of life and niche or place in nature being much the same.

[12] Three distinct species of Pocket Mice occur in the Yosemite region; in fact two distinct systematic groups are represented. But they are all treated together here, due in part to our scanty knowledge of their habits and in part to the slight attention that is likely to be given to such elusive animals by most visitors to the region. It will be noted that the ranges of these three species do not overlap, so that specimens found in the field can be referred with confidence to the proper species on the basis of locality alone.

CALIFORNIA POCKET MOUSE, *Perognathus californicus californicus* Merriam, a large-sized spiny-haired species (pl. 26*b*) which occurs widely through the Upper Sonoran Zone in central California, was found from Pleasant Valley eastward to Smith Creek (6 miles east of Coulterville) and to El Portal where it lives on dry chaparral-covered slopes. The largest and darkest colored species in the region. Head and body 3⅕ to 3½ inches (81–90 mm.), tail 4 to 5 inches (103–125 mm.), hind foot about 1 inch (24–27 mm.), ear from crown ⅓ to ½ inch (8–14 mm.), weight ⅔ to 1 ounce (19.9–30.0 grams). Pelage coarse with many long grooved spine-like over-hairs on side and rump; tail with a 'pencil' or tuft at tip; soles of hind feet naked. Upper surface reddish buff, darkened by numerous black hair tippings; under surface white.

SAN JOAQUIN POCKET MOUSE, *Perognathus inornatus inornatus* Merriam, a small-sized, soft haired species (pl. 26*c*) of the San Joaquin Valley, was recorded at Snelling where it lives in sparse grass on the dry mesa. Head and body 2½ to 2⅞ inches (65–74 mm.), tail 2½ to 3⅛ inches (66–79 mm.), hind foot ⅔ to ⅘ inch (17–20 mm.), ear from crown ⅓ inch (8–9 mm.), weight about ⅓ ounce (10.2 grams). Tail not tufted. Coloration pale sandy buff above, with numerous black hair endings; under surface pure white.

GREAT BASIN POCKET MOUSE, *Perognathus parvus olivaceus* Merriam, a medium-sized, soft haired species distributed through much of the Great Basin country east of the Sierra Nevada, was found abundantly in the neighborhood of Mono Lake, being recorded from Silver Lake and near Walker Lake north and east to Mono Lake Post Office and Mono Mills. It inhabits dry sandy situations and makes its burrows under sagebrush. Head and body 2¾ to 3⅝ inches (69–92 mm.), tail 3⅛ to 4 inches (80–100 mm.), hind foot ⅞ to 1 inch (22–26 mm.), ear from crown about ¼ inch (6–7 mm.), weight ⅖ to ⅞ ounce (12.5–25.3 grams). Tail not tufted. Coloration above plain buff, with many black hair endings; under surface pure white.

The three species of pocket mice in the Yosemite region belong to distinct groups, and were we as fully informed upon the details of their life histories as we are for example upon those of the chipmunks, these three pocket mice would doubtless merit separate consideration. But at the present time we know little more than their structural characters, their ranges, and the sort of immediate surroundings which each inhabits. The San Joaquin and Great Basin pocket mice live in open situations, recalling in this respect the Merced and Pale-faced kangaroo rats, while the California Pocket Mouse lives in places beneath the foothill chaparral (*Adenostoma*) which are somewhat gravelly or rocky. The latter species parallels in choice of habitat the Heermann Kangaroo Rat. In certain parts of the country 2 or even 3 species of pocket mice are to be found in a single locality, each occupying a separate type of habitat or niche; but in the Yosemite region the ranges of the 3 species are distinct geographically as well as ecologically.

Pocket mice are exclusively nocturnal. They spend the day below ground in their short simple burrows, coming out as soon as darkness falls to forage on the surface of the ground. Their mode of progression is like that of a kangaroo; they bound along on the enlarged and proportionately long hind feet, using the tail as a stabilizer and counterbalance. The forefeet come into particular service when the animals feed. Then they function as hands and are used with great dexterity to hold food materials and to thrust these into the fur-lined pouches or pockets on either side of the face. When the cheek pouches are filled with seeds or other food the animals make for their burrows and store the food there for use at times when it is too cold or rainy out-of-doors for them to venture forth.

A specimen of the Great Basin Pocket Mouse was captured alive at the Farrington ranch on June 21, 1916, and retained in captivity for a time. It was kept in a can, well wrapped with cloth. One morning the mouse was found cold and stiff, seemingly dead; but when the sun had warmed the air it revived completely.

One afternoon this mouse was taken to a large clear sandy area and set loose in order that its habits might be observed. It seemed quite averse to facing the sun and would always turn its back to the strong light. In attempting to dig a burrow the mouse used its front feet to shove out the loosened sand. Its actions in this respect resembled somewhat those of a pocket gopher. When not disturbed the mouse moved along the sand slowly like a cat when stalking a bird, but when alarmed the animal bounded over the sand in three-foot leaps using only its hind legs, at such a rate that the observer could scarcely keep up. When offered some rolled oats the mouse, using its forefeet, stuffed the material into its cheek pouches but ate none.

Scanty data were obtained relative to the breeding of the local pocket mice. At Snelling on May 26, 1915, two female San Joaquin Pocket Mice were captured which contained 2 and 6 embryos respectively. A nearly full grown young-of-the-year in the bluish-tinged soft pelage of immaturity was taken at the same station three days later. On the California Pocket Mouse we have only three notes: Two females with mammae conspicuous were taken on May 21 and 27, 1915, at Pleasant Valley, and a nearly grown juvenile was collected at Smith Creek (6 miles east of Coulterville) on July 28, 1920. For the Great Basin Pocket Mouse, although numerous specimens were obtained, the data are likewise scanty. A female containing 3 embryos was captured at Mono Lake Post Office on July 1, 1916, and an immature animal was trapped on Dry Creek, June 12, 1916. At Walker Lake, September 9 to 13, 1915, and near Williams Butte, September 17 to 22, 1915, numerous smooth-pelaged gray-tinged but nearly or quite full-sized young-of-the-year were procured.

KANGAROO RATS. Genus Dipodomys[13]

Field characters.—Body size between that of House Mouse and House Rat, nearer the latter (see footnote 13 for detailed measurements); tail exceeding head and body in length, well haired, and with a conspicuous tuft at end (pl. 26e); front feet very small, hind feet and legs disproportionately long and large; ear rounded, held close to side of head; a large fur-lined cheek pouch on each side of face opening outside of mouth; eyes large; pelage silky. Coloration above plain sandy brown (varying in tone according to subspecies); a white stripe across each thigh; whole under surface of body pure white; end of nose white with a blackish crescent on each side; tail four-striped—dark stripe above and below, with an intervening white stripe on each side. *Workings:*

[13] Three races of Kangaroo Rats are found in the Yosemite region. They are distinct from one another structurally and occupy separate geographic areas, yet their habits and general appearance are much alike.

HEERMANN KANGAROO RAT, *Dipodomys heermanni heermanni* (Le Conte). Found along the west base of the central Sierra Nevada. It was recorded from 1 mile west of Coulterville to 6 miles east of that place, and probably occupies a much wider range than this indicates. It inhabits the Upper Sonoran Zone, ranging locally into the lower margin of Transition, and lives chiefly amid chaparral. Head and body 4¼ to 4⅞ inches (108–123 mm.), tail 6½ to 7⅜ inches (165–187 mm.), hind foot about 1¾ inches (43–44 mm.), ear from crown about ½ inch (12–16 mm.), weight about 2½ ounces (68.6–72.8 grams).

MERCED KANGAROO RAT, *Dipodomys heermanni dixoni* (Grinnell). A subspecies inhabiting the east side of the San Joaquin Valley (Lower Sonoran Zone). It was recorded at Snelling, near Merced Falls, and below Lagrange. It inhabits open sandy or dusty places. From *heermanni* it is distinguished by smaller size and average lighter color. (See pl. 26e.) Head and body 3⅞ to 4¾ inches (98–119 mm.), tail 6 to 6⅞ inches (155–174 mm.), hind foot about 1⅝ inches (39–42 mm.), ear from crown about ½ inch (12.5–14 mm.), weight 1½ to 2⅖ ounces (43.4–68.4 grams).

PALE-FACED KANGAROO RAT, *Dipodomys leucogenys* (Grinnell). A species distinct from the two preceding in several particulars, and readily separated from them by larger size and paler coloration. It is rather common at Mono Mills, on the slopes of Mono Craters and along Dry Creek; all these localities are near Mono Lake east of the Sierra Nevada. It inhabits sandy places among the sagebrush. Head and body 4⅝ to 5½ inches (117–140 mm.), tail 6⅓ to 7⅓ inches (160–185 mm.), hind foot about 1¾ inches (44–47 mm.), ear from crown about ½ inch (12–13 mm.), weight 2¾ to 3⅛ ounces (78.2–88.5 grams).

3urrows about 2 inches in diameter, in loose soil, usually about bases of bushes; entrance
10le usually filled with earth during the daytime. *Tracks:* Paired impressions of hind
'eet (3 or 4 toes showing forward, connected with a long heel print) in lengthwise series
.t intervals of 7 to 36 inches, the tail track as an interrupted line midway between the
'ootprints (pl. 40*c*).

Occurrence.—Resident along east side of San Joaquin Valley, at Snelling, near
Merced Falls, and below Lagrange (*dixoni*), in western foothills about Coulterville
(*heermanni*), and again east of the Sierra Nevada around Mono Lake (*leucogenys*).[13]
Nocturnal.

The Kangaroo Rat is a type of mammal which has developed in response
to the sandy desert conditions obtaining in the southwestern part of North
America. The territory at either end of the Yosemite cross-section, being
rather arid in character and otherwise suitable, is occupied by a moderate
population of this rodent. The name kangaroo rat refers to the mode of
progression which, like that of the Australian kangaroo, is accomplished
by catapultic leaps with the long hind legs and feet, in which operation the
greatly lengthened tail acts as a stabilizer and support. Another special
feature, the external fur-lined cheek pouch on each side of the face, used,
as with the pocket gopher, for the storage of clean food materials, has led
to the name pocket rat for this rodent.

Further description of the kangaroo rat may be of interest, particularly
as the animal itself is rarely seen in the wild alive though it has been found
to submit readily to captivity. The form is somewhat tapered, the nose
being pointed and leading back to a rather flattish head. The forelegs and
feet are small, but the hind legs and feet, the leaping apparatus, comprise
quite the largest part of the animal (pl. 26*e*). The tail is long, well exceeding the head and body in length, and is covered with hair which, toward
the tip, becomes long and forms a tuft, or better, a 'brush.' The nose is
provided with an elaborate set of vibrissae or 'whiskers,' the longest of
which reach out far beyond the side of the body. The ears are rather small
though the hearing ability of these animals is probably acute to judge from
the enlargement of the back portions of the skull which house the internal
ear structures. The whole pelage of the animal is soft, even silky in texture.
The kangaroo rat habitually travels and rests on its hind feet, the fore ones
being devoted to the handling of food materials and to cleaning the fur.

Most species of kangaroo rats inhabit sandy situations, so that, as a rule,
naturalists have come regularly to look for the animals in such places.
The Merced and Pale-faced kangaroo rats of the Yosemite region frequent
sandy ground. But the Heermann Kangaroo Rat which lives in the western
foothill country dwells in the chaparral where there is seldom any sand
and where usually the ground is gravelly or even rocky in nature. Its
niche is evidently much like that of the California Pocket Mouse. The
special requirement of the kangaroo rat is a location in which it can place

its burrow; the animal does all its foraging out on the surface of the ground. No burrows were opened up by us in the Yosemite region, but in other places the underground retreats have been found to be of relatively simple nature, used as shelters during the daytime and in cold or rainy weather, and as storehouses for food to be eaten when the animals canno' well venture out.

The distance which a kangaroo rat can cover in one leap is apt to be over-estimated. On any of the relatively few occasions when we have seer one of these animals abroad during the daytime, it has made off so suddenly that we were practically at a loss to describe what transpired during the few seconds that the animal continued in sight. In cases where the actions of an animal have been observed successfully the extent of a single leap has been found to be moderate; one jump followed another so rapidly, however, that the rat's progress was amazingly swift. Speedy escape is likely to be interpreted as due to the animal's ability to jump prodigious distances, whereas the real basis is rapidity of action. Animals frightened or turned out of their burrows when ground was being plowed have been seen to cover 3 to 4 feet at a leap. Under extremely favorable circumstances this might be slightly exceeded. The tracks of an undisturbed Heermann Kangaroo Rat seen in a dusty road near Coulterville were (heel to heel) from 7½ to 9 inches (190–230 mm.) apart. Where something in the road had claimed its attention and the animal had loitered the tracks were even closer. (See pl. 40c.)

The normal activity of the kangaroo rat is confined to the hours of darkness. Unless disturbed by man or some native enemy, it rarely or never ventures out in the daytime. But as soon as dusk has fallen it leaves its burrow and goes hunting for food. The animal subsists almost entirely upon small seeds of particularly sought kinds. Material is gathered and stuffed into the cheek pouches, then the rat retires to its burrow where the food materials are deposited in a special chamber, to be shucked out and consumed at leisure. Examination of the cheek pouch contents of captured animals indicates that a variety of wild seeds are used as food; but when cultivated grains are available the animals turn to these, especially where the fields adjoin wild land. Kangaroo rats readily take the poisoned grain put out for ground squirrels and many meet death from this cause. Ploughing of new land destroys their burrows and quickly drives them out, so that this rodent rarely becomes an important enemy of man.

Our specimens of the Heermann Kangaroo Rat were all taken in the neighborhood of Coulterville, from Blacks Creek on the west to Smith Creek, 6 miles east of the town. But the species enjoys a much wider local range, for we found tracks in the dust of roads at Pleasant Valley, closed burrows on the greasewood slopes about El Portal in December (when the rats are loath to come forth), and got reports of the presence of the animals in fields near the town of Mount Bullion. It was our experience that this chaparral-inhabiting species was more difficult to trap than those which live on the sandy plains and deserts. Furthermore, the population of *heermanni* is sparser than that of the other species; perhaps two to the acre would represent the population on favorable slopes. In a few places, as about clearings in the chaparral, there are probably somewhat more than the number indicated.

Mono Kangaroo Mouse. **Microdipodops polionotus** Grinnell

Field characters.—Body size about that of House Mouse; tail about equal to head and body, smoothly haired, but without any tuft; forefeet normal, hind feet relatively large; a fur-lined pouch on each cheek opening alongside of mouth; ears small and rounded. (See pl. 26*d*.) Head and body 2½ to 3⅓ inches (64–83 mm.), tail 2⅝ to 3½ inches (72–88 mm.), hind foot about 1 inch (23–25 mm.), ear from crown ⅓ inch (8–10 mm.); weight about ⅜ ounce (10.6–12.5 grams). General coloration above sandy buff; whole under surface pure white.

Occurrence.—Recorded from Yosemite section only at old Salmon ranch near Mono Lake, east of Sierra Nevada. Lives in dry sandy areas, making burrows in ground at bases of bushes. Nocturnal.

The Mono Kangaroo Mouse is an inhabitant of the dry Great Basin territory east of the Sierra Nevada. It was found by our party at only one locality, near the old Salmon ranch adjacent to Mono Lake. Four specimens were taken on the night of June 19, 1916, in a dry sandy area a hundred yards or more up from the lake margin. Other areas which to the naturalist's eye were exactly the same as to soil, slope exposure, and flora were unproductive when tested by trapping.

Allen Jumping Mouse. **Zapus pacificus alleni** Elliot

Field characters.—Body size somewhat larger than that of House Mouse; tail very long, one-third longer than head and body; tail almost bare of hairs, and scaly (pl. 26*a*). Front surface of upper incisor teeth grooved. Head and body 3⅜ to 4 inches (86–102 mm.), tail 4¾ to 5½ inches (120–140 mm.), hind foot 1⅛ to 1⅓ inches (28–33 mm.), ear from crown ½ to ⅔ inch (12–16 mm.); weight about ⅔ to ⅞ ounce (18–24.5 grams). Coloration above bright reddish yellow with a dark tract along middle of back; whole under surface pure white; tail and feet dusky.

Occurrence.—Common resident in Canadian and Hudsonian zones on both slopes of Sierra Nevada. Recorded from Merced Grove Big Trees and Chinquapin eastward to Mono Lake Post Office and Walker Lake. Present in Yosemite Valley about foot of Yosemite Falls. Lives in wet meadows and cañon bottoms close to water. Nocturnal.

Besides the meadow mice and shrews in the high mountain meadows there is present, amid the same surroundings, another mammal not familiar to many people, namely, the Jumping Mouse. In general form of body and mode of progression this animal recalls the kangaroo rats and pocket mice found at lower levels on either side of the Sierra Nevada, but its habitat predilections are quite different, for it lives in damp meadows and along the banks of streams.

The body of the Allen Jumping Mouse is perhaps a fourth larger than that of a House Mouse; it is similar in size to a Gambel White-footed Mouse. It is of slender form, the ears are comparatively small, and the pelage is long haired and rather harsh. The forelegs and feet are relatively short and small; the hind legs and particularly the hind feet are proportionately very much longer in the jumping mouse than in the white-footed mice. The tail is the most striking feature; it is fully one-third again the length of head and body (pl. 26a). These departures from the normal mouse form are all adaptations to the particular and unusual mode of progression used by this mouse. Instead of running on the surface with all four feet, it bounds along, using the hind pair of feet alone for propulsion and the tail as a counterbalance and support.

At Chinquapin an Allen Jumping Mouse was captured alive, the tail only having been slightly injured by the trap. The animal was released on a sunlit slope and an attempt was made to photograph it, but to no avail. It was off on the instant, bounding downhill two to three feet at a jump. These leaps were the results of catapultic extension of the two hind legs simultaneously. The front feet apparently took no part in the leaping. All the movements were so rapid that it was impossible to observe in detail the methods of its locomotion. Upon reaching a small pool the mouse took to the water readily, and swam steadily and rapidly.

Near Porcupine Flat a jumping mouse was startled from its nest at 7:30 A.M. on June 25, 1915. One of us, in walking through a small grassy place beside a stream, chanced to touch the nest where the animal had been resting and it thereupon darted out into the open. In three leaps it covered about 8 feet and then stopped, humped up in the shadow at the butt of a willow stalk but not under cover. There it remained motionless for some minutes, with its eyes closed and its long tail curled around to one side of its body. When in motion the reddish yellow color of the animal quickly attracted the naturalist's eye; and when the mouse came to rest, partly in sunlight and partly in shadow, its coloration was anything but protective against the gray stem of the willow and the brown leaf-littered ground. Later an unsuccessful effort was made to drive the mouse out into the open, but it alertly avoided this, and darted off in a zigzag course among the willow roots, always by quick hops, barely touching the ground at each bound. Finally it disappeared in a hole beneath a clump of willows.

The nest out of which the mouse at Porcupine Flat was flushed was a spherical affair about 5 inches (130 mm.) in diameter, snugly ensconced n a depression in the ground and surrounded and overtopped by dead and new grasses. There was a short curved outlet run at one side about one inch (25 mm.) wide and 5¼ inches (130 mm.) long which led directly into the grass and then disappeared. The nest proper consisted externally of long flexible blades of grass of the previous year's growth; these were arranged concentrically around the outside. Within was a soft lining which consisted of finely shredded, last-year's grass blades together with a few green ones. It was all perfectly dry though the surrounding meadow was, as usual at this season, quite damp. This nest may have been merely 'living quarters' for an adult, and not intended for the reception of young.

A local colony of Allen Jumping Mice was found on the floor of Yosemite Valley near the foot of Yosemite Falls. To our own senses the air is notably cold in that particular part of the Valley. A cold breeze comes down from the falls much of the time, and the ice-cold water dropping directly from snow fields 3000 feet above until well along in summer also affects the temperature of the place. There is, in addition, a thick canopy of shade from the enclosing dense stand of yellow pines, incense cedars, white firs, and black oaks. In this 'boreal' spot jumping mice, characteristic of the Canadian and Hudsonian zones above the Valley rim, were present in numbers during June of 1915. The ground was covered with a mat of dead pine needles and deciduous leaves, and there were scattered plants of thimble berry, azalea, creek dogwood, and fern. Possibly colonies of this rodent occur elsewhere in similar, cool situations on the Valley floor, but we found no others.

No data were obtained as to breeding, save that indications pointed to the summer months as the breeding period. Elsewhere it has been found that the Allen Jumping Mouse has rather large litters, 6 perhaps being an average. Immature individuals about two-thirds grown were captured at Merced Lake August 25 to 29, 1915, and near Williams Butte September 15, the same year.

YELLOW-HAIRED PORCUPINE. **Erethizon epixanthum epixanthum** (Brandt)

Field characters.—Size larger than that of Sierra Marmot; tail less than half head and body; pelage very long; upper surface and sides of body and tail with many barb-pointed yellow quills which can be raised at will. Head and body 21½ to 27 inches (545–682 mm.), tail 7 to 9 inches (175–225 mm.), hind foot 3¾ to 4¾ inches (95–120 mm.), ear about 1 inch (27 mm.); weight 15 to 20 pounds (estimated). [Measurements from California specimens taken outside Yosemite region.] Body coloration blackish, a few long hairs and the quills yellow except for black tips. *Workings:* Areas on coniferous trees denuded of bark and showing paired marks of incisor teeth, each mark about ¼ inch (6 mm.) broad (pl. 37a). *Droppings:* Found on ground beneath 'barked' trees, about 1 inch long, ⅜ inch in diameter, rounded and slightly curved, composed of undigested wood pulp.

Occurrence.—Moderately common resident in boreal region on Sierra Nevada. Work ings noted from Porcupine Flat eastward to Tuolumne Meadows. Individuals occur (rarely) on floor of Yosemite Valley and are reported at even lower stations. Lives in coniferous trees, chiefly lodgepole pines. Solitary.

The Yellow-haired Porcupine is perhaps one of the best known of our native mammals, by reputation at least, though not all the stories which are current concerning it are accurate. Being of sluggish disposition and active by day as well as night it gives visitors in the high Sierras many opportunities to observe it at close range. And should these fail, the work of the animal is evident in many places.

In general, the porcupine is to be found in the high Sierras above the level of Yosemite Valley; its range is practically the same as that of the lodgepole pine. Occasionally, however, individuals are observed at much lower levels. We were told, for example, of one trapped on the floor of Yosemite Valley in September, between 1916 and 1918. We have been told of individuals seen on Bullion Mountain. And at Snelling one resident told of a porcupine which he had shot in the river bottom a mile from town, and of two or three others, possibly castaways brought down the river in drift, which had been observed in the same locality.

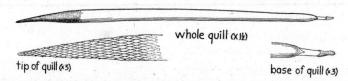

whole quill (×1½)

tip of quill (×3)   base of quill (×3)

Fig. 26. Quill from Yellow-haired Porcupine showing details of tip and base. At the tip are numerous small barbs which when the quill penetrates skin or flesh keep it from being pulled out; at the base is the slender and weak connection which makes for ready separation of the quill from the skin of the Porcupine.

The porcupine's chief claim to attention lies in its covering of sharp-pointed hollow quills which are especially developed on its back and tail. These quills are specialized or modified growths which supplant some of the underfur normally present on a mammal's body. (See fig. 26.) Individually, a quill consists of a hollow tube, closed at both ends, about $\frac{1}{16}$ to $\frac{1}{8}$ inch in diameter and 1 to 3 inches in length. The tip is supplied with a great number of backward-projecting small barbs which upon touching the flesh of another animal instantly engage and hold fast. The bases of the quills are constricted and are weakly held in the porcupine's skin so that they become detached readily when the barbs are imbedded in some victim.

When a porcupine expects attack from another animal it draws its head down, and erects the quills of its back; if the enemy approaches too closely, it also sweeps the tail quickly to one side or the other. This is sufficient warning for most animals, but certain species, and particularly young and inexperienced individuals of those species, do venture to attack porcupines. Often the attacker receives a load of quills for his pains. We have seen a coyote with jaws and feet literally filled with the barbed quills of a porcupine. Occasionally wildcats are found with porcupine quills imbedded in their flesh, particularly about the head and forelegs. Local information is rather scant as to the exact measure of success attained by those species which prey or attempt to prey upon the porcupine.

The Yellow-haired Porcupine is a bark feeder, that is, it subsists on the soft growing tissues (cambium) found at the junction of the inner bark and outermost wood in a growing tree. Its preferred food tree in the Yosemite region is the lodgepole pine, probably because least effort is required to obtain the cambium in that thin-barked tree. This sort of food is available at all seasons of the year and the porcupine therefore has no need to lay up a food supply nor to hibernate, or migrate, as do many of the other herbivorous mammals. The abundance of easily obtained food probably accounts in large measure for the porcupine's sedentary nature. At several points in the Yosemite region we saw trees whose condition indicated that a porcupine had wintered in a very restricted area, and had probably spent many days in each one of the few trees which had been peeled. To get at its food the porcupine shells or scales off the outer bark and then actively gnaws off the tender growing tissue.

A most favorable locality in which to study the work of this animal is the place on the Tioga Road called Porcupine Flat. The territory comprising Porcupine Flat was once occupied by one or more glaciers, and the terminal moraine of one small glacier forms a lake there. This glaciation cleared the surface down to bedrock. Since the glaciers have disappeared only a small amount of soil has accumulated on the surface of the rock. All the trees are therefore shallow rooted and may be easily struck down by storms. The trees newly prostrated provide easily accessible food for the porcupines.

Porcupine Flat is well named, to judge from the amount of the porcupine work which we saw there. The forest on parts of the nearly level floor is purely of lodgepole pine ranging from well spaced trees as much as 3 feet in diameter down to small saplings in dense groves of an acre or so in extent. There was, in June, 1915, much fallen timber, including scores of trees which had been downed the preceding winter or possibly within three months, for much of the foliage was still green. These trees showed that the porcupines had been very busy; they bore marks of incisor teeth on trunks, on large branches, and even on twigs down to half an inch in diameter. (See pl. 37a.) These gnawed places were all 'bleeding' much pitch at the time of our visit. Evidently, for years, the porcupines had regularly taken advantage of these local circumstances, and so avoided the necessity of climbing trees, for other downed trees in various stages of decay indicated that some trees had probably fallen in the storms of each year. Only one standing tree was seen upon which recent work had been done.

An intensive study of the work of the porcupines on one particular tree developed the following facts and inferences. The peelings were confined to the upper, younger half of the tree; the bark there is thinner, and there are fewer rough outer layers; hence the porcupine was able more easily to get at the nutritious parts. The gnawings were further restricted to the sides of such branches as could be reached from some convenient resting place—the ground, or another branch, or a log. The tooth marks were all vertical; if a branch was resting in a horizontal position, the pairs of grooves marking the paths cut by the incisor teeth would cross the grain, and then the bark and outer wood for a distance of from 1 to 4 inches along the grain would be stripped off. Each incisor tooth (in this particular set of gnawings) cut a strip about ¼ inch (6 mm.) wide, and there were of course always two such strips side by side. One branch 9 inches in diameter had been peeled all around.

Ordinarily when working on a standing tree the porcupine makes use of branches or stubs as supports for its body while it gnaws off the bark. If the branches of a tree are so placed that the animal can work all around the tree at one level the tree will be girdled and so killed, unless one of the lower branches is able to take on the function of a new top. An interesting and rather unusual departure with respect to a feeding place was observed on a split tree at Tuolumne Meadows. The porcupine had climbed up by holding to the sides of the crevice and had gnawed off the bark on each side of the split.

The factor which keeps the number of porcupines within bounds is not obvious, but it does not seem to be that of food supply, so potent with most other animals. The lodgepole pine forest could to all appearances support a much larger population of these animals. Possibly the check is occasioned by those of the larger carnivores which remain in the mountains through the winter and, in dire necessity or otherwise, prey upon the slow-moving porcupine. The identity of these effective enemies has already been intimated (p. 153). To judge from the frequency with which we found the remains of porcupines, a good many individuals must come to grief in some way or another. A factor apparently figuring here, however, is the relative imperishableness of the quills; they withstand the usual processes of decay for a long time, much longer than the bones do. In some cases only a mat of quills was to be found, as if every other part of the animal had decayed or possibly been made away with by mice. After all, then, despite the frequent remains found, porcupines, as compared with most other rodents, probably enjoy an 'expectation' of long life.

Sierra Mountain Beaver. **Aplodontia rufa californica** (Peters)

Field characters.—Size of small Marmot, with general appearance of Meadow Mouse; tail so short as to appear to be wanting, shorter than hind foot; head blunt, eyes and ears small (pl. 31a). Head and body 11 to 14 inches (280–354 mm.), tail ¾ to 1⅗ inches (19–40 mm.), hind foot 2⅙ to 2½ inches (55–63 mm.), ear from crown ½ to ⅘ inch (13–21 mm.); weight 30 to 48 ounces (852–1375 grams). General coloration everywhere plain blackish brown. *Workings:* Underground burrows or tunnels about 6 to 7 inches in diameter with numerous openings to surface; located usually along brush-covered banks of swift-flowing streams.

Occurrence.—Resident locally in small numbers in Canadian and Hudsonian zones on west slope of Sierra Nevada. Recorded at Aspen Valley, Gentrys, Chinquapin, near Ostrander Rocks, in both forks of Indian Cañon (above Yosemite Valley), near Porcupine Flat, and in head of Lyell Cañon. Altitudinal range, 5800 to 10,000 feet. Lives along swift-flowing streams bordered by willow and creek dogwood. Colonial; nocturnal.

One of the most interesting and at the same time reclusive members of the Yosemite fauna is the Mountain Beaver or Aplodontia. This animal, like the redwood tree and the wren-tit, is peculiar to the west coast of North America, where it occurs scatteringly in the Sierras and northern coast ranges. Although called Mountain Beaver it is in nowise related by structure or mode of life to the true beaver save that both are rodents. The present species has, indeed, no close living relatives anywhere so far as known. Locally we found that some of the workmen on road gangs who knew of the animals called them 'mush-rats' because of their general resemblance to the muskrat. The latter animal does not, to the best of our knowledge, occur anywhere in the Yosemite region.

The Sierra Mountain Beaver is of the size of a small marmot. If one can imagine a meadow mouse grown to fifteen or twenty times its ordinary size, and practically without any tail, one will have a good idea of the mountain beaver. (See pl. 31a.) The animal is of stout build, has a short blunt head, small eyes, small nearly naked ears, no obvious neck, a thick body, normal legs and feet, and a mere stub of a tail. The tail is less than the hind foot in length, and in this character the animal is unlike all local small mammals except the rabbits and the cony. The body is covered evenly with a uniform blackish brown pelage of considerable length and of soft texture.

Aplodontia is a timid, retiring animal, practically never seen except when trapped. Its activity is confined to the night-time, and it spends the day in underground retreats. When in captivity the least injury seems sufficient to cause its death; its general resistance seems extremely low. When kept as a captive it may be tamed rapidly, and even at the first its only indication of displeasure is a rapid chattering or grinding with its teeth.

Only once, in our rather extended and intensive work in the habitat of Aplodontia, did any of our party happen to see one of the animals abroad. On the evening of June 23, 1915, at 7:05 P.M., one was seen running along the bank of the creek in Indian Cañon (northeast of Yosemite Falls). It moved very rapidly, at perhaps 5 feet a second, and its gait was like the lumbering gallop of a bear. At our Lyell Cañon camp a month later a specimen of Aplodontia was trapped alive and kept for a while in camp (pl. 31*a*).

The manner of life of the mountain beaver is, like its general appearance, suggestive of that of the meadow mouse. It frequents, almost without exception, the near vicinity of streams. When the naturalist goes in search of Aplodontia he seeks creek banks bordered by good growths of willow, creek dogwood, and other riparian shrubs and herbs. On the stems of these, marks of gnawings will be in evidence if the animals are present. Also burrows or tunnels in the ground will be found often within but a yard or so of water. These tunnels, like those of meadow mice, are, in general, parallel with the surface of the ground, and have rather frequent openings to the surface. (See fig. 31*b*.) Within these burrows the animals make their nests, in which they remain during the daytime and within which their young are reared.

At Chinquapin a series of Aplodontia workings was laid open and mapped by one of our party on June 21, 1915. The tunnels ran partly through rocky ground and partly through humous soil. Close by was the north fork of Indian Creek in which the stream of water was about 2 feet wide and 3 to 6 inches deep. Water was also running through one of the tunnels. The tunnel system, for the most part, was in the bank, about 3 feet above the level of the stream. The tunnels averaged between 6 and 7 inches (160 mm.) in diameter, the entrances being slightly larger. No nest was found in the series of tunnels opened, but examination of tunnel systems elsewhere has shown the presence of underground nests, so it may be presumed that the animals which made this particular excavation had their nest in some other burrow. The floor of the tunnel system is usually well packed as a result of constant use and is kept clear of débris of every sort so long as the place is occupied by the animals. The set of tunnels at Chinquapin yielded 2 animals, a male and a female, in the several days of trapping prior to the time when the system was dug out.

Another colony was noted along the East Fork of Indian Cañon (above Yosemite Valley). Here the workings occupied, in 1915, practically all available locations from the crossing of the trail to North Dome northward to the headwaters of the creek. In one place, even during June, the creek practically disappeared from view so great was the amount of water running through the tunnels. Other colonies were found on creeks near

Porcupine Flat; and finally a colony of Aplodontia was discovered at an altitude of 10,000 feet on the slope of Kuna Crest in the head of Lyell Cañon. (See fig. 21.) The lowest record, altitudinally, was made at Gentrys, 5800 feet, where, in the fall of 1915, tunnels were found in fair numbers though none of the animals was obtained.

The 'colonies,' or at least the series of workings so called, are in many cases of considerable extent. In one place an area estimated at 50 by 100 yards was occupied; other colonies were of somewhat less extent. The number of holes in a colony is large, 20 to 30 being noted in one locality on Snow Creek. The population in any one limited series of burrows consists usually of not more than two adults, comprising a pair. If these are trapped out, several days intervene before animals from neighboring burrows move in, to occupy the deserted ones.

The colonies are in most cases fairly well sheltered from view by the vegetational cover of the stream banks. But in early spring, just after the snow has melted off and before the willows and dogwood are leaved out, the burrow openings may be readily seen.

Aplodontia seems to be active, even at the higher levels, throughout the year. There are no data to indicate that the animals hibernate, while much circumstantial evidence points toward regular active life throughout the winter season. In many places we saw willow branches and small coniferous trees which showed signs of beaver activity as high as 5 feet above the ground. This animal is not known to climb to any extent, so the conclusion seems justified that it comes up through the snow, even out on the surface of the snow, and nibbles at the twigs then within easy reach. Along the west fork of Indian Cañon (above Yosemite Falls) a quantity of 'hay' was observed, consisting of a narrow-leaved lupine (*Lupinus longipes*) which had been cut green and piled and cured on dry masses of drift material. This 'hay' when seen on October 30, 1915, was nearly dry. In each pile the butt ends of the stems usually lay in one direction, toward the entrance of the adjacent burrow. Whether this material was for winter food, as with the cony, or for a dry and warm winter nest below-ground, was not ascertainable.

Aplodontia feeds upon most of the plants growing in the vicinity of its burrows. At Chinquapin the following plants gave evidence of being used by the animals: Azalea (*Rhododendron occidentale*), the commonest plant and used very much; hazel, common but little used; Sierran currant (*Ribes nevadense*), common, and many cuttings seen; creek dogwood (*Cornus pubescens*), common, many cuttings; wild cherry, fairly common, a few cut twigs seen; snow-bush (*Ceanothus cordulatus*), abundant at edges of thickets and occasionally used; chinquapin, abundant at edges of inhabited thickets and much used in places; incense cedar, few young trees much used; white fir, many young trees, but rarely used; sugar pine, young trees common but only occasionally used; brake fern (*Pteris aquilina*), fairly common, used slightly.

From the azalea, snow-bush, hazel, and cherry, sticks ¼ inch in diameter and 6 to 8 inches long were cut; the pines and cedars had the smaller twigs pruned off. One azalea stem 1½ inches in diameter had been cut through but had not been carried away. Chinquapin stems which were taken had the leaves still in place.

Elsewhere in the region still other plants showed signs of having been used as food. In one place young aspens had been eaten; and Labrador tea (*Ledum glandulosum*) and another currant (*Ribes viscosissimum*) had been cut by the animals. In one instance a 'whole bush' of creek dogwood had been cut off at about 18 inches above the ground.

Although living in a damp environment, in some places where it must of necessity enter the water at times, there is no evidence that Aplodontia does so by preference. It is not nearly so aquatic in habits as the muskrat or the true beaver. When the fur of Aplodontia is touched by water it wets about as readily as that of other less aquatic animals.

The breeding season of Aplodontia seems to occupy the summer months. Females containing embryos are very seldom taken. We did not secure a single one in the Yosemite region. A quarter-grown youngster weighing about 6 ounces (182 grams) was trapped in Lyell Cañon, July 20, 1915.

Other animals frequent Aplodontia burrows to some extent. Several Sierra Chickarees were caught in traps set in Aplodontia burrows and well out of view from above. One Mountain Weasel was taken in a similar setting. The contrast in vitality between these animals and Aplodontia is marked. Aplodontia even when held lightly by the trap was usually dead when found. The squirrels and weasels had survived, doubtless for several hours.

SOUTHERN SIERRA MARMOT. Marmota flaviventer sierrae Howell

Field characters.—Body size about that of small badger; body stout; legs and tail short. Head and body 14½ to 18¼ inches (370–464 mm.), tail 5⅛ to 8 inches (130–200 mm.), hind foot 2¾ to 3⅓ inches (70–84 mm.), ear from crown ⅔ to 1 inch (15–24 mm.); weight 4⅓ to 7 pounds (1.94 to 3.2 kilograms). General coloration yellowish brown grizzled or 'ticked' above with white; chest and feet dull yellow; a yellowish area on side of neck; muzzle blackish, with narrow whitish cross-band just in front of eye. (See pl. 32a.) Movements generally deliberate. *Workings:* Burrows in ground about 5 to 6 inches in diameter, beneath large boulders or at bases of trees or logs. *Droppings:* Dark brown or black, ⅜ to ½ inch in diameter, elongate, pointed at one end; scattered abundantly about burrows and on nearby flat-topped rocks. *Voice:* A single loud sharp whistle, *sirk;* sometimes repeated.

Upper: Sierra Golden-mantled Ground Squirrel and Belding Ground Squirrel.
Lower: Southern Sierra Marmot.

Occurrence.—Common resident, chiefly in Hudsonian Zone. Recorded from near Porcupine Flat and near Merced Lake eastward to Leevining Creek and to Silver Lake. Altitudinal range 7500 to 11,500 feet. Inhabits meadowland, especially where adjoined by rock slides or large boulders which afford protection for burrows. Solitary. Diurnal.

The largest member of the squirrel tribe in the Yosemite region is the Sierra Marmot which inhabits the high Sierras between altitudes of 7500 and 11,500 feet. It is a ground and rock dwelling species, several times the size of the California Ground Squirrel. Besides the name marmot this animal is often called woodchuck and ground hog. The latter name is not altogether inappropriate, as it suggests the terrestrial habitat of the animal and also its stout body and rather heavy gait. The marmot is a species likely to be seen by any visitor to the higher parts of the region, as it is, like the ground squirrels, abroad during the daylight hours throughout the summer season.

In general demeanor the Southern Sierra Marmot is a lazy appearing animal. When not feeding, it spends much of its time sprawled out in the sunshine. If a person approaches a resting marmot on its rock the animal 'comes to attention' by 'gathering' its feet so that it may, if necessary, move off quickly. At the same time it gives its sharp whistle, which may be taken up and repeated by other marmots in the vicinity. If the person is not in clear view the marmot will sometimes stand up on its hind legs, after the manner of a 'picket-pin.' Then it may utter its whistle several times. If frightened enough to cause it to go below-ground, the animal usually does not appear again for some time. With a marmot that is foraging out in a meadow its first action, on the advent of danger, real or supposed, is to run for its burrow. Like a ground squirrel it usually takes further account of circumstances at a point just short of the entrance, before proceeding farther. When undisturbed a marmot moves at a slow walk. But when frightened it 'gallops,' bear-like, at about the rate that a man can run over the uneven surface of a mountain meadow.

The marmot and badger are sometimes confounded by the casual observer. They are of the same general size, with rather stout bodies and short legs and tails, and both are ground dwellers. But here the resemblance ends. The marmot has a face which is marked chiefly with yellow and brown (pl. 2); that of the badger is conspicuously black and white (pl. 24); the marmot has no white streak over the head while the badger has such a mark. The badger travels steadily, with its body very low and close to the ground; the marmot, especially when excited, gallops along, with undulatory movements of the body. The marmot is strictly vegetarian in diet, whereas the badger is a hunter and subsists upon flesh. The burrow of the marmot is usually under some rock or tree; whereas the badger as a rule sinks its burrow in wholly open ground.

The marmot population of the Yosemite region is to be found chiefly in the Hudsonian Zone and there most commonly about the larger meadows such as Tuolumne Meadows and the floor of Lyell Cañon. The species does, however, in places push down into the upper part of the Canadian Zone, and is found, for example, adjacent to Merced Lake and near Porcupine Flat. In these places, the lower limits of its range, it is but sparsely represented. On the east slope only a few individuals were observed by us below the hemlock belt (Hudsonian Zone). Two individuals taken at Silver Lake in 1916 were objects of marvel to the residents of Mono Valley, who declared that they had not previously seen the species there. The only other low record was of an individual observed in a big rock talus near some chinquapin brush on the Tioga Road in Leevining Creek Cañon at 8500 feet. One of the residents of Yosemite Valley, in 1914, told a member of our party that he had once seen a 'ground hog' in the pile of rock débris below Royal Arches on the floor of the Valley. On some of the main peaks of the Sierran crest, such as Dana and Conness, marmot droppings were found well above timber line, at 11,500 feet altitude. The highest point at which a marmot was actually seen by any member of our party was at 11,000 feet in the head of Lyell Cañon. At least three were heard at 11,500 feet on Parsons Peak.

The Sierra Marmot, like other ground dwelling squirrels, digs a burrow. This it uses as a retreat when seeking escape from enemies, as a place to spend the summer nights, and as a den in which to pass the long hibernating sleep of winter. In the choice of location, the escape from pursuit seems to be the most important consideration, for the marmot so locates its burrow that any enemy too large to enter the tunnel, for example, a coyote, could only with extreme difficulty get at the marmot in its underground retreat. Adjacence to a supply of food, and safety from flooding at the time of the spring thaw, probably also play a part in the choice of site, though these factors are not always apparent. Many of the local marmots have their headquarters in rock slides where the factor of safety is adequately met. (See pl. 32*a*.) How far down within the shelter of these heaps of talus rocks the animals go to place their nests we do not know, as the exploration of rock slides is a thing yet to be accomplished by a naturalist. Other members of the local marmot population have their burrows under large granite boulders in meadowland or at the bases of large trees. In either situation an enemy would have great difficulty in digging out the inhabitant. The burrows in meadows are usually on mounds where the water from melting snow would not be likely to flow into the burrow. The diameter of the burrow is usually about 5 or 6 inches.

Those marmots which live in or along the margins of meadows have a source of food supply close at hand, for this species is more of a grass feeder than are the other members of the squirrel family. But individuals inhabiting the rock slides must either depend, in company with the Bushy-tailed Wood Rat and the Yosemite Cony, upon the plant growths, such as the red elder-berry, which occur among the rocks, or else venture out some distance to vegetation growing in the open.

A feature yet to be mentioned for the majority of marmot burrows is the presence close by, of a flat-topped rock on which the animal can sprawl out to bask in the sunshine, while at the same time keeping watch for the approach of enemies. Specially chosen rocks, used for the same purpose, are to be seen in the case of marmots which live in rock slides. On many of these rocks are large accumulations of droppings indicating occupancy through several successive seasons. (See pl. 32b.) Likewise the smooth worn condition of many of the burrows, the absence of accumulations of earth about the entrances, and the lack of grasses and other plants there, all suggest that those locations have been in use for a number of years.

The food of the marmot consists of green vegetation including various herbaceous plants and grasses. The animal possesses no internal cheek pouches as do the ground squirrels and it is not known to store up a supply of food for winter use as does the cony. The lesser nutritive value of grasses as compared with seeds (used extensively by the squirrels) requires the marmot to take relatively large quantities of the former—and this it does, day after day, throughout the summer season. When the marmots emerge in the spring they are quite lean. As soon as green vegetation is available they feed to repletion, spending the daylight hours between successive feedings simply resting. This process results in a rapid accumulation of fat, which fills every space in the body and lies in great layers between the skin and muscle. This fat serves a double purpose; during the hibernating period it acts as an insulating layer to conserve bodily heat and also as fuel to maintain the life processes which are carried on, though at a lowered rate, during the period of dormancy.

The behavior of the species is indicated by the following account, written in the field after one of us had been watching a marmot for a half-hour or more at the head of Lyell Cañon one day in mid-July (the 20th, 1915).

The animal when first sighted had been feeding in meadow grass, but it took fright at my approach and ran to the shelter of a rock pile. By moving slowly, I was able eventually to get within 15 feet of it and to take several pictures. The animal would move out on some flat-topped rock, remain there for a time with occasional slight changes of posture, and then disappear into the slide, to reappear soon at another similar location. Certain rocks seemed to be used as regular resting places, for the Marmot seemed inclined to stay about these. Often, although not always, the post taken was a slanting rock from which the animal could quickly tumble down into the interstices of the slide at the first intimation of danger. Once, for a short time, it reared up on its hind legs, using the tail to help support the body. Several times the Marmot uttered its sharp whistle, both when out in plain sight and when concealed from view amid the rocks of the talus heap. During the time that this marmot was under observation a Belding Ground Squirrel in the adjacent meadow was uttering its shrill alarm note, and this may have stimulated the Marmot to give its own note.

The seasonal activity of the Sierra Marmot extends from early spring until autumn. The date of first emergence is not known, as few if any people are in the high country early enough in the year to take note of such phenomena. Our own earliest date, June 28, merely indicates our first day within the range of the species. Breeding must take place early in the spring, as young animals, large enough to appear above ground, were trapped on July 10 (1915). Through the summer season the marmots are out every day, but as autumn draws near they are less in evidence, and soon all of them enter the long winter sleep. Our latest record is of a single individual observed near Ten Lakes on October 11 (1915). In late September but few were to be seen on Tuolumne Meadows where earlier in the year the species was common.

Little information is available concerning the home life of the marmot. The young are one-fourth to one-half grown by the middle of July and are then to be seen about the entrances of their home burrows. They probably attain sufficient size during the first season of their lives so that they can go forth before winter and dig their own burrows.

CALIFORNIA GROUND SQUIRREL. **Citellus beecheyi beecheyi** (Richardson)

Field characters.—Size medium for a squirrel (body length about 10 inches), tail long (about 7 inches) and haired at sides, but not so bushy as in tree squirrels; ear short, not tufted. Measurements: Head and body 9⅛ to 10¾ inches (232–273 mm.), tail 6⅓ to 7⅔ inches (161–194 mm.), hind foot 2 to 2⅜ inches (53–60 mm.), ear (from crown) ⅘ to 1 inch (21–27 mm.); weight 15⅝ to 25½ ounces (443–720 grams). General body color dull yellowish brown in effect; triangular area on each side of neck and shoulders, grizzled white; narrow area on fore part of back between whitish shoulder patches, dark brown. *Voice:* A sharp metallic alarm note or whistle, *clink*, usually uttered singly at varying intervals, but, when the squirrel is badly frightened, given two or more times in rapid succession. *Workings:* Burrows in ground, entrance holes about 4½ inches in diameter; also runways, about 3 inches wide, through grass.

Occurrence.—Resident on west side of Sierra Nevada from plains of San Joaquin Valley up to middle altitudes in the mountains (highest record, 8200 feet, east of Merced Lake); observed on east slope of Sierras, at about 8000 feet altitude in Leevining Creek cañon, and locally in vicinity of Mono Lake Post Office. Most abundant on plains and in foothill country (Lower and Upper Sonoran zones), less numerous in the yellow pine belt (Transition Zone), and but sparingly represented in the Jeffrey pine belt (Canadian Zone). Frequents plains, small meadows, tree-covered hillsides, and rocky outcrops or granite taluses; commonest in open situations.

The California Ground Squirrel is probably known by sight to more residents of California than is any other one species of mammal, and it is also the one which most often excites the interest and attention of visitors from other states, because of its different appearance from that of prairie dogs and other squirrel-like animals of the more eastern parts of North America. It is to be seen in numbers from the windows of trains passing through the San Joaquin Valley, and is occasionally observed along the railroad in the Merced Cañon; while along all of the auto roads from the west leading into the Yosemite National Park it compels attention at almost every turn. Here individuals are prone to dash across the road almost under the wheels, uttering their startled cries and stirring up small clouds of dust to mark their precipitate rout. To the residents of the Sierran foothills this species is known as 'digger squirrel' in recognition of its propensity for burrowing and to distinguish it from the 'tree' squirrels, Gray and Red, which inhabit the middle and higher altitudes in the mountains.

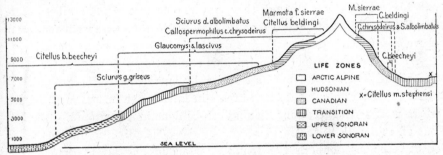

Fig. 27.   Cross-section of the Sierra Nevada through the Yosemite region showing general zonal and altitudinal distribution of Squirrels and Marmot.

The California Ground Squirrel is distinguished from the Gray and Red squirrels by the presence of whitish shoulder patches, by a less bushy tail, and by ground-dwelling habits; from the Belding Ground Squirrel by larger size, and by much longer and broader tail, which undulates as the animal runs along the ground; from the Golden-mantled Ground Squirrel and the species of chipmunks, by larger size and by the absence of stripes of contrasted bright color along the sides of the body.

The California Ground Squirrel is most abundant on the plains of the San Joaquin Valley and in the adjacent foothills, in the Lower and Upper Sonoran zones; it is less numerous in the Transition Zone and but sparingly represented in the Canadian. The highest altitude at which we observed it was 8200 feet, a few miles east of Merced Lake. The California Ground Squirrel shares the Canadian Zone with the Golden-mantled Ground Squirrel, which fact may account in some degree for the lessened numbers of the former in that high zone. (See fig. 27.) Above, in the Hudsonian Zone, the meadowlands are inhabited exclusively by the Belding Ground Squirrel, while about rock slides and on the hillsides only the Golden-mantled is to be found. On the east slope of the mountains the California

Ground Squirrel is present, but in very small numbers; a single individual was seen September 23, 1915, at 8000 feet altitude in Leevining Creek cañon, and a few were found in the vicinity of Mono Lake Post Office in May and July, 1916. On parts of the Great Basin plains beyond, its place is wholly taken by a small round-tailed species, the Stephens Ground Squirrel.

Over its entire range the California Ground Squirrel is resident throughout the year. Those individuals which live above the snow line in the mountains hibernate for considerable periods during the winter months. In Yosemite Valley, ground squirrels in 1920 were first seen out of their burrows about the middle of March, according to Mr. Forest S. Townsley. One exceptional individual was seen out by one of us, on the Big Oak Flat Road below Gentrys, on December 28, 1914. Those squirrels living at still lower levels, even though they may not go into regular hibernation, are still much less active in the winter season, when they are wont to appear above ground only during the mid-day hours of warm, sunny days.

As its common name indicates, this squirrel secures shelter for itself and young, and safety from its enemies, by burrowing in the ground. It seems to prefer to excavate its retreats in hillsides or in low earth banks, where most of the necessary digging can be done in a horizontal direction. But of course those members of the species which live on the plains or on flats or meadows in the foothills or mountains must perforce dig down vertically for considerable distances to gain the requisite protection. Most of the work of tunnel excavation is carried on during the spring months, as is shown by the mounds of fresh, soft earth accumulated at the mouths of the burrows in that season. In the lowlands, where there is a large crop of wild oats in the springtime, this newly excavated earth supports a ranker growth than do the surrounding parts of the field, so that, as one of our party wrote in his field notes, "the plain looks like a cemetery overgrown with grass," with these taller stands of oats about the squirrel holes suggesting grave mounds. To some extent the ground squirrels, like the pocket gophers, thus serve as natural cultivators of the soil. Many of the squirrels which live in the granite country make their homes under large boulders or in rock taluses, where a minimum of burrowing is necessary to ensure safe retreats. This is notably the case in Yosemite Valley.

It is likely that the squirrels construct new burrows from time to time, or, what is even more probable, that each young individual as it comes to maturity and is weaned from its mother leaves the parent burrow and digs a home for itself. In any event, in places, there are many more burrows than individual squirrels present at one time. These tunnels, especially in the plains and foothill country, are joined together below-ground to a greater or less degree, as indicated by the fact that when hurriedly seeking safety squirrels will pitch down into any one of a number of holes in the vicinity of the one about which they were first seen, to reappear later somewhere else. Also, squirrel exterminators, when using gases or smoke in their work, find it necessary to stop up a number of holes adjacent to the one into which they introduce the fumes in order to force them into the lower reaches of the tunnels.

The burrows of the squirrels are often inhabited by species of animals other than the rightful owners. The so-called Burrowing Owls habitually make their homes in squirrel holes, probably deserted ones; and, to a less extent, the holes are frequented by California Toads, Western Gopher Snakes, and Pacific Rattlesnakes. It is likely that the presence of the latter two animals is not particularly congenial to the squirrels, as both of these snakes are known to eat ground squirrels when chance offers.

The burrowing activities of the California Ground Squirrel constitute a matter of considerable economic importance. The Yosemite Valley Railroad Company has found it necessary to reduce the numbers of the ground squirrels along its right of way through the lowlands; for the burrows of the animals weaken the grade embankments and, especially in wet weather, cause them to give way. The company has learned that the results obtained by their anti-squirrel campaigns fully justified the expenditure entailed. Also, ranchers in the irrigated districts near Snelling patrol their ditches so as to discover and promptly plug up any and all squirrel burrows made in the banks, thereby preventing breaks, with consequent loss of the precious water.

Some years ago it was discovered that the ground squirrels in California were harboring fleas which carried the bacillus of bubonic plague. A vigorous campaign of extermination was waged against the animals and they were practically eliminated from many extensive areas. As soon as the efforts against the squirrels were relaxed, however, they began to 'spill in' from adjacent areas until now in most places they are as numerous as ever.

Ranchers living in the mountains find difficulty in keeping their meadowlands rid of squirrels. Mr. W. H. McCarthy, whose ranch is 3 miles east of Coulterville, told us that a regular patrol was necessary to keep his fields even approximately free. On the floor of Yosemite Valley attempts at poisoning ground squirrels have been made at various times during the past decade, but no appreciable diminution in their population was observable as a result of this work. In May, 1919, the squirrel population of the Valley appeared to be the largest of any of the years for which we have record.

Afield, the observer often comes upon ground squirrels which are some distance from their holes. Such animals usually run to the near vicinity of their burrows where they sit upright and can watch the intruder, yet be in readiness to dart down into their holes at an instant's warning. While thus on watch they utter, at short intervals, a rather musical whistled note, *clink*. If the farther advance of the observer seems to portend danger to them they utter a double note, *clink, clink,* sometimes with a sort of chuckle added, and then drop down into the shelter of their subterranean retreats. Ordinarily when thus frightened down, they do not reappear at the surface of the ground for some time, as if to give the suspected enemy plenty of chance to tire of his waiting and to depart. Occasionally, however, a squirrel will crouch motionless almost at the feet of the observer, as if to escape detection by remaining quiet. Extreme fear may be a part of the basis for this manner of behavior.

Ground squirrels, in traveling between their holes and their feeding grounds, frequently traverse the same courses until regular trails are worn through the grass. This is seen particularly well on the rolling lands between Merced and Snelling, where, in the fall, when the grass and weeds are dry, the trails show from a distance very distinctly. In the spring, when the new growth is just appearing, the trails are still conspicuous, as the vegetation is slower in starting there than in the adjacent unbeaten tracts. Soon, however, the trails are entirely obliterated, save as the animals renew them by further use.

It seems likely that ground squirrels can, if necessity demands, go without water for long periods of time, if not indefinitely. Many of the plains-dwelling individuals of this species are so situated that it is impossible for them to get any water except such as may accumulate in small surface depressions or in parts of their burrows for brief periods during the rainy season. As a substitute for bathing in water these animals take dust baths in the soft earth of fields and country roads. We have frequently come upon places where tracks and marks in the dust showed that squirrels had been 'dusting' themselves. This habit may afford partial relief from the many fleas and mites with which they are often afflicted.

Ground squirrels, like chipmunks, are provided with inner cheek pouches which are used while gathering and transporting food. Often when the animals are scared out of bushes or trees, or away from some supply of roots or bulbs which they have discovered, their cheeks are seen to be bulging with the contents of these pouches. They are able to use their teeth even when these pouches are widely distended.

Ground squirrels are chiefly terrestrial in their forage habits, taking whatever may offer in the way of seeds, grasses, fruits, low-growing annual plants, roots, and especially bulbs like those of the common brodiaea. The animals do leave the ground, however, and ascend shrubs and low trees for especially desirable provender. In Yosemite Valley, Mrs. Joseph Grinnell reports that ground squirrels were gathering the green fruits from the top of a 4-foot manzanita bush. At Pleasant Valley we occasionally saw them in low oaks, evidently after acorns; and at El Portal one squirrel was found with three of the large acorns of the Golden Oak, two in one cheek pouch and one in the other. At Snelling, in January, they were eating the coarse fruits of the osage orange, which abounds there as a hedgerow plant; torn remnants of these fruits were scattered about the entrances of the burrows. But the ground squirrel is not entirely restricted to a vegetable diet, as is shown by the fact that it is regularly captured in meat-baited traps set for skunks and other carnivorous animals.

Mr. E. W. Baker, formerly resident in Yosemite Valley, has told us that the ground squirrels about Yosemite Village would, in the fall, come and fill their cheek pouches with acorns and then go off and store them in some safe place for the winter or spring when food would be scarce. He says that the present species, like the gray squirrel, is not averse to stealing young birds. He has seen a California Ground Squirrel carry off a young Western Robin, and he has received report of their capturing young chickens in yards on the floor of the Valley. Numerous visitors to the Valley during the summer months establish feeding tables to attract the birds about their camps, and many of these persons find that ground squirrels give more or less trouble. At first exceedingly shy, the squirrels soon become bold and eventually have to be driven away in order that the birds may have the benefit of the proffered food.

In the lowlands the majority of the young ground squirrels are born in April and May, and by the middle of May some are beginning to appear with their mothers, playing about the mouths of the burrows; but in the higher altitudes the young are born later. Two half-grown young were seen on May 17, 1919, in Yosemite Valley, but in other years some of the females in the Transition Zone and lower part of the Canadian Zone had not yet given birth to their young by the first week in June. 'Spring' in the lowlands comes in April and early May, while the 'spring' of the higher altitudes does not occur until late June or July. Hence the young do appear at the same *season*, considering the differences in temperature conditions at the different elevations.

The annual molt takes place in mid-summer. With the advent of the new pelage, the white areas on the sides of the head and neck become more conspicuous and the pepper-and-salt effect resulting from the banded coloration of the individual hairs is more in evidence. As time goes on the freshness of the coat is lost by wear against the sides of the burrow and in other ways. The brown overwash which the new pelage possesses loses its reddish cast, and the hair becomes yellowish or grayish brown in appearance. There is thus some variation in the tones of coloration shown by squirrels of this species at different times of the year, irrespective of molt.

BELDING GROUND SQUIRREL. Citellus beldingi (Merriam)

Field characters.—Body size about that of House Rat; tail sparsely haired at sides, and short, decidedly less than half length of head and body; ears small and round, not pointed or tufted. (See pl. 2.) Head and body 7 to 8½ inches (180–215 mm.), tail 2⅓ to 3 inches (60–74 mm.), hind foot about 1¾ inches (41–45 mm.), ear from crown ⅓ to ½ inch (8–13 mm.); weight 7¼ to 10¼ ounces (207–294 grams). General coloration light yellowish brown, paler on under surface of body; a broad area of bright reddish brown down middle of back. *Voice:* General warning call of 5 to 8 shrill short whistles, *seek*, in quick succession; females with young utter a single note, *e-chert'*, at intervals. *Workings:* Burrows in ground, surface openings about 2 inches in diameter.

Occurrence.—Common resident in higher and more easterly portions of Yosemite region, chiefly but not entirely in Hudsonian Zone. Recorded from near Porcupine Flat and from near Merced Lake eastward to Mono Lake Post Office and to Farrington ranch near Williams Butte. Ranges upward to 11,500 feet as on Parsons Peak, and higher yet on Conness Mountain. Inhabits chiefly grassland, occasionally rocky places, or floor of open forest. Diurnal.

The Belding Ground Squirrel is a hardy, ground-dwelling member of the squirrel family inhabiting the meadows and other grass-producing areas in the higher and more easterly portions of the Yosemite section. This species is often called 'picket-pin' because of the erect, stake-like posture which it assumes when on the lookout for danger (pl. 2). Some persons have referred to it as "spermophile" (seed eater). Both of these names have a measure of appropriateness not always to be found in vernacular names. This squirrel is named for Lyman Belding, the naturalist formerly resident in Stockton who collected the specimen from which the species was first scientifically described.

The range of the Belding Ground Squirrel begins on the west slope of the Sierras at about the lower margin of the Hudsonian Zone. The westernmost report of its occurrence is from the upper Yosemite Creek in a location west of Porcupine Flat and due north of the Yosemite village. The first specimens actually obtained by our party were collected about two miles east of Porcupine Flat. Merced Lake is the westernmost point of record for the southern part of the section, in the drainage of the upper Merced River. The maximum abundance of the species is to be found on the larger high mountain meadows, such as Tuolumne Meadows, in the heart of the Hudsonian Zone. (See pl. 18b.) While one of us was traversing the meadows in Tioga Pass on July 13, 1915, fully 100 of these squirrels were observed; and an equal number was counted about two weeks later while we were going along the floor of Lyell Cañon. The range of the species extends upward on the Sierran crest to well above timber line, for example, on Conness Mountain, Parsons Peak, and Parker Pass. On the east slope this squirrel is found down through the Canadian Zone (Jeffrey pines) even to the Farrington ranch near Williams Butte and to near Mono Lake Post Office, close to the shore of Mono Lake.

Meadows constitute the preferred habitat of this species, and by far the greater percentage of the animals are to be found in the grassland. But this environment is not absolutely essential to their welfare; for some of them live in rather rocky places and some in areas which bear a moderate stand of trees. In the latter two situations there is usually bunch grass in the neighborhood of the places inhabited by the squirrels. The limited patches of grass about many of the small glacial lakes often support small populations of the Belding Ground Squirrel.

This species is as strictly terrestrial as any ground squirrel of which we know. We have never seen one climb a tree or even a bush. Once one was seen on the top of a boulder about 3 feet in height. The Belding Squirrel is less given to clambering over rocks than the 'copperhead' or any of the chipmunks. Yet the present species, despite its habit of remaining on the ground surface, spies out its enemies, real or supposed, at fairly long distances and communicates at once with others of its kind in a way that puts all the individuals in the neighborhood on their guard.

When the traveler approaches a meadow and is still a hundred yards or more from the nearest Belding Squirrel, his ear is assailed by the alarm call of the animal, a series of shrill piping whistles, loud enough to be heard by any living creature within a quarter-mile radius. Usually there are 5 to 8 (rarely even 12) notes in rapid sequence. Other squirrels take up and repeat this calling so that on some occasions the rocky walls enclosing a meadow resound with their notes. This warning call is responded to according to the circumstances wherein the various individuals find themselves when the call is heard. Those out in the meadows usually at once run toward their burrows; others closer by, within a few yards of their homes, rise straight up on their haunches, with forelimbs pressed against the body. When an individual squirrel has assumed this position, it, too, utters the shrill whistled call. If its curiosity remains unsatisfied, as when its view of the approaching person is imperfect, the squirrel rises still farther until it is standing bolt upright on the soles of its hind feet. The call given then is apt to be of an even more penetrating quality than at first. If the person continues to approach, the squirrel drops to all fours and runs to the entrance of its burrow where sometimes it again assumes the 'picket-pin' position; but it more often remains hunched up on all fours, with its hind feet well under its body, ready to dart down the hole at an instant's further warning. Even when in the upright position at the mouth of the burrow the rapidity with which a squirrel can drop into its retreat is surprising. Once scared into the ground it stays only a short time, then pokes its head out again, to just below the level of its eyes.

When sitting erect and observing its surroundings a squirrel can often be seen to twitch its nose as if sniffing and drawing in the air. Probably it uses the sense of smell to aid its powers of sight and hearing.

On flat open land where grass is at best very short, the usual mode of progression for this squirrel is a heavy run, with little up and down movement of the body, and with the tail down. In high grass, instead of parting the stalks and running between them, the squirrel progresses by a series of jumps; each hop carries the animal up so that it can look about for some distance and be able to spy an approaching enemy.

Once a Belding Squirrel was come upon in a rocky place; the animal ran over some rocks and jumped over a creek which was fully 2 feet wide, in its effort to escape. Another, on Mount Hoffmann, ran along the face of a pinnacle of rock, clinging to small cracks in the surface.

The Belding Ground Squirrel subsists chiefly upon grass and grass seeds, and depends less upon the larger seeds, nuts, and roots such as are eaten by the California Ground Squirrel and the chipmunks. When feeding, the animal sits in a hunched-up position, the hind legs in entire support of the body. The forefeet, when grass is being eaten, are used to draw the grass stalks or heads toward the mouth where they can be cut off. Larger items are held in the forepaws, while small pieces are nibbled off with the front (incisor) teeth and rapidly ground up by the cheek teeth (molars). In a few instances Belding Squirrels were captured in meat-baited traps set for carnivores. Certain other members of the squirrel family seek flesh bait when available, but the present species seems to be more restricted in its food preferences to vegetable material. At the mule corral on Tuolumne Meadows in 1915 the 'picket-pins' were foraging around barley sacks, gleaning scattered grain like rats. Several Belding Squirrels were caught in steel traps set in the entrances to Marmot burrows, and one was captured in a Macabee gopher trap which had been set in a gopher burrow.

Each 'picket-pin' evidently restricts itself closely to use of its own particular burrow and does not, in time of danger, dart into whatever retreat happens to be nearest at hand. On Lyell Meadows one was repeatedly seen to run from the meadowland, where there were numerous holes, to a particular burrow in the granite gravel above the trail. Near the same place, one of our party suddenly came upon one of these squirrels, posted at 'observation,' within one foot of an open burrow. The squirrel, instead of darting into this nearest hole, ran to one fully 30 feet farther away.

The burrows are usually constructed right in the meadows which furnish the animals their food; less frequently they are dug in the rocky soil at the margins of the meadows. Those squirrels which live in the bunch-grass areas at or above timber line make their burrows, of necessity, in the granite soil. A typical meadowland burrow at Snow Flat was opened and studied by the authors on June 28, 1915. This burrow was close to the bank of a small creek, which meandered through the meadow, and was near a large granite boulder. The ground was heavily matted with grass roots to a depth of 1¾ inches (45 mm.) and all the tunnels had been excavated below this mat. The whole tunnel system was remarkably level, unlike those of the California Ground Squirrel in the lowlands; but this may have been conditioned by the nearness of the creek and of the water table. Two short, deeper tunnels which were found may have been prospects toward a deeper system which would have been excavated later in the season. There was melting snow about the meadow and the ground was quite wet on the date of our study, especially below the level of the tunnels laid open. The presence of this extreme amount of moisture may have acted to deter the squirrel from going any deeper.

The total length of all the tunnels in this system was 53.3 feet (16.25 meters) and the average tunnel diameter 2 inches (52 mm.). The total amount of earth excavated was therefore 2010 cubic inches—8.7 gallons of earth, or nearly enough to fill two 5-gallon oil cans. Yet there were no mounds of earth at the entrances to the burrow. The soil had either been pushed into the creek or else washed away by the summer rains and melting snow water.

This burrow system contained no well constructed nest; but in one place there was some grassy material, either the remains of an old nest or, more likely, the beginning of a new one. The inhabitant of this burrow was a female which would have given birth to young, within two weeks probably.

One burrow of this species was noted at the base of a lodgepole pine. In this case there was a mound of earth at the entrance.

The young of the Belding Ground Squirrel are born about the first of July, there being, so far as all our evidence shows, but one brood per year. Yet a pair was seen in what looked like a mating pursuit as late as July 13. The number of young was ascertained definitely in only one case, that of the female containing 5 embryos, at Snow Flat, June 28. A female obtained July 2 east of Porcupine Flat had evidently just given birth to 6 young. In females taken on July 8 and 21, 1915, the mammary glands were functional. The young, when they first appear above ground, are scarcely more than one-third grown. The first young were noted in 1915 on July 25. But near Williams Butte three young only a third grown were seen on June 28 (1916). At the end of July (27–31) in 1915, in Lyell Cañon and on Tuolumne Meadows, young were out at the mouths of burrows in numbers, usually in groups of five and six. At Tenaya Lake on July 29 the young animals seen were larger than those at the higher stations. It is therefore probable that the young are born earlier at the lower altitudes than at the higher levels. The record at Williams Butte goes to substantiate this belief. Full size is not attained for some weeks; young weighing scarcely more than half as much as adults were taken at Merced Lake August 31 and in Tioga Pass September 25, 1915.

As early as July 26 small new burrows with mounds of earth at the entrances were beginning to appear on Tuolumne Meadows. These were evidently made by young which had been turned out of the parental burrows to shift for themselves.

When the young first go above ground they frisk about the entrance to the burrow under the watchful eye of the female parent. In Lyell Cañon on July 25, 1915, one of us came upon a single young animal running in and about some rock crevices adjacent to the burrow at the side of the meadow. The mother was standing guard, uttering her note, *e-chert'*, every few seconds. The observer 'squeaked,' whereupon the parent squirrel at once rose upon her hind feet in the picket-pin position and uttered the shrill piping warning call of the species; the youngster promptly ran into the burrow. The adult remained standing on her hind feet for 48 seconds, then sank down on her haunches.

A day or two later, another family group consisting of a female and 2 half-grown young, on Tuolumne Meadows, was studied at close range for some time.[14] At first the youngsters did not venture very far out of the hole; and when they did they remained on the far side of their mother. Later, they gained courage and came more into view, one being more venturesome than the other. The mother stood much of the time in the picket-pin position giving the *e-chert'* call. At each utterance her body was shrugged up, the head and shoulders thrown forward and the tail given an upward flip; much effort seemed to be put into the production of this note. In cases where families of 5 or 6 young were seen, they all sat close about the entrance of the burrow and when frightened all attempted to crowd into the hole at the same instant. One youngster, bewildered by some horses, ran directly at one of our party and then escaped into a shallow hole some distance from its home burrow.

The Belding Ground Squirrel escapes the rigors of the Sierran winter— when the temperature falls low and all the grasslands are blanketed in

---

[14] This was done by the method of direct approach. The observer garbed in dull brown-colored outing clothes, started about 100 feet away and advanced slowly in a *direct* line toward the squirrels. As he came closer his movements were made slower and slower so as not to startle the animals. Sidewise movement was avoided in every possible way. The squirrel, using monocular vision, was thus less able to appreciate his approach. This method is very useful in getting close to birds or mammals in order to study or photograph them.

snow—by hibernating. The exact duration of the hibernation period is not known. At the Farrington ranch, near Williams Butte, one of these squirrels was obtained on April 29, 1916. In many localities individuals are out before all the snow has disappeared, and in places they have been seen to run over snow banks. At the end of September many of the animals were still abroad in Tioga Pass and on Tuolumne Meadows, even after a slight snowfall. Our latest record is of an individual out at Ten Lakes on October 6, 1915.

The only direct evidence of enemies is a note that at Tuolumne Meadows a Mountain Weasel was seen killing one of these squirrels. The weasel had the squirrel by the back of the neck. The larger high-mountain carnivores probably also levy toll on the Belding Ground Squirrel whenever opportunity offers.

Stephens Soft-haired Ground Squirrel

Citellus mollis stephensi (Merriam)

Field characters.—Size near that of House Rat; ears small; tail short; pelage silky textured. Head and body 6½ inches (162 mm.), tail 2 inches (50 mm.), hind foot 1¼ inches (32 mm.), ear ⅙ inch (4 mm.) [measurements from extralimital specimens]. General coloration buffy gray above, silvery white on under surface; feet dull white; tail drab on upper surface, buffy below. *Workings:* Burrows in ground beneath bushes.

Occurrence.—Resident at extreme southeastern corner of Yosemite section, near Mono Mills. Lives on sandy ground beneath sagebrush.

The Stephens Soft-haired Ground Squirrel is a Great Basin type of rodent which reaches the extreme eastern margin of our Yosemite section in the dry sagebrush-covered, sandy area southeast of Mono Lake. Its presence there is established by two specimens which were captured on June 10 and 11, 1916. These two individuals are not quite full grown. Others were present in the same place, but not obtained. The field notes state that the squirrels slid along on the ground like big lizards and like them stopped and scrutinized the observer from the shelter of the first bush that they reached.

Sierra Nevada Golden-mantled Ground Squirrel

Callospermophilus chrysodeirus chrysodeirus (Merriam)

Field characters.—Size of body about two-thirds that of House Rat; tail about half length of head and body. Head and body 5¾ to 7⅔ inches (147–195 mm.), tail 2⅝ to 4 inches (67–102 mm.), hind foot 1½ to 1¾ inches (38–43 mm.), ear from crown ⅖ to ⅘ inch (11–20 mm.); weight 4¾ to 8½ ounces (135–239 grams). Whole head and neck yellowish or coppery red (pl. 2); on each side of back a broad white stripe bordered above and below by broad black stripes; middle of back grizzled brown; sides and under surface of body pale gray or whitish; tail black centrally, buffy at margin, cinnamon on under surface. *Workings:* Holes in ground 2 to 2½ inches in diameter, usually close to rocks or logs.

Occurrence.—Common resident in Canadian and Hudsonian zones on both slopes of Sierra Nevada. Recorded from Aspen Valley, Merced Big Trees, and near Chinquapin, eastward to Warren Fork of Leevining Creek and to Walker Lake. Lives on ground in open forest and also in rocky situations. Diurnal.

The Golden-mantled Ground Squirrel is one of the most conspicuous members of the high mountain fauna, for it is the most brilliantly marked of all the local squirrel tribe. People living in the mountains usually term this species the "copperhead" or yellow-headed chipmunk, both of which names are appropriate as applying to the coloring on the head and shoulders (pl. 2). In general ecology this squirrel is the high-mountain counterpart of the well-known California Ground Squirrel of the lowland valleys and foothills.

In size the copperhead is our smallest ground squirrel. It is about three-fourths the size of the Belding Ground Squirrel and only one-third or one-fourth the size of the California Ground Squirrel. It is larger, however, than any of the chipmunks. Its general appearance, with stout body and short tail, readily classifies it as a terrestrial squirrel rather than as a climber.

The range of the copperhead practically coincides with that of the lodgepole pine; yet the squirrel is in no way dependent upon this tree directly. The lowest station of record for the "callo," as members of our party got in the habit of calling the animal for short, is at Merced Grove Big Trees, altitude 5500 feet, a place which also marks the western limit of its range. Across the Sierras the whole of the Canadian and Hudsonian zones is inhabited, eastward to Walker Lake; sparingly to Mono Craters. On the high peaks this species does not seem to go much above timber line. Thus, on Mount Florence, the last individual was seen at 10,700 feet, which was just above the highest stunted white-bark pines. On one occasion, at Gaspipe Spring, east of Mono Mills, one of these squirrels was come upon on the ground in the sagebrush, "miles from any timber."

The main habitat or niche of this squirrel is the open rock-strewn floor of the sparse lodgepole pine forest. It keeps closely to this sort of environment, while the Belding Squirrel inhabits the open meadows. At the margins of the meadows, however, the two are often seen in association. The "callo" is strictly a ground dwelling animal. When it wants to look about, it may go to the top of a low boulder or of a log. Only once did we catch sight of one in a tree, and that individual when frightened ran down to the ground and quickly sought its burrow.

The "callo" when first met with is rather shy and usually scampers to the vicinity of its burrow, where it sits hunched up, like a California Ground Squirrel, ready to dart into its underground retreat at an instant's further warning. But its confidence can be won; about camps it may be studied at close range. The gait when running is heavy, with little or none of the bounding or skipping movements of chipmunks. On rare occasions a "callo" will assume the upright picket-pin posture so characteristic of the Belding Ground Squirrel.

The "callo," quite in contrast with the other local squirrels, is seldom heard to utter notes of any sort. On one occasion, near Lake Tenaya, one of these animals was heard to give a high-pitched squeak, repeated three times. In mating chases, when a male pursues a female, low grunting and squeaking notes are uttered; but these are inaudible beyond a few feet.

The Golden-mantled Ground Squirrel spends the winter months, when snow covers the high mountains, in hibernation. Exact data on time of emergence and disappearance are lacking. When we reached Peregoy Meadow on May 20, 1919, the animals were already abroad. At Aspen Valley they were out as late as October 18 (1915). Probably they stay out until the first big storm of the season, which snows them in for the winter.

The summer season is occupied by these squirrels in rearing their broods and in obtaining forage for themselves, not only for their daily needs, but also enough to permit of their acquiring the fat necessary for warmth and sustenance during the long winter sleep. Of one animal collected at Ten Lakes on October 9, 1915, the collector notes that "at least a handful of fat" was removed from the inside of the skin. Not all the individuals, however, acquire fat in equal amounts. Thus, of two males taken on October 3 and 9, respectively, one weighed about 5 ounces (138.5 grams), the other 7¾ ounces (218 grams). And of two females taken at Aspen Valley on October 16, 1915, the respective weights were 5½ ounces (156.5 grams) and 8½ ounces (239 grams).

Once a "callo" was seen to take a dust bath. At Crane Flat, on June 16, 1915, one of our party was resting in a sandy place where large boulders were scattered about. At his approach all the squirrels had disappeared; but after a time one—a Golden-mantled—came forth, frisked about, and repeatedly "dived through" the little heaps of sand; but it did not roll in the sand. Ground squirrels, generally, are afflicted with fleas, and this and other species have been seen to take this method of ridding themselves of these parasites.

About camping and lunching places where summer tourists drop food scraps, copperheads often take advantage of the opportunities afforded to make the getting of food an easy matter. On the summit of Clouds Rest, on August 25, 1915, a "callo" was seen which would come to within three feet or less of a person and take tidbits thrown on the ground. When one of our party offered more material than the squirrel could consume at the moment, it carried the food (in this case dried fruit) in its mouth some distance off, dug a hole in the ground, using the forefeet, thrust the object into the little excavation, then covered the place with earth again, after which it poked small loose stones over the site so as to further disguise it. Probably, as in the case of the California Jay, these caches are temporary affairs, the food being dug up again after a short time and eaten. At Merced Lake four of these squirrels were noted on one occasion gleaning grain scattered on the ground where horses had been fed.

The nest of this species is placed in the ground. At Merced Grove one individual had its burrow in open ground close to several tents. At Crane Flat several of the animals were seen to disappear into burrows surrounded by low brush plants. In the higher altitudes many had their burrows on the open floor of the lodgepole pine forest, sometimes, but not always, beneath rocks. Unfortunately we did not dig out any burrows of this species and no one else seems to have done so in the region, so we know nothing as to the arrangement of the burrow system. Presumably it does not differ greatly from those of the California and Belding ground squirrels; if anything, it might be expected to be simpler in plan.

The animal which had its burrow at Merced Grove was seen to choose as nest material some brown wrapping paper which had been left nearby. This was torn into small pieces by use of both the teeth and forepaws and stuffed into the cheek pouches. Then the squirrel disappeared into its burrow, doubtless to add the paper to the lining of the nest chamber.

Like the other local squirrels the Golden-mantled Ground Squirrel has only one brood a year; this brood is produced in the early part of the summer season. Females containing embryos were taken in 1915 on June 12 (two on this date), 14, 26, and 28, the numbers of embryos in these instances being 2, 5, 6, 6, and 5, respectively. The young stay below ground until about one-third to one-half grown. Mr. Dixon saw numbers of young of this species on the east slope of the Sierras above Mono Lake Post Office between altitudes of 7000 and 7800 feet on July 5, 1916.

Only one bit of information regarding the enemies of the "callo" was obtained. The droppings of a Mountain Coyote on Colby Mountain were found to contain hair of this species.

Tahoe Chipmunk. **Eutamias speciosus frater** (Allen)

Field characters.—Size medium[15] for a chipmunk (head and body 4½ to 5 inches, tail 3¼ to 3¾ inches long). (See pl. 3e.) Tail bushy, flat-appearing, the long hairs on each side bright brown at bases, then black, with buffy white at tips. Back with nine alternating light and dark stripes, the outermost light stripe on each side being conspicuously pure white; side of head with five sharply defined stripes, alternately dark and white from above downward; sides of body bright reddish brown; top of head and rump grayish; under surface of body whitish. Distinguished from *mariposae, quadrimaculatus,* and *senex* by smaller size, and from *monoensis, pictus,* and *alpinus* by larger size; coloration brighter than in any of the others, with light stripes on sides of head, and back whiter. *Voice:* A moderately high-pitched *whisk* repeated at intervals; also a very shrill *tsew*, and, when frightened, a rapid series of notes, *pst-pst-pst-a-kū.*

Occurrence.—Common resident in Canadian and Hudsonian zones on both slopes of Sierra Nevada. Recorded from Crane Flat and near Chinquapin eastward across mountains to Walker Lake. Extreme altitudes, 6200 and 10,350 feet. Lives in forest, foraging both in trees and on ground, rocks, and logs, but habitually *takes refuge in trees,* going 40 feet or more above ground.

The Tahoe Chipmunk is the most widely distributed and perhaps the most abundant of the seven species of chipmunks inhabiting the Yosemite section.[15] Its range embraces all of the forested portions of the ''high Sierras'' between altitudes of 6200 and 10,350 feet. In the wooded territory immediately above Yosemite Valley, as at Glacier Point and back of Yosemite Point, the species is abundant, while farther to the east, at Merced Lake and Tuolumne Meadows, it is also well represented.

The Tahoe Chipmunk is the only one of the local chipmunks which habitually takes refuge well up in trees. This trait alone will, as a rule, serve to distinguish the species from any of its relatives. In point of size

---

[15] Since relative sizes of the whole animals, and proportions of foot, ear, and tail, constitute important characters of the seven species of chipmunks found in the Yosemite section, we give here a table of their measurements and weights. These are based upon ten adult individuals of each species, all of these having been captured within the section.

Species	Head and Body (nose to root of tail)	Tail (excluding hairs at end)	Hind Foot (heel to tip of longest claw)	Ear (from crown)	Weight (Upper figures in ounces, lower in grams)
	(Upper figures in inches, lower in millimeters)				
Tahoe Chipmunk *Eutamias s. frater*	$4^1/_2$–5 114–126	$3^1/_4$–$3^3/_4$ 82–95	$1^1/_4$–$1^3/_8$ 33–36	$^1/_2$–$^5/_8$ 14–16	$1^7/_8$–$2^1/_3$ 52.3–66.1
Allen Chipmunk *Eutamias senex*	$5^1/_4$–6 133–152	4–$4^3/_8$ 102–111	$1^3/_8$ 35–36	$^5/_8$–$^3/_4$ 16–18	$2^2/_3$–$3^3/_8$ 75.2–96.3
Mariposa Chipmunk *Eutamias m. mariposae*	5–$5^3/_4$ 125–147	$4^3/_8$–$4^7/_8$ 110–124	$1^3/_8$–$1^1/_2$ 34–38	$^5/_8$ 15–16	$1^5/_6$–$2^5/_6$ 52.0–80.0
Long-eared Chipmunk *Eutamias quadrimaculatus*	$5^3/_8$–6 135–150	$3^3/_8$–4 85–100	$1^3/_8$–$1^1/_2$ 35–37	$^3/_4$–$^7/_8$ 18–21	$2^2/_3$–$3^2/_3$ 76–105
Alpine Chipmunk *Eutamias alpinus*	$3^7/_8$–$4^3/_8$ 98–112	$2^5/_8$–3 68–77	1–$1^1/_8$ 26–30	$^1/_2$ 11–13	1–$1^2/_5$ 27.5–40.5
Mono Chipmunk *Eutamias a. monoensis*	$4^1/_4$–5 107–127	$2^7/_8$–$3^5/_8$ 73–92	$1^1/_8$–$1^1/_4$ 30–32	$^1/_2$ 12–13	$1^1/_3$–$1^3/_4$ 37.9–48.7
Sagebrush Chipmunk *Eutamias pictus*	$3^7/_8$–$4^1/_4$ 98–108	$2^7/_8$–$3^1/_2$ 73–90	1–$1^1/_8$ 27–30	$^3/_8$–$^1/_2$ 9–11	1–$1^1/_3$ 30.3–37.7

In order of size, as based on average weights of 8 to 10 selected adult examples in each case, the species align themselves from small to large as follows: (1) *Eutamias alpinus* (34.5 g.); (2) *Eutamias pictus* (35.0 g.); (3) *Eutamias a. monoensis* (43.0 g.); (4) *Eutamias s. frater* (59.2 g.); (5) *Eutamias m. mariposae* (63.5 g.); (6) *Eutamias quadrimaculatus* (87.6 g.); (7) *Eutamias senex* (88.1 g.). It will be seen that the largest species is nearly 2½ times as heavy as the smallest.

the Tahoe Chipmunk stands midway among the seven species of the region, being smaller than the Mariposa, Long-eared, and Allen chipmunks and larger than the Mono, Alpine, and Sagebrush chipmunks. The coloration of the Tahoe Chipmunk is brighter reddish in general effect than that of any of the others, and the light stripes on the sides of the head and back stand out as being more definitely or clearly white.   (See pl. 3.)

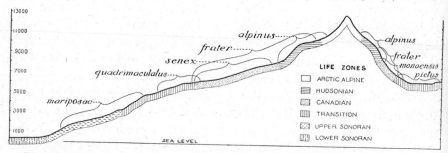

Fig. 28.   Cross-section of the Sierra Nevada through the Yosemite region showing zonal and altitudinal distribution of Chipmunks (genus *Eutamias*).

In the lower part of the Canadian Zone the range of the Tahoe Chipmunk overlaps that of the Long-eared.   (See fig. 28.)   Throughout most of that zone the Tahoe and Allen chipmunks occur on common ground, while the Hudsonian Zone is shared by the Tahoe and Alpine chipmunks. Along the eastern slope of the mountains the Tahoe Chipmunk occurs in localities tenanted by the Mono Chipmunk and in a few places its range touches that of the Sagebrush Chipmunk.   But at no place did we find the Tahoe and Mariposa chipmunks together.   On the Yosemite Falls trail, *mariposae* has been recorded at Columbia Point (5000 feet) while *frater* has been seen only 1600 feet higher, at the top of the zigzags.   But this difference in altitude almost anywhere else than on the nearly vertical walls of the Yosemite gorge would mean a geographical separation of several miles.

It is difficult to determine with any degree of exactness the population of mammals, even of such diurnally active species as chipmunks.   Data obtained from field censuses are not so reliable for mammals as for birds. During the springtime, the regular singing of the male birds makes locating and enumerating individuals simple; then, too, in other seasons the call and flock notes of each species are uttered with more or less frequency. Not so with chipmunks!   When alarmed these animals will call for long periods and then, if there is no new cause for excitement, they will be perfectly quiet for an even longer time.   Many times while we were afield in favorable surroundings we did not hear or see a single chipmunk.   Then, upon the occurrence of some unusual sound, several would call at once from different directions, all voicing curiosity.   In brief, then, while we have census figures to offer, they are not so definitely dependable and show greater discrepancies than do those for most birds. At Porcupine Flat on June 28, 1915, four Tahoe Chipmunks were noted during a single hour, while on two other occasions, once at the same locality and again near Mono Meadow, seven of these animals were recorded during five hours of active observation. It is our impression, gained from extensive field experience, that the Tahoe Chipmunk has its maximum of abundance in the Canadian Zone on the west slope of the Sierras. Again calculating largely from impressions, we would set down the spring population of the Tahoe Chipmunk, before emergence of the young-of-the-season, as about two an acre or 1280 a square mile through the forested portions of the Canadian Zone. In the tree-covered portions of the Hudsonian Zone the population is only about one-half as great. In the late summer when the young are out and all ages are represented, the impression of 'swarms' of chipmunks is given, especially in those localities where forage conditions are most favorable.

The Tahoe Chipmunk shows greater latitude in the matter of its local range than does any of the other Yosemite chipmunks. It runs around a great deal on the ground and over fallen logs, and at times it climbs the brush plants to harvest the crops of seeds or fruit. But the most notable feature in the behavior of the species is its tree-climbing propensity. It habitually goes up into trees at the first hint of danger, climbing many feet above the ground. Even when not frightened the animals do much running around in trees. *Frater* is an adept climber and can go rapidly up the side of a perpendicular trunk, even up such smooth-barked trees as young lodgepole pines and firs. When a frightened animal has gained what it considers a safe height above the ground, it will usually lie quietly on the top of a horizontal branch and peer over the side and down at the scene of its late scare. Its brown and streaked coloration matches so well the various shades of color of the trunk and branches that the animal's location might easily be overlooked were it not for the plume-like tail which often hangs down to one side of the branch, waving back and forth with seeming carelessness.

Tahoe Chipmunks are able to run down comparatively smooth-barked trees head foremost with ease and safety, either at great speed, or moving slowly a few steps at a time. This bespeaks great efficiency in the structure and use of the claws and toes. Individuals have been seen to leap short distances from one branch to another; but, in this respect, the ability of even this most arboreal of our chipmunks is inferior to that of the Gray and Red squirrels.

At Walker Lake one day in September one of our party was walking past a small Jeffrey pine when a Tahoe Chipmunk suddenly dropped to the ground from a height of ten or fifteen feet in the tree. The animal seemed unhurt and quickly made off and climbed a white fir in the vicinity. A jump to earth of considerable magnitude seemed to have been undertaken voluntarily, as an extreme measure of safety, perhaps, and accomplished without injury.

It is not uncommon to see two chipmunks engaged in a play-like pursuit of one another which may last for minutes at a time and carry the two over and beneath logs, through brush, across open places in the forest, and not infrequently up, around, and down the trunks of one or more trees. This habit is not peculiar to the Tahoe Chipmunk, but is indulged in by most, if not all, of the other species. Whether it is pure play, or whether it is part of the courting behavior, we do not know, but its occurrence at various seasons of the year and the fact that young animals often engage in it, indicate that it is not related immediately to mating. As pointed out in the chapter on the Alpine Chipmunk, there are various and diverse relations borne between individuals of the same species, and some of these seemingly mild-mannered chases may, in actuality, be instances where one individual has invaded the small area of territory over which some other chipmunk already exercises 'property rights' and is 'defending title.' The study of behavior in chipmunks in a state of nature would prove a fascinating one, and the plentiful population of these animals at easily accessible spots in the Yosemite region affords excellent opportunities for such a study.

The fact that the Tahoe Chipmunk is the only one of seven local species which habitually climbs high in the trees is a point of evidence that restriction to a particular type of habitat or mode of behavior does not always rest upon the possession of conspicuous special structural features of an adaptive nature. So far as can be seen by an examination of specimens in hand, none of the other species of chipmunks is physically incapacitated for tree climbing; in fact, individuals of these others are occasionally observed well up in the trees. There doubtless *are* minor features of structure, associated with a different psychology, which account for the differing traits indicated. Age-long segregation, in separate areas of differentiation, of the several stocks may be the basis of this divergence of habitat preference. The shifting of climatic barriers, with the resulting migrations of populations, has thrown the species together as very near neighbors or as actual companions. Fatal competition is prevented as a result of these initial predilections, whereby *frater* favors the trees, *alpinus* the rocks, and *senex* and *quadrimaculatus* the brush patches and logs.

A Tahoe Chipmunk three-fourths grown was caught lightly by one front paw in a mouse trap at our Lyell Cañon camp in late July, 1915. One of the members of the party kept the animal in captivity for a time to learn something of its habits. From the time of its capture the chipmunk never attempted to bite, although at first it struggled when handled. Later, when permitted to run about camp and even to climb trees it was recaptured easily. The first night in captivity the animal was placed in a roll of cotton in a pail. During the night it worked out of the cotton and became very cold and numb, in fact it was seemingly lifeless; but a little warming soon revived it completely. The chipmunk drank and ate readily in captivity, taking about a quarter of a teaspoonful of water and several pinches of rolled oats daily. The water it sucked, not lapped, into the mouth; but sometimes it would put its tongue out into the water before actual drinking began. Rolled oats seemed to supply its needs in the way of food, but it also accepted various other items from the camp breakfast. Beans and sugar were eaten readily. The chipmunk would often lick the hands of a person holding it, probably because of the salt deposited on the skin by perspiration.

When holding food materials, this chipmunk used its forefeet like hands; usually it employed both feet, but sometimes only one. If hungry it would stuff kernels of grain into its cheek pouches, but without putting its paws clear into the mouth. Again, after the pouches were crammed with food, it would slip out one grain at a time (and this also was done by working the muscles of the jaws without help from the paws), and nibble the kernel while holding it in the paws.

Much of the activity of chipmunks in summer and fall has to do with the getting and storing of food materials against a season of the year when such supplies are scant or lacking. Although we did not find any large food cache of any of the chipmunks it is probable that the animals do lay by stores in considerable quantity in particular spots. But whether or not they accumulate much food material, we do know that chipmunks are accustomed to bury seeds and nuts of various kinds, a few in a place or singly. After having gathered one or more such articles the chipmunk, using its forepaws in the digging, will excavate a small hole, often deep enough to conceal the animal's head from the view of a person off to one side. Then the contents of the cheek pouches are transferred to the hole, the hole is filled up, and the surface more or less smoothed over and patted down. Some, at least, of such caches are subsequently opened by the chipmunks, as we ourselves have witnessed. Whether the recovery is made by the animal which originally buried the material is not known, though this is believed usually to be the case. A considerable number of the seeds, however, are not dug up by any rodent, and being planted at a proper depth, begin to germinate, when conditions of warmth and moisture are right, and give rise to seedling plants. In this way the chipmunks doubtless atone in full for the toll which they levy on the forest trees and brush plants in the way of seeds actually consumed. The manner in which the chipmunks relocate stores which have been buried is not known definitely, but the sense of smell is probably of important service.

The chipmunks, constituting a group of rodents usually thought of as tree-dwelling animals, are in reality more closely related to certain of the ground squirrels than to the tree squirrels. One feature possessed in common is the cheek pouch. This is a thin membrane-like sac, one on each side of the face beneath the outer furry skin and opening inside the mouth. Seeds or nuts can be passed from the mouth to the pouches or vice versa merely by action of the cheek muscles and tongue, without aid from the forepaws. The Gray and Red squirrels have no cheek pouches of any sort.

When foraging, the Tahoe Chipmunk is likely to be seen in a wide variety of situations. In the Canadian Zone it was often noted climbing about in different sorts of brush plants to gather the seeds or fruits. Some food, such as scattered pine seeds, certain kinds of fungi, and scraps from persons' lunches is sought on the ground. In the fall months many different members of the squirrel family busy themselves in harvesting grass seed, and the Tahoe Chipmunk was sometimes seen so engaged. At Porcupine Flat, in late June, the animals were at work on the cones of the lodgepole pine. At Ten Lakes, in October, two of these chipmunks which had their faces smeared with pitch were encountered, suggesting that the animals had been working on unripe cones.

The contents of the cheek pouches of 10 individual Tahoe Chipmunks, collected for specimens, were saved by us for analysis. In 6, seeds of coniferous trees exclusively were represented; in 5 of these cases the seeds were those of the Jeffrey pine, the remaining one being (doubtfully) of the lodgepole pine. The numbers of pine seeds which were contained in the cheek pouches of individual animals varied from 1 to 20, the latter (of Jeffrey pine) constituting seemingly the full capacity of the two cheek pouches of a chipmunk.

The other 4 sets of contents of cheek pouches gave analyses as follows: (1) Fragments of a brown-colored fungus; (2) 62 hulled seeds of a grass, probably wild brome; (3) 90 seeds of black bindweed (an introduced plant); (4) a mixed lot of seeds including those of a geranium, a phacelia, a borage, and a sedge.

The season of activity for this chipmunk extends through the greater portion of the year. Even the light snows of early winter do not drive all the individuals into hibernation, although they probably all disappear with the first heavy snowfall of the season. In the spring, they are out and active when travelers are first able to climb to the higher levels, in May. The little fellows are then to be seen skipping over the packed snow banks between logs and tree trunks with no seeming discomfiture.

Chipmunks of the Yosemite Section.

a. Sagebrush Chipmunk (*Eutamias pictus*).

b. Alpine Chipmunk (*E. alpinus*).
d. Long-eared Chipmunk (*E. quadrimaculatus*).
f. Mariposa Chipmunk (*E. merriami mariposae*).

c. Mono Chipmunk (*E. amoenus monoensis*).
e. Tahoe Chipmunk (*E. speciosus frater*).
g. Allen Chipmunk (*E. senex*).

Few data are available concerning the exact time or duration of the breeding season in this or any of our other species of chipmunks. Among ground squirrels one species is known to take somewhat less than one month for gestation, and it seems probable that the period is at most not longer in chipmunks. This would require, on the basis of young being born in late June or early July (as shown by the data given beyond), mating toward the end of May. At this season, though the ''high Sierras'' are still fairly well covered with snow, the daily temperature reaches a relatively high point, and spots of bare ground are beginning to appear.

Our records for the Tahoe Chipmunk, based upon the taking of specimens, show pregnant females as follows:

Crane Flat,   6400 feet, June 16, 1915, 6 small embryos
Mono Meadow,   7400 feet, June 16, 1915, 3 embryos
Mono Meadow,   7400 feet, June 18, 1915, 3 large embryos
Porcupine Flat, 8100 feet, June 27, 1915, 4 embryos
Porcupine Flat, 8100 feet, June 28, 1915, 3 large embryos
Porcupine Flat, 8100 feet, July 1, 1915, 6 large embryos

Many young were abroad at Tuolumne Meadows by July 31, 1915. The number of young in a litter we may infer to vary from 3 to 6, and to average about 4.

Allen Chipmunk. **Eutamias senex** (Allen)

Field characters.—Size large for a chipmunk (head and body about 5½ inches long, tail about 4¼ inches). (See table in footnote 15, page 177, for detailed measurements.) Usual chipmunk pattern, markings indistinct; general tone of coloration dark grayish. (See pl. 3g.) Distinguished from *frater* by larger size, duller coloration, and less conspicuous light striping on sides of head and back; from *quadrimaculatus* by more grayish coloration, shorter ears, and less conspicuous light spots behind bases of ears; from *alpinus* by much larger size and by duller and darker coloration. *Voice:* Similar to that of the Long-eared Chipmunk.

Occurrence.—Common resident in Canadian Zone on west slope of Sierra Nevada. Recorded from Aspen Valley, Cascade Creek (near Gentrys) and Chinquapin eastward to Glen Aulin and Washburn Lake, at altitudes of 6200 to 7700 feet regularly, and exceptionally at 4600 feet (Lady Franklin Rock) and 8100 feet (Porcupine Flat). Lives in thickets and about logs, rarely going over 5 feet above the ground.

The Allen Chipmunk is the common brush and log inhabiting species in the belt of country on the west slope of the Sierra Nevada characterized by the presence of huckleberry oak, chinquapin, and snow bush (*C. cordulatus*). By reason of its large size (pl. 3g), gray coloration, and terrestrial proclivities it may be told at a glance from the smaller, more brightly-marked tree-climbing Tahoe Chipmunk sharing the same belt.

Along the lower margin of the Canadian Zone the Allen and Long-eared chipmunks are found together. The former exhibits a grayer-toned pelage, with more obscured striping, shorter ears, and a much less conspicuous

whitish spot behind the base of each ear. The habits of the two, so fa
as we know them at present, are alike, save perhaps that the species no
under discussion is the more closely confined to the ground, low brush
and prostrate logs. At the upper edge of the Canadian Zone the Alle
Chipmunk in a few places meets the small, pale-colored, rock-dwellin
Alpine Chipmunk, from which it differs so greatly as to be easily dis
tinguished. At no station visited by our party were the Allen and
Mariposa chipmunks found near each other. An interval of a thousand
feet or more of altitude ordinarily separates the ranges of these tw
species, which are of similar size and much alike in general markings
They may thus be identified most conveniently, perhaps, on the basis o
the altitude of their occurrence.

One rather notable departure in range for the Allen Chipmunk wa
shown by the capture of an individual at Lady Franklin Rock (altitude
4600 feet) in the gorge of the Merced just below Vernal Falls. We rather
expected to find the Long-eared Chipmunk there, but instead the one
animal taken turned out to be an Allen Chipmunk. The spot named is
an attractive picnic place for leisurely inclined tourists from the Valley
and a way station for hikers en route to or from Glacier Point or the Little
Yosemite, and the chipmunks (for there are usually two or more about)
profit by the crumbs and scraps of lunch dropped there or intentionally
thrown out to attract the animals to close view.

The few facts at hand regarding the breeding season of this species
indicate that it begins in May or perhaps even earlier. A female captured
near Tamarack Flat, May 26, 1919, contained 4 embryos, another captured
near the upper Yosemite Creek on June 4, 1915, contained 5 embryos, and
one taken near Porcupine Flat, June 27, 1915, contained 2 embryos.
Several individuals obtained in Indian Cañon between June 20 and 25,
1915, gave indication of having recently suckled young. The young
probably appear abroad in early July. A young-of-the-year taken near
Merced Lake on August 25, 1915, was already over three-fourths grown.

In the Canadian Zone woods one may find many of the vantage places
to which these chipmunks have repaired when shucking out seeds. One
such place was seen near Tamarack Flat. It was on the top of a mass of
granite which stood up in rather solitary fashion overlooking much brushy
territory. A chipmunk had been seen at the place and upon our climbing
to the spot we found some shells from seeds and scales from pine cones.
There is never so large an accumulation as that which constitutes the
'kitchen middens' of a Red Squirrel, probably because in many instances
the chipmunk is apt to carry seeds about in its cheek pouches and shuck
them out here or there wherever opportunity offers, instead of resorting
to one fixed shelling station.

Contents of cheek pouches in four of these chipmunks gave analyses as follows: (1) Aspen Valley, October 19, 5 seeds of sugar pine; (2) near Glen Aulin, October 1, 15 seeds of Jeffrey pine; (3) Washburn Lake, August 28, 45 shelled grass seeds, probably of wild brome; (4) Merced Lake, August 20, 42 grains of barley (rolled), picked up where horses had been fed.

MARIPOSA CHIPMUNK. **Eutamias merriami mariposae** Grinnell and Storer

Field characters.—Large for a chipmunk (pl. 3*f*); length of head and body about 5¼ inches, tail 4½ to 4¾ inches (see table in footnote 15, p. 177, for detailed measurements). Dullest colored of all the Yosemite section chipmunks; light stripes indistinct, not white; spot behind ear grayish; general tone of coloration dull reddish brown in summer coat and grayish brown in winter. *Voice:* A hollow-sounding *bock*, repeated at regular intervals; when excited, a high-pitched *whisk*, repeated; also a rapid sputter of four or more syllables.

Occurrence.—Resident in small to moderate numbers in Upper Sonoran and low Transition Zones, on west slope of Sierra Nevada. Recorded from Mast (700 feet altitude near Pleasant Valley), eastward to Columbia Point (altitude 5000 feet) on north wall of Yosemite Valley. Inhabits brush and trees, especially oaks, rarely ascending latter to 25 feet or so above the ground.

The Mariposa Chipmunk is the local representative of a group (the Merriam Chipmunks) which is found commonly at middle altitudes in the mountainous portions of southern California. This is the only chipmunk known to occur on the floor of Yosemite Valley, and there, as well as at other stations within its local range, it is remarkably scarce as compared with the number of chipmunks higher in the Yosemite section.

The westernmost station of record for the Mariposa Chipmunk is Mast, in the lower Merced Cañon. Upon none of our visits to Pleasant Valley, only a little lower down, did we get any trace whatsoever of chipmunks. The animals were moderately common in the mixed stands of trees and brush near the old Merced Gold Mine mill west of Coulterville, and a number were recorded at El Portal. In Yosemite Valley, as at Rocky Point and similar places along the sides of the Valley floor, the rough talus slopes grown over with manzanita and golden oaks were found to be the best locations in which to seek the animals. No Mariposa Chipmunk was seen higher than Columbia Point, altitude 5000 feet, on the Yosemite Falls trail.

Compared with other chipmunks of the region this species is the largest and the least strikingly colored. (See pl. 3*f*.) There is a prevailing dullness to the pelage, especially to the gray winter coat, even more noticeable than in the Allen Chipmunk. We did not actually see Mariposa Chipmunks at any locality where any of the other species occurred. It seems not unlikely, however, that the range of the Mariposa will be found to touch that of the Long-eared Chipmunk in certain places. The Mariposa Chipmunk is much duller colored (decidedly less brightly brownish), as compared with the Long-eared, and the spot at the hinder base of each ear is only imperfectly indicated—dull gray instead of pure white; the ear itself is decidedly smaller, not so tall.

It seems likely that those Mariposa Chipmunks which live in the Upper Sonoran Zone do not actually hibernate at any season of the year. They probably remain in their retreats during rainstorms and come out on warm days at any time during the winter months. But those individuals which live in Yosemite Valley and elsewhere in the territory where snow remains for some time during the winter months (Transition Zone), do, in all probability, hibernate. Thus at El Portal, in the fall and early winter of 1914, Mariposa Chipmunks were out and active until December 7, perhaps later. The latest seasonal record on the ˙wall of Yosemite Valley is for November 19 (1915). None was seen anywhere in the Valley during our intensive work there in December, 1914; nor was anything noted of the animals during a visit to the Valley at the end of February, 1916.

On the whole, the Mariposa Chipmunk seems to be a reclusive species. It adheres to a dense type of vegetational cover, where also the range of the observer's view is short. We found that occasional individuals would *chip* noisily when one of us 'squeaked' at them, but more often the chipmunks became silent after the first bit of noise or movement on our part. At Blacks Creek one of several of these chipmunks to which we 'squeaked' came within close range. The animal sat partly hidden from view in a thicket and called *bŏck, bŏck, bŏck,* in long series about as fast as a person could pronounce the syllables easily. Usually each note was accompanied by a sidewise wave of the tail. When frightened by a movement on the part of the observer, the chipmunk gave a rapid series of sibilant notes and dashed off along branches toward some refuge, after which it remained silent and gave no clue to its new location.

The Mariposa Chipmunk, like others of its kind, is given to burying food supplies in small pockets in the ground. Under some manzanita brush on a hill west of the McCarthy ranch and about 3 miles east of Coulterville, we found these caches common, though the animals themselves were notably successful in keeping out of sight.

The favorite haunts of this species in the foothill country seem to be the mixed growths of brush and small trees. Seldom did we find them in continuous or pure chaparral. They do not seem to affect the monotonous stretches of greasewood at all. On several occasions the animals have been seen in oak trees, in one instance about 30 feet from the ground.

A common resort for chipmunks in the vicinity of Dudley was along the rail fences bounding the ranches and bordering the hillside chaparral.

In places like this, on July 22, 1920, 5 chipmunks were checked in a 3½ hours' census walk. A rattlesnake coiled under the lowest rail of a fence was found to contain a partially digested chipmunk; the snake had evidently found the fence a favorable place for his own foraging.

The actual floor of Yosemite Valley does not afford much appropriate cover for the Mariposa Chipmunk. The animals live on the boulder talus overgrown with brush and golden oaks along either wall; they are most numerously represented on the warmer north side of the Valley. In 1915, several chipmunks lived in woodpiles near certain of the buildings in the Village, and they came regularly to take nuts and other food placed out for them in front of the village barber shop. Once, on the north side of the Valley, one of these chipmunks was seen to run across the road and climb the slanting trunk of a willow which stood only about fifty feet from the bank of the Merced River.

The breeding season of the Mariposa Chipmunk begins very early in the spring. A female captured at Blacks Creek, May 10 (1919), was already suckling young; another individual taken that same day was a young animal of the current season already over half-grown. On June 8, 1915, a half-grown young-of-the-year was collected on the ridge of hills 3 miles east of Coulterville, and another a little larger was taken on Smith Creek July 16, 1920. All these young animals have the characteristic pelage of young chipmunks, soft and rather scanty, with colors darker, more blackish, than in adults. A female taken in Yosemite Valley July 29, 1915, was a young-of-the-year, of nearly adult size. It had assumed its first summer coat. The Mariposa Chipmunk evidently breeds earlier than does any of the other local species of chipmunk; this fact is consistent with the greater warmth of the animal's habitat. Its young are abroad in the spring long before the young of high-mountain species have been born.

LONG-EARED CHIPMUNK. **Eutamias quadrimaculatus** (Gray)

Field characters.—A large chipmunk (head and body about 5½ inches, tail 3¾ inches long); usual chipmunk pattern of markings; ears proportionately taller than in any other species, and light spot behind base of each ear larger and more conspicuously clear white. (See pls. 3*d*, 33*a*.) Distinguished from *mariposae* and *senex* by deep ruddy brown rather than grayish tone of coloration, as well as by taller ears and conspicuous white spot at base of same; may be separated from *frater* by larger size, taller ears and darker tone of coloration. (For comparative measurements see footnote 15, p. 177.) *Voice:* A sharp *whsst* or *psst;* also a low-pitched *bock.*

Occurrence.—Common resident in a narrow belt on west slope of Sierra Nevada between altitudes of 5000 and 7300 feet (upper part of Transition Zone and lower part of Canadian). Recorded from Sequoia, Hazel Green, and Chinquapin eastward to Indian Cañon and to junction of Sunrise and Clouds Rest trails. Lives about brush patches and logs, seldom going up in trees and then usually only a few feet above the ground.

The Long-eared Chipmunk is the most restricted in range of any of the chipmunks occurring on the west slope of the Yosemite region. It is found only in a narrow belt of territory between altitudes of 5000 and 7300 feet, hence chiefly in the upper half of the Transition Zone. Its range is almost complementary to that of the Mariposa and Allen chipmunks, the other two large sized species in the region, for the former does not anywhere go above 5000 feet, and the latter is seldom found far below the 7000-foot contour.

As suggested by the vernacular name, this chipmunk is noted for its rather tall and slender-appearing ears, the general effect of which is enhanced by the large conspicuous patch of pure white on the head just behind each ear. (See pls. 3*d*, 33*a*.) The general pattern of markings on this species is the same as in other species but the effect is somewhat different, in that the Long-eared is more brownish and sharply streaked than the Allen and Mariposa chipmunks, and larger and darker toned with less conspicuous white stripes than the Tahoe Chipmunk.

This chipmunk lives about brush thickets and fallen logs and is much like the Allen Chipmunk in general behavior. Indeed in localities where the two occur together we could detect no appreciable difference in their habits. Both keep close to the ground, running over the surface and along logs, and, when frightened, both seek safety in dense brush or in hollows in logs rather than in trees. This feature alone is enough in most cases to distinguish these two larger animals from the Tahoe Chipmunk. But on a few occasions individual Long-eared Chipmunks have been noted well up in trees, once on a dead stub at a height of fifty feet or more above the ground.

The call note of the Long-eared Chipmunk is an incisive *whsst* or *psst*, thought to be sharper than that of the Tahoe Chipmunk, and usually given singly. There is also the hollow *bock* uttered at measured intervals.

At Hazel Green on May 15, 1919, one of us sat quietly for a time in a thicket of incense cedars and Douglas spruces and watched one of these chipmunks which had been running along and near a stake-and-rider fence which surrounded the adjacent meadow. The animal circled about the observer as close as three feet and not more than ten feet away, so that every movement could be clearly seen. The bright patches of white behind the bases of the ears made recognition easy and positive. At first the chipmunk gave the hollow *bock* a few times, accompanying each of the separated utterances by a forward jerk of the tail. Then the shrill explosive *psst* was uttered once or twice with less action of the tail. The movements were all quick and the chipmunk would freeze after each change of position, whereupon its variegated pattern fairly melted into the mixed background. This individual stayed on the ground or on logs and never ascended a tree. Others were seen the same day along the fence, usually running on some rail below the top one.

Along the 'short' trail to Glacier Point above the 5700 foot contour several chipmunks of this species were noted on October 9, 1914, running about over rocks and beneath the brush. The observer stopped and 'squeaked,' whereupon one of the chipmunks perched on a rock beneath a bush and began to wave his tail slowly back and forth. Presently he began to utter the low guttural *chuck* or *bock* at short regularly spaced intervals, thrashing the tail spasmodically from side to side or diagonally fore-and-aft in unison with the notes. The note, while low at first, later became clear and resonant, with a far-carrying quality. A movement on the part of the observer caused the chipmunk to whisk away through the brush.

In the warmer months of the year these chipmunks become active by sunrise. At Merced Grove Big Trees on June 10, 1915, four were out and running about near our camp at 6:10 A.M., just after the sun had appeared over the nearby ridge. The animals are active throughout the day, but usually disappear at sunset or as soon as the chill of evening sets in. The period of hibernation for this species is shorter than for any other save the foothill-inhabiting *mariposae*. Long-eared Chipmunks were out in force at Hazel Green on May 14, 1915, and had probably been out there for some time previously. When we visited Yosemite Point on October 30, 1915, we found the species still abroad in numbers; several brush-inhabiting chipmunks, probably of this species, were noted at Chinquapin on November 26, 1914. But on December 30, 1914, a visit to Gentrys where Long-eared Chipmunks are common in summer revealed none of the animals; they were then doubtless all in hibernation.

The breeding season of the Long-eared Chipmunk occurs at about the same time as does that of the other local chipmunks. A female taken at Merced Grove Big Trees on June 11, 1915, contained 4 small embryos, and another taken on the same date had 5 large ones. Two females taken June 10 and 24, respectively, in 1915, gave indications of having suckled young recently. We were not in the range of this species at the season when the young might be expected to appear, and by early fall we found the young-of-the-year indistinguishable in point of size from the adults.

Chipmunks, like many other wild animals, are often troubled with fleas and not infrequently they may be seen scratching themselves to get rid of the parasites. A Long-eared Chipmunk was watched one day while so engaged. The animal scratched vigorously, but that seemed not to bring the desired relief. He then resorted to a 'dry' bath. Pulling off some of the hard outer wood on a piece of decayed log the chipmunk repeatedly dragged his body through the rotted wood dust inside. The ground adjacent had just been freed of snow and was still wet; this fact probably accounts for the animal's use of the powdery rotted wood.

While coming down the zigzags on the Tenaya trail near Snow Creek on September 29, 1915, one of us found a rattlesnake which had been killed and left in the trail. The tail of a chipmunk was sticking out of the rattler's mouth. When we pulled out the body, which was head-down in the throat of the snake, it proved to be that of a Long-eared Chipmunk.

The food of this chipmunk consists of a variety of seeds and fruits occurring in the belt of snow bush (*Ceanothus cordulatus*). In addition, pine seeds are gathered where they drop out of the ripened cones on the ground. The cheek pouches of three individual chipmunks, collected at Gentrys and Aspen Valley, October 14 and 23, 1915, contained 1, 12, and 5 seeds, respectively, of the sugar pine.

ALPINE CHIPMUNK. **Eutamias alpinus** (Merriam)

Field characters.—Smallest and palest colored of the Yosemite chipmunks (head and body about 4 inches long, tail scarcely 3 inches long). (See comparative measurements in footnote 15, p. 177.) Usual chipmunk pattern of coloration; sides of body pale buff; tail showing more yellowish buff than black. (See pl. 3*b*.) *Voice:* A wiry, not loud, *sweet* repeated frequently; this sometimes modified to *whit* when uttered more slowly and with emphasis; also a low chuckle.

Occurrence.—Common resident of Hudsonian Zone, ranging locally into Alpine-Arctic. Recorded on Mount Hoffmann and on Mount Clark, and from Glen Aulin and near Vogelsang Lake eastward to Mono Pass and Ellery Lake. Seldom below 8500 feet altitude. Lives chiefly among rocks, sometimes about fallen logs; climbs trees but rarely.

The Alpine Chipmunk is the smallest and palest colored of all the chipmunks occurring in the Yosemite section. It lives habitually at higher altitudes than do the other species. In only one place was it observed below 8000 feet; the greater part of the population of the species lives far above that altitude.

Only one other chipmunk, the Tahoe Chipmunk, is found regularly within the territory inhabited by the Alpine Chipmunk. From that species the Alpine may be distinguished by its smaller size and paler tone of coloration and by its marked preference for the rocks. (See pl. 3*b*.) Furthermore, *alpinus* shows much less curiosity than does its relative. If the observer makes a squeaking noise with his lips, the Tahoe Chipmunk will usually be attracted to investigate, whereas the Alpine Chipmunk will either pay no attention whatsoever or else hasten away.

Along the eastern margin of the range of the Alpine Chipmunk is to be found the Mono Chipmunk, a species of only slightly larger size but of somewhat more brilliant coloration. Both may be seen about rocks, and then only close scrutiny of individuals will enable an observer to distinguish between the two. However, *alpinus* has not been found east of Warren Fork of Leevining Creek and Mono Pass and *monoensis* is not known to occur west of those stations. At Glen Aulin the range of the Allen Chipmunk meets that of the Alpine. But the latter is only about half the bulk of the former and its coloration is obviously lighter, so that no difficulty will be experienced in distinguishing these two species.

The range of the Alpine Chipmunk comprises chiefly the Hudsonian Zone, including the 'tongues' of that zone which extend westward from the main Sierran crest to such outstanding peaks as Mount Hoffmann and Mount Clark. The species ranges upward beyond the limits of the main forest, and in a few instances was noted above the highest indication of timber line and hence within the Arctic-Alpine Zone. For example, one was seen at 11,500 feet altitude on Parsons Peak.

This species inhabits for the most part rocky situations, either the large masses of slide rock on the cañon sides or the scattered boulders within the rather open stands of lodgepole pine. Not infrequently it is seen scampering over and about logs lying on the ground, and in a few instances individuals were seen in trees. On Mount Hoffmann an Alpine Chipmunk was seen 3 feet above the ground in a white-bark pine, and another at Ellery Lake was 6 feet up in a lodgepole pine; at Young Lake one of the animals was seen to climb several feet up into a lodgepole pine on the lake shore. But the rock piles constitute the accustomed habitat; individuals traverse these with great facility, and venture much farther into such places than do the Tahoe Chipmunks. Although we found no nests, we believe that the Alpine Chipmunk finds its shelter and suitable breeding dens either amid the rocks or in the ground beneath them.

Bearing in mind the liveliness of chipmunks in general, the Alpine Chipmunk must be put down as exhibiting the extreme of agility, so nimbly and lightly does it skip about from place to place in carrying on its daily activities. When running on the ground it usually holds the tail up vertically and so gives the impression that this member is larger and longer than actual measurements show it to be. When a chipmunk is perched on some rock, and calling, its tail is usually jerked upward at the instant each note is given.

This chipmunk does not seem to be so talkative as some of its relatives. Certainly upon many occasions when the presence of an observer would provoke other species to loud and persistent chipping, *alpinus* gave few or no notes. Its calls as compared with those of the Tahoe Chipmunk are fainter and higher pitched. Once learned by an observer they can be used with considerable certainty in identifying the species. A common call is a repeated *sweet, sweet, sweet,* etc., with rather short intervals between the notes and continued for varying lengths of time. If badly frightened a chipmunk will utter a startled *whip-per'r'r* as it runs to shelter. On occasion a low chuckling note is given, similar to the hollow-sounding 'barks' of the larger species.

The Alpine Chipmunks, despite their boreal home, are active through a rather long season. Our earliest contact with them seasonally was on June 28, 1915, when a number were noted on Mount Hoffmann. As the breeding season was then well advanced or nearly over it seems likely that they had begun to be active much earlier in the year. On October 11, 1915, several of the animals were seen still abroad in the vicinity of Ten Lakes. At Tuolumne Meadows we were told that during a storm in mid-September the Alpine Chipmunks had taken to cover, but that they had reappeared as soon as snow ceased to fall. The individuals seen on Mount Hoffmann were, in several instances, running across the snow banks. Judging from observations made elsewhere upon other species of chipmunks, it seems probable that weather rather than temperature alone is the determining factor in limiting the season of activity for the Alpine Chipmunk.

The time of mating is unknown. Two females collected June 30, 1915, contained 4 and 5 large embryos, respectively, and others captured between July 5 and 17 had been recently suckling young. Males collected in July gave evidence that the period of sexual activity was well past. On July 30, young individuals were abroad around Tuolumne Meadows. A young female weighing 19.5 grams, which is only about half of the weight of an average adult, was collected at 10,500 feet altitude on Mount Florence, August 20, and two individuals obtained on Mount Clark on August 22 were scarcely two-thirds grown. By early October young-of-the-year had reached nearly or quite the size of adults.

The Alpine Chipmunks obtained at the end of June and in early July are passing from the much worn and dulled winter pelage into the more brightly colored new coat. By October this new pelage is completely assumed and is then not only longer and denser but more grayish in tone than when it first starts to appear.

The habit of pursuing one another, noted of other chipmunks, is conspicuous in the present species. A pair will go at great speed, one individual after the other, up over logs and rocks and down through crevices, the two keeping always only a few inches apart. This habit is marked long after the close of the mating season. One explanatory theory states that this practice serves to keep the animals 'in training,' so that when a real menace threatens, as, for example, when a marauding Least Weasel makes its appearance, a chipmunk will find itself in optimum condition for escape to some safe refuge. Another suggestion offered is to the effect that this habit is acquired in order that when male pursues female for the purpose of accomplishing the mating act, only the swiftest males will succeed. If swiftness be a point of advantage to the species, then a sort of sexual selection by which swiftness will become an accentuated trait, will here be operative.

There is always more or less competition between the members of a species in the struggle for existence, and considerable individuality in behavior is exhibited whenever several animals of any one species are gathered at close quarters, as when they are attracted by a common food supply. This individuality was illustrated at Tuolumne Meadows one afternoon in late September, when several Alpine Chipmunks were seen contesting with one another for possession of some scraps of bread which had been discarded from a lunch. At first but one chipmunk was in evidence and he busied himself with a piece of the bread. He was soon observed by another of his kind who shortly arrived on the scene, and this second animal made an attempt to gain possession of the piece held by the first. Being unsuccessful, the second then found another fragment for himself. Later a third and then a fourth chipmunk arrived. Only one animal would eat at any particular piece at one time; if another attempted to join in, a contest would ensue. Sometimes the original possessor successfully defended his rights, sometimes the interloper gained control. Just as among human beings, one, for the time, might dominate the group, another might be bullied about by all, and the others would hold their ground between these two extremes.

In spite of the seemingly barren appearance of its chosen habitat the Alpine Chipmunk finds, at the proper season, an abundance of food in the way of ripe seeds. But the season of harvest is short and many of the seeds are of very small size; to secure these seeds in adequate quantity both for immediate use and for storage therefore requires a rare concentration of effort and a high degree of industry on the part of the harvesters. This industriousness is fully apparent if a person takes the time to watch the animals from a vantage point where his presence does not, through fear or alarm, distract the attention of the chipmunks. Analyses of cheek-pouch contents are instructive in this connection also; and the following selections seem worth placing on record here.

(1) Fletcher Creek at 10,000 feet altitude, September 4: some fragments of a brown fungus.
(2) Colby Mountain at 9200 feet, October 9: two seeds of pine (thought to be silver pine).
(3) Ten Lakes at 9200 feet, October 8: 47 seeds of a grass (stipa).
(4) Ten Lakes at 9200 feet, October 11: 324 seeds of sedge and 1 of stipa.
(5) McClure Fork at 9200 feet, August 29: 165 seeds of sedge and 24 of galingale; total 189.
(6) Mount Hoffmann at 10,300 feet, June 30: 388 seeds of sedge and 1 of pussy-paws.
(7) Mount Florence at 10,500 feet, August 21: 1113 seeds of willow-herb, 1 of pussy-paws, 19 of stipa, 36 of galingale; total 1169 seeds.

(8) Mount Clark at 10,500 feet, August 22: 27 seeds of pussy-paws, 1 of rush, 1080 of a very small undetermined seed; total 1108 seeds.
(9) Mount Florence at 10,500 feet, August 21: 1550 seeds of sedge, 5 of stipa; total 1555 seeds.
(10) Ten Lakes at 9200 feet, October 9: 4796 seeds of pussy-paws, 174 of sedge; total 4970 (counted seed by seed into groups of 10 and these into 100's and 1000's).

The seeds of the plant known as pussy-paws (*Spraguea umbellata*) seem, wherever obtainable, to be especially sought after by chipmunks. These seeds are very small (0.7 to 1.2 mm. in diameter), flattish, smooth, and glistening black; and they prove exceedingly elusive to human handling. The fact that the mass of seeds in a chipmunk's cheek pouches is invariably free of chaff or any other useless material bespeaks a marvelous degree of dexterity on the part of the harvester. When we note that one load contained practically 5000 seeds, and recall the complicated nature and rapidity of the movements of the forefeet, lips, and tongue which must be involved in the act of gathering seeds, our wonder at the effectiveness of the chipmunk's nervous and muscular organization is beyond expression.

MONO CHIPMUNK. **Eutamias amoenus monoensis** Grinnell and Storer

Field characters.—Size small (head and body about 4½ inches, tail 3¼ inches long). (For comparative measurements see footnote 15, p. 177.) Usual chipmunk pattern of coloration; flanks light brown. (See pl. 3c.) Distinguished from *frater* by smaller size, paler coloration generally, less conspicuous white markings, and yellowish rather than reddish color on bases of tail hairs; from *alpinus* and *pictus* by larger size, relatively longer tail and darker general tone of coloration. *Voice:* Similar to that of Tahoe Chipmunk.

Occurrence.—Moderately common in Canadian Zone on east base of Sierra Nevada; recorded on Mono Craters and from Leevining Creek south to Gem Lake and Silver Lake. Altitudes of capture, 7000 to 9100 feet. Lives largely within the belt of mountain mahogany, where it stays in brushy and rocky places.

The Mono Chipmunk in the Yosemite section is limited in its range to the east slope of the Sierras. It touches or overlaps the ranges of three other species of small chipmunks, and difficulty may therefore be experienced in identifying the animals in the field.

The Mono Chipmunk seems to be restricted to the arid Canadian Zone, and it there dwells chiefly within the belt of mountain mahogany. While typically a ground dweller, like the Allen Chipmunk of the west slope, it does sometimes ascend the smaller trees up to a height of 6 or 8 feet. It perches commonly on the tops of boulders where it obtains an unobstructed view over the tops of the bushes roundabout.

In September, 1915, around Williams Butte, the Mono Chipmunks were busily engaged in harvesting seed crops of one sort or another. At Gem

Lake they ranged down from the nearby brush and rocks to the border of a meadow and were seen under the willows there pulling down the grass heads and gathering the ripening seeds. Elsewhere they ranged out under the sagebushes, sharing this sort of cover with the Sagebrush Chipmunk.

Sagebrush Chipmunk. **Eutamias pictus** (Allen)

Field characters.—Size small (head and body 4 inches, tail about 3 inches long). (For comparative measurements see footnote 15, p. 177.) Usual chipmunk pattern of markings; general tone of coloration pale, grayish. (See pl. 3*a*.) Stripes on back dark brown and white, more highly contrasted than in Alpine Chipmunk; size somewhat smaller, tail shorter, and sides of body less deeply brownish than in Mono Chipmunk. *Voice:* A high-pitched *tsew;* also a rapid series of *chip*-ing notes.

Occurrence.—Abundant in Transition Zone east of Sierra Nevada, from Williams Butte eastward all around Mono Lake. Altitude ranging from 6400 to 8000 feet. Restricted to sagebrush association where it runs on ground or climbs up into the bushes.

The Sagebrush Chipmunk is to be looked for in the extensive tracts of sagebrush which cover the floor of the elevated inland desert surrounding Mono Lake. The prevailing gray tone of the region has been impressed on the chipmunk's pelage, though not to the degree shown in certain birds of the region. (See pl. 3*a*.) Yet the alternating stripes of dark brown and ashy white on the back are well contrasted. The species name *pictus*, meaning painted, seems highly appropriate, for the coloring looks as if it had been applied by lengthwise strokes of a brush.

No one need have special difficulty in identifying the Sagebrush Chipmunk in the Yosemite region, for it here keeps almost entirely to the one sort of shelter, namely, pure growths of the sagebrush, and it is the only species of chipmunk ordinarily found there. Along the line of contact where the sagebrush and mountain mahogany meet, the Sagebrush and Mono chipmunks may at times occur together. There is no certain way of distinguishing these two out of hand. A larger, heavier, and more brownish colored animal which keeps to the heavier chaparral and vicinity of trees is likely to be *monoensis,* while a smallish gray-toned individual which runs on the ground beneath the bushes is probably *pictus*.

In size and general habits the Sagebrush Chipmunk is most like the Alpine Chipmunk. It is an active animal, running about on the ground a great deal, and carrying its tail up in a prominent manner, nearly or quite perpendicular to the back, as it goes. Sometimes several of these animals will play about a brush patch, as many as six having been noted together on one occasion. Now and then one individual will give chase to another and a long continued pursuit will follow. Although giving voice to the usual calls of chipmunks when occasion demands, this species is, as a rule, rather quiet. When frightened, an individual will take shelter beneath or within the densest brush.

The Sagebrush Chipmunks were still active when our party quitted the Mono country on September 23, 1915. In the spring of 1916, the first definite record for the species was made on May 18, although the animals must have emerged from hibernation at a much earlier date. A female captured on this date was already suckling young. In favorable areas there is a large population of these animals. More than two dozen were noted in one hour on the morning of September 17, 1915, while one of our party was going from Williams Butte toward Mono Craters. On several other occasions during the same week six an hour was the average seen.

Some Sagebrush Chipmunks captured near Williams Butte on September 23, 1915, had their cheek pouches crammed with seeds of *Kunzia*, which, to the human taste, are exceedingly bitter.

CALIFORNIA GRAY SQUIRREL. **Sciurus griseus griseus** Ord

Field characters.—A typical squirrel, of large size; general form slender; tail a conspicuous 'brush,' about equaling body in length, broad and flat. (See pls. 33*b*, 34.) Head and body 10 to 11⅝ inches (256–296 mm.), tail (excluding hairs at end) 9½ to 11 inches (240–280 mm.), hind foot about 3 inches (72–80 mm.), ear (from crown) 1⅛ to 1½ inches (28–36 mm.); weight 26 to 32 ounces (733–913 grams). Coloration above uniform gray, with light steel gray pepper and salt effect at close range; under surface of body pure white; tail gray margined with white. *Voice:* A hoarse, asthmatic coughing note, uttered usually in slow series. *Workings:* Kitchen middens, consisting of remains of pine cones dissected to obtain seeds; nests of large size among branches of coniferous trees, or else in cavities in oaks.

Occurrence.—Resident in Upper Sonoran and Transition zones on west slope of Sierra Nevada. Recorded from Pleasant Valley eastward to Aspen Valley, Yosemite Valley, and Chinquapin. Inhabits large trees and ground close by. Diurnal. Solitary.

California Gray Squirrels are present in small numbers throughout the digger pine belt of the western foothills (Upper Sonoran Zone). The relatively small number of trees there and the consequent limited supply of nuts (upon which these animals largely subsist) is probably at the base of this sparseness of the squirrel population in that belt of territory. Immediately upon passing into the main forest belt of the mountains (Transition Zone), characterized by the presence of the yellow pine, the observer marks an increase in the numbers of these squirrels, doubtless correlated with the denser stand of trees and much larger crop of various nuts. At the upper margin of the Transition Zone the range of the Gray Squirrel meets that of the Red Squirrel or Chickaree, a species of similar food habits; and the ensuing competition seems to be one of the factors operative in limiting the upward extension of the Gray Squirrel's range. (See fig. 27.)

The California Gray Squirrel population in the tree-clothed parts of the foothills is perhaps not more than one animal to every 10 acres; in the yellow pine belt there is perhaps one to every 3 or 4 acres. On the floor of Yosemite Valley, in certain years at least, the density of population reaches one an acre. In October of 1914 the numbers were at their maximum; more than 4000 were computed to be on the Valley floor and the lower slopes adjacent. But the squirrel population is subject to fluctuations from time to time and place to place. In the spring of 1916 the number of these animals on the floor of Yosemite Valley was very much less than in the fall of 1914.

The California Gray Squirrel is the largest of the local squirrels (save the marmot), being somewhat heavier than the California Ground Squirrel and very much bigger than any of the other species. The Gray Squirrel shows specialization for life in trees in several obvious ways. Its body and legs are long and slender and very strongly muscled so that it can leap considerable distances between branches. The toes are all provided with sharp curved claws which serve well in enabling the animal to cling to the irregularities of the bark of trees and to sprays of foliage. The tail is long and broadly haired to serve as rudder and counterbalance in the various movements of the animal. (See pls. 33b, 34.)

On the ground a Gray Squirrel moves by a series of jumps. The front and hind legs act in pairs, the front ones being held close together while the hind ones spread out widely and are carried forward beyond the body. When traveling at full speed one of these squirrels has been found to have covered as much as 4 feet in a single bound over snow. When ascending a tree its movement is similar; the squirrel 'gallops' up the trunk, often with all four feet off the bark at the same instant. The fine curved claws on the toes of each foot catch readily in the bark and hence the squirrel often has an even firmer hold when in a tree than when on the ground. In descending a tree, which the squirrel does head first, the hind feet are turned outward so that the claws of the hind toes will catch on the bark; and the feet are moved alternately.

Where trees are so close that the branches overlap or nearly touch, a Gray Squirrel may travel aloft for long distances without once coming to the ground; if occasion demands, the animal can run through the tree tops at a relatively high rate of speed.

California Gray Squirrels are active throughout the year, showing no tendency to hibernate as do the ground squirrels. On stormy days they usually remain in their nests, but they promptly fare forth as soon as the weather clears. Their ability to be abroad during the winter is probably due to the fact that their food, consisting of fruits, nuts, and fungi, is practically all aboveground, and that it persists nearly or quite through the winter. Moreover, when this food is most plentiful, in the autumn, the squirrels lay by a reserve, to be drawn upon later as needed. The greatest activity on the part of the Gray Squirrels comes in the fall months, when the season for acorns and pine cones is at its height, and when the squirrels embrace the opportunity to gather in reserve supplies. These nuts they store for the most part by burial in the ground, a nut here and a nut there over a considerable area in the vicinity of their headquarters.

The only note which the California Gray Squirrel has been heard to utter is a coarse, harsh 'cough' or bark which to the ears of most persons is anything but pleasant. While sometimes uttered singly, the notes are usually given in series of 4 to 6 at relatively short intervals; when a squirrel is excited several series of notes may be run together so as to be practically continuous. The Gray Squirrel's vocabulary is thus much less varied than that of the Red Squirrel. Twice, when members of our party were watching Gray Squirrels up in trees, the animals were seen to beat rapidly with one front foot (the left, in one of the cases, the right in the other) on the limbs on which they were resting. The noise in one case sounded like that made by a woodpecker. The squirrel seemed surprised or concerned at the observer's presence and this may have stimulated the pattering. Other mammals, for example wood rats and rabbits, are known to stamp with their feet when excited.

Gray Squirrels build nests as shelters in which to rear their young and as places in which the adults can find refuge during inclement weather and at night. Instead of choosing one type of location, two very different sorts of places are selected, and separate kinds of nests accordingly constructed. When natural cavities, resulting from the rotting out of good-sized branches, are available in oak trees, the squirrels line these cavities with soft material and use them. Failing to find some appropriate shelter the animals build regular nests, out in the open branch-work of trees, somewhat after the manner of many birds. The case is roughly paralleled by that of the Streator Wood Rat, which either builds stick 'houses' on the ground or in trees, or else occupies the interior of fallen logs or crevices in rocks.

Two 'outside' nests of the Gray Squirrel were found in separate but adjacent yellow pines of medium size on the divide between Bean and Smith creeks, east of Coulterville, on June 6, 1915. The two were so nearly alike as to location and details of construction that description of one will suffice. The height of the nest above the ground was about 60 feet; it was placed against the trunk of the tree (which at that height was about 3 inches in diameter) and it was supported by a whorl of branches. The outer, coarse framework of the nest was of yellow pine twigs ¼ to ½ inch in diameter and 6 to 18 inches in length; on many of these the dried terminal tassel of needles was still adhering. Within this broom-like envelope was a packed mass of softer material consisting of yellow pine needles, shredded bark of incense cedar, and grass stems, all dried. Here also were acorn hulls and shells of manzanita berries, suggesting that the occupant had eaten food while in the nest. There were also a few pebbles in this layer, but the reason for their presence was not evident. The innermost element, or nest proper, at the top of the structure, was of bark and grasses, finely shredded and consequently of very soft texture. The main bulk of the structure, below the nest cavity, was very damp, probably as a result of rains a couple of weeks previously. The outside dimensions of the whole structure were: average diameter 17½ inches, height 11 inches. The soft-lined cavity at the top was about 6 inches across and 3 inches deep at the center. After being removed from the tree the whole structure was found to weigh 10 pounds. There was no canopy or covering to this particular nest, though as a rule outside nests are roofed over.

Other nests of California Gray Squirrels were 'spotted,' by members of our field party seeing the squirrels go to them. One outside nest, in Yosemite Valley, was about 75 feet above the ground in a lodgepole pine. At Smith Creek a nest was found in a black oak, in a cavity formed by the rotting out of a large branch 35 feet above the ground. The soft nest in which the young had been reared was 2 feet below the entrance hole. In Yosemite Valley several squirrels were seen to disappear into cavities high up in black oaks. On three occasions in early September, Gray Squirrels were seen carrying to such nests loads of lining material. One animal in particular, seen scampering along a road, had long wisps of grass sticking out on both sides of its mouth. The squirrel ran up a black oak and disappeared with the material into a hole near the top of the tree. Another, in Yosemite Valley on December 24, 1914, was carrying in a great roll of needles of the yellow pine.

The two principal items in the diet of the California Gray Squirrel are the seeds of pines and the acorns of oaks. These, together, are available over a long season; and the squirrel tides over the balance of the year by gathering and hiding away a surplus. 'Bracket fungi' growing on the trunks of trees are eaten at times. There is a strong suspicion, supported by much circumstantial evidence but by little direct observation, that Gray Squirrels rob birds' nests in season. A change to a diet of fresh meat may be sometimes welcome.

The seeds of the yellow pine and sugar pine are eagerly sought by all the Gray Squirrels living within the territory occupied by these trees. In the foothill country the seeds of the digger pine are gathered. With the advent of the first new seed-bearing cones in midsummer the squirrels turn their attention to the pine trees and continue to use the cones until the last of them are gone, in late winter.

When in search of food, a squirrel will run about the branches of a tree until it finds a suitable cone and then with a few quick strokes of the sharp incisor teeth will cut through the stem of the cone. Light cones are usually seized, carried to some convenient place in the tree, and there opened up, but a heavy cone is let fall to the ground. Often several cones are cut off in quick succession, then the squirrel descends, to attend further to its harvest. If the cones are not too heavy the squirrel seizes one in its mouth and repairs to some log or lower branch in the tree. But if too heavy to carry, as in the case of the cone of a sugar pine, the cone is opened right on the ground where it fell, or it may be dragged a little ways, up close to the base of the tree. The procedure in opening the cone to obtain the seeds is practically always the same; most cones are held in the forepaws, but very heavy ones are turned over and over on the ground.

A pine cone consists of a central core upon which the flattened scales are disposed in spiral series. Beneath each scale, in the case of the pines and firs, lie two seeds. The squirrel, to obtain the seeds in the green cone, begins at the upper (stem) end and systematically cuts off the scales at their points of attachment to the core. To do this the cone is rotated so as to bring fresh uncut scales before the animal's chisel-like teeth. At the upper end of the cone, seeds are small or wanting; but as soon as this region is passed, the removal of each scale uncovers two large seeds. These, in the green cone, already have the covering which later becomes the shell of the pine nut, and also the flat wing; but the seed coat is still soft and a stroke or two of the teeth exposes the green yet tasty meat which is, of course, the objective of all the squirrel's efforts. This process of cutting off scales and disposing of the seeds is continued until nothing remains but the stripped core and a pile of scales and shells of seeds. All through the summer, autumn, and winter months these fresh kitchen middens are to be seen on the ground at the bases of large trees, or on logs or boulders, showing where the squirrels have been feasting.

Acorns from the black, golden, or live oaks are either picked in the trees, one at a time, or else gathered up after they have ripened and fallen to the ground. If to be consumed on the spot only a few strokes of the teeth are needed to shell out the meat or 'mast.' But many of the acorns are buried entire in the ground, single nuts being placed in little pits dug here and there, and then carefully covered up. There is no doubt whatsoever that this habit of the Gray Squirrels is a beneficent one with respect to reforestation, in that they *plant* the seeds of valuable trees; for probably some of their caches are never found. Then, too, many a squirrel comes to grief before it has had a chance to benefit from its storage proclivities.

A female Gray Squirrel watched in Yosemite Valley on May 19, 1919, was spending much of her time on the ground seeking out acorns buried (presumably by the same animal) during the preceding autumn. The squirrel went along hesitatingly, with her nose close to the ground, moving this way and that, as though she were *smelling* for the nuts. When she found a promising prospect she would whisk aside the winter's deposit of pine needles with her forefeet and then dig rapidly down 2 inches or less, pulling the earth toward her and heaping it beneath her chest. If an acorn was found, the squirrel would dislodge it with her teeth and then and there, sitting back on her haunches, immediately shell out and eat the nut. In one instance an acorn which was dug up was buried again in a new place ten feet away. The squirrel tamped the earth down over it with her nose and forepaws and then raked pine needles over the place. Only about one in three of the places which were prospected yielded acorns; so we may infer that these animals are not infallible. It would seem that the sense of smell must be relied upon to find these 'planted' acorns. After the winter's snow, rain, and wind, with much movement of oak leaves and pine needles on the surface of the ground, accurate memory of the sites is apparently out of the question. Furthermore, one of the acorns which the squirrel dug up and replanted, and which one of us later examined, had a distinctly sour odor, clearly perceptible to our gross sense of smell.

In this particular instance we have support for the belief that instinct rather than reason controls the squirrel's food-getting activities. There was no real need for this squirrel's activity, because there had been an extremely abundant crop of acorns on the black oaks during the preceding winter and acorns were still to be found on the ground in large numbers. The squirrel could have found much more forage in a given period of time by moving a short distance into the oak forest; yet she remained and foraged beneath the pines in the instinctive manner which serves her in a season of shortage.

In Yosemite Valley on October 8, 1914, a large 'bracket' fungus growing at a height of 15 feet on the trunk of a black oak showed many tooth marks of Gray Squirrels (and possibly some made by Flying Squirrels); there were also many 'crumbs' on the ground beneath. The tooth marks were mostly on the under surface; the top surface was tough and leathery. The free edge had been gnawed literally to shreds and the indication was that most of the mass had been eaten away. When found, the base against the tree was 9 inches (230 mm.) wide and 3½ inches (90 mm.) high, and the mass projected out 5 inches (120 mm.) from the trunk. The taste, to the naturalist's tongue, was not unpleasant, somewhat like raw mushrooms, but rather woody. At other times gray squirrels were observed digging a tough kind of fungus out of the ground.

The conduct of the California Gray Squirrel in cutting down the green cones of the two important lumber trees, yellow and sugar pine, has been commented upon adversely by foresters. The claim is made that the squirrels consume so much of the seed that not enough is left for natural reforestation. This point, so far as we know, has not been thoroughly tested by experimentation; the issue now stands between the judgment of the forester on one hand, and that of the naturalist on the other. We do know that many other factors, such as parasitism of the growing trees by mistletoe or fungus, destruction by fire started by lightning or by human agency, and killing of young growth by grazing, operate to limit the numbers of the trees. And of the seeds which remain in cones on the tree, a very considerable percentage is attacked by certain insects whose young subsist on the embryo plant. The squirrels thus comprise but one factor out of many; attention is likely to be focused upon their work because of its conspicuousness; it is carried on in the open. Other agencies fully as significant operate in an unobtrusive manner, and their importance is thus likely to be underestimated.

It is our opinion that in most places where natural conditions still obtain, the necessary reseeding progresses as fast as is possible anyway, and that the activities of the squirrels do not retard the regeneration of the forest. Where man has interfered by logging off much of the timber or by close grazing, the case may be different.

One resident at Snyder Gulch stated to us that he believed that Gray Squirrels indirectly do damage to sugar pines by leaving heaps of cone scales at the bases of trees when shucking out seeds. When a forest fire sweeps over the country these piles take fire easily and start 'burns' at the bases of the trees. As bearing on this contention we noted many sugar pine trees with kitchen middens at their bases, and many trees showed basal burns which may have been made in the manner indicated. At Hazel Green there were heaps of scales about several oak trees, and at one particular tree there was a kitchen midden fully 18 inches high within the hollowed base of the tree.

The California Gray Squirrel, so far as known, rears but one brood of young each year, and this is brought off during the early summer months. None of the female squirrels which we obtained contained embryos; but litters elsewhere are known to range from 2 to 4. By midsummer the young animals are beginning to appear abroad, being then, on the average, about half the size of adults.

The Gray Squirrel population is affected by a number of factors. Birds of prey capture a certain percentage of the animals; some young are killed by falling out of the nest; other young animals are caught by dogs, and in wild country probably also by native carnivores; disease greatly reduces the ranks of the Gray Squirrels from time to time, as is known to have been the case in other places in California; and, most important of all, the downward fluctuations in the crops of seeds on the principal food trees operate to limit the population.

Locally, interference by man is operating to reduce the pressure exerted by native carnivorous species on the Gray Squirrel. In Yosemite Valley, the government authorities have favored the elimination of coyotes, bob-cats, and other natural checks. This has evidently worked to the advantage of the Gray Squirrels, and accounts, in part at least, for the great numbers of animals present during certain recent years on the floor of the Valley. To our way of thinking, this sort of interference is doubly disadvantageous. A National Park ought to be a "natural" park, where the "balance of nature" can remain undisturbed.

SIERRA CHICKAREE. **Sciurus douglasii albolimbatus** Allen

Field characters.—Body size a third that of Gray Squirrel, about equal to that of House Rat; tail about ⅔ length of head and body, brush-like, with long hairs at sides; ears tall, slightly tufted (fig. 29). Head and body 7⅜ to 8¼ inches (188–209 mm.), tail 4⅜ to 5½ inches (111–139 mm.), hind foot about 2 inches (48–54 mm.), ear (from crown) ⅘ to 1⅕ inches (21–30 mm.); weight 7¾ to 10½ ounces (218–299 grams). General coloration above dark brown; a reddish tinge along back; a black line along each side sharply marking off the white or buffy color of under surface; feet light reddish brown; tail blackish with silvery white hair-tippings. *Voice:* A short explosive note, *quer-o,* often repeated; also a prolonged whickering or whinneying, of high-pitched notes uttered 4 or 5 a second and continued for several seconds. *Workings:* Pine and fir cones cut green and cached on ground about logs; kitchen middens consisting of remains of cones which have been dissected, on the ground (fig. 31), on tops of logs (pl. 36b), or on large rocks; freshly cut foliage scattered on ground beneath trees (pl. 35b).

Occurrence.—Common resident throughout Canadian and Hudsonian zones to extreme upper limit of forest on both slopes of Sierra Nevada; sparingly represented in upper part of Transition Zone on west slope. Recorded from Sequoia, Hazel Green, and Chin-quapin eastward across mountains to Leevining Creek and Walker Lake. Also on Mono Craters. Found at times in Yosemite Valley. Altitudinal range 4000 to 11,000 feet. Inhabits coniferous trees. Diurnal. Solitary.

From the lower border of the fir woods to the extreme upper limit of tree growth, the most conspicuous day-moving mammal is the Sierra Chickaree or Red Squirrel. This species is not found in the company of its relative, the Gray Squirrel, save where the ranges of the two overlap slightly on the west slope and in the exceptional instances when the chick-arees in numbers move down into the Transition Zone. Near Sequoia, at Hazel Green, and at Chinquapin the two have been found together. Occasional individuals are to be seen in Yosemite Valley; in the winter of 1918 large numbers of Red Squirrels moved down into the Valley from the surrounding high country, and some of them were still present at the beginning of summer in 1919. Individuals were seen in May of that year near Stoneman Bridge and opposite the base of Rocky Point. Locally the chickaree is known as pine squirrel, Douglas squirrel, and "bummer" squirrel.

The Sierra Chickaree is characteristically arboreal, and comes to the ground less often even than the California Gray Squirrel. Ordinarily it comes down only when attending to the disposition of cones which it has cut down, when going to drink, and when crossing open spaces between widely separated trees. Whenever possible it travels aloft, through the trees, jumping from one to another across gaps between their adjacent branches. The following account of the behavior of one of these squirrels at Glen Aulin, October 4, 1915, will indicate something of the strong desire of the animal to keep aboveground in the presence of danger. This squirrel, when come upon by one of our party, was on the ground. It ran quickly to the nearest lodgepole pine, ascended about 25 feet, ran out on a branch and jumped to a second tree. There it ascended about 5 feet higher and jumped to a third tree. This tree was separated from other neighboring trees by a distance too great for the animal to negotiate in a jump from branch to branch. The squirrel recognized this fact very quickly after running out on a limb, for almost immediately it returned to the trunk, descended rapidly to the ground, and ran to a fourth tree. This tree, too, was isolated from its neighbors, and the squirrel after climbing a few feet dropped down and ran to a fifth tree from which it was able to make off through the dense forest without having again to come to the ground. These squirrels will climb to the uppermost branches of forest trees, well out of shotgun range. In jumping, the animals can cover 3 or 4 feet at a single leap.

The Sierra Chickaree is remarkably endowed with 'vocabulary,' and in this respect is far better off than any of the other local squirrels. If the curiosity of a chickaree is piqued by a person's 'squeaking,' or from other cause, the animal will often come within a few feet of the observer and while clinging to the side of a tree by means of its sharp claws will utter a sharp interrogative-sounding note, *quer-o* or *quir-o,* every few seconds, accompanying each utterance by a spasmodic jump and a quick jerk of the tail. Not infrequently, if a person sits down under the tree in which one of these squirrels is performing, the animal will keep up this behavior for many minutes, occasionally retiring and then coming back for another look at the intruder and another series of vocal expressions. If the observer happens to jump up suddenly, the startled squirrel usually makes off up the tree, uttering a series of high-pitched squealing notes and 'galloping' so vigorously and rapidly up the trunk that a shower of bark slivers is dislodged as it goes. When undisturbed, off in the depths of the forest, the chickaree from time to time utters a prolonged series of whickering or whinneying notes of somewhat the same character as the single note, but in rapid succession, 4 or 5 a second, and this is kept up for several seconds. Such a series is sometimes answered by other squirrels in the neighborhood. When come upon suddenly a squirrel may give a single, startled, high-pitched squeal as it bounds toward safety. The young, during the fall months, can often be distinguished from the adults by their softer, less penetrating voices.

Fig. 29. Sierra Chickaree or "Red Squirrel." Photographed from fresh specimen taken near Yosemite Point, June 4, 1915; slightly over ⅓ natural size.

The chickaree, like the Gray Squirrel, is admirably adapted for life in the trees. The body is lithe yet muscular; the claws on all of the feet are curved and sharp so as to catch readily on the bark. (See fig. 29.) In going up a tree, the animal gallops, using the fore and hind feet in pairs; but in descending, it goes head downward moving the feet individually. On the ground the gait is also a gallop with the hind feet spread widely apart, carried forward at each bound, and planted ahead of the forefeet.

Despite the agility of the chickaree, occasionally an individual loses its foothold in a tree and falls to the ground. A young badly frightened animal at Gentrys in October, 1915, lost its footing and fell a distance of about 20 feet. Yet it immediately picked itself up and scampered up another tree. A tree squirrel seems able to distribute the shock of impact with the ground by spreading out all of its feet widely, thus saving itself from serious injury.

Tree squirrels, generally, are abroad all the winter. They are able to find food in greater or less abundance, even when the ground is covered with snow. Furthermore, the chickaree goes to great pains to provide a winter store of food, to be used to supplement whatever the animal can find by random foraging. In the late summer and early autumn, when the cones of many of the evergreen trees have attained full or nearly full size but are still green, the chickarees begin their annual harvest. The busy animals gnaw off the cones, and as a person walks through the forest where the squirrels are operating, cones may be seen or heard falling at frequent intervals. In fact there is some danger in being under the trees, especially when the heavy green cones of the Jeffrey pine, weighing several pounds apiece, come down from a height of a hundred feet or so. The cutting is more or less indiscriminate, as cones in all stages of development are cut—those in which seeds are well advanced as well as others in which the seeds are but partly formed. (See figs. 30, 31.)

a   b   c

Fig. 30. Sugar pine cones, (a) as cut down green by the Sierra Chickaree, (b) as matured and dropped naturally by the tree, and (c) the green cone core left after a squirrel has cut off the scales and eaten the seeds.

After cutting for a while a squirrel will descend to the ground and proceed to dispose of the cones which it has detached. Such cones as are not wanted for immediate use are cached on the ground under the sides of downed tree trunks and in other nooks and crannies in the vicinity of the animal's home. Cones so sheltered do not dry out so rapidly as they would if left out in the open. This is particularly important in the case of the cones of the white and red firs, as these, upon drying, go to pieces quickly and the seeds are scattered. In winter, when snow is on the ground, or in early spring, when other forage material is scarce, these cones which have been in cold storage are dug out and the seeds eaten.

An idea of the amount of work done by the chickarees in the Yosemite region may be gained from the following counts and estimates. At Aspen Valley, in October, 1915, a chickaree was found to have its headquarters close to our camp. The animal inhabited a group of seven white firs beneath which was a prostrate trunk. Within an area 50 by 50 feet in extent the junior author gathered 484 cones which had been cut down, evidently by this one squirrel (pl. 35a). Most of these had been carried to the side of the log where some had been partially buried in the ground. Others had been put into crevices in nearby trees. In one case a hole in a log about 18 inches deep had been crammed full of the green cones.

Above Yosemite Point, that same month, the senior author found the head-quarters of another chickaree which had been similarly engaged. This animal had cut down about 180 cones and these were cached at the two sides of a log within an area about 20 by 60 feet. If we assume that there is 1 chickaree to every 4 acres of territory in the Canadian Zone of our Yosemite section, then the 250 or more square miles of this zone harbor approximately 40,000 squirrels. If each squirrel on the average cuts but 250 cones a season, the annual harvest of fir cones in the Canadian Zone on the west slope of the Yosemite region would be about 10 million. In

Fig. 31. Kitchen middens of Sierra Chickaree: shelled-out green cones of Jeffrey pine; Merced Lake, August 28, 1915.

addition there are many Red Squirrels in the Hudsonian Zone, and some in the Canadian Zone of the Mono region, all cutting down cones of the various species of coniferous trees present in those areas.

One morning in mid-October at Aspen Valley, the same squirrel that had garnered the great number of white fir cones referred to above was seen to run down the home tree, grasp a cone in its mouth, and ascend the trunk to a short horizontal stub about 30 feet above the ground. Here it sat up on its haunches, grasped the two ends of the cone by its forefeet, and proceeded to rapidly strip off the scales. After a few scales had been removed there would ensue a few moments of rapid chewing of the exposed seeds and then more scales would be cut off and come fluttering to the ground. Most frequently the squirrel begins at the stem end and, gradually rotating the cone, strips the scales off in the order in which they are attached to the core, from base to tip. But sometimes work is begun at the tip of the cone and occasionally in the middle.

Among the great number of cones lying on the ground there are many which have been only partially dissected, and this is true also of the cones comprising the caches. These may have been sampled and then put away for future use, or perhaps an animal has been frightened and forced to drop the cone before finishing it.

At Porcupine Flat on July 1, 1915, a typical kitchen midden of a chickaree was found by the authors on top of a prostrate tree trunk (pl. 36*b*). The material comprised remains of red fir cones, namely cone-cores, scales, and seed wings. Several other logs in the vicinity were littered with similar débris, with accumulations on the ground beside them. Evidently there had been a fruiting fir tree near by from which the squirrel had gathered a large stock of cones the previous autumn. From time to time during the winter, as needed, the squirrel had retrieved the cones from their places of concealment, and had repaired to these logs to shell out the seeds. In early spring such logs, projecting above the snow, would also afford good lookouts whence a squirrel while at work could watch for possible danger— for the approach of a red fox, a pine marten, or a hawk.

Practically all the cone-bearing trees within the range of the chickaree are levied upon for food. We saw work upon the cones of the red and white firs, the alpine hemlock, and the lodgepole, Jeffrey, and mountain pines. The white-bark pine fruits only at long intervals, so it does not play any very important part in supplying food for the chickaree.

As might be expected, the faces of the squirrels, especially during the autumn, get somewhat smeared with pitch, and from time to time individuals may be seen engaged in vigorously cleaning their faces with their forepaws. But on the whole, the animals keep remarkably clean. If a person tries to get at the seeds in a green cone he will soon come to have respect for the skill of the squirrels in handling such material without becoming hopelessly pitchy.

It might be expected that such wholesale consumption of fir seeds by the chickaree would be detrimental to the forest. But in those protected areas of the Yosemite region where man has interfered slightly or not at all with the natural balance and where tree squirrels have lived for untold generations, the forest appears to be of maximum density and the young growth coming along is sufficient to effect full replacement of natural loss among the mature trees. Despite the heavy inroads which the squirrels make, a certain percentage of cones always escapes their attention, and remains on the trees; these cones mature and scatter their seed in usual fashion. Indeed the cutting off of a considerable percentage of the fruits (cones with seeds) by the squirrels may even be of benefit to the trees. It is analogous to the operations of an orchardist who thins out the fruit on his trees in order to obtain a moderate number of full-sized, vigorous fruits rather than many small or average ones. Examination of the ground beneath pine trees patronized by chickarees shows, during the spring and summer, considerable numbers of cones in which the seed has matured naturally and has fallen before the cones themselves have dropped. It would appear that the squirrels merely harvest a surplus. At Aspen Valley, in the autumn of 1915, where tree squirrels were present in as goodly numbers as in any place which we have studied, there were in addition to mature trees many close stands of healthy young firs and pines.

Like the California Gray Squirrel the present species is thought at times to raid birds' nests, though the extent to which this is practiced is not known with any degree of accuracy. At Merced Lake on August 23, 1915, a Wood Pewee was seen vigorously pursuing a chickaree. The pewee was scolding furiously and the squirrel was retreating rapidly. At Chinquapin, on May 20, 1919, a robin was seen flying at a chickaree, snapping her beak within a short distance of the latter. The squirrel was in full retreat down a tree. Instances of this sort have been taken to mean that the squirrels prey upon eggs or young; but much direct observation is needed to prove the actual extent of the squirrel's operations in this regard.

We have, on one occasion, seen a chickaree eating the small pollen-bearing (staminate) cones of a yellow pine. This was on May 18, 1919, in the neighborhood of Nevada Falls. In late summer the tender 'needle-buds' of coniferous trees are eaten. A squirrel in Lyell Cañon on July 24, 1915, had its stomach filled with chewed-up buds of the lodgepole pine.

Red Squirrels are often attracted by meat bait placed about steel traps for the larger animals, and a considerable number of these squirrels was obtained in our efforts to trap coyotes, badgers, martens, and similar carnivores. At Merced Lake a chickaree was taken in a trip baited with fish entrails and set for mink. We also captured chickarees in unbaited traps set in burrows of Aplodontia and out of sight from aboveground. Some, at least, of the squirrels taken under the latter circumstances were probably en route to drinking places.

The autumn of 1915 witnessed great activity on the part of the chickarees in the Yosemite region. The animals were very busy harvesting their food for winter use. Old-timers in the mountains remarked to us upon this activity by the squirrels, saying that it was sign of a heavy winter coming. There was a big crop of cones that fall; and the winter of 1915–1916 did prove to be marked by heavy snowfall. But that there is any ability on the part of the native animals to predict the nature of the whole season is exceedingly doubtful.

A nest of the Sierra Chickaree was found at Merced Lake on August 27, 1915, the identity being established by seeing the squirrel itself visit the place. The nest was located in an old, much rotted and burned out Jeffrey pine stub about 15 feet high and between 5 and 6 feet in diameter. The entrance to the nest was about 12 feet above the ground, on the north side of the stub, and measured about 2 inches in vertical diameter and 2½ inches transversely. This entrance hole led into an old woodpecker excavation some 6 inches in diameter and 12 or 13 inches high. In the bottom of this cavity was about a pint of fine dry material, small chips remaining from the woodpecker tenancy, and twigs, dry grass, cone scales, and squirrel faeces. From this old cavity a passageway or hollow place in the wood (of which there were many) led down into a larger cavity 18 inches in transverse diameter and nearly 36 inches in the vertical dimension. The chickaree's nest was in this place and to judge from the condition of some of the material the location had been occupied for several seasons or at least for more than one. The total bulk of material which had been carried in by the squirrel was estimated at about 12 quarts. Included were the following items: leaves and twigs of the aspen which had evidently been brought in fresh during the current and previous season; shredded bark of the aspen; moss, both green and dry; staminate cones of lodgepole pine; cores and scales of dissected pistillate cones of both lodgepole pine and Jeffrey pine; mistletoe from coniferous trees; and on top of the whole, as 'bedding,' many freshly cut twig ends of lodgepole pine, with green needles still adhering. These latter varied in length from 1½ to 6 inches, averaging about 3 inches. Droppings were found in but one place in the main nest.

The outer surface of this Jeffrey pine stub was quite smooth; yet it offered no particular difficulties to the squirrel, which was seen to run down from the top past the hole, then turn around and enter the cavity. Adjacent to the stub was a thicket of aspens and lodgepole pines. The nearest live Jeffrey pine was about 50 feet away.

On June 29, 1915, we found a place on the Tioga Road a short distance east of Porcupine Flat where a chickaree had been getting material for a nest. From a slender lodgepole pine about 90 feet high and 12 inches in diameter the squirrel had cut off numerous terminal branchlets with their adhering needles, and left them strewn about on the ground beneath the tree (pl. 35b.) In an area about 15 feet square we counted more than 350 twigs, and it was estimated that there were more than 500 altogether. The pieces varied from 2 to 12 inches in length, averaging about 6 inches. None of the twigs, save one or two from which apparently the young cones had been removed, showed any indication that they had been worked upon after being cut off. Comparison with other trees in the vicinity showed that one-half or more of the terminal foliage of this particular tree had been removed.

Other cuttings of similar sort were seen in the head of Lyell Cañon in mid-July. On July 24, 1915, in the same locality, a chickaree was shot while running over a rock slide. The animal was found to have a bundle of bark in its mouth. This was probably intended for nest lining.

Most of the young chickarees in the Yosemite region are born in June and July, though our data leading to this statement are rather meager. An adult female taken July 19, 1915, in Lyell Cañon contained 5 embryos. This is probably an average litter. A female taken as late as October 3 (1915) was found to have the mammary glands functional; hence, to be the mother of a late litter. The young are cared for by the parent until late September or early October, when they are half- or two-thirds grown; at this time the visible chickaree population is considerably augmented by the appearance of the young, whose softer voices are then to be heard on every hand.

SIERRA FLYING SQUIRREL. **Glaucomys sabrinus lascivus** (Bangs)

Field characters.—Body size about ⅔ that of House Rat; body flattened, with a broad fur-covered extension of the skin along each side between fore and hind feet (fig. 32); tail heavily furred, flat; eyes large; pelage dense and soft, silky in texture. Head and body 5½ to 6½ inches (142–166 mm.), tail 4½ to 5¾ inches (116–145 mm.), hind foot about 1½ inches (36–39 mm.), ear from crown ¾ to 1 inch (18 to 26 mm.); weight 3½ to 5¾ ounces (103.5–164.5 grams). General color above dark leaden gray; under surface of body dull white; both surfaces of tail dark gray. *Voice:* A low *whurr.*

Occurrence.—Moderately common resident in Transition and Canadian zones on west slope of Sierra Nevada. Recorded from Smith Creek, 6 miles east of Coulterville, and from Sweetwater Creek, eastward to Merced Lake and Porcupine Flat. Inhabits trees, chiefly black oaks and red firs, dwelling in holes in daytime, coming forth at night.

The Sierra Flying Squirrel is relatively common in the main coniferous belt of the Sierra Nevada, and a considerable population of the species lives right in Yosemite Valley. Yet, because it comes forth only under cover of darkness and then goes about in a very quiet manner, its activities and even its presence are known to very few persons.

The use of the word 'flying' in connection with this squirrel is not strictly accurate. The animal is unable to course about freely in the air, in the way of a bat or a bird. It can only volplane from a high perch to a lower one and is therefore a 'glider,' rather than a 'flyer.' The structure of the Flying Squirrel is modified importantly in several respects to ensure success in this mode of progression. Yet it has not, of course, reached an extreme specialization of structure anywhere near that of a bat. Its feet are nearly normal in form, and its toes are provided with claws like those of other squirrels, so that it is able to run about on all fours. It has a broad brush-like tail, roughly similar to that of other arboreal squirrels.

The body of the Flying Squirrel is somewhat flattened and along each side there is a fur-covered double layer of skin extending between the fore and hind legs and out to the 'wrist' and 'ankle.' (See fig. 32.) This sort of membrane, when extended, about doubles the area of the lower surface of the animal and thus contributes to the success of the squirrel's passage through the air. The tail is broad, due to a thick, close covering of long hairs at the sides, and is remarkably thin, reminding one, *in toto*, of a single tail feather of a bird. The fur everywhere is dense, of even length, and of a silky texture. The under surface of the body, which is of course exposed during 'flight,' has a proportionately heavier covering of fur than is present on other squirrels. Indeed, this heavy furring covers even the feet, save for the sole pads. This type of pelage, besides serving to keep the animal warm during the cold Sierran nights when it is abroad, also makes for passage *quietly* through the air, a necessary precaution in a region where owls are abundant.

Fig. 32. Sierra Flying Squirrel. Photographed from fresh specimen trapped in Yosemite Valley, December 24, 1914; about ⅔ natural size.

The head of the Flying Squirrel, and particularly the eyes, are proportionately large as compared with the head and eyes of other members of the squirrel tribe. Indeed the combination of large head and eyes and soft body covering reminds one strongly of the condition found in such nocturnal birds as the poor-wills and nighthawks.

Information concerning the Flying Squirrel is much more difficult to obtain than concerning the species of squirrels which are abroad in the daytime. Our own knowledge of it was gained partly by sleeping out at night under the trees, where the animals might be expected to occur, and partly by trapping. A large number of traps was set at likely places, such as the mounds at the bases of black oaks and red firs and the tops of fallen logs adjacent to standing trees.

At Merced Grove on the night of June 15, 1915, at about 10 P.M., one of us while in his sleeping bag was aroused by a soft thud made by a Flying Squirrel which alighted on the base of a white fir close by. It scuttled up the tree, and in the dim light the observer was able to note that this particular animal carried its tail above its back like other tree squirrels. In climbing up the bark it made less noise than a Red Squirrel. In Yosemite Valley, one night in June, one of us heard the low chuckling notes of a Flying Squirrel and the scratching of the animal's claws on the bark of a big yellow pine.

At Gentrys, Flying Squirrels were heard on several nights in October of 1915. Their voices reminded one of the low vibrant *whurr* of a cord suddenly whipped through the air. Needles and other small débris kept falling from the trees, shaken down by the squirrels. At 8 P.M. on October 22 they were heard in at least three places, all within 150 feet of the location of our camp amid some sugar pines and white firs.

At Chinquapin at about 6 P.M. on May 19, 1919, one of us, while searching for occupied woodpecker holes, tapped the side of a dead bole. At this, a Flying Squirrel put its head out of a hole about 12 feet above the ground, gazed down at the disturber for a few seconds, and then drew back inside again.

In Yosemite Valley a young Flying Squirrel was captured by a cat on July 13, 1915. Another young squirrel was brought to us by a Valley resident on September 16, 1915. It had fallen from the nest hole high in a black oak near the government stables adjacent to the old presidio.

At Merced Grove in June, 1915, the cook of a construction crew complained that some animal had been getting into a box of crackers in the cook tent. This was close by our own camp. A rat trap was set on the box and at about 8 P.M. it was heard to go off. Investigation showed a Flying Squirrel caught across the back. It was still alive and so was taken out of the trap and placed in an improvised cage. Another squirrel was taken similarly at about 2 A.M. a few nights later. It was placed with the first. Neither of these squirrels seemed harmed by being caught in the rat trap. Possibly the heavy pelage and broad body so distributed the blow that it was not as serious as it might otherwise have been. One squirrel was in the trap half an hour before being rescued. The first squirrel was active on the morning following its capture, probably because of its unusual surroundings. Thereafter it spent most of the daytime in sleep, becoming active at night. When asleep the broad furry tail was wrapped over the face. Some redwood bark was put into the cage and the squirrel soon began to fashion a nest with it. Various items from the camp food supply were offered. Oatmeal was taken by preference, then bread crusts. Dried prunes, put in at the same time, were not touched until later. Once during the day one of the squirrels washed its face by licking its forepaws and then rubbing them over its face.

At Porcupine Flat a red fir stub was found to be inhabited by Flying Squirrels. Two of the animals were trapped there and evidence of a third obtained, after which the trunk was cut down and examined. The stub was about 40 feet high and 5 feet in diameter, hollow at the base, and well rotted interiorly. Inside, just beneath the bark, at a height of 10 feet above the level of the ground, was a nest which was at least one year old. It was composed chiefly of shredded bark. In a cavity in the center of the tree, at the same level, was a new nest, evidently incomplete. This was made of twig ends from the red fir, rolled into a spherical mass about 5½ inches (140 mm.) in diameter. The twigs used were ⅛ inch or less in diameter and from 1 to 4 inches in length. They had been cut off neatly from the extreme ends of the smaller branches of the fir, and green needles were still adhering to the twigs. There was as yet no internal cavity in this nest. Below the newer nest was a large mass of fir twigs. Various cavities in the stump below the two nests contained droppings, suggesting extended occupancy. Lumbermen near Chinquapin told of cutting down a tree in which a nest containing two young was found.

A pure albino Flying Squirrel, with pink eyes and pink claws, was found in Yosemite Valley in August, 1918. It had been drowned in a water bucket in Camp 17. This specimen was mounted and on exhibition in the Superintendent's Office in 1919.

The young of the Flying Squirrel are produced during the summer season. The broods are small, and evidently but one brood is reared each season. Four females containing embryos were collected, as follows: June 11, Merced Grove Big Trees, 2 small embryos; June 18, Mono Meadow, 4 embryos; June 29, Porcupine Flat, two specimens, one with 2 small embryos, the other with 4 large embryos. A young individual, scarcely half-grown, was taken in Yosemite Valley on July 13. A quarter-grown youngster, which fell out of its nest in a black oak, was obtained in the Valley on September 16; this represented an exceptionally late brood. Two individuals, obtained at Aspen Valley on October 17 and at Sweetwater Creek on October 31, were about half-grown. All these young animals were well furred and all, including the smallest one, had obvious 'flight membranes.'

The enemies of the Sierra Flying Squirrel are not known with certainty. Several individuals which had come to grief in different ways were noted by our party. In Yosemite Valley the dried remains of one was found on the ground. On the Yosemite Falls trail, November 19, 1915, one was

.een partly buried in the snow and minus its head; some predatory animal
vas probably responsible. At Smith Creek, Mr. Donald D. McLean once
'ound a Flying Squirrel hanging on a barbed wire fence. It had probably
ailed against the wire in the dark and received a mortal wound.

GOLDEN BEAVER. Castor canadensis subauratus Taylor

Field characters.—Body stout and heavy; head blunt; tail flattened, paddle-like,
scaly; hind feet webbed; pelage dense, with long over-hair and plush-like underfur.
Head and body 24½ to 31¾ inches (625–805 mm.), tail 11½ to 16½ inches (295–420
mm.), hind foot 7 to 8 inches (180–205 mm.), ear (from crown) ⅞ to 1⅛ inches
(23–28 mm.); weight 34 to 50 pounds (15.4–21.8 kilograms). General coloration rich
golden brown; tail blackish. *Workings:* Dams composed of brush and mud, backing
up water and forming ponds; 'houses' composed of twigs and brush, located at the edges
of ponds; gnawings on saplings and tree trunks; holes or burrows about 15 inches in
diameter in banks of rivers.

Occurrence.—Resident in some numbers along Merced River at Snelling and along
Tuolumne River below Lagrange. Inhabits slow-moving streams and sloughs. Nocturnal.
Somewhat colonial.

Under original conditions, before the advent of the white man, the
lowland streams of central California were heavily populated by the Golden
Beaver, a race of beaver peculiar to the Great Central Valley of California.
Trapping, especially in the early part of the nineteenth century, reduced
the beaver population almost to the point of extermination. Happily,
legislation of more recent years has afforded the animals the fullest sort
of legal protection and the prospects for their perpetuation are now bright.

One of the regions where beavers are still to be found, and in some
numbers, is the extreme western end of the Yosemite section, along the
lower courses of the Merced and Tuolumne rivers west of the foothills.
In fact, in 1920, in the neighborhood of Snelling, permission was granted
to certain persons by the State authorities for the trapping of a number
of beavers. The animals had become numerous enough to cause some
trouble in irrigation.

The beaver is essentially an aquatic animal. It is to be found only
in places where there are considerable and permanent bodies of water
together with vegetation suited to the food requirements of the animal.
The water serves the beaver as a place of escape in time of danger, and as
a highway for travel and for transportation of the pieces of trees which
it uses in its many operations.

The food of the Golden Beaver consists chiefly of young bark of the
willow and the cottonwood, the two commonest trees along the rivers. To
get at this material, the animal cuts down trees or shrubby growths and
cuts off the branches, of which it eats the bark of the terminal, newer parts.
The peeled wood and other remaining materials are often used for building

dams and houses. In 1915, near Snelling, beaver work was seen on cotton woods up to 2 feet in diameter, though stems and boles of much smaller size are more often sought.

One particular cottonwood 10 inches in diameter was seen east of Snelling on which a beaver had been at work for some time. The tooth marks showed that the beaver had turned its head sideways when cutting. The chips lying on the ground below the notch in the tree were from to 2 inches long, ⅛ to ½ inch wide, and 1/16 inch thick. Each consisted of two or more flakes, loosely joined, indicating that several bites had to be taken before a chip was entirely severed. The cutting on this tree was on the side away from the water, yet the tree when downed would have fallen into the river.

In the neighborhood of Snelling, both above and below the town, much work of the beaver can be found along the Merced River and in the ponds and sloughs which were formed there in past years when gold dredgers were operating. On the Tuolumne River, also, within 3 miles below Lagrange, the industry of the beavers is manifest. Most or all of the work of the beaver is done under the cover of darkness, so that the activities of the animal have to be inferred from evidence of a circumstantial nature; but such evidence is in this case unmistakable. It consists of trees upon which the animals are cutting or which they have cut down, pieces of wood from which the bark has been peeled, refuge or nest holes in the banks of sloughs, broad runways beneath the stream-side vegetation or up over dikes, dams across the larger sloughs, and, lastly, houses in or on the banks of the ponds formed by these dams.

On January 9, 1915, two beaver dams near Snelling were examined in detail by the senior author. The first dam was across a narrow and shallow slough between a rock pile left by a dredger on the one side and a river-cut bank on the other. The dam, though small, was perfect, and was curved, with the convex side downstream. (See pl. 37b.) The bottom of the pond just above the dam had been deepened by digging out rocks and mud to contribute to the dam. The dimensions of the dam were as follows: length along curve 12½ feet (3.8 meters); radius of arc about 10 feet (3 meters); thickness of base at middle, 31 inches (0.78 meters); total height on lower side 19½ inches (0.5 meter); depth of water just inside dam, 15¼ inches (0.39 meter); rise in water level of pond due to dam, 12 inches (0.3 meter). The dam consisted of two types of sticks, dead drift, and freshly cut green willow, some with the bark gnawed off. The pieces used were up to 2 inches (50 mm.) in diameter. Some freshly peeled sections of young willow stems and twigs averaging a yard in length were used. There were also whole untrimmed tops of willows, just as cut off, on the adjacent margins of the slough within 100 yards of the place. The interstices of the dam were filled in with small peeled willow twigs, grass pulled up by the roots, roots of other vegetation, and rocks up to 6 inches (150 mm.) in diameter. Some of these rounded rocks had been placed on the rim of the dam, on top of everything else, as if to weight down the mass. The whole structure was notably level-topped and symmetrical in curvature. Although newly made and relatively small, it already served to raise the water level in the slough.

The second dam, a much larger affair, was built across the mouth of a slough where it emptied into the main Merced. This dam was built by the beavers on a foundation of large rocks which some boys had placed to deepen the water in a swimming hole above; but the curvature (or rather the two arcs of the curvature) did not, evidently, relate in any way to the foundation which had been put down by the boys. One end of this dam had been carried away by flood water in the slough. It had been about 40 feet (12 meters) long originally; about one-third had been washed away. The width at base was about 5 feet (1.5 meters) and the height 27 inches (0.68 meter). The material used was much the same as for the first one described.

At one place in the bank of a sluggish stream a beaver's refuge hole 1½ feet in diameter was found. This opened beneath the level of the water in the slough and led into a tunnel in the adjacent bank of hard packed sand. The tunnel when opened up was found to be about 10 feet in length, and the upper inner end was 4 feet below the surface of the bank but above the water level in the slough. It contained no nest, nor was there any branching to the passageway. Beaver runways were seen on the bank and there were fresh chewings on the new shoots rising from the trunk of a prostrate willow near by.

In one place a large 'bed' was found on a bank heavily overgrown by willows and other plant growths along the adjacent stream. This bed was about 4 inches in thickness and 5 feet in diameter and was composed of bark which had been stripped off from some large sections of willow trunk which were lying water-logged in the stream near by.

Beavers when present in a region stand in varying relations to the different persons who are carrying on agricultural operations there. For example, one resident at Snelling considered that the beavers, by raising the water level in the sloughs where their ponds were formed, were of aid to him in that they kept the water-table beneath his land high, and thus secured for him good subirrigation. On the other hand, certain farmers held the animals to be a nuisance, because they persisted in stopping up irrigation ditches. In former years, when the animals were numerous, their damming operations are said to have resulted in the frequent flooding of fields.

With the protection now afforded, we may hope that beavers will continue to live along these streams in goodly numbers especially in those places where their presence is not troublesome to the ranchers. From the standpoint of the naturalist and nature-lover, the beaver is one of the most interesting mammals in the fauna of the Yosemite region.

YOSEMITE CONY. **Ochotona schisticeps muiri** Grinnell and Storer

Field characters.—Body size near that of House Rat; body short, face region rounded, ears large and round, eyes small; tail so short as to be not visible. (See pl. 38*a*.) Head and body 6 to 7 inches (155–180 mm.), tail (vertebrae) ⅖ to ⅗ inch (10–16 mm.), hind foot 1⅛ to 1¼ inches (28–32 mm.), ear (from crown) ⅞ to 1⅛ inches (22–27 mm.); weight 4 to 5½ ounces (112–159 grams). General coloration pale gray, with more or less of a reddish cast, especially in summer. *Voice:* A high-pitched, 'stony' *check-ick,* uttered once; at times, a more excited, repeated, *check-ick, check-ick, check-icky,* which may be kept up for 10 to 15 seconds. *Workings:* Small piles and scattered bits of grasses and other plants, cut green and cured as 'hay.' *Droppings:* rabbit-like, flattened spheres ⅛ inch in diameter deposited in groups on rocks; also stains of liquid excrement at or near tops of peaked, or roof-shaped, rocks, with other higher, sheltering rocks about.

Occurrence.—Common resident in Hudsonian Zone, extending down locally into upper part of Canadian Zone and up into Arctic-Alpine. Recorded from Ten Lakes, Tenaya Lake, and Washburn Lake eastward to Bloody Cañon and to Ellery Lake. Lives in rock slides (pl. 36*a*). Chiefly diurnal.

The Yosemite Cony is an alpine species, found only in the higher parts of the mountains above the fir belt, chiefly in the zone occupied by the alpine hemlock, white-bark pine, Sierran heather, and cassiope. Even within this narrow area it does not live everywhere, but is restricted to a single type of habitat, that comprised in moraines or taluses of broken granite. (See pl. 36*a*.) Altitudinally, the cony is found, in the Yosemite National Park, as low as 7700 feet, for example, near Glen Aulin, on the Tuolumne River; upward it ranges to about 12,000 feet, as on the slopes of Mount Dana and on the very summit of Parsons Peak, 12,120 feet.

In one typical rock slide, at the head of Lyell Cañon, our estimates indicated a population of at least one cony for every 750 square yards. This would mean a population of about six to an acre. The extent of one individual's range is limited, probably rarely exceeding the boundaries of the particular rock slide in which the animal has its headquarters. While a cony will go some distance among rocks for food materials, it will not ordinarily venture more than two or three yards beyond the limits of that kind of shelter.

The summer traveler in the mountains is first apprised of the presence of conies by hearing one of the animals utter its far-off-sounding 'bleat.' In fact, this call is such a valuable introductory aid that the experienced field observer finds it the best practicable means of locating the animals.

Hence he waits in a suitable locality and listens intently until one of them utters its note and then seeks out and scrutinizes the small area whence the sound comes until its maker is discerned. This call is a moderately loud two or three-syllabled utterance, and it has a nasal intonation. The quality of the note suggests the clinking together of two flakes of granite. It has been variously rendered by our field observers. One writes it *yink, yink;* another, *ke-ack, ke-ack,* or *ke-ack, ke-ack, ke-ick-y;* and another *e-chack', e-chack', chee-ick', chee-ick', chee-ick'-y.* Sometimes the call is uttered but once; again it may be repeated for ten or fifteen seconds, at first rapidly, then more slowly, as if the cony's breath were being gradually exhausted. The animal accompanies its calls with certain movements which seem essential to their production. The whole body is jerked violently forward, as if considerable exertion were necessary to expel the air from the lungs, and at the same time the ears are twitched upward, so that in face view their outlines suddenly catch the observer's eye.

For several months of each year snow covers everything within the range of the Yosemite Cony. The various species of animals which dwell there meet the resulting food scarcity in a number of different ways. Most of the birds emigrate, the deer and coyote descend to lower altitudes, the marmot hibernates, the gopher constructs tunnels through the snow so as to reach the vegetation enveloped in the snow mantle, and the white-tailed jack rabbit turns white and develops big 'snow-shoes' on its feet so that it can forage upon the plants that stick above the surface of the snow. The cony has still another method of meeting the situation.

During the late summer and early autumn the Yosemite Cony is busy at all hours of the day gathering materials to serve as food while it is imprisoned among the rocks beneath the snow. It cuts and stores away grasses and sedges and other plants which grow in the vicinity of its home. These are carried into the rock slides and stored in a dry, well-drained, shady yet airy place, sheltered above from snow and rain, and free from the danger of running water below—an ideal hay barn from the stand-point of a farmer. This mode of treatment, as it happens, preserves unfaded the natural colors of the plants, whose fragrance is that of well-cured hay free from mold. One such 'hay-pile' seen by the senior author on Warren Peak, Mono County, September 26, 1915, was situated under a huge flat rock and was composed of about a bushel of material. Samples from a pile examined at 8300 feet altitude on McClure Fork of Merced River, August 26, 1915, included twigs and needles of lodgepole pine, sprigs of "ocean spray" (*Holodiscus discolor dumosa*), two or more alpine species of sedge (*Carex*), with their characteristically rough stems of triangular cross-section, a grass (*Poa*), and an epilobium. The nearest sedge was twenty-five feet downhill in a wet place, while the nearest bush of *Holodiscus* was at least seventy-five feet up the steep adjacent slope. Currant and red-elderberry bushes grew nearer than any of the other plants named, but neither had been touched. Evidently the cony exercises some selection in the choice of its food materials.

When foraging, the Yosemite Cony gets as large an amount of cut greens as it can hold crosswise in its mouth and then carries the bundle to the 'barn.' Often stems of considerable length are transported in this manner, and as the animal moves about, the ends of these stems trail along beside or behind him. Many of the pieces found in the hay piles were over a foot in length. One piece of cut sedge measured forty-five inches in length; but it had been folded several times. Six adult-sized conies and one juvenile were trapped at a hay pile near Vogelsang Lake, and it may be that hay piles are community or at least family affairs.

When not foraging and not occupied beneath the surface of the slide, a cony sits in some partly protected place, often under or near a large overhanging rock. The post usually selected is the crest of a backward-slanting rock on a steep slope where the animal can enjoy a wide angle of view below and yet be in position, when danger threatens, seemingly to tumble back into the shelter of the slide. These perches, or observation posts (pl. 38*b*), are marked by accumulations of droppings, each one of an oblately spherical shape like that of a rabbit but much smaller, and by whitish stains due to the accumulation and action of the liquid excrement on the granite. When perching the animal sits hunched up, usually with its back higher than its head. It may maintain this position without any change for several minutes at a time. When a cony "comes to attention" on an observation post the head is often raised, the nose wiggled, and the feet shuffled, all suggestive of mannerisms of a rabbit; but the movements of the head are much quicker. The hobbling gait reminds one somewhat of the hopping of a brush-rabbit. The cony moves rapidly and with apparent ease almost everywhere in a slide, even over very steep and smooth rock surfaces. We have never seen one of these animals assume the erect posture which is common to rabbits.

The Yosemite Cony occupies the same rock-slide home with the Bushy-tailed Wood Rat and the Sierra Marmot, but we have learned nothing to indicate that these two large rodents molest it in any way. In the matter of enemies, there are only three carnivorous animals which dwell in the same situation and which we have reason to believe may prey upon the cony. These are the Sierra Pine Marten and the Least and Mountain weasels. At Vogelsang Lake, before sunrise of August 31, 1915, two conies were heard 'bleating' vociferously and they were seen to run excitedly here and there among the rocks. Investigation showed the cause of the disturbance to be a Least Weasel. From the commotion which these conies made, it was inferred that they had recognized the weasel as an enemy; a general alarm was being sounded. It is improbable that birds of prey, hawks and owls, levy much toll, because of the protected situations in which the cony lives; and there are no large snakes to search out and devour this animal, as would be the case if it lived at lower altitudes.

Conies seem to be most active during the early morning and evening hours; but they evince more or less activity at all times of the day, and they have been heard bleating on moonlight nights. They seem to enjoy coming out and running about among the rocks or sitting on their observations posts just as the afternoon shadows have begun to creep over the rock slides. Sometimes they will sit for considerable periods of time in perfect quietness, and the observer must do likewise if he expects to catch sight of them.

The young of the Yosemite Cony are brought forth during the warmer months of the year, and, as is the case with some of the rabbits, the breeding season is an extended one. Thus, a young-of-the-year, already nearly the size of adults, was taken on July 11, 1915, while as late as September 2 a female containing embryos was found. Between July 3 and September 2, 1915, 4 pregnant females were obtained; these held 3, 4, 3, and 4 embryos, respectively. The young are precocious and venture abroad when only a third grown. Thus in a rock slide near the Soda Springs on Tuolumne Meadows, an individual weighing only 1½ ounces (40 grams) was collected on July 12, and another even smaller individual (weighing 35 grams) was taken on July 25, 1915. In form the young resemble the adults closely save that, as with young of many other mammals, the feet and head are disproportionately large.

BLACK-TAILED JACK RABBITS. Lepus californicus Gray[16]

Field characters.—Of rabbit form but racy in build; ears longer than head (fig. 33); legs and feet relatively long and slender. Head and body 18 to 19 inches (460–480 mm.), tail 2⅓ to 3½ inches (60–90 mm.), hind foot 4½ to 5½ inches (118–140 mm.), ear from crown 5¾ to 6½ inches (147–165 mm.); weight about 5 pounds (2.3–2.4 kilograms). General coloration above pale yellowish brown, ticked with black; under surface of body varying from pale buff to white; tail black above. *Workings:* 'Forms' (resting places) on ground beneath bushes; also paths leading in direct course across open

[16] Two races of the Black-tailed Jack Rabbit are found at the opposite ends of the Yosemite cross-section. A form of intermediate characters in the southern San Joaquin Valley connects these two, and so they are treated as subspecies of one species.

CALIFORNIA JACK RABBIT, *Lepus californicus californicus* Gray, inhabits the coastal region of central California, the Sacramento Valley, and the northern part of the San Joaquin Valley, and is common in the western part of our Yosemite section from the plains below Snelling and Lagrange eastward into the foothill country to near Bower Cave and to the slopes of Bullion Mountain.

DESERT JACK RABBIT, *Lepus californicus deserticola* Mearns, ranges over the interior deserts of California and the Great Basin and was found present in small numbers near Mono Lake Post Office, east of the Sierra Nevada. It differs from the preceding in its paler, more ashy coloration and in its slightly smaller average size.

country. *Droppings:* Flattened spheres, yellowish brown in color, about ⅜ inch in diameter, scattered on ground.

Occurrence.—Common resident in Lower and Upper Sonoran zones on west slope of Sierra Nevada where recorded from Snelling and Lagrange eastward to Bower Cave and to slopes of Bullion Mountain (subspecies *californicus*). Also present in small numbers east of mountains in neighborhood of Mono Lake, as at Mono Lake Post Office (subspecies *deserticola*). See footnote for details. Inhabit chiefly open plains country, though some individuals live about clear areas in the chaparral or in open woods. Diurnal.

The California Jack Rabbit is a common species on the plains and rolling lands at the eastern margin of the San Joaquin Valley where our Yosemite section begins, and it also occurs to a limited extent in open areas in the foothills among digger pines and chaparral. In a few places jack rabbits enter the lower margin of the yellow pine belt, but they go no farther upward. The main forest belt of the central Sierras, the Transition and Canadian zones of the west slope, is devoid of rabbits of any sort. On the east side of the mountains there is a closely allied form, the Desert Jack Rabbit, which occurs in small numbers about Mono Lake.

Our jack rabbit is strictly speaking a hare, more closely related to the White-tailed Jack Rabbit than to the cottontail and brush rabbits. The present species lives entirely out on the surface of the ground without taking to underground shelters. Its young at birth are fully haired and almost ready for independent existence. The adults when alarmed instead of hiding in shrubbery or bolting down into holes make off in the open and trust to their legs for safety. These are all characters of hares as contrasted with true rabbits.

The present species is a black-tailed jack rabbit. The upper side of the tail, which is the surface presented to view when a hare is running, is extensively black and hence different in appearance from that of all the other rabbits of the region.

The jack rabbit is of slender build throughout. The legs and feet are proportionately longer than in the cottontail and brush rabbit. When foraging quietly, the jack rabbit moves by short hops, keeping the soles of the hind feet on the ground and the long ears erect (fig. 33). But when thoroughly frightened, as when closely pursued by a hound, a coyote, or an eagle, the animal stretches out to the utmost extent, the ears are laid down on the back, only the toes touch the ground, and the body is carried low. In this position the rabbit covers two to three yards at each bound. The jack rabbit's whole being is modified for this sort of travel, for escape by speed in the open.

Only once did we find a jack rabbit taking shelter in a hole, and that was a wounded animal. One shot near Lagrange lay quietly on the ground until the collector made a move to pick it up. Then the 'Jack' scrambled into a hole under some rim rock, whence it could not be dislodged.

A typical meeting with a jack rabbit, near Coulterville, is described in our notes of May 11, 1919.

One of these animals was started up in a hillside field above the main road. He ran a short distance up the slope, then stopped, standing first on the toes, then settled down until the soles of the hind feet rested on the ground. I remained perfectly quiet for several minutes and so did the rabbit. He stood in a quartering position and eyed me monocularly. All this time the immense ears, appearing more than twice the length of the head, were kept erect. I partially closed my eyes and then noted how readily the rabbit melted into the background, so that if it had not moved, it could easily have been overlooked. Finally I started on and at once the Jack bounded off and was lost to view behind some brush plants.

While we were camped along the shore of the Tuolumne River below Lagrange in May of 1919, jack rabbits were often seen close to the margin of the stream. Tracks and droppings indicated that they frequented the place. Whether they came down (off the adjacent mesa) to drink we were unable to ascertain. Their repeated occurrence close to the river, where there was no particular sort of forage to attract them, made this at least a possible explanation. Yet jack rabbits do live in many places where there is no water at all to drink.

The jack rabbit forages for a variety of materials, including not only grasses but also parts of brushy plants. Where man has taken possession of the country and planted alfalfa, grains, or other crops these animals naturally turn to the new materials and often take extensive toll. The erection of rabbit-proof fences and

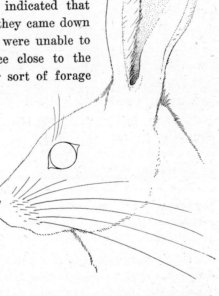

Fig. 33. Head of California Jack Rabbit, one-half natural size. Compare with figs. 34 and 35.

the killing off of the animals by various means have been resorted to in efforts to protect crops. In earlier years rabbit drives, participated in by all the residents of a region, were held in attempts to reduce the numbers of jack rabbits.

Seasonal fluctuations occur in the jack rabbit population. In 1915 the numbers of the animals in the western part of the Yosemite section were moderate, not great enough to excite comment on the part of our field party. But in 1919 their numbers were notably greater. On the hills about

Lagrange an animal would be started up every hundred yards or so. The rabbits were then common even through the chaparral as far into the hills as Coulterville. In the vicinity of the latter place individuals were come upon wherever there was any grass in the small clearings. Rabbits, like meadow mice, sometimes increase until they overrun the country, then suddenly decrease to a minimum. In earlier years this was true of the jack rabbits in the lower San Joaquin Valley, but since the great rabbit drives of the nineties, when thousands were killed by the ranchers, this great variation in numbers seems not to occur.

The young of the jack rabbit when born are far advanced in their development as compared with the young of true rabbits. The body is fully covered with hair and the eyes are open. The body length at birth is about 6 inches and the animal weighs about 2 ounces. Growth is rapid and the young soon take on the rangy form of the adult. Even in the very young the ears are large (about 2 inches long at birth) and exceed the head in length so that no difficulty is experienced in identifying them as young jack rabbits. In the cottontail the ears are very short at birth, shorter than the head.

The breeding season of the jack rabbit extends through most of the year, though a somewhat larger percentage of young is produced in the spring than in other seasons. A female (*deserticola*) taken at Mono Mills on June 19, 1916, contained 5 embryos. The average number in a litter, taking the country at large, is between 4 and 5.

SIERRA WHITE-TAILED JACK RABBIT. Lepus townsendii sierrae Merriam

Field characters.—Form that of Black-tailed Jack Rabbit, but size larger and general build heavier (fig. 34); feet heavily furred; tail large and fluffy. Head and body 19¼ to 20½ inches (491–519 mm.), tail 3½ inches (89–92 mm.), hind foot 6⅓ inches (160–164 mm.), ear from crown 6 inches (151 mm.). Body coloration (including ears) pale brown, ticked with black in summer, solidly pure white in winter; tail and feet wholly white at all seasons. *Droppings:* Flattened spheres about ½ inch in diameter.

Occurrence.—Resident in moderate numbers in high Sierras and at east base of mountains. Recorded from Tuolumne Meadows, and near Half Dome, eastward to vicinity of Mono Mills and slopes of Mono Craters. Ranges upward to 12,000 feet on higher peaks. Lives chiefly in open or sparsely wooded situations. Active mostly in late evening. Solitary.

The Sierra White-tailed Jack Rabbit is known to many persons as the "snowshoe rabbit"; occasionally it is called Sierra Hare. Like many of the other mammals and birds which occur along the crest of the Sierras this hare is a member of a northern group which finds conditions suitable for its existence in the boreal region of high altitude on the main Sierra mountain mass and at its colder east base. Locally, even in the midst of its range, this species is much less common than is the Black-tailed Jack

Rabbit in the low plains country. For this reason among others exact information on many points in the life history of the Sierra Hare is still to be obtained.

The main range of the White-tailed Jack Rabbit begins at Tuolumne Meadows and Vogelsang Lake, where evidence of the species, in the way of droppings scattered on open ground, was found by us to be fairly abundant. An exceptional occurrence, reported by Mr. Lawrence Souvelewski, was that of a White-tailed Jack Rabbit at the immediate east base of Half Dome (altitude about 7500 feet). The animal was seen there on numerous occasions during the summer of 1919. On none of the western peaks (such as Mount Hoffmann, Mount Clark, or Clouds Rest) did we find evidence of the presence of this species; but along the main crest of the Sierras, rabbits were found to inhabit the gentler slopes of all the higher peaks such as Parsons Peak, Mount Florence, Mount Dana, and Warren Mountain, even up to altitudes of 12,000 feet. On the east slope, White-tailed Jack Rabbits were observed at Walker Lake, near Williams Butte, near Mono Mills, and on the slopes of Mono Craters.

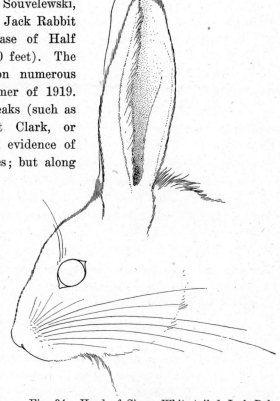

Fig. 34. Head of Sierra White-tailed Jack Rabbit, one-half natural size. Compare with fig. 33.

When fully adult, this species is half again the size of its black-tailed relative. Compared with the latter its ears are slightly longer and proportionately broader, its head is more massive (fig. 34), its pelage denser and longer, and its tail longer and more fluffy in appearance; its feet are always heavily clad in fur (whence the name "snowshoe rabbit"). The white-tail has two regular molts each year. One in the fall changes the color of the animal from the pale brown summer coat to the pure white of winter. The second molt, in the spring, accomplishes a return to the brown pelage. The feet and tail do not participate in this color change but remain white all summer, save as discolored by contact with the ground.

Sometimes certain areas on the body retain remnants of the brown coloration when the animal is in the white coat, and vice versa.

These big rabbits seem generally to keep to open places where they can see unobstructedly for long distances. Around Tuolumne Meadows, flat-topped hills bearing moderately open stands of trees together with some brush were often occupied. To this choice of habitat on the part of the rabbits, and to their crepuscular or nocturnal forage habits, we must attribute the general failure of interested persons to see more of them. Probably the rabbit sees the approaching person from afar and either makes off or else lies close in the shelter of rocks or bushes. In the few cases where a member of our party did catch sight of a rabbit it was usually from far off; the rabbit promptly went still farther away and was soon lost to sight. Near the Sierra Club camp of 1915 at the soda springs on Tuolumne Meadows one or two White-tailed Jack Rabbits were seen repeatedly by members of the Sierra Club and on a couple of occasions by some of our party. At this point the animals had evidently become somewhat accustomed to the presence of people.

On the Farrington ranch near Williams Butte one of our party stayed out for over an hour, from dusk until after dark, on the evening of September 21, 1915, watching for White-tailed Jack Rabbits in a wild hay meadow. One of the animals came into view at 6:35 P.M. It ran out from some tall grass and willow brush into a place where the grass had been cut, and there at some distance from the observer it sat bolt upright. Walking quietly, the observer attempted to approach, but the rabbit became frightened and started for another willow clump across the field. It did not appear to hurry, but its easy run carried it out of sight in an incredibly short time.

On another occasion, at Walker Lake, September 13, 1915, a White-tailed Jack Rabbit was come upon in a meadow. This was after 6 o'clock, in the late dusk of evening, and snow was gently falling. The rabbit, upon being frightened, loped away in easy fashion, and disappeared among the trees. We were told that in winters when the snow gets deep, the "snowshoes" visit the haystacks of the Farrington ranch in numbers to feed. They are then ambushed by the Indians.

The young of the White-tailed Jack Rabbit are produced in the early spring months, to judge from the data at hand. A half-grown animal was seen at close range near Mono Mills on June 8, 1916, and another of about the same stage of growth was shot on the Farrington ranch near Williams Butte on June 25 the same year. The latter animal already weighed 3¾ pounds (1.7 kilograms).

SACRAMENTO COTTONTAIL. **Sylvilagus audubonii audubonii** (Baird)

WASHINGTON COTTONTAIL. **Sylvilagus nuttallii nuttallii** (Bachman)[17]

Field characters.—Size smaller than in either common domestic rabbit or jack rabbit; tail cottony white on whole under surface; ears moderate, about length of head (fig. 35*b*). Head and body 12¼ to 13¾ inches (310–348 mm.), tail about 2 inches (40–55 mm.), hind foot 3¼ to 3¾ inches (81–94 mm.), ear (from crown of head) 2⅔ to 3½ inches (68–90 mm.); weight about 2 pounds or slightly over (1 kilogram). [Measurements from *audubonii*.] Coloration above yellowish brown with moderate amount of blackish overwash; whole under surface of body, tops of hind feet, and under side of tail, pure white. *Droppings:* Flattened spheres about ¼ inch in diameter; scattered on ground where the rabbits feed.

Occurrence.—Common resident in Lower Sonoran and part of Upper Sonoran Zone on west side of Yosemite region. Recorded at Snelling, Lagrange, and Pleasant Valley (*S. audubonii*); also east of Sierra Nevada in neighborhood of Mono Lake (*S. nuttallii*). See footnote for details. Inhabits brushy situations interspersed with clearings. Active in morning and late afternoon.

Cottontail rabbits are present along the western and eastern bases of the Sierra Nevada, but they do not invade the adjacent hill country to any extent. On the west slope, the range of the cottontail is nearly complementary to that of the brush rabbit, though the two are not necessarily mutually exclusive. Cottontails are much different in their habits from jack rabbits (which are hares, and not true rabbits), and so these two types can and do occur in the same general localities without competing seriously with one another.

The cottontail is nearly twice the weight of a brush rabbit but only about one-third that of a jack rabbit. In general, it resembles the former, possessing rather short legs and feet, and ears of moderate length (fig. 35*b*). The cottony white of the tail, which has given rise to the common name, is much more conspicuous in this species than in the brush rabbit. The cottontail is essentially an inhabitant of thickets, although it does not require such dense cover as does the brush rabbit and it forages farther out into the open than does that species. The growths which line the banks of the Merced and Tuolumne rivers on their courses through the San

---

17 Two distinct species of Cottontail Rabbit are found at the opposite ends of the Yosemite section. Their habits are not known to differ to any great extent save perhaps in adaptation to the different types of country in which they live. Because of the lack of knowledge as to many of the details of their life histories, they are here considered together.

SACRAMENTO COTTONTAIL, *Sylvilagus audubonii audubonii* (Baird). The species which inhabits north-central California, and reaches its southern limit in the vicinity of the Yosemite section. It is common near Snelling and Lagrange, and a few were noted in the hills near Pleasant Valley.

WASHINGTON COTTONTAIL, *Sylvilagus nuttallii nuttallii* (Bachman). A Great Basin species. Occurs at localities on the east side of the Sierra Nevada in the neighborhood of Mono Lake (noted by us on Rush Creek, on Williams Butte, and near Mono Lake Post Office). It may be distinguished from the west-side species by grayer tone of coloration, especially on sides of body, and greater amount of rufous on back.

Joaquin Valley afford ideal conditions for cottontails; there they are numerous. But cottontails do not always live about shrubbery. On some of the open hillsides between Lagrange and Merced Falls, cottontails occur in numbers, their only shelter being burrows in the ground, presumably those deserted by ground squirrels and remodelled by the rabbits.

Cottontails are abroad chiefly in the early morning and late afternoon hours; the duration of these daily periods of activity is somewhat longer than that of the brush rabbits. At Snelling, in May, they were seen abroad between 6 and 8 A.M. and were probably out much earlier in the morning. Near Hayward (on the road to Coulterville) a cottontail was seen to cross the road about 9 A.M. one day in early May. In the afternoon, during the summer months, these animals may be abroad as early as 4 o'clock, in places shaded from direct sunshine, but at that season more are apt to be seen toward dusk of evening. In favorable places two or three, and on occasion even more, of the animals forage in close proximity to one another.

The cottontail seems to prefer thickets interspersed with small clearings or grassy glades in which it may feed. In one case three individuals were noted in an alfalfa patch in the river bottomland at Snelling. They were about 25 feet out from thickets of willows and blackberries, and each individual, though feeding, was actively alert and ready to dash back to cover at the first intimation of danger.

Like all of the rabbit tribe the cottontail is speedy when running, though for safety it depends on seeking shelter quickly rather than on outdistancing its enemy. Rarely is there a chance to judge even roughly of the speed at which a cottontail can run. Once, on December 20, 1914, one was seen as it ran for a short distance parallel to the railroad train near Merced Falls. The speed of the train was estimated to be 20 miles an hour and the rabbit appeared to be going about three-fourths as fast or about 15 miles an hour.

Concerning the breeding of the cottontail, little of a definite character is known. On May 24, 1915, a half-grown individual (*S. audubonii*) was captured at Pleasant Valley. This would point to breeding early in the year. A young Washington Cottontail was seen near Mono Lake Post Office on June 30, 1916.

Mariposa Brush Rabbit

Sylvilagus bachmani mariposae Grinnell and Storer

Field characters.—General appearance much like that of small domestic rabbit; ears shorter than head (fig. 35a), half as broad as long; tail short, white of tail much restricted. Head and body 10 to 12½ inches (255–315 mm.), tail 1 to 1¼ inches (25–32 mm.), hind foot 2⅔ to 3 inches (68–75 mm.), ear (from crown of head) 2½ to 3⅛ inches (65–80 mm.); weight 17½ to 22 ounces (500–631 grams). Coloration dark brown with heavy overwash of black; general effect of coloration deep gray rather than brown;

inder side of body grayish white; under side of tail white. *Workings:* Paths or runways 2½ to 3 inches wide, on ground beneath chaparral. *Droppings:* Flattened spheres about ¼ inch in diameter, scattered on ground at feeding places and along runways.

Occurrence.—Common resident in foothill region (Upper Sonoran Zone) on west slope of Sierra Nevada. Recorded from Lagrange and Pleasant Valley eastward to El Portal (to altitude of 4000 feet on south facing mountain side immediately north of El Portal). Lives on ground beneath chaparral, seldom venturing into the open. Seen actively abroad at dusk of evening and morning.

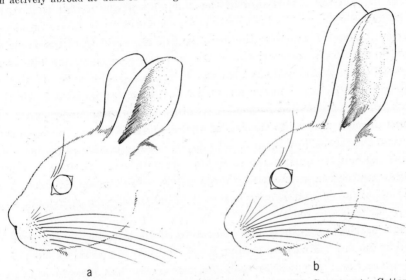

a   b

Fig. 35. Heads of (*a*) Mariposa Brush Rabbit and (*b*) Sacramento Cottontail Rabbit; one-half natural size. See pp. 227, 228.

Smallest in point of size among the rabbits of the Yosemite section is the Mariposa Brush Rabbit of the western foothill country. Hunters refer to this as the "blue rabbit" because of its distinctly bluish gray cast of coloration in contrast with the brownish tones of the cottontail. The average visitor will be likely to see more of the cottontail and jack rabbit than of the brush rabbit, as the former species forage generally in rather open situations, while the latter habitually keeps close beneath the chaparral, even when foraging, and, moreover, is to be seen as a rule only in the early morning and in late evening.

In general form and appearance the brush rabbit resembles the cottontail, to which it is not distantly related. The two species are 'rabbits' in the restricted sense of the word, in that their young are hairless at birth and are born in sheltered nests of some sort, and in that the adults browse close to cover and when frightened seek safety beneath shrubbery or in holes rather than in flight as do the hares (jack rabbits).

The brush rabbit is about half the weight of a cottontail and measures, on the average, smaller in all dimensions than that species. The ear of the brush rabbit is shorter than the head; its greatest length, as measured from the crown of the head, is only about twice its width. (See fig. 35.) The head of the brush rabbit is blunter and broader as compared with that of the cotton tail, and the tail is smaller and shows less white. There is a conspicuously darker, colder, grayish tone of coloration in the brush rabbit, which is to be contrasted with the yellowish brown coat color of the cottontail.

In general the deportment of the Mariposa Brush Rabbit is like that of its nearer relative. It habitually carries its ears up in a nearly vertical position. Not infrequently the red tinge of the ears, resulting from the sunlight shining through them, is the first thing to catch the observer's eye. Usually, when suddenly come upon, a brush rabbit will 'freeze' and remain perfectly still; under such circumstances it might easily be mistaken for a rock. When it decides to move it does so abruptly and a few jumps place it under the shadow of the chaparral. There the observer's eye can scarcely follow it, so closely does the color of the animal's pelage match the general tone of the environment; with a few further scurrying movements the rabbit is entirely lost to view. This animal is an adept at dodging about in and among bushes. As long as cover is available, its safety is fairly assured.

The Mariposa Brush Rabbit does most of its foraging in the dusk of evening and in the early morning hours. Sundown, whatever hour that may be in the different seasons of the year, is the best time to watch for brush rabbits. Then they come out to the margins of the brush thickets to browse, or go hopping about here and there in the spaces under the canopy of chaparral. At El Portal, in early December, they suddenly became active at about 5 P.M.; near Coulterville, in May, they were not out in the evening until about 7 o'clock. The time of appearance of the brush rabbit is roughly parallel to that of the various species of bats. Probably the early hours of the night are spent in foraging. The early hours of the morning soon after daybreak are also spent in some activity. In May and June the animals were seen not infrequently between 5:30 and 6.30 A.M. But soon after they disappeared for the day.

Individual brush rabbits are localized in their range. Once having found the haunts of a particular animal, the observer can be almost certain of finding it there subsequently at the proper hour. Thus near Coulterville one was sighted one evening in May. Next morning it was within 5 feet of where it had been seen before, and later that morning it was again seen close to the same spot.

The Mariposa Brush Rabbits, at least during the fall months, get much of their forage from the brush plants. The greasewood, which serves them as shelter, is not ordinarily used for food; but two other foothill shrubs, the blue brush (*Ceanothus cuneatus*) and wild broom (*Hosackia glabra*), which has a clump of long, flexible, hay-like stems, are resorted to freely. The rabbits nip off the stems of these two plants and eat them, discarding the leaves. Much rabbit sign, indicating repeated visits by the animals, was seen wherever these plants formed the chief vegetation. In the spring months grass and other fresh herbage grows about the borders of the chaparral and the rabbits turn then to this food source. With the food habits just indicated, and with its timid and retiring disposition, the brush rabbit is never likely to become the pest to agriculture that the cottontail is. On the other hand, it is a desirable game animal.

Brush rabbits bring forth their young chiefly during the early months of the year. Two juvenal animals, taken near Coulterville on May 11 and 12, 1919, weighed only about one-third as much as adults and were in the dusky-hued first pelage. To judge from the growth of domestic rabbits these animals were probably not over six weeks old when found by us, and so had been born in the later part of March. These youngsters, however, were already out and foraging independently at the margin of the chaparral, just as adults are wont to do. A female, giving evidence of suckling young, was taken 3 miles east of Coulterville on June 1, 1915.

Several of the local carnivorous birds and mammals are known to prey upon rabbits and this is probably one reason why the Mariposa Brush Rabbit keeps so closely to the cover of the chaparral. The presence of these natural enemies, and the limited forage available to the brush rabbit, are two factors which serve to keep down the numbers of the species.

Mule Deer. **Odocoileus hemionus hemionus** (Rafinesque)

Field characters.—Size large, mature individuals standing 32 to 42 inches high at shoulder. Males more than one year old bear short spike-like antlers; in later years antlers more or less branched. Ears very large, 8 to 9 inches tall from base to tip, 4 inches across at greatest width. (See pl. 39b). Tail narrowed near base, black on outer surface, white on under side. Adults, bright reddish brown in summer, grayish brown in winter; rump and throat whitish; young fawns reddish brown, spotted with white. Footprints small for size of animal, sheep-like, but sharply pointed (pl. 40d). Droppings elliptical, ½ inch long or less, black.

Occurrence.—More or less common, according to season and altitude, almost throughout the Yosemite region; recorded from hills west of Pleasant Valley eastward across the mountains to Mono Craters. Summer range chiefly between altitudes of 3500 and 8500 feet; winter range, below level of deep snow, that is, mostly below 5500 feet. Prefers chaparral country. Seen singly or in small bands.

In the days of '49, when white men first thronged the Sierran foothills, no less than four species of horned or antlered big game animals inhabited the Yosemite region. At the eastern border of the San Joaquin Valley was the Dwarf or Tule Elk; on the plains of the San Joaquin and in Mono Valley was the American Antelope; on the highest parts of the Sierra

Nevada was the Sierra Mountain Sheep; and in the intervening middle altitudes was the Mule Deer. Now all save the last have vanished, probably never to return; but the Mule Deer is still present over most of its early range, though doubtless in but a fraction of its original numbers.

Mule Deer are most frequently seen by foot travelers in the summer on and near the trails above the rim of Yosemite Valley, but autoists en route to or from the Valley, especially during the fall months, often see them along the roadsides. The deer range over practically all of the hilly and mountainous country in the Yosemite region, from the westernmost extension of the brush belt bordering the San Joaquin Valley east over the crest of the Sierra Nevada to Mono Valley. They are not uniformly distributed over the whole area, however, nor do they occur in all portions of it at all times of the year. A small number remain in the Upper Sonoran chaparral belt of the western foothills during the summer season, and a few also occur on the east base of the Sierras, but the great majority of the animals are to be found at this time in the brush country of the higher mountains, in the Transition and Canadian life zones, at altitudes of from 3500 to 8500 feet. Some wander up toward timber line, our highest record being 10,600 feet, near Fletcher Lake. In winter they descend to lower altitudes, there being thus a distinct migratory movement twice each year. Those on the western side of the mountains migrate to the region from Bridal Veil Meadow (3900 feet) and the southern slope of Pilot Peak (at 4500 feet) west to Forty-nine Gap (1500 feet), while the animals on the east slope cross Mono Valley to the country east of Mono Craters. Individuals occasionally range on the west as low as Snelling, in the Merced River bottom well beyond the westernmost foothills.

The two factors controlling the local distribution of deer in the Yosemite region are the presence of the right kind of brush for food and shelter, and the absence of deep snow. Deer depend chiefly on certain brush plants for their sustenance. When these shrubs are covered with snow, or surrounded by snow more than 18 inches deep, the animals are unable to feed. Their altitudinal migrations seem to be controlled entirely by snowfall; they ordinarily remain in the high mountains in the fall until the first snow of the season sends them downhill and concentrates them along the western boundary of the Park. As a rule, they do not stay where the snow lies to a depth of more than 1½ feet, but, other conditions permitting, they do remain just below this level. Their numbers in the most favorable localities may tend to become larger than the supply of forage will support, and then competition forces many of them still lower down, into the foothill chaparral belt entirely west of the Park boundary. The migrant deer go farther westward than do those animals which reside throughout the year in the foothills. Large numbers of deer from the northern part of the Park winter on the sunny, snow-free, south-facing slopes of Rancheria and North mountains in the Tuolumne drainage; while those from farther south range over the slopes within ten miles west of Chinquapin, on the Merced watershed.

Park rangers see more deer in the early and late winter months than during the midwinter or midsummer seasons. This is, in part, because of the fact that in the former periods the animals are on the move, leaving the tracts of heavy brush, and often using the roads or trails. For example, 261 deer were seen in November, 1915, 43 being noted in a single day near Chinquapin. In December of the same year 396 were observed, 37 being seen by one ranger in a single day. But in January, 1916, only 8 deer were seen; storms and deep snow had driven them far to the westward. In March, 1916, 318 deer were noted by the rangers, 60 being seen in one day at Wawona. During the period of heavy snow referred to above, residents of El Portal reported seeing a band of 60 to 70 deer in the hills a few miles south of that place.

If the first storm is a heavy one the deer leave the altitudes with a rush. Mr. C. C. Bull has told us that in Hetch Hetchy Valley after a big storm so many deer have passed a certain point in single file as to leave a beaten trail in the 10 or 12 inches of snow which lay on the ground. If the winter is a light one, with alternate periods of clear and stormy weather, the deer move back and forth, going up as the snow recedes and descending again when a fresh fall occurs. The deer which summer on the east slope of the Sierras, in migrating to the mountains east of Mono Craters either pass along the slopes of the Craters or else go directly across the open plains just south of Mono Lake. According to our experience in 1914–1916, deer are not commonly observed on the floor of Yosemite Valley in summer, though several does and their fawns may appear there in August; by October, and throughout the winter, a good many frequent the lower end of the Valley. In later years, 1919–1920, more have been seen throughout the summer in the Valley, even bucks.

The relative deer populations of the foothills and high mountains during the summer were probably originally determined by food supply—as many as could be supported throughout the year by the forage and shelter of the foothill country remained there, while the balance were led to seek the higher altitudes for the summer season. Habits so developed in the deer of the two different belts have persisted even in the reduced populations of the present day. There is, indeed, some evidence that slight differences in size and structural features exist on an average between the deer resident in the foothill belt (Upper Sonoran Zone) and those which seek in summer the higher altitudes.

The Mule Deer which inhabit the Yosemite National Park seem to have responded favorably to the protection afforded them; they are remarkably tame, and will usually permit a person who moves slowly to approach very near. Despite their size, their somber coloration renders them surprisingly inconspicuous when in brush thickets, but the recurrent flapping of their big mule-like ears sometimes betrays their presence. They exhibit great curiosity and often when frightened out of a trail will circle about the traveler and may soon be discovered gazing at him from some new position. The following excerpt from the notebook of the senior author describes an interesting meeting with some of these animals.

Ridge between Yosemite and Indian creeks, June 4, 1915.—Four deer, an old doe and three smaller deer without evident horns, were walking about 50 feet from me. I first came upon them suddenly; the three smaller ones stampeded over a rise of ground; but the old doe was curious and even came toward me. I remained quiet, only wiggling my fingers, and this interested her. The three young had vanished. Presently she began to look back at intervals, and they finally appeared again. She evidently wished to follow up the ridge, so she walked in a half-circle around me, the other three following at a little distance, single file. . . . They all disappeared over the ridge a few minutes ago, but at this moment three of them are staring at me over a log 60 yards off. The female has a (bullet?) hole through her left ear. I can see daylight through it. The others are about two-thirds the size of the female; probably last year's fawns (could she have had three?). . . . The doe has just now become excited and uttered 8 rather loud snorts in irregular succession, *schfew,* and has given several stiff-legged bounds over the ridge. The young ones have vanished. They all did a great deal of flapping of their big ears, as if the flies bothered them.

On June 24, 1920, about 9 A.M., a company of 5 deer were come upon in a grove of close-growing yellow pines on the floor of Yosemite Valley near Clarke Bridge. They were all males, but no two were of the same size. The antlers, in the velvet with knobby ends, varied from short 'spikes' less than half the height of the ear to the big three-forked type. These deer, the largest one in the lead, moved along slowly, paying little attention to the human observers only 40 yards or so off. They kept reaching up to nip off the highest sprays of ceanothus, which here was shade-grown and sparse of leafage.

Trainmen on the Yosemite Valley Railroad told us that deer are frequently encountered on the tracks at night. The animals seem dazed by the glare of the headlight. The enginemen always slow up so as to give the animals a chance to 'come to' and get off the track.

Mule Deer are browsing rather than grazing animals; that is to say, they prefer leaves and young shoots of certain shrubs and trees to grasses and other terrestrial plants. At all times and in all altitudes their preferred forage is deer brush, mountain lilac, snow bush, and other representatives of the plant genus *Ceanothus.* Among all of these, *Ceanothus integerrimus,* the big-leaved, sweet-flowered bush of middle altitudes, is the favorite. When several other shrubs such as manzanitas and scrub oaks are available, ceanothus will be the only one showing bite marks. A deer nips at the foliage with a diagonal movement of the head and neck, and leaves the bark of the twig ends raveled out instead of cut off evenly. Deer are known to eat the bark of the incense cedar, particularly from young trees, and occasionally leaves of the black oak. In spring they nibble young shoots of dogwood along streams where they come down to drink. When the supply of acorns or chinquapin burrs is large, the deer feed on them with evident relish. At times, as when browse is scant or of poor quality, the deer feed on grass. This is notably true in the semi-barren Hudsonian Zone, where brush of any sort is almost wanting. They may also take willow leaves there. A buck seen at Forty-nine Gap, in the lower foothills, in December, 1915, was feeding on grass, even though several kinds of brush plants were available nearby; but this was an exceptional instance.

The deer of this region have profited, to some extent, through civilization. At the Chinquapin barns they frequently pick up hay which has been scattered when bales are being unloaded, and the men employed there and at Eight-mile have attracted and tamed the deer by putting out salt for them. Deer also visit the salt licks established by cattle men for their stock both inside and outside the western boundary of the Park. Hunters, however, take advantage of this habit and often lie in wait for the animals at these artificial licks. Finally, deer have been seen consuming the remains of lunches. A doe seen near a garbage can above Yosemite Falls one afternoon in late June, 1915, was munching a discarded sandwich with evident satisfaction.

Deer may be seen moving about at any hour of the day or night, but they are active chiefly during the late afternoon and early evening hours. Then the brush is free from dew and presumably more relished by them. On moonlight nights they have been seen foraging on the scanty growth of grass to be found on the forest floor; and they are often heard running at night. They are least active during the heat of the day. Then they are lying down, in their 'beds,' resting and sleeping.

A deer bed is nothing more than a slight depression in the surface of the ground, 2 to 3 feet in diameter, sometimes scraped free of such surface litter as pine needles. It is usually placed in the shade on a sidehill some distance below the top of a ridge, from which the animal can have unrestricted view for a considerable distance. The situation most favored is a small clearing in the brush, sheltered by some small coniferous tree. Certain warm, south-facing slopes near the crests of the higher ridges are much frequented for resting places by large bucks. Park rangers term these animals ''granite bucks'' and say that they are unusually large individuals and that they are able to winter at higher altitudes than do the other deer.

Aside from actual sight of the animals, the presence of 'sign' (characteristic droppings and footprints) is, of course, dependable evidence of the presence of deer in a region. Footprints of deer are much smaller than those of cattle and more pointed than those of either calves or sheep. The largest hoof mark which any of our party saw was that of an old buck. It measured 2 by 2¾ inches. In general the tracks of does (pl. 40*d*) are smaller and more acutely tipped than those of bucks, but, in examining many individual tracks, it has proved impossible to say whether they were made by a buck or by a doe. In late summer the river-side sand bars in the vicinity of Merced Lake are in some places literally plowed up by the little tracks of fawns which have been led down there by their mothers to drink.

Deer take more notice of noise than of motion. If the observer moves quietly and slowly the deer usually will not become frightened, but should a twig be broken under foot or any other sharp noise be made, they are apt to be off at once. The relatively large size of their ears (pl. 39*b*) probably means that, as a rule, they depend on hearing rather than on sight for the detection of enemies.

When frightened or excited, Mule Deer utter a sharp snort, and when running away often 'flash' the tail and rump so as to form a white 'flag' against the darker color of the rest of the body, reminding one of the appearance of a cottontail rabbit. Possibly this is a warning sign, to other deer, of the proximity of danger, or a signal for fawns to flee. When, however, two or more deer are alarmed and retreat from the vicinity of the observer, they usually separate and go in different directions, reuniting when they again feel safe. This is commonly true of does with young fawns, although sometimes the fawns accompany their mothers closely in a retreat.

By passing back and forth over a preferred route through the brush or forest, deer often make distinct trails. These are easily distinguished from horse or cow trails by the facts that they are narrower and do not continue for any great distance in a given direction; they end as soon as a good browsing area is reached. Deer do not follow man-made trails consistently but often take short-cuts. On the zigzags between Illilouette Creek and Glacier Point we have seen both deer and bear tracks in abundance. The bears had plodded along, following every twist and turn, while the deer had taken short-cuts up or down steep slopes.

The summer coat of the Mule Deer, which is worn from about June until October, is of a reddish brown color and the hairs are sparse, short, and straight. The winter coat, which is worn during the remaining portion of the year, is much darker, being grayish brown ("blue," in the hunter's language), and composed of longer, much more numerous, and slightly crinkled hairs. The greater number and length of the hairs and their irregular form are probably for the purpose of furnishing a greater number of discontinuous air spaces in the coat, which help to keep the animals warm during the cold of winter.

The ground color of the coat of a newborn fawn is reddish brown heavily marked with large (½ inch) white spots. The original brilliant contrast of this pattern persists only a short time, as the spots soon become dulled and finally disappear. Such evidence as we have indicates that this change is accomplished by wear and also by the appearance of numerous long reddish hairs. Thus by mid-August the fawn is reddish brown, similar in color to the summer coat of its parents. This in turn gives way in October to the regular gray winter coat. The hair of all these pelages is much softer, and in the first winter coat less crinkled, than is that of the adults.

Mule Deer have three gaits, all of them stiff-legged. When foraging or moving quietly along they walk with a peculiarly individual movement of the legs, each foot being lifted and set vertically down. This, combined with the very small size of the hoofs, results in a surprisingly quiet tread. In fact we are led to the belief that the smallness of the hoof is an adaptation in the direction of quiet movement. The second gait is a stiff-legged trot, in which the feet move alternately; and the third is a gallop, or "peg-legged lope," in which the fore and hind feet move in pairs simultaneously. This last is the gait which is used when the animals are beating a hurried retreat after being thoroughly frightened, and the speed which they make over short distances is surprising. This bounding gait serves two further purposes—to permit the animal to clear the brush in which it characteristically lives, and, with each upward leap of the animal, to enable it to see above the brush and thus to extend considerably its field of vision. Does, especially when carrying young, are said to lope with an easier carriage of the body than the bucks.

Every adult male deer normally possesses antlers and these are used for display and combat during the mating season. These are solid bony structures borne on the skull, grown and shed each year, and entirely different in form and origin from the permanent 'hollow' horns of cattle and sheep. The antlers begin to grow out in early spring and when first in evidence are nothing more than short knobs on top of the head between and a little above the eyes. While growing they are covered with a thick densely haired skin called 'velvet,' and this skin is richly supplied with blood vessels which serve to bring the materials necessary for growth. While growing, the antlers are very sensitive to touch and the deer are then notably careful of them; usually they forage in the open where there is less danger of coming in contact with limbs of trees or with other objects. The development of the antlers is rapid; by late May or mid-June they are one-third to one-half longer than the ears though still blunt-ended; by August their growth is complete, and they have become sharp-pointed. The blood supply ceases, the velvet dries, and the deer gets rid of it by rubbing the antlers against trees and shrubs. At this season bucks are often seen with pieces of dried velvet dangling loosely from their antlers. The bucks retain their antlers through the autumnal mating season and until early winter, when they shed them. A buck seen by Mr. C. C. Bull on March 16, 1916, was still carrying its antlers; but this was exceptionally late.

The number of 'points' or 'tines' on each one of a pair of antlers is commonly thought to be an index to the age of the animal bearing them. Yearling males with simple, unbranched antlers are called 'spike bucks,' while older animals are termed 'two-point bucks,' 'three-point bucks,' and so on, according as each of their antlers bears two, three, or more tines. Very old bucks are said not to have the number of points their years would prescribe. The largest number of points seen by us on any deer in the Yosemite region was six, but Lawrence Souvelewsky reported seeing a seven-point buck in the vicinity of Merced Lake.

The mating or rutting season occurs chiefly in October. Very little is known about the mating habits of the Mule Deer save that the animals are then very wary. Two does seen in Ten Lakes basin on October 10, and a buck and a doe at Aspen Valley on October 15, were all very wild. By November this wildness has passed and the animals may again be closely approached. Soon after this the bucks shed their antlers.

The fawns are born about the first of July, but the does keep their charges hidden in the brush for a month or more before permitting them to forage in the open. In 1915 the first one was seen on July 27, and by early August fawns were observed almost daily. Two constitute the usual number although sometimes there is only one and occasionally there are three. By the time they are seen regularly with their mothers the young animals are about one-fourth to one-third grown, and pretty well able to take care of themselves. The fawns run with their mothers through the first year. Early in June we saw many groups comprising a doe and 1, 2, or 3 fawns which were about two-thirds grown. By the latter part of the same month the does desert these yearlings in anticipation of the arrival of the next litter. It is a common belief, substantiated by known facts, that fawns which are born at low altitudes remain there throughout their lives, while those born in the mountains migrate up and down every season.

Coyotes, especially the big Mountain Coyotes, occasionally 'pull down' fawns or sickly adults. If caught in snow more than 18 inches deep, even adult and able-bodied deer are apt to be run down by these predators. The coyotes run easily on the top crust of the snow, but the deer break through and flounder helplessly in the deeper drifts. In the Yosemite region, however, the chief wild enemy of the Mule Deer is the Mountain Lion. The way in which lions capture deer is described in another chapter (p. 97), where also the numbers probably killed each year are estimated.

The interrelation of Mountain Lion and Deer has naturally become an important subject of discussion and concern among sportsmen, to whom a deer is something to be sought after, both for its flesh and as a trophy. In a very definite sense the Mountain Lion is, in territory open for hunting, the sportsman's rival; hence, from the sportsman's standpoint, the lion should be eliminated. But in the Yosemite National Park, where the aim is to preserve free from human interference *all* the animal life, it is the hunter who is eliminated, and so the situation is altogether different.

The close grazing of cattle in the territory to the west of the Park, which is comprised in the wintering grounds of a good proportion of the Yosemite deer population, has inevitably reduced, especially in hard years, the number of deer which can be carried over there through the winter. Not only the grasses, but most especially certain thin-leafed kinds of deer brush, have been browsed down by cattle and goats to mere vestiges of their former quantity; and the deer are hard put to it when the snow lies far down on the west Sierran slopes. In last analysis, counting out man, the important factor in the reduction of the numbers of deer is the reduction in the quantity of food available to them at the most critical time of the year, rather than the levy upon their numbers by lions.

Except as the factor of hunting and poaching in the territory along the western edge of the Park also affects the deer population of the Yosemite, we do not see that the permanent existence, in relatively normal numbers, of Mountain Lions within the area in question can be expected to reduce the total population of the deer which will be maintained from year to year. In other words, if the Yosemite Park is administered as a true 'refuge' for its animal as well as its plant life, then primitive conditions should be maintained absolutely, to the end that all the constituent species persist in the same relative numbers as they did in early times. The maximum numbers of any and all herbivores which can exist will be determined by the amount of plant food available at the season of least supply; and the numbers of carnivores which can exist will be determined by the amount of animal food available to them at the season of scantiest supply.

Occasional purely fortuitous accidents happen to deer. One of the Park rangers found a deer held fast by one of its forefeet in the crotch of a young black oak. The animal had twisted its leg nearly off in its attempt to free itself.

Within the boundaries of the Yosemite National Park the Mule Deer receive every possible protection. The rangers are careful of the interests of the deer and little if any poaching takes place. But in the area lying immediately to the west little regard seems to be paid to the game laws. Some residents of this region believe that they have a vested right to kill deer "whenever and wherever they please." When confronted with the statement that there is a State law protecting the animals, they ask, "Can you blame a man for going after a deer [despite the law] when meat is scarce?" To this we answer, "We most certainly do." The doctrine that our wild game belongs to *all* the people (to be conserved in the interests of *all*) and not just to those residing in the immediate vicinity seems not to have reached them as yet. A resident of El Portal openly boasted to one of our field party that he had been on a deer hunt during the first week in December, nearly two months after the close of the legal season for killing deer.

Certain residents stated that deer are not now more than 50 per cent as numerous as in earlier years. When pressed for the reasons why deer have decreased the replies were:

1. The deer have moved back.

2. Mountain Lions and other "varmints" have of recent years made disproportionate inroads on them.

3. The closed season on deer has favored the increase of "varmints."

4. "Of course a lot have been shot" (but little stress was laid on this).

Despite all statements to the contrary the most relentless enemy of the Mule Deer is man. The persistence or elimination of the animals in the Yosemite region rests entirely with him. Since many of the deer in the Park proper move out into unpatrolled territory in winter it would seem that complete protection ought to be provided throughout this adjacent territory, at least until there is a sufficient natural increase to warrant reopening a hunting season there. At the present time, so far as the Yosemite National Park is concerned, the greatest potential value of the deer lies in their esthetic appeal; in observing them the visitor is thrilled with delight, and his mind and senses are acutely stimulated.

DWARF ELK. **Cervus nannodes** Merriam

The history of the Dwarf or Tule Elk, the largest hoofed game animal known to have occurred in the Yosemite section, is a closed chapter. Once abundant on the plains of the San Joaquin Valley along the Tuolumne and Merced rivers, it is now entirely extinct there. Being of large size as compared with other native game, and possessing flesh that was highly palatable, the elk was singled out for first attention in a country plentifully supplied with game. Its disappearance was evidently more rapid than that of the Mountain Sheep and Pronghorn Antelope. We cannot, however, feel so great regret in the passing of the elk as in the case of the Mountain Sheep. Elk, in numbers, could not exist today in the San Joaquin Valley where intensive agriculture is practiced, without inflicting great damage.

Records of elk within the Yosemite section are fragmentary. Edward Bosqui in his Memoirs (1904, p. 66) tells of meeting with a herd of elk on Dry Creek, north of the present town of Snelling, in the winter of 1850–1851. He was camped on the then dry bed of the watercourse in a grove of big cottonwoods.

At daylight the next morning I was suddenly awakened by the heavy tramp and noise of large animals, and on looking through the fog which prevailed I could see indistinctly, not thirty yards away, giant-like figures of elk passing, so to speak, in procession before me. They were tossing their great antlers about and sniffing excitedly. Suddenly, with one accord and with an impulse that shook the ground like an earthquake, they swept out of sight. It was a procession of phantoms such as one might conceive in a nightmare, and left an impression on my youthful mind never to be forgotten.

W. L. Manly in a book entitled "Death Valley in '49" (San José, 1894, p. 392) tells of following up the Merced River [below Snelling]. "As we [he] came near groves of willows, big, stately elk would start out and trot off proudly into the open plains to avoid danger. These proud, big-horned monarchs of the plains could be seen in bunches scattered over the broad meadows, as well as an equal amount of antelope. They all seemed to fear us, which was wise on their part, and kept out of rifle shot." Later, this author and a companion came down from Big Oak Flat to the plains to try to get some elk meat to use on a contemplated trip. But they were altogether outwitted by the elk and had to shoot some antelope instead.

The Tule Elk was deer-like in general appearance, but of much larger size and different coloration. The antlers of the old males were large, widely spreading, and considerably branched. The coloration of the Tule Elk was pale brown, with a large whitish area on the rump.

PRONGHORN ANTELOPE. **Antilocapra americana americana** Ord

The American Antelope, or Pronghorn, was, under original conditions, an inhabitant of the plains country at both ends of the Yosemite section. Edward Bosqui in his Memoirs (1904, p. 62) states that in December, 1850, he went with a party of freighters from Stockton to Mariposa, and that "as we [he] approached the foothills [near the present town of Snelling] game became more plentiful. At times we saw bands of elk, deer, and antelope in such numbers that they actually darkened the plains for miles and looked in the distance like great herds of cattle." Another early traveler, W. L. Manly (Death Valley in '49) tells of a trip up the Merced River to the crossing of the Stockton-Mariposa road [at Snelling] and of the numbers of antelope which were scattered over the plain at the time.

In general form the Pronghorn is deer-like. The head of the male is surmounted by a pair of upright flattened blackish horns, each with a single forward-pointing prong; the females have similar but smaller horns. On the rump is a large patch of long white hairs that can be raised at will, as a 'flag' to attract the attention of others of its kind. The body coloration above is uniform pale sandy brown, with patches of white on sides of face and chin, and two patches on throat; the whole under surface of the body is white. In size the antelope about equals a small deer. The height at the shoulder is about 33 inches, the weight of an adult about 100 pounds.

The Pronghorn was an animal of open plains country such as is found widely in the San Joaquin Valley and in the Great Basin. It never occurred far into the foothill districts. Its sustenance was gained from grasses and small plants. For safety it depended upon its running ability, and in escaping from its natural enemies this was sufficient.

With the coming of the white man, possessed of firearms, the fortunes of the antelope declined. Antelope were shot extensively for food and probably also for sport. Miners coming down from the foothills killed antelope for meat, especially when they could not obtain elk. There was a rapid decrease in the numbers of the animals soon after the country began to fill up with settlers. The antelope, adjusted as a species to small annual toll, did not reproduce at a rate sufficiently rapid to make up the losses inflicted by shooting. Even if these matters had been adjusted, however, it is doubtful whether the antelope could have long persisted in view of the agricultural developments which have taken place over nearly all of their range.

Mr. G. B. Neighbor, a long-time resident of Snelling, told us in 1915 that the last antelope he had known of in the vicinity were seen in 1880, and that they had never been abundant there in his time (since about 1874).

One man who had lived at Snelling all his life (since about 1880) said that the antelope had all gone before he became old enough to remember; but that his father, who had resided at the place before 1880, had told him that there used to be numbers of the animals there.

When Mr. Dixon visited the vicinity of Mono Lake in 1916 he was told that prior to 1910 one lone antelope had frequented the flat near the railroad along the eastern side of Mono Lake; but nothing had been seen of the animal after that year.

SIERRA NEVADA MOUNTAIN SHEEP. **Ovis canadensis sierrae** Grinnell

Mountain Sheep or Bighorns originally inhabited the higher slopes and ridges of the Yosemite region in numbers. To the south of the Yosemite section, in the vicinity of Mammoth Pass and thence south to the neighborhood of Mount Whitney, these animals still exist in moderate numbers, but elsewhere in the Sierra Nevada they are things of the past. The rush of white men to the mines of Tioga and Mammoth doubtless resulted in many mountain sheep being killed for food; and later, when domestic sheep were run into the mountains, it is known that the herders levied toll on all the wild game to the limit of their hunting equipment; so we may believe that they had a hand in the reduction of the native sheep. Some of the killing of mountain sheep is to be laid to persons hunting for sport, but such killing was probably a minor factor in their reduction in the Yosemite region. Whatever the several agencies were, the fact remains that mountain sheep, once well represented in the mountains of the Yosemite region, are now entirely gone, with only faint prospect for return, by gradual reinvasion from the more southern parts of the Sierra Nevada or by introduction.

John Muir in his Mountains of California (1894, pp. 308–324) tells of meeting with a flock of 25 or so mountain sheep on the headwaters of the San Joaquin River near Mounts Emerson and Humphrey, in the autumn of 1873. He also tells of finding a weather-whitened skull on the slopes of Mount Ritter. The only reference by him to wild sheep in the Yosemite region proper is to a band of three ''discovered snow-bound in Bloody Cañon a few years'' previously to 1874 and ''killed with an ax by mountaineers, who chanced to be crossing the range in winter.''

One of the men who served us as packer in 1915, Mr. George Smith, told a member of our party that he saw mountain sheep in the summers of 1876 to 1878 on the eastern slope of Sonora Pass, which is at the junction of Alpine, Mono, and Tuolumne counties. During each one of these years he would see about a dozen sheep. This location is some miles north of the present boundary of the Park. Jim Bartel, a resident of Yosemite

Valley, stated that sheep had not existed in the Park since his coming there in 1893. We may thus conclude that sheep probably occurred within the territory at present included in the Yosemite National Park until some time in the seventies or possibly the early eighties. Occasional individuals may have wandered in after that time. One resident of the region told us in 1915 that he believed that sheep were then still present in the territory north of the Park; but of this we have no further evidence.

The skull of the mountain sheep, particularly that part of the head which bears the massive bony horn cores and the horns, is very thick and solid so that when exposed to the elements it disintegrates slowly. Conditions along the crest of the Sierras are conducive to long persistence of such relics (fig. 36b). There are few or no rodents to gnaw at the bones as they would in lower altitudes, and the climatic conditions are also favorable. The winter snow packs the bones in 'cold storage' for long periods of time. Hence, such relics, when found by naturalists, merely indicate that sheep once occurred in the region; no close estimate can be formed of the time which has elapsed since the particular animal represented by the relic lived there.

Three fragments of this sort came to attention in 1915. Mr. Forest S. Townsley of the Park Ranger Service discovered the frontal portion of a mountain sheep skull on the slopes of Mount Dana. The senior author, on September 6, 1915, while descending the upper slopes of Parsons Peak, came upon a weathered horn and a portion of a skull in a grassy place at about 11,500 feet altitude. Later, on September 24, he discovered another relic toward the head of Warren Fork of Leevining Creek, at about 9500 feet altitude. This fragment was partially buried in the gravelly surface of a sagebrush-covered slope.

The best specimen of mountain sheep from the Yosemite Region which has come to light is a skull of a big ram, with horns, all in good condition, killed somewhere east of Crescent Lake, at an unknown date (fig. 36a.) This trophy was for many years in the possession of Mrs. John S. Washburn of Wawona, and from her it passed, in 1920, to the California Museum of Vertebrate Zoology. The measurements of this specimen, as compared with those of a ram of the domestic sheep (fig. 36c), are given in the following table. Both animals, as judged from the growth-rings of the horns, were eight years old. The vastly greater basal circumference of the horn of the wild sheep is the outstanding feature of difference.

(Measurements in inches)	Mountain Sheep (Ram)		Domestic Sheep (Ram)	
	Left	Right	Left	Right
Circumference of horn at base	15½	15½	8	8
Length of horn along outer curve	32	30	26	25½
Greatest spread of horns	23		18¼	
Spread of horns, tip to tip	19¼		18¼	

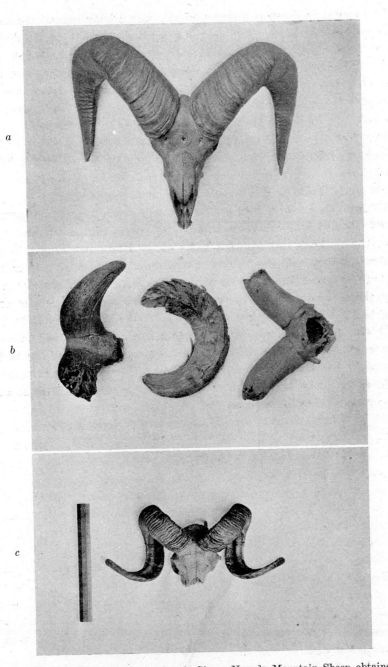

Fig. 36. (a) Skull and horns of male Sierra Nevada Mountain Sheep obtained east of Crescent Lake many years ago; the "Washburn" specimen. (b) Weathered fragments of Mountain Sheep skulls and horn picked up by the senior author on Parsons Peak and on Warren Mountain in 1915. (c) Skull and horns of male Domestic Sheep.

All about 1/10 natural size.

The mountain sheep is a large animal, with a body somewhat like that of a deer, but with horns resembling in general structure those of a domestic sheep. The name 'Bighorn' has reference to the size of the horns in the male. Both sexes in the mountain sheep bear horns, although those of the ewes (females) are much smaller, flatter, and less curved than those of the males; they are goat-like. A full-grown sheep of the Sierra race (as shown by specimens from Mount Baxter, farther to the south) stands about 3 feet high at the shoulder and weighs in the neighborhood of 200 pounds. The body is densely covered with long crinkly hairs at the bases of which there is a minute 'wool' (underfur). The color of the pelage is pale sandy brown, with a large whitish patch on the rump.

The wild sheep of the Sierra Nevada under original conditions occupied for the most part the highest and wildest parts of the mountains, the Alpine-Arctic Zone and adjacent parts of the Hudsonian Zone. In these high places they subsisted on the native bunch grasses and other small plants to be found there. In the winter time the animals sometimes moved down the east slope of the Sierras to where the snow mantle was not so deep, but there was no general exodus as in the case of the Mule Deer. The Sierra Nevada Mountain Sheep was a hardy animal, fitted to live in the narrow belt of alpine conditions found along the crest of the Sierras, and would be there in numbers today had it received any reasonable consideration from the white man. Its gradual return, from the southern remnant, is a thing to be hoped for.

THE BIRDS

AMERICAN EARED GREBE. **Colymbus nigricollis californicus** (Heermann)

Field characters.—Size about that of teal duck; total length about 12 inches; body plump, neck and bill slender; tail so short as to appear to be lacking altogether. Upper surface of body brownish black; lower surface chiefly glistening white; a white patch on wing, shown in flight; in summer, head and chest slate, with yellowish brown streak on side of head; sides of body chestnut. Seen mostly in scattered flocks on lakes; sits low in water with neck straight up and head and bill horizontal; dives below surface at but slight provocation.

Occurrence.—Common on Mono Lake during the summer and autumn months; seen on Gem Lake, September 13, 1915. Reported on Mirror Lake in Yosemite Valley, August 21, 1917 (Mailliard, 1918, pp. 16, 18).

Mono Lake, in spite of its strongly alkaline waters, contains an abundance of animal life consisting chiefly of brine-shrimps and the larvae of a kind of fly. Since many different kinds of water birds are able to subsist, for a time at least, on this kind of food, many migrants stop here to rest and to feed, on their way to or from the north.

One of the commonest of these transient species is the American Eared Grebe. This bird spends practically all of its time on or in the water. Its thick, silky-textured plumage is well adapted for this aquatic mode of life. It is wonderfully expert as a diver and ordinarily seeks safety by diving below the surface of the water rather than by flight, being commonly reputed to "dive at the flash of the gun."

In late May, 1916, fully 150 Eared Grebes were to be seen on Mono Lake in the vicinity of the mouth of Leevining Creek. The birds were associated in pairs, and there was much chasing about and uttering of the shrill courting notes, but there was no evidence to show that they were actually nesting. Since the shores of the lake do not afford the type of surroundings required by these birds during the nesting season, it is probable that they were non-breeders, tempted to remain there by the abundant supply of food. Most of the birds seen at this time were molting, and one individual had entirely lost the power of flight; all its old primary wing feathers had dropped out almost simultaneously and the new ones were not yet fully grown.

PIED-BILLED GREBE. **Podilymbus podiceps** (Linnaeus)

Field characters.—Size and coloration about that of American Eared Grebe (which see), but neck thicker; bill stouter and usually with black bar across middle. Throat (in summer) with black patch; neck, chest, and sides dull brown. Seen singly on ponds and sluggish streams; sits low in water and when frightened sinks beneath surface with no splash and little rippling of water.

Occurrence.—In winter, visits lower course of Merced River, below Yosemite Valley, and sloughs in vicinity of Snelling.

Solitary individuals of the Pied-billed Grebe have been sighted on different occasions in December and January on slow-flowing portions of the Merced River. On the water of a deeply dredged section of the rock-walled channel near Goff, December 12, 1914, a good view of one was obtained from the passing train. Another was seen the last of November, 1915, on the river near Cascade Falls. We may surmise that small trout were the attraction at these places. The only part of the Yosemite region offering the surroundings ordinarily preferred by this grebe is the Merced River bottom below Merced Falls. There the secluded tule-bordered sloughs are likely to afford summer homes and appropriate nesting sites; birds were actually seen there by us only in winter.

CALIFORNIA GULL. **Larus californicus** Lawrence

Field characters.—A gull of medium size; total length 20 inches or more. Plumage of adults (pl. 41a) white on whole head, neck, lower surface and tail; back neutral gray; wings black-ended, with white spots near tips; bill yellow, with dark band near tip and an orange spot near end of lower mandible. Plumage of immatures mixed dark and light brown. Wings long and pointed, tail short and square-ended; flies gracefully, frequently sailing or circling on set wings; when on water sits high, with tips of wings crossed behind back.

Occurrence.—Common in summer on Mono Lake, nesting on Paoha Island; occasionally straggles over Sierran crest to lakes on west slope; noted at Tuolumne Meadows (8600 feet), July 5, 1915, at Young Lake, altitude 10,000 feet, July 8, 1915, and at Tenaya Lake, altitude 8141 feet, July 29 and September 26, 1915.

Most people associate gulls with the seashore. This disposition in general is correct in so far as the winter season is concerned, but during the summer months several of the species leave their maritime haunts altogether and seek bodies of water far inland. Such is the case with the California Gull.

In 1915 we saw California Gulls only four times, as detailed above; but in the late spring and early summer of 1916, when Mr. Dixon visited Mono Lake, he found them there in numbers. On May 6 three birds were seen at the mouth of Leevining Creek; by the latter part of the same month the species had become common there.

On May 27, 1916, Mr. Dixon visited the nesting colony of California Gulls on Paoha Island, the larger of the two islands in Mono Lake. (See pl. 41.) From the north side of Paoha two ridges of black obsidian-like rock extend northward about 200 yards out into the lake. These ridges are about 20 feet high and enclose a long narrow bay about 10 or 15 yards wide and 100 yards in length. Gulls nest on both of these peninsulas but chiefly on the eastern one which bears a rather dense growth of a shrubby plant. Here, over an area of 1½ to 2 acres, there was an average of at least one nest for every 100 square feet; in some places it was estimated that there was one to each 10 square feet. The total number of breeding birds was believed to be close to 1000 pairs.

The nests were placed on the rocky shingle of the beach, in depressions under bushes and on the tops of rocks. Nesting material was scanty, consisting chiefly of old wing feathers, molted in previous years. Many mummified bodies of half-grown young of last year's brood were lying about, and in one instance one of these mummies formed the principal part of the nest. Nests containing 2 eggs were more common than those with one or with 3 eggs, the latter occurring in about equal numbers. One nest held 4 eggs, but this large number was clearly the result of two birds laying in the same nest; for 2 of the eggs were relatively short with a light greenish ground color, while the other 2 were longer, more pointed, and of a brownish ground color. Laying had evidently commenced about May 15, for many of the eggs contained half-developed embryos, but none had yet hatched. The parent gulls seemed to appreciate the need for sheltering their eggs from the intense heat of the sun, which beat down on the bare black rocks. They were often seen standing so as to cast a shadow over their eggs, while they themselves held their mouths open and panted from the heat. Males were seen whose actions seemed to show them to be urging their mates to return to the nests; in some instances they accompanied the females when the latter returned to their duties.

On July 3 a second visit was made to the Paoha Island colony. By this time practically all of the eggs had hatched; about one-third of the young were running about, well feathered and almost half grown. Four nests were found with chicks not more than a day old, and one contained a downy gull so recently hatched from the egg that it was not yet dry. Despite its recent emergence from the shell, this chick was able to scramble about until it found shelter in the shade of a rock. Apparently the adult birds had been more successful with their broods this year, for there were few dead bodies of young gulls about and no infertile eggs. It is possible, however, that abandoned or infertile eggs are promptly eaten by neighboring members of the colony.

In one part of the colony there are many hop-sage bushes about 3 feet high and 3 or 4 feet in diameter. These grow close to the ground, and the strong wind which continually sweeps the island blows the molted white body feathers of the parent gulls against these bushes until each bush has at its base a feathery white windrow often six inches thick. When alarmed, the gray downy young gulls rush headlong into these windrows and do not stop until they are entirely hidden. The larger young, in dusky juvenal plumage, are not so fortunate. They cannot hide their whole bodies in the windrows, and their stubby black tails remain projecting out beyond the drifted feathers in a very grotesque manner. Six youngsters were pulled out of one windrow and there were still other, smaller chicks hidden in the mass. Holes in the rocks were also favorite shelters and places of concealment for the small young; often a chick would shade its head in a small cavity while its body remained out in the broiling heat of the sun.

When disturbed, the larger young headed for the beach, jumping and tumbling over the rocks faster than a man could walk. When they reached the ten-foot bank which borders the waters of the lake they did not hesitate, but plunged over the edge. Once in the water they seemed perfectly at home and swam about, 100 yards offshore, where they were herded into 'rafts' by the parents and prevented from going farther out. (See pl. 41c.) As soon as the intruder retired, the young turned back toward the beach. Once, when a party of a dozen juvenile gulls started down the slope toward the water, they loosened a veritable avalanche of small rocks. Gulls and rocks were pretty well mixed by the time the water was reached and it seemed as though some of the birds would certainly be killed; but they all swam away apparently unharmed.

The young gulls when first hatched eat bits of eggshell, but soon their diet consists exclusively of brine shrimps. Birds 3 or 4 days old had, we found, a considerable number of these crustaceans in their stomachs. When handled, the first thing a young gull does is to throw up quantities of brine shrimps; and the adults, flying overhead, show their displeasure at the disturbance of the young by pouring down similar disgorgements. When undisturbed the adults stand on guard at the nest site. The young play around in the vicinity, but seem always to return to the nest site for feeding. The larger young frequently climb up on the tops of the rocks to await the return of the parents.

The old birds often visit fresh-water lakes in the vicinity to feed on the huge frog tadpoles which there abound. An adult bird captured near Williams Butte on June 23, 1916, disgorged several of these large tadpoles.

Forster Tern. **Sterna forsteri** Nuttall

Field characters.—Approaching pigeon in size; of slender build; tail deeply forked and wings long and narrow. Head black capped; back lavender-gray; whole under surface pure white. Flight airy and swallow-like; bill held pointing downward (nearly at right angle to axis of body).

Occurrence.—Casual visitant to lowland waters. One seen over Tuolumne River 2 miles southwest of Lagrange, May 6, 1919. Usually seen over open water.

Only one Forster Tern was seen by us, as noted above. But the species probably visits regularly, during migrations, the low country on both sides of the mountains. The tern in question was flying along over the Tuolumne River, maintaining a height of from 20 to 40 feet, its bill held down, mosquito-like, as the bird watched for prey in the water beneath. Once it saw something, hesitated a moment, and then went down in a spiral course and splashed into the water after the object it sought, presumably some small fish.

Black Tern. **Hydrochelidon nigra surinamensis** (Gmelin)

Field characters.—As small as Robin; resembling a swallow in form and flight; wings long and pointed, tail somewhat forked. Head and most of body (in summer adults) black; back, tail, and wings, dark gray. Usually seen coursing over lakes or smooth-running streams. *Voice:* A grating cry.

Occurrence.—A transient through the region. Observed by us only at Mono Lake.

The terns are mostly associated with the seashore, but this member of the family is partial to inland waters. Black Terns were seen on two occasions at Mono Lake in 1916. On May 6, six were observed foraging about the marginal ponds near the mouth of Rush Creek. On June 3, one was seen. The graceful aerial evolutions of the birds, which resemble those of swallows, and the black and dark gray plumage and forked tail serve easily to identify this species.

Farallon Cormorant. **Phalacrocorax auritus albociliatus** Ridgway

Field characters.—General appearance goose-like; neck long and slender, wings long but narrow, tail narrow. Plumage wholly black in adults; in immatures, brownish above, gray or whitish below. Bare skin on chin and throat (involving ''gular sac'') yellowish orange. In flight, course direct, wing beats continuous, neck outstretched and often crooked.

Occurrence.—Observed along Tuolumne River below Lagrange, May 6 and 7, 1919. One individual taken in Yosemite Valley (see below). Usually frequents vicinity of lakes or reservoirs.

The Farallon Cormorant, although thought of chiefly as a bird of the seacoast, is well known to visit and nest on a number of the larger inland lakes of California. Small colonies may possibly occur about some of the larger reservoirs in the foothills of the Yosemite region. Three different times on May 6 and 7, 1919, single individuals were seen flying down the Tuolumne River below Lagrange. As the bird or birds seen all took a course leading toward a reservoir in the hills nearby, it was thought that there might be a small colony established there.

A single bird of this species on exhibit in the superintendent's office in Yosemite Valley was taken in the Valley by Ranger Townsley some time between 1916 and 1919.

White Pelican. **Pelecanus erythrorhynchos** Gmelin

Field characters.—Very large size (largest bird of flight seen in the Yosemite region); total length five feet; bill a foot or more long, about three times length of head. Plumage pure white save for black tipping of wings. Flies in flocks, the individuals either abreast or in echelon, that is, in rows diagonal to line of flight; wing strokes intermittent, the birds alternately flapping and sailing; the head drawn in on body distinguishes pelicans in flight from geese, in which the head and neck are outstretched.

Occurrence.—A migrant through the region. Once noted at Snelling.

The White Pelican is only a transient in the Yosemite region. On May 26, 1915, at Snelling, a flock of about 65 of these impressive birds was seen flying north, high overhead. Five minutes later another flock of about 100 passed over, and then one of 19. Although the birds were fully 1000 feet above the observer, they were easily identified by means of the field characters given above.

American Merganser. **Mergus americanus** Cassin

Field characters.—Size large for a duck; head, neck, and bill slender; large patch on wing, and whole lower surface of body, pure white. Male: head greenish black; middle of back black. Female: head reddish brown; back grayish brown.

Occurrence.—Casual visitant. Flock of six seen on Merced River about Merced Falls, January 2, 1915.

The American Merganser is the only species of 'fish duck' we saw in the Yosemite section. Either this species or its relative, the Red-breasted Merganser, is likely to visit any fish-inhabited pond or sluggish stream during the winter months. The American Merganser is known to nest farther north in the Sierra Nevada, but the conditions afforded in the Yosemite region do not seem to attract the birds to remain here during the summer months.

Mallard. **Anas platyrhynchos** Linnaeus

Field characters.—A duck of large size and general similarity to domesticated varieties; bright iridescent steel-blue patch on wing, bordered in front and behind with white; under surface of wing, as shown in flight, white. Male: Head and neck green; ring at base of neck, white; tail whitish with black center and with up-curled feathers near end; back and belly grayish white. Female: Whole plumage streaked with light and dark yellowish brown. *Voice:* Of female, a loud oft-repeated quack; of male, similar but softer, more wheezy.

Occurrence.—Casual visitant on lakes and smoother flowing waters on both sides of the mountains; noted on Merced River in Yosemite Valley, in Little Yosemite Valley, and on Grant and Mono lakes.

In the Yosemite region ducks are to be found in large numbers only on Mono Lake, and there chiefly during the seasons of migration. The Mallard, the best known of all our wild ducks because of its esculent qualities, is the species most frequently seen elsewhere in the region.

The Mallard is a typical river duck and a surface feeder. It seeks its forage in shallow ponds, and 'tips up' to reach down for the coveted morsels instead of diving for them in deeper water as does the Harlequin Duck.

The Mallard probably nests on the marshy lands bordering some of the smoother flowing waters at low elevations on the west slope of the mountains, and about the sage-bordered lakes at the east base of the Sierras.

Baldpate. **Mareca americana** (Gmelin)

Field characters.—Size medium for a duck; feathers at junction of wing and body below (axillars) white. Male: top of head white (whence the name ''baldpate''), green patch behind eye; wing with patch of white followed by one of green; patch on flank white; under tail coverts black; back and sides pale brown; under surface chiefly white. Female: Upper surface barred grayish and yellowish brown; a black patch on wing.

Occurrence.—Transient. Several seen on Mono Lake, September 20, 1915.

The Baldpate or American Widgeon occurs with probable regularity, during both of the migration seasons, on the lakes at the eastern base of the Sierras. It is apt also to be found on the slower streams of the lower west slope.

Cinnamon Teal. **Querquedula cyanoptera** (Vieillot)

Field characters.—Small for a duck; wing with a large blue patch on forward part. Male (except in mid-summer, when like female): Entire head and whole under surface rich chestnut brown; upper surface streaked with light and dark brown. Female: Upper surface dark brown with lighter feather edgings; breast and under surface mottled on a light brown ground.

Occurrence.—Summer visitant along both bases of the Sierras. Noted at Mono Lake, September 20, 1915, and May 30 and June 3, 1916.

Cinnamon Teal are more likely to be found in the Yosemite region during the summer season than any other species of duck. As they breed at Laws, Inyo County, not far southeast of Mono Lake, they probably nest also at Mono Lake itself. The bright chestnut or deep cinnamon plumage of the male makes him easy to identify even at a long distance. A flock of twenty-five was noted on September 20, 1915, not on Mono Lake proper, but in a small lagoon formed by a barrier beach at the edge of the main body of water. Presumably they were in quest of brine-shrimps. Like the Mallard, these birds feed by 'tipping up.'

SHOVELLER. **Spatula clypeata** (Linnaeus)

Field characters.—Size medium for a duck, smaller than Mallard; bill broad at end, spoon-shaped; outer surface of wing with patch of blue and one of green. Male: Head and neck metallic green; breast and under surfaces of wings white; belly cinnamon. Female: Chiefly dull brown.

Occurrence.—Casual visitant. Noted on Merced River below Sentinel Bridge, December 26, 1914.

Only one instance of occurrence of the Shoveller ('spoonbill') was recorded by our party, as given above; yet this species is apt to be seen on the open streams and lakes of the Yosemite region at almost any time during the year. The flock observed was wary; when flushed the birds flew up the Valley and returned down the river, high overhead. The huge bill, the light under surface of the wings, light color throughout of the females, and the dark head and under parts of the males were all seen distinctly.

PINTAIL. **Dafila acuta** (Linnaeus)

Field characters.—Somewhat smaller than Mallard, and of more slender build; neck long. Male: Central tail feathers greatly elongated; head brown; a white stripe up neck on each side; belly white. Female: Similar to female Mallard, but much slenderer; under surface of wing, as seen in flight, grayish brown.

Occurrence.—Transient. A pair on fresh-water pond near mouth of Rush Creek, Mono Lake, May 6, 1916.

The Pintail, or 'sprig' of the hunter, is another of the fresh-water ducks that may be expected, during the seasons of migration, on smooth water anywhere in the Yosemite region. Its long neck, as seen either in flight or on the water, facilitates identification. When feeding in shallow ponds these birds do not 'tip up' so often as do Mallards, for their long necks usually enable them to reach down a sufficient distance without tipping.

Harlequin Duck. **Histrionicus histrionicus** (Linnaeus)

Field characters.—Size, smaller than Mallard; bill small for a duck's; general color-ation very dark. Male: Dark slate blue, strikingly marked with white patches on head, body and wings, and white ring around neck; flanks chestnut. Female: Dull dark brown with two white patches on each side of head—one on cheek, and one on ear region. (See fig. 37.)

Occurrence.—Infrequent summer visitant to the larger streams of the Transition Zone. Adults and young seen on Merced River in Yosemite Valley near Sentinel Bridge.

Fig. 37. The Harlequin Duck (female at left, male at right).

At dusk on several evenings in late April, 1916, a small dark-colored duck was seen to fly up the Merced River in the vicinity of Sentinel Bridge, Yosemite Valley, and then to begin diving and drifting down-stream. On May 7 of the same year, this or another duck of the same species, which was unquestionably the Harlequin, was seen on the river with four duck-lings about four days old. In 1920, Mr. C. W. Michael (MS) saw a pair in the same place on May 11 and 26, and June 4, and he saw a lone female on July 28. These are the only actual occurrences of this species in the area included in our field studies, recorded to the end of 1920. But the Harlequin Duck has several times been recorded as breeding along swift-flowing streams on the west flank of the Sierra Nevada at localities in the Transition Zone immediately to the north of Yosemite Park. It is reason-able to expect that a careful watch in early summer will bring to notice other instances of the nesting of this remarkable bird within the Park itself. So far, very little is known of its summer habits.

The Harlequin Duck, strange to say, belongs to the class of sea ducks and spends the winter exclusively along the roughest, surf-beaten ocean shores, such as, for instance, those around Point Reyes. Curiously, the birds have never been observed at any point between their mountain and seacoast haunts.

AMERICAN BITTERN. **Botaurus lentiginosus** (Montagu)

Field characters.—Large size (height, standing, about 22 inches); heron-like build, but much smaller than Great Blue Heron. Plumage streaked light and dark rusty brown, closely resembling dead tules in general effect.

Occurrence.—Casual transient. Individuals seen by Donald D. McLean along Smith Creek, east of Coulterville, during the fall months.

The American Bittern, which is typically a bird of the tule swamps, does not often venture out into the open as does the Great Blue Heron. Its whole plumage blends so well in color with the dry tules in which it lives that it is ordinarily overlooked, save when flushed. Then it flies in typical heron fashion, with head drawn in, legs trailing behind, and broad wings slowly beating, to soon drop again into the marsh vegetation. This bird will not be found with regularity in the Yosemite section, because of the scarcity there of suitable cover.

LEAST BITTERN. **Ixobrychus exilis exilis** (Gmelin)

Field characters.—Our smallest Heron; little larger than Killdeer; bill and legs long and slender. Male: Top of head and whole back greenish black; flight feathers dull black; sides of neck reddish brown; whole under surface mixed white and light tan color. Female: similar, but top of head and back dark reddish brown.

Occurrence.—One instance: a male obtained at a pond at mouth of Rush Creek, Mono Lake, June 3, 1916. Frequents tule marshes.

The single specimen of this elusive species obtained by our party, as detailed above, was the only one seen anywhere. Its weight was 66 grams (about 2.3 ounces). It is of interest to compare this weight with the 475 grams (about 17 ounces) of the American Bittern and the 1530 grams (3.4 pounds) of the Great Blue Heron. In other words, the Great Blue Heron is 23 times the size of its smallest relative, the Least Bittern.

GREAT BLUE HERONS. **Ardea herodias** Linnaeus[18]

Field characters.—Tallest bird occurring regularly in the Yosemite region (stands 3 feet high or more); general form slender; neck and legs very long. General color slaty blue; head marked with white and black; neck brownish; pattern of under surface

---

[18] Two races of this species occur in the Yosemite region, a darker form, the California Great Blue Heron (*Ardea herodias hyperonca* Oberholser), which ranges from the plains of the San Joaquin eastward at least to Yosemite; and a paler Great Basin form, the Pallid Great Blue Heron (*Ardea herodias treganzai* Court), which is found about Mono Lake and strays westward at least to Tuolumne Meadows. These two forms cannot be distinguished except as specimens in hand.

streaked black and white. Flight direct, with slow, regular flapping of the broad wings; neck crooked in flight (not held out straight, as with cranes and geese); legs held out behind, extending beyond end of tail in line with body. Forages singly or in pairs. *Voice:* A deep guttural squawk, not often uttered.

Occurrence.—Resident in the western lowlands; may occur almost anywhere else in the region during the summer season; most frequently noted along Merced River, between Snelling and Yosemite Valley and along Tuolumne River near Lagrange; has been observed at Merced Lake, Glen Aulin, and Tuolumne Meadows. Found chiefly along streams or about lake borders, but sometimes also in fields and meadows.

In the mountainous parts of the Yosemite region the Great Blue Heron is only an irregular visitant, but at lower altitudes, in appropriate parts of the San Joaquin Valley and adjacent foothills, it is a fairly common resident. Along the river in the Merced Cañon between Merced Falls and the Yosemite Valley one or more individual birds may usually be seen, at close range, from the windows of the passing train. Single birds are occasionally observed in Yosemite Valley and, more rarely, about bodies of water in the higher country to the eastward.

The Great Blue Heron is a marsh and stream-side bird; its whole bodily make-up is adapted to gaining a livelihood in these situations and in a special manner associated with the conditions therein. Its long legs easily allow it to wade in water of considerable depth, and its long sharp bill and long neck enable it to capture fishes and other aquatic animals from a vantage point some distance above the surface. The species is also, however, an efficient catcher of terrestrial rodents. Not infrequently a bird may be seen standing motionless in an alfalfa field on the watch for pocket gophers. Although known locally by the name of ''Blue Crane,'' this bird is a true heron, with habits not at all like those of the real cranes.

Although accustomed to civilization to the extent that it will frequently allow railroad trains to pass close by without being disturbed from its perch on rock or snag, the Great Blue Heron has not learned to avoid overhead wires; from time to time a bird is found dead or injured under telegraph lines against which it has flown. In the plains country where the birds are able to see long distances they lay their courses from place to place at once in a direct line; but in the high mountains the surrounding cañon walls force them to adopt another procedure. When they rise from the shore of a mountain lake they begin to circle upward and continue spiraling until they reach a height which will give an uninterrupted view of the surrounding elevated country; then they make off in a straight line in the desired direction. The deliberate flapping of the broad wings gives the observer the impression that the Great Blue Heron is a very slow flier. And it is, at times; individual birds have been seen by us to keep barely ahead of the train traveling about 20 miles per hour along the Merced.

Near Snelling the Great Blue Heron builds its bulky stick nests in the tall cottonwoods along the river. The belief is held locally that once the birds select and use a tree for this purpose the tree immediately dies. It is probably true, however, that the birds choose the oldest trees in the vicinity, such as are likely soon to die anyway. In the Yosemite Valley and higher country these birds are reputed to be very destructive to trout. The one bird obtained on Tuolumne Meadows, probably a straggler from the vicinity of Mono Lake, had only mammal hair and parts of a crustacean in its stomach.

ANTHONY GREEN HERON. **Butorides virescens anthonyi** (Mearns)

Field characters.—Size small for a heron; length about 16 inches. Top of head greenish black; back and wings, grayish green; neck and shoulders, reddish brown; under surface chiefly grayish. Flight labored but direct; legs extending backward beyond tail. *Voice:* A moderately loud hoarse squawk; also clucking notes.

Occurrence.—Summer visitant in small numbers along Merced and Tuolumne rivers. Seen near Mountain King Mine, August 17, 1915, near Snelling, April 26, 1916, and 2 miles southwest of Lagrange, May 7, 1919. Frequents vicinity of sluggish water, perching on lower branches of overhanging willows; usually flies out over the water when changing position.

The Anthony Green Heron is to be met with only at low elevations and then chiefly along the slower moving streams and the ponds bordered by willows. Only three of the birds were actually seen by us, but the species is undoubtedly a regular summer visitant along the lower reaches of both the Merced and Tuolumne rivers. We have two records of birds seen from the windows of a moving train. Travelers en route to the Yosemite Valley are thus likely to catch sight of this heron while traversing the lower Merced cañon.

Our most intimate knowledge of the Anthony Green Heron was obtained on May 7, 1919, when a nest was discovered in a dense stand of willow and cottonwood trees on the bank of a slough near the Tuolumne River about 2 miles southwest of Lagrange. Great Blue and Night herons breed in colonies and place their bulky nests in plain sight in the tops of tall trees where the birds can command a wide range of vision. But the little Anthony Green Heron nests solitarily; it shows a marked preference for seclusion; it hides its nest in dense growths of willow or cottonwood, just beneath the green leafy crowns of these trees. The nest found by us was so located, about 25 feet above the ground in a slender willow, one of many that slanted toward the adjacent pond. The nest was supported on three twigs about 10 millimeters in diameter, which grew out on the under side of the trunk. The sitting bird had an almost clear view of the ground below, as there were but few bare dead branches beneath her, and practically no undergrowth. When disturbed she flushed directly through the leaves above her head and made off over the nearby water.

The nest was of very loose construction, as are all herons' nests, a mere pile of dead brittle willow twigs from 1 to 5 millimeters in diameter and up to 400 millimeters in length. It measured 280 to 300 millimeters in outside diameter and about 180 millimeters in depth. In profile it was triangular, with the apex downward. There was a rounded depression in the top, 70 millimeters deep at the center, from which point it sloped up to the very rim of the nest. This depression held the 5 eggs, which were of the vivid unspotted green color common to eggs of most herons. Four of the eggs weighed 18.1, 19.3, 19.5, and 20.0 grams, respectively.

As the observer first approached, he could see, from below, the sitting bird; her dully streaked under tail coverts, her slender neck and bill, and her glistening eye showed plainly. When the observer started to climb the tree, she left the nest and, as she took off over the slough, he was able to see the cinnamon brown of her neck. The bird remained in the vicinity and her harsh squawk was heard twice at short intervals, followed in one instance by a series of clucking notes, such as one would give when urging a horse to start. This heron, like herons in general, gave little attention to cleanliness about the nest, and the ground and vegetation beneath the nest tree were spattered with white excrement, a telltale feature marking the location of the nest.

BLACK-CROWNED NIGHT HERON. **Nycticorax nycticorax naevius** (Boddaert)

Field characters.—Considerably smaller than Great Blue Heron, and with noticeably shorter legs and neck. Prevailing coloration of body and wings light gray; under surface whitish; top of head and back greenish black. (There are usually two or three long slender plumes, ⅛ inch wide, extending backward from crown of head to middle of back.) Young birds are streaked all over with light and dark brown. Flight slow, direct, with deliberate wing beats. *Voice:* A sharp harsh squawk.

Occurrence.—Thinly scattered as a resident west of foothills. Frequents vicinity of water and roosts and nests in trees near by. Seen at Snelling May 26, 1915, and near Lagrange, December 14, 1915, and May 8, 1919.

Black-crowned Night Herons are resident in small numbers along the Merced and Tuolumne rivers below their exit from the foothills. The harsh-voiced notes of the birds, of frequent utterance during the night when they are active, have given them the common name of "squawk." Like most other herons they get their food from the margins of ponds and sluggish streams. The birds roost throughout the day in concealment, congregated in dense willow thickets, whence they issue forth at dusk to forage singly over the surrounding bottomlands.

Virginia Rail. **Rallus virginianus** Linnaeus

Field characters.—Size of Robin or Killdeer; body very narrow (compressed); bill slender, over 1¼ inches long; tail very short, upstanding; breast cinnamon colored, back streaked with olive brown and black. Walks with jerking movement of head and neck.

Occurrence.—Resident in small numbers in marshy situations. Noted at Smith Creek, Snelling, and Lagrange. Lives secluded, in streamside or pond-margin thickets, rarely venturing into the open.

Only the observer who can take time to search thoroughly the dense vegetation of the marshlands will be at all likely to see the Virgina Rail. Even if present plentifully, the bird is so elusive that a clear view of one is obtained only by chance. At Lagrange, on December 10, 1915, a small rail was heard and seen, and the next day a Virginia Rail was caught in a steel trap. At Snelling, on January 9, 1915, a bird of this species was caught in an oat-baited mouse trap placed in a marshy situation close to the Merced River. The stealthy, mouse-like habits of the bird are indicated by these captures, which, as far as bait was concerned, were in all probability purely accidental. The Virginia Rail's food consists almost entirely of small invertebrate animals, in search of which it slips through the narrow passageways in swamp vegetation. The mouse trap had been set in such a natural runway.

Mr. Donald D. McLean (1916, p. 229) records the finding of a nest of the Virginia Rail, at Smith Creek, east of Coulterville, on June 5, 1916. The structure was tower-like, composed of grasses from the surrounding wet meadow, and was 8 inches in diameter and about the same in height. The 10 brown-and-lilac-spotted eggs were just beginning to be incubated.

The grass clump in which the nest was situated was not disturbed when the meadow was mowed. When anyone approached the vicinity, the incubating bird would slip off quietly; sometimes she could be heard splashing through the water as she ran away. Usually she did not go more than six feet from the nest, and there would remain standing quietly, appearing merely as a dark shadow. She uttered occasionally a low clucking sound.

Nothing was seen of the male until June 18, when a shrill whistle came from him as he stood some distance away in the grass. This was answered by a similar but softer note from his mate. The male showed himself momentarily as he skulked through the grass, trying apparently to distract attention from the nest.

On June 19 there were 6 coal-black young in the nest. They had black-ringed, pink bills and their feet were large in proportion to their bodies. The female now overcame her shyness and walked out into the open within three feet of the observers. She fluffed up her feathers in the manner of a brooding hen, and uttered many clucks and whistles which were answered by the louder notes of the male.

Later the same day the nest was again visited. The female was absent, but soon appeared, after her mate had whistled, swimming and wading toward the nest across a bit of open water. By the evening of the nineteenth, another egg had hatched, and by the morning of the twentieth, 2 more; the last egg hatched that afternoon. On the morning of June 21, the family had departed. Nothing more was seen of them, save for one that showed itself for a moment one day in late July.

One bird, chiefly in the blackish juvenal plumage, was taken at the same locality, July 24, 1920.

Mud-hen. **Fulica americana** Gmelin

Field characters.—Size of a small duck but with short, whitish bill; front toes with broad flaps or lobes, instead of complete webs. Plumage chiefly dark slate; head and neck black; a white V on under side of up-tilted tail. Walks or swims with fore-and-aft movement of head in unison with tread of feet; rises from water with labored effort, and flies with the large feet extending bulkily beyond end of tail. *Voice:* An explosive *pulque*, or *plop*, with hollow intonation.

Occurrence.—Resident in small numbers on slower streams west of foothills; transient on lower foothill streams elsewhere in the region, and summer visitant to smaller lakes east of Sierra Nevada.

To unobserving persons the Mud-hen or ''coot'' often passes for a duck, but students of systematic ornithology recognize it as a forward-pushing relative of the retiring rails. The Mud-hen is a bird of open water; at times it may be seen from the windows of the railroad train passing through the lower Merced Cañon, swimming slowly about on the quieter stretches of the river in search of food, or, when excited, rising with paddling feet and heavily beating wings to take a direct course away from the source of fright.

Mud-hens occasionally stray up the rivers well into the western foothills, for example, one was seen at Kittredge, October 22. In migration they visit certain lakes east of the Sierran crest other than those on which they nest; a flock of a hundred or more was seen on June Lake, near Reversed Peak, September 17, 1915.

Northern Phalarope. **Lobipes lobatus** (Linnaeus)

Field characters.—A 'wader' much smaller than Killdeer; bill needle-like. Whole under surface pure white; back dark brown in spring and summer, pearl gray in fall and winter; sides of neck rusty brown in spring and summer. Swims buoyantly in companies on open water.

Occurrence.—Numerous at Mono Lake during seasons of migration. Observed May 24 and 27, 1916 (Dixon, MS), and in August and between September 2 and 21, 1901 (Fisher, 1902, p. 10).

The Northern Phalarope is one of the small water birds that nests in the far north and winters to the south of us. It thus occurs in our latitude only for a brief period in spring and again in the fall. At these times it is likely to appear on any body of water either east or west of the Sierran divide.

These birds are adept swimmers and gather their food from the surface of the water by rapid darting movements of the head and neck. Their delicate bills serve unerringly to capture the small objects which are taken as food. At times a bird will spin around rapidly so as to produce a miniature whirlpool or vortex and thus swirl the animalicules from below up to within easy reach of its bill. Thus these birds do not need to dive below the surface for their food as do so many of the water birds, as, for instance, the grebes.

Dr. Walter K. Fisher (1902, p. 8) states that in the fall of 1901 large numbers of southbound Northern Phalaropes visited Mono Lake and fed on the brine shrimps which abound there. The phalaropes fell easy prey to hunters, who called them "Mono Lake pigeons."

Wilson Phalarope. **Steganopus tricolor** Vieillot

Field characters.—Larger than Northern Phalarope; size of Robin or Killdeer, but with slender head and neck, and very slender black bill. Upper surface chiefly dark brown, with some black and cinnamon red at side of neck of female; a conspicuous patch of white above base of tail, shown especially in flight; under surface white except for tawny or gray area on fore neck. Swims lightly, as does the Northern Phalarope, but not so habitually.

Occurrence.—Summer visitant along east base of Sierra Nevada; dates of record at or near Mono Lake: May 6 and 20, and June 23, 1916. Frequents marshy meadows and margins of ponds.

The Wilson Phalarope probably nests in wet meadows at Mono Lake and south of Williams Butte; for a female collected there on May 6, 1916, contained an egg ready to be laid. Moreover, two male birds observed by Mr. Dixon at Farrington's Ranch on June 23, 1916, acted as if there were nests near by. Since the male of the phalarope is the sex which does most or all of the work of brooding and of caring for the young, it seems likely that the concern exhibited by these birds meant that they actually were nesting in the vicinity.

Unlike the Northern Phalarope, this larger species gleans most of its forage when wading rather than when swimming.

WILSON SNIPE. **Gallinago delicata** (Ord)

Field characters.—A 'wader' of about size of Robin; bill slender and very long (2½ inches). Head and back longitudinally streaked with black and buff; belly white; breast mottled with buffy drab and dark brown. Of retiring habits and usually solitary. Flight, when flushed, quick and erratic. *Voice:* A rasping *scaipe, scaipe.*

Occurrence.—Transient (and probably also a summer visitant) in vicinity of Mono Lake; winter visitant near Snelling. Frequents moist grasslands, and margins of ponds and irrigation ditches.

Our field workers observed the Wilson Snipe in winter only at Snelling (January 7 and 8, 1915) and Lagrange (December 20, 1915), and in summer only in the marshes near Mono Lake (May 21, 1916). In no instance were more than two birds seen at one time, and these only as they were flushed from the shelter of the grass.

A juvenile male obtained near Williams Butte on September 22, 1915, still had some of the natal down clinging to the plumage of the thighs.

LEAST SANDPIPER. **Pisobia minutilla** (Vieillot)

Field characters.—A 'wader' of about size of Junco; bill slender, about ¾ inch long. Feet and legs greenish, not black. Upper surface streaked brown and black; under surface white save for indistinct belt of ashy or drab across breast. *Voice:* A plaintive *pe-et* or *wheet.*

Occurrence.—Sparse transient. Recorded at Smith Creek, six miles east of Coulterville, in May, and at Mono Lake, east of the Sierra Nevada, in May and September. Runs over flat open margins of lakes or streams. In small active flocks.

The Least Sandpiper, the smallest of our shore birds, is so widely distributed elsewhere during the seasons of migration that it was no surprise to find it in the Yosemite section. At the mouth of Rush Creek on Mono Lake a trio of small sandpipers, believed to be of this species, was seen on May 6, 1916. In September, 1901, the species was identified positively at Mono Lake by Dr. W. K. Fisher (1902, p. 10).

On the west side of the mountains, on Smith Creek, 6 miles east of Coulterville, a Least Sandpiper was taken by Mr. Donald D. McLean on May 5, 1917. It is not unlikely that individual birds or flocks occur with some frequency along open shores elsewhere in the region.

SPOTTED SANDPIPER. **Actitis macularia** (Linnaeus)

Field characters.—A 'wader' between Robin and Junco in size; of slender build, with long legs, slender neck, and short tail. Upper surface olive brown; under surface, in summer adults, white with numerous rounded black spots; wing crossed by a narrow white band, readily seen in flight; outer tail feathers barred with brown and white. Course of flight usually semicircular, the bird skimming low over the water. When on ground bobs hinder parts of body down and up every second or two. *Voice:* A clear, whistle-like *weet* or *weeter*, uttered three or more times in quick succession.

Occurrence.—Summer visitant, irrespective of altitude, along sandy or pebbly shores of lakes and smooth-flowing streams; seen often along Merced River up as far as Yosemite Valley; also on Tuolumne River below Lagrange, on Tuolumne Meadows, and on shores of Mono Lake.

Most of our stream-side birds seem inclined to seclude themselves in the thick deciduous growths which line the water courses; but the Spotted Sandpiper, gleaning its food at the water's edge, lives almost entirely in the open. Along the river in Yosemite Valley, wherever the banks are gently sloping and sandy or pebbly, and on the broad reaches of the Tuolumne as it winds through the lower part of the Tuolumne Meadows, this bird may be seen or heard almost any hour of the day during the summer time. Excepting for the Killdeer, this sandpiper is the only representative of the large and far-ranging group of shore birds to be found regularly in the Yosemite section.

Along the Tuolumne River below Lagrange, in early May, 1919, two or more Spotted Sandpipers were in evidence all through the day and until dusk of evening. At one sandy place at the river's edge the tracks of the birds were to be seen after each fall of the river. At this time the birds were trilling often. *Weet-weet-weet-weeter-weet* was one call heard. On May 18, 1919, a bird flushed from the river margin near Camp Curry, in Yosemite Valley, gave a loud *peet'-peet'-peet'* and a few moments later a fainter, much more musical *weeter, weeter, weeter, weeter.*

On the morning of June 2, 1915, in Yosemite Valley, when the Merced River was swollen bank high by the melting snows of the higher mountains, three Spotted Sandpipers were seen foraging on a high beach near Stoneman Bridge. They moved about in the shallow water at the edge of the river or on the gravel, never farther than a foot or two from the water, walking rapidly for a few steps, and then stopping abruptly to procure some morsel of food sighted among the stones. While a bird was thus occupied, the hinder portion of its body was continually bobbed down and up at regular intervals of a second or two, and while it was walking the head underwent a rapid fore-and-aft movement in unison with the tread of the feet.

Two of the birds seemed by their actions to be males. It was just at the beginning of the mating season at this altitude, and considerable rivalry evidently existed between them. In one tilt, after much manoeuvering, one of these birds drove the other away. Meanwhile the third bird, presumably a female, unconcernedly went on feeding in the vicinity. After routing his rival the successful suitor approached the female and strutted about her, holding his body in a peculiarly erect posture, and partially spreading his wings and tail. The object of his attentions held shyly aloof, with the feathers of her body closely appressed, giving her a smart, trim appearance. She gave no indication that his presence or actions were noticed, except that now and then the barred outer feathers of her tail were slightly spread apart.

In Yosemite Valley, on June 23, 1920, a nest was found on a sand bar 200 yards below Stoneman Bridge. When the site was selected it was on a small island, but the recession of the water had later established connection with the shore. One of the birds was sitting on the nest, and every now and then it called in melodious voice and was answered by the mate 50 yards or so up-stream. The four eggs were later seen to be resting in a rather deep grass-lined depression in the sand and partly shaded by leafy weed stems.

On July 14, 1915, a brood of downy young was discovered on Tuolumne Meadows, and on July 29 of the same year another was observed at Lake Tenaya. One of the three youngsters comprising the latter family was held captive for a few minutes for close observation. When this youngster was first taken the female parent became greatly excited and ventured within 10 feet of the observer, but later she became more wary. The captive's first reaction was to squat, immobile; after some moments it made strenuous efforts to escape. The other two young birds ran about excitedly, through the sparse grass, and attempted to follow their parent as the latter flew in circles near by among the lodgepole pines. Even at this early stage in their existence the bobbing movement of the hinder parts of the body, which is so characteristic a feature of the adults, was well developed. At longer intervals the whole head and foreparts were bobbed abruptly upward.

When flushed from a river shore where they have been running about, foraging, the adult birds usually fly in a semicircular course out over the water to the place to which they are retreating; sometimes they swing in over the land, even if their destination is to be some other point along the same stream. It is when so flushed that the clear whistled call is most frequently uttered, although it is also given occasionally when a pair is running about on the sand.

In 1920 this species was seen daily in Yosemite Valley until September 16 but not thereafter (C. W. Michael, MS).

KILLDEER. Oxyechus vociferus vociferus (Linnaeus)

Field characters.—A Plover, about size of Robin. Two black bands across chest, white collar around hind neck, white bar across wing, tawny rump, white under surface and brown upper surface, and white-tipped and black-banded tail. *Voice:* A shrill, plaintive *kill-dee* or *kill-deer*, oft repeated.

Occurrence.—Common resident in lowlands and western foothill territory. Also occurs during summer at east base of mountains about Mono Lake; casual in Yosemite Valley and on Tuolumne Meadows. Frequents wet meadows, and pond and stream margins, associating in pairs or small flocks.

The familiar noisy Killdeer is a common resident in the western part of the Yosemite region, for example, about Snelling and Merced Falls. Small numbers occur during the summer months about Mono Lake where they nest, while individual birds occasionally stray to higher intervening localities, such as Tuolumne Meadows. While technically a typical shore bird and hence thought of as a water bird, the presence of mere seepage is enough to attract and hold a pair of Killdeers. Wet meadows are characteristic forage grounds.

About a rain pool on the plateau land near Forty-nine Gap, west of Pleasant Valley, five or six were seen on May 28, 1915. They trotted about, bobbing up and down at intervals, permitting one to approach them to within 50 feet, and showing clearly all of their distinctive color markings. The noise of a gun startled them quickly into flight, whereupon they began to circle upward until they were a hundred yards or so above the ground. For three or four minutes after the shot they continued their wild circling flight and kept up a torrent of cries. Then they began to quiet down and soon descended to the ground, to resume their intent search for food.

The striking pattern of coloration, four black cross-bars on a white and brown background, proves to be highly disruptive in effect when the Killdeer is standing still on a pebble-covered flat; in other words, the bird becomes invisible. The smooth gliding run practiced by the birds renders them much less conspicuous and more difficult to follow with the eye than if they were to hop along jerkily in the manner of sparrows.

On the pebbly shores of Bean Creek, east of Coulterville, a nest of the Killdeer was found on June 6, 1915. The 4 darkly splotched eggs were placed, with no attempt at concealment, and without lining of any sort to provide a softer resting place, in a slight depression in the gravel. When we were yet a hundred yards distant on the bank above, the parent bird flushed. As we approached she ran along ahead of us. Now and then she would squat down, adjust her wings, and proceed to incubate—pebbles! Failing in this ruse she trailed her wings as if they were broken, or again played innocently about the creek shore, alternately attempting to decoy us from the eggs and appearing unconcerned. All the while the eggs were resting in the glaring sun on gravel that was hot to our hands.

When we camped along the Tuolumne River below Lagrange from May 5 to 9, 1919, a pair of Killdeer was found to be occupying a pebbly flat of ten acres or so at the side of the river. The birds raised a commotion whenever we stirred about in the vicinity of the flat, but much minute searching was necessary before the nest was actually located. The sitting bird never flew up directly from the nest; but always when the observer was yet 50 yards or so away she (or he) slipped quietly off and slunk along for 50 or 100 feet with head depressed. Then the bird would begin to cry and call and presently fly off with a great clamor, soon to be joined by the other of the pair. The two would then act greatly concerned no matter where the observer went so long as he remained on the flat. The initial 'sneak' of the sitting bird was the critically valuable ruse, but the tactics all through were unquestionably effective. The nest was found to consist of a slight depression in the gravelly and pebbly ground of the open river bottom. The depression was sprinkled with grayish tips of a dead and withered weed and this lining was the only feature which rendered the spot at all different from its surroundings. There was only one egg; yet the bird had been sitting on it persistently during the preceding two days. The egg showed no evidence of incubation and was likely infertile. Ordinarily 4 eggs constitute a set. Less often there are 3 and rarely 2. Another pair of Killdeer in the neighborhood behaved as though they had their nest on a bit of ground closer to the river, but no search was made for it.

One bird of the pair which owned the nest with one egg was seen repeatedly to squat down on the ground, a long distance from its nest, and to vibrate the tail slightly, at the same time uttering a low 'crooning trill. Another bird in a plowed field in the same general region did the same, as did also a Killdeer seen on Blacks Creek near Coulterville a few days later. Evidently birds of this species are thoroughly conscious of being watched and go through a variety of deceptive tactics in an attempt to mislead anyone who even distantly approaches their nests.

At Walker Lake, September 14, 1915, a Killdeer was seen in a fenced pasture, while in early July of the same year one was repeatedly flushed from a certain area on Tuolumne Meadows near the Sierra Club headquarters at Parsons Lodge. The behavior of the latter bird suggested nesting, but no mate was seen. Proof of the nesting of the Killdeer at so high an altitude remains yet to be obtained.

The species was seen along the banks of the Merced River in Yosemite Valley, June 20 to 25, 1893 (Emerson, 1893, p. 178), and there is the possibility that nesting has occurred there.

MOUNTAIN QUAIL. Oreortyx picta plumifera (Gould)

Field characters.—A quail larger than Valley Quail; sexes alike; a long slender, usually backward-directed, black plume on head. Bands of black, white, and chestnut on sides of body; throat chestnut; head, breast, and forepart of back, bluish slate; rest of back and wings, olive brown; belly whitish. Escapes usually by running; flight direct, with heavily whirring wing beats. *Voice:* A single loud resonant *quēē-ärk* or *wŏŏck* uttered at intervals; also other shorter calls when alarmed, *ca-ca-ca-ca-cree'-a,* or *gup-gup-gup, quee'-ar, quee'-ar.*

Occurrence.—Common in Transition and Canadian zones on both slopes of Sierra Nevada, migrating down to below level of heavy snow in winter. Observed west to Mount Bullion and Smith Creek (east of Coulterville) and east to near Williams Butte. Lives in and around brush patches.

The traveler approaching the mountains from the west will first meet the Mountain Quail when he has passed the hot dry slopes of the foothills and enters the cooler shelter of the main forest belt. From here on, in the vicinity of yellow pines, incense cedars, and silver and red firs, these elegant birds are to be encountered in moderate numbers.

With the coming of the warm days of late spring, and on into early summer, the males perch on fallen logs, open spaces on the ground, or even on branches of black oaks, and announce their amatory feelings by giving utterance to their loud calls with such force and vigor that these resound through the forests for a half-mile or more, commanding the attention of all within hearing. One type of call consists of but a single note, *quēē-ärk,* and this is repeated at rather long and irregular intervals. One bird timed by the watch, June 3, 1915, gave his calls at intervals of 7, 6, 8, 5, 8, 6, 7, 5, 7, 9, and 9 seconds, respectively, and continued at about the same rate for a long time afterward. This intermittent utterance lends to the call a distinctiveness and attractiveness which would be lost if it were given in quicker time.

Another type of call consists of a series of sharper notes, *ker,* uttered more rapidly, something after the manner of a flicker. All these notes are to be heard at any time of the year, but not so persistently in December as in June.

The females, so similar to the males in plumage as not to be distinguishable under ordinary circumstances, are not much in evidence after the nesting sites have been selected. Until then, the couples flush together from the ceanothus thickets. So careful are the brooding birds in quitting their nesting precincts, that we did not succeed in finding a single nest. Broods are to be expected on the west slope of the Sierras in late June or early July. A covey of small young was seen abroad at Smith Creek (Dudley) on June 20 (1920). Mr. W. O. Emerson (1893, p. 179) found a brood of downy young in Yosemite Valley on June 19, 1893. To the east of the Sierran crest the season may be somewhat later.

The average number of eggs laid by the Mountain Quail is fairly large (11, according to a summary of data from all over California), and this is directly correlated with the degree of danger incurred in rearing the chicks to maturity. The mortality from various causes is large. Mr. Dave Bolton, one-time roadmaster at Cascades, told us that in midsummer there were usually about 4 broods of Mountain Quail brought off in the vicinity of his home, each comprising 10 to 15 young, but that by Christmas or New Year's Day the entire number of birds would be reduced to 2 or 3. A brood of 14 of the summer of 1915 was reduced to 4 by early November. Mr. Bolton attributed this decrease to wildcats and stated that tracks of these animals were to be seen in the dust of the road almost every morning in summer.

To this we would add that Gray Foxes probably account for the death of a number of quail. On December 24, 1915, in Yosemite Valley, a steel trap set for carnivores was found in the morning to contain the leg and foot of a Mountain Quail. Near-by were feathers of the same species of bird with some dung of the Gray Fox. The inference is easy. A quail had stumbled into our trap and the fox had taken advantage of the meal thus afforded, without himself falling victim to any of the other traps in the setting. But the Gray Fox and the Wildcat are, as the bunches of feathers which we found so often elsewere clearly testified, sufficiently agile to capture these birds in the open. Nevertheless, the large broods enable enough representatives of this species to live through the winter to insure renewal of the population. The young Mountain Quail are rather slow to attain adult size; coveys seen in late September and even early October contained individuals only about two-thirds grown.

The food of the Mountain Quail comprises both animal and vegetable matter and is quite varied in character. Witness the following array of items from the crop of a single bird taken June 6, 1915, at Bean Creek, near Coulterville: Two or more seed pods of Leguminosae; flowers of manzanita (*Arctostaphylos mariposa*); pieces of fern leaves; green berries of *Ceanothus cuneatus;* several unidentified seeds; 2 nymphs and 2 adult 'bugs' (Membracid Hemiptera); many ants (*Camponotus* sp.); several wingless grasshoppers; 1 small centipede; 4 beetles (2 Chrysomelidae, 2 Carabidae); and several small pieces of bone.

Another crop, from near El Portal, November 21, 1914, held 2 seeds of wild oats (*Avena fatua*); 30 seeds of yellow pine (*Pinus ponderosa*); more than 400 seeds and many leaves of clover (*Trifolium obtusiflorum*); 2 ladybird beetles (*Hippodamia convergens*). Another from El Portal taken on December 1, 1914, had only parts of manzanita berries (*Arctostaphylos mariposa*); and one taken from a bird on Feliciana Mountain, October 30, 1915, had 2 capsules and 148 seeds of croton (*Croton* sp.). It is evident that the Mountain Quail feeds on whatever is abundant: flowers and leaves of plants and insects in spring, seeds and leaves of plants in fall when insects are not so abundant.

VALLEY QUAIL. Lophortyx californica vallicola (Ridgway)

Field characters.—A quail with short, blunt-ended, forward-directed topknot on head. Back, wings, and tail uniform grayish brown; breast clear bluish gray; belly marked with crosswise scalings of black on a white or buffy ground. Sexes unlike; males have throat black, outlined with white. Flight direct, with rapidly whirring wings; when on ground runs with celerity. *Voice:* An assembly call sounding somewhat like the syllables *pa-rah'-ho;* when disturbed, an explosive, sputtering *pit, pit,* or *whit, whit,* uttered many times in rapid succession; when on guard during breeding season, males utter a single loud *kyark* at irregular intervals.

Occurrence.—Common resident in Lower and Upper Sonoran zones west of the Sierran divide; observed at Snelling and Lagrange and thence eastward to El Portal (altitude 2000 feet), and to Smith Creek, east of Coulterville (altitude 3200 feet). Frequents hillside chaparral and river-bottom thickets, foraging under these and in adjacent open areas.

The Valley Quail is a characteristic inhabitant of the dry foothill belt and is eminently suited in both structure and habits to gain a livelihood in such an environment. The dense thickets of chaparral which clothe the steep cañon sides afford both food and shelter for the quail, and the intermittent streamlets which thread the deep ravine bottoms afford water sufficient for their daily needs. Quail are also found in the plains region west of the foothills, but only where adequate shelter is afforded by growths along the big rivers, or by berry or other brush patches near farmhouses.

Entering the Yosemite region by train and stage one is not likely to see the Valley Quail at all, unless a pair or a flock be observed at El Portal; but when going in afoot or in an automobile, the species will be noted commonly along any of the regular routes of travel. In the early morning the dusty roads often bear evidence of the presence of quail, the tracks showing plainly their identity, for they are in tandem alignment, one foot in front of the other, with the middle toe dragging between and the hind toe leaving a distinct impression of its own.

Like many other species which are classed as game, quail are essentially gregarious birds and spend most of the year in flocks. They separate into pairs only for the nesting season. By the middle of spring the birds are paired off and from then on, the males are to be seen perched in commanding situations in the brush or in low trees, on guard to sound alarm if need be, while their mates are preparing their nests or caring for the eggs or young chicks.

In May, 1919, at Blacks Creek, just west of Coulterville, we found Valley Quail to be exceedingly common. There were fully 25 pairs in the little basin of which the old Merced Gold Mine is the center. Males were calling all through the day, so that there was an almost continuous chorus of 'guard' notes. Less often we heard one of the birds 'explode,' when unusually excited, the note then sounding like that made by striking a long wire strung between two supports. Often in the afternoon and early evening, as they came down from the dry hillsides to quench their thirst at the creek, two or three pairs would be in sight at once. The males seemed more than ordinarily solicitous at this time. Near Lagrange one was seen following along close behind his mate as she foraged in an open field. Then while she hunted through the long grass at the roadside he perched with drooping topknot on a convenient fence post and watched all about. When she was ready to cross the road he flew down and led her across and then the two disappeared into other forage grounds in the field beyond.

Mr. Donald D. McLean, residing at Smith Creek, on the Coulterville Road, says that the nesting season of the Valley Quail extends until harvest time, in July. When the broods are full-grown, old and young associate together in flocks, and two or more families join into single bands numbering 25 to 50 or more. In the autumn, Valley and Mountain quail have been seen together in the Smith Creek country in mixed flocks numbering 50 or more individuals.

The flocks of Valley Quail do not appear to decrease as rapidly in late fall and early winter as do those of the Mountain Quail. Flocks of 10 to 30 birds were seen by us on a number of occasions in January and February. Since trapping by man for fur-bearing animals (carnivores), the natural enemies of the quail, is now more intensive in the range of the valley bird, the pressure from enemies is probably somewhat lessened in the winter season. The absence of snow is also a factor, permitting the birds to forage far and wide throughout the year. The hardest pinch comes for the quail in early spring, when the seed and berry crops are approaching exhaustion, and before the new growth of the coming year is available. It is in this same early spring season that most of the carnivorous mammals and raptorial birds rear their young, and hence are put to the necessity of providing greater quantities of food for themselves and their offspring. Because the quail is a favorite food of Wildcats and Gray Foxes, and also of Cooper Hawks and Horned Owls, the quail population is subject to relatively greater persecution at this most critical period.

When foraging, quail work in a quiet but industrious manner, each individual moving forward independently, yet keeping within easy call of one another, each contributing to a general murmur of low conversational notes. They are quick to take advantage of easily obtained food such as may be provided in ranch yards. For example, at the McCarthy Ranch east of Coulterville, Valley Quail are to be seen at almost all times of the year, foraging industriously in the barnyard chaff.

When disturbed while foraging, Valley Quail usually depend for safety first upon their wings. A flock seen on Rancheria Flat near El Portal in December, 1914, all flew off in one direction. Then the birds took shelter in some golden oaks whence, when followed up, they scattered out. For the most part they remained in the trees and kept quiet; only one individual sought refuge on the ground. In other places the quail have been found to make use of their legs after the first flight, running rapidly off, then, beneath the shelter of the brush.

Mr. J. B. Varain said that quail are now (1915) relatively scarce compared with their abundance when he first came to Pleasant Valley, in 1867.

SIERRA GROUSE. **Dendragapus obscurus sierrae** Chapman

Field characters.—Fowl-like in appearance; size large (fully five times bulk of Mountain Quail); general effect of coloration dark bluish gray; tail almost square-ended, with a light band across tip (often appearing almost white by contrast). Close view shows the plumage to have a complex pattern of lighter markings. Flight direct, heavy, with loudly whirring wings; when descending, often sails with wings set. *Voice:* Of male in breeding season a deep, wooden, far-carrying ventriloquial *unt, wunt, wunt', wunt', tu-wunt', wunt, wunt;* of female with young, clucking notes; of both sexes, an alarm note, *kŭk, kŭk.*

Occurrence.—Fairly common resident, chiefly in Canadian Zone and locally in upper Transition; ranges upward into Hudsonian Zone during late summer. Westernmost station of occurrence, Merced Grove; easternmost, Williams Butte. Noted frequently around rim of Yosemite Valley, as at Glacier Point, Artist Point, and in vicinity of Yosemite Point. Lives in or near the heavier coniferous trees.

Acquaintance with the Sierra Grouse may begin in several ways, but rarely does it come in the conventional manner through which we learn to know most birds. Upon entering the Jeffrey pine and red fir forests of the Canadian Zone in spring and early summer, one may often hear a very un-bird-like, dull sodden series of booming notes that have a ventriloquial quality. These are the courting notes of the male grouse. Less often, whatever the time of year, the introduction may come suddenly and much more impressively when, close at hand, a heavy-bodied 'blue grouse' rises quickly from the ground and makes off through the forest on loudly whirring wings, and showing an expanse of square-ended gray-banded tail. When a small flock of the birds get up, as they often do, in rapid succession, or even simultaneously, the aggregate effect is bewildering, to say the least.

The Sierra Grouse lives in the high country throughout the year, never migrating to lower levels as does the Mountain Quail. The thick heavy plumage and legs feathered clear down to the toes enable the grouse to withstand the cold of the midwinter months; while their ability to subsist on pine and fir needles assures them at any season an abundance of food to be easily obtained without seeking the ground.

During the spring and early summer, the males are in the habit of taking solitary positions near the tops of pines or firs, sixty or more feet above the ground, where they stand on horizontal limbs close to the trunk. They hold such positions continuously for hours, one day after another, and send forth at intervals their reverberant booming. With different birds the series of notes comprising this booming consists of from five to seven syllables, six on an average. The quality of the sound can be likened to that produced by beating on a water-logged tub, *boont, boont, boont', boont', boont, boont,* crescendo at the first, diminuendo toward the end of the series. As each note is uttered the tail of the bird is depressed an inch or two—perhaps an index to the effort involved. The separate series of notes in two instances were uttered at intervals of 40, 20, 25, 45, 12, 21, and 29 seconds, and again 10, 10, 20, 26, 14, 15, 17, 12, 11, 15, 13, 28, 17, and 11 seconds respectively. These two birds had been heard booming for a long time before we began to pay special attention to them; and they continued long after we finished this record. The ventriloquial quality is discovered when one attempts to locate the producer, a difficult feat as a rule. The observer may succeed in locating the proper tree, but is likely to circle it many times, peering upward with painfully aching neck, and still utterly failing to locate the avian performer amid the foliage high overhead. The notes are commonly supposed to be produced by the bird's inflating and exhausting the glandular air sacs on the sides of the neck. These sacs are covered by unfeathered yellow skin, and we think it more likely that they serve only as resonators, being kept continually inflated, while the air actually producing the sound passes to and from the lungs along the regular air passage. It rests with someone gifted with patience for long continued observation to determine exactly how the notes are produced.

By early July the new broods of grouse are to be looked for in the brush-bordered glades of the forests. Two downy young were noted on the trail to Nevada Falls so early as June 21, 1893 (W. O. Emerson, 1893, p. 179). When the chicks have been partly reared the males desert their mates, and, forming in flocks of 6 or 8, work higher in the mountains. The females remain with, and continue to care for, their offspring, these family units remaining separate for the time being. Finally, as the summer wanes, they, too, work up into the Hudsonian Zone. Thus, while the Mountail Quail go *down-hill* in the fall, the grouse go *up-hill*.

A 'stag' flock of 8 Sierra Grouse was encountered by the senior author on Warren Fork of Leevining Creek, September 26, 1915, after a light fall of snow. The birds were in lodgepole pines on a level bench at 10,500 feet altitude. They flushed one after another with a startling succession of loud whirs, all taking off in the same general direction and alighting about four hundred yards away. When followed up 5 were flushed again, 3 from the ground and 2 from the trees.

One of the above mentioned male birds was shot and its crop was found to contain 1520 needle tips of the lodgepole pine. The bitten-off ends of needles varied from one-fourth to one inch in length. The crop also contained a few fragments of very young pistillate cones. The bill of this bird was smeared with pitch. The crop of an adult female grouse obtained at Walker Lake held eleven ripe rose hips, and the gizzard was filled with the hard seeds of the rose, together with grains of quartz which of course had served to grind the resistant portions of the bird's food.

We have only one incident to record concerning the enemies of the Sierra Grouse. While camped at Walker Lake on September 10, 1915, our packer noted a large hawk eating something in a pine tree. At his approach the hawk flew away, leaving its meal unfinished, and the packer found the remains of a Sierra Grouse. The victim was an old female in worn plumage and had just begun to molt. The hawk had eaten the flesh on one half of the grouse's breast. The identity of this particular hawk must remain unknown; but we have reason to believe the Western Goshawk to be an important enemy of the Sierra Grouse. Tree-climbing carnivores such as the Sierra Pine Marten and Pacific Fisher probably destroy some grouse each year.

SAGE-HEN. **Centrocercus urophasianus** (Bonaparte)

Field characters.—Largest ground-inhabiting bird in the Yosemite region; fowl-like in general appearance. Tail long with slender, pointed feathers; belly black; rest of plumage a variegated mixture of black, white and varying shades of brown. Takes flight with loudly whirring wings, and when descending sails on set wings. *Voice:* A slowly repeated hoarse guttural *kŭk, kŭk, kŭk,* uttered when flushed.

Occurrence.—Resident in small numbers locally on the open sage-covered levels east of the Sierra Nevada. Reported west to vicinity of Walker Lake and lower Parker Creek.

The Sage-hen is restricted in range within the Yosemite region and will not come under the observation of any save those who cross the Sierran divide and traverse the Mono Basin. The name Sage-hen Meadow given on the topographic map to a spring-fed patch of grass on a sagebrush flat about six miles east of Mono Mills well marks the present metropolis of this bird in the region. Residents say Sage-hens were seen in the winter of 1915–16 between Walker Lake and Parker Creek and that they were common there ten years previously; but we observed none there ourselves.

Near Gaspipe Spring, east of Mono Mills, on April 26, 1916, a single large male of this species was flushed by Mr. Dixon at the edge of a snow bank. The bird whirred rapidly over the snowcapped ridge, then set his wings and sailed off down the valley. His flight was heavy but rapid as he went with the wind. As he left the ground, rather slowly, he uttered a deep hoarse cackle. On other occasions tracks of six or more birds were seen near the same place, and tracks were much in evidence about a small spring in the vicinity where the birds had come down to water.

BAND-TAILED PIGEON. **Columba fasciata fasciata** Say

Field characters.—Size and proportions of domestic pigeon; general effect of coloration of upper surface bluish gray, of under surface pinkish brown; a distinct dark band across middle of square-ended tail. (See pl. 4.) Flight swift and direct, with steadily flapping wings; leaves perch with a loud clapping of wings. *Voice:* A deep, rolled, *coo'-coo*, or *too-coo'*, resembling that of a domestic pigeon.

Occurrence.—Common summer visitant to Transition Zone on west slope of Sierra Nevada. During winter season, ranges down through Upper Sonoran Zone, following food supply as available. Observed in Yosemite Valley at almost all times of the year. Usually encountered in small flocks in open forests near or in oak trees or berry producing shrubs.

A visit to the Yosemite offers to the naturalist, among other attractions, an exceptional opportunity to study Band-tailed Pigeons. These handsome birds (pl. 4) are likely to be found in the Valley in some numbers at almost all times of the year. They are commonest in spring and fall; flocks of from ten to a hundred were noted by us almost daily in those seasons. But they were present, also, all summer, though in lesser numbers, and during winter as well, save when heavy snow covered the trees and the ground.

Band-tailed Pigeons have the flocking habit strongly developed. To be sure, they scatter out when nesting; but even during this period, when not actually engaged in caring for eggs or squabs, the parent birds assemble in small flocks for feeding. The gregarious habit of the pigeons probably serves them usefully in two ways: a larger measure of protection from enemies is secured through the increased vigilance possible with many pairs of eyes; and, by the same means, a better chance of finding adequate food supplies is provided. The individual bird, and hence the species, profits by a certain degree of coöperation. The flocks are loosely constituted, and when disturbed while foraging the individuals flush scatteringly. At times small companies leave the main flock to seek safety independently.

Often as we ascended the steep trails which lead out of the Yosemite Valley we would come upon Band-tailed Pigeons sunning and preening themselves on the exposed upper branches of the oaks or cedar trees which cling to the cañon walls. Once we noted a group of eight contentedly drinking and preening on a flat rock bordering the rushing waters above

Vernal Falls. While some of the birds were thus enjoying repose, others in the neighborhood were to be found seeking acorns in the densely foliaged golden oaks bordering the trails. At times, a bird which was perched high on the Valley wall, would take flight and precipitate itself into the cañon below, going at lightning speed, with wings set almost at its sides, and body veering slightly from side to side. The sense of the vast depth below was intensified by this downward rush, for although it was made too swiftly to permit the eye to focus upon the bird as it flashed by, yet the pigeon remained in view for some seconds before it reached the vanishing point in its downward course.

One would surmise from the relatively large size of these pigeons that they would be conspicuous when perched in open trees such as black oaks; but such is not the case. It often happens that the first intimation of the presence of a flock of pigeons comes when one or more leave precipitately on loudly clapping wings and make off in direct course to some other perch. The birds get under way with surprising rapidity, due to the forceful jump by which they launch into the air and also to the initial strokes of their wide-sweeping wings. A small flock perched in the top of a dead pine was seen to leave with such force that several of the dry weathered branches were broken by the vigorous jumps of the birds. The crashing of the falling branches and the clapping of the pigeons' wings made a vivid impression upon the observer. When a flock of pigeons is engaged in foraging, a person can often hear them at a considerable distance, for the birds flap noisily as they change their positions or seek to balance their heavy bodies on the slender twigs.

The manner of foraging and of eluding approach in the open is well illustrated by the behavior of a large flock watched on the floor of Yosemite Valley near Indian Creek on the afternoon of April 28, 1916. Our note-book record reads:

At the edge of a newly planted grain field where tree shelter was near, fully a hundred of the big blue birds were feeding on the ground. They moved forward as a flock, several feet a minute, those in the rear continually flying up and beyond those at the front. At my distant approach they all flew up into the adjacent yellow pines and cottonwoods; the flapping of their wings as they arose produced a surprising amount of noise, and as they alighted the ends of their fan-shaped, spread tails gave the effect of a scattered series of white crescents against the dark green trees. The birds continued wary and as I came under their perches they flushed in small parties or singly and flew to another clump of trees some distance away. From there, as I followed, they made off in one large band and three smaller ones, circling widely out over the field. As they left, the only color impression I got was of dark blue, but later, when outlined in flight against the sky, the pinkish blush of their breasts was clearly seen.

A few days later, opportunity was afforded to observe at closer range a small flock in the dooryard of a home among the black oaks on the north side of the Valley (pl. 43a).

As the big birds alighted, the air currents caused by their wings and tails stirred up the dust and chaff of the yard to form small whirlwinds. When feeding, the birds walked about actively, their big bodies swinging from side to side as they stretched their short legs in endeavoring to move quickly. Usually the head was held so low that the back of the neck and body and tail were in one plane parallel to the ground, and they would look up only when some moving object or unusual sound prompted them to be on guard. Otherwise they pecked greedily at the abundant supply of grain scattered about. One bird seemed exceptionally thick-breasted, as though it had a very full crop. When in the trees a few of the birds uttered a mild *tuck-oo′*, not spirited; but as a rule they were silent. When disturbed they arose abruptly, almost simultaneously, with a great clapping of wings, displaying spread tails. When descending to the ground they often made two or three short flights, from one elevation to another lower one, rather than one direct descent.

Mr. Gabriel Souvelewsky told us that once when blasting was being carried on in the Valley a flock of Band-tailed Pigeons feeding on the ground in his yard would rise 3 or 4 feet at each blast and then drop back again quickly as their alarm subsided.

We did not succeed in locating any nests of the Band-tailed Pigeon. Nests in other parts of California have been found in airy situations, for example, on large horizontal limbs of trees where the birds could flush directly at the approach of danger. It yet remains for someone to observe and report an instance of nesting in the Yosemite region. The continued presence of pigeons in the Valley throughout the summer months makes it almost certain that they nest there.

Acorns form the main item in the food of the Band-tailed Pigeon. We often saw birds foraging in the golden oaks on the north wall of the Yosemite, and several birds collected there were found to have nothing but acorns in their crops. A resident of Mount Bullion told us that he had shot a pigeon near that place whose crop contained 13 acorns of the black oak. Other common food materials include berries of the manzanita, toyon, chokeberry and coffeeberry. Grain, when available, affords attractive forage; they eagerly glean shelled-out kernels. This last trait works to their disadvantage in those cases where strychnine-poisoned grain has been put out on top of the ground to kill ground squirrels. On several occasions grain so exposed in the Valley has been eaten by the pigeons and some of the birds are known to have succumbed.

People who have resided for a long time in Yosemite Valley state that pigeons used to be found there in much larger numbers than now. Mr. C. W. Baker said that fully 2000 were observed by him in one flock some years previous to 1915. Excessive hunting in the foothill belt during the winter months has probably been the direct cause of most of this decrease. The pigeon is not a species that can recover rapidly from serious reduction, for normally only one young bird is reared by each pair each year. Variation in the available supply of food there and elsewhere probably has also had a marked effect on the number of pigeons visiting the Yosemite Valley from year to year. Fluctuations for such reasons make it difficult to determine with accuracy to what extent the birds have actually been reduced in numbers in the region.

WESTERN MOURNING DOVE. **Zenaidura macroura marginella** (Woodhouse)

Field characters.—Much smaller than domestic pigeon, and with a pointed, white margined tail; upper surface olive brown, breast pale brown. Wings produce a whistling sound, loudest as bird takes flight. Flight, when fully under way, swift and direct with regular and sweeping wing strokes. *Voice:* A series of four mellow yet far-reaching notes, *ah-coo', roo coo,* repeated at rather long intervals.

Occurrence.—Abundant resident in the western lowlands and foothills (Lower and Upper Sonoran zones), ranging in summer locally into lower part of Transition Zone. Twice observed in Yosemite Valley (May 28, 1911, and September 24, 1915), once at Hazel Green, 5600 feet altitude (May 14, 1919), and once at 10,300 feet altitude near Vogelsang Lake, September 4, 1915 (single birds in each instance). Found also east of the Sierras (where likely only a summer visitant), in Mono Basin and thence west to Walker Lake. Partial to open situations; to be seen usually in pairs, or, in fall, winter, and early spring, in flocks numbering up to fifty or even more individuals.

The Western Mourning Dove is to be seen in numbers over the western lowlands at all seasons of the year. On almost every trip we made by train from Merced into the mountains we saw these birds flying over the adjacent fields, often flushing at the side of the railroad and keeping abreast of the train for a time as it traveled twenty or more miles an hour. In all of the foothill country doves are to be looked for as of regular occurrence. Near Lagrange they were about continually, visiting the river margin to drink or resting momentarily on the boulder heaps nearby. At Blacks Creek near Coulterville they came down to drink at the creek every evening at early dusk. In Yosemite Valley doves occur only as stragglers. In our own experience, as noted above, but 2 lone birds were recorded there.

The breeding season extends from April or May well through the summer. Nests are to be looked for in a variety of situations. We found 4. One noted near Snelling on May 28, 1915, was situated 8 feet above the ground in a blue oak. It contained one egg. On the meadows east of Coulterville, at an elevation of 3200 feet, 2 nests were discovered on June 7, 1915. They were both situated on the slanting side of a small gulley that ran through the meadow. One contained 2 eggs and the other, one. On June 8, 1916, in Mono Basin, east of Mono Mills, at an altitude of 8400 feet, a dove was seen incubating 2 eggs in a nest situated on the bare ground at the side of a sagebush.

After the broods are reared, old and young doves combine into flocks and then range far and wide in search of ripening flower and weed seeds,

BAND-TAILED PIGEON

eding in open fields, coming to streams and springs morning and evening
drink, and roosting in trees or along roadside fences. On June 11, 1916,
flock of at least 75 doves was seen by Mr. Donald D. McLean on Smith
reek, east of Coulterville. The birds were feeding on the seeds of wild
ortulaca.

TURKEY VULTURE. **Cathartes aura septentrionalis** Wied

Field characters.—General appearance that of ''bird of prey;'' size large, about
hat of Red-tailed Hawk; plumage black, with faintly gray area on lower surface of
ving (pl. 44e); head red, nearly naked. *Voice:* A low hiss, rarely uttered. Usually
een soaring overhead in wide circles, with wings slanting upward. When perched, sits
n a hunched-up posture, with head drawn in between shoulders.

Occurrence.—Common in summer on west slope of Sierra Nevada, in both Lower and
Upper Sonoran zones. Easternmost point of regular observation, 3 miles east of Coulter-
ville, at 3200 feet altitude. Twice noted over Yosemite Valley in summer of 1920
(C. W. Michael, MS).

As a rule, most large birds of the Yosemite section are so uncommon
that to observe one of them is a notable occurrence. The Turkey Vulture,
or Buzzard as it is called locally, is, within its range, a conspicuous exception. All over the western country below the Transition Zone, it is common
and present throughout the greater portion of the year.

In bulk the Turkey Buzzard about equals the Red-tailed Hawk; it is
of only about one-third the weight of the Golden Eagle. Its black plumage,
and the grayish patch on the under surface of each wing, make it easy
to distinguish from all our other birds of prey. In flight the tips of the
outermost five or six primary flight feathers are distinctly separated like
the spread fingers on a person's hand (pl. 44e), but the tail is held closed
so that, seen from below, it has a narrow, wedge-shaped outline. The
Turkey Buzzard spends a very large share of its time on the wing, sailing
about in almost unceasing watch for food. When soaring, the buzzard
usually holds its wings bent upward, so that a more or less distinct angle,
with the apex downwards, is formed between them. Ofter a bird will soar
in circles for several minutes at a time without appearing to alter the
position of a single feather, accommodation to differences in the air currents seemingly being made by movement of the body as a whole. As
the bird glides down over the brush of a cañon side, it often careens from
side to side, but without changing the relative positions of wings or tail.

These big birds distribute themselves over their range with remarkable
uniformity. Probably the average population is but one or two individuals
to the square mile. Each seems to be scrutinizing a definite area; if one
bird discovers any large item of food the others quickly take notice. As
the original discoverer of the food with obviously increased animation
drops down onto his find, his nearest neighbors cease their patrolling and

close in toward the place where he descended. In turn the birds beyon
them close in and so on until, if the object be a large one, such as th
carcass of a horse or cow, as many as thirty or forty will finally congregat
at the one spot.

The buzzards' inspection of the country over which they range i
exceedingly minute, and rarely does even so small an object as the body
of a ground squirrel escape their detection. In fact, bodies of small bird
and even of mice, used as bait for traps and placed under shelter of bushes
are often detected by the buzzards. Much of this keenness is in their
eyesight; they seem to depend but little, primarily, upon the sense of
smell, although this latter sense may also be highly developed as an
auxiliary faculty in locating food.

The flight of the Turkey Buzzard in migration is an impressive sight.
At Pleasant Valley on the afternoon of February 26, 1916, about 75 were
seen manoeuvering about over a hill to the west, and at the moment their
general movement was toward the south. Half an hour later, the flock
was again seen, from the Baxter road. They were then in an elongated
formation and sailing rather low. A few seconds later the leaders turned
and soon all members of the flock were circling about, each one weaving
its course in and out between its companions, much in the manner of
participants in a Maypole dance. All the while this circling continued the
birds were rising higher and higher. Finally, having probably attained
an altitude which gave unobstructed view up and down the foothills, the
flock, with surprising concert, again assumed the elongated formation,
with usually not more than four nearly abreast, and quickly passed north-
eastward over the hills and out of sight. While circling, and even when
moving forward, the birds engaged in a relatively small amount of flapping; usually they would sail for a half-minute or more without perceptible
change in the posture of body, wings, or tail. After the flock had passed
on, a single bird was seen circling in the place where its companions had
lately been and three other birds sailed slowly about over the opposite
wall of the Merced Cañon. Residents said that these birds were the first
for that season. Next day the newly arrived individuals behaved as though
perfectly at home, and had their coming not been witnessed on the previous
day there would have been no reason to believe that they had been there
only overnight. Evidently no time is lost in settling down.

In the early morning hours just before or just after sunrise, buzzards
perch in hunched-up postures, on trees by the roadside. Often four or more
birds may be observed in a single tree, evidently waiting until the air
conditions become such as to enable them to soar about in their accustomed
manner. When approached, these birds often spread their wings and hold
them extended for several minutes, and sometimes they successively expand

and fold these members several times before jumping into the air. Only a few strokes of the wings are used when starting. Often the birds' positions will enable them to strike down a cañon so as to gain the necessary initial momentum, and they then slowly rise by repeated circlings with few or no further wing strokes.

Residents say that in the spring Turkey Buzzards appear with the advent of good weather and vanish temporarily during storms. Possibly they repair to tree perches in remote ravines, or to the shelter of the caves on the adjacent rocky hillsides where they are known to nest during the summer months.

Near Hayward (an old roadhouse on the road between Lagrange and Coulterville), a partially albino Turkey Buzzard was seen in flight on May 9, 1919. The back and upper surface of the wings were almost solidly white, but the remainder of the plumage, as seen with the binoculars, appeared to be of normal color. This is just another instance in the seemingly endless series in which albinism makes its appearance. Albinos always excite great curiosity, perhaps more than they really deserve.

WHITE-TAILED KITE. **Elanus leucurus** (Vieillot)

Field characters.—Hawk-like; size somewhat larger than that of Pigeon; wings long and narrow. Whole upper surface of body pale gray; whole under surface of body and forehead pure white; a large patch of black at 'bend' of wing, showing conspicuously in flight. Flies in open, with much poising on beating wings.

Occurrence.—Not seen by us. Reported on several occasions near Bean Creek, east of Coulterville, and recorded once from Yosemite Valley, as detailed below. Lives about open marshlands or meadows, perching in adjacent willows or oaks. Solitary or in pairs.

The White-tailed Kite is, or was in the days of its abundance, a regular resident of the lowland districts of California. It sometimes appears in foothill localities and has been seen by Mr. Donald D. McLean on a number of occasions over the meadows of Bean Creek, east of Coulterville. There is a single record of the occurrence of the species in Yosemite Valley. Mr. Otto Widmann (1904, p. 68) records that "about 9 a.m. on May 24 [1903] a great commotion was heard in a clump of trees near the Yosemite Falls, and presently a White-tailed Kite, chased by two vireos, flew out and across an opening into a tall yellow pine." None of the members of our own party chanced to see this species anywhere in the Yosemite section.

MARSH HAWK. **Circus hudsonius** (Linnaeus)

Field characters.—Much smaller than Red-tailed Hawk, and with relatively longer and narrower tail and wings (pl. 44a); a white (rump) patch above base of tail. Adult male pale bluish gray above, whitish below; adult female, and immature of both sexes, dark brown above and paler brown, somewhat streaked, below. Flight slow, indirect, with deliberate wing beats and frequent skimming low over ground. Never circles like Red-tail.

Occurrence.—Resident at lower altitudes on west slope of Sierra Nevada and passes in migration east of mountains. Observed at Snelling and reported from Smith Creek east of Coulterville. Noted in Yosemite Valley by us, May 16, 1919, and by Mr. Joseph Mailliard (1918, p. 18), September 26, 1917. Seen during fall months near Walker Lake and Williams Butte. Frequents vicinity of meadows and marshes.

The Marsh Hawk is to be looked for over large open pasture lands and marshes where it hunts, in its own special manner, for the small animals which live in the short vegetation. Over such territory it floats about with an appearance of laziness or indifference, slowly flapping its long wings a few times and then sailing. It often skims low over the meadows, but it never mounts high in the air to circle or soar like the Red-tailed Hawk. When on the wing the bird's white 'rump' patch gives an effect of its tail being disconnected from the body. The whole demeanor of the bird, totally unlike that of the active "bullet hawks" or speedy falcons, is one of deliberation.

In mid-September of 1915, near Williams Butte, we saw five Marsh Hawks harrying over a small meadow in search of grasshoppers. On another occasion one was seen perched on a post beside an alfalfa field. Meadow Mice, too, are known to constitute a staple article in the diet of this hawk.

SHARP-SHINNED HAWK. **Accipiter velox** (Wilson)

Field characters.—In size, between Robin and Pigeon; spread wings rounded in outline; tail narrow and nearly square-ended. (See pl. 44*f*.) Upper surface dark bluish gray in adults, brown in immatures; under surface mixed reddish brown and white, cross-barred in adults, streaked in immatures; tail barred with blackish brown above and grayish white below. Flight rapid and direct; not often seen to circle, and never to poise on beating wings. Rarely utters any kind of notes.

Occurrence.—Fairly common on west flank of the Sierras. Recorded in summer in Transition and Canadian zones, in winter only below the level of heavy snow. Frequents woods and bottom-land thickets.

Against the broad-winged soaring hawks and the sharp-winged falcons the bird lover in the Sierras holds no brief, for these birds prey chiefly on rodents and insects and only on rare occasions attack song birds. But against the long-tailed, round-winged 'bullet hawks' he must make complaint, for these species are the unremitting enemies of other birds. Of the three species of bullet hawks in the Yosemite region, the Sharp-shinned Hawk is the smallest in size and probably the most important single enemy of the smaller song birds.

By reason of its relatively short, rounded wings and long tail this hawk is able to pursue small birds into such retreats as dense trees and bushes. It is thus often to be seen dashing into or through a thicket in pursuit of some one songster it has marked down, while consternation reigns among all the feathered creatures in the vicinity.

The nature of the Sharp-shin's depredations may best be illustrated by citing a few actual instances which came under our own observation. On December 30, 1914, a hawk of this species was seen in a grove of golden oaks on the north side of Yosemite Valley, flying in and out among the branches, and causing evident panic in a scattering flock of Western Blue-birds which had gathered there to feed on the mistletoe berries. A few days later, at Snelling, a male Sharp-shin was collected which was found to weigh 117 grams. The distended gullet and contents alone weighed 15.4 grams. Upon being opened the gullet was found to be crammed with the remains of a Linnet, including both wings (which had been plucked by the hawk before being eaten), the neck, one foot, and several other parts. A Linnet weighs about 23 grams; since the hawk had eaten nearly two-thirds of the bird, it is to be seen that it had consumed at one meal a quantity of material equal to more than one-seventh of its own body weight.

The most interesting incident concerning this hawk was recorded on December 26, 1914, near an occupied dwelling on the floor of Yosemite Valley. The observer was first attracted by a noise which sounded like that made by a weasel when caught in a trap. Upon seeking the source, he discovered a female Sharp-shinned Hawk struggling with a Blue-fronted Jay, a bird of nearly two-thirds its own bulk. The hawk was shot and killed, but even then its grip on the throat of the jay was not relaxed. Only when approached closely did the jay, apparently little injured, free himself from the talons of his fallen enemy and fly away.

The Sharp-shinned Hawk may be best distinguished from its larger and otherwise almost identical relative, the Cooper Hawk, by its nearly square-ended tail. (See pl. 44.) The tail of the latter species always appears more or less rounded even when but slightly spread. The Gos-hawk, the other bullet hawk of the region, is a giant compared with either of the other two species. As compared with the Sparrow Hawk, the male Sharp-shin is of about the same size, but shows more rounded wings, no black streaks on cheeks, and bright reddish markings are totally lacking.

Females of the Sharp-shin are about one-fourth longer and almost twice the bulk of the males of the same species. There are decided differences in coloration between the immature and the adult birds. The immatures have brown backs with narrow reddish brown feather marginings and their breasts are streaked, while the adults have dark bluish gray backs without lighter feather margins and their breasts have a cross-barred pattern of markings. There is also a difference in the color of the iris, that of the young birds being yellow, that of the adults, chrome orange.

The legs of the Sharp-shinned Hawk are very long and slender, and bare of feathers almost to the top of the tarsus, while the claws are slender and very sharp. These are all adaptations of use in grasping the feathered prey.

COOPER HAWK. **Accipiter cooperi** (Bonaparte)

Field characters.—Similar in all respects to Sharp-shinned Hark (which see), except that size is about double and end of tail is distinctly rounded (pl. 44*g*). *Voice:* Of adults a rather harsh *kluk, kluk, kluk, kluk;* of young a shrill *quick, quick, quick,* many times in rapid succession, and also a far-carrying *swēē'-ew* or *psēē'-ŭr*.

Occurrence.—Moderately common resident, chiefly in Upper Sonoran and Transition zones, on both slopes of Sierra Nevada. Partial to growths of tall trees in vicinity of streams. Observed up to 7700 feet (Dark Hole) on the west slope and to 8000 feet (Walker Lake) on the east side.

The Cooper Hawk is a larger replica of the Sharp-shinned Hawk in both form and structure, and it also closely resembles its smaller congener in habits. Its greater size enables it to prey upon larger birds such as quail and young grouse, but it is guilty of killing all manner of smaller birds as well, even down to those of the size of the Yellow Warbler.

In flight the Cooper Hawk exhibits the rounded wings and the relatively long tail characteristic of the bullet hawks (*Accipiter* and *Astur*), but the end of its tail is slightly rounded, a character which serves well to distinguish it from the Sharp-shin. (See pl. 44.) It also indulges in more soaring and circling during flight than its smaller relative. From the Goshawk it differs in much smaller size as well as in its brown rather than gray effect of under surface.

As indicative of the stealthy nature of the Cooper Hawk, we recite our experience with a family of these birds. In the course of our field studies on the floor of the Yosemite Valley, we many times passed a dense stand of young yellow pines and black oaks situated between the foot of the Yosemite Falls trail and the Ahwahnee footbridge. We did not note anything there, however, except the usual assemblage of small songsters. But on the morning of July 25, 1915, 3 young Cooper Hawks were discovered in this thicket. Their characteristic calls drew our attention, and we located the birds through finding a large amount of white excrement spattered about on the ground and shrubbery. This excrement, moreover, gave a decisive clue to the situation of the forsaken nest overhead. The thicket of trees had been passed repeatedly during the preceding six weeks by members of our field party while searching for nests of small birds without our once catching sight of the old hawks, who must of course have been going to and fro many times a day.

The nest was about 60 feet up in a tall slender black oak growing in a dense thicket of oaks and pines about a hundred feet from a small meandering, willow-bordered stream in a meadow. In silhouette the nest could easily be mistaken for one of the many clumps of mistletoe which grew in several of the oaks in the vicinity. It was composed of sticks, and placed against the main trunk on smaller horizontal branches giving the needed support.

The three young hawks were perched about 30 feet above the ground in trees near the nest. Since their wing and tail feathers were not fully out of the sheaths, the birds could not have been long from the nest. Yet when frightened they were able to fly away far enough to hide more or less successfully in the forest.

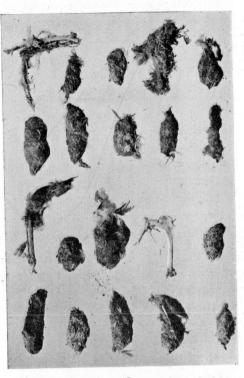

One of the young hawks was shot and upon examination was found to have in its gullet the scalp, eyes, brain, one kidney, and some other parts of an Allen Chipmunk (*Eutamias senex*), a Canadian Zone species, not known to occur anywhere on the floor of the Yosemite Valley, which is itself in the Transition Zone. On this same day one of the parent birds of this family was seen circling high overhead in the direction of Yosemite Falls and may then have been going to forage above the rim of the Valley. It is a well-known habit with this hawk, never to

Fig. 38. Pellets and other débris picked up from beneath nest of Cooper Hawk in Yosemite Valley, July 25, 1915. About ⅔ natural size. See text for analysis.

forage in the near vicinity of its nest, but to seek its prey far afield, presumably so as to avoid any risk of disclosing the location of its own brood. We may thus explain the apparent foraging of a pair of hawks in another life zone, while their nest was located in the zone to which the species characteristically belongs. The bird observed July 2, 1915, at Dark Hole, in the basin of the upper Yosemite Creek, a point well within the Canadian Zone, may well have been one of the pair nesting nearly 4000 feet lower, altitudinally, on the floor of Yosemite Valley.

On the ground below the nest in question we found a large amount of evidence relating to the food habits of the Cooper Hawk. Some of this material, comprising picked bones of victims, scattered feathers, and pellets of indigestible material regurgitated by the hawks, was preserved for subsequent detailed examination (fig. 38). The pellets we find to consist of feathers of birds, and skin and hair of mammals, all of which had been eaten along with the flesh of the victims. Later, when the processes of digestion had removed the meat, the residue had formed into dense pellets and had been disgorged. A great deal of this mass of material, of course, was in a condition to defy recognition; but the following species were identified, in each case to the extent indicated. *Chipmunk:* Much hair and some skin. *Red-shafted Flicker:* Single feather from breast. *Sierra Grouse:* A single, characteristically marked feather from a young bird; a Canadian Zone species, like the Allen Chipmunk mentioned above. *Blue-fronted Jay:* Bones of one wing with two typical feathers attached; also scattered feathers. *Sacramento Spurred Towhee:* One covert from the right wing of a juvenile bird. *Western Tanager:* Several feathers. *California Yellow Warbler:* Several feathers. *Audubon Warbler:* Several feathers from adult birds. *Western Robin:* One claw and part of a toe, the latter with a dark horny sheath indicative of an adult bird; also feathers from juvenile bird. There were also remains of June beetle, ladybird beetle, and of other insects, which may have been taken only incidentally because of their presence in the gullets or stomachs of the avian victims. These hawks are not known to hunt for insects.

Like other hawks the Cooper Hawk is often subjected to attack from kingbirds. At Pleasant Valley we saw one mobbed in flight by Western Kingbirds and Brewer Blackbirds until it took off in rapid retreat, and near Coulterville one seen flying across a cañon was harried by kingbirds until it was driven down close to the brush and there lost to sight.

WESTERN GOSHAWK. **Astur atricapillus striatulus** Ridgway

Field characters.—Size of Red-tailed Hawk, but of more slender build, with shorter, more rounded wings, and longer, more slender tail (pl. 44b); patch at either side of rump, as seen in flight, white. Upper surface uniform dark slate gray in adults, dark brown in immature birds; under surface white, finely barred with black in adults, and broadly streaked with dark brown in immatures. *Voice:* A series of loud, insistent, staccato cries, *kăk, kăk, kăk,* with a ringing quality, sometimes varied to *kēē-är.*

Occurrence.—Resident in small numbers in Canadian Zone on west slope of Sierra Nevada. Visits Yosemite Valley in winter. Lives in or about thick forests.

The Western Goshawk is the largest of the three bullet hawks, which make birds their principal victims. Its large size enables it to prey upon all manner of game; hence, even though present in but small numbers, it must play an important part in limiting the population of quail, grouse, and pigeons in the higher mountainous districts. It is known to visit mountain ranches in fall and winter and to capture domestic chickens. Quite likely at times rabbits and the larger squirrels also fall victims to it.

During the many weeks which we spent in the Canadian Zone we saw goshawks but four times, and only on one occasion was more than a single individual seen; therefore the species is not to be considered at all common in the Yosemite region. On October 3, 1915, an adult goshawk circled about the head of Glen Aulin, and then made off rapidly down-cañon through the lodgepole pine forest. Its rapid flight through the trees suggested strongly its relationship to the smaller Sharp-shinned and Cooper hawks. Another adult was seen to good advantage in the cañon of Florence Creek on August 26.

Near Ostrander Rocks, on June 23, 1915, a pair of adult goshawks was routed out of a growth of dense red firs in a cañon. They showed much solicitude over the observer's presence, and kept flying about overhead, frequently alighting on the uppermost tips of the fir trees and uttering their shrill ringing cries in rapid series of from twelve to thirty-six notes. At this time all of the distinctive field characters enumerated above could be seen to advantage, and when one flew close by, the fine barring on the feathers of the lower surface was easily observed. Search of trees in the vicinity led to the discovery of a nest about sixty feet up in a red fir, supported by the lowermost smaller branches which started from the trunk at that height. The ground below the nest, as in the case of the nest of the Cooper Hawk cited above, was covered with white excrement, suggesting recent or present occupation by young birds.

In Yosemite Valley, on November 1, 1915, Mrs. Jack Gaylor shot an immature female goshawk just as the bird swooped down into her chicken yard. Its crop and gullet were empty. It was reported that five goshawks were killed in the Valley in the fall of 1917. Mr. Donald D. McLean reports that this hawk is occasionally seen in winter in the vicinity of Smith Creek east of Coulterville, altitude about 3000 feet.

WESTERN RED-TAILED HAWK. **Buteo borealis calurus** Cassin

Field characters.—Size large, equaling that of Turkey Buzzard; tail short, usually held broadly fan-shaped in flight (pl. 44c). Upper surface of body (except tail in adults), dark chocolate brown; under surface of body varying from dark brown to almost white, in different individuals; tail bright reddish brown in adults. Most often seen sailing about in circles overhead; sails and glides much, with few wing strokes. *Voice:* A shrill, long-drawn-out, whistled *squee-oo*, uttered once, or several times in slow succession.

Occurrence.—Resident in some numbers throughout the entire Yosemite region. Noted as high as summit of Parson's Peak, over 12,000 feet altitude.

The Western Red-tailed Hawk is a regular resident of the whole Yosemite region, ranging from the cottonwood groves along the Merced River at Snelling up to the Sierran crest, and also farther to the eastward, about Mono Lake. It is not so abundant here, however, as in many other parts of California, for even an experienced observer rarely sees, in a day's walk anywhere in the Yosemite section, more than one or perhaps a pair of the birds.

Sixteen species of diurnal birds of prey inhabit the Yosemite region, but only four of these, the Osprey, Goshawk, Ferruginous Rough-leg, and the Turkey Buzzard, equal the Red-tail in size, and but one, the Golden Eagle, exceeds it. (See pl. 44.) The Eagle has a golden-tinted head and neck; the Osprey's head and under surface are chiefly pure white; the Goshawk is gray-appearing in plumage and it has a long tail; the Ferruginous Rough-leg is conspicuously white beneath and has much white showing at base of tail; and the Turkey Buzzard has a bare red head, black plumage, and a gray area on the under surface of each wing near the tip. Among the hawks of somewhat smaller size, the Swainson has a conspicuously light chin and throat, the Red-bellied, plainly black-and-white barred wings and tail, and the Marsh Hawk, a white rump. None of these other birds has a reddish brown tail in any plumage.

There is much variation in the color of the under surface of the body in different individuals of this species. Some have the under surface as well as the back almost black, while others are nearly white below, with few or no streaks or other markings. Such peculiarities are individual, and cannot be correlated with sex or season. The tail in immature birds is dull, much like the back in color; but all adults, regardless of 'color phase,' have bright reddish brown tails.

The Red-tail is essentially a soaring hawk. The Marsh and Sparrow hawks when hunting beat along over grassland or poise hovering in the air, and the bullet hawks (Cooper and Sharp-shinned hawks, and Goshawks) usually dart after their prey in or through trees or brush; but the Red-tail proceeds in seemingly more leisurely fashion, and in the open. It sails about with wings and tail widely spread (pl. 44c) and watches from on high for its prey. Occasionally it may perch on a fence post and watch the field near by for ground squirrels or gophers, upon which it pounces with alacrity remarkable in a bird with so heavy a body.

At times Red-tails are to be seen perched in conspicuous places on branches of dead trees where they can see for considerable distances. If a person comes suddenly under a bird so resting, it gets up quickly and with heavy sweeps of its large wings rapidly gains momentum and begins to glide and sail in a spiral course; it is soon able, without seeming to change much the relative positions of either wings or tail, to mount high into the air.

The Red-tail is to be considered a beneficial species, as regards the interests of mankind; for it lives to a large extent on ground squirrels and gophers. Despite this fact, many people, having in mind the name 'chicken-hawk' which is erroneously applied to the bird, wage relentless warfare on it when their militant efforts ought by rights to be directed exclusively against the bullet hawks. Of course an occasional Red-tail, just like an occasional human being, departs from the normal habits of its race and becomes harmful to man's general interests, and may quite properly be given summary treatment.

In mid-December near Lagrange five old nests of the Red-tail Hawk were found in an earth bluff about 25 feet high. The nests were in open situations about 8 feet below the top of the bluff and probably represented the choices of sites by one pair of hawks through a number of successive years. Under one of them were found the remains of ground squirrels and much 'white-wash' (droppings), which indicated that a brood of young had been reared there earlier in the year. At Mono Meadow on June 16, 1915, a Red-tail was seen frequenting a neighboring ridge; it kept up its cries so continuously as to suggest the presence of a nest in the vicinity.

The famous "eagle's nest" in Bower Cave is nothing more than a nest of the Red-tailed Hawk. It is situated in a niche of the rock wall below the rim of the cave where, because it is so thoroughly sheltered from the weather, it remains in a fair state of preservation although it has been unused now for many years.

RED-BELLIED HAWK. **Buteo lineatus elegans** Cassin

Field characters.—Proportions of Red-tailed Hawk but size much smaller, though larger than Cooper Hawk. Adults have wings and tail sharply barred with black and white, and under surface of body bright reddish brown; rest of upper surface mixed dark brown, reddish brown and white. There is no white on rump nor red on tail. Wing beats rapid; course usually low over trees, though at times circling high overhead. *Voice:* A series of squealing high-pitched notes, *ker-ker-ker-ker*, repeated every few seconds.

Occurrence.—Resident in moderate numbers in river bottoms of Lower Sonoran Zone. Observed regularly at Snelling.

As one passes by train along the bottom lands of the Merced River past Snelling to Merced Falls, he may often see close at hand a medium-sized hawk with the striking color combination of a red belly and black and white wings and tail, perched on a post or dead tree. This is the Red-bellied Hawk and this is its accustomed haunt, the willow bottoms. We found it nowhere else in the whole region. Its shrill call is not so high in pitch as that of the Sparrow Hawk, yet it is sharper, shorter, and more insistent than that of the Red-tail. When the Red-bellied Hawk takes wing the observer is able to see plainly the black and white barring of its wings and tail, and to note the rapid wing beats and low direct course of flight off over the fields, so different from the heavier flight and more frequent soaring of its larger relative.

Swainson Hawk. **Buteo swainsoni** Bonaparte

Field characters.—Similar to those for Red-tailed Hawk but size somewhat smaller and tail never red; body coloration widely variable; chin abruptly whitish, whatever the phase of color of the plumage (pl. 44*h*). *Voice:* Cry similar to that of Red-tail but clearer and more prolonged.

Occurrence.—Summer visitant in small numbers both east and west of Sierra Nevada. Found near Lagrange, May 8, 1919 (nest with two eggs), and near Williams Butte, May 12 and June 25, 1916 (specimens).

The Swainson Hawk seems to be local in its distribution in the Yosemite region, for, as we note above, it was seen by us on only three occasions. Yet in certain places elsewhere in California it is the commonest of hawks. This is the only species of hawk in our region which migrates south entirely out of the state for the winter months. Its normal breeding range involves only the Upper Sonoran and Transition life zones, and the records given above were from within those zones. Elsewhere in the Sierra Nevada during the fall months this bird has been known to wander up to the higher altitudes, even to the Hudsonian Zone, but we saw none during the several months we spent in the higher portions of the Yosemite region.

In one of the numerous large blue oaks which dot the Upper Sonoran hills about Lagrange a nest of this species was found on May 7, 1919, and the next day we visited it for detailed study. The nest tree was on the crown of a hill and therefore it and the adjacent dead 'perching tree,' about 20 feet off, both commanded view over a wide range of country. The top of the nest was 7 meters (nearly 24 feet) above the ground and close to the top of a vigorous blue oak. The nest was built on a slanting branch 120 millimeters in diameter. At this point the branch forked, each of the subsidiary branches being about 85 millimeters through; there was no other support. The nest proper (pl. 45*a*) was of dead blue oak twigs 4 to 15 millimeters in diameter and 200 to 750 millimeters in length, most of the pieces being very crooked. Many of the twigs showed abrasion where they had been grasped midway of their length by the hawks when building. A few fresh twigs, with leaves still attached to them, were included in the framework of the nest. Within this coarser structure there was a lining composed chiefly of green blue oak leaves (actually twig ends with new leaves of the current season's growth), and a small amount of foxtail grass. The nest measured, outside, about 550 by 750 millimeters and its greatest height was about 200 millimeters; the leafy depression was 200 by 250 millimeters across and at the center was about 100 millimeters below the rim of the nest. Below the nest, lodged in the lower branches of the tree were numerous twigs, evidently dropped during the construction of the nest. Building the nest was probably more or less f a hit or miss process, as was evinced by the loss of these twigs and by the simple manner in which the nest twigs rested one upon another. The irregular form of the twigs doubtless serves a good office in helping to hold the structure together. A few down feathers from the adult birds clung to the leaves in the nest.

When visited on May 7 the nest contained one egg; the next morning there were two, the usual complement for this species. As the nest was approached on the second morning, one of the hawks flushed at long range from its perch in the adjacent dead tree and circled for some minutes high overhead, giving at intervals a loud prolonged cry that was clearer and more sustained than that of a Red-tailed Hawk. This bird, presumably the male, was evidently acting as 'observer'; for the mate remained on the nest until we approached within 50 feet, when it, too, took to flight. Both birds soon disappeared, and were not again seen. The area beneath the nearby dead tree was splashed with 'whitewash' (excrement), showing that it had been occupied frequently as a roost. It was doubtless the accustomed perch and lookout post for the mate of the sitting bird, and its proximity may have determined the selection of the nest tree itself.

Incidentally, it may be remarked that this perching tree of the hawks was tenanted by a pair of Plain Titmouses, with their brood of young, and a pair of Western Bluebirds with a completed set of eggs; while a likely looking hole higher up was being prospected by a pair of Violet-green Swallows. The close proximity of this pair of birds of prey, representatives of a species which rarely if ever eats small birds, was evidently of no more concern to the titmouses and bluebirds than would have been the presence of a pair of California Woodpeckers within similarly close range.

A Swainson Hawk observed in flight showed a light throat (pl. 44*h*), dark chest, rather narrow but bluntly ended wings, and a light patch at the side of the rump. All of these points aided in differentiating the bird from the Red-tailed Hawk. Of course, there is no red on the tail of the Swainson at any age. In motion this bird's wing-beats are quicker and more frequent than those of the Red-tail.

FERRUGINOUS ROUGH-LEGGED HAWK. **Archibuteo ferrugineus** (Lichtenstein)

Field characters.—Size large, slightly greater than that of Red-tailed Hawk; wings broad; tail short. Upper surface of body dark brown appearing; under surface white, with small scattered streaks or bars of dark brown; base of tail in flight appearing white; legs down to bases of toes covered with feathers of a rusty or duller brown tone.

Occurrence.—Sparse winter visitant on west side of Sierra Nevada. Recorded definitely at Smith Creek, 6 miles east of Coulterville, October 17, 1919 (one specimen). Inhabits open ground.

The Ferruginous Rough-legged Hawk is, or was under original conditions, a common winter visitant to the plains of central California and to the larger open tracts in the foothill country, individuals perching in low trees and also often upon the ground. It has been called aptly the California Squirrel Hawk, in recognition of its custom of perching upon squirrel mounds in the prairie country and of preying upon the ground squirrels.

In general form the Rough-leg resembles the well-known Red-tail. It is slightly larger and its coloration is somewhat different. There is no red on the tail of the Rough-leg at any age, and the base of that member shows a considerable amount of white, easily seen when the bird is in flight. The whole under surface of the body in the Rough-leg is white with scattered small streaks of brown which, however, are not apparent at any distance. At close range, or with a specimen in hand, the lower part of the leg (tarsus) clear to the toes is seen to be covered with feathers more or less marked with brown or rusty.

Golden Eagle. Aquila chrysaetos (Linnaeus)

Field characters.—Typical of bird of prey; largest of Sierran land birds (length 30 to 35 inches, spread 6 to 7 feet). Coloration chiefly dark brown, becoming paler, more golden brown, on top and back of head; a grayish white area at base of tail except in old birds, and a whitish area on under side of each wing toward extremity (pl. 44*d*). *Voice:* A single loud cry, sometimes repeated several times in quick succession.

Occurrence.—Moderately common resident in foothill belt (Upper Sonoran Zone) and at middle levels of the mountains (Transition Zone) on west slope of Sierra Nevada; in summer observed at many points elsewhere in the region east to the Sierran crest in vicinity of Mono Pass.

Among Sierran land birds the Golden Eagle is supreme in size and in majesty. It is an inhabitant of the hills and mountains and only rarely strays out into the plains to the west; nor has it been found eastward in the Yosemite section much beyond the crest of the Sierra Nevada. We found the species most common in the western foothill belt, where individuals were seen almost daily; in the higher mountains we observed them less frequently, probably because in this territory a larger forage area is necessary to each individual.

The Golden Eagle may easily be distinguished from the few other birds of prey which approach it in size. The light patch usually present at the base of the tail, and the subterminal light areas under the wings, are readily seen at a moderate distance when the eagle is in flight (pl. 44*d*). The tips of its big primary feathers are rarely spread apart in the manner of a Turkey Vulture, nor are its wings, as seen from in front or behind, inclined upward in the fashion common to the Vulture. Moreover, the least glint of sunlight on the adult eagle's head and neck shows these parts to have a golden brown color unlike that of either the Vulture or the Red-tailed Hawk.

Golden Eagles are seen singly or in pairs; we have never seen more than two at any one time. The birds are wary, by nature as well as by necessity, and in consequence are rarely seen at rest. In flight they exhibit well the strength and power with which an eagle is so closely associated in the average person's mind. Sometimes they are seen to dash across or down a cañon in direct course as if going on a particular mission; again, and more often, they circle with apparent leisure, presumably on watch for prey; and occasionally they spiral up until in spite of their large bodies and broad wings they become mere specks in the sky, seeming to move scarcely at all. In Mono Pass, where the west wind often sweeps through the cañon with such force as to impede the progress of man or animal, a Golden Eagle was seen one day flying against the gale and even he was forced to tack back and forth, seeking a low course behind sheltering crags.

Twice only did we chance to see an eagle perched. In Yosemite Valley on November 9, 1915, after the first fall of snow, a bird alighted on the dead top of a tall pine about 200 yards away. As it grasped the branch, masses of snow, dislodged by the impact of the bird's weight, went showering down through the tree, glittering in the brilliant sunshine. With our field glasses we saw clearly the golden brown tint of the bird's upper plumage.

On the morning of May 19, 1919, while we were driving along the floor of the Valley near Cathedral Spires, a large shadow passed over the road. Looking up we saw a Golden Eagle. The bird alighted in the top of a not distant dead tree where we could see to advantage its characters of size, feathered head, and dark coloration.

At Pleasant Valley we had several conclusive demonstrations that the eagle's reputed keenness of vision is no idle proverb. Several times during our stay, a year-old captive in a cage at the store near by was heard to give its loud clear call. Looking up we would sooner or later detect one or two eagles above the hill-rimmed horizon. Sometimes the approaching birds looked to be mere specks in the sky, too small to attract our attention until it was directed to them by the obvious excitement of the captive; often it was several minutes before they came close enough for us to distinguish them from the ever present Turkey Vultures. But the caged bird had recognized his kind the instant they hove into sight. We were told that this captive bird had been taken in 1914 from a nest in a big digger pine east of the settlement, and that another young eagle in the nest at the same time had been killed accidentally while the tree was being felled.

We have no information concerning the food of the Golden Eagle in the Yosemite region; but we surmise that this bird of prey takes toll from a number of the medium-sized kinds of mammals. The captive bird at Pleasant Valley afforded us an opportunity to learn something of the manner in which an eagle handles its food. When offered a dead ground squirrel this eagle seized it in one foot, dragged it about in the earth at the bottom of the cage for several minutes and then began to eat it. It dug into the squirrel's skull with its strong beak, tore it apart and swallowed the fragments bone and all. The skin and hair were eaten with avidity, but the entrails were carefully avoided.

PRAIRIE FALCON. **Falco mexicanus** Schlegel

Field characters.—Much larger than Sparrow Hawk, the body being somewhat larger than that of Band-tailed Pigeon; wings long and pointed; tail relatively small (pl. 44*j*). A narrow black streak down each side of face below eye and a brownish patch behind eye; upper surface pale brown obscurely barred; under surface white, spotted or narrowly streaked with dark brown on sides and belly.

Occurrence.—Visitant in fall at higher altitudes; possibly resident in small numbers in the arid territory east of Sierran crest. Observed by us only at Vogelsang Lake, August 31 to September 4, 1915, and above Ten Lakes, October 10, 1915. Ordinarily prefers the vicinity of cliffs adjacent to open country.

The Prairie Falcon is far larger than the Sparrow Hawk which, however, it closely resembles in form. It has, indeed, nearly the bulk of the Duck Hawk, but it is paler in color than either of these other falcons. In habits it closely resembles the Duck Hawk, with which, save for the difference in coloration, it might be confused.

We saw representatives of this species at only two places in the Yosemite region, as noted above; but individuals or pairs are likely to be met with anywhere in the more arid parts of the region, from the crest of the main Sierra Nevada eastward. The individual seen repeatedly near Vogelsang Lake, when on the wing showed plainly the glistening white forward under surface which is distinctive of this falcon alone; occasionally it hovered with beating wings like a Sparrow Hawk. It does not seem likely that even a novice could confuse the pale-colored Prairie Falcon with any other raptorial species. (See pl. 44.)

DUCK HAWK. **Falco peregrinus anatum** Bonaparte

Field characters.—Smaller than Red-tailed Hawk, with long slender wings and narrow, relatively short tail. Whole coloration very dark appearing; a broad black band down each side of head below eye. Upper surface dark bluish or brownish black; lower surface heavily barred with black on a light ground in adults, and heavily streaked with black on buff in immatures.

Occurrence.—Resident on Negit Island, Mono Lake, where observed May 27, 1916. Lives about rocky cliffs in vicinity of bodies of water inhabited plentifully by water birds.

The Duck Hawk is the largest and by far the darkest colored of the four falcons in the Yosemite region. Its bodily proportions are similar to those of the Sparrow Hawk, but it is a bird of audacious appearance and behavior, gaining its livelihood by preying almost exclusively on other birds, particularly those which live on or near the water.

Our only first-hand experience with the Duck Hawk was at Negit Island, Mono Lake, where, at the time of his visit on May 27, 1916, Mr. Dixon found a pair living. Concerning these his notebook reads:

Soon after landing on the island a shot roused a male Duck Hawk, and he circled over our party, ki-yi-ing loudly, but being careful to keep out of gunshot range. When we arrived at the top of the crater, after a tiresome climb over the loose talus-strewn slope, the female flushed from a nearby boulder and joined the male in his noisy circling. Both of them left the island before we did. We searched for a nest but were unable to find one, although it seemed certain that the hawks must be nesting in one of the numerous pot-holes in the black volcanic rock.

The skeletons of many Eared Grebes, a species common at most seasons on Mono Lake, were found about the hawks' vantage points, clear evidence of the havoc the hawks had wrought among the water birds that visit the lake.

On the floor of Yosemite Valley close to Rocky Point, on November 15, 1915, a single feather was picked up at the roadside. A comparative study of this feather subsequently, in the Museum, showed that it was one of the secondary flight feathers from the right wing of an adult male Duck Hawk. The features by which it was distinguished from the corresponding feathers of other hawks are the following: actual size, outline, curvature of whole feather, tone of color of outer web (with slaty gray 'bloom') and pattern of barring on inner portion of inner web. We can only surmise that this feather had been lost through molt or accident by a bird casually visiting or flying over the Yosemite.

NORTHERN PIGEON HAWK. **Falco columbarius columbarius** Linnaeus

Field characters.—Somewhat larger than Sparrow Hawk, but of similar build, with narrow wings and long tail. Upper surface blackish brown (immatures) or dark bluish gray (adults); under surface buff, streaked with dark brown; chin buffy white; tail obscurely barred, dark brown and whitish.

Occurrence.—Winter visitant in small numbers in western part of Yosemite region. Recorded in several different years at Smith Creek, 6 miles east of Coulterville, by Donald D. McLean.

The Pigeon Hawk is not much larger than the Sparrow Hawk, but it has the daring, intrepid nature of the larger falcons. It preys chiefly upon small birds and is therefore quite different in habits from the common and better known Sparrow Hawk which in structure it resembles rather closely. Two dates of actual capture of specimens at Smith Creek are February 26, 1919, and December 20, 1919.

AMERICAN SPARROW HAWK. **Falco sparverius sparverius** Linnaeus

Field characters.—Our smallest hawk, only slightly larger than Robin, but appearing bigger because of the longer wings; wings pointed (pl. 44*i*) and, when closed, reaching nearly to end of tail. Two narrow vertical black stripes on side of head below eye; chin and belly white; top of head, back, and most of tail, rusty red; male with basal portions of wings slaty blue and tail with a broad subterminal black band and a white tip; female lacking slaty tone on wings, this being replaced by rusty brown, and tail narrowly barred with black throughout. Flight swift, with frequent quick turns; often hovers in one position for several seconds, with wings rapidly beating. *Voice:* A shrill *kĭll-y, kĭll-y, kĭll-y.*

Occurrence.—Common resident; most numerous in the San Joaquin Valley, but ranges clear up through the Hudsonian Zone, at least in summer; in Yosemite Valley, during most of year. Found chiefly about grass and meadow lands.

Most of our hawks are notably wary and difficult to approach, but the little American Sparrow Hawk may often be seen at a fairly close range. The traveler going into the mountains from the west will have good opportunities to observe this bird on the plains of the San Joaquin Valley, either from the windows of the railroad train or along any of the highways.

The sparrow hawk is decidedly misnamed, for it very rarely captures sparrows or other birds, but devotes its attention to small rodents, such as meadow mice, and to insects. Indeed we would be fully justified in renaming the bird, Grasshopper Hawk, so often are these insects eaten.

The sparrow hawk is to be seen at rest on a telephone pole or other conspicuous perch whence it can watch the surrounding country for the small game which constitutes its prey. Again it hunts over meadow and grassland, now darting along in rapid, sometimes erratic, flight; again hovering in one position for several seconds, its long pointed wings (pl. 44*i*) rapidly beating the air, while its keen eyes search the ground. Should prey of any sort be observed the bird darts down with surprising rapidity and seizes it. Occasionally, as where grasshoppers are abundant, this hawk is seen foraging on the ground much in the manner of a robin. Its shrill *kĭll-y, kĭll-y* is uttered at almost any time, both when the bird is resting and when on the wing.

During the nesting season a sparrow hawk will occasionally mount high into the air and then pitch down head foremost on set wings until close to the earth when it will change to a level course, or else hover, before indulging in further similar behavior.

At Dudley, east of Coulterville, on July 16, 1920, a family of nearly full-grown young was perched about on the branches of a dead pine, the young 'whinnying' whenever the parents came their way. In Yosemite Valley a nest was located high up in a rotted-out cavity of a black oak, north of the village.

Near Lagrange on December 23, 1915, a pair of sparrow hawks was seen pestering a shrike. Every time the latter put its head out of the thick bush in which it had sought safety, first one hawk and then the other would dart at it. Since the shrike could not be seen to have anything in its bill it could hardly have been attacked by the hawks on other grounds than as an object of prey. The hawks finally desisted and left the shrike in peace. Curiously, the same behavior was noted on the part of another pair of sparrow hawks and a shrike on the same day. It might be mentioned, also, that in two cases American Sparrow Hawks were seen pursuing the much larger Red-tailed Hawks, as if to drive the latter from the neighborhood.

The effective rôle of the sparrow hawk in checking the increase of certain kinds of animals and its consequent importance to farming interests, where these interests are dominant, is suggested by the contents of the digestive tract of a bird taken in Yosemite Valley on October 25, 1915. The dilated esophagus contained the heart, liver, and lungs of a meadow mouse (*Microtus*), while the greatly distended stomach held parts of a meadow mouse and of a shrew, a grasshopper, and 20 moth larvae averaging three-fourths of an inch long. As comprising one evening meal this mass of material certainly seemed adequate to last until morning!

American Osprey. **Pandion haliaetus carolinensis** (Gmelin)

Field characters.—Those of a bird of prey; size slightly larger than for Red-tailed Hawk. Whole under surface of body including under surface of wings, pure white; upper surface uniform brown; head chiefly white, but with blackish streak behind eye.

Occurrence.—Transient. Recorded from Yosemite Valley, and from Smith Creek, 6 miles east of Coulterville.

The only American Osprey ('fish hawk') observed by our party was, on June 8, 1915, seen to fly, in Yosemite Valley, from the east past the base of El Capitan, and to alight for a minute, before continuing its westward journey, on a dead-tipped pine. When the bird was in flight the great expanse of narrow wing was noticeable, as was also the pure white under surface; as the bird perched, the back of the head was seen also to be conspicuously white.

The osprey probably visits the Yosemite region only casually, during migration. Mr. Donald D. McLean says that the species is seen occasionally in spring at Dudley, on Smith Creek, east of Coulterville.

Barn Owl. **Tyto pratincola** (Bonaparte)

Field characters.—Medium size for an owl (length 15 or more inches, spread of wings about 45 inches); no ear tufts (fig. 39*g*); eyes relatively small, dark-colored (not yellow). General color of plumage above light golden brown; under surface white or buffy white; face white, heart-shaped, bordered by a rim of brownish feathers. *Voice:* A single prolonged rasping screech, *sksch* or *ksch* - - - -; also a rapid clicking noise, *click, click, click,* etc.

Occurrence.—Common resident wherever appropriate daytime shelter is afforded in the lowlands (Lower Sonoran Zone chiefly). Observed by us only at Snelling and west of Pleasant Valley.

The Barn Owl, as its name might indicate, has become so well adapted to the presence of man that when unmolested it takes up its quarters in a barn, attic, or windmill tower, sleeping quietly by day and issuing forth at dusk to hunt in the neighboring fields for mice and gophers. Its usefulness in this connection is well recognized and can be readily corroborated through an examination of the large collection of pellets found under any long-occupied roost.

The Barn Owl usually begins its nightly forays at late dusk and can be seen at that time, sweeping out over the fields in search of prey. One of these birds was seen abroad on a small plateau west of Pleasant Valley on the cloudy and rainy morning of February 26, 1916. The bird was on the ground near a squirrel hole in a pasture, and probably was on the watch for prey. This owl, if aroused during the daytime, shows itself able to see well, even in strong sunlight, and will fly quickly and unhesitatingly to another retreat. Its flight, like that of owls in general, is exceedingly quiet, evidently due to the very soft quality of its plumage.

The notes of the Barn Owl are of two kinds: One is a single, loud, prolonged, rasping *sksch,* uttered only at long intervals; the other, a series of notes *click, click, click, click, click,* resembling in character the notes of a katydid, but delivered with diminishing emphasis and shortening intervals toward the end of the series. From the changing direction of the sounds, it is evident that the notes are uttered in flight as one bird closely follows another. Sometimes a second bird will start his (or her) series of *clicks* before the first has finished.

The distinctive outline of the Barn Owl's face has given rise in many places to the name Monkey-faced Owl, and the peculiar color of plumage to the name Golden Owl.

Fig. 39. Owls of the Yosemite region: (*a*) California Pigmy; (*b*) Southern California Screech; (*c*) Saw-whet; (*d*) Long-eared; (*e*) Pacific Horned; (*f*) California Spotted; (*g*) Barn; (*h*) Great Gray; (*i*) Burrowing.

LONG-EARED OWL. **Asio wilsonianus** (Lesson)

Field characters.—Size medium for an owl (somewhat larger than pigeon); head an face rounded, with two long ear tufts on top of head just above eyes (fig. 39*d*, pl. 42*a*) plumage chiefly dark and light brown, in fine complex pattern; eyes yellow. *Voice* Of adults, a low, mellow, long-drawn-out *hoot*, uttered at varying intervals; also, o both adults and young, cat-like calls.

Occurrence.—Resident locally both east and west of the Sierra Nevada, below th Canadian Zone. Observed nesting commonly near Williams Butte, and once in Yosemit Valley. Lives in dense tree growths, preferably along or near streams, and forages ove adjacent meadowlands.

The Long-eared Owl seems to be of very local occurrence in the Yosemite region. We found it only in Yosemite Valley and in the open country south of Williams Butte. It probably occurs in some numbers to the westward also, along the lower reaches of the Merced and Tuolumne rivers; but we did not happen to see it there.

This owl differs from the other members of its family in the Yosemite region most especially in its choice of a nesting site. Most of our species of owls roost and nest in cavities in trees or in caves in rocks; but the Long-eared Owl finds shelter for itself and its nest in thickets of trees or shrubs on marshy lands or near streams. None of our owls is known to 'build' a nest in the accepted sense of the word; they all make use of some existing structure, be it a natural shelter or the nest of some other bird.

On the floor of Yosemite Valley at late dusk (8:00 and 7:35 P.M.) on the evenings of July 28 and 29, 1915, strange notes having a grating, tinny quality were heard repeatedly. On the morning of July 31, when the same sound was heard in the same locality, a close scrutiny of trees in the vicinity was undertaken, which disclosed the maker of these sounds to be a young Long-eared Owl, chiefly in the grayish down of the natal plumage. The owlet was perched about twenty feet up on a swaying branch of a young incense cedar standing in a dense thicket of the same sort of trees. The empty nest was close by, about thirty feet above the ground in a small yellow pine, and was partly supported by branches of a slender cedar which were interlaced with those of the pine. This was only about 200 feet from the Cooper Hawk's nest discovered a few days previously (see account of that species), and was probably an old nest of that hawk, for it was similarly constructed of coarse sticks. The nest was smeared with excrement, indicating that a brood of young had been reared in it recently. On the ground directly beneath the young bird there was a fresh, headless Yosemite Meadow Mouse (*Microtus montanus yosemite*) and many disgorged pellets, while the surrounding ground was splashed with white excrement.

When Mr. Dixon first arrived at the Farrington Ranch, near Williams Butte, on April 27, 1916, he found Long-eared Owls numerous there and ready nesting. From that date on, he had excellent opportunity to study the birds as they incubated their eggs and reared their young. (See pl. 42.)

Seven nests or broods of the Long-eared Owl were found, and 3 of these were kept under intermittent observation during the months of May and June. In all cases the owls had preëmpted older nests of the Black-billed Magpie, a bird common in that vicinity. The owls begin to nest somewhat earlier than do the magpies, and hence gain possession of the last year's nests before the original builders have occasion to reclaim them. The magpies thus have to build anew. In almost every instance a newly constructed and occupied magpie's nest was found within 15 to 50 feet of an owl's nest.

The owls were rather easy to photograph, as the accompanying illustrations will indicate. If the sitting bird flushed at his approach it was only necessary for the observer to go away for a few minutes and the bird would return. Then a quiet approach would make it possible to set up the camera at a relatively short range. The owls usually gave little heed to the camera, save to glare at the lens as though the reflection seen there were another and intruding owl. One individual, thought to be a female, was more aggressive, and several times attacked the photographer openly. She would wait until Mr. Dixon put his head under the focusing cloth; then she would swoop down and strike his head. At first the bird used only her wings, but later, becoming emboldened, struck with her claws, and once inflicted slight wounds in his scalp.

In one instance the incubating bird remained on the nest until Mr. Dixon was but 6 feet away (pl. 42a). Then it flushed and began hooting, whereupon its mate appeared. Another time the sitting owl remained until the observer was but 5 feet away. Then she (the bird was thought to be the female) hopped to a drooping willow about 12 feet away, fluffed out her feathers, flapped her wings, hooted and then uttered a *me-ow*-ing call exactly like that of a house cat. This woke her mate, who previously had been sleeping in another willow thicket a few yards away. There then ensued a duet of calls which "sounded like a pair of angry tomcats." Both birds flew about the nest, but would neither alight on it nor quit the vicinity so long as the intruder remained.

The hoot of the adult birds is low, mellow, and long-drawn-out, and bears a resemblance to the note of the Band-tailed Pigeon. With each note the throat expands and contracts but the bill is kept closed. The cat-like cries are accompanied by a spreading of the wings, and while uttering them the bird usually totters and struggles as though caught in a trap. When surprised on the nest the owls would raise their 'ears' (pl. 42a), but when they were left alone, or when perched elsewhere, the ear tufts would be flattened down on the head so as scarcely to be visible.

Sometimes when excited they clicked their bills in the manner common t
most species of owls. Later in the season, when the young were out c
the nest, the adults would fluff up their feathers and strike their wing
against their sides, producing a 'plopping' sound.

A nest seen on May 9 held 4 eggs in which incubation had begun. B
June 2 this nest held 4 young owls which were being brooded by the femal
parent. Three were still in the natal down, but the fourth and larges
one had begun to acquire the gray feathers of the juvenile plumage
When the nest was watched, both the parents attempted by the usua
tactics to distract the intruder's attention. These methods failing, th
female left the vicinity and did not return during the hour that Mr. Dixor
spent at the nest.

This nest was again visited on June 22. By this time the young owl:
were out of the nest and in Shepherdia bushes about a hundred yards
away. They had not yet learned to fly but were able to hop about readily
They uttered low whining notes when the parent birds came to feed them.

Another brood of young owls which was hatched about May 20 had
disappeared ten days later. Either they had been blown out of the nest
by the hard winds of the intervening days or, perhaps, they had fallen
victims to the ever present magpies. The latter were always about the
owl nests while the old owls were incubating, and it seemed as though the
parent birds would have to guard their treasures vigilantly in order to
prevent the magpies from destroying the eggs or young.

In one instance, after the young of a brood were partly grown, one
of the owlets was picked up in the hand. At this the female parent, in
the top of a 15-foot willow near by, let out an "agonized, blood-curdling
squawk," and allowed herself to fall down through the thicket to the
ground, where she fluttered with a well-feigned semblance of injury.

Upon summarizing the nesting data gained at Williams Butte, we find
that of the 7 nests or broods examined 3 were of 5 eggs or young each, and
4 were of 4. All the nests were in willow or Shepherdia thickets. All sets
of eggs were complete by May 1, one had hatched by May 6, and one had
not hatched by May 17. The individual records follow:

No. 1. April 27, 5 eggs; later deserted.
No. 2. April 29, 5 eggs; later destroyed.
No. 3. April 30, 4 eggs.
No. 4. May 6, bird on 2 downy young and 2 pipped eggs.
No. 5. May 9, 4 incubated eggs; June 2, 3 small young in down and 1 larger
       young one with flight feathers partly out; June 22, young out of
       nest and in thickets near by.
No. 6. May 15, 4 young with ear tufts and wing quills beginning to grow out;
       May 18, about half-grown (pl. 42b); June 1, out of nest.
No. 7. June 27, brood of 5, with both parents, encountered together in willow
       thicket.

Unlike the nest found in Yosemite Valley, all of those near Williams Butte were clean and almost altogether free of animal remains, so that little was to be learned concerning the food habits of the Long-eared Owls here. In one instance, a freshly killed White-footed Mouse (*Peromyscus* sp.) was found beneath an occupied nest.

The pellets from the Yosemite nest (fig. 40) upon examination proved to contain chiefly remains of the Yosemite Meadow Mouse. One long pellet contained practically the entire skeleton and hair of a mouse of this species, together with numerous feathers aud bones of a Spurred Towhee. One pellet contained bones from the hinder portion of a Yosemite Pocket Gopher (*Thomomys alpinus awahnee*). The materials in all of the pellets were consolidated into surprisingly compact masses. Often the long bones of the rodent skeletons are thrust into the open parts of a skull; only rarely do they protrude from the surface of a pellet. The hair is felted down so that the whole mass has a smooth exterior, not likely to scratch the owl's gullet.

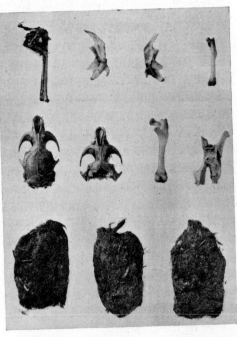

Fig. 40. Pellets and bones picked up under nest of Long-eared Owl in Yosemite Valley, July 31, 1915. About ⅔ natural size. See text for analysis.

Hunting almost exclusively at night, this owl does not capture many birds. The Spurred Towhee here recorded as being captured is notable for being especially active at dusk, just when the Long-eared Owl begins its nightly forays. The Long-eared Owl, although roosting and nesting in dense thickets, does its foraging in the open, and small birds are not as available there, at least at night, as they are in the trees and bushes through which certain other species of owls, known to capture birds, are wont to hunt. The meadow mice and gophers are most active in the early hours of the night, when presumably this owl does most of its foraging.

CALIFORNIA SPOTTED OWL. **Strix occidentalis occidentalis** (Xantus)

Field characters.—Of medium large size for an owl, less than that of Great Horned head round (no ear tufts) (fig. 39f); eyes lead-color (not yellow); plumage brown with numerous abruptly contrasted white spots in transverse rows. *Notes:* Varied perhaps most often a series of yelps like the barking of a small dog.

Occurrence.—Resident in the Transition Zone. Positively identified only in Yosemite Valley, north side, 4000 to 5000 feet altitude, on Sweetwater Creek, 3800 feet, near Feliciana Mountain, and near Bower Cave, 2500 feet. Strictly a night owl, and an inhabitant of woods.

The California Spotted Owl came to our attention first on the evening of October 12, 1914, when we heard its notes from the golden-oak talus near the foot of Yosemite trail, on the north side of Yosemite Valley. These notes differed from those of any other owl of the region, in that they were abrupt rather high-pitched calls, in tone like the distant barking of a dog: *whŭ', whŭ'; whŭ.* The first two were loudest. There was no suggestion of the deep intonation of the Pacific Horned Owl.

Subsequently on many occasions one or more spotted owls were heard near the same place, sometimes farther down toward Rocky Point, but always in or near the golden-oak belt. There could be little doubt that a pair nested there; for the birds were heard at various times throughout the summer of 1915.

The notes were never given until late dusk; for example, on June 7 at 7:50 P.M.; on June 23 at 8:00; on July 24 at 7:32; on July 28 at 7:30; on October 23 at 5:25; and on November 18 at 5:10. It will be observed that these hours closely accord in the changing seasons with a certain degree of darkness.

In only one instance were the numerous attempts to sight this owl in Yosemite Valley successful. On June 23 the first notes for the evening happened to be given by a bird close to the spot where the observer had taken his stand. A little manoeuvering brought the latter beneath the cedar in which the owl was perched; an opening in the foliage permitted a glimpse of its silhouette against the sky; and a quick shot brought it down. Even though here beneath the shaded north wall of the Valley daylight had nearly gone, the bird appeared quite stupid in its lack of fear. The notes heard at this time, close at hand, and as set down at the moment, were thought to resemble the syllables *howk, howk, howk,* given in a rather hollow tone. The specimen procured was an old female in full molt, evidently long past nesting.

Notes, probably of a spotted owl, were heard at Gentry's, 5800 feet altitude, on the evening of October 24. During the last week of October, similar notes were heard in the vicinity of Feliciana Mountain, 3800 to

)00 feet, which proved unquestionably to be given by a spotted owl. On ctober 30, at about 8 o'clock in the morning, the same owl note was heard, nd presently a California Gray Squirrel began barking furiously. This gnal was followed up, but without success. Fifteen minutes later, some inglets, both Ruby-crowned and Golden-crowned, were heard remonstrat- ig in excited fashion, and their interest was found to focus within a Juttall dogwood. Scrutiny of this tree resulted in the discovery of what as at first thought to be a big wasp's nest among the branches about forty eet above the ground. This object, however, soon resolved itself into the utlines of an owl, all hunched-up, so as to quite obscure its true identity. The bird was shot and proved to be an old female spotted owl. Mr. C. A. McCarthy, a rancher in the neighborhood, said that a pair of these owls aad lived in the vicinity for three years, to his knowledge, and had raised a brood of young each year. He appreciated the birds for the variety of their evening voicings.

In the late afternoon of July 23, 1920, on a wooded ridge-slope near Bower Cave, Mr. Donald D. McLean found himself within hearing of a clamor of bird voices. Following the clue he worked cautiously up the slope and discovered the center of the disturbance to be a spotted owl which was perched in an incense cedar, close to the trunk on a branch about 60 feet above the ground. The throng of excited birds included 19 Blue-fronted Jays, 5 or 6 California Jays, half a dozen California Wood- peckers, one Sierra Creeper, and many Cassin, Hutton, and Warbling Vireos, Black-throated Gray Warblers, and Western Flycatchers.

The stomach of the California Spotted Owl obtained in Yosemite Valley was empty—the bird was waylaid probably too early in the evening for it to have dined. The Feliciana Mountain bird taken in the morning had fared well, its stomach containing a mass of foodstuff in which were recognized parts of a wood rat (*Neotoma fuscipes streatori*), a white-footed mouse (*Peromyscus*), and a grasshopper.

GREAT GRAY OWL. **Scotiaptex nebulosa nebulosa** (Forster)

Field characters.—Size very large (largest of our owls); length nearly two feet, expanse four feet and a half; head big and round, without ear tufts; eyes yellow; tail relatively long. General color grayish brown with dull mottlings and streakings of white; no conspicuous white throat patch. (See text fig. 39*h* and pl. 43*c*.) *Voice:* A deep reverberating *whoo*, given at irregular intervals.

Occurrence.—Probably permanently resident. Found by us only in the fir woods of the Canadian Zone. Definite stations: 7400 feet altitude, within one mile south of Ostrander Rocks; 7900 feet, within one mile north of Indian Rock. Seems prone to be active during the daytime, but keeps within thick timber.

The discovery of the Great Gray Owl in the Yosemite section was on of the notable events in our field experience. And what was most surprising was the fact that the bird was apparently quite at home, and nesting. No previous record of the breeding of this northern species of owl south of Canada is known to us, and its occurrence even as a winter visitant within the northernmost of the United States is not frequent.

On June 18, 1915, we were camped to the south of Yosemite Valley on the Glacier Point road within two miles south of Ostrander Rocks. A long trap-line beginning at camp led up the gentle slope toward the latter landmark and through a fine forest of red fir. During inspection of this line on previous days we had distant glimpses, morning or evening, of a large bird in silent flight among the trees. On the day of discovery, however, the diminutive kinglet pointed the way and really deserves all the credit. From a distance through the forest came the low but insistent *wer-rup, wer-rup, wer-rup* of a Ruby-crown, its unmistakable note of anxiety. The clue was traced by the expectant naturalist to a tall fir, out from near the summit of which there presently flew a great owl. The bird alighted at the top of a Jeffrey pine close at hand where it was shot and wounded. As it fell to the ground it gave several deep-pitched *whoo's*. At this, another owl appeared in flight from one fir top to another and was also obtained.

We wanted to photograph it, so the wounded bird was taken back to camp alive. Its huge facial discs (pl. 43c), each centered by a great yellow-irised eye, its snapping bill, and its spasmodically clenching claws, all contributed to profound respect on our part in the necessary handling incidental to taking the pictures.

On succeeding days a careful search of the vicinity was made, and a large nest of sticks, which, it was thought, belonged to the owls, was found one hundred feet above the ground on the close-set branches of a fir next to the trunk. But no close examination of it was made. On June 19 in the same stretch of woods the deep notes of an owl were heard three times repeated, but the bird could not be located. This time the kinglets failed us.

The two specimens obtained proved to be male and female, probably a mated pair. As is usual with owls the female was slightly the larger, measuring: total length 595 millimeters (nearly 2 feet); expanse of wings 1370 millimeters (4½ feet). The male measured: length 580 millimeters; expanse 1350. In both birds the iris was bright straw yellow; bill greenish becoming yellow toward tip; claws lead-color darkening toward tips. The stomach of each bird was empty.

As an indubitable indication of breeding during the current nesting season, the female was found to have a large bare tract on the lower surface

»f the body, including the belly and insides of the thighs, from which the arger feathers had all been removed. Associated with this condition, lirectly beneath the bare skin, were layers of fat, though the bird was »therwise lean. As is well known, many birds show, during the nesting season, the same or similar adaptations for the better performance of the functions of incubation. The male Great Gray Owl lacked any such modifications, and we may infer that in this species the female alone performs the duty of incubation. The reproductive organs of both the birds indicated that the time of actual egg laying was long past. It seems more than likely that a brood of young had been reared in the vicinity and, approaching maturity, had scattered out through the adjacent woods.

On July 1, 1915, a Great Gray Owl was met with on the old Snow Flat trail, a mile or so north of Indian Rock. When first seen it was perched on a low limb of a lodgepole pine not over 10 feet above the ground. Two juncos in the vicinity were in spasms of excitement. The owl, taking alarm, flew to a higher branch of a neighboring tree, and thence made off into a dense stand of red firs. Its species was easily recognized by its great size, dark gray plumage, big round head without ears, and by the slow flapping of its broad rounded wings. No note was given by this bird. This was at 1:30 P.M. As far as our observations went, this species would seem to be more active by daylight than other owls such as the Pacific Horned Owl.

In Aspen Valley, on October 13, 1915, at 7:30 P.M., an owl note, supposedly of the Great Gray, was heard; but it proved impossible to verify the identity. Near Tamarack Flat, on May 24, 1919, similar notes were heard but the birds were not seen. Notes of certain individual Band-tailed Pigeons proved enough like those of this owl to cause confusion until the authors of the notes were actually seen to be pigeons.

SAW-WHET OWL. Cryptoglaux acadica (Gmelin)

Field characters (inferred from specimens).—Size small (between that of Pigmy Owl and Screech Owl); head round (no ear tufts) (fig. 39c); eyes straw yellow; color above cinnamon brown, below white, with broad streakings of warm rusty brown (not blackish). [Living birds not seen by us.]

Occurrence.—Sparse resident on floor of Yosemite Valley and probably also in vicinity of Dudley, 6 miles east of Coulterville.

On July 24, 1915, a Golden-crowned Kinglet's nest, in use earlier the same season, was taken from its site 30 feet above the ground, in a smallish yellow pine standing near Yosemite Falls Camp. This nest, now preserved in the Museum of Vertebrate Zoology, had as part of its constituent material a considerable number of the feathers of a Saw-whet Owl. There were twenty or more of these feathers, broad rusty striped ones from the under surface of the owl, and cinnamon brown ones from the back. In fact, the bulk of the inner lining of the nest cavity consisted of these feathers, of unmistakable identity.

What else could we infer but that a Saw-whet Owl had met with some mishap within the radius in which the kinglets had done their scouting for suitable nesting material? The feathers were full-fluffed, not in the least bedraggled; this would seem to prove that they had not been exposed to wet weather. The accident that made them available to the kinglets must have occurred recently, after the heavy rains of early spring.

Upon visiting Yosemite Valley in May, 1919, we found a specimen of the Saw-whet Owl mounted in the Park Superintendent's office. Inquiry developed that Mrs. Jack Gaylor, a resident in the Valley, had killed three of these owls at different times during the period between 1916 and 1919, and that the bird mounted was one of these. She had "knocked them over with a stick," two, when she discovered them perched on crossbeams under a shed roof, and a third, when she found it in the granary of her barn. The exact dates of these occurrences had not been kept. One individual was seen during the middle of the day while being bothered by a number of Sierra Juncos in Yosemite Valley on August 26, 1920 (C. W. Michael, MS).

On July 13, 1920, the dried remains of a Saw-whet Owl were found in the fire box of a rusty engine boiler at a deserted mine, one mile south of Dudley.

Thus the circumstantial evidence of 1915 indicating the occurrence of the Saw-whet Owl in the Yosemite region was fully corroborated by facts collected later. The birds may be present regularly in parts of the region, though hardly in large numbers. Like other nocturnal animals they could easily have escaped our eyes, and even our ears. Some one more fortunate than we will find them.

SOUTHERN CALIFORNIA SCREECH OWL. **Otus asio quercinus** Grinnell

Field characters.—Size small for an owl (length about 9 inches); head with conspicuous ear tufts (fig. 39b); whole plumage streaked with dark and light gray, in general effect resembling the bark of an oak tree; eyes yellow. *Voice:* A series of low-toned, mellow notes uttered in a rapid series, with diminishing intervals; also single soft clucking notes, especially when adults and young are foraging together.

Occurrence.—Rare resident of foothill belt on west slope of Sierra Nevada (Upper Sonoran and lower part of Transition zones). Frequents live oaks and golden oaks.

In our experience with the Southern California Screech Owl elsewhere in the State we have come to associate it in our minds with the live oak belt. Where live oaks occur there we expect to find this owl common.

Such was not the case, however, as regards the Yosemite region. Although we made special search for it at several likely points in the foothill belt we ourselves failed to find it there at all.

Our only record is of a single bird seen in the golden oaks near the foot of the Yosemite Falls Trail in Yosemite Valley on the evening of November 20, 1915, just as our field work for the season was drawing to a close. The bird was heard and momentarily seen close at hand. Within a quarter of an hour there were also heard in the same vicinity, besides this screech owl, 2 great horned owls, a pigmy owl, and a spotted owl.

On January 13, 1916, Mr. Donald D. McLean succeeded in capturing alive a screech owl at Smith Creek, east of Coulterville.

PACIFIC HORNED OWL. **Bubo virginianus pacificus** Cassin

Field characters.—Large size (length about 20 inches); ear tufts present and conspicuous (fig. 39e); exceeded in size only by Great Gray Owl, which lacks ear tufts. Plumage chiefly a mixture of dark and light brown, streaked on back and barred on under surface; eyes yellow. *Voice:* A deep, reverberant, deliberate, *whoo, whoo-whoo, whoo,* or *too-whoo, whoo.*

Occurrence.—Resident in moderate numbers throughout the region below Hudsonian Zone; observed in Hudsonian Zone once, at Ten Lakes. Lives in open woods in mountains, along wooded ravines in foothills, and in river-bottom timber in the lowlands.

The Pacific Horned Owl is the owl which ranges most widely through the Yosemite region. It is nowhere common, yet it is likely to be met with anywhere from the cottonwood groves along the Merced River at Snelling to the Jeffrey pine woods of the Canadian Zone. In the Hudsonian Zone we found it only at Ten Lakes; its general absence from the higher zones may be due to the lack there of appropriate food. On the east slope of the Sierras we found the species at Walker Lake.

Horned owls, wary birds more often heard than seen, usually will not permit of close approach. It seems probable that in detecting the presence of people they depend fully as much on hearing as on sight. At Lagrange, Mr. Dixon tried several times to get near a horned owl heard regularly on several successive evenings in a certain steep-sided, tree-clothed ravine. Keeping entirely out of sight he tried to approach behind a ledge of rimrock; but the owl, seeming to hear his footsteps, flushed while he was some distance away and still completely out of sight.

These owls begin to stir about at dusk and at that time are wont to take commanding positions on the bare tops of dead trees whence they can watch or listen for prey and detect the distant approach of enemies. Their activity extends throughout the night and until late dawn. Their deep-toned reverberant hooting is most often heard in the evening and morning twilight; but, as many a camper can testify, it may be uttered

as well during the midnight hours. Heard out of doors during the middle
of the night, their heavy voices leave an impression long retained. The
time of their appearance varies with the season. At Lagrange in December
they were out and hooting by 4:30 P.M., while in midsummer they were
not to be heard until 7 o'clock or later. On dark days they were occasionally heard during the daytime. Usually, with the coming of dawn the
birds seek shelter in tall dense-foliaged trees where they spend the day
in quiet.

The Pacific Horned Owl has a reputation for feeding on poultry,
particularly in outlying communities where the fowls are in the habit
of roosting in the trees in the barnyard. Mr. George Smith, our packer,
told us that in his experience a horned owl would not ordinarily pounce
directly down on a sleeping hen, but ''would alight on a limb where a
number of chickens were roosting. Then it would crowd against the birds
until the one on the opposite side was forced to fly,'' whereupon the owl
would also take wing and catch its prey when the latter was in motion.

Mr. Donald D. McLean says that a horned owl taken 8 miles northeast
of Coulterville was captured in a rabbit snare on the ground. At Aspen
Valley we found the mummified remains of a horned owl impaled on a
barbed wire fence. One wing was broken and literally wrapped around
the middle wire of the fence. Evidently the owl had hit the fence while
in flight and its struggles to get free had but fixed its feathers more firmly
on the barbs of the wire.

BURROWING OWL. **Speotyto cunicularia hypogaea** (Bonaparte)

Field characters.—Size small for an owl; about twice bulk of Meadowlark; head
rounded, no ear tufts (fig. 39*i*). Plumage light brown and white in mixed pattern; eyes
yellow. *Voice:* A mellow two-syllabled call, *cuck-oo,* uttered over and over again; heard
most often at dusk during the spring months.

Occurrence.—Common resident in Lower and Upper Sonoran zones; noted by us
only west of Sierra Nevada. Lives in open country in and about ground squirrel
burrows.

The Burrowing Owl, locally known as 'billy owl,' and perhaps better
called 'ground owl,' is to be looked for confidently on the plains of the
San Joaquin Valley and on such larger tracts of level land as are to be
found among the foothills. Living in the open and being active during
part of the day as well as all the night, this owl is likely to be seen by
anyone traversing its habitat. It frequents the vicinity of ground squirrel
burrows, both for shelter and for nesting sites.

Occasionally individuals are to be seen perched on fence posts at the
edges of fields or pastures, and from these vantage points they watch for
insects in the surrounding grasslands. As a person walks past at close

ange the owl turns its head so as to keep the passerby under constant surveillance; should the observer circle about the bird, the latter seemngly finds no difficulty in rotating its head, even so as to look directly over its own back. The dexterity of the bird in this respect has given rise to the popular belief that it can twist its head entirely around several times without inconvenience! A curious mannerism of this owl is a profound bow executed at irregular intervals.

Nests of the Burrowing Owl are situated in squirrel burrows, at varying distances from the entrances, but usually far beyond arm's length. The birds make use of damp horse manure almost exclusively in making the nest proper, hence a scattering of this material seen during the spring months at the entrance to a squirrel hole may be counted on as an indication that a pair of Burrowing Owls has a nest within.

Burrowing Owls are more prolific than tree-nesting species of owls, doubtless because they are more subject to enemies than the latter species. Late in summer family groups of as many as a dozen individuals are occasionally seen within the radius of a few yards.

CALIFORNIA PIGMY OWL. **Glaucidium gnoma californicum** Sclater

Field characters.—Size very small (smallest of our owls); total length only about 7 inches, expanse 14½ inches; head round, without ear tufts (fig. 39a); eyes yellow. Color of plumage above grayish brown, relieved by small white spots; below white, with sharp blackish streaks. *Voice:* Different from that of any other owl, and frequently heard during the day; a single mellow *whoot*, repeated at intervals; or a prolonged slow trill, followed by two or three isolated *whoots: too-too-too-too-too-too-too-too-too; whoot; whoot; whoot.*

Occurrence.—Apparently a common permanent resident of the Transition Zone, and perhaps also of the upper margin of the Upper Sonoran Zone. Inhabits sparse woods. Definite stations: Yosemite Valley, 3900–4200 feet; El Portal, 2000–2500 feet; Smith Creek, on Coulterville Road, 2800 feet.

In Yosemite Valley, the voice of the California Pigmy Owl was heard more frequently than that of any other nocturnally active bird. The first indication of the presence of this owl was a regular concert beginning at early dark and lasting until dark, given on the evening of October 10, 1914, in the strip of pine, cedar, and fir woods between the road and the cliff-wall below LeConte Lodge. Two birds about 300 yards apart were answering one another, and at one time a third was heard in the distance. The calls consisted of a slow trill, rather mellow, but not so mellow nor of such full quality as in the call of the California Screech Owl—more like the slow roll of the flicker. This trill would continue some seconds, then came a pause, then one note, an equal pause, and a second note. In one instance a third note was added. The striking characteristic was the pause after the trill, followed by the two detached notes. Once three far-separated notes were heard, not preceded by any trill. The following syllables, i uttered while one whistles, seem to represent the pigmy owls' usual song *too-too-too-too-too-too-too-too; toot; toot; toot.*

On October 12 similar notes were heard at 6:30 A.M. in the same vicinity; and on October 14, at 9:30 A.M., others were heard from the dark shaded valley wall near Bridal Veil Falls.

During the summer and fall of 1915 the voice of the pigmy owl was heard practically every evening that observations were made, in the vicinity of Yosemite Falls Camp, and from there down to Rocky Point and across the Ahwahnee footbridge. On August 18 and 19 the notes were heard at daybreak; on September 2 at 5:30 A.M., in broad daylight, and again at 6:50 P.M.; on September 4 at daybreak; and on October 23 at 5:22 P.M. On October 24, near Camp Ahwahnee, three owls were heard, the earliest at 5:22 P.M. On the evening of October 25 the first note was heard at 5:21 P.M. On October 27 three owls were heard near Camp Yosemite from as many different directions, beginning at 5:30; they called persistently for about fifteen minutes, after which perfect quiet reigned. On November 1, a clear sunny day, the regular full series of notes was twice heard at 11 A.M.; and on November 3, a day partly overcast, the notes were heard at 12:20 P.M.

Near El Portal, on December 6, 1914, a pigmy owl was obtained through the assistance of solicitous song birds. A bevy of fully fifteen ruby-crowned kinglets was buzzing like bees about the foliage of a tree, each uttering its ratchet-like call, and flitting hither and thither in the most perturbed manner. While the observer was watching, a pair of plain titmouses joined the group, and soon there flew out a pigmy owl, quickly followed by a good part of the excited congregation.

On December 10, 1914, about 11 A.M., near LeConte Lodge, a creeper was heard squeaking emphatically, with its attention fixed on the lower branches of a yellow pine. Presently a pigmy owl disclosed its presence by taking flight. It alighted near by on a pine twig thirty feet above the ground, and there it was shot.

Subsequent dissection of this owl showed its stomach to contain one forefoot, some bones, and much hair of a Yosemite Pocket Gopher. The stomach of a California Pigmy Owl obtained at El Portal, December 26, 1914, contained fragments of a small snake and of several grasshoppers. This further betokens daytime foraging on the part of this, our smallest species of owl.

ROAD-RUNNER. **Geococcyx californianus** (Lesson)

Field characters.—Of fairly large size (near that of Leghorn chicken) with tail long, fully as long as head and body (about 13 inches). General color effect of plumage pale brown, with feathers of back broadly dark centered; tail chiefly black in color, and with a large white 'thumb mark' at end of each feather; bill strong, slender, about 2 inches long; head with an erectile crest; feet and legs stout. *Voice:* A series of low notes, mournful in effect, with descending pitch; also a low clattering sound, repeated.

Occurrence.—Sparse resident of Lower and Upper Sonoran zones on western base of Sierra Nevada. Lives in open chaparral of the foothills, and on the plains adjacent to river-bottom thickets.

The Road-runner was found only in small numbers in the Yosemite region. One was heard 'singing' near Blacks Creek, west of Coulterville, on May 10, 1919, but only one individual was actually seen by any member of our party, and that near Lagrange, on December 18, 1915. There was much hearsay evidence, however, of its occurrence near Pleasant Valley. We were also told that it had been seen twice on a dry flat near El Portal; and Mr. Donald D. McLean reports that Road-runners are seen occasionally in the lower cañon of Bean Creek, east of Coulterville.

At Pleasant Valley, on the morning of May 30, 1915, as we walked out west of the settlement, we saw much evidence of the events of the preceding night and early morning in the dust of the road. Besides the abundant slender tracks of many smaller birds, such as towhees and sparrows, we could see where Valley Quail had crossed or run along the road in several places. There were tracks of a raccoon and of numerous California toads; and spots where kangaroo rats had taken dust baths or sought forage in the scattered chaff. But most interesting of all, because not previously noted by us in this region, were a few tracks of a fairly large bird, totally different from those of the quail. The impressions made by the toes of each foot were in tandem alignment, two in front and two behind, and the footprints were separated by considerable intervals. The evidence was conclusive—a Road-runner had passed that way.

WESTERN BELTED KINGFISHER. **Ceryle alcyon caurina** Grinnell

Field characters.—Size somewhat greater than that of Flicker; head big, tail small, bill stout, and crest prominent. Color above, slaty blue; beneath, silvery white with a broad belt of slate across breast. Female has also a belt, behind the slaty one, of bright rusty brown, with extensions of this color backward along each side. Flight rapid and usually in straightaway course up or down a stream. *Voice:* A loud grating clatter or rattle.

Occurrence.—Frequent along streams and about the margins of lakes up at least to the altitude of Tuolumne Meadows, 8600 feet. Observed along the Merced River, in nearly every month of the year, at many points, from near Snelling to and above El

Portal, and along the Tuolumne River near Lagrange in spring; also, in summer and fall, in Yosemite Valley, in the upper Merced Cañon between Merced and Washburn lakes, and, on the Mono side of the mountains, at Walker Lake and along Rush Creek down nearly to Mono Lake.

Associated closely, as it is, with fish-producing waters, the Western Belted Kingfisher proves to be well represented in the Yosemite region. Along the sloughs and quieter parts of the Merced River, one's attention is often suddenly attracted by the harsh rattling note of one of these birds, as it dashes past in rapid flight. When alighting, it chooses some prominent bare tree branch at the side of the stream, where it can have an uninterrupted view of the water beneath and also have access to a clear 'fly-way' up and down. Here the bird perches with its big head and bill held horizontally, its crest showing in profile conspicuously. It does not keep one perch very long, however, but soon goes rattling off down the river to the next favorable vantage point.

This bird's wing-beat is characteristic, three quick beats followed by two executed in a more leisurely manner, like this: one, two, three; four; five.

A Western Belted Kingfisher watched by Mr. Walter P. Taylor came to a perch on a bare limb overhanging some rapids in the river, and sat there motionless. The outline of the bird's body at once became indistinguishable from the light and shade of its background; in other words it was obliterated because of the disruptive pattern of its coloration, white and slate areas alternating. If the fishes in the water beneath got the same impression as did the human observer, the kingfisher must have become invisible to them, remaining so until the moment of its headlong plunge in their pursuit.

Outlining the behavior of the belted kingfisher in further detail, our notes record an observation at Stoneman bridge, October 12, 1914. It was 5 P.M., and dusk was just coming on. A kingfisher was much in evidence. It flew down to the water, skimmed over its surface for a ways, then up and out into the woods, twisting among the trees with wild headlong flight. Then back to the river it flew, to take its position for a few moments on a cottonwood limb twenty feet above the water. It uttered, at short intervals throughout this flight, the characteristic harsh clatter.

At El Portal, December 5, 1914, a kingfisher was seen to perch on the tip of a sharp-angled boulder out in the swift current. In that locality certain drift snags in mid-stream and dead oak branches extending out over the water were also chosen as perches.

Even to the casual observer the dependence of this bird on a diet of fishes is most apparent. This fact plainly accounts for the antipathy to it displayed by most human fishers, and, as a result, many kingfishers are killed each year, "just to get rid of them." We are convinced that the rate of multiplication of the fishes was long ago adjusted to the "expected depreciation" due to the regular draft on their numbers by kingfishers. Indeed, the birds probably constitute but one of very many causes of fish mortality. Moreover, one bird obtained by us, at Snelling, January 7, 1915, was found to contain in its stomach only sundry fragments of water beetles, indicating occasional departure from a purely fish diet. The numbers of the kingfishers are really not large; for example, we kept a pretty close watch from the train one afternoon, along the whole distance from Merced Falls to El Portal, and yet recorded just six individuals. Anyway, we would forbear to catch our share of trout if this were necessary to preserve in normal numbers so interesting a member of Yosemite's avifauna.

The Western Belted Kingfisher nests in Yosemite Valley proper, probably each year. In 1920, on June 23, a nest hole was located in the high south bank of the Merced River, about 200 yards below Stoneman Bridge. The entrance was 2 feet below the surface of the ground and 6 feet above the base of the bank, which was there washed by the deep water of an outward bow of the river. The otherwise circular hole had two track-like grooves at the entrance, marking the place where an arriving bird gained its first foothold. While the nest was under observation young birds were suddenly heard inside. Then the male (recognizable by the lack of brown coloring in its belt) arrived bearing a fish which protruded lengthwise from his bill. This bird and its mate had their forage range up and down the river between Stoneman and Sentinel bridges. Earth banks of the sort to accommodate nesting burrows occur along the river at several other points below Stoneman Bridge, but some of these, at least, are wholly inundated by the May floods. For instance, when search was made for kingfishers' nests on June 2, 1915, all the possible nesting sites then known were found to be covered with water.

A belted kingfisher was noted in Yosemite Valley in the fall of 1915 almost daily until November 4, but not subsequently. There is every likelihood, however, that the species remains throughout the winter wherever the food supply is adequate, up as high as the streams remain unfrozen.

MODOC WOODPECKER. **Dryobates villosus orius** Oberholser

Field characters.—A woodpecker of size of Robin or slightly less. Upper surface black, with a broad white stripe down middle of back; whole under surface, including outer tail feathers, uniformly white; small spots on wing, stripe below eye, and another stripe behind eye, white. (See pl. 5*f*.) Adult males have narrow fringe of red feathers across back of head, but this is not often to be seen at a distance. *Voice:* A single sharp note, *speenk*, uttered at irregular intervals.

Occurrence.—Resident in moderate numbers throughout the region except in the Lower Sonoran Zone and above timber line. Observed at Pleasant Valley and thence eastward to vicinity of Mono Lake; highest station of record, Warren Fork of Leevining Creek at 9300 feet altitude. Forages in more open stands of both coniferous and deciduous trees.

The Modoc Woodpecker is but a local race of the wide-ranging 'hairy' woodpecker, which is found practically everywhere in the forested regions of North America. As with most of the allied forms, the present race ranges through several life zones, from the scattered digger pines at Pleasant Valley eastward through the main forest belt to the sparse tracts of Jeffrey pines in the vicinity of Mono Lake. It is nowhere really common, even for a woodpecker; it reaches its greatest numbers in the upper part of the Transition Zone and in the Canadian Zone.

The Modoc Woodpecker is identical in pattern of coloration with the much smaller Willow Woodpecker, save that the outer tail feathers of the larger bird are pure white, whereas in the smaller species they are barred with black. The special plumage features which are associated with differences in sex and age are likewise identical in the two species. Adult males have a narrow fringe of red feathers across the back of the head (pl. 5*f*), whereas young males have the whole top of the head red. Adult females entirely lack the red color and young females have only a few scattered red feathers on the crown.

A comparison of the weights of these two woodpeckers shows that the Modoc is about two or three times as heavy as the Willow Woodpecker. Thus, male Modoc Woodpeckers weigh on the average 68.1 grams (2.4 ounces) and females 58.9 (2.1 ounces), whereas Willow Woodpeckers weigh 27.0 (0.95) and 24.4 grams (0.86 ounces) respectively. The Nuttall Woodpecker, a Sonoran Zone species of similar build and proportions to the two species just mentioned, weighs 41.2 (1.45) and 34.4 grams (1.2 ounces), for the two sexes, respectively, being thus fairly intermediate.

During the summer months we rarely saw in a morning's walk more than one individual of the Modoc Woodpecker. But in Yosemite Valley, during the winter season, the birds seemed as noisy and conspicuous as they had been quiet and unobtruding before. Perhaps this impression was enhanced by the absence of the voices of summer birds. One of our notebook records (December 20, 1914) reads:

Four seen in two and a half hours; the most noticeable bird, making enough noise to give the impression of many. No ''rolling,'' but much tapping and frequent high-pitched ''speenks''; birds working on dead limbs of tall cottonwoods and black oaks on the Valley floor.

The Modoc Woodpecker forages on both evergreen and deciduous trees, favoring the latter, perhaps, during the winter months. In summer it is usually rather quiet, particularly so as compared with the noisy California Woodpecker. It gains much of its food in the outer portions of the bark, where a few strokes of moderate intensity enable it to secure any insect or grub living near the surface of the tree.

At the margin of the forest above Coulterville, May 31, 1915, a Modoc Woodpecker was seen foraging in a yellow pine. The tree in question had recently been killed by the boring beetles which were common in the western forests that year. The woodpecker was going over the tree in systematic manner, working out and in along one branch, then ascending the trunk to the next branch where it would repeat the performance. The bird was flaking off the outer layers of the bark without much evident expenditure of effort, for little noise of tapping was heard; it was feeding presumably on the boring beetles or their larvae.

At Gentrys on October 23, 1915, a Modoc Woodpecker was seen enlarging a hole in a pine tree, perhaps preparing a shelter for use during the winter months. The bird worked actively, but paused frequently as if to inspect its work.

At Chinquapin, on May 19, 1919, a pair of these woodpeckers was seen going through their courting antics. A male was in a large yellow pine at the edge of a logged-over area, calling almost incessantly. His usual *speenk* had become *spenk-ter-ter-ter,* a staccato run repeated every few seconds. The female answered in like voice but uttered the trill less often. The male changed his location many times, and after protracted calling on his part, the female flew to the same tree.

On June 24, 1920, in Yosemite Valley, a brood of full-grown young in a row of large cottonwoods near the Ahwahnee footbridge was much in evidence by reason of their calls and active behavior.

Willow Woodpecker. **Dryobates pubescens turati** (Malherbe)

Field characters.—Smallest of our woodpeckers (pl. 5e) about halfway between junco and robin in size. Upper surface, wings and tail chiefly black; lower surface dull white; a white streak over eye, and one across forehead and down along cheek; middle of back continuously white (no bars); outer tail feathers white, barred with black; outer wing feathers marked with white spots near tips. Males have a bright red band across back of head, this, however, not often seen; females without any red at all. Flight-course in short undulations; wing strokes intermittent. *Voice* (seldom heard): A high-pitched run or trill of unique character.

Occurrence.—Sparse resident of deciduous timber in Lower and Upper Sonoran and Transition zones. Observed from river bottom near Snelling to as high as 5750 feet on Yosemite Falls trail above foot of upper Yosemite Falls. Works chiefly on soft-barked deciduous trees such as willow, cottonwood, and apple.

The Willow Woodpecker, a close relative of the eastern Downy Woodpecker, is nowhere abundant in the Yosemite region; in fact scarcely a dozen individuals all told were observed by our party during the entire period of our field work there. In coloration and general behavior the Willow Woodpecker resembles closely the much larger Modoc Woodpecker (see pl. 5), but it is far less noisy. It rarely has anything to do with coniferous trees, foraging, rather, on soft-barked trees such as the willow, cottonwood, and, where it is available about ranches, upon the apple.

The quietness of the Willow Woodpecker, as compared with most other species in its family, is noteworthy. We heard no single call note from it, and only at long intervals did we hear the indescribable short trill characteristic of this bird. Individuals are much restricted in range, foraging along a relatively short line of cottonwoods or willows day after day. Once a bird is located, it can usually be found in the same place regularly. When foraging it moves about with very little commotion, and even when drilling for insects works so quietly that only a keen auditor can detect its presence. No matter what the season of the year, a pair of these birds is to be found usually within hearing of each other. The bird's close adherence to deciduous trees makes it more conspicuous and easier to observe in late fall and winter than in the summertime when the trees are fully leaved out; but even in winter, our experience with the Willow Woodpecker led us to consider it about the most elusive of all the diurnal birds of the Yosemite region.

We had always supposed that the rapid series of notes uttered by this species were given only by the adult male and hence constituted a sort of song. But on June 24, 1920, in Yosemite Valley a juvenile male was found, with his head out of a nest hole eight feet above the ground in a dead branch of a live willow, giving every few moments this very series of notes. The large *crown* patch of red on this bird established its age and sex clearly. There was every indication that the notes were being given as a food call.

A pair of Willow Woodpeckers proved to be regular tenants of Curry's apple orchard on the floor of Yosemite Valley. They, or their ancestors, had evidently worked there for some years, with the result that most of the 150 trees in the orchard showed marks of their attention, and many of the trunks were fairly riddled with drillings somewhat like those of the sapsucker. On November 8, 1915, two of us made a study of the site, with the following results.

A measured area 6 inches (15 cm.) square, 4 feet (130 cm.) above ground on a trunk 12½ inches (32 cm.) in diameter contained 17 fresh pits and 30 old ones, of last year's or older digging. These pits (fig. 41) were horizontally elliptical, each about 2.5 by 4 mm. in surface extent, and therefore were distinctly different in size and shape from true sapsucker drillings. They were arranged in irregular horizontal rows with spaces of 6 to 14 mm. between individual pits and 3 to 8 cm. between rows. On this particular trunk, the pits occurred over a vertical distance of 41 inches (105 cm.), so that there were about 2100 pits in all on this one tree. Limbs less than 4 inches (10 cm.) in diameter usually had not been worked upon. However destructive this drilling may seem to be, it does not seriously affect the vitality of the trees; the pits are but 4 to 5 mm. deep, penetrating only those outer layers of the bark which after a time scale off. We should judge that all evidence of this woodpecker's work is thus removed through natural process within about three years. The heartwood of the tree therefore seems not to be damaged at all by the woodpecker's work; it *is* damaged, however, by the work of the true sapsucker.

Fig. 41. Drillings by Willow Woodpecker in outer layers of bark of apple tree in Yosemite Valley. Photographed November 8, 1915; about ½ natural size.

Our inference from these facts is that the Willow Woodpecker feeds on the inner layers of bark, which the bird exposes through the perforations described above. We watched a bird at work; moreover, bits of inner bark-fibers were found adhering to the bristles around the bill of a bird shot.

Nuttall Woodpecker. Dryobates nuttalli (Gambel)

Field characters.—Size small for a woodpecker, little over half that of Modoc Woodpecker. Whole back, wings, sides of body, and outer tail feathers barred or spotted with black and white; throat and breast white, unmarked; head black, with a white stripe above and another below eye; back of head red in adult males. Juvenile birds of both sexes have more or less red on crown of head. Flight course in short swoops or undulations, with intermittent wing strokes. *Voice:* A loud, high-pitched trill.

Occurrence.—Common resident in Lower and Upper Sonoran zones, west of main Sierra Nevada. Recorded from Snelling and Lagrange eastward to El Portal; casual in Yosemite Valley. Frequents oaks, digger pines, and to a lesser extent cottonwoods and willows.

The Nuttall Woodpecker differs in habits from the slightly smaller Willow Woodpecker in that it usually frequents situations far from water, typically those on the upper hill slopes. At Snelling this species was seen only in cottonwoods, probably because these were the only trees there affording it appropriate forage. But at Pleasant Valley, Mount Bullion, and El Portal the birds were in digger pines and blue oaks. On the morning of May 24, during the taking of a five hour census at Pleasant Valley, a dozen were seen. Some of these showed solicitude and were probably nesting in the vicinity. The call of the Nuttall Woodpecker is louder and more sustained than that of the Willow Woodpecker.

The species was noted at the mouth of Indian Cañon in Yosemite Valley throughout almost the entire months of November and December, 1920 (C. W. Michael, MS).

Northern White-headed Woodpecker

Xenopicus albolarvatus albolarvatus (Cassin)

Field characters.—Size somewhat under that of robin. Plumage wholly black, save for entirely white head (pl. 5g) and white area on wing, the latter showing best in flight. Flight course undulating, wing strokes intermittent. *Voice:* Usually a single-syllabled high-pitched note, *wiek;* this note, or a similar one, repeated in short staccato series when bird is excited.

Occurrence.—Common resident in Transition and Canadian zones on west slope of Sierra Nevada. Observed from Sweetwater Creek (near Feliciana Mountain) and Smith Creek (6 miles east of Coulterville) east to Mono Meadow and near North Dome; not common in Yosemite Valley. Forages chiefly on living coniferous trees, but nests in dead stubs, usually less than 12 feet above the ground.

The Northern White-headed Woodpecker is a conspicuous member of the bird population at middle altitudes in the central Sierra Nevada. In certain places in the Yosemite region it is the commonest species of woodpecker. For example, near Chinquapin, on June 13, 1915, 12 of these birds were recorded during the taking of a seven hour census, while only 4 other woodpeckers were seen, each of which represented a different species.

The black body and white head of the White-headed Woodpecker as seen from behind are distinctive. (See pl. 5g.) A side view of the bird when it is clinging to a tree shows a narrow white stripe along the folded wing. When the bird flies this stripe expands, forming an irregular white patch on the middle of the wing. Adult males have a narrow band of red across the back of the otherwise white head, but their mates lack this coloring. In juvenile males the hinder half of the head is more or less solidly red, and even in juvenile females there is usually a little red in the same place. In late summer the feathers on top of the head in adult birds may be so badly worn as to show the white much less clearly.

The White-headed Woodpecker is not so promiscuous in its foraging as are some other species, but gives most of its attention to live coniferous trees. This probably accounts for the fact that the feathers on its throat are almost always besmeared with pitch, whereas those of the Modoc Woodpecker, for instance, which lives in the same timber belt but forages mostly in dead trees, are relatively clean. So far as we could determine the foraging of this bird seems to be a rather haphazard proceeding. A female near Tamarack Flat was watched for a considerable period of time as she hunted over a number of trees. She would prospect one tree for a while, but when it had been gone over only partially, she would go on to inspect a second and then a third, with similar lack of thoroughness; often after examining portions of several trees the bird would return to one or more of those previously visited.

The usual call note of this woodpecker is a single *wiek*, but when excited, the female calls *cheep-eep-eep-eep*, very fast, and repeats the call every few seconds. The male, under similar circumstances calls *yip, yip, yip, yip*, in a much shriller tone, but in slower time.

Because of the striking appearance of the Northern White-headed Woodpecker, and also because no special pains seem to be taken by the birds to conceal their nesting sites, it is an easy matter to locate the nests. In fact, nests of this species proved to be more easily located than those of any other woodpecker in the Yosemite region. For this reason we shall present some remarks upon the activities and ecologic relationships of woodpeckers in general while writing of this species. The matters here discussed may be readily confirmed as to accuracy by anyone who will watch a few pairs of these birds during the nesting season.

To locate occupied nests the enquirer has merely to tap the bases of stubs containing likely looking holes. If he merely passes by an occupied tree, no bird appears, but upon his tapping on the bole, a scratching sound within is followed shortly by the appearance of a white head framed in the entrance of a hole. If the observer remains, the bird flushes and quits the vicinity, but as it flies off one may usually see whether the back of its head bears the red fringe of the male or the plain white of the female. Our own experiences follow in some detail.

The behavior of a pair seen near LeConte Memorial Lodge in Yosemite Valley, on May 31, 1911, quickly led to the finding of a nest in a black oak close at hand. On June 24, 1915, a female bird, flushing at our approach to a dead stub near the east fork of Indian Cañon, disclosed the location of her nest. In May, 1919, when especial attention was paid to the nesting habits of birds, 9 occupied nests of this woodpecker were discovered. Three of these were found at Hazel Green on May 14 and 15, and 6 near Tamarack Flat May 24 to 26.

Of the 10 nests concerning which we have data, the lowest was located only 58 inches (measured) above ground and the highest, 15 feet (estimated). A nest of the Mountain Chickadee occupying what was evidently an old nest of this woodpecker was but 50 inches above the ground. Probably 7 feet would be the average height at which the nests of this species of woodpecker are placed. Dead stubs, either cut or broken off, seem to be the preferred sites for nest holes, for by far the greater number of nests were in such stubs.

No nest holes of this woodpecker were found in living conifers. Nor, on the other hand, do the birds seek what is commonly known as rotten wood, that is, wood too soft for the nest cavity to be maintained against the incessant wear involved in the birds' passage back and forth, incident to the rearing of a brood. The tree chosen must have been dead a sufficient length of time for the pitch to have hardened or to have descended to the base of the tree, and the outer shell of the tree must still be hard and firm, whereas the interior must have been softened to a moderate degree by decay. These conditions are not to be met with in every standing dead stub; hence the choice of a nest site becomes a matter of rather fine discrimination.

As evidence that considerable investigation by these birds precedes the excavation of the nesting hole finally occupied, we found many 'prospects,' varying from shallow pits, conical in form, where a woodpecker had begun excavation only to leave off without even penetrating the outer hard shell of the tree, to those where a bird had entirely completed the laterally directed tunnel into the softer wood within, but had not sunk the shaft which forms the nesting cavity proper. Often we found numerous fresh prospects on the same bole, and sometimes these were close to a newly completed and occupied nest cavity. We were led to conclude from all this that the White-headed Woodpecker is either notional or else very particular, in the selection of its home. Evidence points strongly to the birds excavating and occupying a new cavity each year, although one set of eggs was found in a hole which had been dug in earlier years.

Some stubs are literally riddled with holes, these probably recording successive years of occupancy. One stub had at least 5 fully excavated holes besides 11 or more prospects. Hence it will be seen that the activities of these and other woodpeckers contribute rather directly toward bringing down the standing dead timber. Drilling by woodpeckers results in an increase in the number of entrances through which insects may get at the heart wood of a tree and thus hasten its ultimate disintegration. Water, also, is thus afforded an easier entrance and this hastens decay. Eventually each and every tree must yield its place in the forest to seedlings. The woodpeckers hasten this process of replacement, once the tree is dead.

Many of the woods-inhabiting animals depend upon this woodpecker to furnish them convenient nest holes or retreats. We have found Mountain Chickadees and Slender-billed Nuthatches incubating their own eggs in holes drilled in earlier years by the White-headed Woodpecker; a Sierra Flying Squirrel was found occupying an old White-head's hole. Probably, tree-dwelling chipmunks and perhaps California Pigmy Owls also occupy holes of this woodpecker.

The nesting cavities of the White-headed Woodpecker are gourd-shaped, the entrance tunnel turning downward into a shaft which expands toward the bottom. The internal dimensions vary somewhat, but the size of the entrance hole is surprisingly constant. Also, the symmetry in the outline of the entrance is remarkable when it is recalled that an excavation just begun is often higher than wide and has an irregular margin. One hole, the first one listed below, measured 43 millimeters in four different directions—practically a perfect circle. The accompanying table shows the measurements (in millimeters) of four nests of this species which were studied.

Height of top of opening from the ground	2760	2047	1480	3040*
Vertical diameter of nest entrance	43	47	47	37
Horizontal diameter of nest entrance	43	42	42	37
Top of hole to surface on which eggs or young rested	300	322	275	400
Diameter of shaft	----	112	70–90	100
Thickness of wall in front of shaft	40	105	15–35	65
Number of eggs or young	5	4	5	5

* "10 ft."

Excavating is done by the removal of small chips or splinters, rarely over 25 millimeters in length by 3 or 4 millimeters in diameter. Because of the way in which chips are broken loose, the inside of the nest hole is usually irregular in surface finish. The small detached splinters of wood are, in the case of the White-headed Woodpecker, merely brought out to the entrance and dropped to the ground directly beneath. No attempt is made to keep the nest site concealed. An accumulation of such splinters below a hole is an infallible guide to a newly dug nest. In the case of the nest mentioned later as having been placed in a branch of a fallen black oak, the chips were strewn for a distance of 3 meters on the ground alongside of the prostrate trunk.

Two of the nest cavities we found were in such unusual sites as to call forth comment. One at Hazel Green was in a slantingly upright limb on a prostrate dead black oak trunk lying in a grassy meadow, fully 150 feet from the margin of the forest. The hole was excavated on the lower side of the stub. The other nest was at Tamarack Flat, in the butt end of an old log, lifted above the ground when the tree fell over a granite outcrop. This hole was about 7½ feet above the ground, and as with the other there were piles of chips immediately beneath it.

We were unable to conclude that the nest holes are located with any special regard to direction of exposure to the sun or weather. There seemed to be no rule as to their position with relation to the cardinal points. Probably the availability of appropriate surfaces in which to excavate is much more important in the choice of a site than is the possible protection from the elements.

In one stub was found a nest hole excavated in some previous year, but again occupied for the current season. This same barkless stub showed four weathered prospects. About the margin of the entrance to this nest were many claw marks, which aggregated into trapezoidal patterns, registering the positions of the toes, two up and two down. The tracks were most numerous immediately above the nest, showing that it was the custom of the woodpeckers, when going to the nest, to alight above the hole in the spot indicated and then back down to the entrance.

Eggs of the White-headed Woodpecker are typical of woodpeckers in general, in that they have a white, shiny surface entirely lacking any natural color markings—"immaculate" in the vernacular of the oologist. The eggs in one set had a wrinkled appearance at the smaller end as though that end had been compressed before the shells had hardened. Eggs which are advanced in incubation are apt to be soiled by pitch; this is doubtless brought in by the parent birds on their bills, feet, or plumage. The eggs always rest on a lining of fine chips or rotten wood, and the nest, even after the young are hatched, is maintained in a marked state of cleanliness.

A set of 4 fresh eggs collected at Hazel Green on May 14, 1919, weighed 20.5 grams, and a set of 5 fresh eggs taken the next day weighed 25.3 grams; while a set of 5, 4 of which were advanced in incubation, taken on the 14th, weighed only 20.7 grams. It is thus evident that these eggs lose considerably (15 to 20%) in weight as incubation advances.

We did not arrive within the range of the White-headed Woodpecker early enough in any year to ascertain whether or not both sexes assist in excavating the nest cavity. But after the eggs are laid, the male and female share alike in the duty of incubation. From the same nest hole we have in turn flushed the female and then the male; and in other instances birds of one sex or the other were flushed, in about equal ratio. Furthermore, the two sexes bear structural evidence of their equal share in the duty of incubation. During the nesting period the skin on the surface of the abdomen becomes thickened and underlain with a stratum of spongy, vascular tissue, the whole serving to transmit readily the necessary heat from the parent's body to the eggs beneath.

At Tamarack Flat, on May 26, 1919, a female White-headed Woodpecker was seen to flush from her nest about ten feet above the ground in a dead pine stub. Tapping by one of us on a nearby bole had caused her to leave, but she returned to the vicinity almost immediately. Then, for fully 25 minutes, while the observer remained within watching distance the bird foraged, preened, and flew about from one to another of the circle of 8 or 10 trees within a 50-foot radius of the nest, but always kept the nest tree in her sight. About every 5 minutes she would fly to the nest. In approaching it, she would swoop below its level and then glide up to the site with decreasing speed so as to end her flight with little or no momentum. Then, having gained claw-hold, she would poke the fore part of her body into the hole, withdraw it at once and repeat this performance four or five times before flying away again. Finally, after fully half an hour had elapsed, and her suspicions had been allayed, she went in, to remain. During this entire time the male kept out of sight and was heard only twice.

On another occasion, following the removal of a set of fresh eggs by chopping out the wall in front of the nest, the observer retired some distance, whereupon the male bird came almost at once to the site. He approached the hole from above and to one side, and upon arriving at the place poked his head into the space which marked the position of the entrance hole; but he did not enter the wide open cavity. He seemed to be puzzled at the sudden change in the configuration of his home. The next day he or his mate was seen busily digging a new nest in a stub about 50 yards distant from the first site.

Near the east fork of Indian Cañon, above Yosemite Valley, a nest containing young birds was discovered on June 24, 1915. The female parent flushed at our approach and lingered about the vicinity, uttering two kinds of notes at short intervals. The voices of the young could be heard within the nest tree, and upon investigation we found 5 of them, only a day or two old and still entirely naked. They lay on the nest lining of fine splinters and with them were the shells from which they had hatched, each of which had been cut around the middle.

A White-headed Woodpecker was watched on June 24, 1920, near the village in Yosemite Valley. It was intently searching the trunk of a large cottonwood and picking naked larvae out from under the bark scales of the living tree, now and then whacking off the edge of a bark plate in order better to explore the space underneath.

Stomachs of two adult birds, obtained at Merced Grove Big Trees on June 10, 1915, and at East Fork of Indian Cañon, June 24, 1915, both held ants, some of which were large carpenter ants. The stomach of one of the young birds from the nest mentioned above contained remains of 2 large spiders, a large ant, 2 boring beetles, and a whole fly larva.

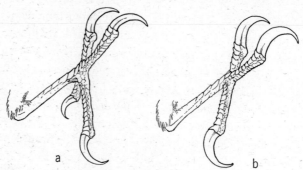

Fig. 42. Feet of (*a*) Northern White-headed Woodpecker, and (*b*) Arctic Three-toed Woodpecker, showing greater size of latter, perhaps compensating for loss of fourth toe. Natural size.

Arctic Three-toed Woodpecker. **Picoides arcticus** (Swainson)

Field characters.—Size somewhat less than that of Robin. Upper surface uniformly black save for golden yellow patch on crown of male (pl. 5*c*); middle of under surface white (sometimes stained tan-color); flanks, sides of body, and under surface of wings barred narrowly with black and white, and outer surface of wings finely spotted with white. (These characters of barring and spotting were confessedly not apparent to us in the field.) *Voice:* A low, single-syllabled note, *pert, week,* or *tup.*

Occurrence.—Sparse resident of Canadian and Hudsonian zones on west slope of Sierra Nevada. Observed at head of Grouse Creek, in basin of Bridal Veil Creek near Mono Meadow, at Lake Tenaya, at Tuolumne Meadows, and at 8600 feet altitude near McGee Lake. Forages chiefly in lodgepole pines.

Like the Great Gray Owl, the Arctic Three-toed Woodpecker is a typically boreal species finding its southern limit of distribution in the central Sierra Nevada. The instances of occurrence cited above are the southernmost now known.

This woodpecker impressed us as being relatively rare. Only twelve individuals were seen or heard in several months of field work in the Canadian and Hudsonian zone forests. Being a quiet bird it may often have been overlooked, and therefore may be actually much more plentiful than our few records indicate. Attention is usually attracted to the birds by the noise they make when drilling.

On June 20, 1915, a nest of this woodpecker was discovered in a dead lodgepole pine which stood less than 10 feet from the bank of Bridal

a

b

c

, e

f

g

h

Woodpeckers of the Yosemite Section (in order, from left to right and top to bottom): *a*. Lewis Woodpecker (in flight and at rest). *b*. California Woodpecker. *c*. Arctic Three-toed Woodpecker. *d*. Sierra Red-breasted Sapsucker. *e*. Willow (Downy) Woodpecker. *f*. Modoc (Hairy) Woodpecker. *g*. Northern White-headed Woodpecker. *h*. Red-shafted Flicker.

Veil Creek and within a hundred yards from the point where that stream is crossed by the Glacier Point road between Peregoy and Mono meadows. The nest was about 50 feet above the ground, and as both parent birds were visiting the site at frequent intervals it likely contained young. One of the adults beat a rolling tattoo on a neighboring dead pine. Two days later, on Mono Meadows, when a tapping sound was followed up, another bird of this species was seen, this time in a red fir. The call note then heard had some of the quality of that of the Hairy Woodpecker, but was far weaker.

A bird collected at the head of Grouse Creek on May 20, 1919, gave evidence that she would have laid within a few days. This, again, would place the time for young in the nest at about mid-June.

While one of our party was traversing the trail from McGee Lake to Lake Tenaya on October 5, 1915, he saw two male Arctic Three-toed Woodpeckers foraging close together on a dead lodgepole pine; a single shot secured the two as specimens. At Tuolumne Meadows at dusk on the evening of July 5, 1915, a male was seen foraging on a lodgepole pine. The bird worked industriously, with a quick succession of strokes, and once was seen to steady itself against the tree by spreading one wing. As it took flight, it uttered a single weak note which reminded the observer of the sound produced in twisting a wet cork out of a bottle.

SIERRA RED-BREASTED SAPSUCKER. **Sphyrapicus varius daggetti** Grinnell

Field characters.—A woodpecker, in size decidedly smaller than robin. Whole head, throat, and breast, rose-red or crimson (pl. 5*d*); back and wings black, spotted with white, rump white; a stripe of white along wing when folded. Whole demeanor of bird very quiet. *Voice* (seldom heard): A single low note, *chürr*, or *cheer-r-r*, burred at end.

Occurrence.—Common in summer in parts of Transition Zone and lower portion of Canadian Zone on west slope of Sierra Nevada; found also at Walker Lake, on the east slope, in same season. Winters in Upper and Lower Sonoran zones on the west side. Seen in Yosemite Valley during fall and early winter months; earliest record, September 16, 1920 (C. W. Michael, MS). Forages in both deciduous and evergreen trees.

Two woodpeckers of a particular type known as Sapsuckers are found in the Yosemite region throughout the year, and a third variety of the same category visits the region during the winter. The subject of the present account, the Sierra Red-breasted Sapsucker, is found in the main forest belt during the spring, summer, and fall, but regularly performs an altitudinal migration which carries it down into the tree growths of the western foothills and valleys for the winter months.

Sapsuckers, of whatever species, seek mainly the juices and to a less extent the softer wood (bast and cambium) of the trees. Hence they work only on living trees, and their relation to the forest is entirely different from that of most other woodpeckers, which forage extensively on dead timber and drill live wood only when in search of boring insects.

The Sierra Red-breasted Sapsucker is in our experience well-nigh voiceless and its work is done in such a quiet manner that it does not ordinarily attract attention, as do the woodpeckers which are wont to pound noisily. The most vigorous drilling of the sapsucker will scarcely be heard more than a hundred feet away. The bird moves its head through a short arc, an inch or two at the most, giving but slight momentum to the blows. The chips cut away are correspondingly small, mere sawdust as compared with the splinters or slabs chiseled off by other woodpeckers. The strokes are delivered in intermittent series, four or five within a second, then a pause of equal duration, then another short series, and so on. From time to time a longer pause ensues, when the sapsucker withdraws its bill and gazes monocularly at the work. The cutting is done first on one side of the little pit and then on the other so that the resulting hole is wide, clear to the bottom, but usually only high enough to easily admit the bill. This shape of hole, exposing a greater breadth of the growing wood through which sap flows, brings the greatest amount of sap with the least expenditure of effort in cutting. The depth of the hole varies with the thickness of the bark, but it always reaches down into the soft growing layer of the wood (fig. 43).

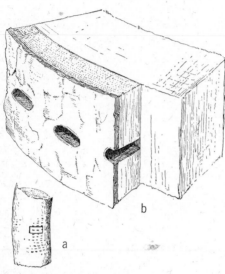

Fig. 43. Diagram of workings of Sierra Red-breasted Sapsucker, showing how the bird drills through the bark to reach (b) the soft growing tissue (cambium) where sap is moving rapidly. Inset figure (a) shows general arrangement of workings on trunk of tree.

Since the location of the drillings is not determined by the presence of any boring insect or larva within the tree, the pits are made in series, in rows transverse to the axis of the trunk or larger limbs; sometimes these series extend nearly around the bole, interrupted only where the bird has been halted by the presence of a branch. Were the holes made one above the other, only the bottom one (or top one, according to the season) would afford any considerable flow of sap; this premise is in part verified by the observation that when a certain tree was drilled repeatedly the newest holes were at the bottom of the series.

Soon after being drilled the holes made by the sapsuckers begin to bleed. The sap flows out and collects in the pits, or runs along in the crevices of the bark. The birds revisit the workings at short intervals, taking the exuded sap and any insects which have been attracted or caught by the sticky juice. Subsequently the drillings may be enlarged, until sometimes they become longitudinal series of flutings or grill work, extending up and down the tree for considerable distances.

The effect of these drillings upon the trees is obvious. Removal of the bark and growing layer of wood causes the trees to lose large quantities of the sap which is essential to growth, and exposes the adjacent parts to attack by fungi and insects. Occasionally the drilling is so continuous around the circumference of a tree as to completely girdle the bark, and thus eventually to cause the death of the tree. But the fact that it is a marked trait of this sapsucker to return again and again to the same tree, even year after year, rather than to seek new forage trees each season, means that only a relatively small number of trees are attacked. In all our field work in the Yosemite region we did not see over a score of trees which showed extensive work by this sapsucker.

The variety of trees worked upon and the seasonal differences in this bird's forage range can best be indicated by citing instances of the work of this species which came to our attention. At Snelling, where the bird is a winter visitant only, old pepper trees (*Schinus molle*) showed numerous drillings, and in the foothills near Pleasant Valley apple trees on the Campbell Ranch had been riddled with holes. At El Portal both digger pines and golden oaks had been drilled, one of the latter trees being heavily pitted on many of its upper branches. Near Sequoia a sugar pine five feet in diameter had an area approximately 3 by 40 feet in extent well grilled by Red-breasted Sapsuckers. Near Sweetwater Creek, a yellow pine had been pitted, and an oak tree showed vertical grillings where sapsuckers had evidently worked for a number of seasons. Several incense cedars were seen which showed abundant work by these sapsuckers. One of these trees at Hazel Green had large deep holes as big as the acorn caches of the California Woodpecker, the size being obviously dictated by the thickness of the cedar bark.

In the apple orchard in Yosemite Valley several trees showed extensive workings, both old and new, of this species, in addition to the less harmful borings by the Willow Woodpecker. Twice we saw 'blazed' scars on pine trees where red-breasted sapsuckers had taken advantage of the thinning of the bark to concentrate their drilling on the small area exposed.

The reason for the vertical migration of the red-breasted sapsucker to lower levels for the winter season is not readily apparent. It may be that the birds are ill adapted to seeking dormant insects during the winter months and so need to descend to lower altitudes where they may find in abundance soft-barked trees from which cambium may be easily obtained. Thus they may tide over the season when there is little or no flow of sap in the forest trees at higher levels.

At Tamarack Flat, on May 24, 1919, a Sierra Red-breasted Sapsucker called from high in a conifer and then flew down to an upstanding stub on a prostrate pine. The bird hopped about on this stub and on small fragments of limbs close to or even upon the ground. It would seem that just after the snow is gone bark foraging species (to which category the sapsucker belongs when not dependent upon sap), finding little forage on tree trunks, seek sustenance near the ground.

No nests of this sapsucker were located by us. A bird taken near Chinquapin on May 21, 1919, judging from the glandular condition of the skin on the abdomen, had already begun incubation; another individual collected near Tamarack Flat on May 25, 1919, was just ready to lay a set of 4 eggs.

Except for the occasional fruit trees attacked during the winter months, we do not believe that the rôle of the red-breasted sapsucker in the central Sierra Nevada is economically important. Its general predilection for deciduous trees and its habit of returning again and again to the same individual tree save the forest as a whole from any serious injury. Certainly the part of this bird in this respect amounts to very much less than the ravages resulting from parasitism by mistletoe, or from attack by insects or by fungous diseases of the bark, wood, or leaves.

RED-NAPED SAPSUCKER. Sphyrapicus varius nuchalis Baird

Field characters.—Similar to Red-breasted Sapsucker but with red color restricted on throat, and replaced on breast by black.

Occurrence.—Winter visitant in small numbers on west slope of Sierra Nevada. Observed in Yosemite Valley near foot of Yosemite Falls, November 19, 1915, and at Cascades, November 24, 1915, one individual in each instance, and two specimens taken 10 miles east of Coulterville, December 12, 1915. Seen foraging on dead pine and incense cedar.

The Red-naped Sapsucker is similar in general appearance and habits to the Red-breasted Sapsucker, and seems, in the central Sierra Nevada, to occupy during the winter season the upper part of the range which the latter species fills in summer. The nearest part of the summer range of the Red-naped Sapsucker is, as far as we know, the Warner Mountains of northeastern California.

WILLIAMSON SAPSUCKER. **Sphyrapicus thyroideus thyroideus** (Cassin)

Field characters.—A woodpecker, in size slightly smaller than robin. Male: Black, with rump and large patch on fore part of wing white. (See pl. 6.) Female: General color tone pale; head light brown, rump white; plumage elsewhere narrowly barred with black and light brown. A bird of notably quiet demeanor. *Voice* (not often heard) : A weak wheezy *whang* or *whether.*

Occurrence.—Common resident of Hudsonian and upper Canadian zones on both slopes of Sierra Nevada. Observed from near Chinquapin eastward to Walker Lake. One record for floor of Yosemite Valley: December 29, 1914. Restricted closely to lodgepole pine belt.

The distribution of the Williamson Sapsucker in the Yosemite region is complementary to that of the Sierra Red-breasted Sapsucker; in other words the two birds do not overlap in range to any important extent. The present species is a high mountain bird, being found only in the upper Canadian and the Hudsonian life zones. It is non-migratory; only rarely is an individual detected in lower zones and then only during the midwinter months. The Williamson Sapsucker is, like its relative of lower altitudes, a quiet bird, rarely uttering its weak note, and never, so far as known to us, drumming in the noisy manner so characteristic of certain other woodpeckers.

Of all species of North American woodpeckers, the Williamson Sapsucker is the most remarkable because of the striking differences in plumage between males and females, and between adults and young. (See pl. 6.) The only color mark of the species common to both sexes, at all ages, is the white rump. Otherwise, males are chiefly black, with a large white patch on the fore part of the wing (and not across the flight feathers as in the California and White-headed woodpeckers). There is also a white stripe backward from the bill across the cheek, and another behind the eye. The black of the adult male plumage has a slight greenish iridescence, while that of the young male is more sooty and of a softer texture. The young have the chin white, this white being replaced by red in the adult plumage.

Females are entirely different. They are narrowly barred with black and light brown or white on the back, wings, sides of body and tail, and the head is uniformly light brown. Old adult females have a spot of solid black on the breast, which the younger birds lack. Adults of both sexes have the middle of the belly bright yellow, whereas in the young of either sex this area is chiefly white. Thus, in each sex, the young is most nearly like the adult of that sex: the young male does not at all resemble the adult female, a condition contrary to rule among other birds the adults of which are of different coloration. Young males acquire the adult plumage, even to the red chin spot, at the first fall molt, and by mid September are in fine feather. Young females acquire most of the adult characters at this same molt save perhaps the black breast spot. The marked differences in plumage between the two sexes in this sapsucker led the early naturalists, in the fifties, to designate the male and female as separate species, and they were so considered until 1874; one author, at least, went so far as to place them in separate genera!

In the Yosemite region the Williamson Sapsucker is closely associated with the lodgepole pine. While this tree seems to furnish the bird's preferred source of forage, practically all other species of trees within its local range are also utilized. We saw workings attributable to this sapsucker on the alpine hemlock, red and white firs, Jeffrey pine, and quaking aspen.

Fig. 44. Close view of fresh work of Williamson Sapsucker on lodgepole pine. Photographed at Porcupine Flat, July 1, 1915; about ⅛ natural size.

The amount of work which this sapsucker will do upon a single tree was impressed upon us while we were at Porcupine Flat in early July, 1915. In that locality there was a lodgepole pine (*Pinus murrayana*) about 60 feet high, which showed no marks of sapsucker work previous to the current year. The tree was in full leafy vigor and measured 8 feet 3¼ inches in girth at 3 feet above the ground. There were numerous live branches down to within 6 feet of the ground. Twenty-six irregularly horizontal rows of fresh punctures were counted on one side of the trunk, the lowest being only 18½ inches above the ground, and the highest about 40 feet. (Part of one series is shown in fig. 44.) No one row of pits completely encircled the tree; a branch had in every instance interfered with the bird's completing the row at that level. But opposite the end of any row, from 1 to 4 inches up or down the trunk, there was the beginning of a complementary row, showing where the sapsucker after ascending to clear its tail or descending to clear its head of the obstructing branch, had continued puncturing in the sidewise direction. Up and down the tree the rows of punctures were from 3 to 24 inches apart. The horizontal length of one series of pits 6 feet above the ground was 35 inches; of

another close by, 44 inches. Individual punctures in a row were 0.4 to
0.6 inches (10 to 15 mm.) apart. Three typical fresh punctures all measured 0.16 inches (4 mm.) high, with respective widths of 0.2, 0.37, and
0.4 inches (5, 9, and 10 mm.). The nearly constant vertical dimension,
just as in the case of the drillings of the Red-breasted Sapsucker, was
probably due to the size of the bird's bill, while the varying horizontal
dimension resulted from varying amounts of work done in the individual
pits. Many of the holes were bleeding and probably would have been
visited again and again by the sapsucker. Earlier drillings of the current
season had stalactite-like streamers of hardened pitch below them, some
being 2 feet in length.

In addition to the exudation of sap, these series of puncturings cause
responsive growth action on the part of the tree. Rings or swellings in
the wood and bark develop at the sites of the punctures. A tree drilled
to the extent of the one described above would in a few years show a series
of swollen rings, one at each
line of punctures (fig. 45). And
the site of each individual puncture develops into a small knot-
like growth. A dead lodgepole
pine at Aspen Valley showed
clearly that it had been drilled
extensively in earlier years; for
the dead and partly barkless
bole was little more than a succession of swollen rings. Many
trees exhibiting intermediate
stages in this scar-like affliction
were observed.

During the winter months
when sap is practically at a
standstill in the coniferous trees
at high altitudes, the Williamson Sapsucker must needs seek
other fare. A few of our own
observations added to those of
other naturalists suggest that

Fig. 45. Result of work of Williamson Sap-
sucker on bark and trunk of old lodgepole pine.
Photographed at Porcupine Flat, July 1, 1915.
See discussion in text.

during the winter season the birds may forage in large part on dormant
insects or on insect larvae hidden in crevices in the bark. If such is the
case, whatever the damage done by these birds to the forest as a whole
during the summer months, it is partially offset by their winter-time
activity. In any event, the attacks of the Williamson Sapsucker on the

lodgepole pines of the central Sierra Nevada cannot be considered as of great economic importance, for these trees are there used little if at all for lumber or for any other commercial purpose.

Several points of importance in regard to the economic bearing of sapsuckers in California remain to be worked out satisfactorily. A prime need is definite knowledge as to the real nature of their food—whether sap, inner bark, growing wood, or insects; and if all of these, the proportion of each in the diet for the entire year.

Several instances of the nesting of Williamson Sapsuckers came to our attention. At Mono Meadow on June 20, 1915, a nest was located 16 feet up in a partly dead lodgepole pine. The tapping of the bole of the tree brought forth a chorus of cries from the young birds within. Two days later, at Peregoy Meadow, an adult was seen carrying ants in its bill, probably on the way to feed its brood. At Tuolumne Meadows on July 13, 1915, another nest was discovered about 20 feet above the ground in a dead lodgepole pine. As the observer stood watching the site the female sapsucker swooped past him and alighted on the trunk of the tree above the nest hole. Then she backed down and clung in front of the hole. The notes of the young increased in volume as the mother bird put her bill, laden with ants, through the entrance. It would seem that wood ants are important as an article of diet for the young, at least while they are in the nest. The marked trait of adults of this species, to go directly to the nest hole when feeding the young and not to approach indirectly, as do so many birds, makes the discovery of nests relatively easy.

NORTHERN PILEATED WOODPECKER. **Phloeotomus pileatus abieticola** (Bangs)

Field characters.—Much the largest of our woodpeckers (length over 17 inches). Body plumage black; a brilliant red crest on head (fig. 46); a large white area on forward part of under surface of wing; a smaller spot of white on middle of outer surface of wing. Flies usually in direct course, sometimes in great undulations, with rather slow and regular wing beats. *Voice:* A loud but low-pitched note, *kuk*, uttered a varying number of times in rather slow and irregular succession.

Occurrence.—Common resident in Transition Zone and lower part of Canadian Zone on west slope of Sierra Nevada. Observed near Feliciana Mountain and 6 miles east of Coulterville, and thence eastward to Mono Meadow (7300 feet altitude), and to Little Yosemite Valley at 6200 feet. Seen in Yosemite Valley at all seasons of the year. Lives chiefly in white fir woods.

The Northern Pileated Woodpecker has been aptly called Cock-of-the-woods, for it is by far the largest woodpecker within our region. It is exceeded in size and in loudness of voice by but few of all the forest birds. In general, the range of this species closely duplicates that of the fir trees, in recognition of which fact, it was called *abieticola* (fir-inhabiting). In the Yosemite region the bird is found chiefly in the belt of forest characterized by the presence of the white fir (*Abies concolor*).

Williamson Sapsuckers.

Family group: Adult male at top, immature males in hole and at bottom, adult female
at left with food, immature female at right on trunk of tree.

The pileated woodpecker is conspicuous either in flight or when perched. When a bird is at rest or working on the side of a dead stub, its brilliant red crest can generally be seen plainly. In the female the forehead is blackish, while in the male the red covers the whole top of the head, forward to the bill. The latter sex has, in addition, a narrow red streak extending backward from the side of the bill along each cheek. The neck of this woodpecker is much longer and relatively more slender than that of other species, and this impression of slenderness is enhanced by the streak of white which extends down each side from the cheek to the side of the body; otherwise the plumage of the resting bird appears solidly black. When it takes to flight a large white area shows forth, intermittently, on the forward part of the under surface of the spread wing, and on the adjacent side of the body; a smaller patch of white is to be seen as well on the middle of the upper surface of the wing.

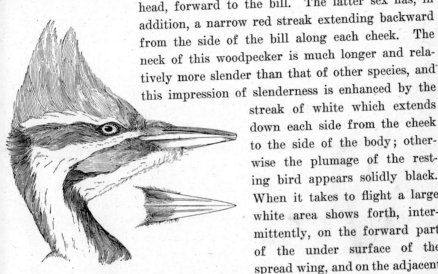

Fig. 46. Head of Northern Pileated Woodpecker showing stout ridged bill, ''mask'' to keep dust from rotten wood out of nostrils, prominent crest, and slender neck. One-half natural size.

The call or alarm note of the pileated woodpecker is a single-syllabled, low-pitched but loud *kuk, kuk, kuk,* etc., uttered in series, at intervals of a half-second or more, depending upon whether the bird is in flight or perched. Sometimes, when a bird is pursuing a long direct course, its notes will be heard from the time it first comes into view until it passes out of hearing in the opposite direction. The call resembles one of the notes of the Red-shafted Flicker, although it is not so high-pitched.

This bird's flight is quite different from that of our other woodpeckers. It ordinarily pursues a direct course, with wings beating continuously though slowly, in a manner resembling the monoplane-like flight of a magpie. Its head meanwhile is drawn in, somewhat after the manner of a heron.

While one of our party was traversing the Glacier Point road near Mono Meadow on the morning of June 13, 1915, he heard a loud pounding which he at first thought might be the noise made by a lineman in repairing the broken-down telephone wire along the road. The racket was followed up—and the observer came upon a pileated woodpecker foraging on a white fir stub. The bird delivered 3 to 8 vigorous blows in rather slow succession, and repeated the series about 4 times a minute. The bird would draw its head far back, so as to move it through an arc fully 8 inches in length and the combination of long neck, heavy head, and stout sharp bill (fig. 46) made for results. With every few series of strokes a large flake of dead bark would fall to the ground with a clatter. Other birds, working with similar industry, have been seen to throw chips fully 2 feet backward as they chiseled off the dead wood.

Another pileated woodpecker was observed working diligently on a dead yellow pine in Yosemite Valley on December 24, 1914. After every few taps the bird would stop and look about intently, thus bearing out the impression of its wariness we had gained elsewhere. It rapidly gouged away the dead pine wood, in long splinters, and often used its strong bill as a pry to give the final loosening touch to a particularly large chunk around which it had chiseled. The noise made, as the bird delivered a blow with all the force in its long neck and powerful body, was as loud as that made by a carpenter when hitting a nail. When two birds are working in the same vicinity the resulting noise is considerable. A pair drilling near Yosemite Point on June 4, 1915, produced tones about an octave apart, evidently due to differences in the wood upon which they were working.

The total amount of excavation done by these birds is surprising. Many dead fir stubs seen near Aspen Valley were literally riddled with surface cavities, some of which were large enough to admit a man's fist. Sometimes great vertical troughs had been dug in the sides of these dead and rotting trees. One such trough measured had a total volume of about 1040 cubic inches. Since no evidence was found of work on living timber, we do not believe that the birds work on any wood that is not dead and populated with insect larvae or ants.

Examination of the stomach contents of two pileated woodpeckers taken at Aspen Valley, October 16, 1915, and Sweetwater Creek, near Feliciana Mountain, October 30, 1915, showed each to contain more than a hundred carpenter ants (*Camponotus herculaneus modoc*). In addition one contained a whole manzanita fruit (*Arctostaphylos* sp.) and the other, 4 large beetle larvae (Cerambycidae) evidently dug out of some dead tree, for the stomach contained also slivers of dead wood (H. C. Bryant, 1916, p. 32).

The Northern Pileated Woodpecker sometimes departs widely from its usual diet of beetle larvae and ants. For instance, on Sweetwater Creek, near Feliciana Mountain, in late October, one was seen feeding on the ripened fruits of the Nuttall dogwood. Because the terminal branchlets which bear the fruit are small and slender, the big bird was forced to hang inverted, chickadee-like, except when the clusters could

e reached from a main branch. When suspended on a swaying stem
he bird would peck at the fruits in the same manner, and apparently
vith as much energy, as when digging into a dead fir stub. Its changes
of position, made after one fruit cluster had been consumed and it sought
another, were accompanied by much flapping of wings and shaking of
branches, and usually by the loud *kuk, kuk* calls. These calls seemed to
be given with the bill closed or at most only slightly opened.

It does not seem likely that the work of the pileated woodpecker, large
as it must be in total quantity, is in any serious way detrimental to the
forest. On the other hand, the birds are probably of material aid in felling
dead timber that would otherwise continue to occupy a place in the forest,
to the discouragement of younger, growing trees.

Two nest sites were seen by us. Near Yosemite Point on June 4, 1915,
two or three holes, of the size for a pileated woodpecker, were located about
twenty feet above the ground in a huge dead and rotting fir. Two birds
were about and seemed attached to the locality. In Aspen Valley, at dusk
on the evening of October 16, 1915, a bird of this species was seen to enter
a nest hole about forty feet up in a dead white fir stub. This instance
would suggest that these birds may make use of old nesting holes as night
shelters during the winter months.

CALIFORNIA WOODPECKER. **Melanerpes formicivorus bairdi** Ridgway

Field characters.—Of medium size for a woodpecker, near that of robin. Conspicuously pied with black and white; patch on wing showing conspicuously in flight, broad
bar across forehead, rump, and belly, white; throat yellowish white; black of chest
broken into streaks toward belly; conspicuous red patch on top of head; iris of eye white.
(See pl. 5b.) Sexes alike save that in female the red crown patch is smaller, being
separated by a black interval from white bar on forehead. Movements typically woodpecker-like. Flight undulating to a degree; a short series of strong flaps, then a deep
sweep on set wings. *Voice:* A nasal *yá-kup, yá-kup, yá-kup;* or *krrá-ka, krrá-ka,* the
r's rolled.

Occurrence.—Most numerous in, and characteristic of, the Upper Sonoran Zone;
present also down along the Merced River, following the bordering strips of valley
oaks out into the Lower Sonoran San Joaquin Valley, as around Snelling; ranges upward
locally into Transition Zone, the highest stations being near Coulterville, at 3500 feet,
and near Columbia Rock, at 5200 feet, in Yosemite Valley. Apparently resident
throughout the year wherever it occurs at all.

The California Woodpecker is emphatically an inhabitant of oaks, more
so indeed than any other species. While foraging sporadically into cottonwoods and conifers, individuals may be almost always traced to headquarters among oak trees of one kind or another. This quercine attraction
is evidently due to the bird's constitutional hankering for acorns as a
staple article of diet. To tide over the annual period of famine in this

particular food source, the California Woodpeckers show high development of the storing habit. In late summer and autumn their industry in gathering and snugly stowing away acorns according to their own peculiar method is perhaps second only to that of the Gray Squirrels. The results of this industry are well advertised, because of the birds' habit of ensconcing each acorn separately in a hole in the surface of a tree trunk, bored accurately to a size to fit. These acorn holes are close set over the surface of the bark, sometimes from within 2 feet of the ground to a height of 75 feet or more. The tree or trees selected by a pair of California Woodpeckers for storage purposes may not be of any species of oak at all. On the floor of Yosemite Valley, ancient, partly dead incense cedars more often, perhaps, than any other tree, show this woodpecker's work. When the acorns have been removed the trunk of the tree is left with a curious pitted appearance as if it had served repeatedly as a target for a large-bore rifle.

On November 5, 1915, along the road below the foot of Yosemite Falls Trail, an old woodpeckered, dead-topped cedar trunk was studied, with the following results (Grinnell, MS). The acorn pits began about 3 feet above the ground and extended to a height of about 45 feet. The circumferences of the trunk at these two limits were, respectively, 15 feet and 9 feet. The pits were pretty evenly distributed all around the trunk; from a series of measurements it was estimated that they averaged 5 inches apart, between centers, all over the surface. This would make 2360 pits on this one trunk. The pits averaged 20 millimeters in diameter by 30 in depth, so they were evidently planned (and doubtless used though now empty) for the fat acorns of the golden oak. This is of interest, as the oaks immediately about were black oaks, which bear much smaller nuts, the nearest golden oaks being about 200 yards away at the base of the talus to the north.

In one large living yellow pine near Camp Ahwahnee in Yosemite Valley which had been very closely pitted, especially on the north side of the trunk, it was estimated that there was an average of 30 acorn holes a square foot placed all the way from 3 to 40 feet above the ground, and that there was a total of 10,500 holes in this one tree! Only the outer layers of the bark were penetrated by the holes, so that no damage appeared to have been done to the growing wood of the tree. In fact, the regular scaling off of bark would probably eliminate the holes altogether within a few years were they not continually deepened or renewed by the birds.

As far as observation goes, only one acorn is carried by one bird at a time. We may well marvel at the ingenuity displayed in the excavation of the holes, always to a diameter to admit of but a tight fit. The holes, too, are just deep enough to bring the butt of the acorn flush with the bark surface—just about 'bill-deep' for this woodpecker. As a usual thing it is impossible to take out, with the fingers, an acorn from its pit, both because of the smooth, elusive surface of the nut and because of its having been forcibly wedged into its socket. There is a great range in the size of the acorns of different species of oaks, from the small slender ones of the interior live oak to the relatively huge ones of the golden oak. Acorns of all sizes are utilized by the birds in the different zones; so that, all in all, an astonishingly acute faculty of adaptation must be credited to the California Woodpecker.

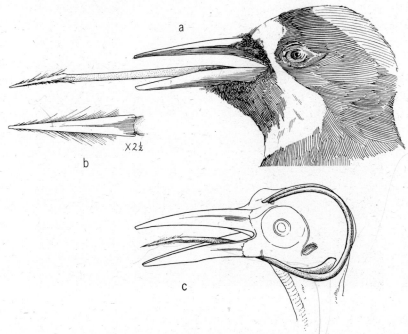

Fig. 47. Head and tongue (*a*) of California Woodpecker, showing general structure of tongue with backward-pointing brush at tip (*b*) and long insertion of base of tongue (*c*) around back of skull. The muscular arrangement within the sheath enclosing the tongue permits the latter to be protruded (as shown in *a*) when the woodpecker is pulling a grub out of a recess in the wood. Natural size.

Near Pleasant Valley, fence posts were riddled with holes (fig. 48*a*), many of which, on May 28, 1915, contained acorns of the previous autumn's crop. Some of these were so loose as to be easily withdrawn, while others were wedged tight. All examined had been inserted point foremost. In some holes only open shells remained, as if the birds had eaten the meat from the nuts without removing them, by breaking them open at the base. Some of the nuts were wormy, probably not a particular misfortune to the birds provided they were not too late for either worm or mast.

Two stomachs of California Woodpeckers shot contained only pieces of shelled acorn, ants, and gravel. At El Portal, in December, a pair of

California Woodpeckers was found to regularly visit the fresh, bleeding borings of a red-breasted sapsucker in a golden oak—evidently sponging on their industrious neighbor.

a   *b*

Fig. 48.   (*a*) Fence-post studded with acorns of blue oak, storage method of the California Woodpecker. Photographed near Pleasant Valley, February 27, 1916.   (*b*) Lewis Woodpecker at nest site in stub of Jeffrey pine. Photographed at Walker Lake, June 26, 1916.

In Yosemite Valley, these woodpeckers were observed during all our visits, winter and summer, in seemingly unvarying though not large numbers. Some days, however, they were very quiet, and might easily be overlooked in one entire morning's census; at other times their nasal chatter sounded almost continually, especially from along the north side of the Valley from the Royal Arches west to below Rocky Point. Often a pair or more made excursions from tree to tree through the cottonwoods around Sentinel Meadow, where they occasionally exhibited the trait of flycatching common to several species of this family. Launching out from a prominent tree top with vigorous wing-beats to waylay a passing insect, they would return in a wide sweep to the starting point. It is not to be inferred from the acorn-storing habit dwelt upon above that insects form an unimportant element in the bird's food. On the contrary, like the other woodpeckers, the California Woodpecker does a great amount of bark foraging, though it does show a decided aversion to *pitchy* conifers.

When alighting on a tree trunk, these birds assume a vertical posture, head out, tail appressed to the bark. They move up by a hitching process —head in, tail out; up; tail in, head out. If a bird perches on a small horizontal branch, his position is more likely to be diagonal than directly crosswise. If a bird alights on the square top of a fence post, he seems ill at ease and soon backs over the edge into a more woodpecker-like posture.

Nest holes about 30 feet above the ground were noted in each of two long-dead and barkless yellow pine stubs standing at the foot of the valley wall back of Yosemite Falls Camp. Individual birds used these for roosting places at night in December, 1914, only one bird occupying each hole. Near Pleasant Valley, May 24, 1915, a nest hole 10 feet above the ground in the trunk of a blue oak held squealing young.

The more intensive occupancy of the Yosemite Valley during recent years and the operations of the government employees in promptly removing dead but standing trees to be cut up for wood has operated to the detriment of the woodpeckers which seek such trees for nesting holes. So it was no surprise, in May, 1919, to find a number of telephone or electric power poles near Redwood Lane which had been prospected for nesting sites by woodpeckers—the California, to judge from the size of hole and general location. Dearth of suitable natural sites had forced the birds to at least investigate these newly established dead-tree substitutes. With no substitutes at all available, the only result to be logically looked for, as a result of man's interference with the natural order of affairs, would be the disappearance of woodpeckers. The question arises here as to the justification of the administration in so altering natural conditions in National Parks as to threaten the persistence there of any of its native denizens.

LEWIS WOODPECKER. **Asyndesmus lewisi** Riley

Field characters.—Size little larger than robin; wings long. Back and head black-appearing; belly pale red; breast and collar around neck hoary white. (See pl. 5a.) No white on wings, tail or rump. Flight nearly direct, with continuously beating wings.

Occurrence.—Irregular, both seasonally and zonally. Stations and dates of record are: Snelling, May 26, 1915; Lagrange, December 15, 1915; Pleasant Valley, May 22 and 24, and December 4, 1915; Goffs, December 12, 1914; above Ten Lakes, October 11, 1915; Walker Lake, May 9 and June 24, 1916; near Williams Butte, September 23, 1915; and Mono Mills, June 8, 1916. Recorded in Yosemite Valley, September 22, 1917 (Mailliard, 1918, p. 18) and September 8 to 13 and 22, 1920 (C. W. Michael, MS). Frequents scattered timber.

The Lewis Woodpecker is a wanderer, and is likely to be seen sometime or another at almost any place in the Yosemite section. It seems to have no preference for any one type of country, save that it avoids the heavier forests; it was apparently as much at home in the blue oaks around Pleasant Valley as in the Jeffrey pines at Walker Lake.

The manner of flight of the Lewis is different from that of all other woodpeckers with which we are familiar. The long wings beat almost continuously, in crow fashion, and the course through the air is nearly direct. These peculiarities in movement together with the black back, wings, and tail, the pinkish cast of the plumage beneath, and the absence of clear white areas, large or small, anywhere on the bird, are the best field marks. (See pl. 5*a*.)

On May 24, 1915, about 8 of these birds were seen at Pleasant Valley, but they gave no indications that they were nesting. On December 15, 1915, at Lagrange, the species was locally common, about 20 being seen in a two hour census. Mr. Charles W. Michael (MS) saw at least 5 daily below the village in Yosemite Valley from September 8 to 13, 1920. The birds were often active in an apple tree there. At Walker Lake, a pair had its nest in a dead pine stub (fig. 48*b*). The young were being fed in this nest on June 24, 1916.

RED-SHAFTED FLICKER. **Colaptes cafer collaris** Vigors

Field characters.—Larger than robin; of woodpecker structure and general habits, save that it does much of its foraging on the ground. In flight shows large white rump patch and flash of dull red from wings and tail. (See pl. 5*h*.) General color above brownish, with narrow bars of black; beneath grayish with numerous sharp polka dots of black and a black crescentic bar across breast. Males have bright red patches at corners of mouth. Flight strong and direct, with quick but infrequent wing-beats. *Voice:* Varied; the most usual note a loud, explosive *claip;* in spring and early summer, a loud rolling *kuk-kuk-kuk-kuk,* etc., repeated at length on one pitch and hence of monotonous though reverberating quality. When two flickers meet, either one, or both, utter a *yuck'-a-yuck'-a-yuck'-a,* or *wee'-chuck, wee'-chuck, wee'-chuck,* reminding one of the sound produced in whetting a scythe. Occasionally drums a rolling tattoo with bill on resonant wood.

Occurrence.—Widely distributed apparently without regard for zonal boundaries; in summer and fall up to timber line, as at 10,200 feet near Parsons Peak, 10,500 feet in Mono Pass, and 10,600 feet, in the pass at the head of Warren Fork of Leevining Creek. Very probably nests from near these limits down throughout all the forested country to the bed of the San Joaquin Valley. Occupied nesting holes in tree trunks, young just out of nest, or adults feeding young, observed at Snelling, near Lagrange, at Pleasant Valley, Buckhorn Peak, Merced Grove, Yosemite Valley, and Farrington's Ranch near Mono Lake. In winter, descends to the region below the level of heavy snows. Highest winter stations: 5100 feet, near Columbia Point, and 4200 feet, in Tenaya Cañon two miles above Mirror Lake.

The tramper in almost any part of the Yosemite region can hardly fail to at least hear one or more Red-shafted Flickers in a half-day's circuit. Although these birds are never seen in true flocks, he may flush from favorable places as many as 6 of them within a few yards. This is paricularly true on the floor of Yosemite Valley during the autumn months. This omnivorous woodpecker then almost completely forsakes the timber and forages in the brush patches, eating berries of various sorts, especially cascara; it often seeks the open meadows where it gathers ants and grasshoppers.

The birds flush one or two at a time, often not until the observer is almost upon them; then the sudden flapping of broad pinkish-red wings, the view of the white rump patch fully displayed, leave no doubt in the observer's mind as to the identity. A bird seldom flies far before alighting, not against an upright tree trunk as with most other woodpeckers, but perching on a branch, to bow deeply this way and that and perhaps utter its explosive *claip.*

In a dead upright stub of a black oak near Stoneman Bridge, in Yosemite Valley, a nest of the Red-shafted Flicker was seen on May 17, 1919. The male bird was foraging actively in the near vicinity and was seen to return to the nest hole, his bill laden with insects for the young. The nest hole was about 25 feet above the ground.

At Coulterville on June 7, 1915, two members of our party engaged in a search for bats in the attics of the larger buildings in town. In one building a persistent series of fine, high-pitched notes was heard for some time and believed to be made by bats, but when we actually located the source it proved to be a brood of quite young Red-shafted Flickers in a nest near the cornice of the building. The young were lodged on a crosspiece in the wall, and an entrance hole, 2 inches or more in diameter, had been cut in one of the boards of the outer wall.

POOR-WILLS. **Phalaenoptilus nuttalli** (Audubon)[19]

Field characters.—Body size appears nearly that of robin, but tail shorter and legs and feet much smaller; head broad; bill small; eyes large. Throat and band at end of tail below, pure white; rest of plumage a variegated yet blended pattern of black, gray and dark and light browns (pl. 43*b*); feathers soft, owl-like. Flight, erratic and silent, usually close over ground or brush; squats on ground when at rest. *Voice:* A mellow yet far-carrying *poor-will-o*, repeated. Also a soft *quirt*, uttered mostly in flight.

Occurrence.—Moderately common summer visitant both east and west of the high Sierra Nevada.[19] Life zone, Upper Sonoran on the western side, Transition on the eastern. Rests on ground in shelter of chaparral during daytime, foraging abroad at dusk and during night.

[19] The Poor-wills at Snelling, Pleasant Valley, Smith Creek, and other west-slope localities belong to a dark-colored subspecies known as *Phalaenoptilus nuttalli californicus* Ridgway, the Dusky Poor-will, which ranges through the central valleys and southern coast region of California; while the birds at Walker Lake, Williams Butte, Mono Lake Post Office and on Negit Island belong to a paler, and slightly larger, Great Basin form called *Phalaenoptilus nuttalli nuttalli* (Audubon), the Nuttall Poor-will. Individuals belonging to these two races cannot be distinguished except in hand, but in the Yosemite region neither race is known to invade the range of the other at any season. They are separated by the high Sierras.

Poor-wills are essentially birds of the night. Along with nighthawk and bats they replace the swallows, swifts, flycatchers, and other birds that feed upon flying insects during the daytime. Soon after sundown of the long summer days the notes of the poor-will are to be heard coming from the grease-wood or sagebrush-covered slopes of the hills, and a little later the birds themselves begin to take wing low over the chaparral or grass-lands in search of their food.

Poor-wills are adapted in many ways for their night-time activities. Their eyes are large, suggesting those of owls. The mouth is broad, extending across the whole width of the head and, when open, forms, with the row of outstanding bristles on either side, a gaping trap into which flying insects can easily be scooped. Their plumage is soft, if anything even more so than that of owls, and so their flight is noiseless, seemingly a necessity in night-foraging birds in general. The wings of the poor-will are relatively long but rounded in outline at their ends, like those of the ground owl. The mottled color pattern of the plumage (pl. 43b) blends well with almost any broken surface, such as gravelly ground, on which the birds may chance to rest, and this may be helpful to them during the daylight hours in making them less easily seen by their enemies when they are resting or sleeping. Certainly the human observer finds difficulty enough in detecting the presence of one of these birds on the ground so long as it remains quiet.

Poor-wills do not usually begin to forage until late dusk, being even more nocturnal in this respect than nighthawks; nor are they seen abroad in the morning as late as are those birds. On the evening of May 20, 1915, at Pleasant Valley, as one of our party was riding along the Baxter Road which winds uphill through the greasewood (Adenostoma), several Dusky Poor-wills were seen along the margin of the chaparral. At the approach of the horse the nearest bird would rise a few feet above the ground, fly a short distance up the road, and then settle down close to the roadway, only to start up again erratically when further disturbed. These birds are active through at least the early hours of the night; for on August 18, 1915, one was heard calling from near Cathedral Spires, in Yosemite Valley, between 9 and 10 o'clock at night.

As regards occurrence in the Yosemite Valley, this last record was made in the season when poor-wills are known to range up the mountains into the lower part of the Transition Zone, where they do not ordinarily occur earlier in the year. We have the statement by Mr. W. O. Emerson (1893, p. 179), however, that the notes of a California Poor-will could be heard "high up on the cliffs above the valley" between June 20 and 25, 1893.

The usual forage range of the poor-will is close to the ground or brush, being thus quite different from that of the high-flying nighthawks. And while actively foraging, the birds pause from time to time and come to rest on the ground or a convenient rock. Indeed they spend much more than half of their forage time at rest. At Mono Lake near the mouth of Rush Creek, on June 3, 1916, three Nuttall Poor-wills were seen foraging on moths about a poplar tree. The birds would fly up and hover about the lower foliage and make short dabs at the insects. At this station the poor-wills were seen to alight lengthwise on old logs rather than on the ground itself.

The mellow two or three-part call of the poor-will is given irregularly, sometimes at long intervals, again in rapid succession. It is heard most persistently at dusk of evening or in the early morning; but near Pleasant Valley on the morning of May 23, 1915, one of these birds suddenly broke out at 10 o'clock and uttered its *poor-will'-o* 85 times (by count, within 2 or 3) at intervals of two or three seconds. At a distance the third syllable may become inaudible.

Near Williams Butte on June 21, 1916, an adult Nuttall Poor-will was captured alive. Next day the bird was taken out in the open, but seemed reluctant to move. It would sit still for a long time, then suddenly fly a hundred yards or so and alight once more. When disturbed it would spread out its tail and wings, open its cavernous mouth, and emit a hissing sound. Altogether the performance recalled the behavior of a rattlesnake when cornered. The bird objected very much to facing the direct sunlight and usually, after a flight, alighted in a shady spot. When forced to sit in the sun it kept its eyes closed most of the time.

A nesting site of the Dusky Poor-will was found near the head of Smith Creek on August 6, 1920. It was on a cleared side-hill where grew scattering plants of 'mountain misery' and brakes. As the neighborhood was approached an adult bird took wing and alighted on a burnt log near by. Search was rewarded by the discovery of 2 half-grown young birds which were lying side to side on the bare ground both facing in the same direction with eyes closed and wings held apart as if to secure coolness. They were in the partial shade of some brakes about 15 inches high. When the young birds were touched they instantly assumed a fighting attitude and struck out, with their mouths wide open, at the same time giving a peculiar hissing note. A space about 5½ feet in diameter in front of the place where the birds were resting was completely cleared of loose material; it had evidently been used by both old and young as a 'take-off' when leaping to capture passing insects.

Bill --
Feet

PACIFIC NIGHTHAWK. **Chordeiles virginianus hesperis** Grinnell

Field characters.—Body size that of robin, but with much longer and more slender wings; these when closed reach to end of tail or beyond. Similar to poor-will in many respects. Chin and narrow band across middle of longer wing feathers, white; rest of plumage barred or spotted with brown, gray, black, and white, in mixed pattern, giving a neutral effect. Flight erratic, with many quick turnings. *Voice:* A one- or two-syllabled note, *zee-nt*, or *pee'-ark*.

Occurrence.—Summer visitant in small numbers to higher open country (Canadian and Hudsonian zones on west slope, and Transition east of Sierran crest). Observed in 1915 at Merced Lake August 25; Vogelsang Lake August 30; Tuolumne Meadows July 5, 7, and 27; and at Williams Butte September 15; Paoha Island, Mono Lake, July 3, 1916; and on ridge 3 miles east of Coulterville, August 9 and 11, 1920. Reported in Yosemite Valley June 28 and 29 and August 24, 1920. Active chiefly in evening and morning; forages high in the air. Spends most of daytime resting lengthwise on large horizontal limbs of trees.

The Pacific Nighthawk is a summer visitant to the higher parts of the Yosemite region. It begins its forays for insects at sundown or soon after and continues its activity well into or through the hours of complete darkness. In July, when the young probably have hatched out, the adult birds forage in the daytime as well. For instance 2 or more were seen abroad foraging over Tuolumne Meadows about 9:30 on the morning of July 27, 1915.

The nighthawk is provided with a wide gaping mouth which enables it to capture flying insects with facility; the long and narrow wings and tail enable the bird to fly rapidly and to turn quickly when in pursuit of moths, flying ants, or other insects which frequent the upper air.

From time to time a Pacific Nighthawk while flying at a considerable height will suddenly drop into an abruptly downward swing with wings held above the back in V-shape. As the bird checks its flight and darts upward, a rushing noise is heard, resembling the syllable 'whoof.' Whether or not this is produced by the wings we do not know.

At Williams Butte on September 15, 1915, 5 nighthawks were seen in flight high overheard about 4:15 P.M.; these were probably in migration, as none was seen after that date in places where they were observed earlier in the season.

Six or more of these birds, actively engaged in foraging, were noted near the crest of the ridge 3 miles east of Coulterville on August 9 and 11, 1920. None was seen in this locality, which is at the lower margin of the Transition Zone, in June of 1915, so those seen later in the season were probably 'vagrants.'

In Yosemite Valley a pair of these birds flew low over the river on the stormy evenings of June 28 and 29, 1920; and during a heavy storm on August 24, 1920, a lone bird coursed for two hours up and down over the Merced River (C. W. Michael, MS).

TEXAS NIGHTHAWK. **Chordeiles acutipennis texensis** Lawrence

Field characters.—Same as those for Pacific Nighthawk (which see), but narrow white band across long flight feathers (primaries) scarcely more than its own length from end of wing; in other words this white bar is well beyond middle of wing rather than close to midway. *Voice:* A mellow, long-continued, rolling trill.

Occurrence.—Common summer visitant to Lower Sonoran Zone. Seen in vicinity of Snelling and near Lagrange. Active during evening and morning twilight and during the night. Forages close over ground, rarely rising over 50 feet into the air. Rests during the day on ground in shade of bush or in open gravelly situation.

The Texas Nighthawk is a summer visitant to the warmer parts of the southwestern United States and in the Yosemite section it was observed only at our lowest stations, west of the foothills. On the evening of May 25, 1915, 3 were noted in flight over the river bottom near Snelling, the first at 7:15 P.M., well after sundown. The next evening 2 were abroad at about the same hour, 'hawking' over the alfalfa fields and doubtless in search of the night-flying insects to be found there.

When we established camp on a gravelly bench beside the Tuolumne River below Lagrange on the evening of May 5, 1919, it was evident at once that we had closely invaded the special domain of this nighthawk, for two pairs were coursing about actively at 6:30 P.M. (sun-time). The mellow trilling notes of the males were heard off and on throughout the succeeding night, so the birds must have been active during most of the hours of darkness. And on the following morning they were flying around now and then until about 8 o'clock.

It was the height of the nesting season and the birds were courting actively. A male, distinguished by the larger and whiter bands on his wings and the more conspicuously white chin patch, was pursuing a female. The male always followed, but at close range, rarely more than two lengths behind the female. Occasionally a second male joined in the pursuit, but evidently with only partial interest, for he frequently circled off by himself. Less often the two male birds pursued one another, weaving an irregular course up and down, in and out, but never rising much if any over 50 feet above the ground. The progress through the air was easy yet swift, a few strokes of the long wings sufficing to carry the birds through a long glide. Often as they passed close over the observer the barred pattern of the under surface was clearly visible, as was also the broad subterminal band of white on the lower side of the tail. While the males were on the wing their low crooning trills were heard almost continually, swelling and diminishing as the birds approached or departed. When they rested on the ground between flights they gave the same notes, prolonged but also with longer intervals of quiet. One trill lasted 25 seconds and another fully a minute. These notes remind one of the quavering call of the Screech Owl save that they are longer continued, on one key, and uttered in almost the same cadence throughout.

Each individual nighthawk seemed to have a favorite resting place to which it returned regularly. This was on the gravel, at the side of, and partially shaded by, a lupine or other bush. The male bird of the pair mentioned was seen to return to the neighborhood of such a spot time and time again, and upon flushing him directly and thus ascertaining its exact location, the site was found to be marked by an accumulation of droppings of characteristic form—each a small spiralled mass composed chiefly of finely triturated insect remains.

Careful scrutiny of the ground within 100 feet of this male bird's 'roost' eventually led to the discovery of a 'nest' with two eggs which were being incubated by the female. The latter flushed when the observer was about 50 feet away, and then made off along the ground with a peculiar dragging flight, her wings fluttering and held downwards from the body, almost touching the ground. When she flew off, the male, who had been resting in his favorite spot, set up his crooning trill and continued it with varying loudness for a full minute, until the female alighted upon the gravel some distance away. When she again took wing he joined and followed close in her wake as she flew about. This was at 1:30 P.M., in the heat of the day.

The eggs lay 2 millimeters apart, and with their long axes at about 30° to each other, evidently just as the body of the female had fitted over them. They were situated on a little sandy area, in a tract generally covered with gravel. When not shielded by the female the eggs were fully exposed to the heat of the sun. The slender branches of a dead weed, 300 millimeters away to the southwest, formed the only semblance of a shelter. The bird could flush only to the northeast although she could easily see all about her for a hundred feet or more. The eggs were found (on May 6) to be about one-fourth incubated and one had a slight "stone bruise" which was covered on the inside by hardened albumen.

As is clearly seen in the illustration (pl. 45*b*) the coloration of the eggs is strikingly like that of many of the water-rounded pebbles in the vicinity. In all stages, egg, chick, and adult, the color scheme of the Texas Nighthawk is to the last degree protective in character—a feature of evident usefulness to a species which spends all of its life, except when foraging, on the open ground.

NORTHERN BLACK SWIFT. **Cypseloides niger borealis** (Kennerly)

Field characters.—Larger than any of our swallows or the White-throated Swift, but resembling the latter in its long slender wings; tail very broad. Plumage black; no white marks ordinarily apparent. Flight more swallow-like, less erratic, than that of White-throated Swift. *Voice:* A high-pitched twitter, not so shrill or long-continued as that of White-throated Swift.

Occurrence.—Flock of about 15 seen by us over Yosemite Valley, May 17, 1919; also noted there June 17 and 18, 1920 (C. W. Michael, MS). Others seen singly or in pairs by us during June and July, 1920, at Dudley, east of Coulterville. Forages in the open air.

The Northern Black Swift is a species notable, at least in California, for the irregularity of its distribution. It is a bird often watched for but seldom seen except in a very few well-known localities where it may be counted upon to occur year after year. So it was a matter of genuine surprise, on the morning of May 17, 1919, to see a flock of 15 of these birds coursing in level formation over the dense stand of slender young pines just north of Stoneman bridge.

The first glance at the flock showed it to consist of swifts rather than swallows, and then a few minutes' study disclosed many important differences between these birds and the smaller, better known, White-throated Swift. The Black Swift is distinctly the larger, and it appears to be all black except for the brownish forehead which sometimes reflects in strong sunlight almost like white. The fore margin of the two wings as viewed from below is a double convex, and not a single continuous arc as in the White-throated Swift; moreover, the movements of the wings are more deliberate than in that species. The tail, nearly square-ended in the larger swift, was broadly spread in fan shape. The birds individually wove courses in and out among their companions, all remaining on about the same level. None was seen to indulge in the downward tumbling flight so characteristic of the smaller, pied species, nor were any of the Black Swifts heard to utter notes of any kind. Our attention was attracted to other birds, and a little later when looked for again the big swifts were gone and were not seen at any other time during the remaining week of our stay in the Valley. None was seen during any of our previous visits to the region.

On July 20, 1920, a pair of these birds was made the subject of special observation at Dudley, where the species had been seen almost daily during the month preceding. Sometimes the two birds were seen together but more often there was one bird alone. They flew very high as a rule so that it took much peering into the blue to descry them. Occasionally they were heard to twitter, in a voice high-pitched but not having nearly the piercing quality characteristic of the White-throated Swift. There was much sailing along on set wings; when the wings were flapped the beating was slower than it is in either the White-throated or the Vaux Swift. When the birds were at certain angles from the observer, striking flashes of silvery gray were given off from the wings.

Mr. Donald D. McLean believes that the Northern Black Swifts nest in this vicinity in burned-out black oak stubs; and he may be right. There are no rock cliffs short of ten miles away; and he says the swifts have been about the locality each summer ever since he can remember. He occasionally sees one bird of a pair dart down from a great height, always to disappear beyond some ridge or behind some large tree. He showed one of us a prostrate hollow oak about which, before it fell, he says these swifts used to be seen; but he never saw a bird actually enter a cavity. With this hint, someone, sometime, with a stock of time, patience, and favoring luck, may enjoy the thrill of the actual discovery of a Black Swift's nest in the Yosemite region.

W. O. Emerson (1893, p. 179) recorded the Northern Black Swift as "very common high up in all the cliffs, particularly [along] the face of Glacier Point" in June, 1893.

VAUX SWIFT. **Chaetura vauxi** (Townsend)

Field characters.—Size about that of Violet-green Swallow; form and behavior like those of White-throated Swift. Plumage plain blackish brown, except for silvery suffusion on breast and throat. No white on flanks.

Occurrence.—Noted in Yosemite Valley in fall (Mailliard, 1918, pp. 16, 18). Not observed by us. Courses in open air, during day time.

The Vaux Swift may be known in flight from the more common and better known White-throated Swift by its smaller size, lesser degree of whiteness on the throat, and by the absence of white on its flanks. It is distinguished from the Northern Black Swift by its much smaller size and by the silvery appearance of its throat and breast.

This swift has been reported from Yosemite Valley by only one observer, Mr. Joseph Mailliard (as above), who found it present in some numbers in the early fall of 1917. "One or two often seen, and quite a flock at times"; this statement referring to occurrence on August 21 and for a few days subsequently (Mailliard, MS).

Mr. Donald D. McLean reports the Vaux Swift as having occasionally been seen by him in spring and summer at his home place 6 miles east of Coulterville.

WHITE-THROATED SWIFT. **Aeronautes melanoleucus** (Baird)

Field characters.—Resembling a swallow but wings much longer and more slender, and tail longer; outline in flight crossbow-like. Plumage black save for white on throat and mid-breast, and white patch on either side of rump. (See pl. 46*g*.) Flight swift and erratic, with very rapid beats of the wings which at times appear to operate alternately. *Voice:* A series of shrill twittering notes.

Occurrence.—Summer visitant locally in small numbers west of the Sierran crest, and below the Canadian Zone. Seen at Pleasant Valley and El Portal, and in Yosemite Valley. Extreme dates of observance, April 27 (1916) and September 29 (1915). Courses about in the open air, usually high over sheer cliffs.

Through our field observations we have come to associate the White-throated Swift with open cañons or valleys flanked by bare rocky cliffs; and as the cañon of the Merced River affords locally just these conditions, it was no surprise to find numbers of these birds at Pleasant Valley and El Portal and in and about Yosemite Valley.

The White-throated Swift may be distinguished from any of the swallows by its crossbow-like outline of body and wings, the latter notably slender, its black plumage sharply relieved by white on throat and middle of breast (pl. 46*g*) and on sides of rump, and by its more reckless manner of flight. Its shrill twittering notes, of insistent quality, are also different from those of swallows.

The much frequented vantage places on the walls of Yosemite Valley, such as Columbia, Yosemite, Union, Sierra and Glacier points, afford good places from which to see White-throated Swifts on almost any day during the summer season. The birds often pass very close to an observer stationed on one of these points, sometimes dashing downward into the valley below at lightning speed, again pursuing a more level course with a half-mile of clear air between themselves and the Valley floor. They begin early in the morning and are active until late evening, even after the last rays of the evening sun have left the surrounding peaks and dusk is creeping into the gorge below. Thus on June 7 and again on June 23, in 1915, swifts were noted still abroad in the neighborhood of the Three Brothers at 7:30 P.M.

In all our watching of White-throated Swifts we have never seen one alight on the ground or upon any sort of perching place. But on one occasion, birds were seen to disappear in the face of the beetling cliff above the upper zigzag on the Yosemite Point trail. Their roosting and nesting places are located in narrow crevices of the rock walls, within which the birds cling, and such sites are, of course, practically inaccessible to any animal save the birds themselves.

From the Big Trees auto road above El Portal, on the morning of April 27, 1916, several White-throated Swifts and Violet-green Swallows were seen coursing about together over the Merced Cañon. Both species exhibited skill in their aerial evolutions, but the swifts were the more daring. They would dart downward, almost vertically, with such velocity that one would think they must be dashed to earth. Yet they checked their flight with apparent ease, and then circled lightly or sailed upward on set wings. Once three swifts swept past within a couple of yards of the observer, going at such high speed that their stiff-feathered wings made a distinct swishing sound as they cut through the air. On two occasions one swift was seen to pursue and grapple with another, as if to mate, and then the two went tumbling over and over, downwards through the air for a couple of hundred feet or more, to break apart and take opposite courses just before they reached the ground.

Black-chinned Hummingbird

Archilochus alexandri (Bourcier and Mulsant)

Field characters.—Male with chin non-iridescent black, bordered immediately below by a narrow iridescent purplish collar; back and top of head dark iridescent green; flanks greenish. (See pl. 46c.) Female with top of head and back bronzy green; under surface grayish, with faint buffy tinge on flanks; no rufous or greenish tinge on sides; ends of outer tail feathers wedge-shaped.

Occurrence.—Summer visitant locally at lower altitudes on both sides of the Sierra Nevada. Recorded at Snelling, Dudley (6 miles east of Coulterville), El Portal, and Mono Lake Post Office.

The Black-chinned Hummingbird is a foothill species, found in the summertime along the beds of cañons and adjacent lower slopes. A male was seen at Snelling on May 28, 1915, perched on a dead willow stub in the tangled river-bottom vegetation; and on May 2, 1916, another was seen in growths of yerba santa on the hillside above El Portal. At Mono Lake Post Office a male was seen feeding at the blossoms of a wild currant, during a snowstorm on May 23, 1916, seemingly unmindful of the state of the weather. Three days later another was seen sitting on a barbed wire fence. Later in the season (June 30), at the same place, four were seen, one of which was driving a Green-backed Goldfinch away from the hummer's favorite perch on a willow twig near an irrigating ditch.

At Dudley, on Smith Creek, 6 miles east of Coulterville, according to Mr. Donald D. McLean, this hummingbird does not arrive until the middle of June. Nesting there takes place, therefore, rather late in the season. Three nests have been found, all on the ranch, close to the house. On July 14, 1920, a nest containing 2 fresh eggs, which the female was beginning to incubate, was found situated 4½ feet above the ground on a slender drooping limb of an apple tree. The nest was saddled in a little crotch where a fine twig was given off. It was but an inch in height by 1⅜ inches in diameter. The materials comprising it included tufts of grayish plant down, and bud scales and seed pods, the whole bound together and to the support with spider web.

Full-grown young-of-the-year were collected at this place July 26 and August 9, 1920.

A 'poker plant' in the ranch garden was the common rendezvous of all the hummingbirds in the vicinity, and here the female of the nest just described and a male Black-chin not infrequently foraged together amicably. But the male was forcibly repelled by the female whenever he attempted to approach the precincts of the nest. Mr. McLean states that earlier in the season at lower altitudes, especially around Coulterville, the species nests more commonly.

Anna Hummingbird. Calypte anna (Lesson)

Field characters.—Largest of the hummingbirds found in the Yosemite region. Male with whole top of head, chin and throat iridescent magenta or rose-red; lower surface grayish green. Back in both sexes metallic green; no rufous or buffy at all in plumage. Female (plate 46*b*) with sides of body tinged with greenish, and with outer tail feathers broadly rounded at ends. *Voice:* 'Song' of male a high-pitched squeaky *zeezy-zeezy-zeezy-zee*, etc., ending usually *e-zeent', e-zeent'*; females utter a low-toned sucking note, *tsup*, when foraging.

Occurrence.—Common resident of Upper Sonoran Zone on west slope of Sierra Nevada. Seen at Pleasant Valley, near Coulterville, and at El Portal. Observed also in Yosemite Valley on July 15, 18, and 28, August 25 and September 5 and 6, 1920 (C. W. Michael, MS); also September 8, 1917 (J. Mailliard, MS).

The Anna Hummingbird is the best known of the California hummingbirds, chiefly because it is resident throughout the year almost wherever found, and is common in the most thickly populated parts of the state. It is common throughout the year at El Portal which is at the upper margin of the Upper Sonoran Zone. Although this bird was not observed by our party in Yosemite Valley it has been seen there in late summer and early fall by other persons as detailed above. It appeared at Smith Creek, east of Coulterville, on July 13, 1920, and was present in numbers at the end of that month.

During November and December of 1914 we saw individuals almost daily at El Portal. At this time of the year there were no flowers of any sort to be found in the vicinity, but the Anna Hummingbirds seemed to find enough good forage on the foliage of the golden oaks, about which they were seen almost exclusively. The minute insects which live on the leaves of the golden oak probably afforded sufficient forage of one sort, but the hummingbirds had another source of food supply.

It was noted that one or more Anna Hummingbirds were to be found regularly about a certain golden oak, but the reason for their attraction to this particular tree was not discerned for several days. Then, on December 11, one of these birds was seen hovering before, and drinking from, some punctures made by a Red-breasted Sapsucker in the bark of the oak tree. The hummer visited puncture after puncture just as it would the individual blossoms in a spike of flowers, and evidently partook of both the sap and the smaller of the insects which had been attracted by the sap. Ruby-crowned Kinglets and California Woodpeckers were also visiting the place, in addition to the sapsucker which had done the work. Thus the hummers, kinglets, and woodpeckers were all benefiting by the industry of the sapsucker without evident disadvantage to the latter, whereas all profited at the expense of the oak tree.

In May, Anna Hummingbirds were foraging among the flowers on the greasewood slopes about Pleasant Valley. A female taken at this time (May 30) had a yolk in the ovary; this would suggest breeding activity at a relatively late date for this species here. It is elsewhere known to nest as early as February, or even January.

RUFOUS HUMMINGBIRD. **Selasphorus rufus** (Gmelin)

Field characters.—Chin and throat of male iridescent coppery red, abruptly bordered below by white; back of male entirely cinnamon rufous, and plumage otherwise mostly rufous; back of female iridescent bronzy green; sides of body and base of tail strongly tinged with rufous. Adult males in flight give forth a tremulous whistling sound.

Occurrence.—Common transient through the Yosemite region. Observed by us as follows: near Yosemite Point, July 1; head of Lyell Cañon, July 23; Washburn Lake, August 24; top of Parsons Peak, September 6; and Silver and Walker lakes, September 14; all dates in 1915. Also, at Smith Creek, 6 miles east of Coulterville, August 8, 9, and 10, 1920.

The Rufous Hummingbird was observed by us only as a transient in the Yosemite region; indeed this species is not definitely known to be other than a transient anywhere in California. The passage of the last northbound spring migrants is so closely approximated by the beginning of the southbound movement in the early summer that individuals are likely to be seen in the region on almost any day during the summer months. Most of the northbound movement probably takes place at low altitudes and in any event occurs too early in the spring to be observed by most visitors to the Yosemite section. But the migration initiated in late June or early July continues until the middle of September, and especially at the higher altitudes is much in evidence.

The adult males take no share in the duties of nesting, which are carried on in the northern Rocky Mountains and in the Pacific Coast district north from Oregon; the first representatives of the species to be seen in the southbound migration are males. Thus the bird seen near Yosemite Point on July 1 was a fully adult male, as it showed an all-rufous back. But later in the same month the females and their young began to pass through. Of the birds seen in Lyell Cañon on July 23 at least one was a female (immature). The southbound migration was evidently in full swing by that date as no less than 5 separate individuals were seen during two or three hours spent on the meadows and adjacent slopes.

A visit to Parsons Peak on September 6, 1915, showed that the migration was still in progress, and further, that the Rufous Hummingbirds were evidently using the crest of the Sierra Nevada as a fly-way. During the short time spent at the top of the peak, 12,120 feet, two of these diminutive travelers were seen flying southward, laboring against the strong southerly breeze; both took advantage of the same gap in the rocks to gain a slight respite from the buffeting of the wind. Other observers have told us of similar incidents noted by them while visiting peaks elsewhere along the backbone of the Sierra Nevada.

Four of the birds seen in Lyell Cañon in late July were drawn to the immediate vicinity of the observer by a red bandana handkerchief which he had purposely hung over his hat in the hope of attracting humming-birds, a ruse which is often successful. The birds presumably mistake the patch of bright color for a group of flowers in bloom. One or more other individuals were seen on the same date visiting red castillejas and other flowers then in blossom on the benches near where the Lyell Fork cascades down from its headwaters to the level meadows below.

At Dudley, on Smith Creek, east of Coulterville, 5 Rufous Humming-birds were collected on August 8, 9, and 10, 1920. These were all young-of-the-year. A great many more rufous-tinged hummingbirds were seen during the last of July and early in August, but determination of their specific identity (as between *rufus* and *alleni*) was not attempted, since the distinguishing characteristics of the two species in immature plumage cannot be noted in birds out of hand.

ALLEN HUMMINGBIRD. **Selasphorus alleni** Henshaw

Field characters.—As for Rufous Hummingbird (which see), but in adult male back green. In hand, the next to middle pair of tail feathers in the adult male are plain (not notched as in the Rufous) and, in both sexes, at all ages, the outermost tail feather on each side is narrow, not more than 2 millimeters wide.

Occurrence.—Sparse transient. Two immature individuals collected at Dudley, 6 miles east of Coulterville, August 5 and 10, 1920.

The Allen Hummingbird is a breeding bird of the coastal district of California, but at the conclusion of nesting both adults and young range widely before departing southward. The flower garden on the Dudley ranch, 6 miles east of Coulterville, is a mecca for many hummingbirds; the "red hot poker plants" are particularly attractive. Among the species found to be represented there in August, 1920, were two individuals of the Allen Hummingbird collected on the 5th and 10th, respectively. One of these was in molt from juvenal to adult plumage; the tail feathers of the adult category showed the absence of notch, and were therefore characteristic of *alleni*. Both specimens showed very narrow outer tail feathers as compared with the distinctly broader ones in the same plumage stage of *rufus*.

CALLIOPE HUMMINGBIRD. Stellula calliope (Gould)

Field characters.—Smallest of the hummingbirds in the region. Throat of male with long, lancet-like feathers (pl. 46a) of a striking lavender iridescence, the whole on a white background; back and top of head green; flanks tinged with buffy. Female with back and top of head iridescent green; lower surface grayish white strongly buffy tinged, but no bright rufous on base of tail as in the female Rufous; outer tail feathers broad-ended instead of narrow as in Rufous. *Voice:* A faint lisping *tweez-e-zeet-zee*, given when one individual is pursuing another; females when foraging utter a faint *seet*.

Occurrence.—Common midsummer visitant to high Transition and Canadian zones on both slopes of Sierra Nevada; observed from middle of May until September 1. Seen by us in Yosemite Valley only in May and June. Frequents alder and willow lined cañons and forest glades, foraging chiefly about castillejas and wild currant blossoms.

The Calliope Hummingbird is the smallest species of bird known to occur in California. Its average weight is only about 3 grams ($\frac{1}{10}$ of an ounce) which is about half that of an Anna Hummingbird, or of a kinglet or bush-tit. Yet this midget is a far migrant. It visits the Yosemite region only in summer; it spends the winter months entirely south of California, and some individuals of the species even go as far south as the City of Mexico and beyond.

Compared with most summer visitants the Calliope Hummer is a late arrival in the region. At Mono Lake it was first seen in 1916 on May 21, a single male bird being observed. Another was seen two days later. On the west slope the earliest record of the bird we have is for May 14 (1919), when a male was seen at Hazel Green. This late time of arrival is probably related to the lack earlier in the season of suitable forage. The appearance of Calliope Hummingbirds in numbers in the vicinity of Chinquapin in 1915 was coincident with the abundant blossoming there of a wild currant (*Ribes viscosissimum*). The stay of these birds is not prolonged into the fall. The bulk of the crop of nectar producing flowers is gone by early August and we find also that most of these hummingbirds have gone by that time. On September 1, 1915, a single individual, the last definitely identified for the season, was seen on the slopes of Mount Clark. The most favorable localities found by us in which to observe these birds were in the vicinity of Chinquapin and Mono Meadow, where certain sun-facing slopes were covered by heavy growths of wild currant.

Adult males of all our species of hummingbirds have on their throats a patch of iridescent feathers of greater or less extent, known as the gorget, the display of which forms a part of the spring courting performance. The distinctive peculiarities of the gorget as to color and extent are set forth by us under the field characters for each species. The males of most species of birds perform before the females during the mating season, and in some of those species which have little or no ability from a vocal standpoint, as is the case with the hummingbirds, the behavior is striking. The courting performance of the hummingbirds takes the form of a special course of flight, distinctive for each species. That of the Rufous is over a semicircular path in a vertical plane, and is repeated many times in rapid succession; that of the Anna is performed in more deliberate manner over a high and narrow U-shaped course; while that of the Black-chinned is on a short horizontal line over which it moves back and forth time after time. The nuptial flight of the Calliope is somewhat like that of the Rufous, but less vigorous and not so extensive or so continuous, two or three swoops being the rule.

In the Calliope Hummingbird the individual feathers of the gorget are long and lancet-like (pl. 46a), and their lavender iridescence is set forth in fine contrast by a white background. John Gould, the most famous student of hummingbirds, named the bird appropriately, *stellula*, meaning the little star. When the male Calliope is excited, as when in chase of a rival, or in courting flight, these slender feathers are raised so that they stand out prominently from the other feathers on the throat.

The nuptial flight of the Calliope Hummingbird was seen by us only a few times. In Yosemite Valley on May 31, 1915, a male and female were seen in a patch of blossoming chokecherries. The male mounted into the air a short distance and swooped down past the female, making a slight metallic sound at the bottom of the arc. Flights of similar sort were seen at Mono Meadow in mid-June but were not accompanied by any sound audible to the human ear. Other male hummingbirds, notably the Anna, when thus performing, produce a loud metallic sound at the moment of reaching the lowest point in the downward swing.

Male hummingbirds are not known to take part in any of the duties of nesting. In fact the location of a male seems to have no relation to that of a female or of an occupied nest. Soon after the mating season the males of the migratory species begin the southward migration; this is evidently true of the Calliope. No male of this species was seen by us after the end of June.

At Hazel Green, Chinquapin, and Mono Meadow the males held rather fixed positions in the wild currant thickets. Each individual presided over a certain definite territory, invasion of which brought prompt pursuit of the intruder who was usually quickly put to rout. The squeaky notes of most hummingbirds, and of the Calliope in particular, are more noticeable during one of these pursuits than at any other time.

A male seen in a cut-over clearing near Chinquapin was found to have his 'beat' on a warm sheltered slope. Several high twigs within a 50-yard radius were occupied in succession. He regularly appeared on a certain one which we kept under observation for some time. While perched there his head turned about almost constantly from side to side, and occasionally he would glance upwards. From time to time he would dart off rapidly, only to return and take position on one or another of the perches.

The males of all our hummingbirds are accustomed to harass birds many times their own size. A Calliope at Mono Meadow was seen to put a Wright Flycatcher to rout, the latter seeking seclusion in a ceanothus thicket. In Yosemite Valley another was seen driving at a Western Robin that was on the ground. The hummer would mount as much as 30 feet into the air and then dash down at the robin. Even Red-tailed Hawks are sometimes 'attacked' by these pugnacious midgets.

At Chinquapin on May 19, 1919, a female Calliope Hummingbird was seen during the late afternoon hovering about the lichen-covered trunks of red firs and Douglas spruces in the cañon of Indian Creek. She was evidently gathering nesting material, but her nest site was not located since she took a course directly up toward the top of one of the trees and was lost to sight.

The hummers at Mono Meadow were active throughout the day and until after sundown. On the evening of June 19, 1915, at this place, 2 males and a female were seen foraging when the crepuscular sphinx- or hummingbird-moths had already begun to fly. In Yosemite Valley, early on the morning of May 17, 1919, a male Calliope was seen perched on a dead stub, in an oak and cedar thicket. The bird was catching flies and from time to time would dart out, pewee-like, after passing insects.

Like other hummingbirds the Calliope is often attracted by red objects. Whether this is a voluntary action based on esthetic appeal, or a reflex based on food-getting instinct, is problematic. At Chinquapin, on June 14, a female of this species darted into the front of our open tent and poised with seeming interest before a red-labeled baking powder can on the table. Then the bird went out into the sunshine, but it returned again twice before finally going away. Two of our three August records of this species were of individuals which were attracted in the same manner, the object being a red handkerchief in one case, and a sweater of the same color in the other.

Western Kingbird. **Tyrannus verticalis** Say

Field characters.—Of rather slender build; somewhat less in bulk than Robin (length 9 inches); head flat-appearing. Upper surface and breast light grayish, throat paler; belly bright yellow; wings brown; tail black, with easily-seen white margins; bill blackish. *Voice:* Loud, harsh, bickering calls.

Occurrence.—Summer visitant to lowland districts on west side of Sierra Nevada; commonest in Lower Sonoran Zone. Recorded at Snelling and from near Lagrange eastward to three miles east of Coulterville and to El Portal; noted in spring near Williams Butte. Casual in Yosemite Valley during early fall. Lives in dry open situations, as along roadways and about isolated trees. In pairs.

As the traveler takes his way over the level plains of the San Joaquin Valley and into the Sierran foothill belt there is constantly in evidence one of the conspicuous members of the lowland avifauna—the Western Kingbird, or Bee Martin. This bird is normally an inhabitant of open country, like that about Snelling, where it may be seen commonly along roadsides. In one instance eight were counted along a single mile of road over the rolling prairie. The bird also penetrates locally far up into the foothill belt, as at El Portal and at the McCarthy ranch on the Coulterville road near the head of Bean Creek (3200 feet). Along the roads in Bear Valley and at Mt. Bullion it was seen at an average frequency of about one pair every quarter of a mile. It was observed also at Farrington's near Mono Lake, probably as a migrant, April 26 and May 18, 1916. In Yosemite Valley one was seen on the meadow near Rocky Point on August 18, 1920 (C. W. Michael, MS), and another on El Capitan Meadows, September 2 and 3, 1917 (Mailliard, 1918, p. 18.)

Kingbirds may often be seen perched on fences or telephone wires, or in other commanding positions, where, with constantly turning heads, they watch for passing insects. When one of these insects ventures near, the waiting bird darts after it, engulfs the hapless bug with an audible click of the bill, and returns to the same or a similar perch. Kingbirds are to be seen frequently on the ground, in grassy situations, preying upon grasshoppers. As might be expected, a wide variety of insects is included in the bill of fare of this species.

A notable feature of the kingbird's behavior is its apparently quarrelsome nature. When a heron, hawk, owl, or crow appears in the vicinity, this flycatcher deems it an especial duty to launch forth and harry the larger bird. This it does by flying over the intruder, uttering intimidating cries, and pecking at the big fellow's head or back; the performance is usually so successful that the larger bird shows discomfiture and makes off with increased speed. Near Coulterville a California Jay was seen on the ground hunting food, and while there a Western Kingbird came and flew several times in pendulum-like course over the jay's head, but without seeming to bother the latter in the least.

If a person happens near a nest of this species during the breeding season he at once becomes the center of a noisy demonstration. Both parent birds, and sometimes other pairs, hover over him, with feet drawn up against the body, tail spread, and wings beating, often poising for several seconds in one position. All the while they pour forth a deafening torrent of protests. At such times the bird's red crown-patch which, under ordinary circumstances, is wholly concealed, is flashed vividly into view. Occasionally, however, one comes upon a kingbird that is quiet. At El Portal one was seen to sit on a telegraph wire for more than ten minutes without once moving or uttering a note.

The nesting season of the Western Kingbird is chiefly in May, soon after the birds have arrived from the south. An empty nest seen at Bagby, May 27, was placed 12 feet above the ground near the top of a small blue oak on the edge of a low bluff along the railroad track. Another nest, seen near Snelling, was 20 feet above the ground, also in a blue oak. The nests are constructed compactly of grasses and weed-stems and measure 5 to 6 inches across the outside and 2 to 3 inches in depth.

Ash-throated Flycatcher

Myiarchus cinerascens cinerascens (Lawrence)

Field characters.—Bulk about twice that of Junco; length 8½ inches; relatively slender in outline, tail as long as body, head with a blunt crest. No sharply contrasted markings; whole coloration pale-toned; breast light gray, belly white tinged with yellow; head and back grayish brown; wings and tail showing reddish brown areas when expanded; closed wing crossed by two dull whitish bars. Perches low in open situations, turning head from side to side, and making frequent changes of position. *Voice:* A throaty, staccato one- or two-syllabled call, descending in pitch, *ker, ker-cherr'*, or *kut-trüh'*, with audible rolling of r's; also a 'song,' a loud rolling *tŭck' a roo*, repeated many times at irregular intervals of a second or more.

Occurrence.—Summer visitant west of Sierras; common throughout Lower and Upper Sonoran zones to as far east as El Portal; once observed by us in Yosemite Valley, on north side near foot of trail to Yosemite Falls, June 7, 1915; noted also in the Valley June 20 to 25, 1893 (Emerson, 1893, p. 179). Frequents open situations, chiefly in chaparral, especially where sparingly interrupted by oaks; forages usually alone, rarely in pairs, never in flocks.

The Ash-throated Flycatcher resembles the Western Kingbird in general form and tone of coloration, but differs unmistakably in habits and demeanor. It has none of the aggressive, belligerent actions which characterize the kingbird, but attends to the business of catching insects in a pleasingly quiet manner. Unlike many of the Flycatcher tribe, the Ash-throat does not often return to the same location after sallying forth o capture an insect, but usually moves on to a new perch, evidently preferring to *go after* its prey rather than passively wait for the latter to chance by. Often, when taking flight for but a short distance, the bird retains the upright posture of its body, and with its tail drooped and slightly expanded flutters from one perch to the next. Nor is it so restricted in home range as the kingbird. Most flycatchers, the kingbird included, are wont to remain in a restricted area after once being established for the season, but the Ash-throat seems to be more enterprising and ranges widely over the brushlands. When perched its rather upright posture, together with its slightly crested head and long tail held in line with the back and body, gives it a characteristic outline, recognizable almost as far as the bird may be seen at all.

In the Upper Sonoran Zone, for example at Pleasant Valley or Coulterville, the Ash-throated Flycatcher is common on the brush-covered hillsides, flying from one dead greasewood stub to another, snapping up various insects attracted there by the flowers of the greasewood, yerba santa, and deer brush, and uttering at intervals its not unpleasant throaty call notes.

In the dry bed of a cañon below the chaparral-covered hills west of Coulterville one of these flycatchers was watched for some time on a morning in May. This particular individual faced *in,* toward the foliage of the live oak in which it perched, and several times was seen to gather insects from the foliage within range by merely reaching for them. Once it took a smooth worm and, gulping it only part way down, flew off to another perch before completing the act of swallowing. Another insect taken earlier was swallowed with much gulping, the contractions of the throat being easily seen.

This flycatcher has access to an abundant food supply in the chaparral belt, and there is no other species of flycatcher there to compete with it. This food supply, however, is greatly reduced or entirely gone during the cold season of the year and so the Ash-throat departs; it migrates south early in the fall and spends the winter months in Mexico and Central America. The species is a late arrival in spring, for on May 24 at Pleasant Valley and on May 26 at Snelling birds of this species, evidently still in migration, were seen working in a general northeasterly direction. On the earlier date about 25 individuals were observed, many more than would have been recorded over the same census route had there been no migrants in the region.

SAY PHOEBE. **Sayornis sayus** (Bonaparte)

Field characters.—But little larger than Junco or Linnet; tail long, as long as body. Coloration ashy brown; tail blackish; belly pale cinnamon. Makes frequent changes of position and flies out after passing insects. *Voice:* A plaintive, protracted *pee-ur*, the two syllables being scarcely distinguishable.

Occurrence.—Common winter visitant to open country in vicinity of Lagrange and Snelling. Recorded also 10 miles east of Coulterville, March 20, 1916. Visits vicinity of Mono Lake after the nesting season. Perches on rocks or fences, or on bare twigs of low bushes.

The Say Phoebe is a flycatcher of desert predilections, and hence not likely to come to the attention of the average Yosemite visitor. In winter it is found on the San Joaquin plains and about the rocky outcrops and earth bluffs of the western foothills. From late June until September or later, in the dispersal which follows the breeding season, it invades the territory about Mono Lake. Near Walker Lake on September 14, 1915, 6 of these birds were seen in a 3½-hour census. Each individual was by itself, perched on some dead twig affording a good view over the general level of the surrounding sagebrush, from which the bird could dart out after passing insects.

BLACK PHOEBE. **Sayornis nigricans** (Swainson)

Field characters.—But slightly longer than English Sparrow (length 6½ inches); build slender; head with a low crest. Plumage solidly black-appearing except for white of belly. Perches on boulders, posts, telephone wires, and buildings; frequently turns head from side to side, and at intervals moves tail up and down. *Voice:* Usually a one-syllabled call, shrill and rather plaintive, *pser;* also, as a 'song,' a persistent repetition of two pairs of similar notes, with alternate rising and falling inflection.

Occurrence.—Resident in Upper and Lower Sonoran zones, barely entering the lower part of the Transition, as at Smith Creek (Dudley's ranch); an occasional individual reaches the floor of Yosemite Valley. Lives along streams and about unpainted buildings.

The black garb and typical flycatcher habits of the Black Phoebe combine to make it one of the easiest of birds to identify; moreover, its preference for open situations along streams and about buildings brings it to the attention of even casual observers within the stretch of country which it inhabits.

Like most flycatchers this species is solitary and the individual birds, even of a mated pair, are usually widely separated. The Black Phoebes are most frequently seen along rock-bordered streams, like the lower Merced River. From the windows of the train as it traverses the Merced Cañon, birds of this species may often be observed perched low on boulders

ear the water or flying rather slowly out over the surface of the river.
n the river bottom at Snelling, in January and again in June, one of
ur party noted six during a three-hour census. The birds were exceptionally numerous there, for seldom does an observer meet with more
han one or two in a morning's walk.

The Black Phoebe does not normally occur higher than the limits of
he Upper Sonoran Zone; but an occasional individual reaches the floor
of Yosemite Valley. On October 23 and November 6, 1915, lone birds
were seen on Sentinel Meadow, perching on telephone wires or on bare
tips of willows in the swales. On May 21 and 22, 1919, one held forth
from a perch over the river near Stoneman bridge. In 1920 (C. W.
Michael, MS) the first one in the Valley was noted on July 29 and thereafter the species was seen daily until September 25.

Whatever its surroundings the Black Phoebe seems to prefer a conspicuous location for its forage perch. Often it posts itself on the tip of
a dead twig at the edge of a stream, or on the corner of a building, whence
it sallies forth for passing insects, making but a short circuit before
returning. When on watch its head moves from side to side almost constantly, and its tail is raised and lowered at short intervals. The short
plaintive one-syllabled call note, *pser,* is uttered simultaneously with an
emphatic movement of the tail. This single call is at times replaced by
a series of four syllables, two with rising and two with falling inflection.
A bird giving this song near Bower Cave on May 13, 1919, was seen to
spread its tail synchronously with each pair of notes so that the narrow
white margin of the outer tail feathers showed momentarily.

Black Phoebes are not distributed locally with the regularity observed
in shrubbery-inhabiting birds such as Wren-tits or Brown Towhees. The
peculiar nesting requirements of the phoebes probably account for this
lack of uniformity in their distribution. They must have sheltered faces
of rocks or wooden walls against which to place their nests, and these
sites must be within carrying distance of some source of the mud used
in nest construction. Such sites are widely and irregularly scattered.
The building of bridges over creeks and the maintenance of stock barns
with watering troughs near by have probably increased the population
of these birds in the country as a whole.

At Dudley's ranch on the Coulterville Road a nest of this species was
seen on June 5, 1915. On that date it contained six young not more than
a day or so old. The nest was a cup-shaped affair, composed of mud pellets
with a few fine grass stems intermixed. It was placed under the gable
of a shed, about fifteen feet above the ground.

OLIVE-SIDED FLYCATCHER. **Nuttallornis borealis** (Swainson)

Field characters.—Smaller than Robin but large for a flycatcher. Head big and tai short as compared with other flycatchers. Middle of lower surface of body from chi backward yellowish white; plumage elsewhere solid olive brown save for patch o white on flank. Perches at tops of tall coniferous trees whence it flies out in typica flycatcher manner after passing insects. *Voice:* Song a loud clear far-carrying *wher whee', whew;* call notes a softer *pŭck,* twice or thrice repeated, most often heard i evening.

Occurrence.—Moderately common summer visitant to Transition and Canadian zone on west slope of Sierra Nevada. Passes through lower zones on both slopes during a least the spring migration. In Yosemite Valley, at least in early summer, but no plentiful there. Arrives in nesting range from middle of May to early June and depart about the end of August. Solitary or in pairs.

The Olive-sided Flycatcher is the patrician among the flycatchers, as it arrives late in the season and departs early, and while here maintains itself in seclusion from most other birds by keeping to the tops of the tallest trees. It spends the winter months in Central America or northern South America and so is a far traveler during its absence from our mountains. During late May and early June birds of this species are to be heard or seen, from time to time, in the foothill country where they pause to rest and feed before resuming the journey to the forests they quitted the previous summer.

At Blacks Creek west of Coulterville, on May 11 and 12, 1919, Olive-sided Flycatchers were moving past our camp on their return to the mountains. One was seen to perch momentarily on a convenient power wire over a greasewood-covered hillside before going on in a northeasterly direction toward the adjacent mountains; another heard calling from a solitary digger pine in the early morning was gone when looked for a little later. At Pleasant Valley, on May 23, 1915, individuals were observed in similar leisurely movement, going toward the cooler pine forests not many miles distant. At Mono Lake Post Office the species first appeared in migration in 1916 on May 22. The latest fall record is for September 1, 1915, when two birds were seen in Jeffrey pines at the head of Sunrise Creek, near Clouds Rest.

The Olive-sided Flycatcher is one of the earliest birds to call in the morning and one of the last to be heard in the evening. This is probably due in some degree to its choice of surroundings, for in the tree tops it is apprized of the coming of dawn long before that news reaches the earthward dwelling species, and in the same places it enjoys the lingering daylight for some time after the glades and thickets below are lost in the shadows of the evening. At Chinquapin on June 17, 1915, where these birds were already located for the summer, the clear three-syllabled

ong, *wher, whee', whew,* or *oh see' view,* was heard at the faintest trace
of dawn; and again at the same place, on May 19, 1919, a pair over our
camp closed the day with their softer *pŭck, pŭck, pŭck,* continuing until
after seven o'clock in the evening. Similar observations were recorded
elsewhere.

At times the clear simple notes of this flycatcher are replaced momentarily by a kingbird-like bickering and the two birds of a pair will flutter
far aloft around the nest site in the manner common to their noisy low-zone
relatives. When feeding young they occasionally indulge in this sort of
behavior, but for the most part they are of quiet demeanor. The observer
may gaze into the tree tops whence the notes are proceeding for minutes
at a time before detecting a movement which will reveal the source.

On June 3, 1915, an Olive-sided Flycatcher was collected from a tree
at the margin of the pine forest above Coulterville. Dissection showed
that the bird was not yet nesting and was likely still in migration. The
stomach of this bird contained beetles one or more of which were of species
which usually dwell on the ground (family Carabidae) and which do not
often ascend trees; presumably they were taken in one of the rare flights
of these insects. This species of flycatcher is known to nest regularly a
few miles farther to the east, at Dudley on Smith Creek, where young
just out of the nest were seen July 19, 1920.

WESTERN WOOD PEWEE. **Myiochanes richardsoni richardsoni** (Swainson)

Field characters.—Size of Junco, with posture and habits of flycatcher. Plumage
above and on sides of body dark brown; middle of lower surface of body yellowish
white. No special markings whatever: no white flank patch, no light eye-ring, wing bars
wanting or else but faint. Perches in upright, straight-backed posture on lower bare
branches of large trees whence it darts out after flying insects. *Voice:* A throaty, slurred
zuweez, or *zweer,* repeated at intervals throughout the day, more frequent (often every
2 or 3 seconds) in early morning and late evening.

Occurrence.—Common summer visitant to Upper Sonoran, Transition, and Canadian
zones on both slopes of Sierra Nevada. Observed from Snelling (in migration) to
Mono Craters. Seen in Yosemite Valley throughout the summer. Arrives about second
week in May and departs about mid-September. Usual forage range about 15 to 40
feet above ground. Solitary except when caring for brood.

The Western Wood Pewee is the commonest and most widely distributed
flycatcher found in the Yosemite region. In form and coloration it
resembles somewhat the Olive-sided Flycatcher, but it is of slenderer
build, lacks the white flank patches of the latter species, and the voices
and forage ranges of the two birds are quite different. The size, of course,
is much less.

From the smaller flycatchers (genus *Empidonax*), the wood pewee is
not very easily distinguishable on grounds of coloration alone. When

closely inspected, the absence of wing bars, or if these are present, as i
the young pewees, their relative dimness, is a serviceable field characte
as also is the presence of a light area down the middle of the bird's unde
surface. The wood pewee, moreover, has no suggestion of an eye-ring
which feature, due to the white or yellowish color of the circlet of smal
feathers immediately around the eye in the Empidonaces, give thes
smaller flycatchers a distinctive, big-eyed expression.

The monotonous droning call of the pewee is altogether unique. Thi
note is one of the commonest of bird voices heard at all places, from th
first digger pines of the foothills to the limit of the red firs and Jeffrey
pines at the upper margin of the Canadian Zone. Wood pewees are activ
and calling from earliest dawn until after dark. They occasionally wake
in the middle of the night to voice a call or two.

The forage range of this bird is usually about the lower periphery
of the forest trees and from about 15 to 40 feet above the ground. It has
no close restriction to one particular habitat or species of tree as do the
smaller flycatchers (genus *Empidonax*), and it may be seen in a great
variety of situations. Occasionally it seeks the top of a tree, after the
manner of the Olive-sided Flycatcher, but it rarely if ever goes so high
above the ground as that bird.

The earliest record at hand for the Western Wood Pewee in the
Yosemite section is for May 9 (1919) when several were seen at Blacks
Creek near Coulterville. None had been seen in the preceding four days
in the lower foothills, nor were any pewees observed in Yosemite Valley
on May 1, 1916. The second week of May evidently marks the time of
arrival of this species in the region. At Snelling, on May 26, 1915, wood
pewees were still in migration, for they were then seen in all sorts of
surroundings. Two days earlier, at Pleasant Valley, 20 were recorded
in a 5-hour census, many more than would likely have been seen in an
equal period of time after the migrant contingent had moved on. By
May 30 they had decreased, only 3 being observed in 3½ hours. East of
the Sierras near Williams Butte the species was first noted in 1916 on
May 18.

A Western Wood Pewee watched in the forest east of Coulterville,
June 1, 1915, occupied in succession, as forage perches, the terminal twigs
of a yellow pine, a fence wire, and the dead limbs of a black oak. At timed
intervals of 15, 10, 15, 10, 15, and 15 seconds it flew out after passing
insects. After taking something particularly large it gulped several times
before swallowing the insect and then carefully wiped its bill on a convenient twig. Between sorties after prey the bird uttered its monotonous
call note at short intervals. Near Porcupine Flat a wood pewee was found
to have a much frequented perch in a certain tree and on the ground

mmediately beneath the perch there was an accumulation of droppings ndicating occupancy for a considerable time.

In the woods on the north side of Yosemite Valley west of Rocky Point wood pewee was seen on her nest on May 18, 1919. This early date of nesting for a species of late arrival indicates that some pairs lose little ime in settling down to the important duties of the season. This nest vas about 40 feet above the ground on a dead horizontal branch of a black oak, well shaded by the new green foliage above. It was situated at a turn in the branch where two small broken-ended twigs started, and from below, it looked like little more than a slight swelling of the branch. The bird was moving about and seemed to be working on the rim with her bill; the nest was evidently still in process of construction. She left, to return soon accompanied by her mate, who uttered a series of low notes, *pĕr, pĕr, pĕr.* She went on the nest again and worked around in it for a few minutes and then again arched her neck, turning her head downward as if modeling or adding again to the rim.

The nesting season of the wood pewee extends over a long time. In Yosemite Valley on July 27, 1915, a family of full-grown young was seen still attended by the parents, and a similar observation was made at Tenaya Lake on July 29, 1915. Near Merced Lake on August 23, 1915, a Western Wood Pewee was seen in vigorous pursuit of a Sierra Chickaree. The bird was scolding furiously, while the squirrel retreated as fast as possible. Since the wood pewee is known to continue its nesting into August, the bird's repulsion of the squirrel may have been incited by a raid upon its nest.

The latest records we have for the Western Wood Pewee in the fall are for September 9, 1915, at Walker Lake, and for September 13, 1915, at Agnew Lake, when four were seen in lodgepole pines. The last seen in 1920 on the floor of Yosemite Valley was noted on September 13 (C. W. Michael, MS).

Wright Flycatcher. **Empidonax wrighti** Baird

Field characters.—Smaller than Junco. No striking white or bright markings anywhere. Whole bird appearing dark grayish brown; color tone on under surface of body yellowish gray; outer surface of closed wing crossed by two light bars; narrow ring around eye, dull whitish, this giving the bird a wide-eyed expression; lower mandible dusky, not yellowish. Perches with drooping wings and tail on prominent twig tips whence it flits out after insects which fly past. *Voice:* Call note *pit,* or *swee'pit,* sometimes a louder *ter, terwhit';* song a varied series of lisping notes, *see'pit, wurt'zel, see'pit, swer'zel, see'wurz,* etc.

Occurrence.—Common summer visitant to Upper Transition, Canadian, and (less commonly) Hudsonian zones on both slopes of Sierra Nevada. Recorded from Hazel Green and Chinquapin east to Mono Lake Post Office. Highest station, head of Lyell

Cañon, 9600 feet (July 19, 1915). Present on floor of Yosemite Valley, at least i
spring. Noted during spring migration at Dudley, April 29, 1916 (D. D. McLean coll.)
and at Pleasant Valley, May 24, 1915. Inhabits brush patches, foraging and singin,
from perches above these and less often from limbs 10 to 30 feet above ground i
adjacent trees.

The Wright Flycatcher is one of a group of small flycatchers (genu:
Empidonax), the members of which are so closely similar in size and
coloration that they cannot always be distinguished from one another ir
life on these characters alone, even by an expert. Fortunately, some of
the species in this assemblage possess distinctive call notes by which they
may be recognized; and each of them occupies a particular habitat or
type of country, so that as a rule they may be identified upon the basis
of these life characteristics with a fair degree of certainty. Thus the
Wright Flycatcher is characterized by the lisping quality of its rather
protracted song (described in detail farther on), and by its preference
for the chaparral slopes of the higher altitudes (mostly above 6000 feet).

The earliest seasonal record we made for the Wright Flycatcher in
the Yosemite region is for April 29, 1916, when an adult male was collected
near Williams Butte, east of the mountains. When we arrived at Hazel
Green, on May 14, 1919, these flycatchers were already present; by May 17,
in the same year, males had established posts in Yosemite Valley, and
by May 19, at Chinquapin. The species probably arrives in the Yosemite
region in numbers during late April or early May. Through the summer
it is common within its proper range, which extends to greater altitudes
than that of any of the other members of the group. After the young
are reared the birds indulge in a slight up-mountain movement to still
higher levels, even to timber line, in an endeavor to profit by the increased
food supply then available there. The latest record of this bird at hand is
for September 13, 1915, when 5 were seen and 2 collected for positive identification, at Gem Lake (altitude 9036 feet). The 5 birds were in willows,
a habitat not usually frequented by the Wright Flycatcher during the
summer season. This of course marked them as transients; for it is well
known that many species of birds during migration forage or seek shelter
in situations totally different from those which they customarily occupy
during the nesting season.

At Chinquapin, on May 21, 1919, a pair of Wright Flycatchers was
found exercising squatter's rights over about an acre of dense chaparral
on a flat near the stage barns. The thicket was about four feet high and
comprised a dense growth of snowbush (*Ceanothus cordulatus*), green
manzanita, and chinquapin. The male bird had a number of forage posts
at the tops of some dwarfed black oaks which struggled up slightly above
the general level of the chaparral; he would progress from one to another

f these in rather regular succession, catching flies en route. Occasionally
e would go up higher, 30 feet or so, to one of the outstanding limbs of
neighboring sugar pine or red fir, and from there he would sing. The
emale did not seek such prominent perches but kept flying low between
he clumps of brush, often disappearing completely within a canopy of
op-foliage, but as far as could be determined at no particular spot. No
nest was located and it is likely that building did not commence until
some days later. At the same locality on June 10, 1915, a bird of this
species was seen carrying nesting material into a similar thicket. Flycatchers generally nest somewhat later than vegetarian birds, probably
because flying insects, especially in the mountains, do not become abundant
enough to ensure successfully rearing a broad of young until the season
is considerably advanced. As one goes up the mountains to higher zones,
'spring' and 'summer' are observed to occur later and later according to
the calendar.

A male Wright Flycatcher which came to our attention on the floor
of Yosemite Valley near Stoneman bridge had evidently located there
for the summer. His singing perch was a limb of a yellow pine about
30 feet above the ground; below him were numerous chokecherry thickets.
No female was seen. The bird was watched on several occasions between
May 19 and 22, and his song translated on the spot as follows: *se-put,
wurt'sel, see'-pit, swer'-zel, see'wurz,* and so on. Another translation was
simpler, *p-sip', reck, p-slip,* or even, *be-sick', wreck, be-sick'.* There was
a lisping quality to the utterance throughout, as indicated by the number
of sibilants. Each phrase of the song was accompanied by a violent tweak
of the head and a synchronized jerk of the tail, and at the time of utterance the wing tips were dropped below and apart from the small and
slender tail. The intervals between songs varied in length and during these
rests the flycatcher would occasionally launch forth after a passing insect.

The song of the Wright Flycatcher appears to be more extensive and
more varied than that of any of the other small flycatchers occurring on
the west side of the mountains. Even so, it is relatively simple as compared with the songs of many of the other woodland birds. These flycatchers (the family Tyrannidae) are not true song birds, their vocal
muscles being fewer in number and less developed than those of the
sparrows, warblers, and thrushes. The call note of the Wright Flycatcher
is *see'pit,* or simply *pit,* and is repeated at short intervals. Occasionally
a throaty *serz* is interpolated. And the combination of these, in variable
series, constitutes the song. When the birds are down in the brush the
soft *pit* is the note most given. Presumably this is the call note exchanged
by two birds of a pair so that each may keep track of the whereabouts of
the other.

HAMMOND FLYCATCHER. **Empidonax hammondi** (Xantus)

Field characters.—Similar to those for Wright Flycatcher (which see). If seen a very close range, the following features (to judge from specimens in hand) might prov usable: Coloration both above and below as in Wright Flycatcher but darker moi slaty gray; size, especially of bill, less. *Voice:* Like that of Wright Flycatcher, but les in volume and thought to be not so varied. Call note a weak *pit;* song, *sēē'wit, psēē swĕrz,* etc., these three notes repeated many times with little variation.

Occurrence.—Moderately common summer visitant to Canadian Zone on west slop of Sierra Nevada. Recorded by us from Merced Grove and Chinquapin east to Porcu pine Flat and Merced Lake. Found in migration at Pleasant Valley (May 25, 1915) One obtained in Yosemite Valley, September 23, 1917 (J. Mailliard, 1918, p. 18) Restricted closely to red fir forests during nesting season; forages singly, 20 to 100 fee above the ground.

The Hammond Flycatcher during its summer sojourn in the Yosemite region is a constant associate of the red firs. This of course means that it is found in only a limited portion of the Canadian Zone and only on the west side of the mountains. The Wright Flycatcher occurs in the same territory, as well as elsewhere, but it usually keeps near the ground in or close above brush patches, while the Hammond rarely strays below a height of 20 feet, keeping, rather, far aloft among the towering firs.

At Pleasant Valley, on May 25, 1915, Hammond Flycatchers were passing through in migration, although on May 25, 1919, birds of this species were found to be already located in the red firs at Tamarack Flat and even earlier (May 20) near Chinquapin. During the nesting season the species keeps close to its favorite forest trees, but after the broods of young are reared the young at least begin to wander higher into the mountains and to invade the Hudsonian Zone. On August 22, 1915, an immature bird was taken at 10,000 feet altitude on the north side of Mount Clark; two others were seen that day at 10,500 feet on the upper slopes of the same peak. The latest seasonal record is for August 28, 1915, when two immature birds were collected one mile east of Merced Lake. A small flycatcher seen at close range in this same locality on September 1, 1915, was thought to be a Hammond.

The call note of the Hammond Flycatcher is weaker than that of the Wright, being a soft *pit.* And the song is usually simpler and weaker in delivery than that of the Wright, and may be written as *see' wit, pseet, swerz,* etc. This three-part song is uttered at varying intervals for many minutes as the bird perches on the terminal twig of some outstanding dead branch two-thirds the way toward the top of a fir. When foraging the birds display considerable activity, changing their locations every 5 or 10 seconds. This may mean that flying insects are less abundant upward of 100 feet above the ground than at lower levels and must be more sought

fter there than within the forage range of the low-dwelling species of
lycatchers.

No nests of the Hammond Flycatcher came to our notice, but birds
aken in late June, 1915, gave indubitable evidence of nesting.

TRAILL FLYCATCHER. **Empidonax trailli trailli** (Audubon)

Field characters.—Similar to those for Wright Flycatcher (which see). Coloration
above more brownish, beneath less deeply grayish than in that species, nearly white.
Voice: A rather soft though staccato *whit'*, or *quip'*, given sometimes 2 or 3 times in
quick succession; also a song consisting of many repetitions of a phrase resembling
whēēt-p'teer.

Occurrence.—Common summer visitant locally in Sonoran Zones, and lower part of
Transition Zone (chiefly in Yosemite Valley), on west slope of Sierra Nevada; also in
Transition Zone in vicinity of Mono Lake. Restricted to willow thickets of broad
bottomlands. Met with in pairs which keep close to cover among the willow stems.

The Traill Flycatcher is essentially a bird of the extensive tracts of
willows marking the meandering stream courses in the broader bottomlands. In the Yosemite region it is most abundant in the Merced river-
bottom near Snelling. Yet it finds conditions favorable again, after the
long interval of narrow cañon, on the floor of Yosemite Valley and is
fairly common there during the midsummer season. It occurs in the same
season east of the mountains, along the lower stream courses in the vicinity
of Mono Lake. The bird's soft-toned yet short call notes, resembling somewhat those of the Russet-backed Thrush though not so full-toned, and the
restricted type of habitat, must ordinarily be depended upon to identify
this flycatcher. No other small flycatcher is found in close association
with this species during the nesting season. The Traill adheres closely
to the cover of thickets; it must be looked for beneath the level of the
willow tops. It is thus very different in perch predilection from most
of the other Empidonaces.

On July 30, 1915, a nest of the Traill Flycatcher was found in a
blackberry bush which grew beside a small slough or ditch near the
Yosemite Valley schoolhouse. The nest was 3 feet above the ground in
the outer edge of the bush; it was made of grass and weed stems and lined
with horsehair. It contained three small young. One parent bird was
about and acted with great concern; but it was shy to the extent of keeping
well hidden within the foliage of the vegetation bordering the slough,
whence it uttered a series of anxious notes. On May 17, 1919, the Traill
Flycatchers were already present in Yosemite Valley. A male heard in
full song on that date repeated over and over again with trying sameness
a phrase something like *whēēt-p'teer.* The bird was so much of the time
out of sight that its location was to be guessed mainly from the direction

of this song. Our latest record, seasonally, is for September 17 (1915) when an immature female was taken near Williams Butte. The latest record for the species in Yosemite Valley is for September 11 (1920 (C. W. Michael, MS).

On Smith Creek, at Dudley, July 14, 1920, a nest was found in a springy place grown luxuriantly to willow, azalea, and blueberry. The nest, measured to the level of the rim, was 37 inches (940 mm.) above the ground, built into the five upright forks of an azalea stem, well beneath the general foliage 'ceiling.' The bird sat until approached within a distance of six feet. There were 3 buff-toned eggs with brown spots, opaque, and therefore far incubated. The nest was the usual compact cup-like structure and consisted entirely of gray weathered bark fibers.

WESTERN FLYCATCHER. **Empidonax difficilis difficilis** Baird

Field characters.—Similar to those for Wright Flycatcher (which see). Upper surface of body olive green, under surface definitely yellowish; lower mandible wholly yellow beneath. *Voice:* Call note a clear shrilly whistled *swee'ip;* song, a shrill, three-part, *see'rip, sip, see'rip,* repeated at short intervals.

Occurrence.—Sparse summer visitant to Transition Zone on west side of Sierra Nevada. Observed in Yosemite Valley from May 1 (1916) to July 30 (1915), at Merced Grove Big Trees, and along Smith Creek (east of Coulterville). Frequents chiefly wooded cañon bottoms where incense cedars and alders line the streams. Forages singly, and perches 10 to 25 feet above the ground.

We found the Western Flycatcher to be rare and local in the Yosemite region, and restricted to the Transition Zone. A single individual was noted at the McCarthy Ranch (altitude 3200 feet) at the beginning of the forest, 3 miles east of Coulterville, and Mr. Donald D. McLean has record of a nest at Dudley, a short distance farther east. Two individuals were seen at Merced Grove Big Trees. All our other records pertain to Yosemite Valley, one of which, made at 5700 feet, on the Yosemite Point Trail, marks the highest place at which the species was observed. Seasonally the records range from May 1 (1916) to July 30 (1915), both dates for the Valley itself. To judge from observations in other parts of California, it seems likely that the birds arrive somewhat earlier and depart later than the limiting dates just given. Our observations on the floor of Yosemite Valley were not continuous during the seasons of migration.

The Western Flycatcher exhibits the same traits in posture and forage habits as do other members of the flycatcher family. When on the lookout for insects, an occupation which fills most of its waking hours, it sits on some twig in erect rather than horizontal posture and there turns its head from side to side, darting out in rapid flight after any suitable insect which may chance to pass close at hand. The Western Warbling Vireo nd the Cassin Vireo, which live in the same sort of territory, bear a superficial resemblance in size and coloration to the Western Flycatcher; but their voices and manner of foraging are totally unlike the flycatcher's, o that there is no need to confuse these birds with this or with any other of the flycatchers.

On the morning of June 3, 1915, a Western Flycatcher was watched as it sang and foraged among the big-trunked incense cedars and huge mossy boulders on the north side of the Yosemite Valley, at the foot of Rocky Point. The greenish yellow of the bird's upper plumage and its yellowish under surface were the only sight characters available, but the call note and song were both distinctive. The former was a single high-pitched, even piercing, *swee'ip* or *twee'it;* less often a fainter *peet* was uttered. The song proper goes *see'rip, sip, see'rip,* or sometimes *see'rip, sert, sip, see'rip,* and is repeated over and over again, often so continuously that the pauses between songs seem no greater than the intervals between the constituent notes. The syllables were given in varying order, and often the single combination, *see'rip,* was uttered over and over again. While singing, this bird was perched on various twigs and branches 10 to 20 feet above the ground. The song is to be heard most often in May and early June, but as late as July 30 a bird was heard in full summer song.

Gray Flycatcher. **Empidonax griseus** Brewster

Field characters.—As for Wright Flycatcher (which see). Judging from specimens in hand the following features might prove usable in life if the bird be seen at close range and be in fresh, unworn plumage: Coloration as in Wright Flycatcher but paler, more ashy gray; general size slightly greater; bill longer and proportionately narrower, with base of lower mandible pale-colored, rather than dark throughout. *Voice:* As far as learned, like that of Wright Flycatcher.

Occurrence.—Summer visitant to lower levels east of the Sierras. Specimens taken in 1916 in Mono Lake district as follows: near Williams Butte, May 6; at Mono Mills, June 8; and on Dry Creek (at 6600 feet altitude) north of Mono Mills, June 11. Also rare transient on west slope of Sierras, at Dudley, 6 miles east of Coulterville (specimen in D. D. McLean collection taken May 20, 1916). Inhabits tracts of large-sized sage and *Kunzia* bushes.

When a group of birds is so difficult of field identification as are the small flycatchers, only through long-continued practice can one expect satisfactorily to approach facility in recognizing the species. The Gray Flycatcher is sharply set off from both the Traill and the Western on the ground of voice; but this test fails absolutely in differentiating the Wright; and, in our experience, the Hammond has not sufficient individuality always to be identified with certainty. Behavior seems to be identical in the Gray, the Wright, and the Hammond, so that there remain, as means of identifying the Gray, only the few structural features indicated above; and these are so small that, even with series of specimens, doubtless as a result of individual variation, uncertainty as to the exact allocation of some particular specimen now and then confronts us.

Of all the Empidonaces, the Gray Flycatcher is largest and grayest; the contrast, when specimens are compared, between the Gray and, say, the Hammond, is quite apparent. But it must still be urged that such differences are not great enough to serve in identification at a distance, with the birds flitting about elusively amid surroundings of varied light and shade.

The Gray Flycatcher, when settled for the summer, is a bird of the arid Great Basin fauna. It enters the Yosemite region in the environs of Mono Lake, where our limited information suggests its restriction to the tracts of sagebrush and Kunzia where these bushes reach largest size. In this sort of 'chaparral,' the Gray Flycatcher doubtless nests, as does its near relative, the Wright, in the darker-hued, more typical chaparral of the Sierras. It is interesting to note that the Wright Flycatcher, as a breeding bird, was found to extend eastward down the slopes of Leevining Peak nearly or quite to the edge of Mono Lake; it there becomes a close neighbor of its very near relative, the Gray Flycatcher.

HORNED LARKS.   Otocoris alpestris (Linnaeus)[20]

Field characters.—In size somewhat larger than Linnet; decidedly smaller than Meadowlark; length about 6 inches. A patch on breast, one on either side of head, and a bar across forehead, black; tail blackish with narrow white margins; upper surface of body light brown, more or less darkly streaked; under surface whitish. Adult male has a short 'horn' (tuft of black feathers) above each eye. When on ground walks rather than hops; runs with celerity. *Voice:* Call notes faint and high pitched, *see-weetle, see-tle,* or *sleet;* song, a series of tinkling notes, *teet, toot, teet-teetle-eetle-eetle,* which is uttered most persistently when the bird circles about high overhead.

Occurrence.—Common resident on the plains of the San Joaquin Valley (Lower Sonoran Zone); occasionally visits small open meadows in foothills west of main Sierra Nevada (race *actia*). Also occurs, at least in summer, locally, east of the Sierras (race *merrilli*). Casual in fall and winter at Smith Creek east of Coulterville, and above Ten Lakes. Live on the ground in open country, usually in loose flocks.

The Horned Lark is a bird of the open country, inhabiting the plains of the San Joaquin Valley and the adjacent rolling grasslands. It also occurs here and there on the meadows in the adjacent western foothills

---

[20] The Horned Larks at Lagrange and Snelling and west of Pleasant Valley belong to the common resident subspecies of the San Joaquin Valley, the California Horned Lark, *Otocoris alpestris actia* Oberholser. Another race, the Dusky Horned Lark, *Otocoris alpestris merrilli* Dwight, is found in the Mono Lake region, and a few individuals stray westward during the fall and winter. With specimens in hand, *merrilli* as compared with *actia* is seen to be of larger size throughout and to have a grayish rather than reddish cast of coloration, with the dark streaks on the upper surface more sharply contrasted.

of the Yosemite section, as well as again in the open country east of the Sierra Nevada. Wherever it nests the species is probably resident through-out the year, as it most certainly is in the San Joaquin Valley. East of the mountains, where heavy snow covers the ground for at least a portion of the winter season, the birds may be partially migratory, although of this we are uncertain, because we made no winter observations in the Mono Lake region.

The Horned Lark is a notably gregarious species. Even during the breeding season, when the pairs severally are attending to the duties of nesting, members of neighboring pairs are wont to convene together, apparently for the mere sake of sociability. Dusty roadways are favorite meeting places and here it is that the Horned Lark is most likely to come to the attention of the traveler. When on the ground the birds walk with alternate tread and a consequent side to side movement of the body and fore and aft movement of the head, resembling, in these respects, Brewer Blackbirds and Pipits. If a bird be excited or frightened its walk changes into a gliding run; when advancing in this manner the straight forward movement of its pale-colored body along the ground renders it decidedly inconspicuous.

If put to flight Horned Larks get under way quickly, each individual pursuing an undulating course; the flock assumes an irregular, scattered formation, circles about, and often alights close to the place from which it was frightened. The dull colored back and pale under surface match well with the earth or sky; but at times, as the birds glide slantingly through the air, the white under lining of the wings shows momentarily in silvery flashes.

The rather faint call notes, *see-weetle, see-tle,* or just *sleet,* are uttered at irregular intervals while the birds are either on the ground or in flight. A distinct flight call is also given when the members of a flock begin to take wing; this resembles the syllables *twee-too-too-too, twee-too,* clear and plaintive. In the spring there is a definite song on the part of the male, consisting of a series of weak finely attenuated notes, with a pleasant tinkling quality: *teet, toot, teet-teetle-eetle-eetle.* This song may be uttered when the bird is perched on a clod or hummock, but is also given, and then much more impressively, when the bird circles high overhead in seemingly aimless course. This it does for many minutes at a time, giving a sug-gestion of the genetic relationship which the Horned Lark bears to the Skylark of the Old World.

The race of Horned Lark occurring east of the mountains is relatively uncommon there, doubtless because of the scarcity of suitable prairie land. On May 12, 1916, a pair was encountered on an open piece of ground which had been cleared of sagebrush and used as a sheep corral. A few others were met with in dry places where the sagebrush was naturally sparse. Some at least of these east-side birds wander westward in the fall and winter seasons, though this movement is not so general as to constitute a real migration. On October 11, 1915, three Horned Larks were seen on an open level spot at an altitude of 9700 feet, above Ten Lakes. The one taken here proved to belong to the race *merrilli*, as did another bird collected at Smith Creek, six miles east of Coulterville, on January 20, 1916.

At Snelling and Lagrange, Horned Larks (of subspecies *actia*) are to be found in considerable numbers throughout the year. In December and January they were seen on the open rolling tableland back from the Merced River on common ground with Pipits. In one instance the two species were mingled in the same flock. On January 8, 1915, Horned Larks at Snelling were darting about erratically, at dusk, in pairs, giving the trilled pursuit notes which mark the beginning of the courting season.

The breeding season in the San Joaquin Valley is early, beginning in early April; and by the latter part of May fully grown young are to be seen in numbers. On May 28, 1915, fully 50 birds, adults and juveniles, were recorded in an hour and a quarter's census at Snelling. East of the mountains the breeding season is somewhat later. The first young bird observed there in 1916 was seen on June 26.

BLACK-BILLED MAGPIE. **Pica pica hudsonia** (Sabine)

Field characters.—Decidedly larger than any of our jays. Total length about 18 inches. Tail much longer than head and body, streamer-like. Plumage black except for abruptly white belly (pl. 56*a*) and large white area on hind part of each wing, the latter area showing best in flight. *Voice:* Not jay-like; various low, chuckling sounds.

Occurrence.—Common resident[21] of Transition Zone east of Sierra Nevada, from near Walker Lake eastward to eastern boundary of Yosemite section and beyond. Frequents vicinity of trees and thickets in open country. More or less socially inclined.

The Black-billed or American Magpie is likely to be one of the first birds to meet the eye of the traveler upon his arrival in the plains-like arid territory east of the Sierra Nevada. In a region where many of the birds and mammals reflect the general tone of their environment by wearing plumage or pelage of a generally pale color, the strikingly contrasted jet black and pure white coloration of the magpie stands out strongly and renders the bird impossible of confusion with any other species in the region.

---

[21] The Yellow-billed Magpie (*Pica nuttalli*), found in various parts of western California, has been recorded from the west base of the Sierra Nevada both north and south of the Yosemite section and is thus likely to occur within our area; but we did not see or hear anything of it. It differs from the Black-billed Magpie chiefly in the possession of a yellow bill, instead of a black one.

The deliberate, seemingly slow, aeroplane-like flight of the magpie, with its long tail trailing out behind, makes an impression not soon to be lost. The observer is reminded of the appearance of a black and white ribbon streaming in the wind. Added to this is an illusionary effect in distant flight when the bird seems alternately to appear and disappear as the strokes of the rounded wings in turn hide and expose the large patches of white on the longer flight feathers.

The general demeanor of the Black-billed Magpie appealed to us as being decidedly quieter than that of most of the other members of the jay-magpie-crow family. Its voice is far softer than that of the jays, and it does not 'bawl out' intruders as do those birds. Many of its notes are low and pleasant chuckling sounds, recalling certain notes of the California Thrasher. On one occasion one of our party was attracted by a noise arising in a mountain mahogany bush and sounding like two of the branches rubbing together. It proved to come from a Black-billed Magpie. Even in early fall, when bluejays and nutcrackers are at their noisiest, the magpie is noticeably quiet.

The nests of the Black-billed Magpie are among the most conspicuous of all the bird structures to be seen about Mono Lake. Large to a degree not known even to most hawks, the 'wicker-work' homes of the magpie loom up from afar, sometimes being visible at a distance of half a mile. The large size of the nest is due in part to the quantity of material used, and also to the fact that the nesting cavity is covered by a dome-shaped 'roof' so that the sitting bird or brood is protected from above as well as from below. When our party visited the vicinity of Mono Lake in the fall of 1915 many of these nests were seen; and in the field work in the spring of 1916 a large number were observed, some newly built and occupied by magpies, others constructed in earlier years and often in use by Long-eared Owls. Near the "Salmon Ranch" on the west shore of Mono Lake, on June 19, 1916, fully 20 old nests of this magpie were observed in the course of one morning's visit, several times, in fact, the number of pairs of the birds seen. This testifies to the durability of the nests, some of which undoubtedly last several years, even when not repaired and reoccupied in successive seasons.

A single nest of the Black-billed Magpie was sent to the Museum of Vertebrate Zoology from Laws, Inyo County, southeast of the Yosemite section, and this is the only one available for detailed study. The structure as a whole measures approximately 20 inches in outside diameter, and the height with the dome in place is almost as much; in other words, the nest is practically a sphere of 20 inches diameter. The cavity within is about 7 inches in diameter and the same or slightly more in height. The construction outwardly is loose, many of the twigs being ready to fall away at a touch. The material comprises pieces of all the common woody plants in the vicinity, such as willow, saltbush, and sagebrush. There is an outer portion comprised only of twigs, then a middle framework which includes a considerable amount of mud applied wet, and then the lining of the inner cavity, which consists of small twigs and which is of a relatively soft texture. These three portions grade insensibly into one another. Another nest, found near Mono Lake and measured in the field, was of more compact construction and was neatly lined with fine rootlets and horse-hair. Outside, this nest measured 24 by 18 by 16 inches, while the cavity was about 6 inches in horizontal diameter and 5 inches deep. The nest was placed in a willow thicket, at a height of about 12 feet from the ground. Of the nests found, both new and old, the greater number were placed 10 to 12 feet above the ground in willow thickets and Shepherdia bushes. One was noted only 6 feet above the ground in a Kunzia bush.

The nesting season of this species begins early in the year, before the storms of winter have entirely ceased, and the broods of young are sometimes out of the nest before the willows are in full summer foliage. At the Farrington Ranch near Williams Butte, in 1916, a nest was found with 6 eggs in it on April 27, and another nest with 7 eggs, already about one-third incubated, on May 1. By May 11 all the eggs in one nest had hatched and the oldest members of the brood had their eyes open and their wing quills started. Eight days later, on May 19, the largest member of this same brood was just able to perch on a branch unassisted, and by June 1 this entire brood, as well as another family not noted earlier, had left the nest. On June 3 a young magpie was collected which had its wing feathers still in the sheaths; one taken on June 23 had these feathers nearly full sized. On June 28 a family of young birds almost fully fledged was seen near Mono Lake. The tail in the young birds taken on June 3 and 23 is only partly grown; indeed the full length of the tail seems not to be attained until well on toward the end of the summer. (See pl. 56a.)

Residents of the region about Mono Lake were unanimous in condemning the magpie. They accuse the bird of stealing hen's eggs from the farmyards, and, further, of alighting on the backs of horses and cattle to peck at any wounds or open sores, thus preventing such spots from healing. As tending to substantiate the above allegation, one of our party saw a magpie that was making obvious efforts to peck a hole in the back of a cow that was down on the ground, helpless, but still alive. Later, when this cow died, the carcass served as a forage place visited regularly by several magpies.

It might be remarked in passing that Williams Butte, near Mono Lake, is an exceptionally good locality at which to study birds of the family Corvidae. In September, 1915, the Black-billed Magpie and Clark Nutcracker, and the Blue-fronted, Woodhouse and Piñon jays were all seen at that station. At no other locality in this country with which we are familiar can so many members of this family be seen at the same time within a few rods of one another.

BLUE-FRONTED JAY. **Cyanocitta stelleri frontalis** (Ridgway)

Field characters.—Somewhat larger than Robin. Head with a conspicuous crest; tail as long as body, broad, and slightly rounded at end; wings short and rounded. Head (including crest) and forepart of body, blackish; wings, tail, and hinder part of body, chiefly deep blue. Young more blackish, less blue, especially on lower surface, and plumage more fluffy. *Voice:* Extremely varied (see below); usual calls harsh and loud, *ksch, kschäk,* or *glöök,* in series of three.

Occurrence.—Common resident of Transition and Canadian zones on west slope of Sierra Nevada and of Canadian Zone on east slope. Recorded from Smith Creek (east of Coulterville) and Feliciana Mountain, east to Lake Tenaya and Lake Merced; also from cañon of Leevining Creek opposite Warren Fork east to Williams Butte. A partial vertical migration to lower altitudes (as to El Portal and even Pleasant Valley) occurs in at least some winters. Remains in Yosemite Valley throughout the year. Frequents wooded territories; seldom descends to ground. Non-flocking, but individuals quickly assemble about any object or sound which incites their curiosity.

The Blue-fronted Jay is the Sierra Nevadan representative of the Steller or crested jays, a wide-ranging group found throughout most of the mountainous regions of western north and middle America. Blue jays, of any species, by reason of their large size, loud voices, and bold manners, bring themselves quickly to the attention of all who visit their haunts, and this is eminently true of the subject of the present account. Locally the Blue-fronted Jay is known as the "mountain blue jay" because of its restriction to the higher altitudes, and to distinguish it from the California, Woodhouse, and Piñon jays found in the lower country on either side of the mountains. The name 'blue-fronted,' designating this particular jay, refers to the streaks of light blue which face the crest in front, that is, just above the base of the bill. This color mark is not conspicuous enough, however, to serve as a mark for field identification.

The Blue-fronted Jay inhabits both the Transition and Canadian zones. On the west slope its range meets that of the crestless or flat-headed California Jay where the main forest belt of the mountains proper gives way to the foothill oaks and chaparral. In a few places along this line or belt of contact these two jays are found together; but each keeps as a rule to its special niche, the Blue-fronted to the pines, the California to the live oaks and blue oaks. Upward, the range of the Blue-fronted ends abruptly at the Canadian-Hudsonian boundary, above which is found the Clark Nutcracker. On the east slope of the mountains, in the Yosemite region, the Blue-fronted Jay is found only in the Canadian Zone. The Transition Zone of the arid interior lacks at this latitude any extensive growth of forest trees, and this fact probably accounts for the absence of Blue-fronted Jays from that part of the Transition Zone.

As a species the Blue-fronted Jay occupies the range outlined above throughout the year, but with the coming of winter there is a down-mountain movement (altitudinal migration) which carries a portion of the jay population to lower zones. This has been observed on the west slope of the Sierras and may occur on the east side as well. At El Portal, on November 28, 1914, an influx of Blue-fronted Jays was observed immediately following the first fall of snow for the season on the adjacent higher ridges. In 1915, on December 8, Blue-fronted Jays suddenly appeared at Pleasant Valley. The jays stayed there "through the winter" according to local testimony, but were gone by the end of February. Mr. Donald D. McLean has told us that a certain number of these jays regularly drop to below Coulterville for the winter months. In certain winters, presumably those marked by severe storms in the mountains, Blue-fronted Jays have migrated down even into the San Joaquin Valley, for instance, to Stockton. It seems likely that difficulty in getting adequate food is a more important factor in influencing this semi-migration than unfavorable weather, especially since a certain number of the jays seem to find no inconvenience in remaining in the higher zones throughout the winter season.

During the nesting season the jays are to be seen in devoted pairs, and after the broods leave the nest the fullgrown young and their parents remain for a time in family parties. With the coming of fall, the parental and filial instincts wane, these family parties break up, and the individuals scatter out rather uniformly through the forest. But the jays retain a strong social sympathy which causes the separated birds to quickly congregate about any object or sound which excites their curiosity. In midwinter, even this interest decreases and the jays then seem to pay little attention to contemporary events, unless food be involved. Heightened curiosity is, for birds in general, an accessory of the nesting season when danger, apparent or real, threatening either the nest or brood, must be guarded against. At the opposite season, midwinter, when nesting instincts are at their lowest ebb, curiosity also lags. *Self*-preservation is then the important factor. But even putting this seasonal variation aside, Blue-fronted Jays show marked interest in most of the events which take place about them. Often when the observer is seeking one of the rarer or more reclusive birds or mammals of the forest, his cautious stalking comes to naught because of the blatant squawking of one of these garrulous informers. In our own case, frustration of our original purpose has more than once resulted in our pointed attention being directed toward the disturbing jay!

The Blue-fronted Jay spends much the greater part of its time in the trees; it does not forage extensively on the ground as does the California Jay. A favorite perch is near the top of a tall tree where it can command a wide range of vision and hence see all that goes on in the forest. Ascending a tree it is wont to keep close to the trunk and hop upward from one limb to another, assisted occasionally by a flutter of the wings. At times a bird will ascend one tree, then sail down on spread wings and tail to the bottom of an adjacent tree and from there repeat the performance. Such actions are usually accompanied by certain of the harsh scolding calls described later. This trait of keeping close to the trunk, "like following a spiral staircase" as one observer has expressed it, makes the birds difficult to watch during the nesting season when they are endeavoring to avoid being seen. At such times they often run along lengthwise on the branches in furtherance of their attempts to elude observation. A mannerism of the bird which particularly impresses the observer at times is its turning the head abruptly this way or that while looking about; in so doing its tall pointed crest is switched from side to side so that the presence of this adornment is emphasized.

The jays are closely related to the crows and share with those birds the possession of an elaborate vocabulary. A commonly heard call of the Blue-fronted Jay is a series of harsh staccato notes variously rendered *chuck, chuck, chuck,* or *quick, quick, quick,* or *kschăk, kschăk, kschăk,* given in quick succession and usually uttered as the jay flies off, on spread wings and tail, and sails into the shelter of a neighboring tree. Then there is a softer though yet harsh, more slowly enunciated, scolding *ksch, ksch, ksch,* or *kwisch, kwisch, kwisch,* given three or more times while a jay is perched or hopping upward in a tree. Again there is a deeper, hollow toned or wooden, *glŏŏk, glŏŏk, glŏŏk.* Occasionally a jay will take position in dense foliage and then utter a clear, whistled *skwee-oo,* resembling the cry of a Red-tailed Hawk as heard at a distance. Under similar circumstances we have heard two other, weird notes, which, since we are unable to express them in syllables or to imitate them, we must merely designate as the 'dry-pump' note, and the 'wheelbarrow' note. A modification of the *ksch* note leads to *kschuey,* more prolonged and more often uttered singly than in series of three. When two jays of a pair are hunting close together a low crackling or growling *ker'r'r'r'r* is uttered. This cannot be heard at any distance and seems to be used most frequently during the nesting season. All these calls are uttered with modifications and different intonations so that a great variety of sound results. It is known that Blue Jays occasionally give a low but musical song and also that at least some individuals can imitate other birds besides hawks. It seems likely, therefore, that these birds are able to comment intelligibly to one another on many different experiences and situations. Here, in this, one of the 'highest' of the birds, we find that a 'language' has been evolved, doubtless to the increased advantage of the species.

Blue-fronted Jays are omnivorous, in that they take any and all kinds of food that the season or place may afford. Camp scraps, bread, fruit, etc., are eaten more or less readily, and pieces of fresh meat are always in demand. An adult male shot on the East Fork of Indian Cañon above Yosemite Valley on June 25, 1915, had its mouth and throat filled with beetles. Two Blue-fronted Jays seen in golden oaks near Yosemite Point on November 19, 1915, along with Band-tailed Pigeons and California Gray Squirrels, were evidently feeding on acorns. The latter source is doubtless a mainstay, resorted to when more desirable food fails.

An interesting habit of the Blue-fronted Jay in hiding food material has been recorded by Dr. Barton Warren Evermann (1915a, p. 58). While his party was eating lunch at Happy Isles on July 12, 1914, one of these jays came down close in quest of food. Bits of cracker were thrown to the bird one at a time. One of these was carried off into the forest, another was eaten, and a third piece was carried to a neighboring incense cedar. This piece the jay wedged and drove into a crevice in the bark and then stripped off several small pieces of bark and placed them in the crack so as to conceal effectively the piece of cracker. The habit recalls that of the California Jay in burying acorns and other bits of provender in the ground.

Enemies of the Blue-fronted Jay do not seem to be numerous. We have already related, in the chapter on the Sharp-shinned Hawk, an encounter between one of those birds and a jay. Mr. Donald D. McLean says that this hawk is the principal enemy of the Blue-fronted Jay at his place east of Coulterville.

No bird in the assemblage of forest-inhabiting species is more secretive with regard to its nesting activities than the Blue-fronted Jay. During the whole of this season, all the artfulness of which the jay is capable is devoted to keeping secret the location of its nest. The structure, although large, as are the nests of most birds of this family, is often hidden in a dense growth of vegetation. And the greatest stealth is observed by the jay in gathering and carrying nest material and in approaching or leaving the site, no matter whether the nest is only under construction or contains eggs or young. No notes are uttered within the immediate environs of a nest and so upon hearing a jay call during the late spring or early summer, one may know at once that the bird is *not* at its nest.

In the Yosemite region the nesting season of this species begins in April or early May and lasts until July. The nest with young, found on May 18, 1919 (see below), must have been begun in late April. The numerous foraging expeditions of the Blue-fronted Jays during June, as announced by the commotions among small birds heard during that month, probably meant that the jays had young at that time, as did the finding of a mass of insects in the throat of an adult jay taken on June 25, 1915. In Yosemite Valley, on June 27, 1915, a family of these birds was seen, the young still being attended by their parents. Only two nests of this jay came to our immediate attention.

On the road between ''Kenneyville'' and Mirror Lake in Yosemite Valley, on May 22, 1919, a pair of Blue-fronted Jays was come upon in the act of gathering material for their nest. Several people had camps on the ground about what proved to be the nest tree, so that the jays did not in this instance seem to mind the presence of an observer and they were watched for some minutes. One of the jays was seen to fly into a black oak, obtain a twig, and carry it off, upward, through the adjacent trees to the nest site, at the top of a yellow pine, fully 40 feet above the ground. Then the other member of the pair came, broke off a twig, dropped it, evidently by accident, and sought another. This bird seemed more particular and hopped about the tree for some time before choosing another twig. Pieces dry enough to break off readily, and a little longer than the jay's body, were chosen, and twisted off by a wrench with the bill. The twig would be worked along between the mandibles until held across the middle and then the jay would ascend by the usual vertical hopping and short flights to the nest. Following the taking of black oak twigs the two jays, together, flew across the river which flowed close by the nest tree, and there, descending quickly to the ground, sought material in an azalea thicket at the edge of the water. Each took a quantity of twigs and grass and apparently also some mud, and flew again to the nest tree. Again they took twigs from the black oak. From this alternate selection of twigs and muddy material it was inferred that the nest was well under way. The jays were not heard to call within 150 feet of the nest tree. One was seen, after depositing material at the nest site, to sail monoplane-like off through the trees, calling only after the nest was well behind.

On May 18, 1919, careful search through a thicket of young pine trees on the floor of Yosemite Valley in the vicinity of Rocky Point led to the discovery of an occupied nest of the Blue-fronted Jay. The nest was in a small yellow pine which stood at the edge of the thicket bordering a clearing which opened onto the Merced River about 30 yards off. The rim of the nest was 2700 millimeters (8 feet 10 inches) above the ground, and the structure was on the south side of the trunk resting on three small branches of the whorl which at that height emanated from the trunk. The nest, when once located, was easily seen on the open side even from a distance. It was a bulky affair, decidedly larger than the usual Robin's nest. It was solid in construction, with a large external basal framework of dead and more or less weathered twigs of irregular shape and small diameter (2 millimeters or less). Many of these were black oak twigs while others were of a very furry herbaceous plant. All of the material of this outer framework, as was attested by the clean, fresh-appearing ends of the pieces, had been freshly broken off by the jays. This suggests that, save for the small amount of herbaceous material, all the outer constituents were gathered above the ground. The outside framework measured about 300 millimeters (12 inches) in one direction and 400 millimeters (16 inches) in the other.

The inner cup of this nest was composed of dry needles of the yellow pine, held together by enough mud to give the structure a firm resistant feel. The mud, however, did not extend to the inner surface. The interior of the cup consisted solely of pine needles, which crossed and recrossed so as to make a porous interior lining. This cup was 100 millimeters (4 inches) in diameter at the rim and 68 millimeters (2⅝ inches) deep at the center. Both the nest and the ground beneath were entirely clean of excrement.

The nest held three young, nearly naked, and hence not over 3 or 4 days old. An adult jay had been covering the young, but flushed at the observer's near approach. The bird slipped off quietly to an adjacent tree and there struck a dumb, statuesque pose which was maintained for a minute or so until the observer showed obvious interest in the nest. Then the bird set up the usual call, *ksch* or *kschuey*, repeated over and over again. This brought another jay, presumably the mate (the two sexes are exactly alike save that the female is very slightly the smaller), and soon afterward two others. All four joined in the vocal demonstration. When the jays first set up their calls, two California Gray Squirrels, a Sierra Chickaree, and a pair of Spurred Towhees began to call, but these all quieted down after a time. When the nest was removed from the tree for closer study the four demonstrative jays came close about and called in raucous chorus, but after a while they began to move away and changed their calls to the more wooden-sounding type of note. Thus the Blue-fronted Jay exhibits a marked concern over the disturbance of its own home.

It remains to tell the jay's relation to other birds at this season. Bird students have for years known that the Blue-fronted Jay, like its lowland counterpart, the California Jay, is a merciless plunderer of the nests of

small birds. And the small birds have known this, evidently for generations, because they almost universally announce with unmistakable tones
of anxiety the presence of a Blue-fronted Jay near their nests. The
period during which this instinct of blue jays is exercised coincides of
course with the nesting season, when eggs or young of the other birds are
available and when the jays themselves have broods or mates to feed. At
other times of the year the jay and its smaller relatives live in peace.
We, ourselves, while in the Yosemite region, did not chance to see one
actual instance of plundering by this jay; such observations can come
but rarely even to a person on the lookout for them. But we have observed
cases elsewhere, and we know of many reliable reports of the depredations
of this jay. We saw evidence of a circumstantial nature, and some of this
is worth while relating.

In Yosemite Valley on June 1, 1915, our attention was attracted
to a Blue-fronted Jay which was beset by an angry Western Warbling
Vireo and then by a Cassin Vireo in similar mood. Each evidently
suspected the jay of sinister intention and each in turn endeavored to
drive the larger bird away. At Chinquapin, on June 14, 1915, two Red-
breasted Nuthatches were heard calling *wă, wă, wă,* in excited tones. Following up the noise, we found their attention to be centered on a pair of
Blue-fronted Jays. The latter were perfectly quiet, a mannerism for
which the marauders are noted when on their plundering expeditions.
On the same day a Ruby-crowned Kinglet was heard calling its *yer-rup,
yer-rup, yer-rup,* over and over again in low but insistent tones. It, too,
was concerned over a pair of the silent but insidious jays. When one of
the latter was shot the kinglet immediately broke into song! At Mono
Meadow on June 22 some anxious bird notes were heard coming from
the top of a lofty red fir. These, again, proved to be due to the presence
of a pair of Blue-fronted Jays in the neighborhood. In this instance there
were at least 11 small birds at the scene of the disturbance. A pair of
Western Warbling Vireos seemed to be the ones most intimately concerned
and their calls had evidently attracted the other birds to the site. "Those
present" in addition to the vireos were two Wright Flycatchers, two
Western Tanagers, two Audubon Warblers, a Red-breasted Nuthatch, and
two Ruby-crowned Kinglets. All were contributing their voices to the
clamor of remonstrance against the jays. Near Bower Cave, on May 13,
1919, a pair of Willow Woodpeckers was seen mobbing a pair of
Blue-fronted Jays, while a California Woodpecker offered half-hearted
sympathy. The first-named were uttering in monotonous succession their
high-pitched call notes.

Because of the depredations of the Blue-fronted Jay among the smaller
song birds of the Park, the rangers, under the direction of the Park

Superintendent, have, for a number of years, carried on a campaign for the reduction of the Blue-fronted Jay, more particularly in the Yosemite Valley itself. Sixty-seven jays were killed in the midwinter of 1915–16, in the vicinity of the government stables where they kept drifting in after the arrival of the winter snow. A 3-hour census by the junior author in this neighborhood a little later the same winter (February 28, 1916) did not reveal the presence of a single jay there; in fact none was seen on the floor of the Valley during a three day visit at that season. But by the end of April the same year jays were again present in fair numbers. And three years later, in 1919, even though the campaign against these birds had been continued with greater or less persistency during the intervening period, we could not see that their numbers on the floor of Yosemite Valley were below normal.

Some figures, even though somewhat speculative, will be suggestive here. The floor of Yosemite Valley, counting the area below the 5000-foot contour, contains roughly 10 square miles. Upon the basis of our many censuses, we estimate the jay population in early spring, before the advent of the new broods, to be 32 birds to a square mile, or a total of 320 jays for the area in question. This, be it noted, is the population at the time of year when the numbers have been reduced by various natural causes to the lowest figure. With the breeding season, assuming that each pair of adults successfully rears three young, the jay population jumps to 80 a square mile, or 800 for the Valley, an increase of 250 per cent! Because the surrounding territory was a reservoir of reserve jay stock, depletion of the jay population locally on the floor of the Valley, in the campaign described above, was quickly followed by a 'spilling in' of birds from the flats adjacent and the slopes above. The pressure of competition for food between the individuals of the species serves under normal conditions to keep the birds spaced out rather uniformly. Whenever the population is suddenly reduced in one particular place, birds from the surrounding territory, beginning to feel the release of pressure, work in, and soon fill the vacancy. The process is somewhat analogous to bailing grain out of a bin; the 'hole' is quickly filled up.

However much we may deplore the ravages of these jays among the woodland songsters, it seems unlikely that any great or permanent reduction in the numbers of the former can be accomplished through human agency, commensurate, at least, with the cost involved. The species is well able to recover quickly from any local reduction, as has been shown so well in Yosemite Valley. The Blue-fronted Jay is resident over a large stretch of territory but sparsely occupied by man; it soon becomes 'gun wise'; and it is very secretive in its nesting habits. All these factors appeal to us as making reduction hopelessly difficult. Furthermore, the sizes of the broods of the small birds were probably long ago adjusted to the toll taken annually by the jays. Plundering the nest of almost any bird, large or small, early in the nesting season, will be quickly followed by the building of a new nest and the laying of another set of eggs. So that loss once sustained need not mark the total failure of any particular bird pair for the season. In other words, the relation we find obtaining between jays and other birds is the natural, normal condition of affairs, which has come about through a long period of adjustment.

INTERIOR CALIFORNIA JAY. **Aphelocoma californica immanis** Grinnell

Field characters.—Body size about that of Robin but tail longer (as long as body), broader, and rounded at end. No crest on head. Top of head, neck, wings, and tail, blue; back grayish brown; under surface of body grayish white, except for incomplete collar of blue low on breast. *Voice:* A variety of mildly harsh notes: *kwish, cheek, chu'-ick, schwee-ick, kschu-ee;* young out of nest utter a ''teasing scold.''

Occurrence.—Abundant resident of Upper Sonoran Zone on west side of Sierra Nevada. Ranges locally down into Lower Sonoran Zone (as at Snelling) and up into Transition Zone (as at Dudley). Reported in Yosemite Valley (near Lost Arrow Camp), September 25, 1917 (Mailliard, 1918, p. 18), and on several dates in 1920 between July 26 and September 11 (C. W. Michael, MS). Frequents blue and live oaks, digger pines, and chaparral. Non-flocking, but socially inclined.

The Interior California Jay is a characteristic inhabitant of the oak, digger pine, and chaparral growths which clothe the slopes of the foothills flanking the west base of the Sierra Nevada. Only locally does it invade the Great Central Valley below and to the west, or the pine covered slopes of higher elevation immediately to the east. Beyond the Sierras, in the vicinity of Mono Lake, its niche is taken by a closely similar species, the Woodhouse Jay. Within most of its range as thus circumscribed it is the only bird of its family and is abundant there at all times of the year.

Whoever chances to invade the domain of the Interior California Jay will speedily make the acquaintance of the bird, for it is quick to sense the arrival of a newcomer within its range and it promptly makes an investigation of the traveler's business. The large size of the bird and the clear blue of the head, wings, and tail readily identify it as a blue jay, while the grayish white color of the under surface mark it as different from the Piñon Jay which may sometimes visit the western foothills. This gray under surface, the paler blue of the upper parts, and the absence of any sort of crest, all combine to make the California Jay easily distinguishable from the Blue-fronted Jay.

The normal habitat of this species is the foothill oak belt; in the oak trees the jays find everything necessary for their existence, food, shelter for their nests, and retreats for themselves and young. They are found also, however, to some extent in other kinds of trees, and also locally in tracts of pure chaparral. Finding such complete satisfaction of all its life requirements within one relatively narrow zone, it is not surprising that the California Jay is a permanent resident. It does not participate, at least to any appreciable extent, in the late summer, up-mountain, food-seeking migration undertaken by so many foothill birds, the bush-tits, the wren-tits, etc., species which are also ordinarily classed as residents. On a few occasions individuals have been found in Yosemite Valley, though our own party did not happen to see any there. On September 25, 1917, Mr. Joseph Mailliard (1918, p. 18) noted a bird near Lost Arrow Camp. In 1920 Mr. C. W. Michael (MS) noted the species on July 26 and 29, and on several dates in August and September until the 11th of the latter month, ten of the birds being seen on August 27.

The Interior California Jay is notoriously bold and forward in its behavior; although it is counted as a non-flocking species, individuals and pairs will gather quickly in response to the excited calls of one of their kin. The birds seem never to be so busy with their own affairs that they cannot stop and investigate any object of an unusual nature. Ordinarily this jay is the picture of animation. Perched, it stands in an attitude of alertness, its head up, tail straight back or tilted slightly upward, and feet slightly spread. Just after alighting a jay will often execute a deep bow involving the entire body, and this may be repeated a number of times and in different directions. The purpose of this bowing is not clear to us. Leaving a perch in the top of one tree the bird will often fly to another of equal elevation, keeping on a direct and nearly level course high in the air during its passage between the two vantage points. Its flight is characteristic, a few strokes of the short rounded wings, then a sail, while from time to time the tail is spread so that its rounded end and kite-shaped outline show well. Descending from the top of a tree to the ground a jay will sometimes drop at a steep angle, with wings and tail closed, only opening them momentarily to check or guide its passage.

If interest lags the jay will seek a perch at the top of an oak or digger pine, and sit there silent and motionless for minutes at a time, with its tail hanging like a dead weight, vertically downward. But the bird evidently watches all that goes on in the vicinity, for it frequently comes out of one of these reveries with a sudden burst of voice and movement.

When going down to water to drink the behavior of the California Jay is in marked contrast to that of most birds. The jays waste no time in looking about for possible enemies; they probably fear none. The two birds of a pair watched near Coulterville came down to the stream one after the other and each drank three or four times, tipping the head back with each swallow.

The voice of the California Jay, although considerably varied, is easily recognized and remembered after once learned, but we find it difficult to describe intelligibly. To one of the present authors (Grinnell) some of the more common notes seem possible of representation as follows: *cheek, cheek, cheek,* etc., staccato, 3 to 10 times in rapid succession; *chu'-ick, chu'-ick, chu'-ick,* etc., usually in 3's, slowly; *schwee-ick,* higher-pitched, 2 to 6 times, uttered still more slowly. To the other author (Storer) the following transcriptions seem to represent the notes most often heard: (1) A series of mildly harsh notes, *kwish, kwish, kwish,* uttered usually 3 to 5 times in quick succession; (2) a more protracted softer note, *kschu-ee,* or *jai-ē,* usually given singly. Birds of a pair when foraging together, and young and adults when in family parties, utter a subdued guttural *krr'r'r'r'r.* When attending young still in the nest, the parent birds utter a low crooning, impossible of representation in syllables; and the young birds, after leaving the nest and before gaining their living independently, have a "teasing scold" which they utter almost incessantly, in keeping their parents apprised of their need for food. Most or all of the above notes are uttered with various modifications, perhaps to indicate different shades of meaning. As is true of some other members of its family the California Jay employs a 'language' which it probably finds of considerable usefulness.

With the coming of early spring, the instincts which accompany the nesting season are revived and the jays commence the construction of their nests. Building, in some instances, probably begins in April, as by early May nests with eggs or young are common. Young birds, out of the nests, were seen in the third week of May, 1915; while at the same time a pair of adults was seen constructing a nest. All broods are not brought off at the same time. Our findings may be given in some detail here to present a more complete record of the nesting of the California Jay in the Yosemite region.

A nest with 4 nearly fresh eggs was found near Lagrange on May 8 (1919). On May 10, that year, a nest with one young bird and the other eggs on the point of hatching was seen near Coulterville. On May 21 (1915) a nest was found under construction near Pleasant Valley, and on May 23 young were heard, out of the nest, near the same place; while on May 30 an adult with 3 young scarcely able to fly was seen there, and on June 3, a family party of 4 of these jays was seen near the McCarthy ranch, 3 miles east of Coulterville. The young birds remain with their parents for a long time, even into August, and so have a long period of dependence or semi-dependence. After that the individuals or pairs scatter out everywhere through the oak covered regions.

The nest mentioned above as found near Lagrange on May 8, 1919, was in a blue oak on the crown of a rounded hill overlooking the Tuolumne River. The rim of the nest was by actual measurement 4780 millimeters (about 16 feet) from the ground, and was at the side of a horizontal branch 80 millimeters in diameter where some small twigs formed a 5-sided frame into which the nest was set. The foundation work of the nest was about 200 millimeters across, and consisted of crooked dry blue oak twigs. There were large interstices in the weaving. Inside of this was an intermediate layer of dry fine yellow grass stems and rootlets. And within this was a thin lining of black horsehair forming an inner cup. The latter was 100 millimeters in diameter at the top and 50 millimeters deep at the center. The four eggs lay on this inner lining. One of the parent jays had been sitting on the nest, which was readily visible from anywhere within a 50-foot radius of the tree; but the bird flushed at our approach and did not again come within a hundred yards of the site while we were there, although both members of the pair called from a distance several times.

Soon after arriving at Blacks Creek, west of Coulterville, in 1919, we discovered a California Jay's nest in the crotch of a willow which leaned over the creek directly opposite where we had made our camp, and not over 30 feet from the tent door. During the succeeding days we had many opportunities to observe the behavior of the parent birds. When one of us climbed to the nest on May 10, it was found to contain one newly hatched youngster and 3 eggs ready to hatch. The sitting bird had remained until closely approached. It then flushed quietly and returned as soon as the observer quitted the tree. The mate was seen only momentarily on this occasion. The remaining eggs evidently hatched on that day or the next, as the adults had by that time begun to busy themselves in obtaining food and bringing it to the nest.

The parent birds had a particular route in approaching and leaving the nest, and this route was adhered to strictly. They would always approach through the trees of a wooded slope to the east, and then, having reached the nest tree, hop by easy stages to a position on the west side of the nest. From there the nestlings would be fed, and then the nest cleaned. After that the bird would work out of the south side of the willow, fly to a digger pine across the creek immediately above our tent, hop upward until near the top of the pine, and from there would take off in a direct course to its next forage ground. Even when the jays had been hunting insects in the open area immediately west of our camp, they would circle about when ready to return to the nest and approach it from the east. Only one adult visited the nest at a time although they often followed one another in quick succession. Save for the low crooning given when standing over the young, no calls were uttered while the parents were in the vicinity of the nest. There was a 'zone of quiet' about their home, within which the owners would not call or raise any alarm.

The California Jay shares with others of its tribe the reputation of a plunderer of the nests of other birds. Both eggs and young are taken in season, but usually the jays' persecution of the smaller species ends by late summer. Mr. Donald D. McLean has told us, however, that on one occasion in midwinter he saw a California Jay kill a Sierra Junco. While near Coulterville we heard and saw several demonstrations by suspicious small birds caused by the presence of jays near the small birds' nests. One jay seen hopping about in some hillside brush caused consternation among some wren-tits and gnatcatchers which evidently had nesting interests there. On another occasion a California Jay was seen to enter a small blue oak and by a few vigorous hops ascend to the top of the tree, where it perched in silence. Upon its arrival, a pair of Western Gnatcatchers which had been in the same tree left off their foraging, and the male of the pair began to swing in vertical pendulum-like arcs over the jay's head, coming within 6 inches at each swoop and rising 2 or 3 feet on either side. No note was uttered by either bird. The performance evidently discomfited the jay to some extent, for it soon began to move. For a while the gnatcatcher followed, continuing his swinging course. The jay's passage from tree to tree was marked for some distance by the movements of its demonstrative satellite. Eventually the jay made off in rapid course and left its small tormentor behind. On another occasion, a California Jay seen on the ground in search of insects was the center of a similar but shorter demonstration by a Western Kingbird.

The California Jay is surprisingly adaptable as regards its food habits; and yet it depends very largely upon a certain few items. In the nesting season various insects are gathered in quantity, together with such eggs and young of the smaller birds as opportunity offers. But the staple diet of the species, during the interval between the close of one nesting season and the beginning of the next, is derived from its favorite tree, the oak. At El Portal in the fall months California Jays were seen on several occasions carrying acorns in their bills. At times they would obtain the nuts from the golden oaks on the south side of the river cañon, and then fly across the river, high overhead, each bird carrying one acorn lengthwise in its bill. They flew eventually to the dry brush-covered slopes which clothe the north wall of the cañon, and there, as was seen in several instances, the acorns were buried, singly, in the ground. With vigorous blows of the stout bill a jay would quickly excavate a steep-sided pit into which he would thrust the nut, cover it over, and tamp the ground. Sometimes leaves would be whisked over the spot, with evident intent to render the place indistinguishable from the surrounding surface of the ground. There is no doubt that the jays themselves fail to recover many of these caches, and thus unconsciously, as planters of seeds, serve the interests of the trees.

Woodhouse Jay.   Aphelocoma woohousei (Baird)

Field characters.—Similar to those of California Jay (which see). Broad area of chin and throat less clearly white and less sharply set off against blue of side of neck and breast. *Voice:* As for California Jay.

Occurrence.—Found in small numbers during the fall months in the piñons on Williams Butte, near Mono Lake.

The Woodhouse Jay is a near relative of the California Jay. In appearance it closely resembles the latter bird, differing chiefly in having a slenderer bill, a paler tone of coloration above, and in being less clearly white below. The light area involving the chin and throat is less sharply set off against the adjoining blue.

Two scattered bands of eight and twelve birds, respectively, were seen in the fine stand of piñon pines on the west side of Williams Butte near the summit on September 21 and 22, 1915. These were possibly fall wanderers from farther to the eastward, for none was anywhere seen in the vicinity of Williams Butte during the field work there, from late April until early July, in 1916.

Western Raven.   Corvus corax sinuatus Wagler

Field characters.—Large size (close to that of Red-tailed Hawk); wholly black, glistening plumage. Flight direct, with deliberate wing beats. *Voice:* Usually a harsh croak.

Occurrence.—Rare straggler; a single individual seen at Pleasant Valley, January 2, 1915.

Conditions in the Yosemite region do not seem to be attractive to the Western Raven, as we saw only a single individual, as noted above, and that bird was doubtless a wanderer from farther south in the San Joaquin Valley. Elsewhere in the Sierra Nevada the species is common locally, as for instance in the vicinity of Whitney Meadows. The general lack of cattle, with which the raven is so often associated, may be a partial explanation of the absence of the species from the Yosemite region.

Western Crow.   Corvus brachyrhynchos hesperis Ridgway

Field characters.—Much smaller than Red-tailed Hawk; plumage solidly black. Flight in direct course, with steadily flapping wings. *Voice:* a loud *caw*, uttered singly or repeated, and with different inflections according to circumstances.

Occurrence.—Resident in the San Joaquin Valley; casual in the nearby foothills. Occasionally seen in Yosemite Valley. Lives in open country, roosting and nesting usually in oak trees.

The Western Crow is locally common in many parts of the San Joaquin Valley, especially along the river bottoms. Small flocks were seen frequenting hog pastures at Snelling during the winter of 1914–15. On May 26, 1915, two individuals were observed there in flight overhead and they may have been nesting in the vicinity. Mr. Donald D. McLean has told us that, in the fall, crows occasionally visit the vicinity of Smith Creek, east of Coulterville; two were shot there in 1914. A mounted specimen exhibited in the Park Superintendent's office in 1919 had been shot in Yosemite Valley at some time within the previous three years. Mr. C. W. Michael (MS) saw two crows feeding on Sentinel Meadow on October 24, 1920.

CLARK NUTCRACKER. **Nucifraga columbiana** (Wilson)

Field characters.—Decidedly larger than Robin or Blue-fronted Jay, but not so big as Crow. Body plumage light gray; wing black, with large white patch at hind margin; tail white with central feathers black. Habits largely crow-like. *Voice:* A nasal cawing note, *kayr*, more or less prolonged, and repeated at irregular intervals.

Occurrence.—Common resident of Hudsonian Zone on crest and upper slopes of Sierra Nevada. Ranges down locally in certain seasons through Canadian Zone to upper portion of Transition Zone, and up above timber line into Arctic-Alpine Zone. Recorded in summer from 9000-foot ridge between basins of Cascade and Yosemite creeks, and from ridge near Ostrander Rocks, eastward to Warren Peak and vicinity of Walker Lake; also on Mono Craters. Observed in mid-August and September at Glacier Point, in October at head of Yosemite Falls, and in December near Gentrys and near Merced Grove Big Trees. Frequents tops of trees at margin of forest, around meadows, and at timber line. Non-flocking yet socially inclined.

The bleak upper altitudes of the Yosemite region with their sparse stands of trees and their broad expanses of bare granite suggest strongly the rigorous climate to which the high country is subjected during the long winter season. Despite this forbidding aspect, a rather large permanent animal population is able to maintain itself there through the year. Among the birds in this group of hardy mountaineers none is more conspicuous than the Clark Nutcracker.

Rarely does the book name of a bird fit so well as in the case of the Clark Nutcracker. The first word of the name makes record of the discoverer of the bird, the earliest United States Government explorer in the far west, Captain William Clark (in some current literature spelled Clarke), one of the principals in the famous Lewis and Clark Expedition across the Rocky Mountains in 1805–1806. And the word nutcracker applies excellently to the food-getting habits of the bird. The name Clark Crow has also been used in referring to the species; and some people in the mountains call the bird the Fremont Crow, thus connecting its name with that of another though later explorer who actually reached the mountains of California.

Although the Clark Nutcracker is a characteristic resident of the Hudsonian Zone, it strays both above and below this belt. In summer, after the broods of the year are fledged, some of the birds move down the mountains. For instance, they appear at Glacier Point in August where they are not ordinarily seen or heard earlier. And at the same season they sometimes wander up over the rock-strewn ridge crests well above timber line. Some of the nutcrackers which stray to the lower altitudes remain there at least until early winter, as the species has been observed about the top of Yosemite Falls in October, and near Gentrys and Merced Grove Big Trees in December. But most of the birds remain at the normal high altitudes through the winter months.

The bird's conspicuously pied plumage, set forth best when in flight, its far-carrying nasal call notes, and its marked preference for the tops of trees bordering on a clearing, all serve to bring the species to the attention of everyone who traverses its domain.

In coloration and habits the Clark Nutcracker cannot be confused with any other bird in the whole Yosemite avifauna. The adults and young, both sexes, are all practically alike. The body is pale gray; the wings are black, each with a large white patch on the hind margin (technically speaking, on the tips of the secondary wing feathers); and the tail is black centrally and broadly pure white on each side. The 'face,' or area around bill and eyes, is whitish in adults, but this can be seen only at close range. In the fresh plumage, which is acquired by a complete molt in July or early August, earlier than in most birds, the body coloration is clear light gray. This color, however, quickly becomes soiled by contact with pitch. The bird's daily round of foraging after seeds in cones either in the trees or on the ground beneath soon results in its plumage acquiring a brownish overtone, and this becomes deeper as the winter comes on. In early summer, before the molt, the old birds present a decidedly bedraggled appearance, the feathers on the top of the head and the back being, in some individuals, literally worn to shreds.

In bodily configuration the Clark Nutcracker shows stout build; its wings are proportionately longer than those of blue jays, and its tail is shorter. These features may be related directly to its life in more open situations. The bill is long, thick at base, tapering to a pointed tip (fig. 49). The bill of the nutcracker thus resembles in form that of the Piñon Jay rather than that of any of the true blue jays.

The nesting season of the Clark Nutcracker commences so early in the spring that few naturalists anywhere, and none in California so far as we know, have seen the eggs of the species. Such information as we have been able to assemble on this matter for the Yosemite region is rather meager and of an indirect nature. The 'evidence' is as follows. Near Williams Butte on April 30, 1916, a pair of adult nutcrackers was seen foraging in some willows, and near Walker Lake on May 9 of that year another pair was encountered. In each case the headquarters of the birds were likely on the higher east face of the Sierras close by. During a visit to the upper margin of the forest on Mono Craters on June 10, 1916, at least four family parties all containing fully fledged young were observed. The young birds were following their parents about and begging assiduously for food. Whether or not these families were reared in the immediate vicinity is problematical. Adult birds collected in Lyell Cañon in mid-July showed by dissection that the breeding season was long passed. It may be safely inferred that the pairs of adults seen by themselves in April

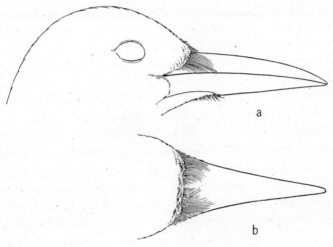

Fig. 49. Head of Clark Nutcracker, showing protecting ''mask'' of feathers which serves to keep snow and other foreign materials out of nostrils. Natural size.

and early May had eggs or young, more likely the latter. All of this evidence points to nest building as beginning in the Yosemite region in March or early April.

The staple article of diet of the Clark Nutcracker seems to be pine nuts. An adult female shot on Williams Butte, September 22, 1915, held in its throat 72 ripe seeds of the piñon, comprising a volume of about one cubic inch. Another female taken September 25 of the same year on Warren Fork of Leevining Creek held in her distended throat 65 mature seeds of the white-bark pine, and some fragments, all together weighing 10 grams or close to 7 per cent of the weight of the bird, which was 146 grams. The nutcrackers on the east side of the mountains often descend to the slopes where piñons are abundant, and the nuts of that tree are known to be a favorite food in many localities elsewhere in its range. During at least a part of the year, however, this vegetarian diet is varied by the birds turning their attention to insects or other forms of animal life. Sometimes they behave as though actually fly-catching. Taking position at the top of a tree, preferably one with dead bare branches at the top, a nutcracker will dart out on the wing as if after passing insects. In Lyell Cañon on July 16, 1915, several of the birds were engaged in this manner. Occasionally one would fly out a hundred feet or more, pursuing an erratic course before finally returning to its perch.

The lusty calls of the Clark Nutcracker are to be heard early and late. The notes have a certain nasal intonation which makes them unmistakable when once the naturalist has heard them. The pleading calls of the young are distinctly different in quality from the notes of the adult birds. During the fall months, when the social tendency of the species is most manifest, a great deal of cawing is indulged in. Feeding and calling may go on without mutual interference. In one instance a bird which had been calling loudly was shot and its throat was found to be distended with a large mass of pine seeds. Nutcrackers, like crows, are apt to sound an alarm when a hawk passes near them. Thus at Vogelsang Lake on August 30, 1915, when a Red-tailed Hawk flew close by our camp a party of nutcrackers in the vicinity set up a great outcry.

Mr. Gabriel Souvelewsky told us that, a number of years ago while climbing about the rocky summits above Vogelsang Lake, he came upon a roosting place of some Clark Nutcrackers. There were about three dozen of the birds in a loose company and the droppings on the rocks indicated that the place had been resorted to for some time as a sort of meeting ground.

Although they are at times shy and hold themselves far aloof, nutcrackers usually impress one as being of a fearless nature. They are wont to visit camps, and will hop down familiarly among the articles of camp equipment to glean scraps of food. This propensity has lead to their being characterized by some mountaineers as camp-robbers. In our experience this familiarity has been of only pleasing consequence, for we have thus become better informed of the birds and their habits.

So far as known the Clark Nutcracker does not commonly stand in the same unfortunate relation to other birds which nest within its range as do the California and Blue-fronted Jays. Still, on July 13, 1915, at Tuolumne Meadows, a Western Robin was seen in excited pursuit of a Clark Crow. The robin gained on the object of its chase and was seen to strike several feathers from the nutcracker's back. Whether the nutcracker had been disturbing the robin's eggs or young was not known.

PIÑON JAY. **Cyanocephalus cyanocephalus** (Maximilian)

Field characters.—One-third larger than Robin. Tail shorter than body. Coloration entirely pale blue; lighter, grayish blue, on under surface. No white markings anywhere, and no crest. *Voice:* A high-pitched, querulous, nasal *kä'-ĕ*, with descending inflection, given singly, or repeated in series.

Occurrence.—Common in the arid region east of the Sierra Nevada. Observed around Williams Butte and Mono Craters, September 16 to 22, 1915, and near Sand Flat, June 7, 1916. Ranges at times widely beyond nesting area, as instanced by flock seen over Indian Cañon above Yosemite Valley, October 11, 1914. Frequents sparse forest or open country; roves about in flocks of varying size.

The Piñon Jay is altogether different in many respects from all the other members of its family found in the Yosemite region. Structurally it differs from both the flat-headed (California and Woodhouse) and crested (Blue-fronted) jays in possessing a longer and more slender bill, smaller head, longer wings, and shorter tail, while its coloration is much paler blue and more uniform. This bird lacks entirely the white markings that render the Clark Nutcracker so conspicuous. In mode of life the Piñon Jay exhibits strong sociable proclivities at all times of the year, traveling about in large flocks during the fall months and even assembling in companies of moderate size to forage during nesting time. It is also a habitual wanderer, and ranges widely both within and beyond its normal habitat, the piñon belt of the arid Great Basin.

In behavior the Piñon Jay is quite the opposite of the California Jay, for it is calm and deliberate in movement rather than excitable and fidgety. The former is dignified and slow to arouse. We have been astonished, on occasion, by the seeming indifference displayed by Piñon Jays even when one of their number had met with violence.

As is suggested by its name, the Piñon Jay is a close associate of the one-leafed nut pine or piñon. This tree, in the Yosemite region, is to be found in numbers only in the vicinity of Williams Butte and Mono Lake. When we visited that section in the fall of 1915 Piñon Jays were encountered almost daily. On September 16 a large flock was seen feeding in the piñons on Williams Butte. The birds were calling back and forth among themselves in high-pitched, querulous tones of voice, giving one the impression that separate conversations were going on among many individuals. Next day near the same place a flock numbering between 30 and 40 birds swooped past one of our party with a loud swish of wings and came to rest momentarily in some sagebrush and Kunzia fully a mile from any real trees. Other bands were seen up until September 22, when we quitted the neighborhood of Mono Lake for the season. On October 11, 1914, a vagrant band of four of these birds was seen and others were heard, passing over the upper reaches of Indian Cañon above Yosemite Valley.

The roving habit of the Piñon Jay and its colonial nature are probably both related to the marked preference of the bird for the seeds of the piñon, which, for most of the year, form the staple article of its diet. The crop of these nuts varies from place to place and from year to year; so that the jays must move about in order to find adequate sustenance. In this search for food, the flocking tendency plays an important part, as many eyes are better than two when the food supply is widely scattered. In this respect the habits of the Piñon Jay recall those of the Band-tailed Pigeon.

Seeds of other pines are eaten when obtainable. An adult female Piñon Jay collected on September 20, 1915, on the Mono Mills road close to one of the Mono Craters had its throat crammed with seeds of the Jeffrey pine, 28 by actual count. Since the cones of that tree were just opening, the birds were afforded ready access to this source of supply. The query arose as to whether the seeds in this jay's throat had been gathered to feed her young which were to be seen near by, still in juvenal dress though fullgrown, or whether she had intended to cache the seeds somewhere against a time of want during the on-coming winter.

On June 7, 1916, three families of Piñon Jays, with young barely able to fly, were seen near Sand Flat, south of Mono Lake. The young birds were being fed grasshoppers by their parents. The diet of the species is thus varied to include insects, wherever this source is readily available.

COWBIRDS. **Molothrus ater** (Boddaert) [22]

Field characters.—Slightly smaller than female Red-winged Blackbird, bill short and thick, sparrow-like. Male with head and chest dull brown, plumage otherwise black with a slight iridescence; female entirely dull brown, paler on under surface where faintly streaked; no contrasted color markings in either sex. General habits of a blackbird. *Voice:* So far as heard by us, a protracted squeal or high-pitched whistle, uttered by male.

Occurrence.—Found as a summer visitant in the Lower Sonoran Zone at Snelling and near Lagrange (race *obscurus*); also east of the Sierras, in the Transition Zone in the vicinity of Mono Lake (race *artemisiae*). One individual of the latter race was picked up dead 3 miles north of Mount Bullion on December 27, 1917. Frequents stream-side willow thickets and also stock corrals and pastures.

Our first record of the Cowbird in the Yosemite section was made on May 29, 1915, when a male of the Dwarf race was obtained at Snelling after attention had been attracted by its high-pitched squeal. This bird was perched at the tip of a tall dead tree standing within the dense growth

---

[22] Two species of Cowbirds are found in the Yosemite region. At Snelling and Lagrange is found the Dwarf Cowbird, *Molothrus ater obscurus* (Gmelin), while east of the mountains in the vicinity of Mono Lake there is the Nevada Cowbird, *Molothrus ater artemisiae* Grinnell. These two races differ chiefly in size, the former being smaller throughout; but these differences can be determined only from specimens in hand.

of willows bordering the Merced River. A pair of Dwarf Cowbirds was seen near the Tuolumne River, 2 miles below Lagrange, on May 8, 1919, but no evidence as to their breeding activities was obtained, nor did we chance to find Cowbirds' eggs in any of the birds' nests examined there.

At Mono Lake in the season of 1916 a number of Nevada Cowbirds were obtained. Two birds taken on May 10 showed little sign of breeding activity, but a female obtained May 23 contained an egg nearly formed which probably would have found its way into the nest of some small bird the following morning. It is to be recalled here that the female Cowbird is a shirker in that she deposits her eggs, singly, in the nests of other birds, usually species smaller than herself. She thus foists upon these other birds the duties of incubating her eggs and rearing her off-spring. On May 31 a second female was taken which contained a good-sized yolk. Another bird taken the same day was a non-breeder, possibly having failed to find a mate. On June 17 a third female was taken which gave indications of laying activity close to the time of capture. Cowbirds were heard in the corrals at the Farrington Ranch near Williams Butte on September 14, 1915, but since none was obtained nor any others observed during the subsequent week when intensive field work was carried on in the vicinity, this may have marked the last appearance of the species in the region for that season.

YELLOW-HEADED BLACKBIRD. **Xanthocephalus xanthocephalus** (Bonaparte)

Field characters.—Male slightly larger than Robin; head, neck, and breast bright yellow; small patch on wing white; plumage otherwise dull black. Female smaller than a Robin; body dark brown, not streaked; head, fore neck, and breast dull yellow. *Voice:* Various harsh and scolding notes, recalling Red-winged Blackbird but distinctly different.

Occurrence.—Uncommon transient. Recorded near Williams Butte, April 27, 1916, and May 11 and 12, 1916, and Yosemite Valley, "about January, 1917." Reported from Dudley, six miles east of Coulterville, in spring.

The Yellow-headed Blackbird belongs to the fields and marshes of the lowlands, hence is not often encountered in the Yosemite section. None was seen by us during our work in the western part of the region, and only three were noted in the vicinity of Mono Lake.

A male bird in full adult plumage was seen near Williams Butte on April 27, 1916, and other individual males were collected on May 11 and 12 of the same year; these latter lacked the white wing patches, and so were probably yearlings. In 1919 there was exhibited in the Park Superintendent's office in Yosemite Valley, a male Yellow-headed Black-bird which was said to have been killed "almost at the door of Sentinel Hotel about January, 1917." It was obviously a stray wanderer from some point on one side or the other of the Sierras.

Mr. Donald D. McLean has told us that Yellow-headed Blackbirds are sometimes seen during the spring months at his home, Dudley, 6 miles east of Coulterville.

RED-WINGED BLACKBIRDS.   **Agelaius phoeniceus** (Linnaeus)[23]

Field characters.—Somewhat smaller than Robin. Males wholly black, except for red 'epaulet' or shoulder patch on each wing at bend. Females brownish black, with under surface more or less streaked with pinkish buff, feathers of back edged with buff, and a light stripe over eye. *Voice:* Song of males a throaty *tong-leur'-lee;* both sexes, adult or young, when excited utter a sharp *chăck;* males whistle and scold when nesting precincts are invaded.

Occurrence.—Common locally below Canadian Zone.[23] Restricted to fresh-water marshes with abundant growths of tules (or willows), or to boggy meadows with thick stands of tall grass. More or less gregarious at all seasons.

The Red-winged Blackbird is closely associated with the fresh-water marshes which border the lower reaches of the Tuolumne and Merced rivers and with the many small seepage depressions and wet meadows which are found along smaller streams on both sides of the Sierra Nevada. In the dense stands of tules, grasses, and willows which characterize these places the Red-wing finds suitable shelter and in the vicinity forage adequate for its existence through a part or all of the year. In the San Joaquin Valley (Lower Sonoran Zone) the Red-wing is resident throughout the year, but in the western foothills (Upper Sonoran and Transition zones) and in Mono Valley (Transition Zone) east of the mountains, it is but a summer visitant, being forced out by the adverse conditions obtaining through the winter months. At all seasons of the year the Red-wing exhibits gregarious tendencies, but it does so most markedly during winter when compact flocks numbering hundreds and often thousands of individuals roam about on the then wet plains of the San Joaquin Valley. Even during the nesting season, when the members of most sociable species separate, this colonial propensity of the bird is manifested by the propinquity of the nests of different pairs.

---

[23] Three subspecies of Red-winged Blackbirds have been found in the Yosemite section, namely: (1) BI-COLORED RED-WINGED BLACKBIRD (*Agelaius phoeniceus californicus* Nelson), the race of central California, characterized by absence of any buff border below the red of wing in males, is resident at Snelling and near Lagrange (Lower Sonoran Zone) and a summer visitant on the meadows of Bean and Smith creeks (Transition Zone), east of Coulterville; (2) NEVADA RED-WINGED BLACKBIRD (*Agelaius phoeniceus nevadensis* Grinnell), of the Great Basin, distinguished by a smaller bill, the presence of a broad buffy edging on red of wing of males and by sharper and more extensive streaking on under surface of females, is a summer visitant to Mono Valley and the vicinity of Walker Lake; (3) KERN RED-WINGED BLACKBIRD (*Agelaius phoeniceus aciculatus* Mailliard), previously known only from Kern Valley east of Bakersfield, with buff wing bar in male and sharp streaking in female (as in *nevadensis*), but notable for its long slender bill, was found as a summer visitant to Yosemite Valley in May, 1919, and June, 1920.

The two sexes of the Red-wing Blackbird are strikingly different in coloration, size, and habits. The male is a showy creature, his solidly jet black plumage being set off by a pair of brilliantly red epaulets or shoulder patches (technically the group of feathers known as the lesser wing coverts), one on the bend of each wing. The males are about one-half larger than the females; for example, males of the Nevada race weigh on the average 61 grams (about 2.2 ounces) and females 42 grams (about 1.5 ounces). The female wears a much duller garb, the ground color of her plumage being brownish black, relieved by streaks of lighter color. The nature of this pattern is believed to be correlated with the greater responsibilities and need for protective or concealing coloration on the part of the female while she is incubating the eggs or caring for the young. Young birds in their first full plumage (after the down) resemble the female, but are even more extensively streaked. There is much variation in the appearance of individual female and young birds. This is conditioned by differential wear of the lighter markings which comprise the feather marginings. Attrition of the feathers against one another and against the harsh siliceous blades of the tules or grasses wears these off and tends to give the plumage in general a darker effect. Certain of the males do not acquire the full black plumage until some time after the fall molt, when wear has removed the buffy feather tippings. In some males the epaulets are orange-colored.

The male Red-wing (of whatever subspecies), is readily distinguishable from the males of other species of blackbirds by the red patch on his wing. He entirely lacks the white which is seen on the wing of the Tricolor. Females are distinguished from female Brewer Blackbirds by their streaked pattern. The Brewer is altogether unstreaked.

It is a marked trait of the Red-winged Blackbird to cling to upright stalks. In the tule swamps few or no horizontal perches are available and the long continued addiction to these situations has resulted in the Red-wings using perches of this sort without evident discomfort. In grain fields the Red-wings will cling to stalks barely stout enough to support their weight, and often sway back and forth as the vegetation is blown by the wind or bends under the weight of the birds. Occasionally one particular spot, such as an approach to a nest in a swamp, is used repeatedly, and the stout sharp claws of the feet perforate the tules and leave series of punctures, three in a row, in the tough blades.

The Red-winged Blackbird remains in large flocks until the end of the rainy season. Several flocks of different sizes, including one of at least 400 individuals, were seen from the window of a train between Merced and Snelling on February 26, 1916. On a trip over the same route two months later, on April 26, 1916, we found the Red-wings all in pairs and scattered out, each little swale in the rolling lands being occupied by one or more pairs. The males were then in full courting display. The break-up of the flocks elsewhere in the San Joaquin Valley occurs about the end of March and probably at about the same time in the Yosemite section. Examination of a colony on the Tuolumne River below Lagrange on May 7, 1919, showed that some of the pairs had commenced nesting early in April; and at Snelling, in 1915, mixed flocks comprising males and females were seen on May 29, and, on that date, there were fully fledged young in the tules. These facts would again place the beginning of nesting early in April. But on May 6, 1919, females seen near Lagrange were carrying wet nesting material, and sets of fresh eggs were found on the following day; and at Snelling, in 1915, young just hatched were found on May 29, so that the nesting season of the Bi-colored Red-wing extends at least from early April to the latter part of June. Once the young are grown, the flocking instinct is quickly manifested, and birds of both sexes and all ages band together and roam about in search of food. It seems probable that the representatives of the Bi-colored Red-wing which summer in the foothills drop down to the San Joaquin Valley for the winter season and thus augment the resident population of the plains during the rainy months.

The Nevada Red-winged Blackbirds which occur in Mono Valley are only summer visitants there. On April 26, 1916, when Mr. Dixon arrived at Williams Butte, the male Red-wings were already on hand and had taken their stations in the willow thickets; but no females were observed until May 6, when a flock of about 15 was noted. Most of the male birds taken during that part of the season gave evidence that they were summer residents and ready to mate, while a small minority were transients, en route to more northern localities. The species remains in the region at least until September, for a flock of 25 or so was seen, in a wet meadow near Williams Butte, on September 14, 1915, and lone individuals were noted on September 21 and 23. On the latter date observations were concluded in that locality for the season.

Our field party first noted Red-winged Blackbirds in Yosemite Valley on May 23, 1919, although Miss Margaret W. Wythe (MS) found a few in the willow thickets east of Sentinel bridge in July, 1914. In 1919 at least 8 pairs were apparently settled for nesting in the wet meadows both east and west of Kenneyville. When the Valley was visited in 1920, the Red-wings were twice as numerous. On June 23 a nest was found in an open field situated 6 inches above wet ground in tall saw-grass. It contained 5 small young. Mr. C. W. Michael (MS) reports that small flocks were seen there on various dates up until September 25, and thereafter a solitary Red-wing was observed on October 7, 1920. The birds of

Yosemite Valley proved to belong to a race (*aciculatus*) recently (1915) described from the Kern Valley east of Bakersfield and until now not known to breed in any other locality.

As soon as the flocks begin to break up, the males commence courting and their displays are carried on with little cessation from daylight to dark throughout the nesting season. For this they seek some open situation, never far from the favorite swampy haunts. The male lowers and opens his tail in wide fan shape, spreads and droops his wings until the tips reach to or below his feet, raises his red wing patches outward and forward like a pair of flaming brands, and having swelled out as large as possible, utters his curious throaty song, *tong-leur'-lee.* Usually this is done while he is perched; less often he mounts into the air and flies slowly over a circling course without departing far from the object of his attention. Interspersed between songs the bird gives other notes, a sharp *chĕck* or *chăck,* a shrill whistle, or a scolding chatter. He closely guards the immediate nesting precincts and tries to drive away all sorts of intruders, including rival males. He even assists in demonstrations against human invaders. When the female is building the nest he often accompanies her as she goes for nesting material. But this is about the extent of his participation in the family work. Some doubt exists in the minds of naturalists as to the strength of the marital tie among the Redwings even during the nest-building period. We think it likely that it varies with different pairs. Polygamy may be practiced to some extent.

On May 5, 1919, we established a camp on a gravelly bench beside the Tuolumne River and about two miles southwest of Lagrange. A gold dredger had worked on the river margin some years previously and had left, in place of the fertile tillable plain of rich bottom-land soil, great irregular heaps of rounded boulders of varying size, totally unsuited for any use by humans. But the series of ponds in which the dredger had floated had become converted into tule sloughs and these with the lines of willows and cottonwoods along the adjacent river afforded splendid nesting situations for the Red-winged Blackbirds and other swamp-loving species. Red-wings, both because of their numbers and their incessant activity, were the conspicuous birds, but associated with them were Rails, Least Vireos, Yellow Warblers, Yellowthroats, and Long-tailed Chats— the usual marsh-border assemblage.

The Red-wings in this colony (all of subspecies *californicus*) were at every stage in the cycle of nesting activities. Nests ready for eggs, fresh eggs, incubated eggs, newly hatched young, and young fully grown were found in different nests, although the account of foraging females given below suggests that most of the young were by this time hatched. The following table summarizes our findings May 6 to 9, 1919.

Nest no. 1. Four young several days old, eyes not yet opened but some down on heads. Rim of nest 390 mm. above surface of water; nest 110 mm in outside diameter and 70 mm. high.

Nest no. 2. Incomplete (presumably deserted); only the outer wall of larger tule material was present. Rim of nest about 400 mm. above water.

Nest no. 3. Complete and ready for eggs.

Nest no. 4. Four eggs, heavily incubated. Rim little over 200 mm. from water.

Nest no. 5. One young bird fully fledged and ready to leave nest.

Nest no. 6. Four eggs, fresh. Nest about 8 feet above the water in a willow sapling, there being no standing tules in the pond where this nest was located.

Nest no. 7. Complete and ready for eggs. Location as for no. 6.

Nest no. 8. Four eggs, fresh. Rim of nest about 300 mm. above water.

Nest no. 9. Four young, only a day or two old.

Nest no. 10. Two eggs, fresh. Rim of nest 310 mm. above water.

Nest no. 11. Three eggs, one with incubation commenced, the other two half incubated. Rim of nest 445 mm. above water. (See detailed description of this nest below.)

It is likely that some of the nests found completed though empty had been built earlier and were subsequently deserted, for the Red-wing is prone to desert a nest disturbed while in process of construction. The finding of a set of four fresh eggs would show, however, that egg laying had not been entirely ended for the season. Elsewhere, eleven days has been recorded as the time necessary to rear a brood after hatching, and a like period for the incubation of the eggs, so that the nest containing the fledged young bird must have been commenced about April 10 or at least shortly thereafter.

Three or four eggs constitute the usual completed set. The set of two eggs in nest no. 10 was watched for two days, but the number was not increased; it may have been deserted before completion. The nest which held the single nearly fledged young bird was tilted at such an angle as to suggest that the other members of the brood had tumbled into the water and been lost to the bass which lurked in the depths below. A nest (of subspecies *californicus*) found at Dudley, on Smith Creek, June 19, 1920, contained six eggs, probably a maximum complement. The ground color of the eggs is pale blue, and the scattered markings of dark brown or black, chiefly at the larger end of the egg, consist of dots, spots, streaks, and lines, the latter often running around the pole of the egg.

The Red-wings at Williams Butte and elsewhere near Mono Lake (subspecies *nevadensis*) lose no time after their spring arrival in commencing their nesting program. The first females were seen on May 6; by May 11 they had paired off with the males, which had arrived earlier. A female taken on May 17 had already begun laying, and on May 26 two nests were found, in one of which the eggs were already partly incubated. But there was considerable variation in the different birds' dates of egg-laying, for

n June 22 a nest with one egg and another with 2 eggs was found, while
fully fledged young bird was seen in a neighboring meadow on the
ame day.

The nests of Red-wings are usually located in tules and at varying
distances above the surface of standing water. Two nests found at Lagrange were in willows at the margin of a pond which had no standing
tules. At Mono Lake Post Office and other localities in the vicinity of
Mono Lake, nests (of subspecies *nevadensis*) were found in willows, 2 nests
being recorded as approximately 5 feet and 10 feet, respectively, above the
water; while one was found only 4 inches above the ground in a grass
clump in a meadow near Williams Butte.

Nest no. 11 listed above was typical of nests (of subspecies *californicus*)
found in tules. The tips of the supporting tules were 1375 mm. above the
water surface, and the nest rim was 445 mm. from the water. The outside
diameter of the nest was 110 mm. and the height 110 mm., while the cavity
measured 80 mm. in diameter and 70 mm. in depth. The internal diameter
was, by comparison, found to be about the length of a female's body. The
nest consists of three parts: (1) An outer loosely woven framework of
tule leaves fastened to the standing (dead) stems and growing leaves of
the tule thicket. The attachment of this outer framework to the tules is
very loose, an arrangement which undoubtedly saves some nests from
being tipped over when one side is attached to growing tules and the
other to a dead stem. (2) Next comes the body of the nest, a firm structure
comprising some tules, but chiefly of finer material. This material is
worked in while wet, either while it is green or, perhaps, after it has been
taken to the stream-side and moistened. Some foxtail grass of the current
season and still partly green was incorporated in this layer of one of the
nests examined. Some of the material, in the particular nest here described,
had a coating of green algae suggesting that tules broken down into the
water had been used. This middle, wet-woven layer when dried and ready
for use is so strong as not to break on moderate pressure with the hands.
This is the important structural element in the nest. (3) Finally there is
an inner lining of fine dry grass stems of the previous year's growth. The
fibers of this layer are chiefly interwoven with each other, but some extend
into the middle layer and hold the two layers together. This inner layer
forms the soft lining on which the eggs and later the newly hatched young
rest. Later still it gives a holdfast for the sharp claws of the growing
young who can thus secure themselves against being tumbled out of the
nest during high winds or when the nest is beset by marauders.

From the time that the nests are built until the young are out, the
parent birds, both male and female, exhibit much concern when an observer
enters or even passes near the colony. They fly up from their perches

chack-ing harshly, and scolding and whistling incessantly. If the observe makes a 'screeping' noise with the lips, the males fly up and hover ove the nest site, with wings and tail widely spread, as if trying to appear a large and absorbing of attention as possible. The females join thes demonstrations at first, but soon retire and leave their otherwise unoccupie mates to continue the protests.

As mentioned above, a single young bird, nearly fledged, was foun in one of the nests examined at Lagrange. When an effort was made t lift this bird from the nest he clung tenaciously to it and each of his sharp claws had to be released in turn from the lining material. Later, when released over dry ground, he flew in a direct line toward the nearest patch of green, a willow tree, and the instant he touched the foliage he seized the latter with clenching claws and hung there until disengaged again. The instinctive traits here exhibited must be of positive value to the young Red-wings as safety measures, just after they leave the nest. The face of this young bird was almost bare of feathers. The query arises as to whether this feature in the young Red-wing is adaptive, for better hygiene and sanitation during life in the nest, or whether it is an ancestral trait, showing the relationship of the Red-wing to certain tropical American members of the family. Furthermore, the ear coverts of the young bird had scarcely begun to grow out, and the under wing coverts were likewise undeveloped, although the bird was otherwise nearly fledged. The bird's first need is for feathers to sustain flight; less important or accessory portions of the plumage make their appearance later on.

Observation along the bank of the Tuolumne River below Lagrange on May 7, 1919, disclosed the fact that the Bi-colored Red-winged Black-birds in that vicinity were using the river as a fly-way between their nests and some rich forage ground up the river. Thus, in fifteen minutes (2:15 to 2:30 P.M.), 49 birds, all females, were seen to fly up the river past a selected post of observation. Fifteen went singly, and 12 in two's, while there were 2 groups of 4 and one each of 3 and 11. So far as could be seen none going in this direction had anything in the bill. In the same interval of time 38 birds, all females, were counted going down stream. All the latter seen closely were carrying what looked like cutworms. The grouping of these birds was as follows: 25 singles, 5 in groups of 2 each, and one of 3. The fact that fewer were seen going down the river than up was probably accounted for by the fact that some individuals on the return journey cut across a gravelly bench beside the river at this point and went down overland behind a line of willows in a more direct course to their nests; 2 or 3 were glimpsed in such a course. These observations prompted the following conclusions: (1) Somewhere down the river there was a breeding colony of Red-wings; (2) many young in this colony were already hatched and being fed; (3) up-stream was a forage ground, rich enough to warrant a flight of a least a half-mile in each direction; (4) only females forage for food for the young; (5) the flocking tendency manifests itself even in nesting time; (6) there is less tendency to flock on the return journey, when each bird may be assumed to have gathered its quota of food after unequal periods of search and also may be prompted by the then more urgent instinct to return to her brood; (7) males stay continually near the nest, on guard, and do not assist in feeding the young.

Tri-colored Blackbird. **Agelaius tricolor** (Audubon)

Field characters.—As for Red-winged Blackbird, but male with red shoulder patch bordered by a striking white bar, and plumage with faint iridescence. Female so similar to this sex in Red-wing that only association with male can be depended upon for identification in the field. *Voice:* Song of male, a scolding *ĕskŏw-ēskēō;* call note of both sexes, a harsh throaty *chĕck.*

Occurrence.—Resident locally in Lower Sonoran Zone; a nesting colony found near Tuolumne River 2 miles southwest of Lagrange. During nesting season frequents dense tule growths, foraging on open ground in vicinity. Gregarious at all seasons.

The Tri-colored Blackbird gains its name from the striking combination of color borne by the adult male. His otherwise solidly black plumage has, by way of contrast, a bright red patch on each wing, and this patch is broadly margined below by white. The female is more dully marked, wearing a streaked plumage closely resembling that of the female Red-wing. The close relationship of the Tri-color to the Red-winged Blackbirds is further evidenced by the similarity in the call notes (though not the song) and by the gregarious habits of the two species. But the Tri-color exhibits a number of differences. The song of the male is shorter and less musical, while the species as a whole maintains the flocking habit to a much more persistent degree, so that there is scarcely any relaxation of it during the breeding season. The Tri-colors nest in more compact colonies, often composed of a great many pairs, and they resort to the densest sort of tule thickets, a shelter requirement which probably explains their absence from many localities otherwise suitable. They are not known to scatter out and nest in small marshes as do the other Red-wings.

In flight the male Tri-colored Blackbird closely resembles the male Red-wing with one notable difference: the red color rarely shows, and the same is true even when the bird is perched, so that the appearance at most times is that of a white-winged blackbird.

A small but typical colony of Tri-colored Blackbirds comprising about 25 pairs was found near the Tuolumne River below Lagrange on May 7, 1919. Several pairs were seen foraging in a meadow near the river. After gathering some food material, the birds would perch in adjacent willows

for a short time and then fly off, all in the same general direction, ove
heaps of boulders left by a gold dredger. Other pairs were arriving from
time to time over the same course. By following up this line of fligh
we discovered the nesting area about a quarter of a mile distant in a lon
dredger pond which supported at its in-shore end an unusually dens
stand of tules, both living and dead. This trait of the Tri-colored Black
bird to fly back and forth over a given air-course or 'highway' may thu
be used in determining the location of a nesting colony, even though the
latter may be a mile or more from the forage ground.

At the colony numerous pairs of adults were perched about in the smal
willows which grew on the shores of the pond. The males exhibited no
jealousy at one another's proximity, and each accompanied his mate as
the latter went in search of food for the nestlings. Zealous guarding of
the nesting precincts, which is so marked a trait in the behavior of the
male Red-wing, is not practiced by the Tri-color. There is not the need
for each and every male to remain at the nest while the female is absent;
the nests are located so very close together that there are always enough
adult birds about the colony to sound an alarm should an enemy appear.
It would seem as though the Tri-colored Blackbirds had attained to a more
successfully communal stage of development in their domestic affairs than
have the Bi-colored Red-winged Blackbirds.

The females did all the work of feeding the young; but despite their
burden they carried on the work in a surprisingly deliberate manner,
totally unlike the incessant activity which characterizes so many birds
when rearing their broods. Each stage in the proceeding was accomplished
in a leisurely manner, and the birds rested at each end of the journey
to and from the forage grounds, and both before and after feeding the
young. While perched near the colony, adult birds of both sexes uttered
the single harsh call note at short intervals, and the males from time to
time gave their short scolding song, which sounded somewhat like the words
get out uttered quickly and harshly. Individual females were continually
entering and leaving the tules, and as each approached her own nest the
squealing calls of the young, *skee, skee skeeeee*, would increase in volume
and then suddenly cease as their wants were satisfied. The nests were
not examined closely, but it was evident that most of the eggs in the
colony had hatched; still no young were seen out of the nest.

WESTERN MEADOWLARK. **Sturnella neglecta** Audubon

Field characters.—Of chunky build, with stout bill, legs, and feet, and short wings and tail. Under surface bright yellow, with a large black crescent across breast; head with three parallel light stripes, one over each eye and a third over crown; upper surface brown, streaked and barred with black and buff; margin of tail white, showing best in flight. Flight direct with continuous and rapid beating of wings; when on ground walks instead of hopping. *Voice:* An elaborate, clear, rolling song of 8 to 12 notes; a clear whistle; a short *chuck'*; a chuckling, throaty *chr-r-r-r-r;* also various combinations of these notes.

Occurrence.—Common resident west of the Sierras in the Lower and Upper Sonoran zones; also in smaller numbers east of Sierras, at Walker Lake, Parker Creek, Mono Lake Post Office, etc. During the fall months single vagrant birds have been observed in Yosemite Valley, on Tuolumne Meadows, and even on a pass at 9700 feet altitude near Ten Lakes (October 11, 1915). One individual was seen in the Valley between June 20 and 25, 1893 (Emerson, 1893, p. 180); in 1920 single birds were noted there on May 23 and November 12 and 15, and two on October 30 (C. W. Michael, MS). Lives on open grassy plains, meadows, and pasturelands.

The Western Meadowlark is by far the most conspicuous and at the same time the most pleasing songster to be found on the grassy plains of the San Joaquin Valley or on the meadowlands of the Sierran foothills. It easily surpasses in vocal attainments any of its blackbird or oriole relatives, and compares favorably with the best of the forest and cañon carollers. Travelers who go to Yosemite by railroad have excellent opportunities to observe the species from the train windows anywhere through the San Joaquin Valley, especially between Merced and the foothills; while the autoist may see the birds in numbers along any of the several roadways leading into the mountains. The bright flashes of yellow glimpsed as the birds whir away across the fields, and the snatches of wonderfully melodious song heard above the noise of train or machine, serve only to increase one's desire to see and hear more of this justly famed songster.

Although essentially a ground dwelling species, as is indicated by its stout legs and feet, the meadowlark often seeks a perch on a fence or in the top of a tree adjacent to its chosen haunts. When so perched it commonly utters various of its shorter calls and whistles, accompanying each utterance by a quick spread of the tail, sufficient to flash into view the white areas on the outermost feathers.

The Western Meadowlark is for the most part a resident species here, being found in the same situations throughout the year. Those individuals which summer on the smaller meadows at the lower edge of the Transition Zone are probably forced by the snows of winter to descend to lower elevations, but this is the only seasonal change in the local distribution of the species. The large flocks which are to be seen in the fall and winter months roam about from field to field; but no part of the general range at least to the west of the Sierras, is entirely deserted at any season.

In spring and early summer meadowlarks are to be seen chiefly in pairs; but throughout the fall and winter they forage in flocks numbering anywhere from 10 to 75 individuals. The flock organization is loose; in fleeing from danger each bird takes its own course, remaining with or leaving the flock at will. It usually happens that certain individual birds fail to take wing when a flock is first flushed, and these belated birds subsequently rise one after another as their field is invaded, to straggle off independently.

Spring is the period of maximum song for the meadowlark. Then, on warm sunny days, their songs ring clear and sharp from every direction in the newly grass-grown fields. Sometimes the birds sing while on the ground; more often they mount a clod or boulder, a fence post or a tree, and not infrequently they pour forth their melodious carolling while on the wing, after the manner of the Skylark of the Old World and of the Horned Lark of the New. At all times of the year their spirits and actions seem to be greatly influenced by the weather. On warm sunny days their voices are heard on all sides, and as the observer walks through the field the birds rise and fly off, their short wings beating rapidly and their white outer tail feathers showing conspicuously. But in cloudy or rainy weather their demeanor is entirely different. Then their voices are rarely heard, they skulk in the grass, loath to flush, preferring to slink quietly to one side rather than to take wing.

The nesting season is rather long, beginning in March or April and extending well into the summer. Three to 5 eggs constitute a full set, and often two broods are reared in a season. The nests are of grass, loosely woven, often overtopped by a flimsy 'dome' of grass, and having a 'runway' leading off through the adjacent vegetation. If approached while incubating, the bird usually manages to flush while the observer is still some distance away so that discovery of the nest is not easy. The most successful method of locating nests is for two persons to drag a long rope between them over a field where the birds are believed to be nesting. This usually results in forcing an incubating bird to rise directly from its nest, thereby disclosing the exact location of the latter. On June 26, 1916, Mr. Dixon found a nest of the meadowlark containing 5 eggs, situated beneath a bunch of salt grass at 7500 feet altitude on Parker Creek, Mono County. Four days later, at Mono Lake Post Office, he saw adults carrying food to their young.

As with so many other resident birds, the food of the meadowlark varies with the season. When the young are being fed, insects are abundant, and both young and adults subsist largely on animal food. At other seasons of the year grain forms a considerable percentage of the food. In the planting season meadowlarks occasionally do some damage to newly sprouting corn and other crops, but this damage seems to be more than offset by the good they do at other seasons of the year by destroying insects. A single meadowlark watched on Sentinel Meadows in Yosemite Valley, October 22, 1915, was engaged in catching the grasshoppers which then abounded there.

The meadowlark's annual molt occurs in the late summer or early fall. When the new plumage is acquired the black breast band is partially obscured by light-colored feather tippings, but these gradually wear off so that as the season advances this black crescent becomes more and more conspicuous. The colors throughout have become brightest by the beginning of the nesting season.

Bullock Oriole. **Icterus bullocki** (Swainson)

Field characters.—Smaller than Robin. Bill moderately slender, sharp pointed. Male: Plumage conspicuously orange, black, and white. Chin and upper surface of body (including wings but not rump), black; rump and whole under surface of body bright orange or yellow; a large patch of white on fore part of wing; tail black centrally, broadly margined with yellow. Female and young: Dull olive brown above; breast yellow, and belly and abdomen whitish; wings and tail like back. *Voice:* Song of male: A slightly varying series of syllables, rhythmically accented, like *hip'-kip-y-ty-hoy'-hoy*, but with a peculiar quality impossible to describe (fide senior author); also a mildly harsh *cha-cha-cha-cha*, etc., in rapid sequence, and a single clear note, *klēēk*. Female and young give simple harsh blackbird-like notes.

Occurrence.—Common summer visitant to Lower and Upper Sonoran zones on west side of Sierra Nevada. Recorded at Snelling and Lagrange, and thence eastward to Mount Bullion, El Portal, and 6 miles east of Coulterville. Also east of the mountains in vicinity of Williams Butte, at least as a transient. In Yosemite Valley one bird was noted on May 15 and several on June 3 and 4, 1920 (C. W. Michael, MS). Frequents blue oaks in foothills, and roadside or orchard trees in lowlands. Non-flocking.

The Bullock Oriole is perhaps the most brilliantly colored bird in the whole valley and foothill avifauna. The flashes of orange or bright yellow, black and white in mixed pattern, seen momentarily as a male oriole passes in front of a background of arboreal foliage or along a grass covered hillside, quickly catch the eye and fix attention on the bird. Along all the highways leading toward the mountains, and near the roadways through the foothill belt, this species is common and readily observable throughout the summer months. Moreover, when the birds are not actually seen, their mildly harsh notes coming from a planted poplar or other shade tree often give a clue to the location of a pair busy with nesting duties.

The Bullock Oriole does not remain in this latitude through the winter months when insect forage is scant or wanting. The birds arrive in the Yosemite region in numbers some time in early April. On April 27,

1916, males were present and well established at El Portal. During May, 1915, and again in 1919, the species was much in evidence at our camps in the foothills. But as the season advanced the birds became less and less conspicuous. Our latest record is for August 17, 1915, when a single bird was seen from the window of a train while near Pleasant Valley. East of the mountains, the first migrant for the season of 1916 appeared near Williams Butte on May 8.

In striking contrast to the behavior of the blackbirds, to which it is not distantly related, the Bullock Oriole is, at least during its stay in our latitude, a non-flocking species. Each pair nests by itself and each male presides over a certain rather definite tract of country.

The song of the male Bullock Oriole, as intimated in the small-type paragraph above, is not readily transcribable. The result of an effort to render the song in syllables is included in the following notebook entry by the junior author written on April 27, 1916, at El Portal:

Seated under some blue oaks I am listening to several Bullock Orioles. Four males are spaced about 50 to 100 feet apart in four large oak trees, and each at intervals utters his song. The song goes about as follows: *chŭck'-ătă-chŭck, chŭck'-ătă-chŭck, tă-wēē'-tăh.* Intervals between songs are filled with a variety of other notes. A scolding *chŭck'-ătă* is often uttered continuously for several seconds. Sometimes this is reduced to *chŭ, chŭ, chŭ.* Also there is a single explosive note, *klēēk.* This last corresponds to the '*chuck*' of the Western Meadowlark. The female scolds in a minor key.

Near Blacks Creek, west of Coulterville, a nearly completed nest of the Bullock Oriole was found on May 10, 1919. The nest was ensconced in the crown of a blue oak which stood beside the main traveled road. The female was doing all the work of building, but her mate stayed within 200 feet of the nest, flying to and from the site at frequent intervals. There were several clumps of mistletoe in this and adjacent trees, but the nest was not hidden in one of these as is often the case with this oriole. To a passer-by the nest might, indeed, at first glance, as seen against the sky amid the oak foliage, have been mistaken for a small clump of the mistletoe. The female was seen to approach the site with a straw in her bill and then to proceed to incorporate it into the structure. She carried the straw inside and there worked it among the grasses already in place. Then she emerged and worked on the outside for a time. The whole structure shook visibly as a result of her energetic efforts. On another occasion when bringing material the female caught sight of the observer. She stopped short and scolded several times, still retaining the straw in her bill. Near Snelling on May 27, 1915, a nest of the Bullock Oriole was seen in a blue oak.

Late in May, 1915, Bullock Orioles at Snelling and Lagrange were busily foraging for insects for their nestlings on the grass covered ravine bottoms and hillsides. A male bird taken on May 26, 1915, at Mount Bullion had some hard parts of grasshoppers in its gizzard.

BREWER BLACKBIRD. **Euphagus cyanocephalus** (Wagler)

Field characters.—Slightly smaller than Robin. Female about one-fourth smaller than male. Male entirely black, the plumage with a distinct sheen; iris white. Female dull brownish black; iris dark brown. No contrasted color marks in either sex. *Voice:* 'Song' of male a wheezy *tseur* or *tshēē;* both sexes utter a harsh *tchick.*

Occurrence.—Common resident of the lowlands and foothills (Lower and Upper Sonoran zones, sparingly Transition) on the west slope and in the vicinity of Mono Lake (Transition) east of the mountains. Nests from Snelling up at least to the floor of Yosemite Valley (4000 feet altitude) and also in vicinity of Mono Lake. In summer and fall months ranges upward in mountains nearly to timber line. In winter abundant in San Joaquin Valley. Forages largely on meadows and grasslands. Nests singly or in small scattered colonies, but assembles in large flocks at other seasons of the year.

The Brewer Blackbird is the most widely ranging species of blackbird found in the Yosemite region. Although it remains at the lower levels for nesting, after the young are reared it ranges widely and is then apt to be found almost anywhere from the plains of the San Joaquin Valley and flats near Mono Lake up to the highest of the mountain meadows. The alert and active demeanor of the bird, its generally fearless nature, and its marked preference for foraging on open grasslands in plain view, all serve to bring it to notice wherever it may happen to be present.

The male Brewer Blackbird is without any of the color adornments which are borne by his red-winged and yellow-headed relatives. His one distinctive mark is the yellowish white iris which makes him a "white-eyed blackbird." The female is much duller colored than her mate and lacks the white of the iris, her eye being dark brown. The young birds in juvenal dress closely resemble the female parent. At no stage in their existence do the birds of this species possess any streaks or contrasted markings of any sort; therefore females and young of the Brewer are easily distinguished from those of the other blackbirds.

The voice of this blackbird is very simple. The male's song is a single whistled note, *tseur* or *tshēē.* Adults and young of both sexes utter a call note, *tchick,* analogous to the *check* of the Red-wing. This note is given when the birds are in flight, as well as when they are walking about on the ground or perched on logs or fences.

Nesting activities are instituted by the Brewer Blackbird in April or early May, and in the latter month the young begin to appear abroad. Near Lagrange, in 1919, broods of young were seen out of the nest and foraging with their parents on May 8, and in Yosemite Valley a nest with six small young was found on May 22 of the same year. In 1915 the season seemed to be slightly later. Our earliest record of young out of the nest in that year was for May 26, when a fully fledged young bird was observed at Mount Bullion. On May 24 at Pleasant Valley and on May 26 at Snelling adult birds were still concerned with young in the nest. Young birds were seen on Sentinel Meadows in Yosemite Valley on May 31. A set of 4 eggs was still being incubated in a nest on the floor of the Valley on July 10. In 1916 at Mono Lake a nest with fresh eggs was found on May 18. The majority of the broods are probably brought off in the earlier part of the period here outlined.

Brewer Blackbirds show great diversity in the location of their nests. At Snelling the birds were using planted hedges of the osage orange as well as the native oak trees, and near Pleasant Valley nests were placed in clumps of mistletoe in blue oaks. In Yosemite Valley nests were seen in small yellow pines and in tangles of the cultivated blackberry. In a meadow near Mono Lake a nest was found at the base of a willow clump and only 4 inches above some standing water. Elsewhere in its range this blackbird often nests at much greater heights above the ground, even as much as 40 feet; but we found none in the Yosemite region more than about 15 feet above the ground. The species never nests in large colonies as do other blackbirds. Occasionally a few pairs have their nests in rather close proximity, but quite as often the structures are placed singly.

In Yosemite Valley, on June 18, 1915, a nest of this species was discovered in a blackberry bush near the Valley schoolhouse. It was situated in a tangle of blossoming branches and well concealed among the leaves. Dried blackberry and weed stems comprised the outer portion of the structure, while the interior was lined with both black and white horsehairs. The nest measured 7 inches vertically, from base to rim, and the inside diameter and depth were each 3½ inches. The base was 28 inches above the ground. Four eggs comprised the set; and 4 to 6 eggs or young were found in the other nests examined by us.

The Brewer Blackbird is an ardent defender of its home during nesting time, and the members of a pair, often assisted by neighboring pairs, will protest vigorously whenever an animal or person, either intentionally or innocently, approaches a nest containing eggs or young. This was well illustrated by an incident which came to our attention in Yosemite Valley. In a meadow near the Valley schoolhouse, where blackbirds of this species had been found more or less regularly, an unusual commotion was noticed at noon of June 18, 1915. Following up the disturbance it was found that four Brewer Blackbirds were pursuing a California Gray Squirrel. The birds were hovering over the animal, snapping their bills a few inches above its head, and scolding in an angry tone. The squirrel when first seen had been near a clump of blackberry bushes. From there it went dodging about in the grass of the open meadow and soon gained the top of a fence post where it perched with its tail up over its back. The long side hairs on the tail moved back and forth, either as blown by the wind or moved intentionally by the animal, and seemingly formed a shield protecting the owner from the irate birds who were continuing their demonstration. While perched on the fence the squirrel was seen to be nibbling at some small object, the nature of which could not be determined by the observer. Soon the animal leaped down, jumped across a ditch, and scrambled up a tall tree. It is entirely possible that the squirrel had not molested the blackbirds in any way but was merely eating some bit of vegetable material picked up on the ground near the nest. But the gray squirrel has been known to raid birds' nests at other times and so the concern exhibited by the adult birds may not have been entirely unwarranted. The day previous a gray squirrel had been seen pursuing a young blackbird in the same vicinity. The fledgling had escaped its pursuer only by fluttering across a pond of water and hiding in some bushes on the opposite side of the pool.

It is a well-known trait of the Brewer Blackbird to badger large birds such as hawks and crows. At Pleasant Valley, on May 24, 1915, a Cooper Hawk flying overhead was mobbed by some of these blackbirds, assisted by several Western Kingbirds. The attack was similar to that upon the Gray Squirrel as described above.

The male Brewer Blackbird during the nesting season seems to be as industrious as his mate, at least as regards attending the young, and in this he differs strikingly from the male Red-wing. As soon as the young are hatched the two parents share alike in the work of gathering food for their offspring. It is a common thing to see the members of a pair walking abreast, with the characteristic swinging gait, through the grass of a meadow, intently searching for insects or larvae. And they are remarkably keen in these searches, for rarely does one of them go far before putting its bill down and pulling something from the grass. As soon as one bird gains a mouth-load of food material it makes off to the nest site, to be followed by the mate when it too has gathered a quota. The birds usually go directly to their nests and thereby readily reveal the location of the latter.

As soon as the young are fully fledged, which in a majority of broods means about the first of July, many of the old and young begin to move up the mountains. The first Brewer Blackbird seen at Tuolumne Meadows in 1915 was observed on July 10. Four were seen in Lyell Cañon on July 14, and thereafter they were observed at many places at high altitudes; for example, in Tioga Pass (9800 feet), September 28, 1915. Their occupancy of the higher level continues until fall, as on October 9 (1915) several were seen at Ten Lakes. In 1920 the species remained in Yosemite Valley at least until October 9 (C. W. Michael, MS). Meanwhile those of the species which have remained at the lower levels gradually assemble in flocks. The approach of winter drives down those individuals which have invaded the mountains and they join the bands in the lower valleys. By December or January the flocks often number hundreds and not infrequently thousands of individuals. At Snelling about one thousand of these birds were seen on the afternoon of January 2, 1915. They were perching on the telephone wires and in the cottonwoods near the river. On January 7, 1915, 1200 were recorded in a three and a half hour census. "Great clouds" were the words used to describe their numbers and the notebook entry states that in addition small flocks were continually passing overhead. Below Lagrange a flock of fully 500 was seen on December 22, 1915.

East of the Sierras gatherings of the same sort are to be seen, although they do not involve such large numbers. On September 13, 1915, fully 200 birds were seen in the vicinity of Silver Lake and in the adjacent sagebrush. At nightfall the birds flew in and roosted in the trees near the lake, and in the morning, between 6 and 7 o'clock, they left in small bands, flying down the cañon of Rush Creek to start anew the daily hunt for food.

During the summer months insects form the principal item of food for the Brewer Blackbird. The young birds seem to be fed largely if not exclusively on this sort of diet. The up-mountain movement of the birds in summer is probably induced by the abundance of insect food then to be obtained in the alpine meadows. At Silver Lake many of the blackbirds were catching grasshoppers among the sagebushes. At Mono Lake, on June 30, 1916, about 50 Brewer Blackbirds were seen feeding on the "Mono Lake fly," myriads of which were hatching out on that date. The birds seemed to be seeking certain individual adult insects, or perhaps the larvae, among the great mass of débris, chiefly pupa cases, which lay along the lake shore. Below Lagrange on December 22, 1915, a large flock of these birds was seen following a gang plow and feeding on worms and insects turned up from beneath the surface of the ground.

CALIFORNIA EVENING GROSBEAK

Hesperiphona vespertina californica Grinnell

Field characters.—Size large for a Sparrow, but less than that of Robin. Body chunky, tail short and indented at end; bill very large and conical (fig. 52b). Male: Body coloration brownish yellow; tail and wings black, each wing with a large white patch (mostly on innermost secondaries); top of head black; forehead and stripe over eye clear yellow. Female: Body coloration grayish brown; wings and tail black, much spotted with white. *Voice:* Song of male three loud high-pitched notes uttered slowly: *zer-r-p, zir-r-p, prilip;* call note a shrill *quer-up* or *killip*, or *plëë-ëk*.

Occurrence.—Irregular, usually sparse, summer visitant to Transition and Canadian zones on west slope of Sierra Nevada. Observed from Crane Flat, Hazel Green, and Chinquapin east to Mono Meadow; also in Yosemite Valley. Irregular winter visitant to foothills, as at Smith Creek. Inhabits forest trees, foraging in crown foliage; less often in shrubs or on ground. Usually in small flocks of loose formation, or in pairs.

The California Evening Grosbeak is so irregular as to its seasonal behavior in the Yosemite region that no prediction can be made concerning its occurrence in any stated locality at any given time of the year. In 1915, when field work was diligently prosecuted by our party in the mountains from June until November, the species came to attention only four times; while during a two weeks' visit to the Yosemite Valley and its environs in May, 1919, the birds proved relatively common. Generally speaking, this grosbeak does not appear to be really common anywhere in the Sierra Nevada.

Early on the morning of June 15, 1915, at Crane Flat, two large mustard colored finches having short black tails and showing much white on their wings were seen to fly into a willow thicket in a meadow. These birds proved to be evening grosbeaks. They flitted about the thicket, evidently foraging, and by their close association with one another were believed to be a pair that was established for nesting in the vicinity. Near Mono Meadow on June 16, at Chinquapin on June 18, and near Yosemite Point on October 30, the same year, birds of this species were observed, three being the most seen at any one time.

In 1919 our first contact with evening grosbeaks came early on the morning of May 14 when several were seen feeding in the chaff at the side of an old barn at Hazel Green. Others were seen later the same day at the same place, and on subsequent days, in Yosemite Valley, at Chinquapin, and at Tamarack Flat. In Yosemite Valley 6 were seen together on May 16, and at Artist Point a flock of 8 or more was observed on May 19.

The California Evening Grosbeak is a finch of very distinctive features, not therefore likely to be confused with any other bird. It has a relatively huge conical bill (fig. 52b) of greenish yellow color, a big head set rather close onto the stout body, and a short tail, indented at the end. The bird is somewhat more chunky in build than the commoner black-headed grosbeak; and in similar way it differs from the pine grosbeak still more emphatically. The outstanding color features of the evening grosbeak are the dark body plumage, and the black wings and tail. In the male there are large markings of solid white on the wings, while the female has many small spots of white on both tail and wings. Often when the birds are feeding in the tops of the trees and are seen against the bright sky no color markings can be distinguished; but then the short thick silhouette is entirely diagnostic.

The vocabulary of the evening grosbeak is not elaborate. The bird has none of the extreme loquacity or versatility of expression of the black-headed grosbeak. The only note to be heard commonly is a high pitched two-syllabled call, variously written by us as *plēē-ēk*, *quer-up*, or *killip*. This is repeated at regular intervals, and is often the first clue to an acquaintance with the species. The song of the male is scarcely more than a succession of these call notes. On one occasion it was written *zer-r-p*, *zir-r-p*, *prilip*. The first two notes of this song were uttered slowly and with a resonant twang, whereas the last note was more high pitched, and uttered with a querulous intonation; the two syllables of it were run together as fast or faster than a person could have pronounced them, forming a sort of trill. The song of another male bird was written *prĭsr-r*, *präs-r-r*, *prĕzer-r;* the three notes being given in three different pitches, and, as before, having a curious twanging timbre.

California Evening Grosbeaks do some of their foraging in the crown foliage of deciduous trees and some of it on the ground. Occasionally they visit fruiting bushes of the cascara or some other berry-producing plant. In Yosemite Valley, in May, 1919, some of the birds watched seemed to be eating the tender, newly unfolded leaves of the black oak, while others gleaned forage from the carpet of pine needles and oak leaves on the forest floor. When on the ground the birds progress rather slowly; they turn their heads first to one side and then the other, just as when they are feeding in the trees.

A suggestion as to the courting behavior of the California Evening Grosbeak was obtained in Yosemite Valley near Stoneman Bridge on the afternoon of May 16, 1919. Three males and three females, closely associated in pairs, were actively engaged in foraging on the ground under some black oaks. While the rest of the flock was busily hunting for food, one of the males was seen to spread his wings slightly and droop them so that their tips nearly touched the ground. Then his tail, ordinarily held in line with the back, was cocked up at an angle. The partially opened wings were quivered for a few seconds and then held quiet for a time.

No notes were uttered during this display. When this male began his movements another of the male birds quitted his own mate and moved toward the performer; but no real belligerency was manifested.

In the fall and winter months the evening grosbeaks sometimes assemble in flocks numbering many individuals and these bands may stray down into the foothill country. Flocks were noted in Yosemite Valley in September, 1920, and one large flock was seen there October 2, 1920 (C. W. Michael, MS). Large flocks were reported by Mr. Donald D. McLean from Smith Creek, east of Coulterville, in October, 1916. Specimens were obtained at that place on October 11 and December 18 of that year. During the summer season the grosbeaks are sometimes seen in small bands of a dozen individuals or less. It may be that even during the nesting season the adults assemble in flocks for feeding. The flock formation is always loose and the flight of the individuals is strongly undulating, each rising and falling quite independently of its companions. Indeed the band seen at Artist Point looked like nothing so much as 'giant' gold-finches, both their coloration and manner of flight contributing to this impression.

We obtained only one hint relative to the nesting of the evening grosbeak. At Hazel Green, on May 14, 1919, a female was seen flying through the scattering trees of a meadow, carrying a long twig in her bill. She was about 25 feet above the ground, and was followed by a male. Both were soon lost to sight as they made off into the forest of firs.

CALIFORNIA PINE GROSBEAK. **Pinicola enucleator californica** Price

Field characters.—Size large for a sparrow, only slightly less than that of Robin; tail long appearing. Plumage in general, including wings and tail, dark gray, without any white markings. Males have head, breast, and rump pinkish red; females and immature birds have top of head and rump dull yellow. *Voice:* Call note, a loud clear *woit-leek*, repeated.

Occurrence.—Sparse resident in Hudsonian Zone on west slope of Sierra Nevada. Observed on ridge at 9000 feet four miles southwest of Dark Hole, July 2, 1915, and in Ten Lakes basin, October 8 and 11, 1915. Frequents coniferous trees of its zone.

The two large grosbeaks of the higher part of the Sierra Nevada are by no means as abundant as the Black-headed Grosbeak is at the lower levels, and the California Pine Grosbeak is decidedly the rarer of the two mountain species. According to the authors' knowledge the present species does not, in the Yosemite region, occur below the Hudsonian Zone even in midwinter.

Being a bird of predominantly gray coloration and medium size, the California Pine Grosbeak is not likely to be confused with any other species in the region, save perhaps the Townsend Solitaire. The pine grosbeak is of somewhat stouter build than the solitaire, has no light markings under the wings or on the tail, and possesses a stout conical bill. The male of course may be known by the great amount of red on its head, breast, and rump.

The call notes of the pine grosbeak, as written in the field by two of our party, sound like *woit-leek, woit-leek,* and *klink, kerink.* They recall the simpler notes of the linnet or purple finch, but are louder and clearer. They also remind one of the sound produced by clinking a metal spoon in a tin cup. In addition to these notes, there is said to be a pleasing song; but this we did not hear. During the whole season of field work in 1915, we encountered the pine grosbeak at but two places. A single adult male was found on July 2 in an alpine hemlock on a hill four miles southwest of Dark Hole. This locality proved to be the westernmost 'island' of the Hudsonian Zone in the Yosemite region. The species was not met with again until early on the morning of October 8, when an adult male in red plumage and at least four yellow-crowned young were observed in some alpine hemlocks at Ten Lakes. They were all evidently feeding on the foliage and seeds, for they were clinging to the outermost swinging branchlets where the needle buds are tenderest, and sometimes would reach down almost directly beneath their perches to get some desired bit of food. On October 11 two other birds in the gray and yellow plumage were seen in the same vicinity. When perched on the outer twigs of a pine tree they held their tails up at a distinct angle with the body after the manner of a White-crowned Sparrow, and decidedly unlike the posture ordinarily assumed by grosbeaks. One bird which was collected at Ten Lakes held in its gizzard needle buds of some coniferous tree and the remains of a single insect.

CALIFORNIA PURPLE FINCH.   **Carpodacus purpureus californicus** Baird

Field characters.—Size of a Junco (length 5½ inches); tail shorter than body, end decidedly notched (fig. 50a). Male: Top of head, rump, and lower surface of body from chin to breast, dull purplish red; belly whitish, unstreaked; rest of plumage dark brown, more or less tinged with red. Female: Entirely lacking red, the plumage above grayish brown (tinged with greenish) and the under surface broadly streaked with dark brown. (See pl. 7c, d.) *Voice:* Song of male a rapid rolling warble lasting about two seconds and repeated at irregular intervals; both sexes give a low one-syllabled call note, *pert.*

Occurrence.—Moderately common summer visitant to Transition Zone on west slope of Sierra Nevada; descends to foothill region (Upper Sonoran Zone) for the winter. Observed at Smith Creek (in June and July), at Hazel Green (May), in Yosemite Valley (May to August), at El Portal (October to December), and at Pleasant Valley and Lagrange (both in December). In pairs or in small flocks.

Three finches occur in the Yosemite region which comprise a distinct group with conspicuous red in the male coloration. These are the California Linnet of the lower valleys and western foothills, the Cassin Purple

Finch of the higher mountains, and the California Purple Finch of middle altitudes, the subject of the present chapter. The California Purple Finch is the species most likely to be seen by the average visitor to the Yosemite region, for it is the one to be found on the floor of Yosemite Valley during the summer months, and, in the winter season, it is abundant at El Portal, the main entrance to the Park. It is noteworthy as being the only migratory member of the group, both of the others being practically resident in their respective ranges throughout the year. The name purple finch, as applied to two of these birds, refers to the color of the plumage of the adult males, which is the ancient reddish, or Tyrian, purple. To most persons, however, this name is misleading, for the tone is not purple in the sense of violet. The females and young males are much duller colored than the old males, altogether lacking the red.

In both of the purple finches the tail is notched or indented at the end (emarginate), while that of the linnet is practically square ended (fig. 50); and these respective characters of the tail are shared by both sexes and all ages so that they become satisfactory field marks when the observer finds himself in a position to use them. Old male purple finches have the whole crown of the head red while in the male linnet the crown is brown,

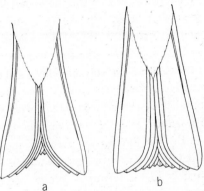

Fig. 50. Tail of (*a*) California Purple Finch and of (*b*) California Linnet, showing the "notching" in the tail of the former: a useful field characteristic for distinguishing these rather similar species. Natural size.

the red being restricted to a band across the forehead and along the sides of the head. Male purple finches in the 'purple' plumage are unstreaked beneath, while the male linnet, of more carmine hue, has the belly and flanks marked with narrow longitudinal streaks of brown. Contrasting the two purple finches, now, one with the other, the California is seen to be somewhat smaller than the Cassin, and whereas the male of the former has the red on the breast and rump of practically the same shade as the color of the head, in the latter species those areas are decidedly paler, more pinkish, than the crown. The female California has a greenish yellow tinge to the plumage, while the female Cassin is in mass effect ashy gray. (See pl. 7.)

The two purple finches in common differ further from the linnet in that the male birds take more than one year to acquire the red plumage. In the early spring months one finds certain purple finches (both California and Cassin) in a plumage which looks like that of the adult female.

But these birds sing typical male songs, and when any are collected they are found to be males in breeding condition. The ordinary supposition is that the male birds do not attain the red coloring until the second fall after they are hatched, that is, when they are about fifteen months old. Male linnets on the other hand acquire the red at the first fall molt, when they are but three or four months old.

The California Purple Finch is regularly migratory in the Yosemite region. During the summer months the species is restricted closely to the Transition Zone. It is then to be seen in fair numbers on the floor of Yosemite Valley. Thus, on May 31, 1915, a 4-hour census there revealed 6 singing males. The latest date upon which the species was observed by us in the Valley was August 19 (1915), but it undoubtedly occurs there somewhat later. In the fall and winter the bird descends to the foothill country; we have found it then at El Portal, at Pleasant Valley, and even at Lagrange. At the first-named place the species was seen on October 7 (1914), and on the one day of December 7 the same year more than a hundred of the birds were seen there. At the lower stations only a small number of these birds were recorded, and not until December. They leave Pleasant Valley before the end of February.

Purple finches are never found in large flocks as are linnets. Small bands numbering at most a dozen birds seem to be the rule. They forage largely in the terminal foliage of trees or bushes where they seek the buds or fruits. At times they descend to open ground to forage. We do not recall having seen them in pure chaparral. At El Portal in December the birds were giving attention almost exclusively to the scattering bushes of *Rhamnus californicus,* the coffee-berry or cascara, the fruits of which were being eagerly eaten. When willows come into blossom the purple finches are accustomed to visit these trees and feed on portions of the catkins as well as on the buds. At Dudley on July 21, 1920, California Purple Finches were feeding on the fruits of the manzanita (*Arctostaphylos mariposa*), and the plumage on the head and breast of a bird collected was gummy from contact with the sticky coating on the berries.

On December 2, 1914, a company of about 15 California Purple Finches was seen gathered about a small quiet willow-bordered pool near the Merced River at El Portal. There in company with Sierra Juncos and brown towhees they were bathing and then coming out on the adjoining shrubbery to dry and preen their feathers. The purple finches were notably quiet, not singing at all and only occasionally uttering a few simple call notes. The purple finch does not sing so continuously or through such a long season as does the linnet. Indeed the former is a characteristically quiet bird, quite in contrast to its loquacious lowland relative. At Dudley, in 1920, one was heard in song as late as July 15.

a, b. Cassin Purple Finch.   *c, d.* California Purple Finch.   *e, f.* California Linnet.
Males at left, females at right.

Cassin Purple Finch. **Carpodacus cassini** Baird

Field characters.—Slightly larger than Junco or California Purple Finch; tail with decided notch at end. Male: Crown bright crimson, breast and rump pale pink; upper surface of body suffused with reddish. Streaks of brown on back but none on belly. (See pl. 7a, b.) Female: Upper surface dark brown, without any greenish tinge; under surface whitish streaked with brown; no prominent spot on chest. *Voice:* Male has a clear song, resembling that of California Linnet yet different; both sexes have a single-syllabled call note.

Occurrence.—Common resident of Canadian and Hudsonian zones on both slopes of Sierra Nevada; recorded from Hazel Green and Pinoche Peak ridge (west of Chinquapin) eastward to Williams Butte and Mono Mills. Casual in winter at Smith Creek, 6 miles east of Coulterville. Once observed in Yosemite Valley, November 16, 1915. Frequents tops of forest trees and also open ground beneath. Seen singly, in pairs, or in small flocks.

The Cassin Purple Finch is the largest of the three red-headed finches, and its range is the uppermost. It is a hardy species, adapted to life in a rigorous climate; for it is resident in its boreal habitat throughout the year and drops to lower levels only individually and rarely. In the Yosemite region it is to be found commonly above the range of the California Purple Finch, that is, throughout the "high Sierras." One is sure to meet with it upon attaining the rim of Yosemite Valley, as at Glacier Point or above Yosemite Falls.

The Cassin Purple Finch is somewhat larger than either the California Purple Finch or the California Linnet and it differs somewhat in coloration from those species. (See pl. 7.) In the male Cassin the top of the head is bright crimson whereas the breast and rump are much lighter, being a pale pink. The female is likewise paler toned, the ground color of her under surface being whitish and her upper surface lacking entirely the greenish tinge of the California Purple Finch. The male Cassin Purple Finch requires more than one year (probably two) to acquire the red plumage, although it probably breeds while still in the dull plumage.

The song of the Cassin Purple Finch is more varied than that of either the California Purple Finch or the linnet, yet it reminds one strongly of the linnet's song. There are full rounded notes and also some 'squeals' like those in the song of the linnet.

At Hazel Green early on the morning of May 14, 1919, we found a number of Cassin Purple Finches foraging in company with several Sierra Crossbills and a few California Evening Grosbeaks. The object of attraction for this mixed assemblage was a pile of chaff on the east side of an old stage barn. By stationing ourselves inside the barn we were able to watch the birds at close range. In the flock were about twelve of the present species, two of them old males in red plumage, the rest in the indeterminate brown female-like plumage. Upon collecting some of the latter birds we found them all to be males and in breeding condition. Apparently, so far as the Cassin Purple Finches were concerned, this was a 'stag' flock, the males flocking separately, a trait of the species which has been noted elsewhere in the mountains of California.

Throughout the course of our field work at the higher altitudes Cassin Purple Finches were encountered frequently. In early summer when nesting duties were engaging their attention, single birds or pairs were seen as a rule; but later, after the broods had been reared, family parties were encountered. Close to the top of Mt. Hoffmann on June 29, 1915, fully 6 males of this species were singing volubly. Probably 6 singing birds would be the average number to be observed during a morning. Later in the year our censuses record about 10 birds seen in an hour in favorable country. The flocks are never large, rarely exceeding a dozen birds.

At Merced Grove Big Trees in June, 1915, a male bird, which probably had a mate on a nest in the vicinity, used to come to the ground near the ranger cabin in the early morning and hop about confidingly in the litter of needles, searching for food.

We found no occupied nests of the Cassin Purple Finch. At Mono Mills on May 17, 1916, an individual was seen finishing a nest 40 feet above ground in the outermost crotch of a pine branch. Near Peregoy Meadow on May 20, 1919, a female was seen to disappear into a dense fir bough 60 feet above the ground. At Ellery Lake, 9500 feet altitude, on July 6, 1916, a female Cassin Purple Finch was observed feeding fully grown young, while at the same time the members of another pair were engaged in building a nest. A male bird taken in Lyell Cañon on July 23, 1915, had passed the height of the breeding season. It would seem, therefore, that the Cassin Purple Finch here as elsewhere has a long nesting season, beginning in late May and lasting at least until the end of July.

The feeding habits of the Cassin Purple Finch are like those of the California. It forages either in the tops of the trees or on the ground, rarely feeding in bushes and then only on the outer foliage. Near Tamarack Flat, on May 24, 1919, a male of this species was seen feeding on the urn-like buds of the green manzanita. Young buds of one sort or another, especially needle buds of the coniferous trees, seem to be the preferred food. These and similar tender growths are likely the staple food of the Cassin Purple Finch during the long winter season when the ground is covered with snow.

CALIFORNIA LINNET. **Carpodacus mexicanus frontalis** (Say)

Field characters.—Size of a Junco (length 5½ inches); only slightly smaller than California Purple Finch; tail practically square-ended (fig. 50*b*). Wings and tail brown with no white or yellow markings. Male: Head (except crown), whole fore part of body, and rump, bright red; belly dull whitish, streaked sharply with brown. Female: Brown, entirely lacking either red or any tinge of green; whole under surface of body streaked with brown on a clayey white ground. (See pl. 7*e*, *f*.) Flight markedly undulating. *Voice:* Male has a prolonged and varied, bubbling song, to be heard at almost any time of year except in late summer and fall; both sexes utter a pleasing call note which has a rising inflection, *che-eep*.

Occurrence.—Common resident of lowlands and foothills (Lower and Upper Sonoran zones) on west side of Sierra Nevada, from Snelling and Lagrange eastward to 6 miles east of Coulterville, to El Portal, and to Mount Bullion. Rare in Yosemite Valley. Common east of the mountains, in vicinity of Mono Lake. Usually in flocks except during nesting season, when in attentive pairs or family groups.

The California Linnet or House Finch is, in California, the lowland counterpart of the purple finches. Because of its greater abundance and its occurrence in settled districts it is more widely known than its mountain-dwelling relatives. In the Yosemite section it is abundant in the western valleys and foothills and is found also in smaller numbers beyond the mountains, about Mono Lake. In spring when attending to the rearing of their broods the birds are to be seen in pairs or family parties, but later in the year after the young are abroad, adults and immatures join in flocks often of large size and forage together in fields, gardens, and orchards as well as on various sorts of wild land where seeds of such plants as sunflower and thistle abound.

The red coloration of the male linnet is of a brighter hue than that of the male of either of the purple finches, but this color does not in the present species cover the whole crown of the head. The under part of the male linnet's body is streaked, while in the purple finches it is plain. (See pl. 7.) The female linnet lacks any tint of green, it is narrowly streaked beneath, and the ground color of the lower surface is tinged with clay color or ocher. From either of the purple finches the linnet may be distinguished from beneath by its square-ended instead of emarginate tail (fig. 50).

It is a well-known fact that the red areas on the male linnet in fall are dull, and that the color gradually increases in brilliancy as the season progresses. Attempts to explain this transition as a change of color without molt involved much speculation on the part of naturalists two or three decades ago. It is now known that the change is entirely the result of the mechanical process of wear. In new plumage the red feathers are tipped and faced with minute structural elements which are white. As these parts are gradually worn off, the red is unmasked and thereby the bird increases in brilliancy. Thus the male linnets when foraging in the mixed flocks during fall and winter are dull-hued, pinkish rather than bright red. By the time that singing and courting are commenced in earnest, in early spring, the birds have become much more brilliant in hue, and so they make more of a display when they sue animatedly for the attention of the dull plumaged females.

Linnets, like purple finches, when frightened usually seek safety in flight rather than in dodging into the protection of trees or brush as many sparrows are wont to do. If a flock of linnets is come upon suddenly, while feeding in a weed patch or on the ground, they get up quickly with an audible whirring of wings and make rapidly off in ascending course. The flock is usually dense when it first rises. Then it opens out and the individuality of the members is expressed as each pursues its own undulating course. Linnets, more perhaps than any other of the finches, are accustomed to strike out into the open, mounting high into the sky and circling for a time, before descending again.

The song of the male linnet is heard off and on through the greater part of the year. After the annual molt begins, in late summer, singing is indulged in sparingly and the birds usually remain relatively quiet until some protracted warm spell during the late winter, or until the first days of actual spring. From then on, their voices resound, in favorable places, from early dawn until late dusk. During the courting season they are as apt to pour forth their melodies while in flight high overhead as when perched.

After the couples have become established, the male and female of each pair stay close together, both when perched or when in flight, and when alone or with other pairs. In flight, the male usually keeps a little behind and to one side of the female, and when foraging he is quick to follow any changes in her location. After she begins the work of incubation he is wont to post himself on a perch close to the nest, where he is to be seen and heard much of the time.

Linnets build their nests in a wide variety of situations. Near Lagrange, on May 6, 1919, a nest was found on the up-stream side of a pile of drift close beside the Tuolumne River. It was ensconced in a natural niche in the mass of drift about 5 feet above the ground. Near Coulterville, on May 10, 1919, an incomplete nest was found about 8 feet above the ground in a slender blue oak. At Pleasant Valley, on May 23, 1915, a nest with two fresh eggs was seen 5 feet above the ground in a small blue oak. At Snelling on May 28, 1915, a nest with 5 fresh eggs was found in an old cliff swallow's nest on the wall of a gully and only 61 inches above the bed of the wash (pl. 47b.) At Smith Creek, east of Coulterville, on June 5, 1915, a nest with 2 young birds in it was seen 5 feet 4 inches above the ground in a young yellow pine.

The nests are simple affairs, of rather loose construction, composed of plant stems and fibers of various kinds, and often lined with horsehair. A typical nest measured externally 4 inches in diameter and 2½ inches deep. Four is probably the usual complement of eggs, although we found one nest with 5 eggs and another held but 2 young birds. The nesting season probably begins in April, as on May 26, 1915, some young of the year were already out of the nest. Two days later a set of fresh eggs was seen.

A rather unusual case was that of partnership nesting, noted at Dudley, 6 miles east of Coulterville, on July 14, 1920, where two nests had been built on one beam inside a barn. The nests were placed so close to one another that the constituent materials were interwoven on the adjacent sides. The centers of the two nests were but 4½ inches apart. Each nest contained 4 fresh eggs, and so far as could be seen the householders were deporting themselves with model comity.

Linnets seem to find enough forage in the lowlands to sustain them throughout the year, as they do not ordinarily invade the high mountains in late summer and fall after the manner of some insect-eating birds. A probably casual occurrence is that in the vicinity of Le Conte Lodge in Yosemite Valley, August 19, 1917 (Mailliard, 1918, p. 15). Those linnets which summer on the Mono Lake side of the mountains probably leave that region in the winter season. Our earliest and latest records of birds actually observed there are, respectively, May 21 (1916) and September 20 (1915), both near the shore of Mono Lake. One of the surprising discoveries made on Paoha Island in Mono Lake was a colony of about 30 linnets which was established there for the summer at the time of Mr. Dixon's visit on May 27, 1916. Nests were seen in and about the old buildings on the island.

Several linnets shot on the Dudley Ranch, along Smith Creek east of Coulterville, on July 23, 1920, had been eating the then green and sticky fruits of the mountain lilac (*Ceanothus integerrimus*). A week or two later, as the apples in the ranch orchard began to ripen, linnets, young and old, congregated there. The birds were expert at keeping quiet amid the thick foliage, where they were taking generous toll of the fruit; the gullets of those that were shot were full of 'apple sauce.' Shooting seemed to avail little against the tide of incoming birds, which seemed to sense the feast from afar. Those persons who decry the killing of birds on the plea that they are, at least part of the year, in one locality or another, of economic importance (by destroying weed seeds, in the case of the linnet) should put themselves in the place of the mountain rancher at harvest time, when hungry young birds continually pour in from the surrounding wild lands and fatten on his crops.

SIERRA CROSSBILL. **Loxia curvirostra bendirei** Ridgway

Field characters.—Somewhat larger than Junco but of more chunky build. Hea
large appearing; tail small, short, and decidedly notched at end. Bill heavy, mandible
much curved, and crossed near end (whence the common name). (See fig. 51.) Bod
plumage dark gray, variously tinged with greenish, orange or red (see below). Fligh
undulating, goldfinch-like. *Voice:* Call notes, *sйp* or *chйp*, usually uttered in three's
and most often given as the birds take wing or fly from place to place.

Occurrence.—Moderately common resident in the Boreal region (Upper Transition
Canadian, and Hudsonian zones) on both slopes of Sierra Nevada. Observed at severa
stations, from Hazel Green east to Mono Mills. Also reported to visit Smith Creek
6 miles east of Coulterville, in fall and spring (D. D. McLean). Frequents cone
bearing trees usually far above ground; occasionally forages on ground. Seen by
us in small parties of a dozen or less, sometimes in company with other finches.

The Sierra Crossbill is the local representative of a species which is
found throughout the more boreal parts of the northern hemisphere. In
our latitude in summer it is an inhabitant of the mountains, and it quite
likely remains there through the winter as well, though flocks may some
years descend in the latter season to the foothills and valleys. It is
impossible to predict with certainty concerning its appearance at any
one time in a particular locality; for its local occurrence varies with the
changes in food conditions. Nor, as regards the Yosemite region, can
any definite information be given relative to the time or place of its nesting.

The Sierra Crossbill is likely to be encountered at one time or another
at almost any place in the upper part of the Yosemite region. Our first
definite record of the occurrence of the species came on September 28,
1915, when three of the birds were seen on Tuolumne Meadows. Others
were noted at the same place on September 29, and near Glen Aulin on
the latter date. Four were seen near Mono Mills on June 10, 1916. At
Hazel Green on May 14 and 15, 1919, the species was relatively common,
and it was noted once near Tamarack Flat, on May 24, 1919. On each
of the dates mentioned the birds came to notice at close range and appeared
to be relatively unwary. The irregularity of their observance must be
attributed not to shyness, but, first, to their habit of foraging high above
the ground, near the summits of lofty trees, where their presence may
be altogether unsuspected, and second, to their propensity for wandering.

The plumage of the male crossbill, as exhibited by a series of specimens,
shows much variation in coloration. It is generally assumed that as the
birds increase in age they acquire, at successive molts, more and more red
in the coloration; but this supposition remains to be proved. Male birds,
which by dissection are shown to be in breeding condition and hence mature
in the generally accepted sense of the word, exhibit a wide range of coloration, from greenish yellow through orange to brilliant red. The bright

olor is distributed rather generally over the under surface of the body,
and on the head and rump. It is least in evidence on the back and
practically absent on the wings and tail. Females are different in color
from most males, in that they retain the gray plumage, tinged with greenish
or at most with a suggestion of yellow, throughout life. The young of
both sexes are streaked on the under surface of the body, looking at this
time much like the female of a California Purple Finch.

At Tuolumne Meadows on September 28, 1915, three crossbills came
to the seepage area within 75 feet of the log hut which protected the main
outlet of the soda springs. The birds seemed to drink, stayed a few
minutes, and then flew to a lodgepole pine close to the Sierra Club lodge.
There they set to work on the new cones, hanging head downward as they
worked at the ends of the terminal twigs. They gave an occasional chirp,
and when one of the birds started to fly this note was repeated often in
couplets, *chip-chip, chip-chip, chip-chip,* reminding one of the chirps given
by linnets under similar circumstances. The flight, too, was suggestive
of that of the latter bird. One of these crossbills was a male in the red
livery, whereas the other two were evidently females. Later, the birds
descended to the ground and foraged among the fallen débris. Another
small assemblage composed of a red male, an orange-colored male, and
two supposed females, was seen momentarily at Mono Mills on June 10,
1916, as they came to drink at a tub near a water tank. On this occasion
the observer remarked upon the resemblance of the birds in voice and
flight to goldfinches.

At Hazel Green a mixed flock of finches, comprising 8 or 10 Sierra
Crossbills, about half a dozen California Evening Grosbeaks, and about
a dozen Cassin Purple Finches, was seen industriously foraging in the
chaff at the side of an old stage barn early on the morning of May 14,
1919. This assemblage seemed to stay together for the morning meal,
but broke up as the day progressed. By hiding inside the barn the
observer was able to get within a yard of the birds without arousing their
fear and so to watch closely their movements. The crossbills seemed to
take the preferred positions and were less wary than the other two species.
When hunting in the chaff, the crossbills used their pinkish tongues
repeatedly and opened their bills wider than the other finches, probably
because of the peculiar form of their mandibles. When taking flight the
birds separated into pairs, although as stated elsewhere it was not likely
that they were nesting at the time.

These crossbills usually uttered their notes when in flight or when
just about to take flight. The notes were uttered in chains of three,
with diminishing emphasis toward the end, *chŭp', chŭp', chŭp; chŭp',
chŭp', chŭp.* In flight the notes were given in unison with their aerial

swings, as are the flight notes of the Willow Goldfinch. While feeding either on the ground or in the terminal foliage of the lofty trees, the crossbills were silent.

The usual forage niche of the Sierra Crossbill is in the tops of coniferous trees where the bird obtains the seeds from the ripening cones. In extracting these seeds the peculiarly crossed mandibles are believed to be especially helpful, for by their use a bird, in turning its head, gets a double leverage to separate the scales of the cone. (See fig. 51.) Some of the crossbills' subsistence is gained on the ground. Like the purple finches, they do not forage in, or frequent, intermediate situations such as brush patches. One of the birds at Tuolumne Meadows, upon being collected, was found to have its throat crammed with seeds of the lodgepole pine; the birds at Hazel Green were getting a variety of seeds and grain from the barnyard litter.

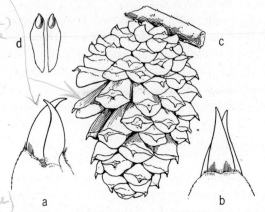

Fig. 51. Bill of Sierra Crossbill, from (*a*) side and (*b*) above; and (*c*) cone and (*d*) seeds of lodgepole pine; all natural size. The twisted mandibles enable the bird easily to spread the scales of the pine cone and to obtain the seeds thus released.

We found no direct evidence of nesting on the part of the crossbills which we saw or collected, nor were any young in the streaked juvenal plumage observed. The skin of the abdomen of a female collected at Hazel Green on May 14, 1919, was bare and wrinkled, and rather leathery in texture, as if it had been glandular. Its condition was that to be expected in a bird which had been incubating perhaps two months previously.

SIERRA NEVADA ROSY FINCH. **Leucosticte tephrocotis dawsoni** Grinnell

Field characters.—Larger than Junco; size of White-crowned Sparrow. Color chiefly deep chestnut brown, with rosy red edges or tippings to feathers on rump, tail, and base of wing; forehead black, joined behind by a broad gray patch which extends down to level of eye. Female lighter than male in tones of color; body plumage of young more grayish. (See pl. 1.) Forages in scattered flocks on open ground, usually above timber line. Flight and manner much as in Siskins, though size considerably greater. *Voice:* Loud, rather hoarse chirps, few together, rarely anything like a chorus. No song of any sort heard by us.

Occurrence.—Resident in Alpine-Arctic Zone, descending at times into Hudsonian Most often seen in summer on open ground around edges of snow banks above the 10,500-foot contour. Westernmost stations, Mount Hoffmann and Mount Clark; easternmost, Warren Mountain. In pairs at nesting time; flocking at other seasons.

The Sierra Nevada Rosy Finch, or Leucosticte, is the most typically alpine of all Californian birds. The mountaineer does not meet with it until he reaches the main Sierran crest or at least the loftiest of the outstanding spurs. Constantly surrounded by extremes of cold and bleakness, and by vast declivities, a combination most forbidding to us, the rosy finch excites our astonishment at his choice of habitat if for nothing else. He is one of the innumerable sparrow tribe, not so very different in many features from the finches of the lower altitudes. It seems that he has been crowded out of the better parts of the land by his more successful relatives, until now he has left for himself only the last and least hospitable strip of territory. He certainly has no competition there; he is usually the sole avian tenant of his domain, save for, in summer, some vagrant rock wren

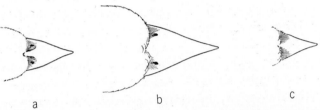

a   b   c

Fig. 52. Bills of (*a*) Cassin Purple Finch, (*b*) California Evening Grosbeak, and (*c*) Sierra Nevada Rosy Finch, from above. Natural size. The Rosy Finch remains in the cold high country throughout the winter and is well provided with a ''snow-mask'' over the nostrils.

or junco from below. No one is contesting with him for possession. The following typical experience, recorded on the spot by the senior author, gives an idea of some of the peculiarities of the bird and of its habitation.

On treeless ridge at about 11,000 feet, above Vogelsang Lake, afternoon of August 31: sharp west wind; black clouds piling along; reverberating peals of thunder at intervals; dashes of rain now and then, driving over the ridge. A dozen or more rosy finches are in sight, forming a loose flock which flies bravely from the lee side up into the teeth of the wind, only to be overwhelmed and swept back into space above the great glacial basin lying below. Presently they rally and come up again, this time tacking diagonally; then they dash by, across the wind, skimming the ledges in a headlong course toward a distant snow bank, to be quickly lost to the eye. All the while quaint chirps apprise the observer of the presence of the birds somewhere in the vicinity, although direction becomes hopelessly mixed amid the eddying gusts. No matter how far adrift the birds go in their wild flights, the snow field seems to hold them magnetized, for back they always swing. The flights themselves *seem* of no use in the economy of existence: Can they be expressions of jubilance resulting from excess of vigor? One can imagine the rosy finches similarly disporting themselves in midwinter about the selfsame ridges. The scanty vegetation now going to seed is then uncovered periodically by the winter gales, so that their accustomed fare is continually available at one place or another.

Our findings in the Yosemite Park and elsewhere along the Sierras tend to show that the food of the Leucosticte even in summer consists predominantly of seeds, with possibly buds, of the dwarfed plants which grow at and above timber line. This is contrary to the testimony of several observers, who, upon seeing the birds hopping about the edges of snow banks where numbers of benumbed insects are often seen stranded on the snow, conclude that the birds are engaged solely in gathering these 'cold storage bugs.' To most members of our field party who watched them the birds on or around snow banks appeared to be shucking out the seeds of the previous year's crop, which the melting snow continually exposed. Such a food supply carries over until the new crop is ripe. Some of the seeds are sifted through the snow as it is swept into drifts by the autumn winds; others are buried while still in the head, to be revealed only with the receding of the snowfields as summer advances. One bird watched by the junior author at the head of Lyell Cañon, July 17, was getting seeds out of dry grass-heads at the rate of sixty a minute.

On the other hand, two of our party reported undoubted instances of animal food being taken. Mr. Camp noted numbers of Leucostictes about the top of Conness Mountain above the 12,000-foot level, July 8, 1915. Here they were, as usual hopping about the snow banks, and one bird was plainly seen to pick up the cold-storage insects "continuously for two minutes at the rate of one insect per second." The insects seen in the snow were mostly small flies. Butterflies, moths, beetles, and squash-bugs were also represented. The birds were in companies of six or less, and would usually allow of an approach to within fifty feet. Again, on Dana Meadows, July 6, 1916, Mr. Dixon watched two adult rosy finches "pulling worms out of the turf." The birds were approached to within a distance of twenty feet and even then they kept at their business with extraordinary indifference.

The present contention as to the prevalently vegetable character of the food of the Sierra Nevada Rosy Finch is upheld by the contents of the crops of several of the birds taken for specimens in August, 1911, in the Mount Whitney region. These crops, ten in number, were subjected to careful examination and their contents found to consist 91 per cent of small seeds, and 9 per cent only of insects. The dilated gullet of a bob-tailed young one taken August 22, 1915, on Mount Clark contained a gruel-like mixture of shelled seeds (35 per cent) and insects (65 per cent),[24] evidently just fed to it by one of the parents. This last bit of evidence is most important; for in certain seed-eating birds, which adhere closely to a vegetable diet most of the year, the young are fed with a greater or less proportion of insects. The rosy finch seems to belong, along with chipping sparrows and juncos, to this category of fringillids, rather than with the strict vegetarians, like the linnets and goldfinches, to which structurally it is thought to be more nearly related.

[24] Stomach examinations made for us by the United States Biological Survey, through Dr. E. W. Nelson, Chief.

We were not fortunate in finding any nest of the Sierra Nevada Rosy Finch in the Yosemite region. We have considerately left this accomplishment for someone with marked cliff-climbing predilections, together with unlimited patience and tireless powers of observation. An essential element in the search for a Leucosticte's nest would be time, but there might be an element of luck, too. We would suggest, first, the watching of a pair of birds to determine the focus of their interests; then the searching of the crevices of the rock chute or fractured brink of fluted cirque about which their fixed headquarters are almost sure to be found.

The nearest to finding a nest that any of us came, knowingly, was on the side of Mount Clark, August 22, when a half-grown young rosy finch, yet unable to fly, was traced by its hoarse *chirp* or *chirrup* to its hiding place in a rock crevice close to a snow cornice on the verge of a thousand-foot declivity facing toward the northwest. The nest must have been close by, though possibly altogether out of reach deep down in some one of the many clefts. This instance would indicate a late date of egg laying, probably about August 1. On the other hand, a female bird collected at 10,500 feet on Mount Hoffmann, June 30, contained a full-sized egg and showed evidences of having already deposited other eggs.

Young-of-the-year, fully feathered and flying about in restless flocks, were first observed August 29, at Vogelsang Pass. On September 26, flocks were seen along the ridge at the extreme head of Warren Fork of Leevining Creek, 10,500 to 11,000 feet. Not far away was found an adult male all alone on a rocky slope among lodgepole pines at only 10,000 feet altitude. He proved to be undergoing the fall molt, being extremely ragged in appearance, and doubtless unable to keep up readily with the flock of full-feathered young-of-the-year. As with certain other members of the finch family which are of flocking habit most of the year, the adults at molting time in the fall (there being no spring molt in this species) sequester themselves during the period of impairment preceding the acquisition of a complete new garb.

While our party was on the summit of Mount Lyell, 13,090 feet, July 18, a pair of rosy finches was foraging about among the rocks apparently picking up crumbs left from luncheons. On July 8, Leucostictes were seen about Young Lake (10,000 feet) and on August 21 a small company was seen on Mount Florence at 11,500 feet. One lone Leucosticte was seen at the Soda Spring, Tuolumne Meadows, only 8600 feet altitude, on the the evening of July 27, 1915, this being the lowest station of observation.

WILLOW GOLDFINCH. **Astragalinus tristis salicamans** (Grinnell)

Field characters.—About half size of Junco. Sexes different in summer, nearly alik
in winter. Male in summer brilliant canary yellow, with wings and tail black and ca
black; edgings of wing feathers white, and white showing in mass at end of tail (fig
53a). Female dull greenish brown, with white markings of male obscurely represented
In winter both sexes brown above and light grayish brown beneath; wings and tail a
in summer, but light edgings on wings more conspicuous. Flight markedly undulating
and buoyant. *Voice:* Male in summer has a spirited and varied song; a characteristic
series of notes is given during flight, and there are simple call notes.

Occurrence.—Common resident of the lowlands (Lower Sonoran Zone), less numerous
in foothills (Upper Sonoran Zone), on west side of Sierra Nevada. Observed at Snelling,
near Lagrange, and at Pleasant Valley, and reported from Yosemite Valley. Shows
marked preference for vicinity of willows. Usually in flocks of varying size.

The Willow Goldfinch is the most brightly garbed of our three species
of 'wild canaries,' the body plumage of the male during the spring and
summer season being clear yellow, set off by black on the head, wings,
and tail. As both its English and Latin names indicate, this bird is a
frequenter of willow growths and is to be looked for accordingly in the
neighborhood of water. In the Yosemite region, however, it is restricted
to the lowlands, and we did not find it in the willows which line the rivers
and creeks at the higher altitudes.

We found Willow Goldfinches in numbers only at Snelling and below
Lagrange; in other words, in the Lower Sonoran Zone. At the former
place in January, 1915, from 6 to 8 could be recorded in a half-day census;
by May of the same year they were much more in evidence, as many as
40 being recorded on the morning of May 26, 1915. Then they were flying
about continually, in pairs or little companies, and some were foraging
with linnets in patches of star thistle. As late as October 22, 1915, they
were abundant, 32 being seen in 13 minutes from the window of a train
going from Snelling to Merced Falls. A single bird was collected at
Pleasant Valley on December 1, 1915. We saw nothing of the species at
any of our other camps in the foothills, but Mr. Donald D. McLean tells
us that the Willow Goldfinch occurs regularly at his home 6 miles east
of Coulterville. Mr. Otto Widmann (1904, p. 69) saw this goldfinch in
Yosemite Valley once, on May 21, 1903, and Mr. Joseph Mailliard (1918,
p. 16) reported it there on August 19, 1917. The species was not seen at
all by us east of the Sierras.

The flight of the Willow Goldfinch, and in fact of all of our goldfinches,
is markedly undulating in its course and the bird is light in its carriage.
The wings do not beat continuously, but after a few strokes there is a
slight pause. The beats carry the bird upward and then as the wings
remain closed it swings down again. This succession is repeated over and

over by each individual so that when a number are flying together in open company, as is their custom, each rises and falls rhythmically but independently of its companions. The relation between the lifting power of the relatively large spread of flight feathers to the total bulk of the body is such that a few rapid strokes of the wings will carry the bird in a buoyant manner quite different from the direct flight of the heavy-bodied, round-winged, brush-inhabiting sparrows.

The Willow Goldfinch molts twice each year, once in the fall when the entire plumage is replaced and again in late winter and spring when only the body feathers are changed. The brilliant yellow garb of summer is exchanged in August or September for a coat of greenish brown, and the black cap of the male is lost. The prenuptial or spring molt is less definite in time of occurrence. Some birds show new yellow feathers as early as January while others still retain some brown winter feathers as late as May.

The nesting activities of this goldfinch do not usually begin until summer is well advanced, that is to say, until July. A female bird was seen at Snelling carrying material for a nest on May 29 (1915), but other birds observed on that date gave no indication of nesting. Our field work at the lower altitudes did not cover the summer months when these birds would ordinarily be expected to be nesting in numbers.

GREEN-BACKED GOLDFINCH. **Astragalinus psaltria hesperophilus** Oberholser

Field characters.—Half the size of Junco. Sexes different from one another both summer and winter. Male: Body plumage dark greenish above, yellow below; whole top of head, and wings and tail, black; in flight a patch of pure white appears on middle of each wing and another shows at base of tail (fig. 53b). Female: Dull brown, green-tinged above, and dull yellowish beneath; white patches, showing on wing and tail in flight, small or obscure. Flight course of both sexes undulating. *Voice:* Male has a pleasing canary-like song; both sexes have plaintive-toned call notes.

Occurrence.—Common resident at lower altitudes on both sides of Sierra Nevada. Recorded from Snelling and Lagrange eastward to Yosemite Valley; also, east of the Sierras, near Williams Butte and Mono Lake Post Office. Frequents open situations among scattering trees or bushes; forages mostly in weed patches. Usually in pairs, sometimes in small companies.

The Green-backed Goldfinch is the most abundant and the most widely distributed in the Yosemite region of the three goldfinches found there. It is the least conspicuously marked of the three, the females in particular being somber-hued.

The Green-backed Goldfinch is slightly smaller than either the Willow or the Lawrence, and differs from them, for one thing, in having yellow rather than white at the lower base of its tail (the under tail coverts). The white on the inner webs of the outer tail feathers of the Green-backed

Goldfinch extends to the bases of the feathers, but not to the tips, whereas in the Willow Goldfinch the white extends to the tips of the feathers but not to their bases. (See fig. 53.) In the Lawrence Goldfinch the white is confined to the middle of the feathers, reaching neither bases nor tips. Sharp observation of the birds is necessary to determine these points, and the marks on the tail are to be seen satisfactorily only when a bird is in flight. There are other characters, however, upon which to depend for identification of the goldfinches.

The Green-backed Goldfinch never shows any yellow on the wing, whereas the Lawrence Goldfinch always shows this color in considerable amount. The male Green-backed Goldfinch is quite dark colored above, darker than the males of either of the other two species. It never has the black chin which characterizes the Lawrence Goldfinch. The female Green-backed Goldfinch is merely greenish, with the upper surface brown-tinged; and she lacks prominently contrasted markings of any sort.

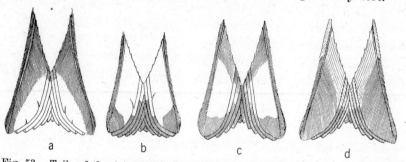

Fig. 53.   Tails of the (a) Willow, (b) Green-backed, and (c) Lawrence goldfinches, and (d) Pine Siskin; natural size. The distribution of white (clear) is diagnostic in the three Goldfinches; the Siskin has yellow (sparse shading) at base of tail. These differences can often be made out when the birds are in flight.

We found Green-backed Goldfinches common in the lowlands and foot-hills, for example, at Snelling, Lagrange, and El Portal; and on June 24, 1915, two were noted in Yosemite Valley. By the end of July the same year the species had become common on the floor of the Valley, due no doubt to an up-mountain migration of birds which had nested earlier in the season at the lower levels to the west. On August 19, 1915, fully 15 of the birds were seen on the north side near Yosemite Falls and on September 5 two were noted near the Kenneyville stables. In 1920 individual birds were in the Valley as late as October 24 (C. W. Michael, MS). East of the Sierras the seasonal status of the Green-backed Gold-finch is not definitely known. It was already present in May, and continued there as late as September 20 (1915); but that the birds continue through the winter in that region is doubtful. Eighteen individuals were seen near Williams Butte during an hour's census on the morning of September 18, 1915.

On June 23, 1920, a nest of this goldfinch was under construction 7 feet above the ground on a lower outswaying branch of a lodgepole pine growing on the floor of Yosemite Valley. The female was gathering material and the male was attending her closely; but when they visited the site he did not get into the nest, as she did.

On July 14, 1920, two nests of the Green-backed Goldfinch were found at Dudley, 6 miles east of Coulterville. One was 18 feet above the ground in an upward-shooting 'water-sprout' of a pear tree and the other at an equal height and similarly situated in an apple tree. The eggs numbered 3 and 4, respectively, and were all fresh.

Throughout the year the Green-backed Goldfinch feeds very largely on seeds of herbaceous plants, shelling them out deftly while clinging to the dry flower heads. Plants of the sunflower-thistle order (Asterales) furnish the greater portion of the forage of these, our smallest finches. The dry nature of this food evidently makes it necessary for the birds to drink frequently for they are regularly seen visiting watering places to quench their thirst. About human habitations they are often seen drinking from dripping hydrants. In doing this a bird will perch on the faucet, lean downward, and, maintaining its balance by an occasional flutter of the wings, catch the drops of water as they emerge from the spout.

LAWRENCE GOLDFINCH. Astragalinus lawrencei (Cassin)

Field characters.—Half size of Junco. Plumage gray-appearing; yellow on under surface restricted to breast; outer surface of wing marked with yellow. Male: Chin, face, and top of head, black; wing and tail feathers chiefly black, the former showing yellow and the latter white in flight (fig. 53c); rump yellowish. Female: Lacks any black on head; general tone of color grayish brown except for yellow on wings; white markings of male dully represented. Flight like that of other goldfinches. *Voice:* Song of male weak but varied and distinctive. Call notes single, low, and with a tinkling quality.

Occurrence.—Uncommon summer visitant. Two individuals seen at Pleasant Valley, May 23, 1915, and specimens taken at Smith Creek, east of Coulterville, August 5 and 9, 1920.

The Lawrence Goldfinch is least common of the three species of goldfinches to be found in the Yosemite region. It was recorded by us upon only the three occasions above specified. The black chin patch of the male, the yellow instead of white edgings on the wings in both sexes, and the generally gray instead of yellow tinge of the plumage, all aid in distinguishing this goldfinch from its two relatives. With each of our three species of goldfinches, the song and call notes are so distinctive as to provide, after once learned, the readiest means of identification.

Mr. Donald D. McLean reports that this species nests occasionally on the Dudley ranch, 6 miles east of Coulterville.

PINE SISKIN. **Spinus pinus pinus** (Wilson)

Field characters.—About half size of Junco; size and general habits of a goldfinch. Sexes practically alike. Tail deeply notched at end (fig. 53d). Whole body plumage both above and below, streaked brown and dull white; middle of wing and whole base of tail canary yellow, these areas of bright color showing best as birds take flight. Flight undulating to marked degree. *Voice:* A plaintive call note, *swe-ak'*, with rising inflection; also a throaty 'watch-winding' note, *zwe-e-e-e-et* or *zree-e-e-e-eet*, the inflection rising and the intensity increasing until the call is ended abruptly; in summer there is also a goldfinch-like song.

Occurrence.—Common in spring, summer, and fall in Transition, Canadian, and Hudsonian zones west of Sierran crest; recorded from Hazel Green eastward to Tioga Pass. In winter small numbers are found in the Sonoran zones, as at Snelling. Present in Yosemite Valley at least from April to December. Frequents both coniferous and deciduous trees, and also often forages about meadows on flower heads close to or on ground. Usually in flocks.

In general characteristics the Pine Siskin is very much like the goldfinches, but it does not wear so bright a pattern of plumage, at least as regards the male sex. Indeed, its dully streaked pattern recalls more the coloration of some kind of ground-dwelling sparrow. Only by a yellow bar on the wing and by yellow at the base of the tail (fig. 53d), which markings are partially concealed, does its coloration suggest kinship with the more brilliantly marked birds.

In the forested region on the west slope of the Sierra Nevada from Hazel Green, Chinquapin, and Yosemite Valley east to the crest line of the mountains, Pine Siskins are relatively common from early spring to late fall. Our earliest seasonal record for the species in Yosemite Valley is for April 30 (1916) and the latest, made on the margin of the Valley, at Fort Monroe, is for November 26 (1914). In January a few were noted at Snelling. We saw none east of the Sierran crest at any time, nor were any observed in the Yosemite Valley or its environs during the season of heavy snow. It remains to be determined whether any of the siskin population stays in the higher altitudes throughout the winter. The numbers which occur at the lower levels to the west in that season are relatively small, and some of the birds may go entirely out of the mountains, wintering still farther west or to the southward.

The general behavior of Pine Siskins is much like that of the goldfinches. The siskin is, perhaps, more persistently flocking in habit. The flocks vary in size from a half-dozen to a half-hundred or even more individuals. In flight each member of the band rises and falls independently of its companions yet the flock formation in this species is usually more compact than is that of the goldfinches. The flight course of a flock is apt to be roundabout or circling, both when the birds are leaving and arriving at a perch. Sometimes when stirred up they will fly around in a wide circle several times and then settle down again practically in the place whence they arose; and this same repeated circling is apt to occur when they arrive from a distance and are settling down preparatory to foraging in some particular spot.

At times a flock of siskins will act as if greatly perturbed, and fly about seemingly without definite purpose. The flock will alight in one tree only to leave precipitately a few seconds later and make off in a circling course to some other temporary resting place. Such a performance is usually accompanied by frequent utterances of the gasping 'watch-winding' note. When actively foraging, the individuals perch every which way, some upside down like chickadees. Often a large feeding flock will be perfectly quiet save for the patter of falling bud scales or seed hulls.

The Pine Siskin subsists upon a somewhat different class of food than its goldfinch relatives. Its usual diet comprises tree buds of various kinds, material from seed cones and catkins of alders and willows, and tender young needle tips from coniferous trees. Some of the siskins seen at Fort Monroe on November 26, 1914, were feeding on buds in the black oaks, while others were searching for seeds in the little cones of the Douglas spruces. At Tuolumne Meadows on July 5, 1915, the birds were feeding in the terminal foliage of lodgepole pines and an adult bird taken had its crop filled with needle buds of that tree. A certain amount of the foraging of siskins is done on the ground in openings between forest trees, or in meadows, where ripening seeds of plants of the sunflower tribe are diligently sought after.

We obtained only one suggestion as to the nesting activities of the Pine Siskin. At Tuolumne Meadows on July 6, 1915, a young bird, not able to fly, was picked up from the ground. It had evidently fallen from a nest somewhere in the lodgepole pines near by.

ENGLISH SPARROW. **Passer domesticus** (Linnaeus)

Field characters.—Size of Junco but of more chunky build. Sexes different. Female and young: upper surface of body brown, the upper back and wings streaked with black; under surface of body without markings, grayish white often soiled to dark sooty brown. Male: Similar, but with large patch involving middle of chin and throat, and more or less of breast, black; also much chestnut on side of head, back, and wings. *Voice:* No regular song; a variety of unmelodious notes. Most usual call a harsh *chis-sick.*

Occurrence.—Resident at Snelling, Mount Bullion and Coulterville; reported in Yosemite Valley, September 2, 1920 (C. W. Michael, MS). Lives in streets of towns and sometimes about farmhouses or stables. In flocks except when nesting.

An account of the 'natural' history of a region ought, perhaps, not take notice of 'introduced' species; but so forcefully has the English Sparrow made a place for itself in our fauna that we feel we must accord it brief mention. The status of this species in the West is still rapidly changing, and so whatever we write of it here must be considered only as showing its condition for the years 1914 to 1920, when we worked in the region.

In May, 1915, it was seen at Mount Bullion, and the Marre Brothers, long residents at that place, stated that the birds had been present for between 10 and 15 years. At Snelling on May 28, 1915, it was fairly common, and numerous young were noted about the corrals of the town livery stable. In May, 1919, it was seen in the streets of Coulterville, and residents told us that it had been present for a number of years. We did not see it there on either of two brief visits to the town in 1915. At Pleasant Valley no trace of the species was found when we worked the locality in May, 1915, but Mr. Donald D. McLean tells us (1919) that since that time he has noted a flock of the birds there. Up to 1919 nothing had been seen of the English Sparrow in Yosemite Valley, but in 1920 a pair, probably the entering wedge for establishment of this intruder in the Valley, was seen in the barnyard at Kenneyville on September 2 (C. W. Michael, MS). As the English Sparrow seems still to be extending its range in California it would not be surprising to find it as time goes on at other localities in the Yosemite region.

VESPER SPARROWS. **Pooecetes gramineus** (Gmelin)[25]

Field characters.—Size near that of Junco. Upper surface of body streaked with brown and black; under surface whitish, narrowly streaked on breast and sides with dark brown; outermost tail feather on each side mostly white (fig. 54b); patch at bend of wing bay-colored, though not so striking a mark as to be readily seen at any distance. *Voice:* Song of male somewhat like that of White-crowned Sparrow but yet distinct; two or three low clear notes, then two or more higher ones, and finally a succession of buzzy trills.

Occurrence.—Common summer visitant east of Sierras, from Silver and Walker lakes eastward around Mono Lake (race *confinis*). Also winter visitant in moderate numbers on west side of mountains, where found at Lagrange and Dudley (race *affinis*). Frequents dry grassy ground, either entirely open or among scattering bushes. Met with singly or (in winter) in scattering assemblages.

---

[25] Two subspecies of the Vesper Sparrow occur in the Yosemite region. The WESTERN VESPER SPARROW, *Pooecetes gramineus confinis* Baird, a summer visitant to the Great Basin and known by its larger size and grayer tone of coloration, is to be found from May until September in the vicinity of Mono Lake. The OREGON VESPER SPARROW, *Pooecetes gramineus affinis* Miller, which summers in the western parts of Oregon and Washington and is known by its smaller size and warm brownish coloration, has been found as a winter visitant in the western part of the Yosemite section, more definitely, at Lagrange on December 19, 1915, and at Dudley, October 8, 1916. The differences between these races are so slight that individuals of the two would scarcely be distinguishable in the field, even should representatives chance to occur on common ground.

Several species of ground-dwelling sparrows with dull streaked pattern of coloration and of quiet or retiring disposition are found during certain seasons of the year at the lower altitudes on either side of the Sierra Nevada. At first glance they seem confusingly alike, but as the observer studies them closely and learns their peculiarities, each species is found to exhibit quite definite characteristics as to structure, coloration, and habits. The vesper sparrow is a member of this group.

The vesper sparrow in coloration combines streaking, both above and below, and a distinctly white-margined tail (fig. 54b), with the general features of a sparrow. In gross appearance it recalls the pipit, but it has none of the nervous 'wagtail' mannerism of that bird; indeed, the vesper sparrow gives one the impression of being unusually phlegmatic in disposition.

From the Savannah sparrow, which often occurs in company with, or on practically the same ground as, the vesper sparrow, the latter may be known by its larger size, relatively longer and white-bordered tail, and patch of bay color at the bend of the wing. The vesper sparrow frequents as a rule drier and more open situations where grass or other terrestrial vegetation is scantier; and it is somewhat less retiring in its behavior than is the Savannah sparrow.

The habitat of the Western Vesper Sparrow during the summer months, in the Mono Lake country, is flat ground sparsely clothed with grass, and with scattered sagebrush or other small shrubs. On December 19, 1915, a far-scattered aggregation of about 50 Oregon Vesper Sparrows was found by Mr. Dixon on an open grassy area of about ten acres extent near Lagrange, exactly the same sort of country as that which was inhabited at that season by Western Savannah Sparrows. Mr. Donald D. McLean found this race once in the fall at Dudley (see footnote 25). The Western Vesper Sparrow, also, is to be expected at the west base of the Sierras in winter, but we ourselves failed to find it there.

The vesper sparrow gains its name from the supposition that the male bird sings at his best at early evening. During the spring months in the Mono country the males perch in the tops of sagebushes to sing, and from these vantage points, in our experience, they give voice to their rather stereotyped song quite as vigorously at one time of the day as another.

No nests of the Western Vesper Sparrow came to our attention, although near Rush Creek, on May 10, 1916, the males seen acted as though they had nests in the vicinity.

In the flock of Oregon Vesper Sparrows seen near Lagrange there was one individual much paler than the rest. This bird was shot and upon close scrutiny was seen to lack one of the component elements in its coloration, namely, the black pigment. The yellow pigment was present and the pattern developed, but the dark feather centers on the upper surface were wanting.

SAVANNAH SPARROWS. **Passerculus sandwichensis** (Gmelin) [26]

Field characters.—Smaller than Junco; tail shorter than body. No prominent white markings on tail or wings. Upper surface streaked with black and various tones of brown; lower surface of body white, with narrow streaks of dark brown on sides of throat and on breast; a narrow stripe of light color runs backward over crown and another over each eye, the latter stripe being bright yellow in some individuals (pl. 8*j*). Usually stays on ground, at most perching on weed stems or fence wires but a few inches above the ground. *Voice:* Song of male 'dry,' two or three sharp notes followed by a buzzing sound; both sexes utter a weak *seet*.

Occurrence.—Common winter visitant along west base of Sierra Nevada (race *alaudinus* common, race *sandwichensis* rare); also common summer visitant in vicinity of Mono Lake (race *nevadensis*).[26] Inhabits open grasslands at all seasons. Sociable but not definitely flocking in habit.

The Savannah Sparrow finds the most congenial conditions both as to shelter and food upon open meadow lands; here the birds are likely to be found, either summer or winter, or during their migrations. Since grassland of one variety or another is found over much of North America, so are Savannah sparrows, represented by several geographic races. In the Yosemite region two races or subspecies of the Savannah sparrow occur in the winter months on the grass covered hillslopes and plains west of the mountains, and a third is found about Mono Lake in the summertime.

Savannah sparrows during most of the year are of a retiring disposition and if undisturbed will rarely come into prominent view. They do not expose themselves as do brush or tree-dwelling species. If started up from their favorite retreats they fly off quickly, in a jerky, hesitating manner, and after proceeding a short distance in zigzag course, drop down

---

[26] Three subspecies of the Savannah Sparrow are found in the Yosemite region: (1) ALEUTIAN SAVANNAH SPARROW, *Passerculus sandwichensis sandwichensis* (Gmelin), which nests on the Aleutian Islands and which is distinguished by its relatively large size, is a rare winter visitant, and was found only at Snelling, on January 6 and 8, 1915; (2) WESTERN SAVANNAH SPARROW, *Passerculus sandwichensis alaudinus* Bonaparte, which summers in western North America (west and north of the Great Basin), and which is characterized by intermediate size and coloration, is a common winter visitant at Snelling and near Lagrange and Pleasant Valley and was once taken at Smith Creek, 6 miles east of Coulterville; (3) NEVADA SAVANNAH SPARROW, *Passerculus sandwichensis nevadensis* Grinnell, is a Great Basin race notable for its small size and grayish coloration, and is found as a common summer visitant in the vicinity of Mono Lake. One individual of this race was obtained by us at 9700 feet altitude above Ten Lakes on October 11, 1915, and another was obtained by Mr. Joseph Mailliard (1918, p. 17) in willows along Merced River in Yosemite Valley, September 27, 1917.

Sandwichensis is enough larger and slower in movement than *alaudinus* to render the two distinguishable when seen together in the field. *Nevadensis* is not likely to be found west of the Sierras in numbers at any time of year. By far the most plentiful race west of the Sierras in winter is *alaudinus*.

abruptly into the shelter of the grass again. Their notes are rather faint and almost ventriloquial in quality, hence one cannot upon hearing them always readily locate the producers.

The Nevada Savannah Sparrow is present about Mono Lake at least from late April until mid-September (latest, September 20, 1915), but is not believed to winter in the region. In May representatives of the species are common there in the low wet meadows. Some of these are doubtless transients, resting temporarily from their migration flights. By early June the migrants have passed on and only the birds which are to spend the summer in the region remain, and these are then busy with nesting duties. A young bird, out of the nest and able to fly, was seen on June 22, 1916.

Western Grasshopper Sparrow

Ammodramus savannarum bimaculatus Swainson

Field characters.—Decidedly smaller than Junco; tail small, shorter than body. Upper surface mixed black, tan, and chestnut; under surface unstreaked, buffy white; head with a light stripe over each eye and another over crown, the three bounding two broader blackish stripes (pl. 8*k*). Keeps on ground where dodges about through grass and is extremely averse to being routed out. *Voice:* Not heard by us; said to be ''grasshopper-like.''

Occurrence.—Found in summer at Smith Creek, 6 miles east of Coulterville, June 6, 1915, June 16, 1916, and July 16, 1920. Inhabits grasslands. Non-flocking.

The Western Grasshopper Sparrow as a species is so reclusive and so local in its occurrence that we ourselves did not chance to encounter it in our work in the Yosemite region. We record it here on the basis of the experience of a resident of the region, Mr. Donald D. McLean, of Smith Creek, 6 miles east of Coulterville. The first specimen of the Western Grasshopper Sparrow taken by him was obtained on June 6, 1915, in a grassy meadow bordering Smith Creek. In 1916 he found the species represented there by a number of individuals, and on June 16 he succeeded in shooting two males. These three individuals were added to the collection of birds of the Yosemite section at the Museum of Vertebrate Zoology. The bird taken in 1915 was found upon dissection to be in breeding condition and there is every likelihood that the species nested in the region in both seasons—in the latter year, in some numbers. The particular meadow which was inhabited by the birds was covered chiefly with a species of saw-grass.

In this instance we find illustrated one of the fascinations in the study of bird life, namely, the ever-present possibility of a new discovery. No amount of attention to any given region, even by persons of relatively large experience, will exhaust its entire resources; something is always waiting for a subsequent diligent observer to seek out.

Western Lark Sparrow. **Chondestes grammacus strigatus** Swainson

Field characters.—Somewhat larger than Junco. Top of head and ear region chestnut, with a light stripe over crown and another over each eye; side of face white with three lines of black running backward from bill; tail rounded at end (often spread by the bird even when perched), blackish centrally, broadly bounded with white (fig. 54a); upper surface of body brown, streaked with black; lower surface gleaming white without markings other than a rounded black spot on breast. *Voice:* Song of male lowtoned, long-continued, and much varied, but always with numerous buzzing or purring notes; both sexes utter a *seep*.

Occurrence.—Common resident of Upper Sonoran Zone on west slope of Sierra Nevada, ranging down into Lower Sonoran. Observed from Snelling and near Lagrange eastward to El Portal, and to 3 miles east of Coulterville. One pair seen in Yosemite Valley May 5 and 9, 1920 (C. W. Michael, MS). Also found east of the Sierras, around Mono Lake. Lives in semi-open country, in and about clearings and on dry grasslands with scattering trees or bushes. Seen usually in pairs in summer, in small companies in fall and winter.

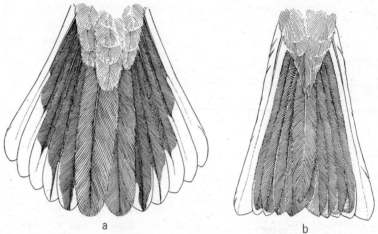

a   b

Fig. 54. Tails of (*a*) Western Lark Sparrow and (*b*) Western Vesper Sparrow, natural size, showing differences in outline of partly spread tail and in distribution of the white.

The observant traveler who enters the Yosemite region over any of the highways which traverse the western foothills will be likely to see a sparrow with strikingly variegated plumage fly up from the roadside and perch on some fence or low tree, showing as it goes a fan-shaped tail that is dark centrally but broadly white at the end. And if, during the spring months, the same traveler should walk along any of these roadways or across the adjacent grassy oak-dotted hillsides he will probably hear the unique purring song of this bird, the Western Lark Sparrow.

Few of our sparrows wear such a distinctive pattern of coloration as the lark sparrow. The head is striped and recalls the coloration of the white-crowned sparrows, only in the lark sparrow the broad crown stripes are chestnut, separated and bordered by buffy white. There is a large patch of chestnut on the ear region of this bird; on the white face, extending backward from the bill on each side, are three lines of black. The otherwise white under surface has a single small rounded black spot low on the breast.

But the lark sparrow's most prominent feature is its tail. On each tail feather, excepting the middle pair, there is an extensive terminal spot of white and these spots increase in size from the center outward so that the outermost feather is almost entirely white. (See fig. 54a.) The tail instead of being square-ended, as is that of most sparrows, is rounded; furthermore, it is a marked trait of the bird to spread the tail widely when it flies up from the ground and often even while perching quietly. The two sexes are alike; but the young, in juvenal dress, differ from the adults in having the throat and breast narrowly streaked with brownish black, and the pattern on the head less sharply contrasted.

The song of the male lark sparrow is not one that can be readily expressed in syllables; and so, beyond giving some of the general characteristics of the song, we must leave the reader to analyze it farther for himself. There are certain 'words' or 'phrases' and the stringing together of these, in varying sequence, constitutes the song. The latter is therefore not a set utterance such as is given by so many birds. One recognizes the lark sparrow's song by this irregular combination of soft notes, trills, and buzzing or purring notes, by its varying intensity, and by its long continuance. Few if any other local birds sing so incessantly as the lark sparrow. Many of its individual songs last for a minute or more, and during the late spring and early summer the male birds sing through most of the daylight hours. The song, even at best, lacks carrying power; to an auditor at a distance the song seems alternately to die away and to revive. At close range the song is heard to be continuous, but increases and decreases in loudness with every few notes. The lark sparrow often sings until late dusk and on several occasions we have heard it give a few bars long after nightfall.

By May the Western Lark Sparrows are busying themselves with nesting affairs and in June the young begin to appear abroad. At Snelling on May 27, 1915, an adult bird was seen carrying nesting material, and others behaved as though their headquarters were already well established. At Pleasant Valley on May 28, 1915, a nest with four eggs was discovered at the base of a yerba santa bush on a dry sun-heated hillside. Near the McCarthy ranch, 3 miles east of Coulterville, on June 2, 1915, another nest was found. This last nest had been placed on the ground on a gentle hillslope, in a spot sheltered by an accumulation of cones and branches from the yellow pines above. When first seen the nest held four eggs and as none were added by the following morning the set was believed to be complete. When this nest was again visited, on June 4, it was found to have been raided; one egg was gone and another lay broken outside the nest. Neither of the birds was seen on this last visit. The nature of the enemy was not determinable but it seemed likely that he had been frightened away before his meal was completed, as even the egg which was broken open still held some of its contents.

During the fall and winter months the lark sparrows gather into flocks which are usually small. But at El Portal, in December, at least 25 of the birds were seen together in a live oak standing out by itself in an open field. The species habitually forages upon the ground among grasses and other low vegetation; but when the individuals are alarmed they seek perches a few feet above the ground, whence, when further pressed, they fly off in an open course to a distance. They do not as a rule dive into the brush as do the White-crowns; nor do they run aside through the grass, as do the Savannahs.

Although these birds are permanent residents west of the mountains, they are probably only summer visitants in the elevated Mono Lake country. The first lark sparrow observed in the latter region was seen in the garden at Farrington's ranch, near Williams Butte, May 2 (1916). Others were encountered later the same month at this ranch, and also at Mono Lake Post Office.

WHITE-CROWNED SPARROWS. Zonotrichia leucophrys (Forster)[27]

Field characters.—Slightly larger than Junco (length about 7 inches). Sexes alike. Top and back of head with three white and four black stripes alternating, the middle stripe over the crown being white (pl. 8a, c); upper surface of body streaked with brown on a gray ground; tail plain brown; some small white spots forming two rows on wing; under surface of body grayish white, unstreaked. Immature birds have black and white on head replaced by reddish brown and dull buff, respectively. (See pl. 8b.) *Voice:* Males have a clear set song; both sexes utter a sharp call or alarm note, *peenk*.

Occurrence.—Common summer visitant to Hudsonian Zone (subspecies *leucophrys*); common fall visitant to Transition Zone and winter visitant to Sonoran Zones on west side of Sierras, and fall and spring migrant east of the mountains in vicinity of Mono Lake (subspecies *gambeli*).[27]

---

[27] Two subspecies of the White-crowned Sparrow occur in the Yosemite region, namely: (1) The HUDSONIAN WHITE-CROWNED SPARROW, *Zonotrichia leucophrys leucophrys* (Forster), which summers in the northeastern and mountainous parts of North America east of the Pacific humid coast strip, and which is distinguished principally by the small area between bill and eye (technically, the lores) being black (pl. 8a), is a summer visitant to the Hudsonian Zone of the Yosemite section of the Sierra Nevada. It was found established for the summer from near Mono Meadow and Porcupine Flat eastward to the vicinity of Williams Butte; it passes through the lower levels on both sides of the mountains during the spring migration. One case of nesting in Yosemite Valley has been reported (Dawson, 1916, p. 28). It arrives in Yosemite region by early May at least and departs about the end of September. It frequents willow thickets, in pairs or family parties.

(2) The INTERMEDIATE WHITE-CROWNED SPARROW, *Zonotrichia leucophrys gambeli* (Nuttall), which is found in summer in the interior of northwestern North America from

White-crowned Sparrows occur somewhere in the Yosemite region at all times of the year, but the same individuals are not continuously in residence at any one place nor is the species to be found in any one locality at all seasons. As explained in footnote 27 there are two subspecies represented in the region. One of these, the Hudsonian White-crowned Sparrow, is the summer representative at the higher altitudes, while the other, the Intermediate White-crowned Sparrow, or Gambel Sparrow, is to be found in winter at the lower elevations to the west, and elsewhere in migration. The change, while involving considerable time during the spring and fall seasons of migration, is eventually complete, for none of the former race has been found in the region in winter nor do any of the latter remain there to nest in summer.

The earliest definite records of the arrival of the Hudsonian White-crown in the Yosemite region are for May 10 (1916) near Williams Butte and for May 8 (1917) at Smith Creek, east of Coulterville. Migration was still in progress on May 22 (1919), as a male bird in Yosemite Valley on that date tarried only a short time before moving on. The birds often establish themselves in the leafless willow thickets which border the streams in the boreal meadows before human invasion of those heights is easy. Hence, the first travelers of the season are apt to find the White-crowns already busy with nesting duties. Some individuals continue in their summer haunts until the end of September, several having been noted by us at Tuolumne Meadows on September 29, 1915, but none anywhere later than that date.

Our highest record for the Hudsonian White-crowned Sparrow was close to 11,000 feet altitude, in a patch of stunted willows in a draw between Mount Gibbs and Mount Dana, July 29, 1915.

The occurrence of the Intermediate Sparrow in the lower zones is practically complementary to that of its congener at the higher altitudes. Our earliest fall record for *gambeli* was made near Williams Butte on September 17, 1915. In Yosemite Valley the earliest date of its occurrence is September 18, 1917 (Mailliard, 1918, p. 18). Numbers were seen in the Valley on September 24, 1915. After mid-September the birds are to be met with commonly in the brush lands below 4500 feet. We think it likely

---

British Columbia northward, and which is distinguished by having grayish white (instead of black) between bill and eye (pl. 8c) is a winter visitant in the lower zones (Sonoran) from Snelling and Lagrange eastward to El Portal; it also passes as a migrant, in fall and spring, along the east side of the Sierras in vicinity of Mono Lake, west to Walker Lake and Warren Fork of Leevining Creek, and is common in Yosemite Valley in the fall. It arrives in mid-September (September 17, 1915, near Williams Butte) and departs in late spring, remaining as late as May 6 (1919, at Lagrange). Frequents brush and small trees. Loosely flocking.

White-crowned sparrows may often be approached closely enough in the field for the observer to see whether the small area between bill and eye is black (*leucophrys*) or gray (*gambeli*). The two subspecies will not often be found on common ground, and any particular bird not closely seen may usually be guessed as to name by giving consideration to date and place of occurrence.

that the Intermediate Sparrow does not winter in the vicinity of Mono Lake, although it is common there during the last half of September; probably it moves still farther south when the snow comes. On the west slope of the mountains some of the birds which arrive first appear in the Transition Zone, as in Yosemite Valley. Then, with or before the coming of the snow, they drop down to the foothill country where they remain throughout the winter and spring. They evidently do not move up the mountains again after the snow has gone but tarry at the lower levels until ready to depart directly to their nesting grounds in the north. On May 6, 1919, near Lagrange, about a dozen Intermediate Sparrows were seen and one was collected. The fact that some of the birds linger late in spring should not lead anyone into believing that this subspecies nests in California.

The two white-crowned sparrows may be readily distinguished in adult plumage from all other sparrows in the Yosemite region by the striping on their heads. Of the only two species which approach these birds in coloration the Golden-crowned Sparrow has a broad, golden-yellow patch on the middle of its crown and entirely lacks any pure white about its head, and the Lark Sparrow has at all ages, a brown-striped head. The latter has a conspicuously white-marked tail, as well.

White-crowned sparrows are thicket-dwelling birds at all seasons. (See pl. 18a and text fig. 21.) Often they may be seen on open level ground or grassland but never far from some hedge or bush to which they can resort if frightened. Their preference is for isolated or scattered shrubs rather than for broad areas of solid chaparral. When frightened they always seek shelter in brush instead of making off in the open, and when resting between periods of foraging they perch in the tops of thickets.

If a flock of White-crowns is come upon while it is foraging on the ground, the birds get up quickly and dart into the shelter of some nearby thicket, each pursuing a separate course. There they remain for a short time, silent and motionless, but peering furtively at the intruder. After a short period of quiet, if there be no further cause for fright, they become active again, giving voice to faint *seeps* and, individually, they begin to hop up in the brush where they can see about before venturing into the open again.

The general demeanor of the White-crown is almost sedate, just opposite to that of the Song Sparrow; every movement is made with seeming deliberation. As the White-crowns hop about on the ground they present a trim appearance, due in part to their long legs and manner of standing more nearly in an upright posture than most ground-feeding birds. Practically all of their foraging is done on the ground, but they do not habitually scratch like the heavier bodied and stouter clawed Fox Sparrows and towhees.

During the nesting season the White-crowns are in pairs, each pair occupying a separate and well-defined small area in the willows; but at other seasons they associate in loose flocks. This is true of the Hudsonian White-crowns in early fall before they migrate southward and of the Intermediate Sparrows throughout their stay in our latitude.

The song of the Hudsonian White-crowned Sparrow is a fairly loud clear lay, which carries well over the open meadows at the higher altitudes. The traveler may often hear a song long before getting close enough to see the performer. One transcription of the song, written in the field, is as follows: *wĕ chēē′ äh wēēēēē äh;* the last syllable is sometimes omitted. The theme is brief and unvaried. The White-crown, like several of its close relatives, occasionally sings at night. Both male and female utter a sharp call note, *peenk*, and this is repeated frequently when the birds are disturbed. At late dusk they are especially active in their favorite willow thickets and the call notes are given many times ere the birds settle down for the night. Seasonally the song is heard from the time the first migrants arrive up until early July. During the molting season they are quiet. By the end of August some have completed the renewal of their feathers, and songs of a more or less fragmentary character are given from then on until they depart southward for the winter.

The song of the Intermediate Sparrow may be heard in the foothills from time to time during the winter months, but it is then often incomplete. While to the trained ear distinct, it resembles that of the Hudsonian White-crown so much that a person having heard either one readily recognizes the song of the other as that of a closely related bird.

Nests of the Hudsonian White-crown are not difficult to locate, for the birds are quick to set up a disturbance whenever their home sites are approached. On June 25, 1916, at the Farrington Ranch near Mono Lake a nest with 4 eggs was discovered, sunk even with the surface of the ground beneath a willow bush in a meadow. It was made of rootlets and grass, with a lining of black horsehair. Outside, the diameter was about 4 inches and the height (after removal of the nest), 2¼ inches; while inside the diameter was 2¼ inches and the depth at the center about 1¾ inches. The 4 eggs were well advanced in incubation. At Tuolumne Meadows on July 5, 1915, a nest was found 12 inches above the ground in a willow shrub close to the river bank. It contained three young birds about half-grown, and the parents evinced great solicitude during our examination of the nest. A week later these young had left the nest but were evidently still in the vicinity, for whenever we approached the place the old birds exhibited marked concern.

The juvenal Hudsonian White-crowned Sparrows wear a much more streaked pattern of coloration than their parents, the breast as well as the whole upper surface bearing a pattern of narrow streaks. This plumage is worn but a short time. In August all of it (except the wing and tail feathers) is molted, and the bird then acquires the immature or first winter plumage, which resembles that of the adult save for the coloration of the crown, which is brown and buff instead of black and white. In this plumage the immature birds go south to spend the winter, but before they return, another partial molt in early spring gives them the crown coloration of the adults.

When the Intermediate Sparrows come south in the fall the immature birds have dull colored heads, but at the end of winter, in March or April, the prenuptial molt gives them black-and-white striped heads like their parents. This spring molt is participated in by both adults and immatures, but, obviously, the change in color is conspicuous only in the latter.

The stomach of an adult male Hudsonian White-crowned Sparrow taken at Lake Tenaya on July 3, 1915, contained, in so far as its contents were recognizable, nothing but beetles. General observation leads to the belief that a considerable part of this sparrow's food during the summer consists of insects. The birds which winter in the foothills (*gambeli*) subsist largely if not entirely on vegetable material (the cotyledons of newly sprouting plants, and seeds) most of which is gleaned from the open ground near thickets. At Lagrange they take advantage of easy forage obtained in the gardens, and in so doing conflict with the interests of the truck gardeners there.

GOLDEN-CROWNED SPARROW. Zonotrichia coronata (Pallas)

Field characters.—Decidedly larger than Junco. Upper surface of body dull brown, streaked on back with black; under surface of body not streaked, light grayish brown, palest on belly; top of head in adults golden yellow, margined with black (pl. 8*f*), in immatures dull mottled brown; two rows of white spots across closed wing. *Voice:* Song, three clear whistled notes, in minor key, descending in pitch and suggesting the words *oh dear me;* both sexes utter a rather sharp single-syllabled call note.

Occurrence.—Common winter visitant to foothill and plains country (Sonoran zones) from Snelling east to El Portal; during autumn invades higher portions of west slope of Sierra Nevada, east to vicinity of McGee Lake. Stays in or near thickets. Often in loose flocks.

The brush thickets and adjacent feeding grounds which serve the Intermediate White-crowned Sparrow through the winter months are shared by another sparrow of slightly larger size and somewhat different coloration and voice, but of similar habits. This is the Golden-crowned Sparrow, another of our many winter visitants from the far north.

Our earliest seasonal record for the Golden-crowned Sparrow was made on October 2 (1915) when at least 7 adult and immature birds were seen in a coffee-berry thicket in Yosemite Valley. Thereafter, for a month or so, the species was noted in a number of places in the higher country; for example, near McGee Lake (October 5), at Aspen Valley (October 15 and 16), and above Yosemite Point (October 30). In 1914, at El Portal, these sparrows were regularly noted from November 21 to the end of December. At Pleasant Valley in 1915 the species was seen on December 3. It seems very likely that those Golden-crowns which go first into the higher zones drop down the western slope with the advent of heavy snow. They are entirely absent from Yosemite Valley during the mid-winter months. Furthermore, there is no evidence of a return to the higher zones in the spring. Like the Intermediate Sparrows the Golden-crowns continue in the foothill brush belt until they leave for their nesting grounds. They often remain in our latitude until relatively late in the spring. Thus, on May 10, 1919, near Coulterville, one was collected and the next day at least four others were noted. The bird collected, a female, was fat and contained only small ova. The first fact testified that it was in condition to begin the long northward migration to its summer habitat and to undertake the trying task of rearing its brood there, while the second indicated that it would not have begun actual nesting activities for some time. None was seen after May 11. As in the case of the Intermediate Sparrow, this regular late occurrence of the Golden-crown has resulted in some bird students believing that the species nests in California; but as far as we know there is no other ground for the belief.

The Golden-crowned Sparrow receives its name from the presence of an area of golden yellow on the top of its head. In the immature birds this area is duller and smaller and not set off by contrasted color, but in the adults the area in question is decidedly a clear yellow, bordered in front and at the sides by solid black. This pattern on the head is sufficient to distinguish the Golden-crown from either of the white-crowned sparrows and from the lark sparrow. It differs further from all of these in having a dark toned under surface. But in general behavior it closely resembles the White-crowns, staying about brush patches and taking shelter under or within these when frightened.

The song of the Golden-crowned Sparrow is distinctive. It consists of three remarkably clear whistled notes, of a minor quality, and descending in pitch from the first to the third. Often, especially in the winter months, the song, short as it is, is given incompletely, only one or two of the notes being uttered, and then with a quavering intonation. But as spring comes on, the full three syllables are given vigorously and often. On occasion the Golden-crown is heard to indulge in a 'whisper song,' which is so faint as to be heard only at a very few yards' range. This has none of the clear whistles which characterize the usual utterance, but is remindful of the song of the lark sparrow. In addition, like other crowned sparrows, the Golden-crown, when disturbed, utters sharp metallic call notes.

In foraging, these sparrows, in scattered formation, advance out from the margins of the brush patches onto open ground where they hop here and there seeking their food, which is chiefly of a vegetable nature. They feed in particular upon the green seedlings of various 'weeds.' When the birds chop up between the edges of their mandibles the sprouting succulent seedlings, the exuding juice soils their faces and not infrequently even the plumage of their breasts. After the first rains have started the new growth of annuals, the bills of the birds are quite characteristically gummed up with dried green stuff.

WESTERN CHIPPING SPARROW. **Spizella passerina arizonae** Coues

Field characters.—Decidedly smaller than Junco, and with narrower tail. Crown of head chiefly bright reddish brown (pl. 8*d*); stripe over eye ashy white; upper surface of body brown, with black streaks on back; under surface of body ashy white, unmarked in adults, streaked in juveniles. No white on tail. *Voice:* Song of male a monotonous cicada-like buzz, lasting several seconds; both sexes utter a weak *tseet.*

Occurrence.—Summer visitant widely from floor of San Joaquin Valley to near timber line on Sierra Nevada; found in nesting season from Snelling east to Tioga Pass. Most abundant in Transition Zone and least numerous in Lower Sonoran and Hudsonian zones. Passes through Mono Lake country during spring migration. Winters in small numbers at Snelling. Frequents various situations, most often margins of clearings adjacent to small trees. Forages chiefly on ground. Flocks loosely after nesting.

The Western Chipping Sparrow possesses special characteristics which serve to bring it quickly to the notice of anyone who goes camping in the Sierras. Smaller even than a junco, and marked by neither brilliancy of coloration nor attractiveness of song, it might easily be overlooked. But it has the regular habit of coming close about a camp site and hopping, with many quick movements of both head and body, and with seeming fearlessness, over the open ground. It thus chooses as its own forage area the same sort of place that the vacationist selects for his camp; and so the bird happens to come much more than halfway toward bringing about an early acquaintanceship.

As regards coloration, the Western Chipping Sparrow is more easily distinguished by lack of conspicuous features than by the possession of any positive color marks. Only one, the reddish brown crown patch (pl. 8*d*), stands forth with any prominence; otherwise, the adult bird shows ashy white, unstreaked lower surface, dull brown wings and tail, and inconspicuously streaked back. Young birds, up to two months or so of age, are narrowly streaked on the under surface as well as above. With the first autumnal molt they become plain on the lower surface, while the crown patch (pl. 8*g*) does not appear until the first pre-nuptial molt, the following spring.

The Brewer Sparrow which summers in the sagebrush east of the mountains is much like the chipping sparrow but never has the bright brown crown patch. The Black-chinned Sparrow of the foothill chaparral has a black chin and blue-gray head and hind neck. During the summer season the bill of the chipping sparrow is black or nearly so, but in other seasons it is light-colored. In neither of the two other species named does the bill ever become black.

An interesting instance of adventitious coloration was met with at Dudley, on Smith Creek, on July 11, 1920. An adult female chipping sparrow was captured which had the plumage of the whole under surface of the body strongly tinged with a pinkish color. This was doubtless due to a 'dust bath' that the bird had taken in the roadway a mile or so up the valley where the soil is predominatingly reddish in color.

Western Chipping Sparrows are notably active, ever moving rapidly about from place to place. They seek much of their food on the top of the ground in open spots under trees, and they must needs hunt for it over a considerable area rather than dig it out in one place; their claws are relatively small and weak as compared with those of the ground-scratchers, like towhees and fox sparrows. Their activity seems never at an end, for they are as busy in the heat of midday as in the chill of morning or cool of evening.

The notes of the chipping sparrow are very simple. Both sexes utter a single short weak *tseet*, while the song of the male is nothing more than a cicada-like trill or buzz, monotonous to a degree, and strongly sustained throughout. It lasts several seconds (2 to 9 in instances timed by us) and is repeated over and over again at short intervals.

The Western Chipping Sparrow is one of the most notable of our passerine species in respect to the wide range of its occurrence. Indeed, it is exceptional for the great diversity of climatic conditions under which it thrives in the Yosemite section, this being, also, an index to its great degree of hardihood. Some individual birds nest in the hot, dry, almost parched San Joaquin Valley, where the temperature in summer is often 100° F.; and others rear their broods about the cool snow-covered alpine meadows almost at timber line. Yet, within these extreme life zones, as well as through all the intervening territory, it is associated with a type of habitat or niche which upon analysis is seen to recur with corresponding regularity. This niche is the one in which small trees dot open expanses of smooth, relatively dry ground, either practically bare, or grassy. Such an 'association' is illustrated by an orchard at Snelling, by a blue oak hillside at Pleasant Valley, by a tract of young yellow pines adjacent to a meadow in Yosemite Valley, or by a stand of smallish lodgepole pines on the edge of Tuolumne Meadows. In other words, the Chipping Sparrow is to be found in almost any climate, providing its special associational needs are met. Here is a case, then, where character of habitat (niche) weighs more in the economy of existence than do the factors of climate.

The chipping sparrow population is not uniform throughout its wide range but varies in the different zones. The birds are perhaps most numerous in the Transition Zone and least common in the Lower Sonoran and Hudsonian zones. A continuous census along the Tioga road between Porcupine Flat and Snow Flat, on June 28, 1915, revealed one or two birds an hour. About this same number an hour was noted in the Upper Sonoran Zone at Pleasant Valley in May, 1915. In the Transition Zone, in Yosemite Valley, the average was six or more, seen or heard, in an hour's census.

The Western Chipping Sparrow arrives in the Yosemite section in April or May, and leaves by late September or early October (the 7th in 1920 [C. W. Michael, MS]). A few winter at Snelling where one was collected January 9, 1915, from a flock of about 20 in company with some Sierra Juncos. But the host which fills the foothills and mountains in summer-time spends the winter somewhere to the southward, either on the deserts of southeastern California or beyond, on the tablelands of Mexico. The birds arrive in April, as nest building was already in progress in Yosemite Valley on April 30 (1916); and individuals were well established in the foothills between Lagrange and Coulterville on May 9 (1919). Occupation of the higher mountains seems to be accomplished with little if any delay. By May 24 (1919) the species was well established at Tamarack Flat (altitude 6400 feet). Near Mono Lake on May 6 (1916) chipping sparrows were passing in migration, but they were not found there later that season. The return migration sets in during September, and by the end of that month most of the birds have gone. The last to be reported in Yosemite Valley were seen on September 29 (1917) (Mailliard, 1918, p. 16). Our latest record for any point above the level of the San Joaquin Valley is for October 7 (1914), when a few were noted at El Portal.

But little time elapses after their arrival in the spring before the chipping sparrows settle down to nesting duties; yet not all the birds complete the rearing of their broods at an early date. Pairs engaged in caring for eggs or young are apt to be found at almost any time up until early July. Our earliest record of nest building is for April 30 (1916), and the latest, of young still in the nest, was made on July 15 (1920). Probably the bulk of the birds in the Transition Zone and above begin nesting between the middle of May and the middle of June. At the higher

Some Sparrows of the Yosemite Section: *a*. White-crowned Sparrow, adult. *b*. Same, immature. *c*. Intermediate Sparrow, adult. *d*. Western Chipping Sparrow, summer adult. *e*. Brewer Sparrow, adult. *f*. Golden-crowned Sparrow, adult. *g*. Western Chipping Sparrow, winter. *h*. Nevada Sage Sparrow. *i*. Bell Sparrow. *j*. Nevada Savannah Sparrow. *k*. Western Grasshopper Sparrow. *l*. Rufous-crowned Sparrow.

altitudes, nesting comes later, probably because, due to the persistence of a low temperature there to a later date in the spring, sufficient food is not available earlier. But the discrepancy from this cause is not so great as might be supposed. At the lower levels the chipping sparrows nest after the first burst of bloom from the herbaceous plants is over, whereas around the high mountain meadows the birds have their nesting already well under way when the alpine flowers have only begun to appear. Thus, to a certain degree, the spring calendar for the birds is different from that for the flowers. The birds maintain their own body temperature in spite of the prevalent conditions about them, and may therefore be controlled more directly by other factors, such as that of available supply of food.

At El Portal on the morning of April 27, 1916, a male chipping sparrow was seen in courting display before a female. He uttered notes sharper than the usual ones, more like the syllable *tsā*, uttered singly or trilled in series. As the notes were given, each was accompanied by a slight shrug of the body and downward movement of the tail. The two birds passed back and forth, hopping and flying, amid red-bud, buckeye, and live oaks.

A majority of the nests of this bird are placed between 4 and 6 feet from the ground; very few are more than 12 feet up. The lowest nest found by us in the Yosemite section was only 2 feet above the ground and the highest approximately 16 feet. Almost any sort of tree or large bush is used for a site. In a bush or small tree the nest is most often placed near or at the top; while in a large tree it is situated near the end of a lower outreaching branch. We saw nests in blue oak, live oak, incense cedar, yellow pine, lodgepole pine, and orchard trees, as well as in deer brush and wild rose, and once in a cultivated blackberry vine.

The nests of the Western Chipping Sparrow are of such an unique type that they may be readily identified without the necessity of seeing the makers. No other bird of the Yosemite region builds a nest of the same form or constituency. The foundation is of long fine weathered stems of grasses and other plants, so laid together and interlaced that they constitute a firm yet porous structure not easily shaken to pieces. Internally, the nest proper is of a deep cup-shape, walled with a neatly woven layer consisting solely of long mammal hairs, wound about so as to produce a perfectly smooth interior surface. This inner lining is so well woven that it can be lifted free of the foundation part of the nest and still retain its shape, almost like a piece of hair cloth. This type of nest seems well adapted to the kind of site preferred by the chipping sparrow, namely, the outer loose foliage of trees, upon a large area of which the nest platform can rest without danger of disintegration or of falling from place. The nest cavity measures in ascertained cases 1⅞ inches in diameter by 1¼ inches deep. Externally there is naturally much variation in dimension; one nest measured in place was 3¼ inches in diameter and 2¼ inches high.

Four is the usual number of eggs laid; none of the nests seen by us held more. Several nests held only 3 to 2 eggs or young, but in these cases there is the possibility that some of the clutch or brood had been lost.

During the nesting season chipping sparrows are as fearless as at other times. The observer can often approach very close to a nest before the sitting bird will leave. We have set up our camera, unscreened, within two feet of a nest, and the female remained on the nest during most or all of the manipulations incident to the taking of a picture.

After the broods are reared, parents and young join in family parties and wander about in their daily quest for food. Sometimes several of these groups gather in a loose flock of a score or more. After the late-summer molt, there is no renewal of the song, as with some sparrows; only the weak call notes are given. In early autumn the "chippies" quietly take their leave, and by the first week in October the observer finds the species no more among the birds recorded in his daily census.

Brewer Sparrow. **Spizella breweri** Cassin

Field characters.—Size, proportions, and coloration close to those of Chipping Sparrow. No reddish brown on crown or distinct light line over eye. (See pl. 8e.) Top of head, like back, brownish gray streaked with black; lower surface plain ashy white. *Voice:* Song of male more varied and more musical than that of Chipping Sparrow, remindful of some themes in song of tame canary; call note, a weak *tseet*.

Occurrence.—Common summer visitant along east side of Sierra Nevada, in vicinity of Mono Lake. Recorded from Silver and Walker lakes eastward. Occurs, also, in spring migration, along west base of Sierra Nevada, as at Lagrange (May 6, 1919) and Smith Creek, east of Coulterville (March 23, 1916). Noted in Yosemite Valley, September 18, 1917 (Mailliard, 1918, p. 17). A few appear at higher altitudes in early fall, as near Merced Lake (August 25 and September 5, 1915). Habitually in sagebrush. In pairs while nesting; in loose flocks at other times.

The Brewer Sparrow is a common and characteristic summer visitant in the great inland sea of sagebrush which covers the floor of the Great Basin. It is a near relative of the Western Chipping Sparrow, but wears still duller colors, having none of the bright markings on its head which characterize the latter bird. (See pl. 8e.) The general tone of its whole coloration is subdued to a pale tint of gray which closely matches the gray color of the brush in which it lives.

The time at which the Brewer Sparrow arrives in the Yosemite region has not been ascertained closely. Birds which were undoubtedly migrants were observed at Smith Creek, 6 miles east of Coulterville, on March 23, 1916, and near Lagrange, on May 6, 1919. About Mono Lake, in 1916, the first were observed, near Williams Butte, on May 6, although they may have arrived there somewhat earlier. Southeast of the Mono Lake region the migration begins in late March or early April.

On September 18, 1917, Mr. Joseph Mailliard (1918, p. 17) identified one of these birds among some Western Chipping Sparrows on the floor of the Yosemite Valley.

Throughout the summer months Brewer Sparrows are to be seen everywhere in the sagebrush country perhaps more commonly than any other bird species. In early autumn the number of birds about Mono Lake seems to be augmented, either by the arrival of migrants from the north or by a post-aestival movement toward the Sierras from the drier flats and valleys to the east. Whatever the cause of increase in local population, our censuses at that season record 10 to 36 of these birds an hour in sage-covered areas. The Brewers were still abundant when we quitted the Mono Lake country on September 23, 1915. The wintering grounds of these birds are on the deserts of the Southwest and so their migration, whatever the date of departure from the Mono region, is not a very extensive one.

A nest of the Brewer Sparrow was found only about 10 inches above the ground in a sagebush near the mouth of Rush Creek on June 3, 1916. It held two blue eggs, far advanced in incubation; the sitting bird flushed as the observer grazed the side of the bush in passing. On June 30, 1916, adults were seen carrying food to young in the nest. The young, with the streaked breasts of the juvenal plumage, do not appear abroad in numbers until slightly later, that is in July; by the middle of August many of them have already completed the fall molt which brings them into a plumage almost exactly like that of the adults.

Brewer Sparrows occasionally work up into the high eastern portions of the Sierra Nevada in much the same way that many other kinds of birds which nest at the west base of the mountains move up to Yosemite Valley or beyond in late summer. But with the Brewer the movement is not so general and when the birds do thus appear out of their normal range they seek out, and keep close to, their accustomed shelter plant. On August 25, and again on September 5, 1915, flocks of a dozen or more of these sparrows were seen in some stunted sagebrush on a sun-heated gravelly bench between Echo and Sunrise creeks, not far from Merced Lake.

BLACK-CHINNED SPARROW. **Spizella atrogularis** (Cabanis)

Field characters.—Size near that of Chipping Sparrow. Tail as long or longer than body. Head and neck and most of under surface of body plain dark gray; middle of back reddish brown, streaked with black; wings and tail plain blackish brown. Chin black and bill reddish brown in male. *Voice:* Song of male a series of high-pitched wiry notes, all on about the same key, beginning slowly but running together at the end, *tseey, tseey, tsey, tse, se-se-se;* call note a low sharp *chit.*

Occurrence.—One bird heard in song near Black's Creek, west of Coulterville, May 11, 1919. Possibly present in small numbers as a summer visitant in Upper Sonoran Zone on west side of mountains. Lives in greasewood chaparral.

Our inclusion of the Black-chinned Sparrow as a member of the Yosemite avifauna rests upon our hearing the characteristic song of the male repeatedly on the one occasion instanced above. This sparrow is moderately common on many of the chaparral covered hillsides of southern California, but it has not previously been reported from any locality along the west flank of the Sierra Nevada. Careful search of the greasewood brush (*Adenostoma*) between Pleasant Valley and Coulterville would likely reveal the presence of the species in small numbers.

SLATE-COLORED JUNCO. **Junco hyemalis hyemalis** (Linnaeus)

Field characters.—As for Sierra Junco (which see), but coloration more slaty black, the adult male being entirely without reddish brown on either sides or back. Female much as in Sierra Junco, but less distinctly pinkish on sides and less brown on back. Habits like those of Sierra Junco.

Occurrence.—Irregular winter visitant. Definite records (specimens taken) are as follows: Gentrys, on Big Oak Flat Road, December 30, 1914 (one); Yosemite Valley near Rocky Point, November 12, 1915 (two individuals); Smith Creek, 6 miles east of Coulterville, January 28, 1919, and March 9, 1919 (one in each case). Most likely to be associated as single individuals in flocks of Sierra Junco.

Individuals of the Slate-colored or 'eastern' Junco turn up almost every year in different parts of California, so it was no great surprise to find a few of this species in the Yosemite region. When this bird is found within our boundaries it is usually only to the extent of an individual or two in a large flock of the common wintering species, the Sierra Junco. This was the case with the birds obtained by us and with those taken by Mr. Donald D. McLean at his home east of Coulterville. When seen in association with its relative, the Slate-colored Junco immediately impresses the close observer as being darker, more slaty in color. Its habits do not seem to differ in any appreciable way from those of the Sierra Junco.

SIERRA JUNCO. **Junco oreganus thurberi** Anthony[28]

Field characters.—A small sparrow (total length about 6 inches, tail about 2½ inches long). Head, neck, and breast covered by solid black (most intense in males, grayish toned in females and immatures), sharply set off from white on under surface of body. Bill whitish-appearing. Back and wings dark brown, unmarked; tail black centrally, two outer feathers on each side pure white. Juvenile birds lack the black 'cowl' and have the whole head and body, both above and below, streaked. When on ground, hops about rapidly in zigzag course; if flushed, rises quickly, spreading tail so that white margin shows conspicuously; usually takes refuge within nearby trees or large bushes. *Voice:* Song of male a quavering trill, metallic in quality, rapid in utterance, *eetle, eetle, eetle, eetle* . . . . continued for from one to three seconds, weakening in intensity toward the end; repeated at irregular intervals. Call of both sexes a low *seep* or sharper *tsick;* one of these notes often given several times in quick succession as birds of a family or flock rise from ground.

Occurrence.—Abundant summer visitant throughout the Transition, Canadian, and Hudsonian zones on both sides of Sierra Nevada. Recorded in summer from 3 miles east of Coulterville and from Bullion Mountain eastward across the mountains to Parker Creek (at 7500 feet) and Warren Mountain. As a rule the range of this bird is limited altitudinally at timber line; the highest elevation at which we saw it was 11,000 feet on Parsons Peak, September 6, 1915. In winter descends to below the level of heavy snow, occupying the whole of foothill and lowland country; a few may remain as high as Yosemite Valley. Found in numbers in winter at El Portal and 6 miles east of Coulterville and from there westward to Lagrange and Snelling. In summer lives in and about openings in forest or along open stream banks; in winter ranges widely, but not onto open prairie. In pairs at nesting time, but in flocks of varying size during other parts of year.

The Sierra Junco or Snowbird has proved, by actual census, to be the most abundant species of bird in the Yosemite section. During the summer season it is common throughout the forested portions of the mountains embracing the Transition, Canadian, and Hudsonian zones, on both slopes, while in winter it is abundant in the Upper Sonoran foothills of the west slope, and occurs in some numbers in the Transition and Lower Sonoran zones as well. Because it is thus a species of wide occurrence, and in addition possesses a distinctive type of coloration, we have chosen it for our standard of comparison in discussing the other small birds of the region.

The whole forepart of the Sierra Junco's body is covered by a solid dark cowl, jet black in the adult males, but grayish toned in female and immature birds. This black ends below abruptly against the white of the belly. The back and wings lack contrasted markings of any sort, but when

---

[28] In addition to the prevalent Sierra Junco there is present in winter in small numbers another subspecies of the 'Oregon' Junco, the Shufeldt Junco, *Junco oreganus shufeldti* Coale, which summers in northwestern North America interiorly. This race has the wing and tail somewhat longer, the sides more dusky (less pink tinged), and the back of a duller brown than has the Sierra Junco. Specimens are at hand from Dudley (on Smith Creek), six miles east of Coulterville, taken December 25, 1918, and January 27, 1919.

the bird takes to flight the tail is seen to be broadly margined with white. The young in the juvenal plumage, which they acquire in the nest and wear until the first fall molt, are streaked over the whole body, and they lack any indication of the black cowl, but their white outer tail feathers are just as conspicuous as those of the parent birds. The middle of the back and sides of the body are reddish brown in the adult Sierra Junco, a feature which helps to separate this species from the near-related Shufeldt and Slate-colored juncos. No other bird is likely to be confused with the junco. The Spurred Towhee has a black cowl similar to that of the junco, but the former is a much larger bird, has white spots on the black wings and tail, and stays almost exclusively within heavy brush, instead of foraging out on open ground.

The Sierra Junco, in summer, is found throughout the main forest belt of the Sierra Nevada. It eschews dense growths of timber, preferring to live in clear areas beneath the larger trees or between tracts of timber, but always where there is convenient cover close by, to be sought if danger threatens. The bird gains the greater portion of its forage on open ground and nests there, but it uses the trees and large bushes as song perches and as safety refuges. In winter a lesser degree of restriction in habitation is evident, for then the juncos invade all sorts of vegetational environments save open prairie where no cover of any sort is available.

The total junco population on the Sierra Nevada during the summer months is in excess of that of any other one species of bird. Three to five an hour will usually be seen at this season in any part of its range, save perhaps in Yosemite Valley. The Sierra Junco is outnumbered by the Western Chipping Sparrow on the floor of the Valley, but it is much better represented in the zones above, especially in the Canadian. The junco population is larger, relatively as well as absolutely, on the west slope of the Sierras than on the east slope. The winter distribution is less uniform. Then the birds are in flocks and their inclusion in a census depends upon the observer's meeting one of these companies, which may aggregate 15 to 50 birds.

Many juncos remain in the highlands through the crisp fall weather, and the birds are then present literally in droves in the red fir territory immediately above and surrounding the Yosemite Valley. But the first flurry of snow, forecasting the approach of winter, starts them down-slope rapidly and soon relatively few remain even as high as Yosemite Valley. Some depart for the lower altitudes by October; these are joined later by those which linger until they are literally forced out of the high mountains by the snow mantle which covers up their food supply there. The bulk of the population at this season is concentrated in the foothills, but some go down still farther to the west, into the San Joaquin Valley.

It is during the fall and winter months that individuals of the Slate-colored and Shufeldt juncos are occasionally encountered in flocks of the Sierran birds. These have probably traveled all the way from summer localities in British Columbia and beyond.

In the fall of 1915 we remained in Yosemite Valley through the first real snowfall of the season which began on the evening of November 8 and continued into the following day. On the morning of the 9th juncos were in active migration down the Valley. They did not fly along continuously nor did they alight in the snow, but from the clear ground about the base of one thick-foliaged tree they dashed on a few rods to another similar shelter and hopped about there for a minute or so before moving farther. Each individual was moving independently, yet all in the flock were going in the same general direction. One bird would fly ahead, loiter a minute, and be passed by others previously left behind, and so on. At any one point there would be a rapid succession of juncos while the flock as a whole moved more slowly. It was quite evident that the birds from the plateau above the Valley were migrating down-slope and westward, as more juncos were seen on that morning passing one place on the north side of the Valley than had been seen all told in the preceding month on the whole floor of the Valley.

On December 26 and 28, 1914, when the early snows of that season had largely melted off on the north (sunny) side of the Valley, several companies of juncos were observed there, and it is possible that amelioration of conditions had led them to come in again from the westward. Some of the birds were around the buildings of the old Presidio, foraging far back within the open basements. Subsequently, a resident of the Valley reported that about 25 juncos had stayed around his house during the winter of 1915–16, as he thought, because of the food continually put out for them.

In general demeanor the junco is more active than many of the sparrows. On the ground it gets about with quick movements, turning first to one side and then the other, but not often hopping many paces before stopping to examine its surroundings. It does little scratching, and indeed neither its claws nor its bill are of the stout type found in birds such as the fox sparrows which dig out their food. The Sierra Junco, like the Western Chipping Sparrow, is a surface forager and gets its provender by moving about rapidly and scanning a relatively large area of ground. This is as true of the members of a winter flock as of individual birds in summer.

When frightened, a junco flies directly to cover, taking shelter usually within trees or large bushes. Its general procedure is to fly along a short distance above the ground, usually reaching the nearest foliage at the first flight; then, after a pause, and some hopping about from branch to branch, it descends again to the ground near by. If badly scared the bird will make off to a distance, though usually going from one tree to another rather than making a continuous, direct flight in the open.

While foraging on the ground a junco opens and shuts the tail slightly from time to time, so that the white margins show for an instant. Upon taking flight either from the ground or a tree the bird spreads its tail widely and then the white shows broadly and conspicuously. Some naturalists believe that the bird's flashing of these contrasting areas serves to apprize other members of the species of the particular individual's location and of the direction taken by it when it moves off; any threatening danger seen by one bird may thus be reported to other juncos in the vicinity which, in turn, seek safety. Accompanying the display of white when an alarmed junco flies up are the well-known call notes given in rhythm with the wing-beats and movements of the tail; and these notes are believed to be of similar purport. The sense of hearing is thus brought into service to supplement that of sight.

The song of the male junco is to be heard throughout the spring and early summer months; it usually ceases some time in July. It is a quavering trill, pleasing to the human ear, given rapidly and possessing a tinkling quality. The syllables are practically alike, *eetle, eetle, eetle, eetle,* on about the same key, but with the intensity lessening toward the end. In spring the male gives his song at practically any hour of the day, perhaps not so much at dawn and dusk as during the mid-day hours. Yet we have heard it as early at 5:15 A.M. (June 2), in Yosemite Valley, and sometimes the birds break out in song in the middle of the night. The sharp call note, *seep* or *tsick,* uttered by both sexes, is usually repeated several times as the birds rise from the ground, and if given while foraging there, its utterance is often accompanied by momentary flashing of the white outer tail feathers. A heavier note, of alarm, is also given, *tsup.*

The courting of the junco is not so elaborate or varied a performance as that of some birds. The pursuit of females by males or of rival males by one another may occasionally be observed, but for the most part the birds are rather quiet. Occasionally males either on the ground or perched, when females are close by, will hold the tail spread for some seconds so that the white margin shows forth with extraordinary brilliance. The song seems to be the principal factor in courting. In order to study this subject satisfactorily, an observer would need to keep track of flocks just before they break up in the spring and then watch the behavior of the pairs during the whole course of the development of the mating instincts.

When the first rush of human travelers reaches the Yosemite region in May the juncos are preparing to nest, and by early June many pairs of the birds have their nesting well under way. Our earliest record of a completed nest with eggs was made on June 10 (1915) at Chinquapin. But earlier instances will doubtless be found upon further search; for we saw a bird carrying nest material on May 20 (1919). The peak of nesting activity is reached in June, during which month, in 1915, we found, without special search, over a dozen nests. The first young noted out of the nest in that year were observed in Yosemite Valley on June 21, soon after which new broods were common. But nesting does not cease at an early date. Either some pairs are delayed, through accident or other cause, or else they rear more than one brood. A nest found at Merced Lake on August 20, 1915, held two young not old enough to fly; and bob-tailed youngsters were seen near Washburn Lake on August 24 the same year.

The majority of the nests observed were located either at the margins of wet meadows, or along open creek banks. The birds seemingly prefer to be able to fly to and from the nest unimpeded by vegetation. The nest is a compactly woven cup, about three inches in outside diameter and the same in depth. It is almost invariably sunk in the ground so that the rim is flush with the surface. Sometimes it is placed at the side of a log or beneath a fallen branch, but as often it is on open ground amid the grasses, and one nest was seen in the center of a traveled road. As an exception to the general rule may be cited a nest placed on an overhead beam under the roof of a painted cottage porch in Yosemite Valley. This nest was bulkier than usual, and the materials composing it straggled down the side of the beam. It was evidently built in good faith because two eggs were laid ere a gust of wind cast it to the ground.

The average nest is composed largely of small plant or grass leaves and stems compactly woven together. The larger pieces are on the outside, and the size of the pieces of material gradually decreases as the center is approached. The inside lining is usually of horse hair, but occasionally shed hairs from some of the native mammals are used. Four is the usual number of eggs laid and no more than this complement were seen in any nest examined by us. Sometimes but three seemed to constitute the completed set.

During the summer the members of a pair of Sierra Juncos keep in close company, and if the vicinity of their nest is approached the two will often exhibit a high degree of concern. If the female is incubating she will usually leave in a flurry, with the tail widely spread (whereby the eye catches the white quickly), and then trail along the ground, giving an appearance of being injured in an effort to focus interest upon herself and draw attention from the nest. Soon the male, if not already at hand, will appear and the two will hop excitedly about either on the ground or among the low branches of an adjacent conifer, repeating their call notes with an intonation which suggests extreme anxiety.

After the broods are reared the adults continue to guard and care for their charges for some time; in some cases, at least, the family stays together through the fall molt. From this initial grouping it is but a step to the formation of the flocks in which the birds spend the winter. Flock formation persists until the birds seek their nesting grounds again the following spring.

From late April until July pairs are the rule. Then young begin to appear in numbers and family parties are of common observation. Such groups were seen at Merced Lake on August 23, and in Yosemite Valley even as late as September 24 (1915). Flock formation is under way about the latter date; one band of 20 was seen in Yosemite Valley on September 25, and several of 20 to 50 each in Tioga Pass, September 28, 1915. The flocks hold together through the winter months, sometimes becoming mixed with those of Chipping Sparrows in the valleys, but more often keeping by themselves. At Pleasant Valley on February 27 and 28, 1916, bands of 12 to 35 were seen; and a flock of 15 was observed in Yosemite Valley on February 29 the same year. By April 27, the time of our next visit, the lowlands were cleared of juncos, and the birds seen in Yosemite Valley on April 28, 1916, were not in flocks. On May 14, 1919, juncos at Hazel Green were paired and the males were trilling their songs.

BELL SPARROW. **Amphispiza belli** (Cassin)

Field characters.—Size of Junco or Linnet; tail as long as body. Upper surface plain dull brown, becoming iron gray on head; area in front of eye, and conspicuous stripe down side of neck from bill, black (pl. 8*i*); spot on each side of brow, lower cheek, and throat and under surface of body, white; a distinct black spot on center of breast. *Voice:* Song of male a set utterance of tinkling quality, *tweesitity-slip, tweesitity-slip, swer;* also a faint one-syllabled call note, *seet.*

Occurrence.—Common resident in Upper Sonoran Zone over western base of Sierras. Lives almost exclusively in greasewood chaparral. Observed by us at Pleasant Valley, near Coulterville, and near El Portal. To be seen in pairs or scattered family parties.

The Bell Sparrow is closely associated with that type of chaparral, made up almost purely of the greasewood, which clothes so much of the dry foothill country flanking the west base of the Sierra Nevada. Since this is a bird of dull colors and retiring habits, it will not likely be seen by a person passing quickly along any of the dusty roadways through this 'chamisal.' The bird student interested in forming an acquaintance with this sparrow will need to tarry at some place in the foothills and spend a few hours amid the greasewood itself.

In 1914 and 1915 we saw but little of the Bell Sparrow, and that only incidentally, as we were endeavoring to get a general idea of the fauna in the vicinity of El Portal and Pleasant Valley; but in 1919 some time was spent at Blacks Creek, west of Coulterville, in seeking a special acquaintance with this species. To do this we left the beaten roadway and grassy clearings and pushed our way up onto the slopes covered solidly with greasewood. Here we followed a growth of young bushes which had sprung up where once a narrow clearing had been made for miles across the country beneath a power line. Our field notes of this day, May 12, 1919, are substantially as follows.

The hillside was a dry, south-facing one, of slaty formation covered with a typical California chaparral composed of greasewood (*Adenostoma fasciculatum*) with scattering bushes of wedge-leafed ceanothus (*Ceanothus cuneatus*) and manzanita (*Arctostaphylos mariposa*). Here a Bell Sparrow was found, its headquarters proving to be on a subsidiary ridge running down into an oak lined ravine. We located the bird first by hearing from a distance its tinkling song. This may be variously written, *inksely-inksely-inksely-ser*, or *tweesitity-slip, tweesitity-slip, swer*, or *sweesely-swer, sweesely-swer, swer*, according to different attempts at transcription. The rhythm of this utterance was notable. The bird sang every 9 or 10 seconds, each song lasting about 2½ seconds. The song would be repeated for several minutes from one perch and then the bird would change to another location. It would perch on the topmost shoot of a greasewood bush, facing away from the wind, its feathers blown outward somewhat, and would rock back and forth in keeping its balance on the swaying twig. This individual bird seemed to be centering his attentions on some particular portion of the hillslope, for he circled about within a radius of not over 150 feet, singing from one perch, then changing to another. Between song periods he would disappear, presumably to forage, within the mantle of brush, where also probably was his mate, though she kept well out of our sight.

Searching around amid the smaller greasewood bushes on the one-time clearing, we found 8 old nests belonging undoubtedly to this species. These ranged from 6 to 30 inches above the ground, but most of them were not more than 10 inches up. All were in small greasewood bushes, not over 24 inches tall, and placed within the cluster of upright stems. The nests were composed of small twigs of the greasewood, with the dry whitish stems of some annual plant as a felting for the interior. A typical weathered nest measured approximately 3 inches in outside diameter. So large a number of nests found in the one area (not over 150 feet in diameter) would suggest continued occupancy of the little tract of an acre or so for a number of years by this one pair of birds or their ancestors.

No other bird of any species was encountered during our stay in this area of an acre or more. It would seem that the Bell Sparrow, at least at nesting time, closely restricts itself to a type of territory such as is not sought out by other birds; it is not consequently bothered by competition.

Moving on to the next little hillslope we observed another singing male Bell Sparrow; a careful examination of the many hillsides in the basin of Blacks Creek would probably have revealed a pair of Bell Sparrows on each one. Hence, while the number of Bell Sparrows to be found in any one limited area is small, the total population in the entire greasewood belt of the western foothills must be large. As already stated, not one of these birds is likely to come to the attention even of the careful bird student save as he or she makes particular effort to find the species.

NEVADA SAGE SPARROW. **Amphispiza nevadensis nevadensis** (Ridgway)

Field characters.—Slightly larger than Junco or Bell Sparrow. Whole bird gray-toned; upper surface of body, wings and tail, ashy brown; head pure ashy gray (pl. 8*h*); under surface white with a dusky spot on center of breast; a broad streak of dull black runs from bill through eye, and there is a narrower dark gray stripe on each side of throat. *Voice:* As for Bell Sparrow.

Occurrence.—Common summer visitant to Transition Zone east of Sierra Nevada. Observed widely about Mono Lake and around Mono Craters. Habitually in sagebrush. In pairs or scattering companies; never in close flocks.

The Nevada Sage Sparrow is the counterpart of the Bell Sparrow and takes the niche of that bird on the east side of the Sierra Nevada, where sagebrush takes the place of the greasewood of the west slope. In various portions of the plains-like, sage-covered country about Mono Lake these sparrows were seen in moderate numbers during mid-September, 1915. In the spring and early summer of 1916 they were met with only once, on June 20, close to the old Salmon Ranch near Mono Lake Post Office.

Sage sparrows do all their foraging upon the ground between bushes, where they hop about in a peculiar hesitating manner. When alarmed they run with astonishing celerity, being able easily to keep several bushes between themselves and their pursuers. If closely pressed they take to flight and scatter out, to drop out of sight again shortly. When singing, and often at other times, individuals will perch many minutes at a time at the tips of tall bushes, where they are visible considerable distances over the sea of sage.

RUFOUS-CROWNED SPARROW. **Aimophila ruficeps ruficeps** (Cassin)

Field characters.—Size of Junco, but tail and wings shorter. No contrasted white markings; top of head reddish brown (rufous) (pl. 8*l*); plumage brown toned, tinged with rufous on back; line over eye ashy gray; chin buffy white, bordered on each side by black line extending a little way downward from bill; otherwise no streaks or markings of any sort beneath. Movements quick and frequent. Seldom flies far; keeps closely within protection of low bushes. *Voice:* Song of male resembling in general effect song of Lazuli Bunting; both sexes utter a slow series of notes, *kiew, kiew, kew-kew-kew;* last of the series fainter, and quality throughout nasal.

Occurrence.—Resident in small numbers and locally, in Upper Sonoran Zone. Found by us at Pleasant Valley and El Portal. Lives on dry sun-facing hillsides among low scattered shrubs (*not* in dense or high chaparral). To be met with in pairs or singly, never in flocks.

The Rufous-crowned Sparrow is a bird of the chaparral belt, but, unlike the Wren-tit, it lives exclusively in open stands of low bushes on the driest slopes. Such tracts are to be found on the sun-facing slopes at the heads of the smaller ravines. The bird is not known to us to occur in the dense brush at any time. These areas of dwarf chaparral are quite limited in extent in the Yosemite section and the Rufous-crowned Sparrows are restricted in like measure. They seem to be strictly resident and are as likely to be found in the particular locality of their choice in winter as in summer. We observed the birds at only two places, Pleasant Valley and El Portal, but careful search of the foothill districts would doubtless show them to be present in many other localities of similar nature.

The Rufous-crowned Sparrow resembles in some ways the Bell and Nevada Sage sparrows, but yet it differs from these birds in certain noteworthy respects. It is decidedly brown rather than grayish in tone of color, it possesses a reddish brown crown patch (pl. 8*l*), and it has no dark spot on the chest. Its niche is different from that of either of the species named, and it does not habitually perch in prominent view on the tops of bushes as do the other two birds.

The song of the male Rufous-crowned Sparrow is rarely heard. It is somewhat like that of the Lazuli Bunting but is weaker and less elaborate. For singing the bird will perch a foot or so above the ground on the top of one of the small bushes of the neighborhood, where it will sing a few times and then take itself off to forage. Its curious whining or nasal call note, as described above, is uttered by both sexes and as a rule without any apparent cause, such as danger.

Nesting activities with the Rufous-crowned Sparrows are evidently commenced in April. We found no occupied nests, but on the 25th of May, 1915, near Pleasant Valley, we obtained a fully fledged juvenile bird. The young birds do not differ greatly in appearance from their parents.

The plumage, as is generally the case with juvenile birds, is laxer, the crown is not so bright and the breast is narrowly streaked with blackish. These differences, accompaniments of immaturity, disappear at the first fall molt.

Our attention was attracted to the young bird just mentioned by our hearing a pair of adults uttering their nasal notes in a rapid scolding series, unlike the usual slow enunciation. Meanwhile the birds kept hopping about in a concerned manner in the low brush on a ravine side. A Bell Sparrow and a Lazuli Bunting were calling close by, but the notes of these birds did not indicate so great a degree of solicitude as was evinced by the voices and behavior of the adult Rufous-crowns. While we were cautiously approaching the focus of the commotion, a California Gray Fox suddenly broke from cover in the bottom of the little cañon. The parent Rufous-crowns were quite justified in finding his presence a cause of concern; there were evidently other juveniles of that species in the brush beside the one we found.

A Rufous-crowned Sparrow was seen in some thick brush on the side of a small cañon near El Portal on the morning of November 25, 1914. Its brownish coloration, light stripe over eye, light throat, and quick movements reminded the observer of the San Joaquin Bewick Wren. While moving close about the observer and on the alert, this sparrow was seen to fluff out and then press down its feathers; and the rufous feathers of the crown of the head were held continually in a slightly elevated position. The faint call note was given several times while the bird was in view, and from time to time other birds of the same species were heard calling in the vicinity.

SONG SPARROWS. **Melospiza melodia** (Wilson)[29]

Field characters.—Somewhat larger than Junco. Body streaked both above and below; ground color above dark, below white; a distinct dark spot on breast; no white marks on wing or tail; a light stripe over each eye and another over mid crown. Tail short-appearing, not longer than body, habitually carried up at decided angle with back. A quick-moving sparrow, almost as active as a wren. *Voice:* Song of male set as to theme, much varied as to rendering; begun with two or three separate clear notes, followed by a buzz and ended with a trill; both sexes utter various call notes.

----

[29] Four subspecies of the Song Sparrow were found in the Yosemite region. The case with these birds is different from that with the Fox Sparrows, as one subspecies of song sparrow is much more numerously represented than the others, both winter and summer, and there are very few if any Song Sparrows present in the western portion of the region during the summer months. Furthermore, in summer, the Song Sparrow occurs altogether below the range of the Fox Sparrow. The subspecies represented are as follows:

MODOC SONG SPARROW, *Melospiza melodia fisherella* Oberholser, a gray-toned form with light brown streaking, is a summer visitant to the Great Basin region east of the mountains where it was found by us at Mono Lake Post Office, near Williams Butte, and at Silver and Walker lakes. Single individuals (strays?) noted at Gem Lake, 9036 feet,

Occurrence.—Winter visitant in small to moderate numbers at various places on west slope of Sierra Nevada below 4500 feet altitude. Also present during summer season locally east of the mountains, around Mono Lake; in fall stragglers reach to 9000 feet on east slope.[29] Inhabits bushes and thickets nearly always close to water or over damp ground. Solitary except when pairs are engaged in nesting.

The Song Sparrow is not so conspicuous a member of the avifauna in the Yosemite section as it is in many other parts of North America. In summer, it is present only east of the mountains, while in winter, when some representatives of the species do occur on the west side of the Sierra Nevada, its numbers are never large, as compared for instance with those in the coastal region of California. This deficiency is due perhaps to the relative dearth of suitable stream-side cover.

Both summer and winter the Modoc Song Sparrow (*Melospiza melodia fisherella*) is the most abundant of the several subspecies of song sparrow occurring in the Yosemite region. East of the mountains, in the spring of 1916, it was found near Williams Butte as early as April 29, and in the fall of 1915 it was still present on September 20. It probably leaves the east side of the mountains during the winter months, though it doubtless returns there as soon as weather conditions permit. In Yosemite Valley, our earliest fall record for song sparrows was made on October 10 (1914), when two were noted in some willows. A bird captured there on October 28 (1915), proved to be the Modoc Song Sparrow. Subsequently, Mr. Joseph Mailliard (1918, p. 17) took one of these birds on September 27 (1917). None was seen by us at any station on the west side of the mountains higher than the floor of Yosemite Valley. In November and December, a few of this race were found along the Merced River at El Portal and Pleasant Valley; and it was fairly common at Snelling and Lagrange.

The song sparrow resembles in general appearance the Lincoln sparrow which occurs in one part or another of the Yosemite region throughout the year. The song sparrow is of larger size and stouter build, has no buffy band across its breast, and the streaks on the breast are heavier. In

September 13, 1915, and at Warren Fork of Leevining Creek, September 25, 1915. Also occurs on the west slope, but only in winter, being then found from Yosemite Valley westward to Snelling and Lagrange. This is the commonest subspecies in the region.

RUSTY SONG SPARROW, *Melospiza melodia rufina* (Bonaparte), a reddish brown colored form which summers in the coastal district of northwest America from southeastern Alaska to Washington, was taken at Snelling, January 6, 1915, and at Smith Creek, east of Coulterville, March 3, 1917, and November 26, 1918.

HEERMANN SONG SPARROW, *Melospiza melodia heermanni* Baird, a large billed subspecies with black streaking on a pale ground, which nests in the San Joaquin Valley, was found at Snelling, January 2, 1915, and at Lagrange, December 10, 1915. It is possible that this race nests within our limits, although we found no song sparrow at Snelling or Lagrange in May.

MERRILL SONG SPARROW, *Melospiza melodia merrilli* Brewster, a large, brownish form, yet paler than *rufina*, summering in the northern interior states between the Cascade and Rocky mountains, was found once, in winter, at Snelling, January 7, 1915.

the summer season, however, there is no overlapping in the ranges of these two sparrows. The Lincoln is then almost altogether above the 6000-foot level, and on the west slope only.

No nests of the song sparrow came to our attention. But in the vicinity of Mono Lake the presence in mid-September, 1915, of yet unmolted juvenile examples of *fisherella* pointed toward broods having been reared in the vicinity. On September 20, 1915, song sparrows were seen around the edge of Mono Lake, where the birds seemed to be feeding on the then abundant supply of Mono Lake flies and their larvae.

LINCOLN SPARROWS. Melospiza lincolni (Audubon)[30]

Field characters.—Slightly smaller than Junco; tail shorter than body. No white markings on wing or tail; body narrowly streaked both above and below; head and upper surface of body streaked with brown and black; a gray stripe over each eye; sides of throat and body, and band across breast, buff, narrowly streaked with dark brown; chin white. Behavior much like that of Song Sparrow. *Voice:* Song of male an extremely rapid gurgling utterance, remindful of Western House Wren: *zee zee zee ti ter-r-r-r-r-r;* call note of both sexes a low *sip;* a chuckling note is also given.

Occurrence.—Moderately common summer visitant in Canadian Zone (and locally in the Hudsonian and Transition zones) on west slope of Sierra Nevada (subspecies *lincolni*). Also fall and winter visitant on west flank of mountains from Snelling to Yosemite (subspecies *gracilis*).[30] Lives in thickets near streams. In pairs at nesting time, otherwise solitary.

The Northeastern Lincoln Sparrow (*Melospiza lincolni lincolni*) is a summer visitant to the higher portions of the Sierra Nevada. While there, it inhabits dense willow and dogwood thickets, such as line streams or occur around the edges of wet meadows. It is thus found at the higher altitudes on the same ground with the white-crowned sparrow. The Lincoln sparrow, however, keeps much more closely to cover, and as its song is not loud or its markings or actions conspicuous, it is not nearly so likely to come to notice as its clearer voiced and more brightly marked

[30] Two subspecies of the Lincoln Sparrow occur in the Yosemite region, at different times of the year.

NORTHEASTERN LINCOLN SPARROW, *Melospiza lincolni lincolni* (Audubon), a larger and paler toned form, which summers in the boreal portions of North America and in the Boreal Zone of southward-extending mountain ranges in the west, is a summer visitant to the Canadian Zone (and to a less extent the Hudsonian and Transition zones) on the west slope of the Sierra Nevada. It was found by us from above Chinquapin (at 6500 feet altitude) east to Mono Meadow (7300 feet), near Porcupine Flat (at 8100 feet), and at the head of Lyell Cañon (at 9000 feet). While in the region it lives in dense thickets of creek dogwood and willow along streams and on borders of wet meadows. Seen singly; in pairs at nesting time.

NORTHWESTERN LINCOLN SPARROW, or Forbush Sparrow, *Melospiza lincolni gracilis* (Kittlitz), a smaller darker toned subspecies, which nests in the coast region of southeastern Alaska, is a winter visitant along the lower west flank of the Sierra Nevada. It was found in Yosemite Valley in fall and at Pleasant Valley, Lagrange, and Snelling in winter. At these stations it lives in thick stands of grass, or amid root tangles and brush along streams; forages singly.

and forward-acting associate. In habits, and in the niche which it occupies, the Lincoln sparrow is similar to its better known relative, the song sparrow. Its voice, however, is altogether different.

The Lincoln sparrow arrives in the Yosemite region at least by the middle of May. In 1919, near Chinquapin, the species was already present on May 20. On May 18 and 23 the same year individuals were seen in Yosemite Valley, and on May 28 (1911), a bird was noted in full song near Happy Isles. On June 23, 1920, two pairs were located along drainage ditches in the field near Kenneyville. One bird was seen carrying insects, so that young were doubtless being reared close by. This is an exceptionally low station for nesting. From late May until at least the end of July the Lincoln sparrow may commonly be looked for in willow thickets between extreme altitudes of 6500 and 9000 feet. During August we saw nothing of the birds; they were probably engaged in molting and, being notably reclusive at other times, were then able to avoid observation altogether. Nor were Lincoln sparrows of this race (*lincolni*) seen on any subsequent date in the fall; they took their departure southward without coming to our attention again.

The Northwestern Lincoln Sparrow, or Forbush Sparrow (subspecies *gracilis*), arrives in the region in the early fall. In Yosemite Valley, Mr. Joseph Mailliard (1918, p. 17) took birds belonging to this subspecies on September 15 and 18, 1917. Our own earliest record is for October 12, 1914, when one came to grief in a mouse trap set under an overhanging bank near the Merced River in Yosemite Valley. In January (1915) the birds were noted almost daily at Snelling, and several were recorded at Pleasant Valley and Lagrange in December (1915).

The little we saw of the Lincoln sparrow in the Yosemite region gave us the impression that the bird is much more retiring in its disposition than the song sparrow. The latter often perches out on top of a bush, at least when singing, and does much flying to and fro in the open; but the Lincoln sparrow keeps close within the thickets at all times. Its foraging, and even its singing, is carried on beneath the vegetational 'ceiling.' Unlike the song sparrow, the Lincoln sparrow has but a short song period, restricted to the nesting season.

A nest of the Northeastern Lincoln Sparrow was discovered on June 28, 1915, in a dense growth of willows covering a quarter acre or more on a wet seepage slope near Porcupine Flat. (See pl. 49b.) The willows which surrounded it were still almost leafless, and prostrate, having only recently been released from their heavy blanket of snow. While walking through the bog one of us chanced to step close to the nest, whereupon the incubating bird flushed and made off, dodging silently between the willow stems. The nest was on wet ground, between two small streams a yard apart. It was sunk in the dead grass of the previous season's growth, but was above the level of the sod proper, the extreme bottom of the structure barely touching the ground. The nest had been built at the base of a leaning willow stem. Three inches above it, another stem formed a sort of ridge-pole, supporting a canopy of last year's grasses. These had to be parted in order to permit the observer to look down into the nest cavity. The nest was constructed exteriorly of coarse grasses woven into a loose framework; the interior lining consisted solely of dried and yellowed grass stems of the finest sort. There were five eggs, with a pale greenish blue ground color, rather heavily marked with irregular spots of light reddish brown. Incubation was found to have proceeded about halfway toward hatching.

Fox Sparrows. **Passerella iliaca** (Merrem) [31]

Field characters.—Of chunky build, between Robin and Junco in size. Upper surface almost uniform dark brown, grayish, or reddish in tone, according to subspecies; wings and tail in any case with more or less of a foxy red tinge; under surface white, with bold triangular spots of dark brown or grayish brown, most numerous on fore neck (pl. 48*a*); no white markings on either wings or tail; bill varyingly stout, dark-colored, in some races yellow below at base. *Voice:* Of both sexes, a loud sharp single call note, *clink;* song of male notably clear and melodious in quality.

Occurrence.—Common in summer in Canadian Zone on both slopes of Sierra Nevada, ranging down to 5500 feet altitude, as near Chinquapin, and up to more than 8000 feet, as at Porcupine Flat. Also, in different subspecific forms, a migrant and winter visitant, rare in Lower Sonoran Zone, but common in Upper Sonoran and (except during periods of heavy snows) Transition zones, throughout the region. Inhabits thick brush, under which it industriously forages with much sound of scratching in the dry litter; found singly or in pairs, never in flocks.

---

[31] The eight subspecies of Fox Sparrow which occur in the Yosemite region differ in varying degree from one another in one or more characters. Some of these minor points of discrimination cannot be seen except by close examination of specimens in hand, but others are determinable even in the field. For example, even a novice, remaining in the region throughout the year, could recognize the differences between the gray-backed birds of summer with big bills (*mariposae* and *monoensis*) and the brown-backed subspecies of winter with medium-sized or small bills (*unalaschcensis, sinuosa, insularis,* and *altivagans*). *Schistacea* is a gray-backed winter visitor with very small bill. *Megarhyncha* is gray-backed, with large but relatively short bill, and of rare occurrence in early winter. Such data as we have do not show any regularity or restriction in the occurrence of these different wintering subspecies. Probably all of them could be recorded in any one of a number of localities on the west slope, were collecting extended over a sufficient period of time.

The names and ranges of the birds occurring in the region at different seasons of the year are given in the following paragraphs. For the criteria of discrimination between these races we must refer the reader to the detailed account of the Fox Sparrows given elsewhere by Swarth (Univ. Calif. Publ. Zool., **21**, 1920, pp. 75–224, pls. 4–7, 30 figs. in text).

SHUMAGIN FOX SPARROW, *Passerella iliaca unalaschcensis* (Gmelin), winter visitant to west slope of Sierra Nevada; found by us from Snelling (250 feet altitude) to Yosemite Creek (at 7800 feet). Earliest record, at latter locality, October 6, 1915. Summers on Alaska Peninsula and nearby islands.

KADIAK FOX SPARROW, *Passerella iliaca insularis* Ridgway, winter visitant to west slope of Sierra Nevada; found by us from El Portal (2000 feet) to near top of Yosemite Falls (6500 feet). Earliest record, October 14 (1915), from Aspen Valley (6400 feet). Summers on Kadiak Island, Alaska.

When the summer traveler in the Yosemite region reaches the Canadian Zone, with its thickets of huckleberry oak, chinquapin, and snow bush, he encounters the conspicuously distinctive inhabitant of this zone, the Fox Sparrow. It is true that the Green-tailed Towhee inhabits practically the same territory, but here the Fox Sparrow is the predominant species, outnumbering this towhee fully three to one.

The Fox Sparrow is a sprightly bird of trim and pleasing appearance, easily recognized by its distinctive coloration, as described above. Its upper surface entirely lacks any contrasted markings, but the under surface of its body is white, strikingly patterned with large triangular spots of dark brown. (See pl. 48a.) These spots have their apexes pointed upward, and on the lower part of the throat they are massed together forming a more or less distinct patch. No other sparrow in the region possesses this combination of uniform upper surface and patterned under parts. The Song Sparrows have streaked upper surfaces and are also considerably smaller in size. The Hermit Thrush is similar in general coloration to the Fox Sparrow, but differs in its slender bill, big-eyed expression of face, and, most emphatically, in mannerisms and voice.

The fox sparrows are essentially birds of the brush, and they rarely venture far into the open. In late spring and summer the males, when giving voice to their clear melodious songs, perch on the uppermost twig-tips of their favorite thickets, and occasionally even mount 30 or more feet to some bare branch in an adjacent coniferous tree. But at other

---

VALDEZ FOX SPARROW, *Passerella iliaca sinuosa* Grinnell, winter visitant to west slope, from Lagrange (300 feet) to Aspen Valley (6400 feet). Earliest record, October 14, 1915, from latter locality. Summers in vicinity of Prince William Sound, Alaska.

ALBERTA FOX SPARROW, *Passerella iliaca altivagans* Riley, late winter visitant: near El Portal (at 3800 feet), December 15, 1914; Pleasant Valley, December 4, 1915; six miles east of Coulterville, December 25, 1918, and January 20 and 27, 1919; Aspen Valley (6400 feet), October 14, 1915. Summers on Canadian Rockies along boundary between Alberta and British Columbia.

SLATE-COLORED FOX SPARROW, *Passerella iliaca schistacea* Baird, winter visitant to both slopes of Sierra Nevada, from Pleasant Valley (600 feet) to Warren Fork of Leevining Creek (at 9200 feet). Earliest record, September 13, 1915, at Gem Lake (9036 feet). Only migrant species observed on east slope. Summers in Great Basin and included mountain ranges from British Columbia south to Colorado.

MARIPOSA FOX SPARROW, *Passerella iliaca mariposae* Swarth, summers in Canadian Zone on west slope of Sierra Nevada, from Hazel Green (5600 feet) to near Porcupine Flat (at 8100 feet) and Washburn Lake (at 7800 feet). The majority depart about October 1. One apparently wintering individual captured six miles east of Coulterville, January 20, 1919. Winters chiefly in southern California.

MONO FOX SPARROW, *Passerella iliaca monoensis* Grinnell and Storer, summers in Canadian Zone on east slope of Sierra Nevada, as at Mono Lake Post Office (6500 feet), Walker Lake (8000 feet), and on Parker Creek (at 7500 and 8600 feet). Earliest spring record May 9, 1916, at Walker Lake; last fall occurrence recorded, September 11, 1915, at same station. A specimen taken on the Tuolumne River at 6300 feet, October 1, 1915, was probably a transient. Found in winter six miles east of Coulterville, December 25, 1918, and January 20 and 27, 1919.

THICK-BILLED FOX SPARROW, *Passerella iliaca megarhyncha* Baird, rare winter visitant to west slope of Sierra Nevada. One instance of occurrence: El Portal (2000 feet), November 28, 1914. Summer range not yet known.

seasons the males as well as the females are invariably of retiring disposition. They both always do their foraging under or near brush, and when pursued prefer to dive deeper into the home thicket rather than to fly off to another shelter as do Golden-crowned, White-crowned and Intermediate sparrows; if finally driven out they often circle about in erratic flight and return to the same thicket from which they were flushed. Often when an observer moves around trying to catch sight of one of the birds the latter will hop about, uttering its sharp *clink,* and manage to elude observation by keeping on the opposite side of the thicket or behind a tree trunk or branch. Their movements are mouse-like, but as they move about, one notes at close range an audible flutter of the wings such as characterizes so many other brush-inhabiting sparrows.

The fox sparrow forages exclusively on the ground, and does not even seek the berry crops which are commonly borne on bushes within but a few feet of the earth. It scratches persistently in foraging beneath the brush thickets, jumping up and kicking vigorously backward with both feet simultaneously. This procedure sends a small shower of leaves and loose earth back from where a bird is digging, and often shallow holes 2 or 3 inches in diameter are left as a result. The quantity of food material obtained evidently justifies the seemingly large amount of energy expended in the search, as the birds can be seen to stop frequently and glean titbits uncovered in their scratching. It is when absorbed in scratching under the bushes that the coloration of the fox sparrows serves best to conceal them from view; if the birds remain moderately quiet they fairly melt into the background of brown earth and dry leaves.

When perching these birds assume a peculiarly upright posture; but they seldom remain long in one location, and as they move about from twig to twig in the bushes, or on the ground, their strong legs and feet enable them to move with marked grace and precision. Although this sparrow is continually busy through most of the daylight hours, the twilight of evening and morning marks its period of greatest activity. In summer the males often leave their favorite haunts early in the morning and move uphill, even ascending to the summit of some conifer to catch the first rays of the coming sun, which they greet with full-toned songs. At Hazel Green on May 15, 1919, a male sang twice at 3:50 A.M., which was at the earliest peep of daylight.

The song of the male fox sparrow is among the most pleasing of the bird songs of the high mountains. The individual notes ring out strongly and clearly, the major ones being well enunciated. At Hazel Green, on May 14, 1919, a singing bird was watched for a long time as he sat perched at the top of a 9-foot Douglas spruce. He was motionless, except when singing, and even after his song had been heard a number of times it required some search to determine his exact location among the many small trees in that particular glade. At intervals of from 8 to 20 seconds up would go his head, his bill would open, and forth would come the song, his entire body quivering with the effort of utterance. His songs were of two types, neither of which was satisfactorily expressible in writing. The number of syllables in each group of notes varied somewhat, but otherwise the songs differed only by occasional omission of a trill which was the conspicuous element in one of the types.

The male fox sparrow seems not to indulge in any elaborate courting behavior such as is characteristic of certain other birds. His song is evidently a sufficient demonstration. But at Chinquapin, on May 19, 1919, a singing male while perched had its tail widely spread. This habit is very common among the males of some birds during the spring months, but its use by the fox sparrow shows that it is not peculiar to species with white tail markings, in which the display is so much more conspicuous.

These birds are quite secretive as regards their nesting. In 1915, when necessary attention to many other species limited the time which could be devoted to fox sparrows, we did not find any occupied nests, and but one bob-tailed fledgling (fig. 55a) came to our attention. But in 1919 several nests were discovered, although only after a careful and continued search.

The first nest, located at Chinquapin on May 21, 1919, was scarcely 300 feet from the government barns on the stage road. It was situated on a small level bench covered with snow bush and chinquapin and close to a forest of firs and sugar pine on the slopes of Indian Creek. A male had been noted there singing regularly at short intervals during the preceding two days. His song perch was about 6 feet above the ground and halfway up in a clump of small black oaks which were just coming into leaf. Occasionally he would go to another perch a few yards distant and above the chaparral; and more rarely he mounted 40 feet or even more above the ground to one of the dead lower branches of a nearby sugar pine. But fully four-fifths of his singing was done from the first mentioned perch, which was found to closely overlook the nest site 50 feet distant and due south. The female was usually out of sight.

Once both birds were observed together, the female feeding along the ground and frequently fluffing out her plumage as is the custom of an incubating bird. She uttered the Brown Towhee-like 'clink' note at short intervals. The male was in close attendance but not singing. Presently the female, followed by her mate, flew to the top of a patch of *Ceanothus cordulatus* about 25 feet in diameter, and after a look around, disappeared into the clump. The male thereupon repaired to his usual post and sang. After a minute or so the observer, who had been watching at some distance, went to the brush patch where the female had disappeared and shook one side of it, whereupon the female slipped through beneath the mat of the thicket and then hopped across the adjacent opening, unconcernedly picking here and there in the loose earth and débris. A moment's search revealed the nest, examination of which elicited no evident anxiety on the part of the female bird. The observer returned to the spot later and as he approached, the female slipped from the nest when he was only about 8 feet away. She was not seen again for some minutes; then she came within 15 or 20 feet giving the sharp call note. The male had meanwhile ceased to sing.

The nest was well concealed from above, although when once located it was easily seen from one side. It rested on a low dense tangled mat of Ceanothus twigs and foliage, both living and dead, about 6 feet in from the margin of the patch and 3 feet out from where a group of stems emerged from the ground at a common root center. There was a canopy of green Ceanothus leaves 150 millimeters above the nest, the rim of which was 240 millimeters above the surface of the ground. The basal portion of the structure was composed of short coarse twigs, not interlaced, and these fell apart when an attempt was made to lift the whole nest clear of the tangle. This basal portion was about 280 millimeters in diameter. Then came a layer of pine needles more closely laid, and finally the lining of the nest cavity, of deer hair (deer are particularly abundant at Chinquapin), together with a few long black mane or tail hairs of horses. The cavity measured 65 millimeters in diameter by 37 millimeters deep.

Four nests found near Tamarack Flat on May 25 and 26, 1919, were in various stages of construction and, in practically all respects, were identical with the nest just described. The heights of the nests above the ground were, respectively, 200, 380, 450, and 600 millimeters, and they were all in snow bushes.

The three fresh eggs which the Chinquapin nest contained were of very dark color, the ground tint of blue being heavily overlaid with brown marks which coalesced in many places and completely obscured the deeper-lying pigment. This heavy coloration is characteristic of fox sparrow eggs generally, as contrasted for instance with those of the Green-tailed Towhee inhabiting the same sort of country, which are notably light colored.

The contents of this nest indicated that nesting activities had begun some time during the first half of May. The fledgling bird referred to above was found near the same station, Chinquapin (at 5500 feet altitude), on June 13, 1915, which again would place the beginning of nesting near the middle of May. The season continues for some time, for birds at Tamarack Flat on May 25 and 26, 1919, had nests only in process of construction or barely completed, and other evidence which we have obtained points to a nesting season lasting until mid-July.

During the nesting season the birds are noisy and the males are belligerent, each jealously guarding his home precinct. A male watched at Mono Meadow, June 20, drove away in quick succession a Western Tanager and a Wright Flycatcher. On August 17, 1915, an adult and one juvenile fox sparrow were seen under some golden oak brush near Glacier Point. The adult seemed unusually forward in its actions as if it were attempting to distract attention from the young bird.

Up till late in the fall, as in summer, the thickets of the Canadian Zone, so long as they are free from snow, are inhabited by fox sparrows. The mannerisms of the birds then in evidence are the same as in summer and the same places are frequented—but the grayish brown birds of summer have been replaced by birds with reddish brown backs. The former, the Mariposa and Mono fox sparrows, have emigrated elsewhere, and from the north, from various places in Canada and Alaska (see footnote 31) have come several races of brown-backed birds. The replacement is complete and yet so gradual that the casual observer would not detect the exchange. These winter visitants from the north also take possession of the lower zones, the Lower Sonoran as at Snelling, Upper Sonoran as at El Portal, and Transition as in the western part of Yosemite Valley. We believe that in summer the temperature conditions in these lower zones are unsuited to the requirements of the fox sparrows, or else that the niche which they occupy there in the winter is in summer filled by other species. Then, too, fox sparrows, being ground-feeding birds, must live below the altitude at which snow lies on the ground for any length of time. Thus the brown-backed birds which migrate into the Canadian Zone in the fall drop to lower elevations when the heavy snows of winter come.

SPURRED TOWHEES. **Pipilo maculatus** Swainson[32]

Field characters.—Size large for a sparrow, bulk between that of Junco and Robin; tail about as long as body, and usually carried up at an angle with back. Whole upper surface and forepart of body, black; small spots ('tear drops') in rows on wings, larger

---

[32] Two subspecies of the Spurred Towhee inhabit the Yosemite region, occupying separate territory, on the western and eastern flanks of the Sierra Nevada respectively.

SACRAMENTO SPURRED TOWHEE, *Pipilo maculatus falcinellus* Swarth. This is the race of the western slope of the Sierras, ranging in the breeding season from the vicinity of Snelling up as high as the floor of Yosemite Valley. In autumn, wanders still higher, as to Aspen Valley at 7000 feet and on Illilouette Creek at 6200 feet.

NEVADA SPURRED TOWHEE, *Pipilo maculatus curtatus* Grinnell, the race of the Great Basin area, enters the Yosemite region from the east and breeds in the vicinity of Mono Lake, where found by us at Mono Lake Post Office, near the mouth of Leevining Creek, and about the base of Williams Butte. One individual was obtained in Glen Aulin, 7700 feet altitude, October 4, 1915, which would seem to indicate a westward movement of this interior race in autumn over the Sierran crest.

The differences between the two races, *falcinellus* and *curtatus*, are so slight that only specimens in hand can be distinguished. *Curtatus*, as compared with *falcinellus*, shows a shorter hind claw, a smaller bill, a shorter tail, a greater amount of white on shoulders, wing coverts, and tail, and paler tone of coloration on sides and lower tail coverts.

spots ('thumb marks') at end of tail, and belly, white; sides of body orange brown. (See pl. 48c.)   Male with black more intense than in female; young quite different, streaked. *Voice:* A cat-like mewing call or alarm note, and a trilled song sounding like *to-whee-e-e-e*, the first syllable inaudible beyond a short radius.

Occurrence.—Fairly common at lower altitudes both east and west of Sierra Nevada. On west slope common in Upper Sonoran Zone but ranges up into Transition and downward locally into Lower Sonoran (subspecies *falcinellus*).   Also east of the mountains in vicinity of Mono Lake (subspecies *curtatus*).   In late summer and until severe winter weather, individuals wander upward through the Canadian Zone.[32]   Lives in brush thickets and forages on ground beneath such cover, seldom venturing into the open. Solitary.

In the group of big ground-dwelling sparrows which includes the towhees and fox sparrows, the Spurred Towhee exhibits an extreme type in both structure and coloration. Its stout body, long tail, short rounded wings, large legs and feet, and heavy curved claws (pl. 48c) proclaim it to be a brush dweller and ground forager. The short wings and long tail may serve to enable it to move about rapidly within obstructing growths where locomotion must be accompanied by many short turns and twists, while the heavy armament of claws makes scratching a productive method of unearthing food.

The preferred haunt of the Spurred Towhee is a ravine-side thicket within ready reach of water. The birds venture into the open somewhat more than do fox sparrows but not so much as do the brown towhees. During the warmer months the leaf-covered brush and tall growths of grass and other annual plants form protecting shelters under which the Spurred Towhees can forage unseen; but in midwinter and early spring when rain and wind have battered down the grasses and shaken off most of the leaves the birds are much more exposed. Even then their broken pattern of coloration would be protective in effect were it not for their almost incessant activity. But when a towhee takes flight from one thicket to another its brilliant coloration flashes forth vividly; a predominance of black is seen, but the white dots on the shoulders and wings, and the white 'thumb marks' at the end of the fan-shaped spread tail, introduce a decided element of contrast.

The spotted towhees closely resemble the fox sparrows in manner of foraging. They habitually scratch in the earth and leaf mold under thickets and berry tangles, repeatedly springing up and kicking backwards with both feet at the same time. Often an observer's attention is first attracted to the presence of the birds by the sight or sound of the small showers of débris resulting from this vigorous mode of foraging.

During the breeding season the males are accustomed, particularly toward evening, to ascend by series of short hops and flights to the tops of large bushes or small trees, and there to repeat their monotonous but not unpleasant song, *tu-whēēze*. At other seasons of the year they are content to remain within the shelter of the brush. In the breeding season the birds are very excitable and readily respond to squeaking noises. This trait is undoubtedly correlated with a feeling of concern for mates or young; for in midwinter when the reproductive instincts are at a low ebb the Spurred Towhees are not easily to be 'squeaked' out into full view.

The nest of the Spurred Towhee is a deep cup-shaped affair placed on or sunk in the surface of the ground. One found by Mrs. Joseph Grinnell in Yosemite Valley was a deep cup of pine needles, bark, and grass stems, lined with fine round grass stems and a little black horsehair. It was situated among strawberry plants and under a small chokecherry bush. The four eggs were finely marked with reddish brown on a creamy ground color. Two days after discovery this nest was raided, seemingly by some animal which had burrowed up into it from the ground beneath. Whenever the nest was visited, even after the contents had disappeared, the parents were always in attendance and scolded violently. A second nest, of similar construction, was located under a canopy of dried ferns at the base of a small stump. When first found, on June 12, 1915, it contained 4 eggs. On the morning of June 24 it held one young bird, and two more hatched out that same afternoon. The fourth chick died while attempting to crack open its shell. Up to the time the eggs were hatched the owners of this second nest, upon being disturbed, slipped away quietly, but after their brood had emerged they changed their behavior, and were then accustomed to stay about and insistently voice their solicitude. The young in juvenile plumage have streaked breasts, but by fall they have assumed the plumage of their parents.

In the fall after the breeding season and before the arrival of winter snows, the Spurred Towhees wander higher in the mountains, ranging throughout the greater portion of the Canadian Zone. In late September and in October they have been seen on Illilouette Creek above the falls, on the Snow Creek trail at 6000 feet, and at 7000 feet, near Aspen Valley. This spilling upward is thought to be due to overpopulation of the lower zones as a consequence of the appearance of the fully grown young of the year. It has been further suggested that the young of the year, among animals generally, exhibit instinctively a sort of wanderlust, of benefit to the species in that new territory is thereby sought out and sustenance made available for an increased number of individuals. Of course, when winter comes on, burying the food at the higher levels, this wave of vagrant individuals is pressed back again; but beneficial readjustments doubtless occur in the population even within the regularly occupied area.

NORTHERN BROWN TOWHEE. **Pipilo crissalis carolae** McGregor

Field characters.—Size large for a sparrow; length nearly that of Robin, but body smaller, more plump-appearing, and tail longer (nearly as long as body). Plumage almost uniformly brown, with no contrasted white or black markings; area beneath base of tail bright reddish brown. *Voice:* Call or alarm note, a single, rather loud metallic *peep;* song merely a rapid repetition of the same sort of note with decreasing intervals between them; occasionally, as when courting, a series of curious whining or squealing sounds is given.

Occurrence.—Resident west of Sierra Nevada in both Sonoran zones but more common in Upper Sonoran; ranges sparingly up into lower edge of Transition, as at Smith Creek (2800 feet) and above El Portal (to 3300 feet). Hops about margins of brush patches and along trails and roads, ordinarily in pairs, even through the winter, never in flocks.

No more characteristic bird of the lower chaparral belt could be named that the brown towhee; none takes kindlier to the modifications wrought by human occupancy. This trait of the bird, together with its choice of forage ground, in openings at the margins of thickets, about clearings, and along roads, renders it one of the first species to meet the eye of the traveler. El Portal lies well within the range of the brown towhee, and here one may see the bird commonly about the buildings and even from the stage as the latter starts off with its load up the road toward Yosemite. The foraging birds are so loath to leave the open road ahead of the approaching stage that they are often nearly overtaken before they realize their plight and take to the brush in pell-mell flight, uttering a startled succession of alarm notes.

Brown, in a word, characterizes the coloring of this towhee. Among all the many members of the sparrow family which inhabit the Yosemite region there is none more somber colored. True, the garb of the female blue grosbeak is dull, but she is of much smaller size and has a shorter tail, and is to be found only along watercourses in the Lower Sonoran Zone. The brown towhee on the other hand is found in a wide variety of situations, up as far as the beginning of the yellow pine belt. The two sexes are exactly alike, and entirely lack spots, streaks, or stripes of either white or black.

Roadways over the brush-covered hillsides, grassy spots beneath digger pines or blue oaks, and gardens and similar spots adjacent to human habitations are the common haunts of these birds. They spend most of their time in the open but never venture far from some good shelter such as a brush thicket, blackberry tangle or osage-orange hedge. They come about barns or dwellings where there are oaks or other trees or vines near at hand in which they can take quick refuge.

The manner in which the brown towhee makes use of any new source of food is shown by an incident which occurred at El Portal early in December, 1914. As a freight truck laden with grain moved up the road en route to Yosemite one of the sacks which it carried dropped a narrow stream of rolled barley. Soon brown towhees, in company with California jays and spurred towhees, had found the trail and were industriously gleaning the scattered grains all along the road. The towhees also appropriate grain which has dropped from horses' feed bags or which has been accidentally scattered in a barnyard.

When hopping about in search of food the brown towhee carries its tail straight out behind, or often slightly drooped. In flying the tail is widely spread and much used in steering and stopping; its large area when spread makes of it an effective rudder for a bird dodging about through brush or low trees. In courting, the male sometimes carries his tail up at a decided angle with the back, at the same time hopping 'cornerwise' toward his mate.

In late May and early June of 1915, when our field parties were at Snelling, Pleasant Valley, and Smith Creek, many nests of the brown towhee were found. The season was already well advanced, and of the nests which had not been disturbed by natural enemies all but one held young. At Snelling on May 26, bob-tailed young were out of the nest and with their parents in the willow and blackberry thickets, while on June 5 at Smith Creek a nest was found with young only two or three days old, and another held eggs nearly ready to hatch. In 1919, a nest found near Lagrange on May 6 held four eggs far advanced in incubation while another nest was found completed but without eggs. Three or four constituted a brood in all the instances recorded.

The nests are placed in shrubs such as Ceanothus, or in small oak trees, and are situated from 3 to 8 feet above the ground. At Smith Creek all the nests found but one were placed in *Ceanothus integerrimus* bushes, although there were several other kinds of shrubs available in the vicinity. The exceptional nest found at the last named locality was placed on the ground and constructed entirely of strips of bark of the incense cedar. The usual nest measures 5 or 6 inches across and 5 inches high, and has a central cavity 2 inches deep by about 3 wide. The material used in construction consists of twigs and weed stems with fine grasses and frequently, for lining, horsehair.

The brown towhee subsists upon a wide variety of food materials, almost entirely of a vegetable nature, and, as indicated above, is quick to make use of any unusual source that may offer itself.

GREEN-TAILED TOWHEE. **Oberholseria chlorura** (Audubon)

Field characters.—Size and habits recalling both Fox Sparrow and Spurred Towhee, but coloration and voice very different from either. Crown of head bright chestnut; throat abruptly pure white, surrounded by uniform light gray of neck and breast; wings and tail dull yellowish green; back greenish brown, not streaked; no white spots on wings or tail, or dark spots on breast. (See pl. 48*b*.) Young streaked. Seeks safety under brush rather than by flight. *Voice:* Song of male, a wheezy *sŭp-sĕ-tew'-sēē-sĭ-sĕ*, or *eet-ter-te-te-te-si-si-si-seur;* call note of both sexes a cat-like *mē-ū* or *zew*, or a more prolonged *mee a-yew.*

Occurrence.—Moderately common summer visitant to Canadian Zone on both slopes of the Sierra Nevada, and to Transition Zone east of the mountains. Observed at Crane Flat and Chinquapin and thence eastward to Porcupine Flat and Mono Meadow; and again, beyond the mountains, near Walker Lake, Williams Butte, at Mono Mills, and at Mono Lake Post Office. Seen in Yosemite Valley October 2, 1915, September 5, 1917, May 15 to 23, 1919, and June 23, 1920. Ranges more widely after nesting season; for example, noted at 10,700 feet on Mount Florence, August 21, 1915. Nests in brush thickets, and forages near or beneath these. In pairs during nesting season, solitary at other times.

The Canadian Zone thickets of snowbush, chinquapin, and green manzanita which harbor the Mariposa Fox Sparrow during the summer months are at the same time often frequented by another big towhee-like sparrow, but one of altogether different coloration and voice. This is the Green-tailed Towhee. It wears a very unusual pattern of coloration, distinguishing it from all other birds in the Sierras, and its call note is as distinctive as its plumage. The Green-tailed Towhee is not so abundant as the fox sparrow on the west slope of the mountains; our censuses there show about one individual of the former to four of the latter. On the east slope, however, the Green-tailed Towhee is found in many places to the exclusion of the fox sparrow; in fact, the former seems to be inherently a Great Basin product, along with the sagebrush and sage thrasher, and its occurrence to the westward is in the nature of a spilling over on the extreme margin of its geographic range.

The combination of conical bill, long tail, short wings, and stout legs and feet, proclaim the Green-tailed Towhee to be adapted for foraging beneath brush patches. (See pl. 48*b*.) And that is exactly the manner in which it gains its livelihood. For safety it depends upon dodging into the recesses of the thickets, its short wings and long tail being suited to this means of escape.

Nesting with the Green-tailed Towhee begins about the middle of May, and from then until the end of July the birds are busy with family duties. Upon our arrival at Chinquapin on May 19, 1919, we found the birds in pairs with the males in full song, and at Tamarack Flat, on May 25, 1919, two completed nests were found, one of which contained one fresh egg and the other two. The nesting season must be somewhat protracted, for on June 21 (1915) at Mono Meadow a bird was observed with nesting material in her bill, although she was seen to fluff her feathers and shake herself as though she had already been engaged in the confining duty of incubation. East of the Sierras, at Mono Lake Post Office, on June 30, 1916, an adult was seen carrying food to young. The young, which are narrowly streaked like the young of the White-crowned Sparrow, but which have greenish wings and tail, are much in evidence toward the end of July, when the up-mountain scattering which follows the breeding season begins.

In 1919 three Green-tailed Towhees were seen in Yosemite Valley between May 15 and 23, and two of these (males, for they were singing) acted as if they were located for the season. The headquarters of these two were in chokecherry thickets near Redwood Lane, while the third individual was seen on two occasions near Stoneman Bridge. The species was reported by residents of the Valley to have nested there in 1918, but of this there was no conclusive proof. A singing male was present in Sequoia Lane in the Valley on June 23, 1920.

A typical nest found near Tamarack Flat on May 25, 1919, was 620 millimeters above the ground at the rim, and was situated in a nearly upright spray of snow bush (*Ceanothus cordulatus*) which stood out in the center of a large patch of the same plant. (See pl. 49*a*.) The nest was thick walled and the cavity measured 67 millimeters across by 40 millimeters deep. The basal portion was of long slender branching fir twigs, well interlaced. Then came a middle layer of weathered pine needles and fine plant stems, and inside of this was a smooth lining of long horse tail or mane hairs and fine rootlets. The one fresh egg was pale greenish white in ground color and was marked, chiefly at the larger end, with minute spots of reddish brown. Four eggs is the usual complement. The other nest found was similar in all respects, save that its height above the ground was greater, 700 millimeters to the rim. The nest of this species is much more compactly formed than that of the Mariposa Fox Sparrow.

During the courting season the male Green-tailed Towhee sings at frequent intervals, although on the whole somewhat less often than the male fox sparrow. For singing the bird mounts to the topmost twig of his selected thicket and there says in rapid wheezy sequence, *sŭp-sĕ-tew'-sĭ-sĕ*, or *eet-ter-te-te-te-si-si-si-seur* (according to the transcriptions of two different observers). Individual syllables may be added or dropped, but the general plan of the song remains about the same. The song is buzzy, distinctly like that of the Western Lark Sparrow, and not so much like the impressively clear lay of the fox sparrow. Between songs the cat-call is given at irregular intervals, and it is frequently uttered when the bird is disturbed or excited. Thus when the two nests mentioned above were being examined, the owners remained in the vicinity, at a distance of 30 or 40 feet, hopping about on the ground, exhibiting some concern, and voicing a kitten-like *mew-weé*.

East of the Sierras in the fall months the number of Green-tailed Towhees seems to be augmented over and above the normal seasonal increase by the appearance of migrants. When trapping for mammals was being carried on in the sagebrush near Williams Butte several of these towhees, attracted by the rolled oats placed on the traps as bait, fell undesired victims.

We have no data as to the time of arrival of the Green-tailed Towhees on the west side of the Sierras, nor is the route of their migration thitherward known. On the east side, at Williams Butte, the first was seen in 1916 on May 6, after which the species was common. They were still there, at least as migrants, on September 22 (1915), when field work for the season was concluded in that locality. In Yosemite Valley on October 2, 1915, Green-tailed Towhees were frequenting the same thickets as the Golden-crowned Sparrows which had then just arrived from the north. The Green-tails were evidently on the verge of departing, as the last record for the season is of one seen near Glen Aulin on October 4, 1915, although field observations were continued on the west slope that year until late in November.

Mr. Joseph Mailliard (1918, p. 15), who visited Yosemite Valley from August 18 to September 29, 1917, states that he found no Green-tailed Towhees there until September 5; after that date they increased in numbers until, in favorable spots, such as the eastern end of Sequoia Lane, 8 or 10 could be seen within 200 yards.

Pacific Black-headed Grosbeak
Zamelodia melanocephala capitalis Baird

Field characters.—Between Junco and Robin in size; tail shorter than body; bill large and blunt. Adult male in summer: Upper surface largely black; end of tail and middle of wing with large spots of white; collar around hind neck, rump, and under surface of body, light reddish brown. Female and immature: Head with a light stripe over each eye and another over crown; rest of upper surface dull brown, streaked with blackish; under surface brownish white. Yearling males often wear a plumage intermediate between that of adult male and of female. *Voice:* Song of male elaborate—a rapidly timed series of full warbling notes with both ascending and descending inflection; call note, uttered by both sexes, a sharp *spick*.

Occurrence.—Abundant summer visitant at lower altitudes on both sides of Sierra Nevada (chiefly in Upper Sonoran and Transition zones). Recorded from Snelling and near Lagrange eastward to Hazel Green, floor of Yosemite Valley, and near Chinquapin; also at Mono Lake Post Office and near Williams Butte. Forages largely in crown foliage of deciduous trees, sometimes in shrubs, occasionally on ground. Non-flocking.

There is probably no species of bird better known to summer visitors to the Yosemite Valley than the black-headed grosbeak. This is the bird which is wont to fly down from the trees surrounding a camp and pilfer viands, especially butter, from the dinner table. Indeed so well has this trait been developed among the grosbeaks in Yosemite that they have been nicknamed "butter birds." The species is likely to bring itself to the attention of visitors in other ways as well, for it is of large size for a finch, and the male possesses bright and contrasted coloration and a loud and pleasing song.

The black-headed grosbeak arrives on the west slope of the Yosemite section during April. The species was common in Yosemite Valley on April 29, 1916; and in early May, 1919, it was well established in the western foothill country. East of the mountains its migrations are somewhat later. The first seen there in 1916 was observed on May 14. During the summer season the birds are much in evidence and can scarcely be missed by anyone who enters their domain. They quiet down in July, and thenceforth are much less noticeable. Mr. Joseph Mailliard (1918, p. 19) states that in 1917 none was seen in Yosemite Valley after September 20. This accords with our own findings in 1915; in that year the birds departed from the Valley prior to September 24.

These grosbeaks are abundant in both the Upper Sonoran and Transition zones. At Pleasant Valley on May 23, 1915, 20 were recorded during a 4-hour census, and two days later 12 were noted in 2 hours. In Yosemite Valley at the same season 8 to 12 birds were observed during each of several 4-hour trips on the floor of the Valley. At Snelling the population was smaller, and along the shores of Mono Lake the numbers were likewise small, only 3 being seen in 3 hours at the latter locality on May 31, 1916. In general, the preference of the species is for rather open foliaged, broad-leaved trees, such as blue oaks, black oaks, and willows. The birds are most likely to be found in scattered growths rather than in thick woods, and generally they are not very far from water.

The adult male black-headed grosbeak is a strikingly colored bird. At first glance one gets an impression of black, white, and brown in highly mixed pattern. Upon closer examination this coloring is seen to consist of black on the head, back, wings, and tail, a large white patch on middle of spread wing, and white thumb marks at the ends of the outer tail feathers. There are also numerous scattered white spots elsewhere on the wings. The rump, the collar around the back of the neck, and the under surface of the body are colored brown, of a bright tone but not so red as the breast of the robin. The female grosbeak is quite different. Dull brown everywhere replaces the black, the amount of white is much smaller, and the head and back are coarsely streaked. There is a conspicuous light stripe over each eye and another over the crown. The big bill, in either sex, can easily be made out at ordinary field distance, and in making identifications, its presence helps to rule out other birds of roughly similar appearance.

Some spring breeding males exhibit a plumage intermediate between those just described for the adult male and female. In these "peculiar" birds some or all of the flight feathers in the wings and tail are old, faded, and worn, much more so than in males which are in the black plumage. This condition of the flight feathers shows that the birds which wear them are from broods of the previous season and therefore are just under a year in age. The small percentage of these differently plumaged birds suggests that they represent cases of incomplete molt. Reports of 'singing females' are probably explained by the fact that these so-called singing females are males in this more or less immature condition of plumage.

The black-headed grosbeak possesses a rich voluble song that forces itself upon the attention of everyone in the neighborhood. In fact at the height of the song season this is the noisiest of all the birds. The song resembles in some respects that of a robin, and novices sometimes confuse the two. The grosbeak's song is much fuller and more varied, contains many little trills, and is given in more rapid time. Now and then it bursts forth fortissimo and after several rounds of burbling, winds up with a number of 'squeals,' the last one attenuated and dying out slowly.

Early in the season the males are to be seen, now and then, in ecstatic song flights. These are most likely to occur just as the sun touches the tops of the trees in the early morning. Launching forth on a horizontal course, circling out from the summit of a tree, with wings and tail spread to fullest extent, every feather seemingly held tense, the bird utters an almost continuous "bold breathless, bubbling song," richer and fuller even than the usual utterance and almost torrential in its delivery.

Of lesser notes there is a sharp explosive call or alarm note, *spink* or *spick*, sometimes repeated at short intervals and given by both males and females. The males are in song upon their arrival in spring and continue to sing until some time in July (July 15, 1920, at Dudley). Thenceforth, until the departure of the species in September, only the sharp call is given and this but seldom. The young have a distinct call, a soft musical whistle. This note is to be heard coming from berry patches and fruit trees all through the summer. The adults at nesting time evince extreme concern for their broods, and if their precincts are raided give voice to squalls, loud and ear-piercing. The effect, as demonstrated in our own experience, is to absorb the invader's attention so that he fails to look farther for the eggs or young.

In late April and early May, soon after their arrival from the south, the grosbeaks engage actively in courting. Sometimes two or even three males will be singing and flying about in the vicinity of one female. Near Lagrange on May 6 to 8, 1919, there was much frenzied chasing of females by males and of rival males by one another. In some places it seemed as though there was a surplus of males. The same conditions existed near Coulterville on May 9 to 12; but by May 16 in Yosemite Valley, nesting was well under way. Here, a female was seen gathering building material on that date; on the 17th another bird had already completed her nest and laid five eggs. At Pleasant Valley, in 1915, a brood of bob-tailed young already out of the nest was seen on May 25; nesting in this instance must have been commenced close to the first of May. Two nests with small young were seen in Yosemite Valley on June 24, 1915. Another with the male brooding one small youngster was seen there as late as July 29 (1915). Hence nesting may commence about the first of May; it is well under way by the middle of that month; broods are emerging in numbers toward the end of June, while a few pairs whose nesting program has been delayed or interrupted are still busy with nestlings as late as the last week in July.

Nests of the black-headed grosbeak are placed in trees or large brushes, usually at a height of not more than 12 feet from the ground. We have record of several at approximately 8 feet, and others at 4, 6, 7, 15, 20, and 30 feet, respectively. Young black oaks, small incense cedars, mountain lilac, apple trees, and chokecherry bushes, all had been used in instances noted by us. A crotch, or a group of horizontal twigs, forms the usual support, and the nest is frequently located against the main vertical stem or trunk. The nest itself is an openly constructed affair, often little more than a platform slightly concave above, and is so thin in weave that the contents can be seen, at least in outline, from beneath. Sometimes the nests are firmer and more cup-shaped than this usual type, although they still exhibit the open-work style of construction. Small long plant stems, grasses, and crinkly rootlets are the important structural elements. One nest, rather deeper than the average, measured 5 inches across the outside and $2\frac{1}{2}$ inches in height, while the interior was $3\frac{1}{4}$ inches across at the rim and about $1\frac{3}{4}$ inches deep at the center.

A female was watched gathering nest material in Yosemite Valley on May 16, 1919. She hopped about in a mountain lilac bush, finally selected a small twig which, with a few pulls assisted by the cutting edges of her mandibles, she broke off. Then she worked the twig along in her bill until it was held across the middle. Still retaining the first twig, she gathered a second in the same manner, after which she made off in irregular course through the trees, en route to her nest.

In late May and during June it is a relatively easy matter to locate occupied nests of the black-headed grosbeak, for the male bird does much of its singing within a hundred feet of the nest and often even while actually on the nest. Several nests in Yosemite Valley were found by following up singing males. On one occasion, while one of us was walking along the road near the Royal Arches, a female flew across the road to a black oak in which the male had been perching. After giving a few calls she flew away. The male then flew directly over the observer, alighting in the same general vicinity whence the female had first come. After a minute he hopped farther onto what was then seen to be the nest. The bird sang a number of times, *spicked* between songs, and then worked himself down close over the eggs so that only his head and tail showed above the low rim of the nest. Another male bird, on a nest in a black oak at the roadside, was watched from a distance of but 15 feet. He sang snatches of song off and on for many minutes; each utterance was marked by an up-and-down twitching of the tail, which projected over the edge of the nest and could be easily seen beating time, as it were, to the rhythm of the singing.

Still another nest of the black-headed grosbeak was found in a coffee-berry bush on the north side of Yosemite Valley on the morning of June 19, 1915 (Mrs. Joseph Grinnell, MS). Some workmen had removed all adjacent shrubbery a few days previously, evidently leaving this bush only because of the nest. Originally the site had possessed a measure of seclusion, but now it was exposed to the view of all passers-by. Attention was quickly drawn to the nest by the male voicing his loud song as he brooded the four small young. The latter were clad in the white natal down which was about one-fourth of an inch in length and quite thick, though the yellowish pink skin showed through in places. At sundown the same day, when we passed, the female was seen to be brooding. Next morning at 8:30 the male was seen to feed each youngster in turn and then brood them. At 5:30 this second afternoon the female was again on the nest. On June 26 the eyes of the young were open. The nest was not watched further, but the young must have left soon afterward.

No nest of the black-headed grosbeak was watched continuously; but brief observations on a number of nests including others than those specifically mentioned above make possible the following summary. Courting and selection of mates is carried on after the birds arrive within their summer haunts. The female alone gathers nest material. After the eggs are laid both members of the pair engage in the function of incubation. When the eggs hatch the male does a good share of the food-gathering and brooding. The young (fig. 55b) remain in the nest at least 8 days, and likely somewhat longer. The male sings frequently while on the nest, both before and after the eggs hatch.

Four is the usual number of eggs laid although we saw sets of both 3 and 5 in which incubation had commenced. Several nests seen held 4 young but no unhatched eggs, indicating that all the eggs in these particular sets were fertile and had hatched successfully.

During their residence here the black-headed grosbeaks levy upon a wide variety of materials for food. At Snelling, on May 26, 1915, the birds were feasting on the wild blackberries which were then ripening in abundance. At Pleasant Valley at the same season, males were noted on the ground in search of insects. At Lagrange birds of both sexes were

a   b

Fig. 55. (*a*) Young Mariposa Fox Sparrow; Chinquapin, July 13, 1915. (*b*) Young Pacific Black-headed Grosbeak; Pleasant Valley, May 25, 1915.

seen flying out from the trees to capture passing 'bugs.' In Yosemite Valley Mr. Joseph Mailliard records (1918, p. 14) that he saw family parties of these birds foraging in barnyard chaff at the ''Kenneyville'' stables; grains from the dried stalks of oats, wheat or barley were being picked out. At Mono Lake Post Office on May 21, 1916, two males were seen feeding upon the hearts of cherry blossoms. These birds were working rather rapidly and a blossom would drop every fifteen or twenty seconds.

The black-headed grosbeaks in Yosemite have become accustomed to the presence of people and also have learned to patronize habitually the bird-feeding tables, which many persons establish during the period of their sojourn in the Valley. The grosbeaks often dominate these places to the exclusion of other birds, even the robins; and among the grosbeaks themselves certain individuals seem to be more aggressive than others.

California Blue Grosbeak. Guiraca caerulea salicarius Grinnell

Field characters.—Decidedly larger than Junco or Linnet; tail shorter than body; bill heavy, very thick at base. Sexes different. Adult male: Almost solidly dark blue; wing with a broad bar of reddish brown. Female and young: Pale yellowish brown, the wings and tail darker; two light bars across wing. Behavior similar to that of Linnet. *Voice:* Song of male a rather weak rhythmical warble of short duration and uttered at relatively long intervals; call note of both sexes a sharp *clink*.

Occurrence.—Common summer visitant in Lower Sonoran Zone. Found by us only at Snelling. Lives in willows and similar vegetation along river bottoms. To be seen singly or in pairs.

The California Blue Grosbeak is restricted to the Lower Sonoran Zone where it lives in the low dense thickets of willow on the bottom lands of the big rivers. It is therefore not likely to come to the attention of the mountain-seeking visitor unless he should stop off at some place in the lowlands and make special search for the bird.

The blue grosbeak takes its name from the color of the male bird which is almost entirely blue of a dark ultramarine hue and not cerulean or the usual sky blue as one of the scientific names of the species would suggest. The female and young birds are almost solidly brown, with no conspicuously contrasted markings. Not infrequently breeding males are to be seen which have only a few irregular patches of blue on an otherwise brownish plumage. The males in this imperfect stage have their wing and tail feathers much more worn than those of the males with full blue plumage. This latter fact suggests that the birds in mixed plumage are of the previous season's brood and hence just under a year in age. The flight feathers acquired in the nest (juvenal plumage) are not shed at the first fall molt. These feathers, retained throughout the first year of life, show relatively more wear than the wing and tail feathers of the adults, which are newly acquired at some time in the fall following completion, for the season, of the nesting duties.

The blue grosbeak is the only one of our emphatically big-billed finches which has blue in its scheme of coloration, and it can be distinguished, as regards the male, on this score alone. The Lazuli Bunting, which is conspicuously blue (of a lighter tone) is much smaller, with white on belly and with a smaller bill. The Western Bluebird is slender of bill and brown of chest.

During the nesting season the blue grosbeak seems to prefer the vicinity of water, the banks of an irrigating ditch grown up to tall weeds or willows being an acceptable location. After the broods are reared the birds range more widely and often invade much drier situations. They do not linger long in the region, and after the middle of July, few if any are to be seen. The fall molt is deferred until after the birds leave our latitude for their far southern winter home.

At Snelling, on May 26, 1915, 6 blue grosbeaks were seen during a three-hour trip through the bottom lands of the Merced River. At that season wild blackberries were bearing abundantly and these grosbeaks in company with other species had been feasting on the berries.

LAZULI BUNTING. **Passerina amoena** (Say)

Field characters.—Decidedly smaller than Junco; tail shorter than body. Sexes different. Male: Head, throat, back, and rump, clear light blue; breast crossed by a bright tawny band; under parts otherwise white; tail and wings blackish brown with a white bar (sometimes a narrower one also) across each wing. Female and young: Dull dark brown above, buffy and white on under surface, without contrasted markings of any sort. *Voice:* Song of male a rather long, high-pitched hurried utterance, of set character; both sexes give a rather weak call note, *tsip.*

Occurrence.—Common summer visitant at lower altitudes on both sides of Sierra Nevada; most abundant in Upper Sonoran Zone on west slope. Recorded from Snelling east to floor of Yosemite Valley, and to 6 miles east of Coulterville; also at Mono Lake Post Office. In migration, noted east of Sierran crest at Grant Lake, Walker Lake, and near Warren Fork of Leevining Creek. Lives in low growths along ravine bottoms and near streams. Seen in pairs or singly, the male more often than the female.

The Lazuli Bunting is a common summer species in the low growths which line the water courses at the lower altitudes on the west side of the Sierra Nevada It is found in some numbers at Snelling and on the floor of Yosemite Valley, and is abundant in the foothills of the Upper Sonoran Zone. East of the mountains small numbers occur in the vicinity of Mono Lake.

The male Lazuli Bunting wears a plumage the striking feature of which is the lapis lazuli or sky blue of his head, throat, back, and rump. The female and young are merely dull brown and white, and hence are quite inconspicuous amid the sort of surroundings which the species affects. The Lazuli Bunting is, in structure, obviously a sparrow, but in coloration the male reminds one of the bluebirds. The latter, however, are of larger size, with slender bill, and have no white bar on the wing. They are, too, very different in voice and mannerisms. The male blue grosbeak is a larger bird and of much darker tone of blue than the bunting. It has no buff band across the breast or white on the belly. The female bunting and grosbeak are to be distinguished by the larger size and heavier bill in the latter.

This finch is but a summer visitant to the Yosemite section and is one of the last of the lowland migrant species to arrive on its nesting grounds. None was seen during visits to El Portal and Yosemite Valley on April 29 and 30, 1916, so it had probably not yet arrived in those localities. Our earliest record is for May 12, 1919, when two individuals, male and female, were encountered separately west of Coulterville. These were obviously migrants as the species does not inhabit at nesting time the dry chaparral, such as that in which the two birds in question were seen. In Yosemite Valley a male was seen on May 17, 1919. At Pleasant Valley, in 1915, the species was present on May 19, and was established in considerable numbers there by May 23. East of the mountains, in 1916, the Lazuli Bunting was not encountered until May 23 when a single male was recorded.

The fall departure of this bird takes place in September. One individual was noted at Walker Lake on September 14, 1915, and three at Grant Lake on the same date, while two, singly, were seen near Warren Fork of Leevining Creek (at 9000 feet, the highest station at which we saw it), on September 25, 1915. Mr. Joseph Mailliard states (1918, p. 19) that in Yosemite Valley in 1917 the species became scarce toward the end of September, and that his latest record was made on September 28.

During the nesting season Lazuli Buntings live in low thickets of various kinds, not on wet ground, yet within a hundred yards or so of streams or cañon beds. The males perch at the tops of the taller bushes or the smaller trees to sing, but the females remain closely within the shelter of the vegetation and are far less often seen. At Pleasant Valley, on May 23, 1915, adults to the number of 24 were recorded during a 4-hour census; singing males were spaced about 100 to 200 yards apart along the Merced River and tributary ravines. At Snelling 10 were observed amid blackberries and nettles, during a 3-hour census on May 26, 1915. Four males were noted at El Portal on the morning of May 31, 1915. The song season in Yosemite lasts through July, for a male was heard singing in the Valley on July 24 (1915).

The Lazuli Bunting is one of our most persistent singers. It does not confine its utterances to the morning and early evening hours, but is heard if anything less often at those times than during the warmest part of the day. In our memory the song is associated with the drowsy heat of early afternoon. The song is rather high pitched, like that of the California Yellow Warbler, yet is not nearly so shrill. It is rather set in character. Certain syllables may be added or dropped, but the general theme remains the same, and is uttered over and over again at intervals of about 12 seconds. One of our transcriptions of the song is as follows: *see-see-see, sweert, sweert, sweert, zee, see, sweet, zeer, see-see.* These notes follow one another with rapidity; it is really with difficulty that any syllabic rendering, such as the one just given, can be made.

The nests of the Lazuli Bunting are usually ensconced in low growths along cañon bottoms in situations near which the adult birds spend most of their time. A nest found in Yosemite Valley on June 7, 1915, was at the edge of a meadow near Rocky Point. It was 18 inches above the ground in the crotch of a small chokecherry growing in a rather sparse stand of the same sort of bush. The nest was rather thick walled, not tightly woven, and its exterior was composed of dried and weathered grass and plant stems of the previous season's growth. A few leaves of the cherry growing on the small branches upon which the nest had been built were incorporated into the surface of the structure. The inner portion of this nest was made of fine rounded grass stems, while the cup was lined with horsehair rather loosely placed. The outside dimensions were, height 3 inches, diameter 4 inches; the cup was about 2 inches across and nearly the same in depth. Within were four pale blue eggs in which incubation had just commenced.

When this nest was approached and the observer was yet about 25 feet away, the female parent left and flitted off through the brush, but she soon reappeared and uttered her weak call note. The male also came to the neighborhood but instead of evincing any concern during the examination of the nest, uttered his song at regular intervals from successive perches in the upper foliage of nearby black oaks.

Another nest, seen at Smith Creek, near Coulterville, on June 5, 1915, was 4 feet above the ground in a mountain lilac (*Ceanothus integerrimus*). It, too, held four eggs.

WESTERN TANAGER. **Piranga ludoviciana** (Wilson)

Field characters.—Between Robin and Junco in size. Sexes different. Male: Head red; wings, upper back, and tail, black; rest of body plain lemon yellow. Female: Dull yellowish brown (sometimes greenish in effect) on upper surface; dull yellowish white beneath. Both sexes notably deliberate in all movements, the opposite of nervous. *Voice:* Song of male a hoarse drawling note, *chĕr'-wĕr*, repeated three to many times in rather rapid succession with but slight changes in intonation; call note a hoarse *chĕr'-tig*, or *chĕē'-tik*, or *prĭt'-it*, frequently repeated.

Occurrence.—Common summer visitant in Transition and Canadian zones on west slope of Sierra Nevada; sparingly represented on east slope. Observed by us from 3 miles east of Coulterville and from El Portal eastward to Tenaya Lake and Merced Lake; also in vicinity of Mono Lake. Passes through lowland and foothill country on west side (Snelling, Lagrange, Pleasant Valley, Coulterville, etc.) in spring migration. Keeps to open forest during nesting season. In pairs at nesting time; otherwise seen singly except as small flocks may be formed in early fall, before departure.

The Western Tanager, often called Louisiana Tanager in books, is among the most conspicuous birds of the Yosemite fauna, combining as it does brilliant coloration and unfearful disposition with a preference for open portions of the forest. The male wears a livery of bright yellow, with a red head and black wings and tail, while his mate is garbed in dull yellow and greenish brown. The species is so well represented on the floor of Yosemite Valley and in the Canadian Zone forest on the slopes adjacent that the tanager will usually be one of the first birds to gain the visitor's attention after his arrival within the Park.

The northward passage of the tanagers through the lowland and foothill districts of California in late spring constitutes one of the most conspicuous migratory movements among our birds. The brilliant coloration of the males and the distinctive call note of the species, so different from that of any of the resident low zone birds, together serve to focus the attention of even casual observers on this seasonal movement. Near Lagrange on May 7, 1919, five or more Western Tanagers were seen during an hour and a half in the blue-oak belt. On the slopes of Penon Blanco the birds were moving through the greasewood chaparral on May 9, 1919, and near Coulterville on the following day transient tanagers were notably numerous. In 1915, at Pleasant Valley, about 10 migrants were seen during a 5-hour census on May 24, and a single one was noted there on May 30, while two were observed at Snelling on May 29, and one near Coulterville on May 31, of the same year. East of the Sierras, at Walker Lake, one tanager was seen May 9, 1916. Thus the spring migration is known to occupy much of the month of May.

During the summer season tanagers inhabit mainly the more open portions of the forest. Their preference in Yosemite Valley seems to be for black oaks and incense cedars, although they are seen in most other trees as well. Numerically, the tanager is not an abundant species. Our censuses show on the average one or two birds to an hour of observation. In some localities the number is larger, but never up to that of the robin or of the chipping sparrow. Of course there is a sudden doubling or trebling of the tanager population in July when the broods of young leave the nest. In late August, when cascara and other berry-producing shrubs are fruiting, the tanagers often assemble in flocks numbering under a dozen individuals, and this gathering of the birds is likely to give an observer the impression of still further increase in numbers. It is not unlikely that some of the tanagers from the Canadian Zone drop down into Yosemite Valley before all depart southward.

The Western Tanagers remain in the mountains of the Yosemite region until some time in September. Single individuals were observed by us at Walker Lake on September 13 and 15, 1915, and small numbers were noted in Yosemite Valley up until September 5 of the same year. In 1920 tanagers were observed regularly until the middle of September; the last individual was noted on September 28 (C. W. Michael, MS). All are gone certainly before the first of October.

The vocabulary of the Western Tanager is not elaborate. The song is but little more than a repetition of notes like those which constitute the call. There is a peculiar droning quality to the utterances which makes them readily distinguishable from those of other birds. Once learned, the notes are the best clue to the presence of tanagers, either when they are on their nesting grounds in the mountains or when they are passing in migration through the lowland country. The call note is a drawling, two-syllabled *prĭt-it* or *prēē-tert,* sometimes changed to a more abrupt *chĕr-tig,* or *chēē-tik.* The song consists of a rapid repetition of the syllables *chĕr'-wĕr,* sometimes modified to *chēē'-wĕr,* or *chir'-rup,* or *zĕr'-wĕr,* or *zēē'-wĕr.* The song season of the tanagers lasts from the time of their arrival on their nesting grounds until some time in July. The tanager sings at all hours of the day. It begins almost as early as the wood pewee and the robin. At El Portal on May 31, 1915, our notes record the tanager as the most insistent singer in the morning chorus there. At least four were within hearing of the hotel at 4:30 A.M. They were also singing until late dusk of evening.

The Western Tanager is a bird of deliberate movement; indeed it might even be characterized as apathetic in temperament. In perching, foraging, or flying, its demeanor is ever the same; this sedateness of manner seems never to be lost, even under stress of sudden surprise. It may be that this mode of behavior is related to the male's brilliant coloration. In a bird the size of a tanager showing large areas of bright color, quick movements like those of a warbler would almost surely serve to draw attention. But by adopting a slow deliberate type of action the tanager is much more likely to escape observation, despite its bright coloration. Frequently we have gazed at a tree for some moments before realizing that a Western Tanager was sitting there in plain sight before us. The *fact* is, that the bird had escaped detection. Whether this is to be explained on the basis of protective, concealing, or disruptive coloration is a matter for speculation. However this may be, the factor of the bird's quietude seems to us to play an important rôle in its protection.

We learned of no case of a tanager being beset by any sort of enemy. Only one instance of death from natural cause came to our notice. This was at Mono Lake Post Office on May 24, 1916, following a night when snow fell. A pair of tanagers that had roosted in an old building were found dead and frozen in the morning, but whether the cold itself was the direct cause of death was not determined.

The Western Tanagers begin nesting activities soon after they arrive in the Yosemite region. Little or nothing in the way of courting, other than the persistent singing of the males, has been noticed of these birds. On May 23 (1919) in Yosemite Valley a female was first seen at work on a nest, and immediately after that date quite a number of other females were observed gathering material, or building. Nest construction may be looked for with confidence regularly during the last week of May; in 1911 one female was seen building on May 26 and another, in 1915, on May 31.

The work of nest construction is carried on entirely by the female, and even when searching for material she is rarely if ever accompanied by her mate. She employs no subterfuge, but usually gathers the material on the ground in the near vicinity and then flies directly to the nest site. The nest is located in trees and placed well above the ground, supported by several small diverging twigs toward the end of some horizontal branch. The height of the nests seen by us was about 20 to 25 feet, although one was estimated to be 60 feet above the ground. Another, situated in a rose bush (an exception to the rule above given) was within 10 feet of the earth. The nests are loosely constructed and flattish, the height being about half the breadth. Pine needles, long crinkly rootlets, and dried grasses are used as building materials; these are put together in lattice-work fashion, so that from below it is often possible to see light through the interstices.

Prior to the time that incubation commences, the members of a pair are seen often together; but after the female begins to sit the two birds forage in company only for brief periods during the early morning and evening hours. Through the day the male goes about by himself, foraging on the ground or singing somewhere well up in the trees. He evidently takes little or no part in the family duties until the eggs hatch, but after that event he is almost as busy as his mate in caring for the brood; he takes food to the nest at frequent intervals through the day. The young appear abroad in July. The juvenal plumage, which is much like that of the parent female save for obscure streaking on the under surface, seems to be worn only while the young birds are in the nest. By the time they are old enough to leave, or at least very shortly thereafter, they have molted and are then indistinguishable from the adult female.

After the breeding season the tanagers do not wander to any appreciable degree up into the higher zones. Only one individual, a male, was observed by us in the Hudsonian Zone. He was seen near the Soda Springs on Tuolumne Meadows on July 13, 1915.

Tanagers in summer forage to a large extent in the trees for insects, but some of their provender is apparently gathered also on the ground. In late summer and early fall they turn to a vegetable diet and feed upon berries of several kinds which are usually abundant on the floor of Yosemite Valley in that season. Mr. Joseph Mailliard (1918, p. 14) says of the Western Tanagers seen in the Valley in 1917:

They were occasionally seen in August, but grew more and more numerous, evidently gathering from far and wide, as the berries of the 'cascara sagrada' [=*Rhamnus californicus*] became ripe, upon which they regaled themselves seemingly almost to the point of bursting. At the foot of a cedar tree close to the writer's tent in Camp Curry was one of these bushes covered with fruit, near which many people passed in the course of the day along one of the camp avenues. Almost touching the bush was a round table three or four feet in diameter, and beside it a rustic rocking chair. In spite of people passing, tanagers would drop down from the cedar tree, even when the chair was occupied, and if the occupant kept still and was apparently indifferent to their actions, would go so far as to alight on the table.

WESTERN MARTIN. **Progne subis hesperia** Brewster

Field characters.—General appearance that of our other swallows, but size much greater; tail forked, though not deeply so, as in the Barn Swallow. Male: Solidly black with purplish sheen to plumage of body. Female and young: Brownish black above, with little or no gloss on feathers; breast dull brown; belly grayish white. *Voice:* Loud, and usually mellow; male gives a series of full 'burbling' notes, constituting a sort of song.

Occurrence.—Not seen by us. Reported in Yosemite Valley June 20 to 25, 1893, and in foothills along Coulterville road. Lives in open, nesting in cavities in dead trees. In pairs.

Mr. W. O. Emerson (1893, p. 181) records that between June 20 and June 25, 1893, he heard the notes of the "Purple" Martin from some old oaks near the Stoneman house in Yosemite Valley, and that at two of his camping places on the way into the Valley (doubtless along the Coulterville road) he had noticed young martins. Mr. Donald D. McLean reports it as appearing occasionally, in spring, in the vicinity of his home east of Coulterville. We, ourselves, however, failed to see anything of this ordinarily conspicuous bird.

It is strange that it should be so rare in the Yosemite region, where the great range of conditions afforded would surely meet its needs in one place or another.

CLIFF SWALLOW. **Petrochelidon lunifrons lunifrons** (Say)

Field characters.—Body size about that of Linnet or Junco; wings long and narrow; tail short, practically square-ended. (See pl. 46*d*.) Forehead creamy white; back, wings, and tail black-appearing; rump yellowish brown; cheeks and chin dark reddish brown, with a blackish patch on throat. *Voice:* A weak chuckle.

Occurrence.—Common summer visitant locally at the lower altitudes on both sides of Sierra Nevada. Recorded from Snelling and near Lagrange eastward to Bower Cave. Also, east of mountains, near Williams Butte and on Rush Creek. Local distribution controlled largely by availability of rough rock walls or of weathered buildings upon which to place nests. In colonies of few to many pairs. Forages over open fields or smooth water.

The Cliff Swallow is probably the best known of all our species of swallows because of its common occurrence about human habitations. Originally, as its name indicates, this bird placed its nests on the rocky walls of cañons and on river bluffs, in consequence of which it was correspondingly restricted as to local occurrence. With man's erection of barns and other rough-walled buildings, the Cliff Swallows took to nesting on these structures and so appeared in many new localities. In addition to extending its local range, it is certain that this swallow, in many parts of the west, has increased in aggregate numbers.

The Cliff Swallow is the most colonial of our six species of the swallow family. Wherever found it is represented in some numbers and its nests are placed in the closest sort of mutual proximity. At Pleasant Valley on May 25, 1915, ten or a dozen pairs had their nests on the weather-beaten station house, and near Merced Falls on May 28, the same year, a colony of about 20 pairs was nesting on the undercut walls of a small gully in the prairie. (See pl. 47a.) Near Lagrange on May 6, 1919, an assemblage of fully 75 pairs was busily engaged in constructing nests on the face of a stratified cliff at the side of the Tuolumne River. At the McCarthy ranch east of Coulterville, and at Bower Cave, Cliff Swallow nests were seen on the *inside* of farm buildings, access to the interior in each case being provided by a large open doorway through which the birds could fly to and from their nests.

The swallows of the Yosemite section can be divided into three groups according to their manner of nesting. The Rough-winged Swallow nests in a hole in a bank, the Western Martin and the Tree and Violet-green swallows seek natural cavities in trees or, in the latter species, also in rocks, while the Barn and Cliff swallows being skilled masons build elaborate nests outside of any cavity, using mud for structural material.

The home of the Cliff Swallow is shaped like a gourd or retort, having a rather narrow entrance and expanding basally to accommodate the nest proper. (See pl. 47a.) The structure is built entirely of mud (save for a slight lining of soft fibrous materials) which is gathered and applied wet in the form of small pellets. The building of such a nest is a labor which must extend over several days in order that the basal portion of the nest may dry and thus gain strength to hold the later additions. When a nest is well under construction the observer finds it composed of mud in several stages, from the entirely dry base to the wet, most recently applied, material at the rim. While gathering the small rounded pieces of mud the birds at most barely alight upon the ground, balancing with their wings upraised and quivering. As the source of supply for mud is often at some distance from the colony the total amount of energy expended in the construction of a nest by a single pair of birds is considerable. Moreover, work must be suspended at frequent intervals in order that the birds may hunt for food.

The Cliff Swallow arrives in the western part of the Yosemite region some time in March, but the birds there do not begin nesting until early May. This delay is probably due to the relative paucity of insect life in April as compared with the plenty in May and June. When the adults arrive they can find sufficient forage for themselves, but at that season there is not enough to enable them to feed a brood of young. Hence they delay until the food supply is adequate for the increased needs of nesting time. East of the mountains, near Williams Butte, in 1916, the birds returned for the season on April 27.

Barn Swallow. **Hirundo erythrogaster erythrogaster** Boddaert

Field characters.—Body size about that of a Linnet but tail and wings much longer and slenderer; tail deeply forked, with the outermost feathers very narrow toward tips (pl. 46e). Upper surface of body iridescent dark blue; forehead and under surface of body light reddish brown; chest with a dark band, not often complete. *Voice:* A series of twittering notes.

Occurrence.—Common summer visitant locally at low altitudes both east and west of Sierra Nevada. Recorded from Snelling and near Lagrange eastward to Bower Cave, 12 miles east of Coulterville; also, east of mountains, in neighborhood of Mono Lake. Chiefly near smooth flowing water; local distribution controlled largely by availability of suitable nesting sites such as low bridges. Usually in pairs, at most in small companies.

The general range of the Barn Swallow in the Yosemite region is practically the same as that of the Cliff Swallow, but as the nesting requirements of the two species are different, their local distribution is not the same. While the Cliff Swallow must have an expanse of wall, either of rock or board, and nests in colonies, the Barn Swallow prefers to live more apart and places its solitary nest on a beam beneath a bridge. Thus the Cliff Swallow is to be found in considerable numbers in a few localities, whereas small numbers of the Barn Swallow are found in many places through the lowland and foothill districts. By reason of its choice of nest site the Barn Swallow is often associated with the Black Phoebe.

The Barn Swallow differs conspicuously from all its fellows in the possession of a deeply forked tail (pl. 46e). This, in flight, is the most easily noted field character. When the bird is perched on a wire or twig the observer sees four points of feathers projecting backward from its body; these comprise the tips of the elongated and narrowed wings and the long outermost tail feathers. The six species of swallows found in the Yosemite section exhibit little difference in skill of flight, yet the Barn Swallow, with its attenuated tail, seems to us to be slightly more adept and certainly more graceful in its aerial coursing than its square-tailed relatives.

Like other hunting birds which feed exclusively on flying insects these swallows spend most of the daylight hours on the wing. At times they come to rest on a wire or other convenient perch where they are wont to spend some minutes in dressing and preening the long flight feathers of the wings. Depending as they do so completely on these organs for gaining their livelihood it is not to be wondered at that the swallows take exceedingly good care of their wings. In consequence of their care of their plumage and of the open nature of their forage area, the primary feathers do not show anywhere near so much wear as do the flight feathers of birds which inhabit shrubbery, grass or trees, whose feathers come in direct contact with these objects.

The Barn Swallow arrives in the Yosemite region during March and lingers until late summer or even early fall. Six individuals, including some young of the year already on the wing, were seen near Merced Falls on August 17, 1915. About 12 birds of this species were observed near Grant Lake, east of the Sierras, on September 14, 1915.

At Mono Mills on June 19, 1916, a nest of the Barn Swallow was found at the side of an old cellar which had once been used for the storage of potatoes. No bridge beams being available the birds had made use of the one site most nearly like that usually chosen. The nest contained five eggs in which incubation was well advanced.

In Bower Cave on July 18, 1920, a pair of these swallows was seen to enter a dark cavern at the bottom of the pit, skimming close over the water. One bird was carrying a fluffy white chicken feather which could be followed by the eye after the bird itself had become invisible in the gloom. Nest construction was probably under way even though, seasonally, the date was late. On July 20, 1920, near Dudley, 6 miles east of Coulterville, a nest containing two fresh eggs was discovered in a mining shaft 30 feet below the surface of the ground.

The Barn Swallow, like the Cliff Swallow, constructs a mud nest. But the nest of the former is open-topped, like a phoebe's, instead of retort-shaped, and has more straws and feathers incorporated into it.

Tree Swallow. Iridoprocne bicolor (Vieillot)

Field characters.—Body size about that of Linnet or Junco; tail nearly square-ended. Upper surface of body black with a steely blue iridescence; whole under surface white; no white on rump. *Voice:* Faint single notes, *seet*, sometimes given several together to form a weak twitter.

Occurrence.—Sparse summer visitant. Recorded only in vicinity of Snelling and Lagrange, and, east of the mountains, at Mono Lake Post Office. Usually near standing water. In pairs or loose companies.

The Tree Swallow resembles the Violet-green Swallow in general plan of coloration and in habits, but it does not range so high altitudinally as does the latter species, nor was it anywhere so abundant. We found the Tree Swallow in May and June along the lower reaches of the Merced and Tuolumne rivers west of the foothills, and in the neighborhood of Mono Lake, beyond the Sierras.

The Tree Swallow is, perhaps, more prone to perch than other swallows. A pair will be seen a good deal of the time sunning themselves on twigs of the dead tree in which their nesting site has been chosen. The nest is hidden as a rule within an old woodpecker hole in some tree standing at the edge of quiet water.

NORTHERN VIOLET-GREEN SWALLOW. **Tachycineta thalassina lepida** Mearns

Field characters.—Body size slightly less than that of Linnet or Junco; wings long and pointed, when closed reaching an inch beyond the slightly notched tail. Whole under surface of body, and sides of rump, pure white (pl. 46*f*); upper surface of body intense green, with violet tinge on rump discernible at short range. *Voice:* A plaintive *tsee* or *che*, sometimes repeated to form a twitter.

Occurrence.—Common summer visitant to Upper Sonoran and Transition zones on west slope of Sierra Nevada; also at east base of mountains. Recorded from Pleasant Valley and near Lagrange eastward to floor and walls of Yosemite Valley and to near Chinquapin; also in vicinity of Mono and Walker lakes; seen in migration near Washburn Lake. Forages in the open, roosting and nesting in hollow trees or in rock crevices. Often in loose flocks while foraging.

Of the six species of swallows found in the Yosemite section the Northern Violet-green Swallow is the one most likely to be seen by the summer visitor to the region. During the warmer months of the year it is common in Yosemite Valley (the only swallow regularly there, indeed), and it is plentiful in the blue oak belt of the western foothills. It occurs in some numbers east of the mountains in the same season, and it was observed at Washburn Lake in the fall.

In a general way the Violet-green Swallow resembles the Tree Swallow. Both species have pure white underparts and dark backs, and both nest in natural cavities of trees; but the Violet-green Swallow shows conspicuous white patches on the sides of the rump (pl. 46*f*). Sometimes the white feathers of these patches curl up so as to completely cover the rump, at least in side view, while again a dark space may show between the two. The pure white under surface readily distinguishes the present species from the remaining swallows found in the region.

In Yosemite Valley, and at certain places in the foothills, the Violet-green Swallow and the White-throated Swift may be seen together and the characteristics of the two may be compared closely. The swallow is seen to be of only about half the bulk of the swift and the hind margin of its proportionately broader wing is straight instead of concave as is that of the swift. In flight the Violet-green Swallow, while adept enough, is less speedy and never as daring as the swift, and its notes, even when uttered in series, are not given in the torrential manner characteristic of the swift.

The Violet-green Swallow arrives early in the Yosemite region. It was already present at El Portal upon our visit to that place on April 27, 1916, and was found in Yosemite Valley the following day. East of the Sierras, in 1916, it appeared on May 6, when a scattering flock was observed at the mouth of Rush Creek near Mono Lake. Throughout the summer months and until early September the species is much in evidence below the 7000-foot contour. At Washburn Lake on August 24, 1915, a troop of at least 12 was seen making its way high overhead down the cañon. Two were seen below Vernal Falls on September 1, 1915, and on September 10 the same year, five or more of these birds were noted near Walker Lake. Mr. C. W. Michael (MS) saw the species in Yosemite Valley during stormy weather on September 23, 1920. These are our latest records of the species.

Soon after arriving here the Violet-green Swallows begin hunting for nest sites. Unlike the Cliff and Barn swallows, they seek natural cavities in trees or crevices in rocks. On the blue-oak covered hillsides near La-grange, on May 6 and 7, 1919, several pairs of these birds were prospecting, flying here and there, entering and leaving old woodpecker holes or cavities left by the rotting out of stubs, and doing much twittering. But our impression was that nesting would not commence in earnest yet for some days. The Violet-green Swallows seen on Negit Island in Mono Lake on May 27, 1916, seemed to be searching for nest locations in the cracks of the lava in the rougher parts of the islet. At Sierra Point on May 16, 1919, some of the swallows seen appeared to be settled for the season. Two, in particular, were again and again seen to alight on a certain little bench of rock near a cleft in the cliff. In Yosemite Valley, in 1915, a female was seen gathering nest material on May 31. Other pairs in the Valley that year were more advanced with their nesting program, as young were observed there on the wing, June 24. East of the Sierras, at Mono Lake Post Office on July 1, 1916, a female was found sitting on three incubated eggs in a nest on a cross beam in a barn, entrance to which had been gained through a knothole in the wall of the building.

Like other swallows the present species spends most of the daylight hours on the wing. Much of its hunting, as is noted often in Yosemite, is done high in the air. On the afternoon of May 29, 1911, there was a thunderstorm over the Valley, and another developed at late dusk. Just as the clouds were gathering and the sun was setting, large numbers of these swallows appeared over the meadows, where they alternately skimmed low and mounted almost out of sight, chasing one another, and giving their twittering notes which sounded faintly or loudly according to the distance of the birds from the observer. Probably the cloud formation over the Valley, preceding the shower, had forced the birds down from the upper air where they had been foraging.

ROUGH-WINGED SWALLOW. **Stelgidopteryx serripennis** (Audubon)

Field characters.—Body size about that of Linnet or Junco; tail almost square-ended. Whole upper surface dull brown; throat and chest grayish brown; belly and feathers below base of tail white. No brilliant or iridescent markings whatsoever. *Voice:* Three or four weak notes, *zeetle-tzeet*, repeated at irregular intervals.

Occurrence.—Sparse summer visitant in foothills west of Sierra Nevada. Observed by us only at following points: 2 miles southwest of Lagrange, on Blacks Creek west of Coulterville, and near Bower Cave. Recorded once in Yosemite Valley, May 22, 1903 (Widmann, 1904, p. 70), when two were seen over Sentinel Meadow in company with Violet-green Swallows. Frequents vicinity of gulches having steep earth banks. In pairs or small companies.

The Rough-winged Swallow is the most local in its manner of occurrence of the several species of swallows found in the Yosemite section. Previous to 1919 it escaped our attention entirely, and subsequently was found at only three places in the western foothills, as noted above. The species differs from all of our other swallows as regards nesting site. It chooses a steep earth bank and there digs a horizontal tunnel in which to place its nest. There its spotless, white eggs and later the young are entirely hidden from view.

At Blacks Creek, one mile west of Coulterville, eight Rough-winged Swallows were seen on the morning of May 10, 1919. There were suitable nesting sites close by but the birds seemed not as yet to have settled down for the rearing of broods. They were flying about, sometimes coming to rest on dead weed tips or bare branches of trees; at times they alighted directly on the dry sandy earth of a cow trail.

From time to time the males were seen in pursuit of the females and, while so engaged, to make rather striking use of their seemingly plain garb. They would spread the long white feathers (under tail coverts) at the lower base of the tail until these curled up along either side of the otherwise brownish tail. The effect produced was of white outer tail feathers, such as those of the junco or the pipit. Males can by means of this trick be distinguished from the females at a distance of fully 50 yards. An examination of specimens in hand reveals the fact that the under tail coverts of the males are broader and longer than those of the females.

A nest of this swallow was found by Mr. Donald D. McLean on Jordan Creek near Bower Cave on June 20, 1920. It consisted of a mass of dry grass placed in an excavation in an earth bank and contained three eggs.

Bohemian Waxwing. **Bombycilla garrula** (Linnaeus)

Field characters.—Somewhat smaller than Robin (half again as large as Cedar Waxwing) and with much smaller tail; head crested; sexes alike. General color of plumage dark gray; chin and throat, bill and streak through eye, black; end of tail yellow; two lines of white marks on each wing; under tail coverts reddish brown.

Occurrence.—Rare and irregular fall and winter visitant. A flock seen and specimens taken by Donald D. McLean, at Smith Creek, 6 miles east of Coulterville, January 31, 1917. One individual was noted in Yosemite Valley on September 28, 1920 (C. W. Michael, MS).

The Bohemian Waxwing is even more of a rover than its smaller relative, the Cedar Waxwing, and visits California only at rare intervals. There was a general invasion of the northern portion of the State by this bird in 1892 and again in 1911, but the flock seen at Smith Creek constitutes the only California record of the species for 1917. The flock in question comprised about sixty Bohemian and three Cedar waxwings. These birds were feeding on decaying apples in an orchard.

The Bohemian Waxwing may be readily identified by the characters given above. The average weight of four individuals was 55 grams, which is just one and a half times the weight of the smaller species. Many individuals of both species have the inner flight feathers (secondaries) of the wing provided with red wax-like tips, whence comes the common group name of these birds.

Cedar Waxwing. **Bombycilla cedrorum** Vieillot

Field characters.—Slightly larger than Junco; head crested; plumage soft appearing; tail small; sexes alike. General color of plumage grayish brown; belly yellowish; chin, bill, and streak through eye, black; tail tipped with yellow; under tail coverts whitish. Flight swift, undulating, in a course usually low over or among trees. *Voice:* A series of rather faint, high pitched, hissing notes.

Occurrence.—Sparing visitant in fall, winter and spring on both slopes of Sierra Nevada. Stations and dates of record: Snelling, May 26, 1915 (5 individuals); Smith Creek, 6 miles east of Coulterville, January 31, 1917, and December 7, 1915; El Portal, October 7, 1914 (one); Yosemite Valley, September 28, 1920 (small flock); Warren Fork of Leevining Creek, September 27, 1915 (12); Mono Lake Post Office, May 24, 1916 (one). Seen usually in close flocks, in or near berry producing shrubs or trees.

The Cedar Waxwing is one of the few species of birds which wander about over the country erratically, appearing as a winter visitant in numbers in a given locality for one or more years and then being almost or entirely absent from that locality for a like period. Its movements are probably governed by food supply; yet it seems curious that, patronizing as it does a wide variety of trees and shrubs, it should not readily find one or another of these growths offering in any one locality sufficient food for the season. The Cedar Waxwing appears in winter chiefly in the valleys and lower foothills; but Mr. Donald D. McLean recorded the species at Smith Creek (east of Coulterville) on January 31, 1917, and he says further that it has been seen commonly there in winter and spring of some years. A small flock was seen feeding on mistletoe berries in the top of a tall incense cedar in Yosemite Valley on September 28, 1920, by Mr. C. W. Michael (MS). The birds noted at Snelling and Mono Lake Post Office in late May were probably late migrants bound northward; for the species is not known to nest in the Sierra Nevada.

It is the usual habit of 'Cedar Birds' to travel in flocks of 25 to 50 individuals. A flock will visit some heavily fruiting plant; the individual birds will gorge themselves to satiety, and then rest on perches during the action of their digestive processes, until, presently, they may indulge in further feeding. Mistletoe berries are an important article of their diet in the hill country. Many of the berries eaten by Cedar Birds are retained only long enough to enable the digestive juices to dissolve the outer layers. Then the resistant or indigestible central portion, which in the berry of the pepper tree has a hot and disagreeable taste, is disgorged.

When feeding, the birds are very active, clinging to slender twigs so as to reach the berries, sometimes hanging inverted in chickadee-fashion, twisting, fluttering, making short flights to regain a lost perch, and occasionally uttering their shrill hissing notes. If disturbed while feeding, they fly off swiftly, in close formation and in undulating course, low over the trees, and utter their unique notes in chorus as they go.

PHAINOPEPLA. **Phainopepla nitens** (Swainson)

Field characters.—Body size slightly greater than that of Linnet, but tail longer than body; head crested. Male: Whole plumage black; in flight a large patch of white shows conspicuously on middle of spread wing. Female: Dark grayish brown; wing patch present but obscure. Flight slow, vacillating. *Voice:* Song of male a rather weak wheezy warble, rambling and intermittent in delivery, interspersed with clear notes; call note a single, low-pitched whistle.

Occurrence.—Resident in small numbers in Upper Sonoran Zone at west base of Sierra Nevada. Frequents blue-oak belt, staying about clumps of mistletoe and other berry-producing plants. Solitary or in pairs.

The Phainopepla is typically a bird of the hot arid southwest and occurs in large numbers in southern California; yet it is also to be found regularly in certain localities along the west base of the Sierra Nevada. Since we found it at Pleasant Valley in May and November of 1915, and near Coulterville in August, 1920, it seems likely that the species is resident, though in limited numbers, within the Yosemite section.

The wing patch of pure white on the otherwise glossy black plumage of the male and the peculiar flight of the bird set it apart sharply in general appearance from any other species in the region. The female is a replica of the male save for her duller coloration.

The whole demeanor of the Phainopepla is suggestive of indecision. The flight is vacillating, and the wing-beats are slow. The bird seems to travel with no idea of directness or of desire to reach a certain destination. Even when perched while being stalked, a Phainopepla although visibly alarmed will show uncertainty as to whether or not it shall leave; it makes several false starts—then suddenly it flutters off, with a befuddled air, in zigzag course, to another perch not far away. A bird seen foraging in a mistletoe clump, or a male seen singing from the upper foliage of an oak, presents a very trim and slender outline; the crest of narrow feathers on the top of the head is usually held erect when the bird is perched.

The song of the male is a rather weak utterance, wheezy or throaty in character, and given intermittently. The intervals between successive warbles are punctuated now and then with the clearer, whistle-like call note.

Some of the birds seen at Pleasant Valley during the last week of May, 1915, exhibited the solicitude to be expected at nesting time, but we did not succeed in finding any nests. Eight Phainopeplas were seen in a 5-hour census on May 24, and fourteen in 3½ hours on May 30, in the territory south and west of the settlement. Males were much more in evidence than females. On November 30, 1915, three Phainopeplas were observed, also at Pleasant Valley, during a period of five hours.

SHRIKES. **Lanius ludovicianus** Linnaeus[33]

Field characters.—Between Junco and Robin in size; tail as long as body. Plumage bluish gray above, whitish beneath; wings, tail, and stripe through eye, black; large patch of white shows on each wing in flight, and tail is broadly ended and margined with white. (See pl. 53*b*.) Flight usually low over ground; perches solitarily in exposed situations while watching ground for prey. *Voice:* A harsh call, *skree, skree, skree*, which may be repeated at short intervals; a song of some compass is given at times during late winter and early spring.

[33] Two subspecies of shrike are found in the Yosemite region.

CALIFORNIA SHRIKE, *Lanius ludovicianus gambeli* Ridgway, is a slightly smaller and somewhat darker toned race with only a slight amount of white at upper base of tail. This race is resident in the San Joaquin Valley and penetrates into the foothills even as far as Smith Creek, east of Coulterville.

WHITE-RUMPED SHRIKE, *Lanius ludovicianus excubitorides* Swainson, is a slightly larger bird, of paler tone above and with the rump usually more clearly white. This subspecies was found about Mono Lake in summer, and has occurred in winter (January 20, 1916) at Smith Creek, on the west slope of the Sierras.

A shrike, of unknown subspecies, was noted in Yosemite Valley on September 4 and 6, 1920 (C. W. Michael, MS).

The two forms of the 'Loggerhead' Shrike cannot be distinguished except by measurement and close examination of specimens in hand.

Occurrence.—Common resident at lowest levels on west side of Sierra Nevada. Recorded regularly at Snelling and Lagrange; less often at Smith Creek, 6 miles east of Coulterville (race *gambeli*); once in Yosemite Valley. Sparingly represented east of mountains near Mono Lake (race *excubitorides*). Keeps to open, as along roadways, perching on wires, fences, poles, or exposed portions of trees. Solitary.

The shrike or 'butcherbird' is a common resident along the roadways over the floor of the San Joaquin Valley, but only a few individuals of the species are to be found within the foothill country. There is but one record for Yosemite Valley and none for the higher levels.

The requirements of the shrike are simple. Open fields inhabited by large beetles, grasshoppers, and mice, and some convenient perch four to fifteen feet above the ground from which to watch for prey, will satisfy the bird throughout the entire year. At nesting time a pair will choose some dense bush or tree in the general neighborhood, in which to place the rather bulky and deeply cup-shaped nest. Except when caring for a brood the birds are solitary, and even at this season, the two members of a pair keep spaced well apart so as to avoid the duplication which would result were both to scrutinize the same territory.

The shrike spends most of its time perched quietly on one of its favorite lookout posts. From time to time it changes location to survey a new field, or swoops down to capture some item of prey which by movement has divulged its position to the bird. When leaving one perch for another the bird drops close to the ground, then speeds along in direct line with continuously beating wings, the white patches showing for an instant at each stroke and giving a 'twinkling' effect to the flight. The shrike continues on its low course until close to the new goal, then rises abruptly *up* and *on* to the perch.

At rest, the shrike is seen to be a big-headed bird with a relatively large black bill, resembling that of a hawk in outline. There is a black line continuing backward from the bill through the eye which gives the bird a rather bold, fearsome expression. Closed, the wings and tail are black above, the white markings, save when the tail of a perched bird is seen from beneath, showing forth only when the bird is in flight.

On January 7, 1915, at least 8 California Shrikes were seen during a 3½ hour trip over the flat country near Snelling, and the species was found to be about equally abundant below Lagrange in December of the same year. In the latter month the grain farmers were doing their winter plowing and the shrikes almost "followed the plow," waxing fat on easily captured insects. Birds collected at this season contained remains of beetles of various sorts, grasshoppers, and Jerusalem crickets.

In the midwinter months shrikes often appear at the Dudley ranch, on Smith Creek, east of Coulterville. Most of the birds collected there belong to the California race (*gambeli*), but one, at least, is referable to the subspecies (*excubitorides*) inhabiting the Great Basin. This indicates that some of the shrikes are given, just as are certain other birds of the arid interior, to wandering over to the west slope of the Sierra Nevada during the season of storms and snow in the Great Basin region.

Near Lagrange on May 6, 1919, a family of California Shrikes was found near the home tree, a blue oak on a hill above the county road. The two parents were accompanied by five lusty youngsters, the latter having left the nest only a day or two previously. From time to time the youngsters implored their parents for food by uttering quavering peevish cries, and at the same time they quivered their wings in the manner common to many young birds. The young at this age showed fine brown barrings on the whitish under surface, the white on their wings and tail was clouded with brown, and the plumage looked softer, more fluffy than that of the adults. The nest was about 9 feet above the ground in the foliage of a dense blue oak, and had been much flattened by its late occupants. The rim of the nest and adjacent foliage of the oak were much spattered with excrement. This suggests that a bird of prey, which the shrike is in habits if not in systematic position, does not need to keep the location of its nest a secret after the young are hatched. A couple of days later, two members of this brood were seen perched on fence posts about 150 feet apart, along the roadway. They were watching an adjacent field. Parental supervision had ceased and the young birds had begun to live independently.

WESTERN WARBLING VIREO. **Vireosylva gilva swainsoni** (Baird)

Field characters.—Two-thirds size of Junco; tail shorter than body. Plumage grayish green with no highly contrasted markings; a light line over eye; no light bars on wing. (See pl. 50*b*.) Movements slow as compared with warblers; keeps usually within crown foliage of trees. *Voice:* Song of male a sustained and voluble warble uttered at short intervals; both sexes give a throaty or burred call note, *szhee* or *zree*.

Occurrence.—Summer visitant in Upper Sonoran, Transition, and Canadian zones on both sides of Sierra Nevada; commoner on west slope. Observed from Pleasant Valley and near Lagrange eastward to Porcupine Flat and Merced Lake; also at Walker Lake and Mono Lake Post Office. Frequents deciduous trees chiefly, most often near streams, foraging from 10 to 60 feet above ground. Solitary except when pairs are caring for broods.

The Western Warbling Vireo is the most widely distributed and the commonest of the four species of vireo occurring in the Yosemite section. While usually found in deciduous trees and in the general vicinity of streams it is at times observed well away from water and is occasionally to be seen or heard high in tall coniferous trees.

Vireos as a group are birds of deliberate mien. When an individual is discovered, as often happens, in the same tree with some one of the wood warblers, there is little likelihood of the two being confused. The vireos are more sluggish of movement and never hunt over the trees with the nervous, zigzag movements so characteristic of the warblers.

Each of the four vireos of the Yosemite section offers good clues for field identification (pl. 50) by both coloration and voice, and in general the species may be separated on the basis of local distribution as well. The Western Warbling Vireo, as compared with the other vireos, exhibits a white stripe *over* the eye, and *no* light bars on the wing. Its song is a voluble rolling warble, and is of more nearly continuous production than that of almost any other bird to be heard in the region. The Cassin Vireo is of slightly larger size than the warbling vireo, it has a white circlet *around* the eye, two light bars on the wing, and a more clearly white under surface, while its song consists of bars of alternately rising and falling inflection, separated by rests. In some places, these two species of vireo inhabit much the same sort of territory, yet the warbling vireo usually shows preference for the deciduous growths along streams, while the Cassin is more inclined to frequent the incense cedars and golden oaks in drier situations. The Hutton Vireo is slightly smaller in size than the Western Warbling Vireo and is decidedly more greenish in tone of color than any of the other three species. It has, by way of contrast, a partial ring of buffy white around the eye and two bars of light color across the wing. The niche of this species is in oak trees of which the evergreen live and golden oaks seem to be preferred. The California Least Vireo, as its name implies, is smaller than any of the preceding species. In general tone of coloration it is light grayish and when seen in spring and summer it lacks contrasted markings of any sort. The song is set in character, and rapidly delivered, with first a rising, then a falling inflection. The bird keeps low in the dense thickets which margin the water courses in the San Joaquin Valley.

The Western Warbling Vireo probably arrives in the Yosemite region during April, although we have no exact data on this point. It was well established at El Portal on April 27, 1916, and in Yosemite Valley on April 28 the same year. It continues in the region until the end of summer. Several were seen at Merced Lake on August 23, 1915, and single individuals were noted at Walker Lake on September 10 and 14, 1915. A single bird was noted in Yosemite Valley on September 5, 1920 (C. W. Michael, MS). The greatest numbers are to be found in the vicinity of streams in the Transition Zone where three or four will ordinarily be noted in an hour of observation. Above and below this zone the population is somewhat sparser. East of the mountains the species is represented in small numbers. It was seen there on only a few occasions in spring, at Mono Lake Post Office and near Walker Lake.

During the spring and early summer months the Western Warbling Vireo is, within its range, one of the principal contributors to the early morning chorus of bird voices. At El Portal on May 31, 1915, one of us rated it as fourth among the various contestants, being exceeded in loudness by only the Western Tanager, Pacific Black-headed Grosbeak, and Western House Wren. The song is a voluble rolling warble sustained for several seconds at a time and repeated at very short intervals. It is more varied and slightly more slowly timed than the roll of the Purple Finch and among all the bird songs of almost continuous production it is, to our way of thinking, most pleasing. Often, in the heat of midday, when, for one reason or another, most other species are stilled, the warbling vireo continues its melodious song with little or no indication of lagging. Indeed, it is a warm weather bird, often being silent in the cool of morning or evening, and singing less on cloudy or foggy days than on those marked by bright sunshine. It is a well known trait of the male of this bird to sing while he is taking a turn in the duty of incubation on the nest. The song season lasts from the time the birds first arrive in the region until about mid-July. A male was heard in broken song in Yosemite Valley on July 23, 1915. The call note of the species is a burred *zree* or *szhee*. This note may be repeated over and over again in a very insistent tone, in case a jay has entered the nesting precincts of the vireo.

In a shady spot among some pine trees on the north side of Yosemite Valley, a nest of the Western Warbling Vireo was found on June 17, 1915. It was located 4½ feet above the ground at the forking of two almost leafless branches of a coffee berry bush. The nest was, as usual, strapped to and slung within the crotch between the diverging branches. The cup was about 3 inches in outside diameter at the top and about 6½ inches from rim to rim around the bottom. One of the parent vireos was sitting on the nest, and the color of its back blended well with the gray bark of the bush and the gray nest material, but its bright black-appearing eye was conspicuous. The bird did not flush until the observer was within four feet of the nest. Two of the four eggs in this nest hatched on June 22 and the others were hatched by the 24th. By July 7 this brood had left the nest. Another nest of this species was discovered in a young black oak. It was about 12 feet above the ground and 3 feet out from the trunk. Like the other nest, it was composed of light gray bark fibers and weed stems together with some white egg-cases of spiders. There were 4 tiny young in this nest on June 25 (1915). Upon our visiting the place again on July 7 the then fully feathered young took wing and left the nest as the observer climbed the tree. Some few broods are evidently brought off at later dates, as a family group was seen near Merced Lake on August 23, 1915.

CASSIN VIREO. **Lanivireo solitarius cassini** (Xantus)

Field characters.—Three-fourths bulk of Junco; tail shorter than body. Plumage grayish green above, olive gray on head; under surface whitish; eye encircled by white (pl. 50*a*); two light bars on wing; bill black. Movements deliberate. *Voice:* Song of male a series of detached notes, now rising, now falling in inflection, *quēē'-up, tsēēr,* etc.; call note a harsh *chē.*

Occurrence.—Common summer visitant to Transition Zone (sparing in lower Canadian) on west slope of Sierra Nevada; recorded in nesting season from 3 miles east of Coulterville and from El Portal, eastward to east fork of Indian Cañon at 7300 feet and to near Merced Lake at 7500 feet altitude. In spring migration passes through lowland and foothill country, as at Snelling, Lagrange, and Pleasant Valley. In fall small numbers wander to higher levels, as along McClure Fork to 8300 feet and along course of Rafferty Creek. Not observed on east slope. Frequents chiefly incense cedars and golden oaks. Solitary except when pairs are caring for broods.

The Cassin Vireo is a summer visitant at middle altitudes along the west flank of the Sierra Nevada. Its distribution at nesting time closely parallels the ranges of the golden oak and incense cedar, though the bird does not restrict itself exclusively to these two trees. In and around Yosemite Valley this species and the Western Warbling Vireo are often to be found together, although the Cassin shows preference for the drier portions of the Valley, for example, near and upon the talus slopes along the north and south walls. During the spring migration the Cassin Vireo is a common transient in the western foothill country where, during its passage, it is to be seen in blue oaks and chaparral on the dry hillsides. In early fall after the young are grown a few of these vireos wander up into the Hudsonian Zone before taking final leave of the country for the winter.

The first of the Cassin Vireos probably arrive in the Yosemite region early in April. On our visit to El Portal on April 27, 1916, the species was already well established there, and the same was found to be true in Yosemite Valley the day following. Near Lagrange, in 1919, Cassin Vireos were passing through the blue oak belt in numbers on May 7, and a few transients were observed near Coulterville on May 9 and 10, while in 1915, migration was still in progress at Bullion Mountain on May 26, at Pleasant Valley on May 23 to 28, and at Snelling on May 27. In 1919, however, nesting was already under way in Yosemite Valley on May 22. It seems likely that the late migrants seen in the foothills in 1915 were bound to some much more northerly station rather than that they were going to swell the number in the Transition Zone of the region immediately to the east. The species continued in evidence through August; single birds were seen as late as September 1 near Echo Creek, September 2 in Yosemite Valley, and September 7 along Rafferty Creek, all in the year 1915. Mr. Joseph Mailliard (1918, p. 19) states that a few were still in Yosemite Valley on September 28, 1917.

The Cassin Vireo is the largest of the four species of vireos in the Yosemite section. (See pl. 50.) In general, the bird gives the impression of having an abnormally large head and short tail, and of being big-eyed, the latter obviously by reason of the conspicuous circlet of white around the eye. In good light the head appears an olive slate, the back greenish, and the under surface ashy white, with a yellowish tinge on the sides.

The movements of this vireo are like those of the Warbling Vireo, but they are even more slow and deliberate. It perches stolidly, and when insects are spied captures them by direct thrusts of the bill. Occasionally a bird will poise on fluttering wings to seize some object not otherwise obtainable. But even then, there is little suggestion of the nervous activity of, for example, the Audubon Warbler.

The Cassin Vireo is a slow but persistent singer; the syllables of its song are set off from one another by long rests. With one bird which was kept under observation for some time these breaks varied from about one to ten seconds. Another, similarly studied, sang at intervals which, by the watch, ranged from one to three seconds. After a long series of these closely spaced notes the latter bird was quiet for ten minutes or more save for two series of five or six notes each. Each note is clear cut and loud so that the song rings out, and may be heard for a considerable distance. Successive notes are variously inflected, some rising, others falling; at times a bird will give a regular alternation of rising and falling inflections. Hence the name "question-and-answer bird" has been suggested for the Cassin Vireo. Some of the notes were syllabified by one of us as *tseer'*, *pee'rit, pee'-o-wup, syrup, que'-up, tseer*, etc. Another series was written as *che'weh, cheweuh', che wer*, occasionally *wee'cha*. The notes suggest the words "to eat? to cheer!" The bird has also a scolding or alarm note *chē, chē, chē*, and the two members of a pair when together may indulge in low conversational notes. The Cassin Vireo continues in song through much of the summer, one in song being heard in Yosemite Valley on July 23, 1915. There is a revival of song after the molt; on September 2, 1915, one was heard in the Valley giving a song almost as full and persistent as that ordinarily to be heard in the spring.

A nest of the Cassin Vireo was found in Yosemite Valley on May 22, 1919. It was placed in an incense cedar at the edge of the Merced River. The nest was on a branch which extended out over the rushing stream and was about 18 feet above the surface of the water. The nest was a deep cup lashed by the rim to two forking branchlets forming a crotch. The following day another nest, in an early stage of construction, was found near the road along the north side of the Valley. It was 7½ feet above the ground at a fork in an outswaying branch of a young black oak beneath a larger tree of the same kind. The bird came to the nest singing loudly and, while still singing, proceeded to add material around the rim, standing on one of the supporting twigs while it worked. Two automobiles passed unheeded by the bird, which sang again before departing. Two minutes later the vireo came again with material in its bill, sang, added material to the nest, sang, and departed into the golden oaks across the road. The bird seemed not at all inconvenienced by having its bill laden with supplies, and, indeed, this is generally true of our song birds; movement of the bill is not a necessity in singing.

Hutton Vireo. **Vireo huttoni huttoni** Cassin

Field characters.—About half size of Junco; tail decidedly shorter than body. Plumage nearly uniform greenish olive, only slightly darker above than below; eye partially surrounded by light color; two pale bars on wing (pl. 50c). Movements deliberate; does not habitually twitch or flutter wings as does Kinglet. *Voice:* Song of male a hoarse, drawling *zee'-ey, zee'-ey, zee'-ey;* and again, *zi-ew, zi-ew, zi-ew;* these notes intoned monotonously in long series; there is also a low harsh call note.

Occurrence.—Fairly common resident locally in Upper Sonoran and lower Transition zones on west slope of Sierra Nevada. Observed near Coulterville, about El Portal, in Yosemite Valley, and at Gentrys. Lives almost exclusively in live oaks and golden oaks. Solitary or in pairs.

Four species of vireos or 'greenlets' are found in different portions of the Yosemite section during the summer months, but only one, the Hutton Vireo, remains in the region through the winter as well. This vireo is almost exclusively an inhabitant of the live oaks and golden oaks and this choice of habitat is doubtless the basis for the continuance of the bird here during the winter moths. These 'evergreen' oaks furnish forage in the form of insects throughout the year, as is shown by the number of warblers and kinglets which resort to these trees during the colder months. The Hutton Vireo, by being restricted to this type of tree, is assured of food in all seasons, and does not need to migrate.

The Hutton Vireo is the greenest of our four species. It is smaller than the Cassin and the Warbling and larger than the Least Vireo, and although it resembles the Cassin in possession of a light eye ring and two bars on the wing (pl. 50c), its much greener coloration makes it readily distinguishable from that gray and white-toned species. Its voice is absolutely distinct from that of any of the other three.

The Hutton Vireo bears a remarkable resemblance to the Ruby-crowned Kinglet. The two species are of about the same general tone of coloration and have in common a light eye ring and two light bars on the wing; but the vireo is somewhat larger, has the appearance of big-headedness and has no bright crown-patch such as is worn by the male kinglet. In demeanor the two birds are at most times strikingly different, and the voices are not likely to be confused at all. The deliberate vireo occasionally flutters its wings but never so frequently or nervously as does the smaller bird. During the winter season both of these birds are to be found in the oaks, and so, on occasion, may be compared in life, side by side.

The range of the Hutton Vireo within the Yosemite section is not extensive. The westernmost station at which we observed the species was Blacks Creek, west of Coulterville, and the easternmost was the talus slope on the north side of Yosemite Valley, near Rocky Point. In the winter of 1914 (December 28), one was recorded at 4500 feet altitude on the Big Oak Flat road, and on October 21, 1915, one was found at Gentrys, 5800 feet, also on that road. The species was seen in greatest numbers at El Portal, probably because of the abundance of evergreen oaks in the vicinity.

The restriction of the Hutton Vireo to oak trees seems to be practically complete; not one of our ten recorded observations of the species list it as being seen elsewhere than in one or another kind of these trees. It forages occasionally in black oaks, but more commonly in the non-deciduous oaks. In Yosemite Valley, individuals were discovered by following up the characteristic monotonous drawling song, in June, July, and December. All observed were at the lower end of the valley, west of Yosemite Falls.

California Least Vireo. **Vireo belli pusillus** Coues

Field characters.—Less than half bulk of Junco or Linnet. Plumage appearing light gray above, whitish beneath; a single inconspicuous light bar on wing (pl. 50*d*). Movements quicker than those of other vireos but less nervous than those of warblers or kinglets. *Voice:* Song of male, a rapidly uttered series of three or more warbling notes ending in a short questioning note, a pause, then the series repeated with downward inflection.

Occurrence.—Summer visitant locally in Lower Sonoran Zone. Common at Snelling and below Lagrange; one pair found at Pleasant Valley May 22 and 23, 1915. Keeps low (6 feet or less from ground) in willow and other thickets along streams and sloughs. In pairs or solitary.

The California Least Vireo dwells in the dense thickets of willows and other plants which grow along the lower courses of the Merced and Tuolumne rivers, chiefly west of the foothills. In size, coloration, voice, and habits it is well set off from the other three species of vireos in the Yosemite section, so that chance of confusion with them is slight.

The Least Vireo is decidedly smaller than any of the other species of vireos; it is less fluffy in appearance than the Hutton Vireo, the next in point of weight. Its grayish tone of coloration above, single wing bar (pl. 50*d*) scarcely discernible at a distance, and whitish under surface, taken together distinguish it from its relatives.

Near Snelling, on May 29, 1915, eight Least Vireos were observed within a stretch of about 300 yards in the low growths beside the Merced River. In an approximately similar extent of stream-side brush along the Tuolumne River southwest of Lagrange, on May 6, 1919, three pairs of these vireos were found. Each pair had a definite forage beat, within which the two birds could be found at almost any hour of the day.

As regards the niche occupied, the Least Vireo differs from our other vireos in that it chooses a low zone of vegetation in which to search for its food and place its nest. An individual is rarely seen above 6 feet from the ground, and usually it keeps below four feet. Our impression is that all the other vireos habitually forage well above the six-foot level.

A completed nest of this vireo was found near Lagrange on May 8, 1919. (See pl. 51*a*.) It was in deep shade under a thicket of willows and white alders which grew on the lower slope of a pile of gravel left by a gold dredger. The nest was 19 inches above the gravel, and instead of being placed in one of the stout crotches of the adjacent alder it had been lashed to a slender fork on the brittle stem of a weed of the previous season's growth. This was only 7 feet from the margin of a pool of quiet water. In form the nest was a well rounded, deep and rather thin-walled cup with slightly inrolled rim. It was composed of dry shreds of plants felted compactly with down from cottonwoods and willows. Outside, it measured 2 inches in height and 2½ inches in greatest diameter, while the interior was 1½ inches deep at the center and about 1⅝ inches across the opening.

When first found, this nest was empty, but on the following day, by 6:30 A.M., one egg had been laid. During our second examination of the nest the male came close and sang his song at intervals of 10 or 15 seconds. To one observer the song sounded like this: *we-cher, che we, che we-chey? we cher, che we, che we, cheey!* Each set of syllables was uttered rapidly, with a distinct rest between the two.

Another pair of these little vireos was watched around one of the other small ponds in the same general locality. The female was foraging and she moved about rather rapidly, occasionally flying upward a short distance to get some particular insect on the leafage. Meanwhile the male traveled along with less frequent change of position, keeping to perches fairly close to his mate, and singing at short intervals. When he was giving the song, his whole body vibrated with the effort, the throat swelling visibly at each syllable, and the tail being depressed at the same time. This song was transcribed on the spot as *wretchy, wretchy, wretchy, wretchy, wree? wretchy, wretchy, wretchy, wretcheur, wreer.* The *r*'s here indicate a burred or rolling quality; and the whole song was, as usual, hurried in its delivery. The question-and-answer inflection was striking.

CALAVERAS WARBLER. **Vermivora ruficapilla gutturalis** (Ridgway)

Field characters.—Half bulk of Junco. Body coloration yellow beneath, olive green above; head and neck (except throat) gray; eyelids white; male has a chestnut colored crown patch, visible only at close range. No white or black markings whatsoever on wings or tail. (See pl. 9a.) *Voice:* Song of male 4 or 5 rapidly uttered shrill notes followed by 3 or 4 lower ones: *tsirp, tsirp, tsirp, tsirp, sup sup sup;* call note a *tseep,* or *tsit.*

Occurrence.—Common summer visitant to Transition Zone on west slope of Sierra Nevada. Recorded from 3 miles east of Coulterville and from Sequoia eastward to Yosemite Valley and slopes adjacent. Highest stations, at 7400 feet altitude near Mono Meadow and at 6700 feet above Yosemite Falls. Some few individuals wander higher in mountains after nesting (for example, 8000 feet on McClure Fork of Merced River, August 29, 1915). Sings and forages 10 to 70 feet above ground in broad-leaved trees such as black oak and maple, but nests in shaded situations on ground. Solitary.

The Calaveras Warbler is common during the summer months in the black oaks and maples along each side of Yosemite Valley and in similar situations elsewhere on the western flank of the Sierra Nevada. Among all the warblers to be seen in the Yosemite Valley during the summer months the present species is the only one which does not forage and nest in the same niche. The Calaveras seeks its food and does its singing well up in trees, but places its nest immediately upon the ground.

The niche of the Calaveras Warbler is not invaded by any other species of warbler, although other birds of this group may be close around. (See fig. 56.) In the pines and cedars are the Audubon and Hermit warblers, the golden oaks of the talus slopes harbor the Black-throated Gray Warbler, and in the stream-side willows and cottonwoods is the Yellow Warbler; while the tangles of underbrush above moist ground on the Valley floor shelter Tolmie and Golden Pileolated warblers.

During May and June the song of the Calaveras Warbler may be heard frequently, for the males sing at short intervals through most of the day. One bird watched near Columbia Point on June 2, 1915, was singing at intervals of 7 to 12 seconds, each utterance occupying but a second or two. The pitch is high although the notes are not so piercing as those of a Yellow Warbler and the song as a whole suggests that of the Lazuli Bunting. Four or five notes are given sharply and distinctly, then three or four less sharp ones are uttered in more rapid time. Three phrasings of the song written by us in the field are as follows: *tsirp, tsirp, tsirp, tsirp, sup sup sup; tsu'-ip, tsu'-ip, tsu'-ip, tsu'-ip, seet-seet-seet-seet;* again *seit, seit, seit, seit* (4 or 5), *che-che-che-cha.* Sometimes the terminal group of syllables is omitted.

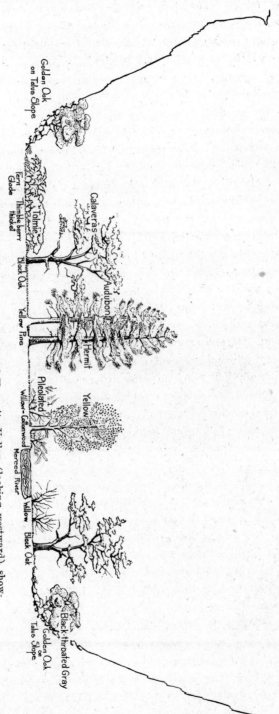

Fig. 56. Diagrammatic cross-section of Yosemite Valley (looking westward) showing principal vegetational associations and the forage ("niches") occupied by the seven species of Warblers which breed in the Valley. The nesting places of some of the species are in different locations from the forage places shown here.

The forage range of this warbler lies chiefly in trees other than conifers. Such trees as the black oak and big-leafed maple renew their foliage every spring and the Calaveras Warblers find excellent forage in the insects and larvae which feed upon this tender new leafage during the spring and summer months. Less often these birds may be found in golden oaks and occasionally in Douglas spruces. They usually forage 25 to 40 feet above the ground, keeping within the stratum of new foliage, but they have been seen as low as 10 feet and as high as 70 feet above the earth. When within the foliage their yellow and green coloration makes it difficult to locate them, especially as the birds do not move about as rapidly as some of the other warblers. At times a Calaveras Warbler will poise on rapidly beating wings to capture some insect otherwise out of reach.

A good view of the male Calaveras Warbler reveals a plainly colored bird, lacking contrasted markings of any sort. (See pl. 9a.) The head is clear gray, the throat and lower surface continuously clear yellow, the upper surface olive green. The female differs only in showing less contrast between the dull gray of the head and the olive green of the back. There is lacking in both sexes the brilliant yellow of the Yellow and Pileolated warblers, and there are none of the black and white markings of the Audubon, Hermit, and Black-throated Gray warblers. The Calaveras Warbler bears somewhat of a resemblance to the Tolmie, especially in the immature plumage, but then the difference in habitat and the smaller size of the former are sufficient for distinguishing the two.

A nest of the Calaveras Warbler was discovered in Yosemite Valley near the base of Sentinel Rock on May 26, 1911. The location was only about 75 feet from the much traveled south road on the Valley floor and at the base of the talus pile of huge boulders. The nest was on the face of one of the larger of these boulders, partly in a diagonal fissure. It was on the north side of the rock and so never received any direct rays of sunlight. The whole face of the boulder was covered densely with yellow-green moss which in places was overlaid by olive-gray lichens. The nest was 43 inches from the base of the rock and about 60 inches from the top. The whole vicinity was densely shaded by black oaks and firs and the ground beneath was strewn with dead last year's leaves of the oaks. There were 5 eggs, and incubation was far advanced. When the nest was first discovered, the parent birds acted very shyly, but after a while they began to show much anxiety, coming down as close as 10 feet from the observer who was sitting below the nest. The female was the bolder of the two birds. Their excited *tsits* attracted other birds for a time, among these being a brilliant male Hermit Warbler, a singing male Golden-crowned Kinglet, and some Ruby-crowned Kinglets and Western Warbling Vireos.

b

d

g

i

Warblers of the Yosemite Section (adult males).

a. Calaveras Warbler.   *b.* Lutescent Warbler.   *c.* California Yellow Warbler.   *d.* Hermit Warbler.   *e.* Audubon Warbler.   *f.* Black-throated Gray Warbler.   *g.* Golden Pileolated Warbler.   *h.* Tolmie Warbler.   *i.* Western Yellowthroat.

On June 5, 1915, we were shown a nest of the Calaveras Warbler in the vicinity of Smith Creek, east of Coulterville. It was in a hollow of the ground at the base of an azalea bush, near an old road along the hillside. The creek itself was about 50 feet distant. This nest was 3 inches across the outside and about 2 inches high, the cavity being 1¼ inches deep. Strips of bark of the incense cedar, plant fibers, and horsehair comprised the building material. When first discovered it had contained five eggs, but prior to our seeing it the nest had been raided and all trace of the eggs was gone. A third nest was discovered near the bridge over Yosemite Creek above Yosemite Falls on July 1, 1915. It was ensconced in a shallow hole in the bank at the side of a well traveled trail. A tuft of grass overhung and nearly concealed the structure. One of the adult birds was flushed from the nest, which, however, contained neither eggs nor young.

Calaveras Warblers continue in the Yosemite region at least throughout August; individuals have been seen along the McClure Fork of the Merced River on August 26 and 29, 1915. The latter is our latest date of noting this species in the region, although Mr. Joseph Mailliard (1918, p. 17) made definite record of an individual in Yosemite Valley as late as September 16 (1917).

Orange-crowned Warblers. **Vermivora celata** (Say)[34]

Field characters.—Half size of Junco. Whole body dull greenish, tinged with yellow beneath. No wing bars or other contrasted markings of any sort (pl. 9b). *Voice:* Song of male a series of tinny notes, uttered rapidly and descending slightly in pitch toward end of series; call note a moderate *chit*.

Occurrence.—Summer visitant in small numbers locally in Upper Sonoran and Transition zones on both slopes of Sierra Nevada. Also passes along both slopes of mountains in migration. Winters in small numbers at Snelling.[34] Keeps to inner foliage of trees on shaded hillslopes, foraging 10 to 30 feet above ground but nesting on ground. Solitary.

---

[34] Two subspecies of the Orange-crowned Warbler occur in the Yosemite section. These are so much alike that they cannot be separately recognized in the field.

Lutescent Warbler, *Vermivora celata lutescens* (Ridgway), a brightly greenish-tinged subspecies (pl. 9b), nests in summer in the Upper Sonoran and Transition zones on west slope of Sierra Nevada, as near Coulterville, and ranges to higher levels after nesting season, as up to 10,500 feet altitude on Mount Clark (August 22, 1915) and to 10,350 feet near Vogelsang Lake (August 31, 1915).

Rocky Mountain Orange-crowned Warbler, *Vermivora celata orestera* Oberholser, a duller colored (less yellow tinged) subspecies, of slightly larger size, which summers in the Rocky Mountains and Great Basin, occurs also at that season sparingly around Mono Lake.

Birds of this species, but of undetermined subspecies, were seen at Snelling in midwinter; these may have represented a third subspecies, namely, the Eastern Orange-crowned Warbler.

Neither of the races of the Orange-crowned Warbler is abundant in the Yosemite section, the birds being greatly outnumbered by that closely related and more typically Sierran species, the Calaveras Warbler. We saw the Lutescent Warbler (the west-Sierran race) on a few occasions, and the other, the Rocky Mountain Orange-crown, came definitely to attention only around Mono Lake Post Office on May 24 and 26, 1916.

In Yosemite Valley we did not record the presence of Lutescent Warblers until June 8, 1915, when three fully grown juvenile birds were seen in a thicket of chokecherry bushes. They came to our attention as a result of their own curiosity concerning our close examination of the nest of a remonstrant Yellow Warbler; otherwise, these Lutescents might have escaped observation altogether. The fact that we did not see or hear adults of this species in the Valley previously suggests that these three were up-mountain migrants. Probably they had been reared at some station in the foothills where the parents were still engaged in the rearing of another brood. Later in the year other representatives of the Lutescent Warbler were encountered still higher in the mountains. At an altitude of 10,500 feet on the slopes of Mount Clark no less than six of these birds were noted on August 22, 1915; single individuals were recorded at Washburn Lake August 24, and near the foot of Vogelsang Pass on August 31 and September 2, 1915. In the western foothill country the Lutescent Warbler was encountered in spring at only two stations, near Coulterville, May 11, 1919, and at Bullion Mountain, May 26, 1915.

Mr. Joseph Mailliard (1918, p. 17) says that in 1917 "the Lutescent Warbler was first seen [by him in Yosemite Valley] September 18, after which its numbers increased slowly until the 26th, when a small wave of migration reached the valley, the eastern end of Sequoia Lane being especially popular as a feeding and resting place." It was estimated that 75 were noted on that one morning. Next day very few were to be seen. Four were noted on the 29th.

The males of these warblers (Orange-crowned and Lutescent) have on the head an orange-colored crown patch whence the common and scientific species names are derived. This crown patch, however, can rarely be seen when the bird is out of hand, and so is not serviceable as a field character. The bird's general greenish coloration, unrelieved by wing bars or tail spots, its tinny-toned song, and its rather deliberate movements for a warbler, must be depended upon for its identification out of doors.

CALIFORNIA YELLOW WARBLER. **Dendroica aestiva brewsteri** Grinnell

Field characters.—Half size of Junco. Yellow color predominating; no black or white markings whatsoever. Male: Clear yellow beneath (narrowly streaked with chestnut, but this not discernible at a distance); upper surface greenish yellow. (See pl. 9c.) Female and young: Pale yellow beneath, unstreaked; upper surface dull greenish yellow. Movements quick and nervous; hops along small branches in zigzag course. *Voice:* Song of male very high pitched, piercingly shrill, 4 or 5 sharply enunciated notes followed by quick series of shorter ones; call note a sharp *tsip*.

Occurrence.—Common summer visitant at both bases and on adjacent lower slopes of Sierra Nevada, extending up through the Transition Zone. Recorded from Snelling and near Lagrange eastward to Yosemite Valley; and again about Mono Lake. Chiefly in cottonwoods and willows along streams, foraging up to 40 feet from the ground; nests in same general surroundings, but usually less than 15 feet from ground. Solitary.

Long ago the appellation "summer yellow bird" was given to the Yellow Warbler in recognition of its clear yellow coloration and of the fact that it comes to our latitudes only during the warmer months of the year. The species is well represented in the Yosemite section from late spring until early fall, and is found from Snelling and Lagrange eastward to Yosemite Valley, and again, east of the mountains, near Mono Lake. Everywhere it exhibits a strong preference for deciduous trees near streams.

The California Yellow Warblers which are to nest on the west slope of the Sierra Nevada arrive there some time before those individuals destined to nest east of the mountains reach their particular haunts. Thus yellow warblers were already present in Yosemite Valley on April 28, 1916, while in the same year the species was not noted near Mono Lake until May 19. The fall departure takes place toward the end of August. The birds do not wander to the higher zones, as do the Lutescent Warblers, for example, but leave their nesting haunts rather early for the lowlands to the west, en route to their winter quarters to the south of the United States. Our own latest definite record for Yosemite Valley was made on August 19 (1915), but Mr. Joseph Mailliard (1918, p. 19) states that in 1917 the species was present until somewhat later, disappearing in early September. In 1920 the last seen by Mr. C. W. Michael (MS) in the Valley was noted on September 11.

Numerically the Yellow Warbler is an abundant bird within its restricted environment. Fully 20 were seen or heard during a 4-hour census taken in Yosemite Valley on May 31, 1915. These were practically all in the cottonwoods, alders, willows, and in other deciduous growths near the Merced River or its tributary streams. Similarly, along the lower reaches of the big rivers where these emerge from the foothills, these birds are plentiful in the month of May.

The song notes of the California Yellow Warbler are shriller than those of any of our other warblers, and, indeed, are exceeded in height of pitch by the notes of only a very few birds. This feature alone is often sufficient to identify the song. Syllabification can do little more than indicate the theme of the song, for the notes are well above those of the human voice. *Wee, wee, wee, sit, sit, sitsitsit, sieu,* is one of our renderings; and *chee, chee, chee, chee-e-e-e-e-er* another. The call note is a loud *chip* or *tsip.* Song is not heard often after the first part of July, but there may be a partial revival of singing in the latter part of August just before the birds depart for the season.

Yellow warblers like many other birds have definite forage beats which they traverse repeatedly through the day. This was well illustrated by observations on a bird of this species seen at Chinquapin in mid-May, 1919. A small black-oak sapling had grown up through the sea of chaparral near our camp and from time to time this tree would be occupied, momentarily, by a California Yellow Warbler. The bird always arrived from a certain direction (coming from another similar station) and upon departing went to still another definite tree situated about 50 yards distant.

Nesting with the California Yellow Warbler begins soon after the birds arrive in the region, our earliest record being for May 29 (1911); on this date, in Yosemite Valley, a female was flushed from a nest containing four eggs. Two nests seen on June 5, 1915, at Smith Creek, east of Coulterville, each contained young a few days old. Nest construction in each of these instances must have commenced in the middle or early part of May. June marks the height of the nesting season for the Yellow Warblers here; in this month the greatest number of nests comes to attention. An adult was seen feeding young recently emerged from the nest, on July 24 (1915) in Yosemite Valley. This instance marked about the close of the nesting season. The one nest found east of the mountains (near Williams Butte) was only under construction on June 23 (1916).

Yellow warblers nest abundantly on the floor of Yosemite Valley. Some of the nests are in growths close to water, whereas others are located in brush tangles or other rank growths back some distance from the streams. A nest found June 7, 1915, may be taken as fairly typical. It was 52 inches above the ground in the crotch of a forking stem of a chokecherry which grew in a clump of the same plant, and was shaded by a black oak. As usual it was higher than wide outside, being 3½ inches in height by 3 to 3¼ inches in diameter. The cup-like cavity was 1¾ inches across at the top and the same in depth at the center. Shreds of bark and flat plant fibers were the principal materials used in construction, the lining being of horsehair and a few feathers.

When found, this nest contained three eggs; the following day a fourth was laid. During our first approach to the nest on the 7th, both male and female were about and voiced their alarm. Returning to the nest later that day we noticed only the female. She departed at once, dropping close to the ground and then speeding off through the underbrush. A nest of this species probably used in the previous year was seen 8 feet away in another cherry bush and 36 inches above the earth. Still another occupied nest was seen 7 feet above the ground in a small incense cedar, close to a well traveled road.

One of the nests found at Smith Creek on June 5, 1915, was 4 feet above ground in a chokecherry bush and near the stream. It was 2½ inches in diameter and 4 inches in outside height, and was made of plant fibers and feathers. There were 3 young, about 2 or 3 days old, and one unhatched (evidently infertile) egg. The other nest was 4 feet above the ground in a mountain lilac (*Ceanothus integerrimus*). It also contained young, 4 in this instance, and not over 3 days from the shell. The parents of this brood were *tsip*-ing excitedly about 30 to 50 feet from the nest.

None of the nests just mentioned was watched until the young emerged; but observations on still another nest, in Yosemite Valley, help to complete the story. This nest was found by Miss Margaret W. Wythe (MS), who watched it at intervals from June 13 to 27, 1915. It was placed about 15 feet above the ground in a small pine tree growing at the margin of a pond. It rested on the next to the topmost whorl of branches and one side was against the slender trunk of the tree. On June 23, the male was seen with his bill full of 'green worms.' The young left the nest on or before June 27; on that day they were perched in adjacent shrubbery while being fed at frequent intervals by the parents. No more than three young birds were seen at any one time.

But little is to be seen of the yellow warblers after the young are grown. They then take to foraging, individually and unobtrusively. Soon the molt with its quieting influence comes on, after which the birds slip off southward for the winter.

ALASKA MYRTLE WARBLER. **Dendroica coronata hooveri** McGregor

Field characters.—Essentially as for Audubon Warbler (which see), but chin always white and tail with spots of white on but three outer feathers on each side (fig. 57*a*). *Voice:* Song similar to that of Audubon Warbler; call note similar, though of slightly different quality.

Occurrence—Sparse winter visitant. Recorded at Smith Creek, 6 miles east of Coulterville, February 12, 1916, and February 6, April 26, and December 23, 1919. Forages in foliage of trees and bushes. Usually in scattering companies with Audubon Warblers.

The Alaska Myrtle Warbler is occasionally to be detected in flocks of the more common Audubon Warbler. In voice, habits, and general appearance it resembles closely the latter species. Discriminating observers will be able to note the lesser amount of white on the tail and the regularly white chin. This warbler has thus far been recorded from a single locality in the Yosemite region, at Dudley on Smith Creek, six miles east of Coulterville. The records listed above were all made at this station by Mr. Donald D. McLean. Continued observations at other localities on the west slope of the mountains would probably show the species to be of regular occurrence, though in limited numbers, during the winter months, perhaps in a ratio of not more than one Myrtle Warbler to a hundred or so of Audubon Warblers.

AUDUBON WARBLER. Dendroica auduboni auduboni (Townsend)

Field characters.—Size two-thirds that of Junco. Rump always yellow (except in young newly out of nest), and tail large-appearing and always with a wide bar of white across it near end (fig. 57b). Chin usually distinctly yellow. Adult male in summer: Top of head, chin, rump, and patch on each side of breast yellow; breast black; upper surface bluish gray streaked with black. (See pl. 9e.) Adult female in summer: Top of head, chin, and rump yellow; breast mottled with gray and black; upper surface bluish gray. Adults and immatures in winter: More or less brownish both above and below; little or no black on breast; chin usually (but not always) distinctly yellow, though rump always so. All movements quick and nervous; often flies out from foliage of tree in semicircular course. *Voice:* Song of male a series of mellow notes, run together rapidly, not loud, and of tinkling quality; call note of both sexes a sharp *tsip*.

Occurrence.—In summer common visitant to Transition, Canadian, and Hudsonian zones on both slopes of Sierra Nevada (most plentiful in Canadian); recorded from 3 miles east of Coulterville eastward clear across the mountains to Mono Lake Post Office. Remains in Transition through October. Keeps chiefly to coniferous trees, foraging 10 to 50 feet or higher above ground, and nests in same situations. In pairs or solitary. In winter common visitant to Lower and Upper Sonoran zones on west side of mountains, as at Snelling, Lagrange, Pleasant Valley, and El Portal. At this season, forages extensively in outer parts of broad-leafed trees. Solitary, or in scattering companies, often with birds of other species.

The Audubon Warbler is the most widely distributed and the most abundant of all the species of wood warblers found in the Yosemite region. It occurs in numbers throughout the main forested districts of the mountains during the summer season, and it frequents the deciduous trees and brush of the foothill and valley country in the winter time.

Altitudinally its summer range extends from the beginning of the Transition Zone yellow pines on the west slope, at 3300 to 3500 feet, up through the lodgepole pines and other conifers of the Canadian and Hudsonian zones to the upper limit of unstunted trees at 10,000 feet or a little higher. It distribution is uninterrupted from near El Portal and the ridge of hills above Coulterville eastwardly across the mountains, through the Tioga and Mono passes, to Williams Butte and Mono Lake.

During the winter months the birds are entirely gone from the high country. In this season the species occupies most of the hill and valley country lying below the level of regular snowfall. The district from El Portal westward to Snelling and Lagrange is tenanted by numerous Audubon Warblers from October until early April. In Mono Valley east of the mountains there are, in all probability, no Audubon Warblers whatever present during the long season of snow and storm there.

The migratory movements of the Audubon Warbler are but imperfectly known. Birds of this species begin to appear in the lower altitudes in late September or early October, but at this time many are still in the mountains where they continue until late in October. Through September there are droves of Audubons in the trees and brush on the east slope of the Sierras. Doubtless these are mostly birds from stations to the north en route to their wintering grounds in southern California and beyond. The return movement of the species is accomplished in April, and by early May the western foothills are practically cleared of the species. It yet remains to be learned whether the birds which leave the Sierras in the fall go directly westward into the foothills, to remain there for the winter, or whether they move southward and individuals from northern localities migrate into the foothill territory.

As to numbers, in the summer time our censuses show one to two singing birds during an hour of ordinary walking through favorable territory. About 10 were noted in 4 hours on the floor of Yosemite Valley May 31, 1915. Eleven were noted in 5 hours in the vicinity of Porcupine Flat on June 27, 1915. And 3 were recorded in 3½ hours at the head of Lyell Cañon on July 16, 1915. After the young are out, better scores are to be made; 13 were noted in 3½ hours along the Tenaya Trail from Tenaya Lake down to Mirror Lake, July 30, 1915. Fully 50 were seen in 6 hours between Vogelsang Lake and Mono Pass on September 7, 1915. At Gem Lake, on September 13, 35 were noted in 2 hours of intensive hunting, this warbler being then the most plentiful bird there. In 1920 Audubon Warblers were abundant in Yosemite Valley during the first three weeks of October; then a sudden decrease in numbers was noted, and the species disappeared on October 28, save for a solitary individual noted on November 3 (C. W. Michael, MS).

More differences in plumage are shown by the Audubon Warbler according to sex, age, or season, than by any other common bird of the Yosemite avifauna. Upon hatching, the young are sparsely clothed with a grayish white natal down. While still in the nest the juvenal plumage is acquired. In this the body feathers are sharply streaked, while the flight feathers are closely similar in color and markings to those of the adult. In these first two plumages the sexes look alike, but upon the replacement of the body feathering, which takes place in August and results in the 'first winter' plumage, the males and females present differences. The males gain considerable clear yellow on the chin, while in the females the chin is only indistinctly yellow. Both males and females then acquire the yellow rump. Thus the young birds, within about three months, have three distinct plumages. The last of these is retained until the following spring (April) and then another molt of the body feathers brings the bluish gray back and bright yellow patches on sides and crown, of the 'first nuptial' plumage. Not until August or September, however, when the birds are about fifteen months old, is there renewal of the flight feathers of the wing and tail, which were acquired with the juvenal plumage. Such long service usually results in these feathers becoming badly worn, and bleached to a pale brown.

In this same molt, the second or adult fall molt, both sexes show more or brighter yellow on the chin, crown, and sides, and in the males the breast and sides are rather heavily mottled with black. These features make possible the distinguishment of birds fifteen months or more old from those only three months of age. It is thus possible to recognize eight different feather assemblages or 'plumages' in this warbler.

The above brief outline of the molt program of the Audubon Warbler will serve to explain why so much variation is apparent among individuals seen in the field at different seasons and even at the same time.

The Audubon Warbler is considerably larger than any of the other common warblers of the Yosemite region. One species, the Alaska Myrtle Warbler, a sparse winter visitant here, is similar in size and general appearance to the Audubon. (See pl. 9e.) It has a yellow rump and white-spotted tail, but its chin is always clear white. In the Audubon Warbler ten of the twelve tail feathers (all but the innermost two) are marked with large white patches near the ends, whereas in the Myrtle Warbler only the three outer feathers on each side are so marked and the spots are smaller. (See fig. 57.) The mass effect of the white on the spread tails in the two species is thus quite different. The Audubon and Myrtle warblers are the only warblers with white-spotted tails, yellow rumps, and dark backs to be found in the region.

A feature common to both of these warblers in comparison with the other warblers of the region, is the relatively great length and breadth of the tail feathers. This may be a special adaptation for the twofold purpose of aiding in the short circuitous flights and in the displaying more conspicuously of the white markings, possibly directive in their function.

Through most of the year the only note heard from the Audubon Warbler is a sharp *tsip* or *chit*, but this is given frequently both when the birds are engaged in foraging and when they are in flight. This note is distinctive enough in character to serve as a means of recognition once it has been learned by the observer. In March or April, before the birds depart from the lowlands, the males begin to sing, and after the birds arrive on their nesting grounds the full songs are to be heard regularly and frequently through May and June and, especially at the higher altitudes, even well into July.

The song resembles most nearly that of the Hermit Warbler, but is more mellow and tinkling, and lacks the burred or 'z' tones of the latter's utterance. One phrasing of the Audubon's songs goes *si-wi, si-wi, si-wi, sissle, sissle, see-see;* another *tŭrly, ŭrly, ŭrly, ŭrly, ŭrly, ĭ-cĭ.* These are given much as if the syllables were spoken rapidly and in a whispering voice.

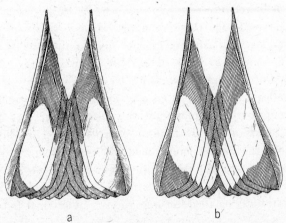

a   b

Fig. 57. Tails of (*a*) Alaska Myrtle Warbler and (*b*) Audubon Warbler; natural size. Note that in the former the white (clear) areas are present on only six feathers, whereas in the latter species ten feathers bear white. This character, under favorable conditions, may be used in field identification.

During the summer season the Audubon Warbler keeps mainly to coniferous trees, foraging from 10 to 50 feet or more above the ground. In the Transition Zone and part of the Canadian Zone it shares this habitat with the Hermit Warbler, but at higher altitudes it is the only warbler present in the evergreen forests. In this same niche its nesting is carried on. After the breeding season this restriction is broken and the Audubons range widely here and there, wherever food offers. In the dry days of autumn when the wind is shaking down the dead leaves of the deciduous trees the birds spend their time about such trees seeking the flying and other insects then available. When they move into the foot-hills and valleys for the winter they take to a variety of situations, hunting often in the live oaks, again in shrubbery or in low chaparral, and not infrequently alighting on the grass or ground in pursuit of some terrestrial insect. Few other insectivorous birds show such seasonal diversity in forage grounds.

This warbler forages most especially about the peripheral foliage of the trees. In seeking the sedentary insects lodged on the leaves and in their axils a bird is accustomed to change its post of view by flying *out beyond* the leafage in a semicircular course toward a new location. This is quite the opposite of the habit of the Lutescent Warbler, for example, which works about *within* the terminal or crown foliage. The special mode of leaf examination, just alluded to, on the part of the Audubon may be accounted for by the greater proneness of this warbler to indulge in fly-catching. The flight out into the open air puts the bird in position to see and seize with least additional expenditure of energy, passing insects, or insects disturbed from the foliage. This fly-catching habit is often practiced toward evening by several of the birds in near proximity to one another. Then insects are active in numbers about the warm sunlit upper portions of the trees. On these short sorties the bird's wing-beats appear rather weak, and a vacillating manner of flight results. The tail is widely spread, and the patches of white in transverse row near the end show forth plainly. In a word, the Audubon Warbler is the most open-acting, above-board, and the least reclusive, of all our wood warblers.

We were not fortunate in finding any nests of the Audubon Warbler in the Yosemite country. But nests elsewhere are known to be placed many feet above the ground on branches well out from the main stem of the tree and so located that they cannot be readily made out from below. Save when the site is disclosed by a female going to the place, carrying material for the nest or food for the young, much time and energy will be expended vainly in hunting for the structure. On May 17, 1919, in Yosemite Valley, a female Audubon Warbler was seen in the top of a small yellow pine gathering dry needles. She moved off toward a group of large trees of the same kind and was soon lost to view. A similar fleeting glimpse was obtained of another bird in Little Yosemite Valley the following day. Bob-tailed young already out of the nest were seen in Yosemite Valley on June 23, 1920. A juvenal bird barely able to fly, and so probably just out of the nest, was seen by one of us at Tuolumne Meadows on July 26, 1915. These dates indicate approximately the extent of the nesting season.

In the fall, and to a less extent during the winter months, Audubon Warblers are given to traveling in small open flocks, either along with their own kind or mixed with bluebirds. Such an aggregation was seen in some black oaks near Camp Curry on October 7, 1914, there being in it about a dozen Audubons in all. The 'location note,' *tsip*, so frequently uttered by each individual in one of these scattering groups, seems to serve well in helping to hold the flock together in its general onward movement. Over El Capitan Meadows eight were seen on October 24, 1915, with an equal number of Western Bluebirds. The Audubon Warbler is thus more sociably inclined than any other member of its family found regularly in the Yosemite section.

In the fall the Audubons range widely, some keeping to the middle altitudes, others dropping to the lowlands or moving south, while a few may range even above timber line. On September 6, 1915, while one of us was traversing the south slope of Parsons Peak at an altitude of 11,500 feet, a lone Audubon Warbler flew past. Others had been seen in the dwarfed pines near Vogelsang Lake at 10,350 feet altitude a few days earlier. Of all our warblers the Audubon is the hardiest as regards ability to stand the cold and storms of the winter season at the lower levels and the variable weather of the summer season at the upper altitudes.

BLACK-THROATED GRAY WARBLER. **Dendroica nigrescens** (Townsend)

Field characters.—Half bulk of Junco. Head, chin, and throat black (mixed with white in female and young), with a white line backward over eye and another from bill down side of throat; sides of body streaked with black; rest of under surface white; upper surface bluish gray; two light bars on wing; tail white margined. No conspicuous yellow in plumage. (See pl. 9*f*.) Movements rather deliberate for a warbler. *Voice:* Song of male a slow drawling *wēē'-zy, wēē'-zy, wēē'zy, wĕr;* call note a low *chit.*

Occurrence.—Moderately common summer visitant locally in Transition Zone on west slope of Sierra Nevada. Recorded from 3 miles east of Coulterville eastward to Yosemite Valley. Seen in fall migration near Mono Lake. In nesting time practically restricted to golden oaks. Solitary or in scattering parties.

The Black-throated Gray Warbler is a bird of the golden oaks and is to be found in fair numbers in the heavy growths of these trees which clothe the talus slopes along the north and south walls of Yosemite Valley. Elsewhere in the Yosemite section the species was found only in stands of this same oak or in nearby situations. This warbler is therefore notable for being one of the very few birds which, in the Yosemite section, is entirely restricted to the Transition Zone. The Yosemite Falls Trail below Yosemite Point, the Glacier Point short trail below Union Point, the Big Oak Flat road below Gentrys, and the Little Yosemite trail below Nevada Falls are good places from which to study this warbler, for all these trails pass through golden oaks.

This bird is preëminently a black and white warbler. (See pl. 9*f*.) At a distance no yellow shows (though a small spot of this color is present in front of the eye). In this feature the bird departs from the color scheme of its local relatives, all of which show, even at a distance, more or less yellow. In the adult male of the present species the head, chin, and throat are chiefly black. The female has less black, her chin often being mixed black and white; this is true also of the young. Adults and immatures of both sexes share in common the white stripe above and behind the eye, the white line from bill down side of throat, the two light wing bars, the white margined tail and, best of all, the *black streaking on the sides* of the otherwise pure white under surface. The back is bluish gray in all.

A striking similarity in markings exists between the Townsend and the Black-throated Gray warblers. One is an exact replica of the other save that the yellow of the former is replaced by white in the latter. This parallelism extends to all ages and both sexes. The Townsend Warbler is only a transient here.

The Black-throated Gray Warbler arrives in the Yosemite region by April; it was already present in Yosemite Valley on April 29, 1916. It continues here until early fall, several being seen in company with some Audubon Warblers, along the Glacier Point trail, on September 25, 1915. The latest seasonal occurrence known is of a single bird recorded near Feliciana Mountain southwest of El Portal, on October 30, 1915. East of the mountains near Williams Butte two of these warblers, doubtless migrants, were seen in a mountain mahogany bush on September 16, 1915.

The population of this bird seems to fluctuate markedly from year to year. During a 50-minute walk up the Yosemite Falls trail to Columbia Point on June 4, 1915, 14 of these birds were recorded. A similar climb, through the somewhat lighter growth on the Sierra Point trail, May 16, 1919, revealed only one singing male, and elsewhere in the Valley, in the latter year, the numbers of this species were unusually small.

The Black-throated Gray Warbler is not a particularly active species and its slow movements combined with a 'disruptive' pattern of coloration sometimes render it difficult to see against the sunlit foliage of the oaks. The bird inhabits largely the crown and middle foliage and so does not often come into plain view. The song of the Black-throated Gray Warbler is a rather lazy, drawling utterance, deep-toned rather than shrill. *Wēē-zy, wēē-zy, wēē-zy, wēē-zy-weet; tsewey, tsewey, tsewey, tsewey-tsew; zuēē, zuēē, zuēē, soop; sĭ-sĭ-wēēzy, wēēzy we-tsu'; owēzē-wēzē-wēzē-wēzē-chŭr*, are syllabifications written by us at different times when individual birds were singing close at hand. There are modifications in the song; sometimes the terminal syllable is omitted and again only three of the two-syllabled notes are given. The ordinary call is a rather low, one-syllabled *chit*.

Near Smith Creek, east of Coulterville, a nest of the Black-throated Gray Warbler was seen on June 5, 1915. It was placed 5 feet 6 inches above ground in a mountain lilac (*Ceanothus integerrimus*) bush against a main stem. Outside, the nest measured 2¼ inches both in diameter and height. There were 4 young birds only 2 or 3 days old. Upon our approach the female flushed and made off, with the broken-wing ruse common to so many species. Then she perched on a nearby limb and fluttered her wings, *chit*-ing every second or so in remonstrance at our intrusion.

The same day, in the forest on the hill above and immediately east of Coulterville, one of our party interrupted an attack by a California Striped Racer upon a brood of Black-throated Gray Warblers. The female parent was much excited, flying from twig to twig, calling, and fluttering her wings. Near by, on the ground, was one of the young warblers. There was good evidence that the snake had already swallowed another member of the brood.

The records of two broods given in the preceding paragraphs indicate that the beginning of nesting was, in one case at least, close to the first of May. A pair of these birds intent upon nesting duties was seen in the oaks near Yosemite Falls on May 23, 1919; their nest, however, was not seen. A family group, with the young birds out of the nest and uttering food calls, was observed in the Valley on July 27, 1915. Nesting is probably mostly over by mid-July, as the song season ends about the first of that month.

TOWNSEND WARBLER. **Dendroica townsendi** (Townsend)

Field characters.—Half bulk of Junco. Head, chin, and throat black (mixed with yellow in females and young), with a line of yellow over eye and another from bill down side of throat; sides of body streaked with black; fore half of belly yellow, the rest white; upper surface black and dull yellow; two white bars on wing; tail white margined. *Voice:* Song not heard; call note a sharp *tsip*.

Occurrence.—Transient along west slope and east base of Sierra Nevada. Observed by us west of Pleasant Valley, May 24, 1915, near Coulterville, May 10, 1919, and at Mono Lake Post Office, May 24 and 31, 1916. Likely to be seen in oak trees or chaparral. To some degree gregarious.

An observer stationed in the western foothills at the appropriate season would probably see much more of the Townsend Warbler than we did. We encountered it upon only two occasions, as a spring transient; but numbers of the birds undoubtedly pass through the foothills in both spring and fall. On one occasion a scattering band of at least a dozen warblers was seen moving northward, some Townsends being distinguished among them. The others could not be recognized because the glimpses obtained of them as they passed through the wind-rocked foliage of some oaks were too fleeting.

HERMIT WARBLER. Dendroica occidentalis (Townsend)

Field characters.—Half size of Junco. Cheeks always yellow; under parts whitish, unstreaked; back bluish or greenish gray; two light bars on each wing; tail white margined. Adult male: Whole head clear yellow except for black throat. (See pl. 9d.) Female and immatures: Head dull yellow, crown mottled with blackish; little or no black on throat. *Voice:* Song of male three or four two-syllabled notes followed by two shorter ones, often with drawling intonation, *zeekle, zeekle, zeekle, zeek, sup-sup;* again, more clearly, *ter'-ley, ter'-ley, ter'-ley, sic' sic';* call note a moderate *tchip.*

Occurrence.—Summer visitant in varying numbers to Transition and Canadian zones on west slope of Sierra Nevada. Recorded from Smith Creek (six miles east of Coulterville), Hazel Green, and near Chinquapin eastward to Merced Lake; common in Yosemite Valley. Transient in spring through western foothills (Lagrange and Coulterville). Forages chiefly in coniferous trees 20 feet or more above ground, and nests in same locations. Solitary.

The name Hermit, applied to a warbler, might lead the novice to expect a bird of dull coloration and retiring habits. The first of these expectations will be dispelled by one glance at the bright yellow head, black throat, white under surface and dark back of the Hermit Warbler, while further acquaintance shows the bird to be a recluse only in the hiding of its nest.

The markings just alluded to will be sufficient to identify this warbler with certainty. (See pl. 9d.) In the adult male the head is clear yellow, with a black throat patch; even female and young birds always show more or less yellow on the cheeks which stands out in contrast to the otherwise dark upper surface. The back, wings, and tail in the Hermit Warbler are dark like the same areas in the Black-throated Gray and Townsend warblers, and there are conspicuous white margins to the tail.

Hermit Warblers arrive in the Yosemite region before the end of April; singing males were already present in Yosemite Valley on April 28, 1916. Two individuals, in migration, were noted near Lagrange on May 7, 1919, and one near Coulterville, May 10, the same year. The species continues in the mountains until the latter part of August, two pairs being seen near Glacier Point on August 17, 1915, and one individual at 9000 feet altitude, a little east of Merced Lake, on August 26, 1915. None was noted east of the mountains at any time.

The population of this species varies somewhat from year to year; ordinarily the birds are not very common. We saw but limited numbers in 1915 and 1916. Yet in 1919, in Yosemite Valley and its immediate environs, the species was more abundant than either the Audubon or the Calaveras Warbler. In Yosemite Valley a 4-hour census on May 31, 1915, revealed about 6 singing males. The same number was recorded in a 5-hour census at Chinquapin, June 10, 1915, all the birds being below an altitude of 7000 feet. The population in 1919 at both these points was obviously larger.

The Hermit Warbler is a bird of the coniferous forests at middle altitudes. Pines and firs afford it suitable forage range and safe nesting sites. The birds keep fairly well up in the trees, most often at 20 to 50 feet from the ground. The Hermit may thus be found in close association with the Audubon Warbler, although the latter ranges to a much greater altitude in the mountains.

The song of the male Hermit Warbler, while varying somewhat with different individuals, is sufficiently distinct from that of the other warblers of the region to make possible identification by voice alone. This song is most nearly like that of the Audubon Warbler but usually not so clear or mellow. A male bird observed at Chinquapin seemed to say *seezle, seezle, seezle, seezle, zeek, zeek;* just that number of syllables, over and over again. The quality was slightly droning, but not so much so as that of the Black-throated Gray Warbler. Another song, clearer in quality, heard in Yosemite Valley, was written *ter'-ley, ter'-ley, ter'-ley, sic', sic',* thus much more nearly like the song of the Audubon Warbler. Other transcriptions ranged between these two as to timbre. A rendering set down at Glacier Point June 16, 1915, was as follows: *ser-weez', ser-weez', ser-weez', ser', ser'.* The marked rhythm throughout, and the stressed terminal syllables, are distinctive features of the Hermit's song. The call note is a moderate *tchip,* used by both sexes.

A Hermit Warbler watched in Yosemite Valley on June 22, 1915, by Miss Margaret W. Wythe (MS) was foraging in the upper parts of the trees and never came to the lower branches. Starting from near the trunk of a pine it would work out to the tip of one branch before going to another. Its demeanor while foraging was much more deliberate than that of any of the other warblers.

The only nest of the Hermit Warbler which came to our notice was discovered by Miss Wythe (MS) on June 28, 1915, in Yosemite Valley. She was following up some rather insistent chirping notes which came from a pine tree beside a road, when a young bird of this species, already fledged enough to be out of the nest, was seen. The yellow on its head was clearly in evidence, but the black chin spot was only beginning to show. The tail was only half an inch in length. The young bird, when first seen, had an insect in its bill, which it soon swallowed. Other similar notes were heard close by and soon the two parents were seen, one of which flew to the tree and evidently fed another member of the brood. Most of the time the birds remained in the outer portions of the trees, where the thick needle tufts screened them from view. Later the nest was located, 15 or 18 feet above the ground in what then proved to be plain view for an observer stationed below. The materials of which it was composed appeared gray in comparison with the green foliage of the pine.

TOLMIE WARBLER. **Oporornis tolmiei** (Townsend)

Field characters.—About two-thirds bulk of Junco. Head, neck, and breast gray, darkest in adult males; eyelids white; belly and under parts yellow; upper surface, wings, and tail, plain dull green. (See pl. 9*h*.) *Voice:* Song of male three to five clear separated notes followed by one or several shorter ones close together and sometimes trilled: *syr-pit', syr-pit', syr-pit', syr-sip sip sip sip;* call note of both sexes a rather loud *tchip.*

Occurrence.—Common summer visitant to Transition and lower Canadian zones on west slope of Sierra Nevada. Recorded from Smith Creek (six miles east of Coulter-ville), Yosemite Valley, and Chinquapin eastward to Washburn Lake. Also common migrant along west side of mountains, as at Snelling and Pleasant Valley, and along east base, at Walker Lake and Mono Lake Post Office. Keeps to low shrubbery, usually over damp ground, foraging 4 feet or less from ground; nests in same sort of surroundings. Solitary, or in pairs.

The Tolmie Warbler, often called Macgillivray Warbler, is a denizen of brush at middle altitudes, living close to the ground in thickets of cherry, thimble-berry, ceanothus, brakes, and other similar plants. It does not commonly inhabit the dry chaparral. On the other hand, it is not so closely dependent upon proximity to streams as is the Pileolated Warbler, although it is at times found amid the same surroundings as the latter. The Tolmie is one of the largest of our warblers and its markings render identification by sight easy; yet it is so given to keeping within the dense shrubbery that it is likely to be more often heard than seen.

The male has the whole head, throat, and breast continuously dark gray, forming a cowl similar to, but not so dark as, that on the Sierra Junco. The body otherwise is clear yellow beneath (with dark flanks) and dull green above. (See pl. 9*h*.) The female and young are colored similarly save that the gray on throat and breast is paler, sometimes gray-ish white. No other of our warblers is similarly marked. The Calaveras Warbler which has gray on the head, has the throat and breast yellow like the rest of the under surface.

The Tolmie Warbler arrives on the west slope of the mountains in May. It was already present at Hazel Green on May 14, 1919, and in Yosemite Valley on May 16, the same year. Some, however, migrate northward still later in the month, for the species was recorded, in 1915, at Pleasant Valley on May 23 and 30, and at Snelling on May 28. East of the mountains, where the Tolmie is thought to be solely transient in mode of occur-rence, none was seen in 1916 until May 21, but immediately thereafter they came with a rush and were of almost daily record until May 31. After the nesting season the species is much less in evidence. Our last records in 1915 on the west slope are for August 28, when individuals were seen near Merced Lake and others at Washburn Lake, and for September 10 and 13, when single birds in migration were noted at Walker Lake. In

1920 Mr. C. W. Michael (MS) observed the species in Yosemite Valley on September 28.

The Tolmie Warbler population is not distributed so uniformly as that of certain other species, so it is more difficult to form a general estimate of the numbers. In the snowbush and huckleberry oak on the high plateau above the Valley between Indian Cañon and North Dome, 6 or 7 were noted in a 3½-hour census, on June 24, 1915. Four or five singing males were recorded along the short trail between Camp Curry and Happy Isles on May 17, 1919. These counts were made in favorable territory; elsewhere the species is much less frequently encountered.

Most of the activities of the Tolmie Warbler are carried on within the cover of the brush. Yet in the late spring and early summer months the males not infrequently fly up into adjoining trees and sing from perches well above the ground. At Hazel Green, on May 14, 1919, a bird was observed fully 50 feet above the ground on one of the lower branches of a large incense cedar. The tree stood directly over a seepage slope covered with creek dogwood, which had evidently been chosen as headquarters for the summer. This bird sang ten times in two minutes, changing position usually after singing twice on one perch. The song was rendered by the observer *sizik, sizik, sizik, lipik, lipik,* little change being detected in successive songs. In the first three 'words' the 'z' sounds were strong, whereas the last two were more liquid. In singing, the bird would throw its head back, and put much bodily effort into the process of utterance. Soon the bird dropped close to the ground and sang from within the shrubbery, changing his position frequently. The sharp *tsip* of the female was heard at this time. After a few songs the male flew up to a perch 30 feet above the ground, sang twice, and then went below again, this time into a tangle of small young incense cedars.

Other individuals studied and timed while they sang gave their songs at intervals of 10 to 14 seconds. Song production is not continuous, however, for at times a bird will be silent for a minute or more. Some males seem to keep entirely within the shelter of the brush, where they alternately sing and forage.

The 'z' sounds heard from the bird at Hazel Green are entirely lacking in other songs studied. Two of these clearer utterances we wrote as follows: *syr-pit', syr-pit', syr-pit', syr-sip-sip-sip-sip* (J. G.), and another *cheek-a, cheek-a, cheek-a, cheek-a, chee-e-e-e* (T. I. S.). The first syllables are loud, clear, and set off from one another, while the shorter ones (*sip*) are given rapidly, faster than a person can pronounce them, and sometimes are run almost into a trill.

Our earliest record of nesting for the Tolmie Warbler is for May 22 (1919) when a completed but empty nest was seen in a thicket of chokecherries along Redwood Lane in Yosemite Valley. The rim of this was

12 inches above the ground. During the season of 1915, 3 nests of this species, all located on the floor of Yosemite Valley, came under more or less continued observation.

The first of these was found June 10 (Mrs. Joseph Grinnell, MS). It was 12 inches above the ground in a thimbleberry bush in a thicket near a stream. The structure was made of pine needles and grass blades and stems, and was lined with fine round grasses and black horsehair. On this date there was in it a single egg, about the size of that of a Western Chipping Sparrow, creamy white with brown splotches around the larger end. Two days later the nest held three eggs, showing that one had been deposited each day. The set was increased to four, presumably, on the day following, although the place was not visited again until June 17. On none of these visits was either of the parents seen. Identification of the nest was only made at a later date when one of the adults was surprised there. When seen on June 24 (pl. 51b) the eggs seemed nearly ready to hatch and this surmise was confirmed the following day, June 25, when four naked pinkish yellow nestlings were found entirely out of their shells. Assuming that the fourth egg was laid on June 13, and that the parent bird began incubation immediately thereafter, the period of incubation in this case was 13 days. On June 26 the young birds showed dark gray down which looked purple when the sunlight touched it. On June 28 the young in this nest had disappeared and since, when last seen, they were entirely too small to leave voluntarily, some prowling enemy must be held to account for their early disappearance.

Another nest, found on June 13, 1915, has been described by Miss Margaret W. Wythe (1916, pp. 123–127). It was discovered soon after the eggs were laid and was watched until the young had left. The nest rim was 9 inches above the ground, the outside diameter and height each 3½ inches, the cavity 2½ inches across and 1½ inches deep. It was placed between four stems of chokecherry, and in construction was similar to the one previously described.

The female alone brooded, sitting very close some days, but being absent continuously for fully twenty minutes on the 18th. Two eggs hatched on June 23 and another by the following morning. The fourth proved infertile. The two young that hatched on the 23d grew appreciably in one day, and on the 24th were about 2 inches in length and the same in stretch of wings. The down was conspicuous on these two on the second day. The female brooded at intervals. An hour's observation at close range on June 27 disclosed the fact that the female came to the nest every 3 to 5 minutes, while the male visited the place but once during the period specified. The three young were now about of equal size and juvenal feathers had appeared on the head, back, and wings. The eyes of one bird were open on this date and those of another the day following.

On June 29 the three young were found asleep, all facing in the same direction. On the observer touching a branch no response was elicited, but her imitation of the adult Tolmie's *tsip* woke two of the young which thereupon threw open their mouths in expectation of food. The tail feathers were beginning to grow out on this date. On the seventh day, June 30, the behavior of the female warbler changed. Previously she had, when disturbed, hopped about within the shelter of the brush. On this date she dropped to the ground within 3 feet of the observer, slowly raised and lowered her wings, and called continually in an anxious manner. She showed increasing wariness in visiting the nest to feed the young, and the latter began to show signs of fear, and 'froze' when the nest was approached by anyone, or the overhanging branches touched. On this date the young first uttered hissing notes at the approach of the parent. July 1 most of the down had disappeared and on July 2 the feathering of the wings was nearing completion. On this, the tenth day after hatching, the young left the nest (Wythe, *loc. cit.*).

Still another nest was noted by us, on June 24, 1915, in a thicket of thimble-berry and coffee-berry bushes and brakes near the old Presidio. It was, at the rim, 28 inches above the ground and supported partly by a coffee-berry stem and partly by several shoots of thimble-berry, the whole area being shaded by a grove of yellow pines. The nest outside was about 4½ inches in diameter and 3 inches high, while the cavity was 2 inches across and 1½ inches deep. The materials used consisted of numerous broad strips of bark, round grass stems bent at sharp angles, a sub-lining of shredded grass stems, and an inner layer of horsehair. When first seen, on June 24, it was empty; by June 26 there were 2 eggs, on June 27, 3, and on June 28, 4; upon the last date the female was first found to be incubating closely. When the nest and eggs were collected, for purposes of record, on July 3, it was found, however, that the 4 eggs were in various stages of incubation, indicating the probability that brooding had actually commenced before the last egg was laid. When this nest was visited, on July 3, the female was on, but she slipped off shyly, and made off along the ground through the vegetation. After a time she was heard at a 50-foot radius uttering occasional *chips*. The male was singing 100 yards away, but later he too showed some anxiety and uttered notes similar to those of his mate.

On June 24, 1920, in Yosemite Valley, a bob-tailed young Tolmie Warbler was seen 10 feet above the ground in a cottonwood where it was being fed by the male parent.

Summarizing the findings with respect to these four nests, we note that building by some pairs is instituted in mid-May, although others (possibly because of accident to earlier nests) are to be found building at the end of June. Eggs are laid on successive days, incubation begins immediately upon the laying of the last egg or possibly before, and is completed in 13 days, the young hatch on the same day, or on two successive days, and leave the nest 8 or 9 days after hatching. The male seems to participate but little in caring for the brood.

YELLOWTHROATS. **Geothlypis trichas** (Linnaeus)[35]

Field characters.—About half size of Junco. Adult male: Forehead and face crossed by a broad band or mask of black, bounded above by white; throat and most of under surface clear yellow; upper surface of body yellowish brown. (See pl. 9i.) Female and young: Yellowish brown above, yellowish white beneath. An active yet reclusive species. *Voice:* Song of male a set theme given three or four times in slow rhythm with rather insistent delivery, *wretch'-et-y, wretch'-et-y, wretch'-et-y;* call note a sharp yet hoarse-sounding *tchack.*

Occurrence.—Common resident at Snelling and below Lagrange (subspecies *scirpicola*). Transient along both flanks of Sierra Nevada and summer visitant at Mono Lake (subspecies *occidentalis*).[35] Lives low in tule marshes and shrubbery bordering streams. Solitary or in pairs.

The Yellowthroats are birds of marshy places and so are found in numbers at both ends of the Yosemite section, but they are of only casual occurrence elsewhere in the region. Individuals pass through the western foothill country during the migrations. A male bird was noted by us May 29, 1911, in Yosemite Valley near Stoneman Bridge; and two birds were noted in Yosemite Valley on the morning of September 29, 1917 (Mailliard, 1918, p. 16). The lack of suitable cover in the form of dense thickets of willow or of tules probably accounts for the failure of the birds to remain there throughout the summer.

The Yellowthroats found at Snelling and Lagrange (subspecies *scirpicola*) are the only really resident members of the whole warbler family in the Yosemite section. Suitable forage and cover are evidently sufficient there at all seasons; they remain in full numbers throughout the colder portion of the year. At Snelling 10 were noted in tangles of blackberry, nettles and willows during a 2½-hour census on January 6, 1915. Eight were recorded in similar cover at that place during a 3-hour trip on May 26; and on May 29 the same year not less than 18 of the birds were noted during an hour and a half in particularly favorable country.

---

[35] Two closely similar subspecies of Yellowthroat occur in the Yosemite section.

WESTERN YELLOWTHROAT, *Geothlypis trichas occidentalis* Brewster, a smaller duller colored race summering in the Great Basin and the Northwest, a transient along both flanks of the Sierra Nevada, and a summer visitant about Mono Lake. It has occurred in the fall migration at Smith Creek, east of Coulterville, and in spring and fall in Yosemite Valley.

TULE YELLOWTHROAT, *Geothlypis trichas scirpicola* Grinnell, a larger, longer tailed and more brightly colored subspecies, resident in the San Joaquin Valley and in southern California, was found in both winter and summer at Snelling and near Lagrange.

Near Lagrange, on May 7, 1919, a pair was observed in the dense cover of green and dried tules. bordering a small pond; the male was singing at short intervals, while the female, glimpsed but once, was carrying nest material.

The birds observed about Mono Lake (*occidentalis*) in 1916, even as late as the last of May, were not yet fully established for nesting. In the fall of 1915 one individual was obtained, September 20, at the shore of Mono Lake nearest Mono Craters.

In the western part of the Yosemite region the Tule Yellowthroat lives in close association with the Least Vireo, individuals of the two species often being seen, in summer, working through the same clump of vegetation. No other warbler of the lowlands lives so close to the ground. The Yellow-throats rarely go even so far as 6 feet above the ground and their nesting and foraging activities usually involve a vegetational stratum of only half this depth.

LONG-TAILED CHAT. **Icteria virens longicauda** Lawrence

Field characters.—Larger than Junco. Sexes alike. Tail about as long as body. Upper surface plain greenish brown; throat and breast solidly clear yellow; belly white; eyelids and stripe over eye white. Active but not nervous. Often flies up above vegetation to sing. *Voice:* Song of male a strikingly varied series of calls and whistles uttered slowly in irregular sequence.

Occurrence.—Common summer visitant along west base of Sierra Nevada, chiefly in Lower Sonoran Zone. Recorded at Snelling and Lagrange, less commonly at Pleasant Valley, and sporadically at Smith Creek, six miles east of Coulterville. Observed once, June 30, 1916, at Mono Lake Post Office, east of the mountains. Lives in willows and shrubbery near water. Solitary or in pairs.

The Long-tailed Chat is common in the thickets which line the margins of the Merced and Tuolumne rivers, in the San Joaquin Valley, and some of the birds penetrate into the foothills. A few were noted at the mouths of the small cañons which join the Merced River at Pleasant Valley, and a pair or more were, in 1915, established along Smith Creek, east of Coulterville. Snelling is a local center of abundance for the species; as many as 20 were recorded during an hour and a half in the bottom lands there on May 29, 1915. Chats and Yellowthroats often live on common ground, but the former, because of their size and actions as well as voice, are much the more conspicuous of the two.

The Long-tailed Chat is a talkative bird; its song is totally different from that of any of the other warblers, recalling, rather, the mockingbird and thrasher in its variety and lack of continuity. The bird utters calls, whistles, and chuckling notes in endless combinations, and it sometimes executes fair imitations of the notes of other species. We have heard the chat in full song as early as 3:15 in the morning, and it continues to sing until late dusk; sometimes it breaks forth in the night time. Its best efforts seem to be put forth in the drowsy heat of early afternoon when many other tuneful creatures are silent. During the course of a song the bird often jumps up high into the air and then flutters slowly down to its perch with curiously drooping wings and tail. Although an active bird the chat does not ordinarily display any nervousness of movement as do the smaller warblers, its actions in general being deliberate.

These birds arrive by the first part of May, having been found already present near Lagrange on May 6, 1919, and they depart by September.

PILEOLATED WARBLERS. **Wilsonia pusilla** (Wilson)[36]

Field characters.—Half size of Junco. Top of head with a black cap (restricted in females) ; plumage plain yellowish green above, yellow on forehead and on under surface of body. No dark streaks or white markings whatsoever. (See pl. 9g.) Movements quick and nervous; often flies out to capture passing insects. *Voice:* Song of male a series of rather flat-toned notes, on about same key, emphasis and intervals between them decreasing toward end of series; call note a similarly flat *tchĕp.*

Occurrence.—Common summer visitant, chiefly to Canadian Zone, on west slope of Sierra Nevada (subspecies *chryseola*). Also found in spring along eastern base of the mountains and as a migrant through the western foothills (subspecies *pileolata*).[36] Lives in thickets over damp ground, usually close to streams, foraging within 6 feet of ground and nesting near or upon the ground. In pairs or solitary.

In the territory surrounding the Yosemite Valley the small streams and boggy meadows bordered by creek dogwood and willow are frequented by small black-capped yellow birds which are likely to be seen capturing insects close to or within the thickets. The species is the Golden Pileolated Warbler and this territory is its regular headquarters during the summer months. A few of the birds have been seen in summer near the Happy Isles in Yosemite Valley, but the main population at that season is to be looked for in the Canadian Zone above, where pairs are found in favorable country every two hundred yards or so.

The Golden Pileolated Warblers arrive on the west slope of the Yosemite section at least by April 29 (1916). Males seemingly precede the females

---

[36] Two subspecies of Pileolated Warbler occur in the Yosemite section. These cannot often be distinguished with certainty in life.

GOLDEN PILEOLATED WARBLER, *Wilsonia pusilla chryseola* Ridgway, a slightly smaller more yellowish backed subspecies with an orange tinge on the forehead. (See pl. 9g.) It nests in California and is a common summer visitant on the west slope of the Sierra Nevada in the Canadian Zone and locally in the Transition Zone. It was recorded sparingly in Yosemite Valley, and commonly from Hazel Green and Chinquapin eastward to Merced Lake.

ALASKA PILEOLATED WARBLER, *Wilsonia pusilla pileolata* (Pallas), a darker toned more greenish subspecies of slightly larger size which summers in the Rocky Mountain district and the Northwest, was found to be common in spring at Mono Lake and in small numbers as a spring transient near Lagrange.

by a few days. By the middle of May their headquarters are established, and with the coming of June nests are to be expected. After the young are abroad some of the birds wander above the boundary of the breeding zone. Two, for example, were seen on Mount Clark at an altitude of 10,500 feet on August 22, 1915. Our last record of the species for the west slope was made August 28, 1915, when an immature bird was taken at Washburn Lake. The species occurs still later, however, for Mr. Joseph Mailliard (1918, p. 19) states that in 1917 it was noticed up to September 22.

The Alaska Pileolated Warbler is a migrant along both sides of the Yosemite region. Near Mono Lake the first (*pileolata*) in 1916 was seen on April 29. Thereafter they continued in evidence until May 31, and it is possible that some of the birds remained there to nest. Only a few were noted on the west slope; one of those seen was obtained near Lagrange on May 8, 1919. The time of the return migration of this race has not yet been determined for the Yosemite region. Pileolated warblers (subspecies undetermined) were noted in Yosemite Valley from August 25 until October 4 in 1920 (C. W. Michael, MS).

The Pileolated Warbler, whichever the race, may be known at a glance by the cap of black on the top of the head (pl. 9*g*). Both males and females, adult and young, have some of this marking. It is largest and most intensely black in adult males. In most warblers the females lack certain of the striking (and to us useful) markings worn by the males, but here the two sexes are closely alike. The present species shows no other contrasting color features; its plumage is yellow, tinged on the back with green. In one of the races (*chryseola*) the color of the forehead has an orange hue.

Pileolated Warblers do the most of their foraging within 6 feet of the ground and practically never ascend far into trees even to sing. They keep within the cover of the lower stratum of foliage and are therefore only to be caught sight of momentarily. The birds are noted for their habit of darting out after flying insects; indeed one book name of the eastern relative of the pileolated is "black-capped fly-catching warbler." Of all our other warblers only the Tolmie is likely to be found in the same cover inhabited by the Pileolated Warbler. (See fig. 56.) The Tolmie often forages out into the drier chaparral, whereas the present species adheres closely to damp situations, either over boggy ground or else within a few yards of a stream. In favorable country, pairs of Pileolated Warblers may occur as frequently as eight or even more to the linear mile.

The song of the Pileolated Warbler is far less shrill than that of the Yellow Warbler and is less clear and more mechanical than that of several other warblers. The syllables are given all on about the same pitch and about as rapidly as a person can pronounce them, but with the intervals shortening and the emphasis decreasing toward the end of the series: *tshup, tshup, tshup-tshup-tshup-tshup*. The call note is not nearly so sharp as that of other warblers, but, on occasion, appeals to one as surprisingly loud for the size of the bird. It has an unmistakable quality of its own. Singing is done largely within the cover of the shrubbery; in other words this species does not, as do so many brush dwellers, seek out prominent song perches.

A nest of the Golden Pileolated Warbler was discovered on Indian Creek, below Chinquapin, at about 5800 feet altitude, on June 11, 1915. The nest was discovered through the observer's seeing the female flush as he stepped within a few feet of the site. The bird made off 40 feet or so and then stayed at about that distance, uttering her call note, *tchep*. The ravine bottom 20 feet away was filled with creek dogwood, Sierran currant, and rank growths of monkey flower and grasses. The slopes adjacent bore incense cedars and sugar pines. The nest was in a depression in an earth bank at the bases of two azalea stems. It was overhung by these stems and also by a mat of dead brakes, which concealed the eggs from view above. The foundation of the nest was of loosely laid dead leaves and this graded into the rest of the structure which was composed of leaves and grass blades. The fine lining was chiefly of deer hair. The structure measured about 3½ inches in diameter outside, and the cavity was 2 inches across and 1¼ inches deep. The 5 eggs were fresh.

A family comprising 4 birds was seen near Merced Lake on August 23, 1915. This would suggest a later nesting date than that in the instance just described.

AMERICAN PIPIT. **Anthus rubescens** (Tunstall)

Field characters.—About size of Junco; body and bill both slender. Upper surface of body plain dark brown; under surface pale brown or buffy, narrowly streaked with dusky on breast and sides; white margin on tail, showing well in flight. On ground bird walks with fore-and-aft movement of head in unison with tread of feet; tail moves up and down, but not in time with feet. *Voice:* Call note a shrill *see, see, seep*, given 3 to 5 times, usually just as bird takes to wing; song rarely heard in our latitudes.

Occurrence.—Common winter visitant along west base of Sierra Nevada. Observed at Snelling and Lagrange and reported from Smith Creek, east of Coulterville, and from Yosemite Valley. Observed near crest of mountains and on east slope during fall months. Keeps to open lands or sparsely grassed fields, especially moist ones; never seeks thick or high vegetation of any sort. In scattering flocks of up to 50 individuals.

The American Pipit is a well-known winter visitor to the lowlands of the west and as such is to be found on the plains and open foothills at the western end of the Yosemite section. There, from October until March, it may be sought wherever the grass is scant enough for the birds to run about unhindered. It is thus frequently to be found on the same ground as the Horned Lark, and comparison shows that the two have much in common with regard to both structure and mode of life.

Pipits are sometimes called ''wag-tails'' because of the almost incessant up-and-down movement of the tail when they are on the ground. When walking or running, the bird also makes a fore-and-aft pecking movement of the head, in unison with the tread of its feet; this is more vigorous when the birds are moving rapidly. The head movement is thus timed rather evenly, but the tail motion is irregular, and practiced whether the pipit be standing still or walking.

The dun-colored plumage of the pipit matches so well the brown earth on which the bird forages while in our latitudes, that the observer often has difficulty in keeping the object of his interest in sight. On plowed ground the difficulty is increased as the many irregularities in the surface afford the bird opportunities to pass behind clods or into furrows and become lost to view.

When running or foraging the pipit is usually silent, but just before taking to wing the birds as a rule utter several short and sharp notes. Then they spring into the air, flashing as they rise the white outer margins of the tail. Unless badly frightened a bird will usually circle about one or more times and then return almost to the spot whence it arose. Safety is sought first by running, and then in flight. The pipit, like most other plains dwellers, never seeks shelter in dense vegetation.

The greatest number of pipits seen at any one time was fully fifty in one flock observed near Snelling on January 8, 1915. East of the mountains they were encountered in small numbers. Near Williams Butte one was seen in flight over a pasture, on September 23, 1915. Three days later, at an altitude of 10,000 feet near the head of Warren Fork, 2 were flushed from a 'buffalo-grass' meadow. Their call notes and actions were just like those seen on the west slope. There was nothing to lead to the belief that they were more than passing transients there. In Yosemite Valley small flocks of pipits were noted by Mr. C. W. Michael (MS) on November 5, 12, and 13, 1920.

AMERICAN DIPPER. Cinclus mexicanus unicolor Bonaparte

Field characters.—Body size nearly that of Robin, but tail very short, about one-half length of body. Whole plumage appearing dark slate gray; young paler toned beneath, with whitish throat. No contrasted markings anywhere in adults save for small white spot on upper eyelid; when perched on rock or bank, bird bobs body down and up at short intervals. (See pl. 52.) *Voice:* Male has an elaborate and varying song; call note a short *zit* or *bzēēt*, given singly or in rapid series.

Occurrence.—Common in Transition, Canadian, and Hudsonian zones on both slopes of Sierra Nevada; resident at least up to Canadian. Recorded in summer from near Bower Cave and El Portal eastward to vicinity of Williams Butte. In winter appears down Merced River as far as Goff. Lives along swift-flowing streams. Solitary.

The Yosemite visitor who has read John Muir's splendid description of the Water Ouzel in The Mountains of California will be keen for a first-hand acquaintance with this most interesting and singular inhabitant of the Sierran creeks and rivers. But even without an introduction the American Dipper merits more than ordinary attention. It is the only one of our local species of 'song-birds' of land dwelling ancestry which has taken to, and has become specially adapted for, gaining a livelihood *in* and *under* the water.

The American Dipper lives along swift-flowing streams in the Transition, Canadian, and Hudsonian zones at altitudes of from 2000 to 10,000 feet, and it is continuously resident, even under the rigors of the Sierran winter, up as high as any water remains open. Streams which afford conditions suitable for trout are likely to be tenanted by the dipper, especially where there are cascades and where scattered rocks in midstream give appropriate resting places. Smooth water is less frequented by the bird. The dashing waters surrounding Happy Isles in the upper part of Yosemite Valley afford optimum conditions for the species.

Examination of a specimen of the dipper in hand shows several notable adaptations to an aquatic mode of life. The covering of feathers on the body is thicker and denser than in either the thrushes or wrens, to which the dipper is closely related. Also, the ends of the feathers are somewhat more loosely formed, as in many of the true water birds, and this seems to help in keeping the plumage from soaking up water. Each nostril is covered by a movable scale, obviously to exclude water when need be. The oil gland at the upper base of the tail is about ten times as large in the dipper as in related land-dwelling birds of equivalent size, and the bird makes frequent use of the product of the gland to dress its feathers. The stout but tapered form of the body, the short tail, the short rounded wings, and the stout legs and feet all would seem to be of advantage to a bird living along and in swiftly moving waters. The nictitating membrane or 'third eyelid' is whitish in the Dipper, and, when drawn backward across the eye, as it is frequently when the bird is above the water, can be seen at a considerable distance. This membrane probably is drawn over the eyeball when the bird is working beneath the surface of the water.

A notable feature in the behavior of the dipper is the frequent bobbing or squatting movement of its body, down and up; hence the name. Such a movement is often the first feature of a bird to catch the observer's eye and it always forms a ready aid in identifying the species. The rock and cañon wrens have a similar movement; but the purpose of this dipping in any of these birds is not known. One dipper seen standing on the margin of the ice in the river in Yosemite Valley, December 22 (1914), was bobbing upon one leg; the other leg was presumably drawn up into its plumage.

The dipper forages along the shore, on rocks in the stream (pl. 52), and on the bottom of the stream beneath the running water. When hunting along the shore the bird moves by short hops, turning to one side and the other, and bobbing its hinder parts almost incessantly. If the shore line be interrupted by a small embayment of quieter water the bird may swim across on the surface, or it may fly, holding its feet stretched forward and downward in readiness to alight when a suitable rock appears or the shore is again reached. When getting food beneath the surface, the dipper dives directly into the stream, usually against the current, and then seemingly walks along the bottom, the wings assisting. As it walks along it searches the crevices between rocks and the submerged surfaces of boulders where are to be found the larvae of certain insects which it seizes and devours. Near El Portal, one day in December, a dipper was seen to plunge head first into the rushing Merced River, to reappear about twenty seconds later some fifteen feet up the stream. Upon emerging, a shrug or two of the body rid the plumage of most of the adhering water. In summer, after the young leave the nest and before they are able to live independently, they perch on rocks along the shore while the parents hunt and dive in search of food for them.

The song of the American Dipper is given throughout most of the year, perhaps more frequently during the winter time than in summer. We have heard it many times in the fall and winter months at El Portal and in Yosemite Valley. Certainly it comes more often to attention in these seasons when most other birds are quiet and when the rush of the rivers and booming of the Valley falls are stilled. On December 22, 1914, several of the birds were playing about the river ice in Yosemite Valley and giving voice to numerous calls; on March 1, 1916, while snow was falling heavily in the Valley, a dipper was heard in full song.

The utterance is not easily transcribed, being varied as to both theme and rendering. Some passages suggest comparison with notes of the California Thrasher, some with those of the mockingbird, and others with certain wren notes; but there is a distinctive quality to the dipper's song which makes direct comparison misleading. Perhaps part of the impressiveness of the song comes from the surroundings amid which it is heard, but certain of its pleasurable features are assuredly intrinsic.

The call note is short and rather burred, uttered singly when the dipper is 'jouncing' on a rock, or given in rapid series when the bird takes to flight. One of our renderings of it is *zit, zit, zit,* . . .; another *bzēēt*, or extended to *bz-ze-ze-ze-ze-ze-et*. It is quite different in character from the song, and resembles in general character the call note of the cañon wren.

The American Dipper nests amid the surroundings which harbor it throughout the year, placing the structure on a rock close to or over rushing water where the surface of the nest will be kept wet by spray. Interiorly the nest is much like that of a cañon wren, but its outer walls consist of moss which, being continually moistened, remains green throughout the period of occupancy. The entrance is at the side, so that the whole structure is oven-like. Occasionally the nest is placed under a waterfall and only comes to view upon the cessation of the flow in the autumn. In former years a pair of dippers nested on the stone abutments to the old bridge near the Sentinel Hotel, but replacement of the structure by a new one of modern type, with smooth-finished surfaces, left no place for the birds; in 1919 no dippers were to be found in that vicinity.

On May 10 (1916) a nest containing five birds about five days old was seen on a beam under the bridge over Rush Creek, southeast of Williams Butte. A two-thirds grown youngster was being fed by an adult on May 26 (1911), in Yosemite Valley near the Sentinel Hotel. A young dipper already able to live independently was seen on Indian Cañon creek in Yosemite Valley on July 6 (1915). These dates indicate a nesting season continuing at least from April until the end of June.

In winter months dippers appear on the Merced River below El Portal and then range westward at least to Goff. They are to be seen readily from passing trains. Whether these are birds forced down from the ice-bound streams of the high Sierras or are migrants from farther north is not known.

SAGE THRASHER. **Oreoscoptes montanus** (Townsend)

Field characters.—Size nearly that of Robin; build more slender. Under surface of body dull white marked with coarse streaks of brown; upper surface plain grayish brown; tail tipped with white. *Voice:* Song a series of clear warbling notes of varying pitch, well sustained to the end.

Occurrence.—Common summer visitant east of Sierra Nevada, from near Silver Lake eastward. Recorded once (April 20, 1919) as a transient on west slope at Smith Creek, east of Coulterville. Keeps close to ground; lives in sagebrush during summer season. Solitary or in pairs.

The Sage Thrasher is to be found in the true sagebrush (*Artemisia tridentata*) which abounds on the flats and gentler slopes east of the main Sierra Nevada. The bird's spotted under surface and plain back both match in color tone the prevailing gray of its environment.

Sage Thrashers visit the Mono region only in summer, spending the winter months on the lower deserts to the south. The species was first recorded in 1916 on May 6, one bird being taken near Williams Butte on that date. In 1915 the birds were still in the region in considerable numbers as late as September 20. Censuses during the third week of September, 1915, yielded 2 to 6 of these thrashers per hour of travel within the sage-covered areas, but this included many young-of-the-year. Counts at nesting time would have revealed a smaller number. The birds perch for singing, or for a survey of the vicinity, on the tips of bushes. They are quick to take alarm, and drop to the ground, scudding away on foot until they have so much of the brushland between themselves and their pursuer that they are entirely lost to view.

WESTERN MOCKINGBIRD. **Mimus polyglottos leucopterus** (Vigors)

Field characters.—Length about that of Robin, but build much more slender; tail longer than body and rounded at end. Upper surface plain dark gray, under surface nearly white (spotted in young); wing with a large white patch, and tail margined with white, these areas showing forth best in flight. (See pl. 53a.) *Voice:* Song exceedingly varied; imitates calls of many other birds (whence the name); call note a harsh *chuck*.

Occurrence.—Sparse resident in Lower Sonoran Zone; found at Snelling, and west of Lagrange and Pleasant Valley; casual visitant (December 12, 1915) at Smith Creek east of Coulterville. Lives usually among scattering small trees. Solitary or in pairs.

Western Mockingbirds are to be found in the orchards at Snelling and Lagrange, and in the scattered blue oaks which intervene between the floor of the San Joaquin Valley and the foothill chaparral belt. The species is by no means so numerous here as in the orange groves of southern California, six individuals being the greatest number seen during any one morning's observations. The open stands of oaks and other small trees seem to offer congenial surroundings to a small resident population.

More than perhaps any other bird is the mockingbird noted for both variety and loquacity of expression. Its voice is to be heard during most of the daylight hours and often from time to time during the night, as also through a large part of the year. In May, October, and January, visits to Snelling found the species in full song. Only during the season of molt, in summer and early fall, is it quiet. At all other times of year this accomplished mimic exercises its art of reproducing, with large measure of success, the calls distinctive of its various feathered associates. Its repertoire includes excerpts or practically complete reproductions from the vocabularies of a large percentage of the birds in the vicinity. One individual listened to at Snelling on January 10, 1915, imitated, with modifications, the California Linnet, the Western Meadowlark, and Shrike;

while another near Pleasant Valley, on May 28 that year, mimicked the Crow, California Jay, Plain Titmouse, and Western Gnatcatcher, besides interpolating some of its own characteristic notes.

On a hill slope below Lagrange a Western Mockingbird was watched one evening early in May, 1919. His demesne was a gentle south-facing slope once cleared of its large blue oaks, and since grown up with small ones, hence giving much the impression of a Pasadena citrus orchard; from the top of one of these orange-tree-shaped oaks, just as the sun sank into a bank of haze, the bird was pouring forth his ecstatic song with all the fervor of his relatives in the southland.

Winter here affords the mockingbirds as plentiful forage as the summer season; mistletoe berries then abound. At Snelling in January, 1915, the birds frequented the cottonwoods laden with the fruits of this parasitic plant, and the one bird taken for a specimen had little else in its stomach.

CALIFORNIA THRASHER. **Toxostoma redivivum redivivum** (Gambel)

Field characters.—General size about that of Robin; tail long and rounded at end, equal to body in length; bill slender, sickle-shaped, over an inch in length. Coloration plain brown, dark above, paler beneath, whitish on chin. On ground runs rapidly with tail up at angle with back. *Voice:* Song, a series of chuckling notes, whistles, etc., in irregular sequence and given at some length; call note a low *chuck*.

Occurrence.—Fairly common resident of Upper Sonoran Zone on west slope of Sierra Nevada. Recorded from near Lagrange and Pleasant Valley eastward to El Portal and to Smith Creek (6 miles east of Coulterville). Lives in mixed chaparral, keeping closely to cover. In pairs.

The California Thrasher is one of the characteristic birds of the foothill chaparral belt. It rarely occurs outside of this kind of habitat, and, within the Upper Sonoran Zone is seldom missing from it. Food, nesting sites, song perches, and shelter from enemies, all as adapted to the thrasher's special needs, are found in this elfin-wood or dwarf forest which covers the foothill slopes from the margin of the San Joaquin Valley eastward to the beginning of the main forest belt on the higher mountains.

The California Thrasher is fitted in several important ways for its life amid the chaparral. Its wings are short and rounded, such wings as are required by a bird which can make only short flights within or close to cover. The tail is long, broad, and rounded, serving as an efficient rudder for quick turning in close quarters and also as a counterbalance when the bird is running on the ground. The brown plumage matches well with the earth tones beneath the chaparral, and the slender curved bill serves as both pick and rake in digging for food on the ground. The thrasher shows marked ability in escaping observation when he so chooses; to do this he drops to the ground and speeds away, using the stout legs and feet to best advantage, dodging this way or that beneath and around the bushes.

The song of the thrasher is the antithesis of a set utterance, such, for example, as that of the Yellow Warbler. It is extremely varied as to quality of the notes, and as to timing and manner of rendering. The bird has, to be sure, certain stock syllables, but these are put together in such variety that no two songs seem quite the same. The individual notes are mostly throaty, sometimes deep and rich, sometimes chuckling, occasionally like short whistles, all subject to modulation. The song recalls that of the mockingbird, but the thrasher is not nearly so much of a mimic and its notes are mellower and more subdued. The singing is most voluble in the spring months. Early morning and evening are the times most favored for singing, although on cloudy days the birds continue to sing until mid-day. For singing, the male mounts to a perch ten to twenty-five feet above the ground. An oak or elderberry bush rising well above the general level of the brush affords a suitable location. From there the thrasher's voice will travel well out over the adjacent territory; from there, at the same time, the bird is ready to drop to cover and safety at an instant's warning. Near Coulterville a thrasher was observed in song while perched just below the topmost branchlets of a 50-foot digger pine. But this was an exceptionally high position. Pairs are spaced out so widely from one another that it is not common to hear more than one male from one place. Yet near Blacks Creek two thrashers were singing in brush on opposite sides of the road and not 50 feet apart.

Thrashers are strictly resident. Hence, once the headquarters of a pair are determined, the observer may visit the place at any time of year and count on finding the birds there. Probably if one of a pair is lost the survivor soon gains a new mate, so that occupancy of the area is continued without interruption. The species is nowhere abundant; perhaps one or two pairs to a quarter section of cover is a fair average.

Near Pleasant Valley, on May 30, 1915, a California Thrasher was followed about and its regular beat determined. This bird, located a few days earlier by his singing, and his mate, lived on a rather open, south-facing rolling slope, sparsely set with blue oaks, a few digger pines, and many large old clumps of wedge-leafed ceanothus (*Ceanothus cuneatus*). These brush clumps in places grew so close together as to form patches a hundred feet or so across, and their very dense system of interlacing branches made an overhead cover with open spaces beneath—an effective shelter for the thrashers.

Two nests of the California Thrasher were found near Coulterville in 1919. On May 10 a nest was discovered on a gentle hill slope covered with a nearly pure stand of greasewood. It rested on a mass of slanting greasewood stems overhung by sprays of foliage of the same plant. The nest rim was 31 inches (770 millimeters) above the ground. There were 3 eggs, one infertile, one half-incubated, and the third nearly ready to hatch. The second nest was found on May 12. It was situated in a small live oak which was growing at the side of a grassy glade bounded by chaparral. The nest was 57 inches (1440 millimeters) above the ground at the rim, and was supported upon a tangle of twigs as well as by the slanting main trunk of the tree. The material used was chiefly dead twigs of greasewood with a few shreds of bark from the same shrub. The interior was lined with smaller twigs and rootlets. Outside, the nest measured approximately 7½ by 12 inches (190 by 300 millimeters), while the saucer-shaped depression was about an inch deep and 4 inches across (25 by 100 millimeters). This nest was well shaded from above, although in plain view from the side. At 7:30 in the morning it contained two fresh eggs, and a third was added by 2:20 P.M. the same day.

Thrashers obtain much of their food by digging with their long bills in leafy débris under bushes; and this habit, when they chance to forage in gardens, brings them into disrepute. At the Campbell place above Pleasant Valley the birds were said to have practically dug up the garden during the summer of 1915. This is only likely to occur where cultivation is attempted close to chaparral-covered areas. General clearing and tilling of the land ordinarily results in the thrashers withdrawing from the vicinity altogether.

Rock Wren. **Salpinctes obsoletus obsoletus** (Say)

Field characters.—Size nearly that of Junco; bill long and slender. Upper surface light grayish brown; under surface whitish, lightly flecked with dusky on breast; tail with a subterminal blackish bar and light tip. Body bobbed down and up at frequent intervals. *Voice:* Song a series of burred and clear notes of varying pitch, with occasional rests, *chr, chr, chr, trr, ter, ter, eche, eche, chr*, etc.; call note a clear tinkling trill.

Occurrence.—Common in summer at numerous points in the Yosemite section from near Merced Falls eastward across the Sierra Nevada to Williams Butte; ranges up to timber line; in winter disappears from the higher country, but remains all the year below level of heavy snow. Lives in rocky situations, either on broken outcrops or about masses of slide rock; also, in winter, on earth walls of gullies. Solitary.

The Rock Wren is one of a considerable group of birds and mammals whose local distribution is dependent upon the presence of a particular type of habitat. In the case of this bird the special requirement is met in bare, steep, or broken surfaces of rock or of hard-packed earth. The domes and rock slides of the high Sierras, the outcrops on the sides of the lower Merced Cañon, and the earth bluffs near Snelling afford suitable conditions for the species. In winter the mountains are deserted, the birds descending to lower levels or going south to the deserts; the numbers in the foothills, too, at this season become small.

The Rock Wren seems to be totally unaffected by conditions of temperature or humidity and is as much at home in the summer heat of the San Joaquin Valley as in the cool and rarified air of North Dome or Ragged Peak. The highest point at which it was seen was in Mono Pass, at about 10,500 feet altitude. Another high place of observation was near Vogelsang Lake, 10,350 feet. The species was observed in Yosemite Valley on August 31, 1917 (Mailliard, 1918, p. 19).

While in general features of structure and behavior a true wren, the Rock Wren presents some peculiarities which clearly adapt it to its particular kind of environment. In shape of body and head it is notably flattened, a feature which enables it to creep far into horizontal fissures and into crevices between boulders; the bill is very long and slender, enabling the bird to reach still farther, into remote niches, in its search for an insect or spider; the legs are short, but the sharp-clawed toes are very long, and have a wide span so that the bird can cling firmly to the vertical or even beetling rock wall; the coloration, *in toto,* is that of the average bare rock; when the bird is examined at close range the indistinct fine pattern of white and dusky dots and bars is seen to resemble, to a suggestive degree, the minute patterning of the rocks.

In size the Rock Wren is the largest of the wrens in the Yosemite avifauna, being more than half again the bulk of the next smaller, the Cañon Wren. From that species, which often occurs in the same territory as the Rock Wren, the latter may be known by its much paler coloration, lack of contrast in color of throat and rest of body, and by its longer, black-and-light-banded tail. The voices of the two are totally different.

In the lowland and foothill country, where birds in general are abundant, the Rock Wren might be easily overlooked through one's attention being absorbed by other species; but in the high mountains, especially on the granite domes and the heaps of slide rock where living things are much scarcer, this bird comes more readily to notice.

Like all wrens this bird is constantly on the move, turning to one side or the other at short intervals. It also bobs its body down and up spasmodically, in the manner of the Cañon Wren or of the American Dipper. When it is perched on a point of rock its repeated movements often carry it through a complete revolution in the course of a few seconds. During this turning and bobbing its short clear trills are uttered, and in spring its song is given.

The song is not set in character, being a series of syllables, repeated in irregular sequence, the successive series separated by short rests. One bird observed near Pleasant Valley sang 4 to 7 notes at a time, the intervals between being 5 or 6 seconds in duration. *Chr, chr, chr, trr, ter, eche, eche, eche,* were some of the 'words' in the song of this particular bird. The whole effort reminds one of the rambling song of the California Thrasher, but it is of much higher pitch.

No nest was found by us; but at Pleasant Valley on May 17, 1915, a pair of these wrens was seen carrying food beneath a large boulder near the Merced River. A bird observed in the same general locality on May 23 was similarly engaged, so the nesting season was probably at its height at this time. A family of young was seen abroad on a schist-like outcrop near Merced Falls on May 28, 1915.

DOTTED CAÑON WREN. **Catherpes mexicanus punctulatus** Ridgway

Field characters.—Size more than half that of Junco; tail shorter than body; bill long (¾ inch) and slender. Coloration rich reddish brown; throat and chest clear white. (See pl. 53c.) Executes squatting movement every few seconds, by which white of throat area is emphasized. *Voice:* Song a series of ten or so loud clear whistled notes, the pitch descending and the timing faster toward end of series; call note a short, hoarse *bzert.*

Occurrence.—Resident in fair numbers from Lower Sonoran Zone up through Transition on west side of Sierra Nevada.[37] Recorded from near Snelling and Lagrange eastward through Yosemite Valley, and, in late summer, to Merced Lake. Chiefly on and about rock walls of the larger cañons. Solitary.

One usually gets his first knowledge of the Dotted Cañon Wren through hearing its clear, musical song from high up on the wall of some cañon. In Yosemite Valley the notes of the song are often to be heard coming from the surrounding cliffs, dominating all other sounds because of their remarkable carrying power. Only persistent observation will bring acquaintance with the bird itself. The emphatic bobbing movement of the body, the rich brown coloration, and the strong contrast between the pure white throat and chest (pl. 53c) and the dark body render this wren, when once within view, easy to recognize both as distinct from the members of its own tribe and from other song birds in general.

The species is common in the lower cañon of the Merced River, from Pleasant Valley to El Portal. Some individuals also live about the earth bluffs and rock outcrops near Merced Falls, and others dwell on the glacier-scoured walls of the Yosemite Valley. A few venture even into the lower Tenaya Cañon and the Little Yosemite. Finally, several birds were noted by us in the vicinity of Merced Lake, well within the Canadian Zone, August 23 to September 1, 1915. Whether these latter had nested at so

[37] The Cañon Wren has been reported from the vicinity of Mono Lake by Dr. W. K. Fisher (1902, pp. 7, 11), who saw one or more of the birds there in September, 1901. None was seen by either of our field parties which visited that region in the fall of 1915 and the spring and summer of 1916. In the absence of specimens the subspecies represented on the east side remains in doubt.

great an altitude, and whether they would have wintered there, were points not determined. It is possible that here was a case of local wandering after the close of the nesting period.

The preferred habitat of the Cañon Wren consists of broken rock surfaces, such as abound in parts of the region; yet fallen logs, old buildings, and even inhabited houses come within the forage range of certain individuals. No satisfactory estimate of numbers can be given, because of the irregularity in the occurrence of suitable surroundings. At Pleasant Valley 6 individuals in different directions could be heard during a certain 10-minute walk; in Yosemite Valley 2 singing males were sometimes within hearing at one time; elsewhere the birds are as a rule much more widely scattered than indicated by the observations just cited.

At El Portal a Cañon Wren frequented the cabin in which our indoor work at that station was done. The bird would come in at various hours of the day and proceed to zigzag about the floor, pursuing flies and spiders. It would poke bill and head into crevices and at times even crawl all through the space between the inner and outer walls of the drafty building. At Pleasant Valley, in May, 1915, the station house was similarly tenanted, and the agent there complained mildly that the birds, hopping across the desk and tables, interfered with his work.

Crevices and crannies in rock walls and caverns and openings between talus rocks are explored to their limits by the birds. Like the Rock Wren, the Cañon Wren has acquired a special flatness of body structure, which is an obvious adaptation to allow it passage through *horizontal* crevices. This is a quite different adaptation from that in a rail, whose narrow compressed body, thin from side to side, allows progress through the *vertical* interstices among standing reeds.

Were the Cañon Wren less active, its disruptive scheme of coloration would be exceedingly effective in rendering it inconspicuous; but its almost incessant bobbing movements make the bird easy to see against almost any tone of background. Even in the dark recesses of a deep cavern the white throat patch is, because of this motion, surprisingly conspicuous.

When foraging, the Cañon Wren travels apparently with equal facility on rock, earth bank, and wall of building; it moves by short hops of two or three inches, and usually changes direction, or zigzags, with every few of these 'hitches.' The bird's legs (tarsi) are short and are held at an acute angle with the surface on which it is traveling, so that the body is close to the substratum. At intervals of two to twelve seconds the hinder parts are slowly raised and then instantaneously depressed. So quickly and violently is this done that the whole body is drawn into the movement. This is the characteristic bobbing referred to above.

The song of the Cañon Wren is one of its most notable features. Many wrens have throaty or bubbling songs; but only in its call note does this species utter anything like the notes of its relatives. The song is a series of clear undulating musical whistles, starting high and, with individual notes well separated but with lessening intervals, descending gradually in pitch to an abrupt low ending. Some songs studied in detail included ten to fifteen notes. The call, a rather hoarse, low-pitched *bzert*, is uttered now and then when the birds are foraging. The song is to be heard at any time of day, from dawn until dark, throughout the nesting season; and it does not entirely cease when the broods are reared, for we have heard it during late July and August. There is a revival or continuance of song in winter. For instance, on December 19, 1914, one of these birds on the cliff near Yosemite Falls gave three full songs at late dusk (5:05 P.M.) when the air was freezing cold and icicles two feet in length were hanging from the rocks.

The nest of the Cañon Wren is commonly placed on ledges in rock caverns, but in the foothills of the Yosemite country situations in weathered buildings are sometimes used. Near Lagrange, on May 8 and 9, 1919, a pair of these birds was engaged in carrying food to a brood of young in a downward slanting crevice at the base of an earth bank in a ravine. The nest was not in sight but was evidently located somewhere below the level of the ground outside.

At Pleasant Valley a nest under construction on May 17, 1915, was situated inside a storehouse, on a beam beneath the gable and about fifteen feet from the floor. On May 25 there were 3 fresh eggs which by May 30 had been increased to 5, 3 of which at that time showed the beginnings of incubation. The base of the nest was composed of a pile of irregularly placed twigs, upon which had been heaped scraps of rotted wood and other débris, while the inner wall was thickly felted with old cotton and then lined separately with mammal hair. Another nest, in which a brood had been reared, was in the station house at the same place. Two fully fledged young birds were seen there on May 29, 1915. A brood of bob-tailed young was seen on the north wall of Yosemite Valley near Rocky Point on July 27, 1915.

The short irregular movements of the Cañon Wren when hopping about the rocks are made largely for the purpose of spying out food. The bird darts here and there, examining crannies and crevices and making selections from the insect population to be found in such places. The wren seen in the cabin at El Portal gathered large numbers of the flies and spiders which had been benumbed by the chilling cold of an early December morning; it was an easy matter then for the wren to accumulate a meal in short order; but later in the day, as the insects became warmed up, the bird did not fare so successfully. The Cañon Wrens which inhabit the walls of the Yosemite Valley seem to find adequate forage in the crevices of the granite and amid the jagged rocks of the talus slopes, where they go into all sorts of dark corners in their searches for food. The mantle of snow in midwinter is no hindrance to their activity. The birds then work far back in the protected caverns, often altogether beyond the reach of the human eye. Only the echoing *bzert* indicates their presence there.

SAN JOAQUIN BEWICK WREN. **Thryomanes bewicki drymoecus** Oberholser

Field characters.—About half bulk of Junco; smaller than Cañon or Rock Wren, but larger than House and Winter Wren; tail, long, nearly as long as body. Plumage plain dull brown above, ashy white beneath; a conspicuous white line over eye; grayish white patches on ends of outer tail feathers. (See pl. 53*d*.) Movements jerky. *Voice:* Song of male a lively series of notes, full of sibilants, ending in three or four clear calls, *seek, seek, suk, terrr, tuh, whoit, seet seet, seet, tsee;* call note a hoarse *tserk,* also a softer *chee-chee-chee-chee.*

Occurrence.—Common resident chiefly of Upper Sonoran Zone, on west slope of Sierra Nevada. Recorded from El Portal and near Coulterville westward to Lagrange and Snelling. Forages in mixed growths, more often in brush than in trees. Solitary.

The San Joaquin Wren, a local race of the widely distributed Bewick Wren (called Vigors Wren in some books on western birds), is common in the Upper Sonoran foothills, and some are to be found still farther to the west, in the San Joaquin Valley, in the bottom lands of the Merced and Tuolumne rivers. There are four species of wrens in the foothill country, yet no two meet each other in serious competition. The Cañon Wren is found on rocky cañon walls, the Rock Wren about earth bluffs and rocky outcrops, the House Wren in oak trees, whereas the San Joaquin Wren inhabits the mixed growths comprising small trees and brush.

This wren is nowhere abundant. Individuals or pairs are located at wide intervals through the chaparral country, usually so far apart that not more than one bird will be within hearing from a single post of observation. Our records show that in a 4-hour census at Pleasant Valley, on May 23, 1915, 6 were heard in song; an equal number were noted during 3 hours of observation at Snelling, on May 26, 1915. At El Portal in November and December, 1914, only one or two of the birds were recorded in an average forenoon's reconnoissance. But then they were more quiet and more absorbed in foraging under dense cover.

The garb of the San Joaquin Wren is quite plain, being dull brown above and ashy white beneath. Over the eye is a conspicuous white stripe which at all times forms the best single character for sight identification of the species. (See pl. 53*d*.) When moving about in its favorite haunts the bird does a great deal of twisting to one side or the other, and jerks the tail this way and that, but it does not 'curtsy' or bob down and up spasmodically like the Cañon Wren or the Rock Wren. While engaged in foraging it is not an uncommon thing for this wren to drop down and hop twistingly about on the ground, with the tail held aloft. But when the male sings he is apt to perch rather quietly; and then his tail hangs directly downward in the manner of a thrasher.

The Bewick Wren has a rather extensive repertoire, consisting of several phrases or 'small songs' each of which is itself set in character. Variety is displayed in the manner or sequence in which these are put together. There is a 'full song,' as indicated at the beginning of this chapter. Another rendering, taken down in the field, was *see, see, see, see, sing, sing, sing, sing, sir.* Always the song is quick timed and full of sibilants. The ending is usually of three or four clear notes, *see, see, see, see;* not infrequently these alone are given as a song. Again a bird will call *eent, eent, eent, eent,* rather slowly, and then sing *zree-ter-er-er-er,* the latter being a trill of short duration. The call notes of the species differ in quality markedly from time to time even in the same individual. Sometimes they are coarse, staccato utterances, given in sharp series; again, they are low, mildly harsh sounds, uttered now and then, singly.

WESTERN HOUSE WREN. **Troglodytes aëdon parkmani** (Audubon)

Field characters.—Much smaller than Junco; more nearly size of Kinglet; bill slender, nearly straight. General coloration dull brown, paler on under surface. No contrasted markings of any sort. (See pl. 54.) Very active and talkative. *Voice:* Song of male a rapidly delivered series of bubbling notes; song repeated at frequent intervals; call note harsh and scolding.

Occurrence.—Common summer visitant to Upper Sonoran Zone on west slope and to Transition Zone on east side of Sierra Nevada. Recorded from Pleasant Valley eastward to El Portal and also about Mono Lake. After nesting season many immature individuals invade higher altitudes, as at Glacier Point (August 17), Merced Lake (August 21), Washburn Lake (August 24), and head of Lyell Cañon at 9200 feet (July 23, all dates in 1915). A few individuals winter in western part of region as at El Portal (December 4, 1914) and Snelling (January 2 and 6, 1915). Lives near ground (usually below 10 feet), chiefly about deciduous trees. Solitary or in pairs.

The Western House Wren or Parkman Wren is a common and conspicuous element in the summer bird life in the oak belt of the western foothill country. It is present also in small numbers from May until September east of the Sierras. Were these two separated areas the only territory visited by the birds, the species would not often come to the attention of the Yosemite traveler. But in the late summer and early fall months the young wrens which have been reared in the Upper Sonoran and Transition zones invade the higher levels, even to the Hudsonian Zone, and continue there for some weeks before departing southward.

The Western House Wren arrives within its nesting range on the west slope of the mountains rather early in the season. The species was found to be already well established at El Portal upon our visit to that place on April 27, 1916. East of the Sierras it was not noticed until May 9 (1916). The latest fall record on the west slope above the Upper Sonoran Zone is for September 15 (1917), in Yosemite Valley (Mailliard, 1918, p. 19); while one of our party saw an individual bird on the east slope near Williams Butte on September 22, 1915. In Yosemite Valley the House Wren appeared in 1920 on July 30, and thereafter the species was noted on August 18 and 27 and on September 4 and 6 and 26 to 28, in the same year (C. W. Michael, MS).

Of the wrens found in the Yosemite region the House Wren is next to the smallest in size. Its coloration is plain brown, only slightly paler below than above, and the bird has no white line over the eye or other contrasted markings of any sort. (See pl. 54.) The Winter Wren is more chunkily built, with a much shorter tail, and warmer tone of coloration; and the San Joaquin (Bewick) Wren is larger, more whitish beneath, and has a white stripe over the eye. The Cañon and Rock wrens are enough larger as not to be confused with the House Wren.

Few birds sing more persistently during a brief period in the spring than the Western House Wren. The song is a series of burred warbling notes, uttered so fast as to defy imitation, and is repeated at frequent intervals. One individual studied at El Portal on April 27, 1916, was giving songs each of which lasted from 2 to 3 seconds, and a new song was commenced every 4 to 6 seconds. The general pitch of each song is about the same throughout, but the intensity weakens at the end. There are none of the clear notes heard in the song of the San Joaquin Wren. When singing, the male House Wren usually perches well above the ground, but still considerably beneath the crown-foliage of the tree in which it happens to be. The song perch is usually situated within a few feet of the nest site. The call note is a rather harsh scold, sometimes repeated rapidly several times.

The name House Wren implies, correctly, that this bird (and more especially the eastern race) has, with the advent of civilization, taken to nesting about dwellings. Throughout its range the species is noted for making use of any cavity, natural or artificial, which is suited to its needs with respect to size of entrance hole and to interior dimensions.

On the east side of the mountains, in 1916, Mr. Dixon found 3 nests of this wren. The first, discovered on June 2, at about 7300 feet altitude near Williams Butte, was in an old nest hole of the Red-shafted Flicker 3 feet above the ground in a dead aspen. (See pl. 54a.) On this date the birds were carrying nest material in the form of small sticks. Trips were being made about 7 minutes apart. The individual which did the singing carried most of the sticks, and it often scolded and chased the mate when the latter ventured to look into the nest hole. On June 23, a nest was observed in an old one-quart oil can which was hanging inside a building. (See pl. 54*b*.) The entrance hole of the can was barely large enough (exactly one inch in diameter), for a parent to pass through. Both adults were bringing food for the six young birds which the nest contained. On June 26 a third nest was found in a natural cavity in an aspen growing near Parker Creek, at an altitude of 7500 feet. There were 7 eggs in this nest.

WESTERN WINTER WREN.   Nannus hiemalis pacificus (Baird)

Field characters.—Smallest of the wrens; body size less than half that of Junco; tail but little more than an inch in length. Coloration dark reddish brown, below as well as above; an indistinct light line over eye. Tail held always up at steep angle with back. Movements of bird quick; squats every now and then. *Voice:* A rather extended and varied song of rapid delivery and high pitch; call note, *tschĕp*, often given twice in quick succession.

Occurrence.—Sparse summer visitant at middle altitudes on west slope of Sierra Nevada; observed in Yosemite Valley and at Merced Grove Big Trees. Winter visitant in fair numbers to Yosemite Valley, to El Portal, and to Smith Creek east of Coulterville. Lives amid root tangles and brush heaps near streams. Solitary.

The smallest and most reclusive of the wrens in the Yosemite region is the Western Winter Wren. It lives at the middle altitudes, amid freshet-bared tangles of rootlets and accumulations of drift materials along shaded stream courses. The bird is of small size (scarcely so large as a kinglet), and wears a livery of rich dark brown which harmonizes well with its shadowy surroundings. These features, together with its retiring disposition, make of it a species to be seen only when particularly sought for and then only under favoring circumstances.

There are Western Winter Wrens in the Yosemite region at practically all times of year, but a larger number of individuals is present in winter, and the species is then to be found in several places not inhabited in summer. Whether the summer population moves out with the coming of fall is not known, but it is obvious that a considerable quota arrives from the north in October and remains here for at least a part of the winter season.

During the summer the Western Winter Wren is extremely local, having been found by us only at Merced Grove Big Trees (June 15, 1915), and in Yosemite Valley near foot of Vernal Falls (May 24, 1911) and near Happy Isles (May 28, 1911). Bradford Torrey (1910, p. 79) records finding a singing bird near "the footpath below Vernal Falls," on May 18, and June 14 and 27, 1909. Mr. Donald D. McLean reports that the species has nested near Bower Cave. With so many seemingly favorable localities in the region it is surprising that other instances of summer occurrence have not been noted.

The winter range includes such stations as Yosemite Valley, El Portal, and Dudley, on Smith Creek, six miles east of Coulterville. An individual bird collected at Ten Lakes on October 9, 1915, is the basis of our earliest record for the species outside the local breeding area; this bird may have been only a transient, for this locality is in the Hudsonian Zone. It seems unlikely that the species could winter successfully in the territory above the Transition Zone.

Individuals were observed along the Wawona road near Chinquapin, November 26, 1914, and on the South Fork of the Tuolumne River at the Hog Ranch road, October 15, 1915. These birds also may have moved to lower stations with the coming of the heavy snows later in the winter.

The number of individuals present in winter, while greatly exceeding the summer population, is not large as compared with the numbers of other species of birds. On Sweetwater Creek, late in October, 1915, 3 Western Winter Wrens were living within a stretch of about 400 feet of cañon bottom; but this was an exceptional concentration. Elsewhere there is perhaps not more than one every two or three hundred yards.

Wrens as a group are possessed of mercurial temperaments and the Winter Wren is among the most 'nervous' of its kind. The bird seems never to be quiet, but is constantly twitching about from side to side, frequently bobbing down and up, always with the short tail cocked at a decided angle with the back. The bird seems to *skip* along and uses both the short wings and long legs in all its ordinary movements. It seems equally at ease on a nearly vertical twig and on a horizontal root or branch-let. A great deal of its foraging is done in under the overhanging banks. Quite often the bird is lost to the observer's sight amid the crannies and shadows about the base of some large stream-side tree, and comes into view only now and then.

The song is difficult to describe. It consists of a number of notes run together quickly with no rests within the song itself. Some one has compared the Winter Wren's song to the noise made by a squeaking gate hinge, but the comparison is not a specially happy one. The song is heard sometimes during the winter months, and commonly, as is indicated by Mr. Torrey's record, at nesting time. The call note of the species, a short *tschĕp*, is heard more frequently, and throughout the year; sometimes it is given twice in quick succession. An observer can make a good imitation of the note by drawing the tongue backward from the clenched teeth and closing the lips at the same instant. We have commonly used this sound in attracting a bird for a close view.

One evening just at sunset, in October, while our party was camped near Sweetwater Creek, a winter wren was watched as it came down to bathe. The bird fluttered down, half flying, half hopping, to a small pool completely screened from above. It would stay a few seconds, splashing in the water, and then move to a perch a few feet above the pool, soon to return for another brief dip. Five or six such short visits were made and then the bird returned to the perch where it stayed for a while, fluffing out all its feathers, and using its bill to press out the water. Two or three minutes sufficed to complete its toilet and then the wren made off down the creek to a brush pile.

The only Yosemite nest of the winter wren of which we have record was seen on May 28, 1911, near Happy Isles. It was a rather bulky affair, made of soft materials and situated in a tangle of pendant rootlets beneath the butt of an old prostrate log. The place was shaded by incense cedars, Douglas spruces, and black oaks. Beneath the log flowed a little stream about 3 feet wide and the nest entrance was only 13 inches above the water. Twenty feet away was the torrent of the Merced River. There were 4 (possibly more) large young in the nest, but only one of the parent birds was in evidence. The presence of two trout in the stream below, and the fear of these shown by the adult wren, suggested that the other member of the pair might have fallen victim to one of the fishes. The parent was busily engaged in feeding large green worms, millers, crane-flies, and other insects to the young. A beam of light reflected into the nest from a mirror did not seem to frighten the wrens and so it was possible to observe closely the process of feeding. The old bird made visits at intervals of 4, 9, 2, 2, 7, 8, and 3 minutes, respectively; twice, at the second and the last of these timed visits, the bird carried away excrement. The young void the excrement (which is enclosed in a gelatinous sac) immediately after being fed; it is dropped by them on the rim of the nest where it lies as a conspicuous spherical white object, the size of a large bean. The old bird seizes this in her bill and in one instance carried it away fully 50 feet before depositing it in a wild currant bush. One sac fell into the small stream and as it floated slowly along the surface the bird snatched nervously at it again and again. Finally it was recovered, whereupon the bird flew off and disposed of it in the usual manner, in a place where it would give no clue to the location of the nest.

WESTERN MARSH WREN. **Telmatodytes palustris plesius** (Oberholser)

Field characters.—Bulk a little more than half that of Junco; tail shorter than body. Upper surface chiefly light brown with lengthwise light streaking; some black on back and head; a conspicuous white stripe over eye; under surface dull white, brownish on sides of body. Tail usually held up at steep angle with body. *Voice:* Song a hurried series of 'rusty' notes; call note a sharp *chuck*, also a scolding sound, repeated.

Occurrence.—Sparse transient and winter visitant in the lower altitudes. Recorded in Yosemite Valley, at Smith Creek (6 miles east of Coulterville), and at Lagrange; on east slope of mountains at Gem Lake. Lives in thickets and growths close to or above standing water. Solitary.

The Western Marsh Wren is sparingly represented in the Yosemite section during the seasons of migration. A few probably pass the winter at the lower altitudes on the west slope. The species was first brought to our notice in Yosemite Valley on October 10, 1914, when an immature male came to grief in an oat-baited mouse trap set in some tall grass beneath a clump of willows bordering a meadow near the Merced River. Another individual was seen in the Valley at the margin of the river three days later, and on November 1, 1915, one was seen in a mass of drift on the bank of Yosemite Creek. The species was recorded at Smith Creek, six miles east of Coulterville, on December 26, 1919, and at Lagrange on December 19, 1915. East of the mountains an immature male in full song was taken in the willows and tall grass bordering Gem Lake, 9036 feet altitude, on September 13, 1915.

The "long-billed" Marsh Wren, although affecting a different habitat, is almost as reclusive as its small relative, the Western Winter Wren. It keeps to dense cover and is to be glimpsed only momentarily while passing from one thicket to another; sometimes it may be brought out to view by the observer making a squeaking sound of a sort to excite the curiosity of the bird, and then, for a moment or two, its color features and other characters may be seen to advantage.

SIERRA CREEPER. **Certhia familiaris zelotes** Osgood

Field characters.—Less than half size of Junco; tail as long as body, each feather stiffened, and pointed at tip (fig. 58*a*); bill slender and curved. Coloration above dark brown streaked with white; under surface of body plain white. (See pl. 10*h*.) Hitches jerkily, upward, on trunks of trees. *Voice:* Fine and wiry; song of male *see′, see′, se-teetle-te, see′;* call note, *see,* often somewhat prolonged, uttered at irregular intervals.

Occurrence.—Common on west slope of Sierra Nevada. Permanently resident in Transition Zone, where recorded from Smith Creek (six miles east of Coulterville) eastward to floor of Yosemite Valley. Present in Canadian Zone at least during summer season when noted from Chinquapin to Porcupine Flat and Merced Lake. Wanders to higher altitudes (as on Dana Fork, 9500 feet) and to east slope of mountains (Walker Lake and Williams Butte) during fall. Winters in small numbers in western foothills, as near Lagrange. Forages on trunks and larger branches of good-sized trees, and nests in crevices behind loose bark. Solitary or in pairs.

The Sierra Creeper is one of the least conspicuous of the common birds found in the Yosemite region. This is not due to any special reclusiveness on the part of the bird, for it often forages in situations quite open to view. Its effacement is due to its special scheme of coloration together with its peculiar manner of movement. Even experienced observers are sometimes put to considerable effort in locating and following one of the birds. The brown back with its narrow streaking of light color harmonizes closely with the warm tones and up-and-down pattern of the bark. (See pl. 10*h*.) Only in side view, when the white under surface shows, and then especially if the bark be wet and so darkened, is the creeper likely to be seen easily.

The Sierra Creeper keeps closely to one restricted sort of environment, namely, the trunks and larger branches of trees. In our experience we do not recall a single exception to this rule. True enough, one of these birds was seen scaling up the slabs of cedar bark covering the exterior of the Camp Curry dining room, but even there the bird was obviously in its proper niche. The creeper's whole scheme of existence, its manner of foraging and of nesting, is more limited and specialized than is that of almost any other bird in the region.

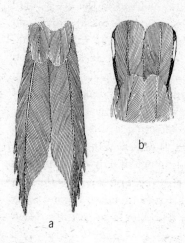

Fig. 58. Tails of (*a*) Sierra Creeper and (*b*) Red-breasted Nuthatch. The Creeper uses its tail as a prop, after the manner of a Woodpecker, and hence climbs chiefly or altogether upward on trees; the Nuthatch makes no use of its tail for support and the bird moves in any direction on a tree.

When on the trunk of a tree the creeper's progress is always upward. Sometimes it moves sidewise a short distance, though always with steeply diagonal posture; often it spirals around the bole while ascending, and occasionally the bird will drop down a step or two; but it never runs down the tree or even turns head downward, as do the nuthatches. After ascending to near the top of one tree the creeper flies down to near the base of the same or a neighboring tree and there starts a fresh ascent.

It moves spasmodically, hopping or 'hitching' upward a few steps, then stopping to make inspection when it sees anything of possible service such as food. The tail with its stiffened and pointed feathers is used habitually to give the bird support (fig. 58*a*). The bird turns its head this way and that, peering into crannies in the bark, and by means of the slender curved bill, used as tweezers, readily picks out insects from the deeper crevices.

The creeper seems never to be at rest. Whatever the time of the day, it is on the move. The query arises: Do these birds need to forage incessantly, do they have to keep continually active in order to get sufficient nourishment? Or is part of their activity a matter of habit or an expenditure of excess energy really unnecessary? Whatever the answer, the fact is that the creeper, like many other small insectivorous species, whenever seen is always on the go.

If the bird watcher in the field had to depend upon eyesight alone, the Sierra Creeper would be one of the 'rarest' birds in our forests. Fully half of our own notebook records have resulted from locating the bird first by hearing. The fine and 'wiry' note which it uses as both call and alarm note, *see,* or *zeetle,* is given practically throughout the year. In the spring season, there is added the song of the male, a series of notes of the same general character as the call, and of the same high pitch, *see', see', se-teetle-te, see'.* The voice of the creeper, especially its call note, is sometimes confused with that of the Golden-crowned Kinglet, and indeed the two are much alike although to the experienced ear there are points of difference. A beginning student should follow up individual birds of the two species and listen to their notes until he learns to distinguish them. It is not unlikely that certain notes of the creeper are so high as to be above the limit of hearing for some persons; this is known to be the case for the Golden-crowned Kinglet.

The nesting activities of the Sierra Creeper are carried on in exactly the same surroundings that afford the bird its food and shelter at all times of the year. The space left where a slab of bark has split away from the trunk a short distance, affording a deep but narrow opening, is the place most often chosen to harbor the nest. Such sites are more common near the bases of trees where the bark is thicker and older and the outer portions often more furrowed and split. It is not surprising, therefore, that creeper nests are often within a very few feet of the ground. Once the site has been selected, both members of the pair busy themselves in bringing the materials needed for the nest. The form of the structure varies with the nature of the crevice which has been chosen, but in all cases the general plan is the same. The lower part of the crevice is filled with various kinds of coarse material such as sticks, old flakes of bark, moss, and rotted wood, until firm enough to support the superstructure. On top of this there is made a shallow cup, longer than wide, somewhat the shape of a narrow gravy dish. This part is composed of soft substances, most often weathered shreds of the inner bark of the willow.

Creepers make direct approach when visiting their nests; the birds practice no subterfuges for keeping secret their location. Hence it is not difficult to follow a bird directly to its home. This was well illustrated by some observations of ours on a pair of creepers in Yosemite Valley on May 22, 1919. The birds had chosen a location about 12 feet above the ground in a large (30-inch) yellow pine. Entrance to the nest site was gained in this instance through a hole about an inch in diameter in one of the large slabs of bark. Both male and female were at work gathering moss from the trunks of black oak trees in the vicinity and carrying this material directly to the nest. When one of the birds entered the nesting cavity it would stay but an instant, and so it seemed that little attention was being given to the arrangement of the material at this, probably early, stage of construction.

A nest was seen in the Valley on May 31, 1911, in a crevice at the tip of a burn on an incense cedar trunk. This was 14 feet above the ground and scarcely 20 feet from the busy office of one of the large camps. Evidence pointed to the presence of young. If young were there, the beginning of nesting must have been close to the first of May.

A nest of the Sierra Creeper which could be studied in detail was found at about 4500 feet altitude near Indian Creek, below Chinquapin, on June 11, 1915. It was in a fire-scarred incense cedar, which had a large plate of bark sprung outward from the base of the tree. Behind this plate, at a height of 7½ feet from the ground, the nest was hidden. The space between the bark slab and the body of the tree for a distance of 21 inches below the eggs had been filled with loosely laid flakes of cedar bark, and a few stray ends of these pieces of bark, projecting beyond the edge of the crevice, had given the observer who had noticed one of the birds his first clue to the exact location of the nest. The nest proper was a mass of felted inner bark of willow, silvery gray in color, longer than wide, about 4 by 2 inches, and was put together in more substantial manner than the underpinning. There were 6 eggs in which incubation had just begun. When the nest was first discovered the female was covering the eggs, while her mate was gathering insects on a tree 30 feet away. As the projecting slab of bark was lifted to gain better view of the nest, the sitting creeper left and joined her mate. Then, while examination of the nest continued, the two birds came down to as close as 8 feet from the observer and voiced their wiry protests almost continually.

As will have been inferred, the Sierra Creeper is an exceedingly local bird, in that, having once selected a favorable neighborhood, it carries on all of its activities within a very short radius. Indeed, at nesting time, once an adult bird is seen, the observer may be confident of finding its mate and its nest close by. The materials for the nest, and the food for both parents and young, are gathered within a remarkably small circle.

SLENDER-BILLED NUTHATCH. **Sitta carolinensis aculeata** Cassin

Field characters.—Size nearly that of Junco; tail about half length of body. Top of head and back of neck black or slate-black; cheeks and under surface of body pure white; back slate gray. (See pl. 10*e*.) Runs about readily on bark of trees, moving in any direction. *Voice:* Song a series of double notes all alike, *cher-wer;* call note a nasal *hănk.*

Occurrence.—Resident in Upper Sonoran Zone on west slope of Sierra Nevada where recorded from near Lagrange and Merced Falls eastward to Smith Creek, east of Coulterville; present in Transition and Canadian zones on west slope except during midwinter; also found east of mountains (Mono Mills) during summer season. Lives low on trunks and larger branches of both coniferous and broad-leaved trees. Solitary.

The Slender-billed Nuthatch is the largest of the three nuthatches found in the Yosemite region. Because it is fairly common and does its foraging chiefly on the lower parts of the trees, it is the species most likely to be seen.

The Slender-billed Nuthatch enjoys a wide distribution in the Yosemite section. It is resident in the blue-oak belt of the western foothills, and is found also, at least from spring until early winter, in the Transition and Canadian zones. Its range on the west slope extends from near Lagrange and Merced Falls eastward. The easternmost summer record was made at Mono Meadow, a few miles south of Glacier Point. In the early fall, as is shown by records from Ten Lakes, McGee Lake trail, and the Clouds Rest trail near Little Yosemite Valley, the birds invade the higher mountains. On the east slope of the mountains Slender-billed Nuthatches were found at Mono Mills on June 7 and 10, 1916, and at Williams Butte, Walker Lake, and Warren Fork of Leevining Creek, in the fall of 1915.

The three species of nuthatches of the Yosemite section agree closely not only in general form of bill, wings, and tail, but also in having bluish gray backs and in possessing white spots on the outer tail feathers. (See pl. 10*e, f, g.*) There are, however, sharp differences between these birds, to be seen if looked for with some little care. The Slender-billed is about twice the size of the Red-breasted and Pigmy nuthatches and the entire side of its head or 'cheek' is white; the under surface of the body also is pure white. In the other two birds the side of the head at least down to the eye is dark, and the lower surface is not clear white. The adult male Slender-billed has the top of the head silky black, whereas in females this area is much duller. This difference in coloring affords a means for distinguishing the sexes in the field.

The word nuthatch comes to us from the Old World where it was first applied to a European relative of our birds which has the habit of wedging nuts into crevices and then hacking them open. Our nuthatches do considerable pounding with their bills both in digging their nest holes and in breaking up food materials. Nuthatches, creepers, and woodpeckers get most or all of their living on the trunks and branches of trees, but the representatives of each of these groups go after their food in different ways. The woodpeckers dig out grubs and insects which burrow in or beneath the bark, while the other birds mentioned get eggs, larvae, and adult insects which take shelter in the furrows in the bark. Probably the smaller sized nuthatches and creepers obtain, on the average, 'bugs' of smaller caliber than are sought out by the woodpeckers. The bill of the creeper is a more delicate instrument than that of the nuthatches. Its slender curved form makes possible to the bird a farther reach, into the narrowest of crevices where small insects lurk.

A creeper moves only upward on the trees, whereas the nuthatches run about without reference to direction, and go up, down, or crosswise seemingly with equal facility. The short tail of a nuthatch is always carried in line with its back and gives the bird no support such as the creeper obtains from its longer and stiff-pointed tail. The nuthatches have long toes provided with stout, well-curved and sharp-pointed claws, and these, catching in small irregularities in the bark, enable the birds to cling readily, whatever their position with reference to the pull of gravity. The bill is straight, rather strong, and sharply pointed, and serves equally well in pulling insects out of crevices, hacking open nuts or seeds, and in excavating or enlarging nesting holes in rotten wood.

Nuthatches usually keep rather closely to their distinctive mode of foraging; yet on one occasion, at Chinquapin, May 20, 1919, a Slender-billed Nuthatch was observed capturing flying insects. The bird was clinging 25 feet above the ground on the trunk of a tree, facing downward but with its head turned outward almost at right angles with the trunk. Upon sighting a passing insect the nuthatch would dart out, with undulating flight resembling that of a small woodpecker. Its tail was spread so that the marginal white spots showed plainly. With this short but broad 'rudder' the bird seemed to be able to change direction easily while pursuing its winged prey. Upon making a capture the nuthatch would alight upon some nearby tree, run along until an appropriate place was found and then, turning head downward, would pound the insect until it was in condition to swallow. Four or five perches within a 50-foot radius were occupied thus during the few minutes that this bird was under observation.

On the same date and at the same place another Slender-billed Nuthatch was watched as it foraged about the bases of the fir trees and on the ground. It seemed rather incongruous for this bark searcher to descend and cross the needle strewn earth between adjacent trees. The bird visited fifteen or so trees and fallen logs during as many minutes but seemed to have no fixed forage beat as these were not visited in any regular sequence. Rarely did the bird go far above the ground; its highest excursion was not over 15 feet. On the fallen logs it worked just as on standing trunks and if it disappeared from sight its travels soon carried it back into view again.

b

e

g

h

Some Small Birds of the Yosemite Forests.

a. Western Ruby-crowned Kinglet, male.   *b.* Western Golden-crowned Kinglet, male.
c. Western Ruby-crowned Kinglet, female.   *d.* Short-tailed Mountain Chickadee.   *e.*
Slender-billed Nuthatch.   *f.* Pigmy Nuthatch.   *g.* Red-breasted Nuthatch.   *h.* Sierra
Creeper.

The voices of the three species of nuthatches are distinct. The call of the Slender-billed Nuthatch is a rather loud *hănk* or *quănk,* repeated at varying intervals. This call possesses somewhat of a nasal intonation but not so much of that quality as there is in the call of the Red-breasted Nuthatch. The Slender-billed never utters any high-pitched, clear, 'chattering' notes such as are given by the Pigmy Nuthatch. In the spring the Slender-billed Nuthatch gives a song which is a mere monotonous repetition of a certain two-syllabled word: *cher-wer, cher-wer, cher-wer,* etc.

The Slender-billed Nuthatch, at least in the Yosemite section, ordinarily makes use of abandoned woodpecker holes for nesting sites. In some other regions the birds are reported to dig out their own nest holes, but here they seemingly find sufficient accommodation in the numerous holes left by woodpeckers. Two instances of nesting were recorded at Tamarack Flat on May 25, 1919, and a third near Pleasant Valley on May 23, 1915. The first of the Tamarack Flat nests was 9 feet above the ground in an old hole of the White-headed Woodpecker in a broken off and barkless Jeffrey pine stump. The male bird was seen to enter with a bill full of insects and there ensued at once from the opening a series of low conversational notes. The contents of this nest were not ascertained. The second nest, also in an abandoned White-head's hole, was 7 feet (2130 millimeters) from the ground, measuring to the top of the hole. The entrance was as made by the woodpeckers (1¾ inches or 43 millimeters in diameter), but the interior had evidently been enlarged, by the nuthatches themselves, to a diameter of over 5 inches (130 mm.) and was filled to within 7½ inches (190 mm.) of the top, with deer and chipmunk hair and feathers from various birds. There were seven slightly incubated eggs. The male kept uttering a special alarm call, *yĕk-yĕk-yĕk-ĕk-ĕk-ĕk,* and circulated about the vicinity anxiously.

The female was on the nest and as she refused to leave even during the hubbub incident to enlarging the entrance, the observer had to lift her from the nest in order to examine the eggs. She seemed to be in a sort of lethargy and did not struggle until actually taken in hand. That the bird had not left the nest for some time was evident from the quantity of excrement which was accumulated in the cloaca. The condition of this female, the food supply which the male of the first nest had been seen to take to his nest, and the further fact that only males had been noted abroad for some days previously, led to the belief that in this species the female alone carries on the duties of incubation and that she remains upon the nest continuously for a greater or less period of time, during which she is fed by the male. In the case of the third nest, mentioned beyond as being seen in the foothill country, and which contained young, both of the parent birds were abroad, engaged in gathering food for the brood. These observations, added to our knowledge of other species of birds, indicate that only accurate observation of a species through the nesting season will establish the exact relations existing in that species between the sexes and between the adults and the young. It is unsafe to attempt to predict the behavior of one species from consideration of the known habits of other, even near-related, species.

Another nest of the Slender-billed Nuthatch was seen on May 23, 1915, in a dead blue oak near Piney Creek not far from Pleasant Valley. The two parent birds were busily engaged in capturing and carrying insects to the young. The presence of a member of our party 6 feet below the nest caused obvious anxiety upon the part of the two members of the pair who flew back and forth for twenty minutes before one of them became courageous enough to enter and feed the brood. Soon after the first had left, the other parent fed the young. Each again filled its bill full of insects, but neither would venture into the nest a second time; they flew back and forth uttering their curious little notes, and in so doing did not seem to find it necessary to open the bill at all.

RED-BREASTED NUTHATCH. **Sitta canadensis** Linnaeus

Field characters.—Half size of Junco; tail about half length of body. Top and sides of head, black in male, slaty in female; a white stripe over eye in both sexes; back slate gray; under surface of body reddish brown. (See pl. 10*g*.) ''Hitches'' about in all directions on bark of trees. *Voice:* A piping nasal *ñă*, uttered singly or in measured series.

Occurrence.—Common in summer in Canadian Zone (less plentiful in Transition and Hudsonian zones) on west flank of Sierra Nevada. Recorded in that season from Smith Creek (at 3000 feet altitude east of Coulterville), and from near Chinquapin, eastward to Tuolumne Meadows. Found on east slope of mountains (Walker Lake) in September. In Yosemite Valley practically throughout the year. Lives on trunks and branches of conifers, usually in the upper halves of the trees. Solitary.

Often when the traveler is following a trail through a forest there comes to his ear from the lofty tree tops the quaint nasal call of the Red-breasted Nuthatch, sounding like the blast of an elfin horn. With careful search he may locate a small form moving about the trunk and branches at the tiptop of a tree. If luck favors and the observer is patient the bird may eventually come low enough so that the black on its head, the white stripe over the eye, the bluish gray back, the reddish brown under surface, and the very short, squared tail will all be seen and the identification rendered certain.

The center of abundance of the Red-breasted Nuthatch lies within the Canadian Zone, but some of the birds are to be found in the zone above and in that below. The seasonal status of the species is not fully known. In Yosemite Valley, which is in the Transition Zone, it is present continually at least from April to the last of December, and it seems likely that a few of the birds stay there throughout the whole winter. On December 30, 1914, four Red-breasted Nuthatches were heard near Gentrys (6000 feet), which suggests that some of the birds may remain even higher in the mountains throughout the year. The species is known to visit the foothills and valleys in other parts of California during some winters, but we did not see it, winter or summer, at any station below the Transition Zone, in the Yosemite section.

The Red-breasted Nuthatch is of about the size of the Pigmy Nuthatch and but half the bulk of the Slender-billed. It has a conspicuous stripe over the eye which is the best single mark by which it may be recognized. (See pl. 10*g*.) The Red-breasted Nuthatch is a solitary bird and so is not likely to be confounded with the Pigmy Nuthatch which is emphatically of flocking habit.

The call note of the Red-breasted Nuthatch is a nasal *ñă* or *wĕh*, reminding some people of the tooting of a child's penny trumpet. Sometimes the note is given singly or, if repeated, with very long intervals between calls, while on other occasions five to nine calls are given close together with measured timing. When the birds are disturbed or excited the *ñă-ñă-ñă*, etc., comes with a more rapid and continued production, even for several minutes at a time. The nature of the call is such that it carries for long distances; the hearer is frequently deceived into believing that the bird is close by. This one call seems to be the only vocal achievement of which this nuthatch is capable.

Even among the three species of nuthatches, which as a group are bark dwellers, there seems to be mutual agreement with respect to forage range, by which each is allotted a separate precinct. The Slender-bill keeps to the smaller trees or around the bases of the larger ones, the Pigmy forages out toward the ends of the branches and amid the needle tufts, while the Red-breasted, although sometimes coming close to the ground, spends most of its time up near the tops of the loftiest trees where it inspects the main shaft and larger branches. Were it not for the bird's far-carrying note, the last-named species would often be passed unnoticed even by the careful observer. Although a nuthatch may be calling constantly the observer often has great difficulty in discerning the 4-inch bird at the top of a tree a hundred feet or more in height.

At Hazel Green on May 14, 1919, a pair of these nuthatches was seen foraging close together and within a few feet of the ground. One of the birds (the male?) kept its tail slightly spread so that the white band showed at each side. Presumably this was a courting display somewhat of the nature to be noticed among fox sparrows, juncos, and other birds at this season, and it is likely that nesting commenced soon afterward.

The Red-breasted Nuthatch probably nests as a rule well up in the trees at about the level at which the birds spend most of their time. On June 14, 1915, near Chinquapin, the mobbing of two Blue-fronted Jays by a pair of nuthatches led to the discovery of the latter's nest site. After the jays had quit the vicinity one of the nuthatches was seen to enter a little round hole in the trunk of a slender and very brittle, dead silver fir. Since the hole was about fifty feet above the ground, the tenants were perfectly safe there from any human intrusion.

Of the nuthatches collected during June, 1915, males predominated, a fact which would suggest that at this season the females were engaged in incubation or in caring for the young. On August 3, 1920, at Smith Creek, 6 miles east of Coulterville, a juvenal bird which was molting into the first winter plumage was taken. The birds collected in August, 1915, at Merced Lake and on Mount Clark (at 8800 feet) were all immatures of the current season; probably the adults were molting and so, as is often the case with birds at that season, were keeping themselves in seclusion.

Once a Red-breasted Nuthatch fell victim to a mouse trap, baited with rolled oats, which had been set beside a log in the forest. Whether the bird had sought the material as food (for some nuthatches do take nuts and seeds) or whether it was led to investigate the trap out of curiosity was not evident. All nuthatches have a more or less well marked trait of curiosity, as have their relatives, the tits and chickadees.

The flight of the Red-breasted Nuthatch is slow and hesitating, the wings beating a few rapid strokes and then being held closed for a short interval. Perhaps this peculiarity of flight is due partly to the extreme shortness of the tail (fig. 58b). The shortness of the tail is a striking feature of the silhouette of the bird in flight.

But little seems to be known concerning the food habits of this species. Its regular patrol of the bark of trunks and branches of trees probably means that insects and their eggs and larvae contribute extensively to the diet of the bird. A freshly captured bird gives off a curious odor quite distinctive of the species, possibly due to its regularly feeding upon some particular sort of insect.

At Aspen Valley one day in October one of these nuthatches was watched as it came down to drink. The bird descended from the trees to the vertical surface of a rock about three feet above the water and then by short flights moved to a twig two inches above a little pool. There it leaned down and drank ten or twelve sips at intervals of three or four seconds. Its bill was in the water less than a second for each drink; the rest of the time the bird spent in looking cautiously about. At this same locality a Red-breasted Nuthatch came several times to a white fir near our camp and drank some of the sap which was oozing from a gash in the bark near the base of the tree.

PIGMY NUTHATCH. **Sitta pygmaea pygmaea** Vigors

Field characters.—About half size of Junco; tail short, about half length of body. Top and sides of head grayish brown; back bluish slate gray; under surface of body pale buff. (See pl. 10*f.*) Goes about in flocks, individual birds clinging to small branches and foliage like Chickadees. *Voice:* An irregular series of light 'chattering' notes, *sŭp, sŭp'-ŭp, sŭp'-ŭp*, etc., uttered by members of a flock, especially when on the move.

Occurrence.—Rather sparse resident at middle altitudes. Recorded around rim of Yosemite Valley (Gentrys, Glacier Point, Nevada Falls, Wawona Road at Grouse Creek, Yosemite Falls trail near top), and at Bean Creek, four miles east of Coulterville; also east of mountains near Walker Lake and on Mono Craters. Lives chiefly in yellow and Jeffrey pines. In flocks except when nesting.

The Pigmy Nuthatch is much less common in the Yosemite region than the other two species of nuthatches. We saw nothing of it ourselves during the summertime. But it came to our attention several times during the fall and early winter months (September 1 to December 30), when flocks appeared in localities around the margin of the Yosemite gorge. The birds seen were foraging chiefly in coniferous trees and of these the yellow and Jeffrey pines seem to be preferred, although sugar pines and the firs were visited as well. Mr. Donald D. McLean has found the species in summer near his home (Dudley) on Smith Creek, east of Coulterville. A full-grown young bird was captured by him on Bean Creek, July 29, 1919.

The Pigmy Nuthatch is small, about the same size as the Red-breasted Nuthatch, and so of about half the size of the Slender-billed. Its color features are chiefly of a negative sort. (See pl. 10*f.*) The head is always grayish brown with neither the white cheeks of the Slender-bill nor the white stripe over the eye of the Red-breasted Nuthatch. The under surface of the body is pale buff, appearing dull white at a distance.

Unlike its relatives, the Pigmy Nuthatch is a persistently flocking species. The bands of Pigmies seen by us in the Yosemite region were all small, the largest comprising about ten individuals and the smallest four; elsewhere larger flocks have been observed. The general behavior of a flock of these birds is suggestive of that of bush-tits. These nuthatches, clinging inverted or upright as circumstances require, work over the smaller twigs and even the foliage at the top and periphery of a tree, rather than the trunk or larger limbs. When absorbed in foraging they are usually quiet; only now and then is a note to be heard. But when the flock is moving through the tree tops, a babel of small voices is heard. These notes remind one of the contented peepings of a brood of chickens when hovered beneath a hen.

PLAIN TITMOUSE. **Baeolophus inornatus inornatus** (Gambel)

Field characters.—Size somewhat less than that of Junco or Linnet. Coloration everywhere plain, grayish brown above, pale gray beneath; no contrasted markings of any sort. Head with a tapered crest, which is habitually kept erect. Manners, flight and notes resembling those of Chickadees. *Voice:* Commonest spring call a sharp whistled *peet'-o,* given several (3–5) times in quick succession; also various other notes not readily transcribed. Ordinary call-note wheezy, chickadee-like.

Occurrence.—Common resident of Upper Sonoran Zone on west slope of Sierra Nevada. Recorded from near Lagrange (at 400 feet altitude), and from Pleasant Valley, eastward to Smith Creek (six miles east of Coulterville), to El Portal, and to Feliciana Mountain (4000 feet). Reported once in Yosemite Valley (C. W. Michael, MS). Lives chiefly in foliage of oak trees. In pairs, except when broods are in care of parents.

The word 'plain' in the name of the Plain Titmouse refers to the exceedingly somber garb of the bird. Even its crest, which is a character so prominent as to serve as a good field identification mark, is uniform grayish brown. But the lively notes and vivacious behavior of the bird, in such decided contrast to its scheme of coloration, easily lead one to guess the rather close relationship of the titmouse to the chickadee. Once within the range of the species the traveler cannot long remain ignorant of the presence of titmouses (the correct plural), for one or more pairs of the birds are likely to be in hearing if not in sight at any locality in the foothill oak belt.

Little or no difficulty need be experienced in identifying this species. The features mentioned in the preceding paragraph are usually sufficient to make the bird known. Its notes, until one has learned their many variations, are less dependable for this purpose than the crest and coloration. The Plain Titmouse is much larger than the bush-tit. As compared with the wren-tit the plain tit is of more chunky build. Moreover, its tail, which is not longer than its body, is seldom or never cocked up at an angle with the back.

The Plain Titmouse is an example of a species that is strictly resident within one zone, winter as well as summer. Individuals of several of the foothill birds such as the bush-tit and wren-tit move up-slope with the close of the nesting season. We have only one record of the Plain Titmouse leaving the Upper Sonoran Zone: A pair was noted near the mouth of Indian Cañon in Yosemite Valley on November 21 and 30, 1920, by Mr. C. W. Michael (MS). The oak foliage about which the species lives so much of the time evidently provides adequate forage not only for the adults at all seasons but for the broods of five or six young which appear at the end of spring. Even at El Portal where two different zones are accessible on the opposing sides of the cañon the titmouses keep to the warmer, north, sun-facing slope where there are live oaks, blue oaks, and digger pines; and although they forage in the golden oaks on that side of the valley they do not cross to the denser stands of golden oaks which grow on the shaded south slope only a fraction of a mile distant. Up the Merced Cañon the range of the Plain Titmouse, like that of the Brown Towhee, ends abruptly where the Transition Zones commences, at about 3300 feet altitude.

At Pleasant Valley 9 of these birds were recorded in a census of 3½ hours on February 27, 1916. On May 24, 1915, about 30 were noted during 5 hours spent in the same general territory. In the latter number were 2 broods; if these be assumed to have numbered 5 each, the average for adults would be 4 an hour, more than were recorded during the winter census mentioned. But titmouses are more in evidence in spring; their voices are heard more frequently then, and this probably accounts for the differences in the two censuses. Six or more, all adults, were seen during an hour and a half spent on the hills near Lagrange on May 7, 1919. During most of the year the birds live in pairs, but in summer when the annual broods have been reared, family parties of 6 or 7 may be found rather commonly.

The Plain Titmouse nests in holes in trees. Old woodpecker holes are used when available, but many, perhaps a majority, of nests are placed in naturally rotted-out cavities. The height above the ground varies according to circumstances. One nest found near Blacks Creek on May 12, 1919, was only 33 inches (830 mm.) from the ground, measured from the entrance, and the nest surface was 6 inches (150 mm.) below that. Another studied in detail near Lagrange on May 8, 1919, was 10½ feet (3170 mm.) from the ground. Both were in blue oaks.

This second nest was in the same tree with, and only 17 inches (440 mm.) from, that of a Western Bluebird; and there was a Swainson Hawk's nest in another oak 12 yards distant. The titmouse's was in a natural cavity of rather large size. The bottom held a mass of fine dry grasses, perhaps 4 inches in depth, and on top of this was a heavy felted lining of cow hair and rabbit fur. The top of this mat was 5½ inches (138 mm.) below the margin of the entrance. There were in the nest 5 half-grown birds and one infertile egg. The young had acquired many of their feathers, though these were still mostly in the feather-sheaths. The finely comminuted remains of such sheaths as had been shed had sifted into the matted hair lining. These young birds would probably have left the nest within a very few days. The other nest mentioned contained three small young.

For purposes of record and study we wished to collect the entire family of this second nest. The young birds were obtained and two adult titmouses which frequented the vicinity and kept voicing disapproval of our actions were shot. Upon dissection the latter proved to be both males! One was undoubtedly the father of the brood but the other was an "innocent by-stander" who fell victim because he had joined in the demonstration. The adults weighed 15.4 and 15.6 grams, respectively, while two of the young birds weighed 14.3 and 14.8 grams. The young at the time of leaving the nest are thus nearly the weight of the parents.

While as a general rule Plain Titmouses keep to the oak trees, the species sometimes invades the digger pines and occasionally drops down to the brush when foraging. An extreme departure from this habit was noted at the Campbell ranch north of Pleasant Valley, where two of these birds were caught in traps set in a field for the capture of kangaroo rats, the nearest trees being fully 50 yards off.

Near Coulterville a Plain Titmouse was watched as it went down to bathe one morning in May. The bird descended by short stages to a pool near a small oak, and after arriving at the margin it spent several seconds in looking about cautiously before venturing to flutter its wings in the water. It did not get drenched; few birds do. Of all the birds we have seen bathing in the wild, none get so wet as not to be able to fly readily.

Short-tailed Mountain Chickadee

Penthestes gambeli abbreviatus Grinnell

Field characters.—About two-thirds size of Junco. Top and back of head, and whole chin and throat, black; side of head below eye and short stripe above eye, white; rest of body chiefly plain gray. (See pl. 10*d*.) Manner active and alert; when foraging, often hangs inverted from smaller twigs. *Voice:* Commonest call a wheezy rendering of the syllables *chick-a-dee-dee;* this often shortened to simply *chee-chee-chee;* also an alarm note, *tsick-a.* Song a clearly whistled *tee-tee, too-too.*

Occurrence.—Common resident in Canadian and Hudsonian zones, less numerous in Transition; present on both slopes of Sierra Nevada. Recorded from Smith Creek, 6 miles east of Coulterville, and from Feliciana Mountain eastward across mountains to Williams Butte and Mono Craters. Lives in trees, mostly conifers, foraging up to 50 feet above the ground. In pairs at nesting time; flocking loosely at other seasons, sometimes in company with other small birds.

The Short-tailed Mountain Chickadee inhabits the whole of the main forested portion of the Yosemite region, beginning at the lower margin of the Transition Zone and ranging up to the highest unstunted trees, at 10,000 feet or higher. It occurs on both slopes of the mountains, down on the west to Feliciana Mountain, and to Smith Creek, east of Coulterville, and on the east slope to Williams Butte and Mono Craters. Within this range the species seems to be strictly resident. We found no indication of an up-mountain migration in summer, nor were chickadees noted in winter at any station in the western foothill country. The birds are as fixed in this respect as the Plain Titmouse is in its range.

During the winter season individual chickadees are not closely restricted as to immediate neighborhood, the birds being then associated in bands which rove through the woods for considerable distances in their daily search for food. But in summer the forage range of individuals is restricted to a small area which has for its center the site chosen for, or occupied by, the nest. Chickadees forage at various heights in the trees, sometimes at 6 feet or less from the ground, again at 50 feet or even higher. On several occasions chickadees have been seen to descend to the surface of the ground and to forage there for a time; but the birds then hop about with seeming awkwardness, as if out of their proper niche.

The chickadee population is greatest in the Canadian Zone. Only a few of the birds are found in the Transition Zone and but moderate numbers occur in the Hudsonian. During June, 1915, before the young were abroad, our censuses in Indian Cañon and at Porcupine Flat gave between 2 and 3 of these birds per hour of observation. A 4-hour census in Yosemite Valley on May 31, 1915, revealed only 2 birds, and the same number were noted during a similar trip there on April 28, 1916. In the Hudsonian Zone, between Young Lake and Tuolumne Meadows, 8 were recorded in 4 hours on July 9, 1915. But by the end of July young were out everywhere and "the woods were full of chickadees." No less than 36 were counted in 3½ hours by one of us going from Tenaya Lake to Mirror Lake on July 31, 1915.

Mountain Chickadees are sociable creatures and spend most of their time in small flocks. The individuals comprising these flocks are continually calling, with the probable purpose of keeping within hearing distance of one another. The company travels along intact, yet spread out through adjacent trees, so that the individuals do not cover each other's ground in their search for food. Apprehension of danger by one is at once communicated to all members of the company, so that each may be instantly on the alert. In the spring, by the end of April if not earlier, these bands break up and pairs are formed as a first step in the nesting program. When the young are fledged enough to leave the nest the family, both parents and young, goes forth and remains as a group at least until time for the fall molt. In early autumn flocks numbering 10 to a dozen individuals are formed, and in this manner the chickadees spend the time until the impulse comes to prepare for nesting once more.

In Yosemite Valley on April 30, 1916, a pair of Mountain Chickadees was followed for about twenty minutes as the birds flew from tree to tree gleaning insect food of various sorts. Black oaks seemed to be preferred and the birds would explore one tree fairly well before going on to another.

Terminal twigs, newly opened foliage and moss-covered trunks seemed to be inspected with equal interest. If the upper side of a twig did not yield food the bird would hang inverted to scrutinize the lower surface, seeming to be quite as much at ease in this reversed position. Most interesting was the way in which the chickadees explored cavities. A bird would disappear into some hollow left by the rotting out of a stub, scan the interior for a few seconds, come to the opening and look about for possible danger, then disappear inside again. It would continue this performance until the cavity had been examined throughout. Occasionally one of the chickadees would drop into a manzanita bush, and twice the birds alighted on the ground for a short while.

The chickadee is ceaselessly active, in large part from necessity, we suppose, for a bird must cover much territory each day to get the requisite amount of daily bread. The birds, although intent in their search, are alert for anything out of the ordinary. They have a large bump of curiosity, and any unusual sight or sound will bring them to the point of interest in a hurry. If a person will sit down at the foot of a fir tree, well screened by the canopy of drooping boughs, and 'screep' with lips to back of hand, he will soon have, literally at arm's length, a number of chickadees. The birds at first are excited and call frequently as they hop and flutter from branch to branch. Then, after some moments of intent peering, they move away quietly, and resume their usual occupation.

The Mountain Chickadee shows considerable range in vocal powers, hardly to be guessed on first acquaintance. The usual call note is the one popularly rendered as *chick-a-dee-dee,* but with an asthmatic, wheezy intonation; often it is reduced to simply *chee-chee-chee.* Sudden surprise is evinced by an explosive *tsick'-a,* repeated several times. On sharp mornings when the birds congregate on the sunny sides of the columnar fir trees, they often indulge in a chorus of cheerful notes, each group of sounds a jumble of sibilants impossible to syllabify and interspersed with the ordinary calls. In addition there is what we consider the real song, a strikingly clear, far-carrying, whistled, *tee-tee, too-too.* The two pairs of notes are on different pitches, higher and lower, respectively. Frequently the second note of the first pair is omitted and the remaining note prolonged: *tee; too-too.* The song is given in winter as well as in spring and summer. It is one of the easiest remembered of Sierran voices, and one that a person can readily imitate by whistling.

In the spring months the chickadees, then foraging in pairs, will be seen to indulge in some of the features of courting behavior exhibited by other birds. At times one of a pair (probably the female) will quiver her wings, whereupon the other will feed her, at the same time holding his tail slightly spread. Now and then a bird which has been calling will be seen while perched on a twig to pound with his bill on the part of the wood between his feet, producing an intermittent tattoo audible for some distance. This possible exhibition of 'spring vigor,' recalls the much louder, rolling tattoo which the flicker and certain other woodpeckers are wont to beat in the spring.

Nesting activities among the Mountain Chickadees are commenced in late April or early May. After the pairs separate off from the winter flocks, the two mates go about in close companionship and begin inspection of old woodpecker holes and of natural cavities either in living trees or in dead and weathered stubs. The nest holes of the White-headed Woodpecker abound in a good part of the chickadee's range, and it is to this bird more than to any other one agency that the chickadee is indebted for suitable nesting places. The White-head digs a new nest hole for itself each season, and as the cavities persist for several years in condition suitable for use by chickadees the latter may even have opportunity for exercising choice. Indeed the chickadees do investigate many holes before settling upon one as the location for the nest of the season. The manner of the birds' work in gathering material was not observed. By the time the nest is ready for eggs there has been accumulated a felted mass of soft material some five to six inches below the entrance. This material consists chiefly of hair. In some nests the soft hair of chipmunks is the principal material, while in others the coarser hair of the Mule Deer predominates. In one nest examined at Porcupine Flat there was hair from meadow mouse, California Ground Squirrel, and chipmunk. In another nest we found down feathers of some bird; and in still another, bones of small mammals were mixed with the hair in such a manner as to suggest that the chickadees had chanced upon some owl pellets and used parts of these in building.

The material composing the nest is closely compacted so as to make a thick felt carpet, and as such, must be of considerable value in conserving warmth when the female chickadee begins to incubate her relatively large clutch of eggs. In some instances this 'carpet' rests directly upon the layer of small chips which served as flooring for the woodpecker tenants of an earlier year. But if the hole is unusually deep, grass and similar coarse material is piled in first so that the nest proper will not be too far below the entrance.

The number of eggs varies, 5 and 8 being the extremes for the complete sets found by us; probably 7 is the most usual number. During the period of incubation, which lasts about 2 weeks, the female occupies herself almost or quite exclusively in covering the eggs. The male, on the other hand, continues to forage actively, and may be seen to visit the nest from time to time, supplying food to his mate. Confirmation of this division

NESTS OF SHORT-TAILED MOUNTAIN CHICKADEE IN THE YOSEMITE REGION

Locality	Date	Site	Height of top of entrance above ground	Level of nest below top of entrance	Material	Contents
Chinquapin	May 20, 1919	concave side of hollow fir stub	19½ in. (500 mm.)	12 in. (300 mm.)	mammal hair	none
Chinquapin	May 20, 1919	low stump	60 in.	———	chiefly chipmunk hair	none
Chinquapin	May 20, 1919	low stump	72 in.	———	chiefly chipmunk hair	none
Tamarack Flat	May 26, 1919	Jeffrey pine stub	102 in. (2600 mm.)	5½ in. (140 mm.)	mammal fur	6 eggs, nearly fresh
Tamarack Flat	May 26, 1919	lodgepole pine bole	50 in. (1270 mm.)	5⅛ in. (130 mm.)	mammal fur	5, fresh
Tamarack Flat	May 26, 1919	blackened stump	85 in. (2150 mm.)	3½ in. (90 mm.)	mammal fur	2, fresh
Mono Meadow	June 21, 1915	rotten stump, 8 ft. high	58 in. (1470 mm.)		fur and down feathers	7, far incubated
Yosemite Valley	June 23, 1920	rock abutment to bridge	5 ft. above base but 2 ft. below road	———		young
Porcupine Flat	June 26, 1915	dead lodgepole pine	27 in. (680 mm.)		mammal hair	8 eggs, far incubated

of labor is found upon examining in hand representatives of the two sexes at this season. The breast and abdomen of the female are bare, the skin rather rough-surfaced and thickened in the manner characteristic of incubating birds generally; while the male lacks any indication of such special modifications. In the first part of the incubatory period the female may flush from the nest when disturbed; but when the eggs are about ready to hatch she will often remain upon them, even if the nest be chopped open. She will then make a hissing sound and whir her wings in a remonstrant manner from time to time whenever the disturbance becomes acute. In one instance the female, fighting valiantly, maintained her place until finally we picked her off from the eggs. In decided contrast is the behavior of the male; he may come around at the beginning of the disturbance but never exhibits much concern, and may wander away again after a little while. After the young are hatched, both parents share equally in the feeding of the brood.

A most striking departure from the usual location for a chickadee's nest was come upon in Yosemite Valley on June 23, 1920. A pair of the birds had placed their nest far back in a crevice in the stone retaining wall of the north approach to the new Sentinel Bridge. The entrance was 5 feet above ground, yet at the same time, 2 feet below the level of the elevated roadway at that place. The young could be heard calling whenever a parent bird brought food. The rumbling of heavy vehicles overhead did not seem to disturb the birds in the least. Choice of such an unique site may have been prompted by the birds failing to find a nest location of the usual sort in the neighborhood—a condition due to the removal of dead trees by the Park authorities, and therefore, in final analysis, one that was man-wrought.

After the nesting season the chickadees and several others of the smaller birds are wont to associate with one another in flocks of varying size. Such a gathering was seen in Yosemite Valley on July 30, 1915. Included in the openly formed yet coherent aggregation were the following species: Mountain Chickadee, Black-throated Gray Warbler, Western Chipping Sparrow, Sierra Creeper, Warbling Vireo, and Cassin Vireo. The birds were foraging through black oaks, incense cedars, and young yellow pines, each kind of bird of course adhering to its own particular niche and own method of getting food.

CALIFORNIA BUSH-TIT. **Psaltriparus minimus californicus** Ridgway

Field characters.—Size small, about one-third that of Junco; tail longer than body. Coloration plain gray, palest beneath; top of head inconspicuously brownish. No contrasted marks anywhere. Habits somewhat like those of chickadee. *Voice:* A low *pst, pst,* inflected variously under different conditions.

Occurrence.—Common resident of Upper Sonoran Zone on west slope of Sierra Nevada where recorded in nesting season from near Lagrange and at Pleasant Valley eastward to Smith Creek, six miles east of Coulterville, and to El Portal. Strays to higher altitudes in summer and fall months, as in Yosemite Valley, near Glacier Point, and on slope north of Mirror Lake. Recorded once east of mountains, at Williams Butte, September 22, 1915. Forages chiefly in foliage of oaks, sometimes in tops of the larger brush plants. In flocks of ten to twenty-five or so, except at nesting time when in pairs.

The California Bush-tit is a common inhabitant of the oak belt in the western foothills of the Sierra Nevada. It is one of the smallest birds found there, and is indeed one of the smallest birds in the Yosemite section, not much larger than a hummingbird. The California Bush-tit's coloration is of the plainest sort, dull gray with no contrasted markings anywhere. The top of its head is brownish, this being one of the features which separate the present species from the Lead-colored Bush-tit found on the east side of the Sierras; but this brown cap can be seen only at close range and when looked for especially. Certain individual bush-tits have the iris of the eye white though in the majority of the birds it is dark-colored. This is a peculiarity which does not seem to be correlated with age, sex, or season.

The bush-tit is characteristically a flocking species and for the greater part of the year the birds go in bands which number from ten to twenty-five or more individuals. The separation into pairs for nesting occupies the period from about late March through May. As soon as the young are fledged the family goes about as a unit, soon joining one or more other families to form the regulation flock.

The flock formation of bush-tits is not so coherent as that of blackbirds or sandpipers; each individual exercises a considerable measure of independence, especially in changing its location. A foraging flock is usually spread out through two or more trees and moves along slowly, the birds stringing along one after another, all going in the same direction from tree to tree, but no two moving at exactly the same instant. Those in the rear fly ahead and in turn are passed by their companions. While engaged in ordinary foraging the members of a flock keep up a series of faint notes which doubtless help to keep the band together. At times an individual will become absorbed in foraging in one particular place and be left behind by his companions. The belated one then utters a series of notes quite insistent in tone, and as soon as he gets a response indicating the new location of the flock he hurries on in direct course to join the others once more.

In general behavior bush-tits remind one of chickadees. Individual birds when hunting food will assume any position, even that of hanging inverted from some small branch or leaf. Their foraging is done very largely in the foliage of the live oaks, the leaves being scrutinized from all sides. The birds pay little or no attention to the larger twigs and branches, and they seldom fly out beyond the leafage as kinglets and Audubon Warblers are accustomed to do.

Mention of kinglets suggests making comparison between these two groups of birds, inasmuch as both are of small size, both feed among foliage, and they are to be found together in the foothill country during the winter season, though they summer in quite different zones. The bush-tit has a short thickish bill, the wing is relatively short, and the tail is decidedly longer than the body. The bird seldom flutters its wings and the members of a flock string along after one another in parallel courses. The kinglets, on the other hand, have proportionately longer and more slender bills, and the wing is longer while the tail is as short as the body; they often twist about, end for end, and they do a great deal of fluttering of the wings. Only the Golden-crown, of the kinglets, is a flocking species, and its flock behavior is not at all like that of bush-tits. In point of color the Bush-tit is predominantly gray, whereas the kinglets are chiefly greenish-colored as to body plumage and each of the kinglets, at least in the male sex, has special bright markings on the head.

The bush-tit is unlike its near relatives, the chickadee and titmouse, for it builds its own nest while both these other birds rear their broods within holes. The bush-tit's nest is an elongated pensile affair, 8 to 11 inches in length and 3 or 4 inches in greatest outside diameter. Entrance is gained through a hole on one side near the top, and the space within is tubular, flared somewhat toward the bottom. The whole cavity bears a suggestive resemblance to the interior of a woodpecker's nest hole, the sort of place so prized by chickadees at nesting time! The bush-tit's nest is composed of soft materials such as moss, lichens, spider web, and willow down, all of which is closely felted together. The structure is usually placed in an oak tree, at a height of 10 or 12 feet above the ground, and so attached that it hangs in or just beneath the crown of the season's new leaves. When engaged in building, and indeed at any stage in the nesting program, the members of a pair stay close about the nest site and make no effort to keep the location a secret. Their home is safe from the usual types of nest robbers.

We did not visit the foothill country early enough in spring to observe the beginning of nesting, but data gained later in the season indicate that building is commenced early in April. A new nest was seen at El Portal on May 2, 1916. At Pleasant Valley, in 1915, numerous pairs were noted on May 23 and 24, and young out of the nest were seen on May 28. Along Smith Creek a family group of adults and young was seen on June 2, 1915. The broods are fairly large, 6 perhaps being an average; thus a group of 8 would constitute but one family.

After the broods leave the nest, the families range about locally and some groups undertake a more extensive wandering which may lead them well up into the mountains. In 1915 the movement had carried at least one flock to Yosemite Valley by July 27. A flock of 12 was seen on that date making rapid time eastward through the golden oaks along the base of the north wall. On July 30 a flock of 8 was noted near the Tenaya trail where it leads down near Mirror Lake, and on various dates in August and September flocks of bush-tits were seen or heard in trees and brush bordering the several trails which ascend the Valley walls. By late fall the birds have returned to the foothills, our latest record for the species above its foothill range being for October 11, 1914, when some were heard on the Tenaya trail at about the 5700-foot level.

In 1920 bush-tits were observed by Mr. C. W. Michael (MS) in the Valley on various dates through the fall months, from August 29 even to as late as December 27. On the latter date "the largest flock yet seen" (17 birds at least) was encountered.

This species was discovered once east of the Sierras. A flock of bush-tits was encountered near Williams Butte on September 22, 1915, and the one individual shot proved to be a California Bush-tit; whether the remainder comprised this species or the Lead-colored Bush-tit was not learned. The former is not known to occur regularly on the east slope of the mountains in this latitude and this may be an extreme case of up-mountain, or rather, cross-mountain wandering from the west slope.

Lead-colored Bush-tit. **Psaltriparus plumbeus** (Baird)

Field characters.—As for California Bush-tit (which see), but top of head gray like back. *Voice:* Like that of California Bush-tit.

Occurrence.—Resident east of Sierra Nevada. Recorded at Williams Butte, September 22, 1915. Lives in low trees. In flocks except when nesting.

The Lead-colored Bust-tit was encountered by us on only one occasion. On the morning of September 22, 1915, a small flock which comprised both adult and immature birds was observed in the piñon pines on Williams Butte. In both voice and mannerisms these bush-tits resembled closely the California Bush-tit, a species which, curiously, had been encountered previously the same day.

Pallid Wren-tit. **Chamaea fasciata henshawi** Ridgway

Field characters.—Size nearly that of Junco; tail long, exceeding body in length, slender, rounded at end, and habitually carried up at decided angle with back. Coloration grayish brown above, pale brown beneath; iris white. *Voice:* Common call a series of clear whistled notes all on nearly or quite the same pitch, uttered slowly at first then more rapidly, running into a trill, *pit, pit, pit, pit-tr-r-r-r-r;* also a subdued, ratchet-like note, repeated in series.

Occurrence.—Common resident on west slope of Sierra Nevada in Upper Sonoran Zone. Recorded from Pleasant Valley eastward to El Portal and to Smith Creek, 6 miles east of Coulterville. During late summer and through the autumn a few individuals range eastward into Transition Zone as along walls of Yosemite Valley to head of Nevada Falls and to Tenaya Cañon above Mirror Lake. Lives mostly in chaparral, sometimes foraging in low trees and occasionally on the ground. Usually in pairs.

The wren-tit is a species peculiar to western North America, and is further limited practically to California; indeed, it does not, as do so many western birds, even have a counterpart in the eastern states. The light-colored race, the Pallid Wren-tit, inhabits the chaparral belt in the western foothills of the Yosemite region and at certain times of the year invades the mountains as far as Yosemite Valley. The wren-tit, as its name indicates, displays some obvious degree of likeness to both wrens and "tits"; yet it stands so far apart from both of these groups as not to be classified with either of them, save in a very broad way.

The most outstanding feature in the wren-tit's make-up is its long and slender tail which is longer than the body of the bird, rounded at the end, and habitually carried up at a considerable angle with the back. This character alone will usually be sufficient to distinguish the wren-tit from all other local species. The wings are short and rounded, a shape which usually goes with a long tail in birds which inhabit shrubbery. The plumage is plain, grayish brown above and somewhat paler beneath, and the body feathers are very soft and lax in texture. At close range the white iris is evident and furthermore, one may then sometimes make out an inconspicuous dusky streaking on the throat and chest.

The regular niche of the Pallid Wren-tit is in the foothill chaparral, beneath the crown-foliage of the brush plants and so usually not more than five feet from the ground. Fully nine-tenths of the bird's existence is passed in this shallow zone. Occasionally wren-tits are to be seen up in oaks or other trees growing amid or close to the brush, while now and then a bird will be noted on the ground, momentarily. But the three essentials for the bird's life, food, shelter from enemies, and safe nesting sites, are afforded in largest measure in the chaparral itself.

Wren-tits go about regularly in pairs in winter as well as during the nesting season. The young after leaving the nest accompany their parents for a time and so four or five birds may be seen together. Occasionally during the winter months loosely formed assemblages of six or eight are noted. Wren-tits are wont to gather quickly about any disturbance in the brush, but they disperse as soon as their curiosity is satisfied or the cause of their concern disappears. In ordinary behavior they are sober, dignified in manner, evincing little or no nervousness such as characterizes the wrens.

In the matter of voice the Pallid Wren-tit differs from most other small birds in that both sexes utter all of the notes characteristic of the species. Furthermore, the birds give their calls throughout the year, with little cessation during the time of the annual molt, and with little if any increase in vocal effort in the courting and nesting season. So far as known, none of the various calls is restricted to use at nesting time; any or all may be heard in fall or winter as well. The most commonly heard utterance, possibly the 'song' of the wren-tit, is a series of whistled notes, all on nearly the same pitch, begun slowly and distinctly, then becoming more rapid, and going into a trill which is ended abruptly: *pit, pit, pit, pit-r-r-r-r*. This call carries well and may be heard easily when the listener is a quarter of a mile or more distant from the bird. Sometimes the notes are given slowly without being run together at the last—*pit, pit, pit, pit,* etc. Occasionally there is heard a series similar in timing to the second, but of different quality—in what might be called a complaining tone—*keer, keer, keer, keer,* etc. There is also a low, ratchet-like note, sometimes interrupted, again given continuously for several seconds, but never so loud as to be audible more than a few yards away. This is uttered when a pair or group of birds is investigating any unusual occurrence in the brush.

At nesting time the wren-tits are extremely localized, each pair keepng within a small area, of which the nest is the pivotal point. The nest is a small structure only three or four inches in diameter and the same in height and is seldom easy to find amid the many dense tufts of leaves and small branches in the chaparral. The location of one nest, in grease-wood brush on the hills a mile west of Coulterville on May 11, 1919, required an hour and a half of intensive search. The details of the manner of finding this nest will, perhaps, be of significance.

When the observer followed up a bird which was calling, it was found to stay in a certain tract about 200 feet square covered with tall grease-wood and scattered small live oaks and toyon bushes. Part of the time two wren-tits could be noted and one of them, which acted somewhat concerned, kept appearing and disappearing. Then the observer began a systematic search, crawling back and forth beneath the brush. After some little time one of the wren-tits came very close, uttering its low 'ratchety, screeping' note at intervals, and thereafter kept close watch, at times coming within six feet of the observer and gazing at him intently with one or the other of her (?) white eyes. The bird continued to move about, now in the brush, then on the ground, in the latter case standing high on her long legs with tail up at a sharp angle to the back. She kept taking in worms (moth larvae), giving each fresh captive a thorough battering on some dead stick and then stuffing it with preceding ones into her bill and throat. Soon she had a mass of these protruding from either side of the bill; but still she failed to go to her nest. The other member of the pair (presumed to be the male) came near once or twice but soon went off again and called in usual wren-tit manner fifty yards or more away. The bird with worms in the bill called occasionally in slower cadence, but with the same distinctive quality to the utterance, it being in no wise muffled by her mouthful. Every bit of the ground adjacent was searched carefully and then the observer turned and gave similar attention to the canopy of brush above him, which showed many small dark masses against the sky. Finally the nest was located, merely a dark spot in the uppermost *Adenostoma* foliage, 7 feet above the ground, much higher than is usual for the nest of this species.

The nest was of globular form, thin-walled but deeply cupped, made of fine grayish vegetable substances which were bound together with cobweb. It rested in the spray of terminal foliage of a slanting greasewood stalk. There were three unfeathered young, and it was for these that the female had been gathering food and showing such cautious concern.

Through the nesting season and until late June or early July all of the wren-tits keep to their foothill haunts. But as soon as the young are fully fledged some of the birds commence to wander and a few range well beyond the limits of their home precincts. In all probability these strays are young-of-the-year as is the case with most other species given to vagrant travel in the late summer months. Our earliest record for a wren-tit above the Upper Sonoran Zone is for July 21 (1915) when one bird was heard near Cascades. On July 30 (the same year) 2 were heard near Rocky Point in Yosemite Valley; on August 17 one was noted near the same place; while on September 1 at least 2 were in evidence near the head of Nevada Falls. This last-named station and the walls of Tenaya Cañon at about the same altitude (6000 feet) seem to mark the eastern limit of the 'wander' zone; at least no wren-tit was seen by us beyond these places. The birds continue to occupy the brush thickets on the Valley wall through September and even to the end of October, two being noted October 30, 1915, high on the Yosemite Falls trail. And even on December 30, 1914, one or more wren-tits were noted close to 'old' Inspiration Point (4943 feet altitude) on the Big Oak Flat road. By spring if not earlier, the species has entirely withdrawn to the foothills.

The aggregate wren-tit population of the whole foothill country with its thousands of acres of chaparral is very large. Yet the birds are so spaced that their numbers are not so impressive as are those of a flocking species. Every little cañon has its pair or more of the birds. At Pleasant Valley in May, before the appearance of the annual broods, it was estimated that there was a pair of wren-tits to every 4 acres of greasewood. In early winter on the south-facing slope above El Portal 6 to 9 wren-tits were recorded for each hour of observation, the birds being in pairs and groups of 3 and 4.

The wren-tit is chiefly an insectivorous species although at times it takes food of a vegetable nature. Insects certainly predominate in the diet during the summer season, and on this sort of material, as indicated above, the young are probably exclusively fed. In fall and winter, berries are eaten to some extent. At the Campbell ranch north of Pleasant Valley several wren-tits were feeding, in company with hermit thrushes, upon berries of the toyon, and others were seen pecking at some old figs which had dried up on the trees.

WESTERN GOLDEN-CROWNED KINGLET. Regulus satrapa olivaceus Baird

Field characters.—Size very small, about one-third that of Junco; tail shorter than body. Crown of head orange and yellow (male) or golden yellow (female) bordered on either side by black; a white stripe over eye; upper surface of body chiefly green; under surface whitish; one or two light bars on wings. (See pl. 10b.) Movements quick, wings fluttered often. *Voice:* Song, a series of fine and wiry notes—*tse; tse, tse, tse-tse-tse-tse, tse, tse;* call notes similar but in shorter series.

Occurrence.—Moderately common, at least during summer season, in Canadian Zone (sparingly in Transition) on west slope of Sierra Nevada. Recorded from Hazel Green and Chinquapin eastward to slopes of Mount Hoffmann (at 8700 feet altitude) and to Merced Lake. Usually in Yosemite Valley throughout the year. Recorded on east side of mountains once, at Walker Lake, September 11, 1915. Inhabits terminal foliage of forest trees, chiefly conifers; in flocks of 4 to 15, usually about 5, except at nesting season when in pairs.

The Western Golden-crowned Kinglet gains its name from the patch of bright color on its head. In the male this is orange red at the center and yellow on the margins, while in the female it is only yellow; distinguishment of the sexes is thus possible in the field. With both sexes the 'crown' is bounded by black on the forehead and sides, and beneath this on each side is a white stripe running from the bill over the eye. The bright and handsome head marking in this species is exposed to view at all times, whereas the 'ruby' crown of its relative is exhibited only when that bird is excited. There are no conspicuous differences as to the body plumage in the two kinglets. (See pl. 10a, b.)

The range of the Western Golden-crowned Kinglet lies chiefly in the Canadian Zone, though some of the birds are usually to be found in the Transition Zone. In most years a few nest in Yosemite Valley, although in 1920 the species seemed to be entirely lacking there. In winter the range is much the same as in summer, there being little if any retreat from the higher altitudes, in so far as the facts at our disposal indicate. Numbers are to be found in Yosemite Valley in December, February, and March, and in all probability the same is true in the Canadian Zone fir belt above the Valley. The Golden-crowns do not visit the foothills to any extent; our only record below the Transition Zone is of one bird at 1700 feet altitude two miles below El Portal on December 18, 1914. On February 29, 1916, Western Golden-crowned Kinglets were the most common birds in Yosemite Valley, 25 being noted among the 51 birds all told recorded in a census which lasted 1½ hours.

Golden-crowned kinglets are to be found in small flocks from the time the broods appear in early summer until the beginning of the next nesting season. It seems not unlikely that some of these may be family groups which have never broken up, as a majority of the bands number about 5 individuals. Occasionally larger flocks are encountered; 3 groups observed in Yosemite Valley in the winter of 1914 had 8, 12, and 15 birds, respectively. Sometimes the kinglets have associated with them other small species such as the Mountain Chickadee and Sierra Creeper, but more often they remain by themselves.

In the vicinity of Feliciana Mountain in the fall of 1915 Golden-crowned Kinglets were abundant, and on October 29 particular attention was given to them. Six groups were heard and their numbers, on the basis of notes alone, were estimated at 2, 2, 2, 1, 2, and 3. Four more groups were sought out and their numbers ascertained by actual count, the results being 5, 6, 5, and 5. On this basis, in the fall months, we should expect to find about *five* Golden-crowned Kinglets in each small flock recorded by ear.

These birds forage in both coniferous and broad-leaved trees, but most of their time is spent in the former. Their food is obtained on the smaller branches and amid the needles and leaves and consists of small insects. At all times the birds are active, hopping lightly this way or that as occasion requires, and often fluttering the wings as a help, perhaps, in maintaining a certain position or in holding their balance when stretching out for some titbit otherwise beyond reach. The members of a flock keep in rather close proximity though each forages irrespectively of his neighbor.

The voice of the Western Golden-crowned Kinglet is so simple and weak as to be a decided disappointment to anyone who has heard and enjoyed the song of the Ruby-crown. The Golden-crown utters nothing but faint high-pitched lisping notes. The full song is a series of these beginning slowly, then given more rapidly, with one or two separated syllables at the end: *tse; tse, tse, tse-tse-tse-tse, tse, tse.* This is to be heard in the spring season and at least until the end of June. During the remainder of the year notes of similar character are uttered, but in shorter series, or singly. So far as we know this is the main difference between song and call in the Golden-crowned Kinglet. It seems rather odd that this bird should be so limited in vocabulary and weak of voice when its relative, the Ruby-crown, is such an elaborate and impressive singer.

There is considerable similarity between the notes of the Golden-crowned Kinglet and the Sierra Creeper. The kinglet's song is longer and the notes in the middle of it are run together more rapidly than are those in the creeper's song. In the winter months the Golden-crown usually utters several notes at a time, whereas the creeper gives at that season only a single or a two-part call. There are differences in timbre, but these can be learned only by following up individual birds of the two species under conditions which allow of comparison.

Mid-May finds the Golden-crowned Kinglets busy with nest building, and by June the parents are carrying food for the young. The latter appear abroad by July if not earlier. At Hazel Green on May 14, 1919, an adult bird (sex not ascertained) was seen about some small Douglas spruces carrying white downy material in the bill. The bird made off through two small white firs and thence into a large sugar pine, where, ascending to a height of 60 feet or more, it disappeared on an outswaying branch into a dark mass which looked like mistletoe.

In Yosemite Valley on May 18, 1919, a pair of Golden-crowned Kinglets was seen displaying considerable anxiety over the presence in a certain yellow pine near Stoneman Bridge of a Blue-fronted Jay. The kinglets were heard about the tree on several subsequent days, and finally on May 23 it was seen that they were actively engaged in nest construction. The site was about 25 feet above the ground and in a thick bunch of needles near the end of an almost horizontal branch about 8 feet long. The exact location was ascertained by watching the female as she carried a tuft of white cottony material directly to the site in a bee line through two adjacent trees. Several installments were brought in quick succession. Once the bird had procured a downy feather which she placed in the nest; but the wind took it away, whereupon she launched into the air and retrieved the feather, to replace it more securely in the nest. Only the female in this case seemed to be carrying material. The nest was, on this date (May 23), only well started, as the light of the sky could be seen through all parts of it by the observer stationed on the ground.

On June 12, 1915, Mrs. Joseph Grinnell saw a Golden-crowned Kinglet in a yellow pine near the old Presidio. The bird had its bill filled with insects and was evidently engaged in feeding a brood. Later in the same season, on July 24, one of our party found a kinglet nest in the same neighborhood, presumably the one used by this bird, 30 feet above the ground in a yellow pine. Upon being brought to hand the nest was found to have been torn open by some bird or mammal. In the substance of the nest the kinglets had included many cocoons of spiders. When the nest was found, it was swarming with young spiders. This nest contained some peculiarly marked feathers which proved to be those of a Saw-whet Owl and these constituted our first and for a long time our only local record for that species, as noted in another chapter.

WESTERN RUBY-CROWNED KINGLET. **Regulus calendula cineraceus** Grinnell

Field characters.—Size very small, about one-third that of Junco; tail shorter than body. Upper surface of body grayish green; under surface buffy white; one or two light bars across each wing, and a light ring around eye. Male has a crown patch of brilliant red, usually concealed, but capable of being flashed into view. (See pl. 10a, c.) Movements quick, nervous; flutters wings frequently. *Voice:* Song of male elaborate, resembling the syllables *see-see-see, oh, oh-oh, cheerily, cheerily, cheerily,* the last three 'words' loud and clearly whistled. Note of concern in summer season a two-syllabled *yer-rup*, repeated at intervals; usual call note a ratchet-like *chĕ*, produced in pairs or else in series for one to several seconds at a time.

Occurrence.—Common in summer in Canadian Zone (sparingly in upper Transition and lower Hudsonian) on Sierra Nevada; altitudes of occurrence chiefly between 5500 and 9000 feet. Recorded from Hazel Green and Chinquapin eastward to Warren Fork of Leevining Creek and to Walker Lake. Also common winter visitant in foothills and valleys on west side of mountains from El Portal and Smith Creek (east of Coulterville) westward to Lagrange and Snelling; transient around Mono Lake. Inhabits terminal foliage, chiefly that of trees; in pairs at nesting time, otherwise usually solitary.

The Western Ruby-crowned Kinglet while resembling its golden-crowned relative in certain respects exhibits a number of features of difference. It is for the most part a solitary bird, it performs a regular migration to lower altitudes for the winter season, and its voice is louder and its song is of quite a different kind from that of the Golden-crown.

In the Ruby-crown the bright crown patch is reserved to the adult male, the female and juvenal birds having no mark of color on the head. (See pl. 10a, c.) The ruby patch is normally nearly or quite concealed by the dull olive green feathering of the head, but it is flashed forth when the owner is excited or angered. Occasionally while foraging a kinglet will keep its red crown feathers in full view for some time. When two of the birds contest with one another over some forage precinct, or when several kinglets 'buzz' about a hawk or owl, the bright color is usually in marked display on each male.

The range of the Ruby-crowned Kinglet is somewhat more extensive than that of the Golden-crown, embracing on the west slope of the Sierras the territory between altitudes of 5500 and 9000 feet. The species occurs on the floor of Yosemite Valley (4000 feet) during some summer seasons, but not regularly or in any numbers. The Canadian Zone is everywhere occupied and is the metropolis for the Ruby-crown during the nesting season. In the Hudsonian Zone the birds are found in moderate numbers but do not seem to go to the upper limit of forest trees. Our highest record for them is 9200 feet on Warren Fork of Leevining Creek, and they are seldom encountered above 8600 feet.

The Ruby-crowned Kinglets leave the higher parts of the mountains (above the Transition Zone) in the fall, our latest records being for upper Yosemite Creek, October 6, 1915, and for Gentrys, October 23, 1915 (one bird). In the winter months the Ruby-crown deserts almost entirely even the Transition Zone; a single entry for Yosemite Valley on December 22, 1914, is our notation of the only exception to this statement. In 1920, however, Mr. C. W. Michael (MS) recorded the species in the Valley as common, and observed almost daily, from October 20 up until December 30. The species is in that season common in the foothill and valley country to the west, having been found by us in numbers at El Portal, Pleasant Valley, Lagrange, and Snelling. At the end of April (28 to 30) in 1916 Ruby-crowns were common once more in Yosemite Valley. East of the mountains near Williams Butte the first for that season were noted on April 29.

The population in the Canadian Zone during early summer is such that an observer will see or hear from two to four birds, usually the higher number, per hour of observation. In either the Hudsonian or Transition Zone this number will at least be halved. At Porcupine Flat 17 Ruby-crowns were noted in 5 hours on June 27, 1915; in Yosemite Valley 7 in 4 hours and 6 in 3½ hours were noted on two days at the end of April, 1916. The winter population in the foothills is denser than that in any part of the summer range. Twelve of these birds were recorded in 2½ hours at Snelling on January 6, 1915, and 8 in the same space of time at Sweetwater Creek on October 28, 1915. Early in the winter of 1914 Ruby-crowned Kinglets were exceedingly abundant at El Portal. About 25 were listed there in 3 hours on November 23; 3 to 5 individuals were observed in a single tree at one time.

Both of our kinglets are busy birds at all times, but the Ruby-crown shows even more activity than does its relative. Its temperament is of the high-strung or nervous sort, which keeps the bird constantly on the go—in decided contrast to the phlegmatic behavior of, for instance, the Hutton Vireo. The kinglet has relatively long legs, and standing up on these its body is kept well clear of any perch so that the bird can hop or turn readily in any direction. Such twists and jumps are often assisted by fluttering movements of the wings. Not infrequently a Ruby-crowned Kinglet will poise on rapidly moving wings while it picks off an insect from some leaf not to be reached from a foothold. In routine foraging the bird moves through the foliage rapidly, peering this way and that as it goes, spending but a moment in any one spot or pose.

The Ruby-crowned Kinglet lacks the sociable attribute of the Golden-crown. During the nesting season the pairs give close attention to the rearing of their broods, but as soon as the young are able to live independently the families break up and each individual takes up a separate existence. While in the foothill and valley country, the Ruby-crowns are to be seen singly, each keeping to a particular forage area and usually resisting approach by another of the same species. When something excites one of their kind, however, other individuals are quick to gather and all unite in a community of effort until the object of their concern has disappeared. Then each kinglet goes its way alone once more.

The Ruby-crowned Kinglet shows considerable latitude in its food-getting activities. Its normal forage beat is about the terminal foliage of trees, in the mountain conifers during the summer time, and around the foothill and valley oaks in the winter season. Other trees than evergreens are patronized, however. Absolutely leafless willows and alders in the dormancy of winter time are resorted to commonly. When searching the twigs of these in their usual fidgety manner the kinglets expose themselves much more prominently to view than at other times. Frequently a Ruby-crown will drop into the lower bushes for a time. Wherever the bird forages it usually stays in the outer zone of foliage, darting in and out in the way of an Audubon Warbler. At times a kinglet will fly out and capture insects passing in the open air, and now and then one of the birds will drop down to the greensward beneath a tree and skip or flutter along from place to place, clinging to the grass blades in such a way that it stands up out of contact with them in so far as is possible. At El Portal a Ruby-crowned Kinglet was seen to poise on hovering wings to drink sap oozing from some fresh punctures which had been made by a Red-breasted Sapsucker in the bark of a golden oak.

Much is to be heard in the way of either song or call notes from the Ruby-crowned Kinglet at all seasons of the year. The song season commences early in the spring, the birds sometimes being in full voice before they leave the lowlands; and complete songs are to be heard until as late as the first of July. In the fall, after the molt has been accomplished, the kinglets sometimes break forth in song once more, though it is not usually complete at that season. The song is distinctive, and easily recognized among all other bird voices. One portion of it is a clear and musical whistled utterance of surprising loudness for a bird which weighs less than a quarter of an ounce (6.2 grams). Two syllabifications of the complete song are as follows: *see, see, see, oh, oh, oh, property, property, property,* and *si-si-si, o, oh-oh, cheerily, cheerily, cheerily.* The beginning notes are attenuated, high-pitched, and, together with the low-pitched middle group, are of a quality that renders them inaudible beyond a few yards. The last portion, consisting of the 'words' "property" or "cheerily," is so clear and full as to carry to astonishingly great distance when atmospheric conditions are favorable. The insistent note of concern used so much in the springtime against the jays and owls sounds like repetition of the syllables *wer-rup* or *yer-rup*. Then there is the 'ratchet' note, *chĕ*, given in pairs or in rapid succession for varying lengths of time and at all seasons of the year. The last is the only note to be heard during most of the winter.

The bird student is often beholden to the Ruby-crowned Kinglet for calling attention to the presence of reclusive birds which might otherwise be overlooked by him. It was to a Ruby-crowned Kinglet that we owe our first definite record of the Great Gray Owl for the Yosemite region; and one of our specimens of the California Spotted Owl was located by reason of the telltale behavior of some of these little birds. On still another occasion the kinglets brought a California Pigmy Owl to our attention. The first two instances have already been detailed in the chapters relating to the owls in question; the third occurred at El Portal on December 6, 1914. At about nine o'clock in the morning one of our party noticed a remarkable assemblage of Ruby-crowned Kinglets about the foliage of a certain tree. Fifteen or more of the birds were buzzing about as actively and excitedly as bees, and each kinglet was uttering its 'ratchet call' with vigorous persistence. A couple of Plain Titmouses joined the group while it was being watched. The cause of the excitement became apparent when a pigmy owl flew out from the foliage of the tree. As the owl made off the crowd of excited kinglets followed in his wake.

In the nesting season Ruby-crowned Kinglets often give warning of the insidious activities of Blue-fronted Jays. On one occasion, at Chinquapin, on June 14, 1915, one of our party followed up a kinglet which was giving its *yer-rup, yer-rup*, over and over again in low but insistent tones. The cause of concern proved to be a pair of silent jays one of which was shot—to the seeming satisfaction of the kinglet, which immediately sang!

At the head of Peregoy Meadow a female Ruby-crowned Kinglet was watched at close range on May 20, 1919, as she was intently gathering bits of fiber or spider web from the twigs of a dead fir. Our expectations of locating a nest were aroused; but when the bird took flight it was to the middle heights of a huge red fir. She did not tarry there but went on and on from fir to fir, higher in each successive tree and was soon lost to view. Somewhere out on a cluster of needles near the end of a branch a nest was being built, but evidently in a location that would be wholly safe from all ground dwellers like ourselves. In the distance the male bird was voicing his clear melody over and over again.

A nest of the Ruby-crowned Kinglet was seen in an incense cedar close by the Sentinel Hotel Annex in Yosemite Valley in late May, 1903 (Widmann, 1904, p. 67).

WESTERN GNATCATCHER. **Polioptila caerulea obscura** Ridgway

Field characters.—Size small, near that of Kinglet but form slenderer; length about 4¼ inches; tail long, equal to body; bill slender, nearly as long as head. Top of head and back bluish gray; tail black centrally, with easily seen margin of white; under surface of body plain grayish white. Males have a narrow black band across forehead. Flight wavering, seemingly indecisive; when perched, tail is persistently 'wig-wagged.' *Voice:* Weak; a series of high-pitched wheezy notes, *zeu, zee, zree,* or *cheu, chee, chree,* three to six of such notes in a series; call notes of both sexes a flat *chee-y,* of similar quality.

Occurrence.—Common summer visitant throughout Upper Sonoran Zone on west slope of Sierra Nevada. Observed at Lagrange and Pleasant Valley and thence east to El Portal and to 6 miles east of Coulterville. Small numbers wander to higher zones after the nesting season; for instance, noted by us at 6300 feet altitude near Glacier Point, August 17, 1915, and at 10,300 feet on ridge near Fletcher Creek, September 4, 1915. Recorded in Yosemite Valley August 22 to September 10, 1920 (C. W. Michael, MS), and on September 25, 1917 (Mailliard, 1918, p. 19). Seen once east of the Sierras, at Williams Butte, September 21, 1915. Forages and nests chiefly in blue oaks, but also in digger pines and greasewood brush. In pairs or family parties, but never in larger assemblages as in the case of the Bush-tit.

The Western Gnatcatcher is a very small bird, of active temperament, which, by habits as well as structure, betrays relationship with the very differently colored kinglets. But instead of living in the mountain coniferous forests inhabited by the latter birds, the gnatcatcher, during the summer season, lives in the warm dry foothills which intervene between the heated San Joaquin Valley and the cooler upper altitudes of the mountains. The traveler who enters the Yosemite region along any of the roads from the west, upon arriving at the frontier outposts of blue oaks which are scattered over the first of the foothills far in advance of the digger pines and chaparral, will almost immediately be apprized of the gnatcatcher's presence there by hearing the fine wheezy notes of the bird. From these outlying foothill oaks on to the margin of the yellow pine belt, at the lower edge of the Transition Zone, the gnatcatcher is, during the summer months, one of the most abundant of birds.

The Western Gnatcatcher is migratory in the Yosemite region, arriving in numbers probably in April and departing in late fall. It was already present at El Portal on April 27 (1916). By early May the birds are busy with nesting duties, and as early as May 30 (1915) young have been noted out of the nest. After the breeding season, a few gnatcatchers wander up into the higher zones, as instanced above, but the bulk of the population remains in the foothills until the time of departure in the fall.

None was seen in early December and late February at either Pleasant Valley or El Portal.

During the early spring immediately after their arrival from the south, the gnatcatchers are to be seen in pairs, the male in close attendance upon the female. When the latter engages in the work of nest construction her mate remains in the vicinity, part of the time accompanying her on trips for building material or on foraging sorties. Otherwise he guards the nesting precincts against invasion of any rival male. All the while, in the heat of mid-afternoon as well as at other hours of the day, the male gnatcatcher utters his fine wheezy song at frequent intervals, and the female answers from time to time in similar tone of voice with single notes.

When settled for nesting each pair of gnatcatchers is strongly localized. Each keeps within a radius of not more than a hundred yards from the nest tree. This localization permits an observer to take a more accurate census of nesting pairs than is possible with many other birds. At Black's Creek, near Coulterville, our own counts led to an estimate of 64 breeding pairs of the Western Gnatcatcher to each square mile in that immediate district. Carrying these figures farther, in consideration of the estimated area of the Upper Sonoran Zone included in our Yosemite section, we find a total gnatcatcher population just before the appearance of the new broods, to consist of 50,000 individuals.

On the hills near Lagrange in early May, 1919, we found the Western Gnatcatchers busily engaged in building their nests in the blue oaks. One nest, complete but without eggs, found on May 8, may be regarded as typical for the species. It was situated about 10 feet above the ground near the periphery of the tree, amid small twigs and branchlets, and rested directly on a horizontal branch about 40 millimeters in diameter. Outside, it measured 80 millimeters in diameter and 45 millimeters in height; the cavity inside was 35 millimeters across—just the diameter to admit snugly the body of the brooding bird.

The nests are of deep cup-shape, and are constructed throughout of light-weight materials. A framework of fine grass stems forms the main wall, and this is covered both inside and out with softer substances. The outside is felted with lichens such as abound on the bark of blue oaks, with a few grass seed hulls, some small oak leaves, and occasionally a feather or two, the whole being held together with spider web. The inside of the nest is lined almost entirely with feathers, laid flat-ways of the inner surface. Whatever the purpose of the bird in constructing such a nest, the form and outside appearance are usually such that the structure might easily be mistaken for a weathered stub or a small accumulation of débris.

Other new nests were seen at Blacks Creek, west of Coulterville, on May 10 and 11, 1919. Some of these were on branches in situations similar to that of the one just described; others were in crotches of small blue oaks, and several were found in greasewood (chamisal) bushes, at a height of not more than 3 feet from the ground. The construction and dimensions were, in all of these nests, practically the same as those of the one described in detail above. Only the height above the ground varied.

One of the nests found at the latter locality on May 10 contained 5 eggs which the female had already begun to incubate. She was on the nest but snuggled so far down into the cavity that, seen from the ground, only her bill and tail, both held at steep angle, were visible above the rim. A casual glance would have passed the whole by as being an aggregation of twigs and leaves in the crotch of the tree. The bird's only act, when the observer climbed the slender tree in which the nest was placed, was to crouch even lower, as if she were endeavoring to escape detection. This sitting bird permitted herself to be touched on the back before quitting the nest.

A late instance of nesting was noted at Dudley, 6 miles east of Coulterville, on July 12, 1920. This was definitely accounted for by the fact that the first nest and its contents had been destroyed. The nest of date cited contained 3 eggs, one-third incubated. It was situated 17 feet above the ground on a crooked, dead and pendant branch of a large live black oak.

The eggs have a ground color of delicate green, and on this are many small rounded dots of reddish brown. The eggs usually number 4 or 5 to the set.

When foraging the Western Gnatcatcher is quick and seemingly nervous in its movements, constantly twitching about, so that, whether intentionally or not, the conspicuously marked black and white tail keeps the bird easily in the eye of the observer. Its temperament is quite the opposite of that of the vireos and some of the wood warblers, which act with a decided air of deliberation. The gnatcatcher has not, however, the spasmodic flutter of the wings which characterizes the Ruby- and Golden-crowned kinglets. The flight of the Western Gnatcatcher is wavering and indirect, and carries the bird rather slowly across the short intervals which it is accustomed to traverse between trees.

Townsend Solitaire. **Myadestes townsendi** (Audubon)

Field characters.—Body about one-third bulk of Robin; tail long, as long as body. General coloration gray; tail narrowly white margined; a narrow circle of white around eye. (See pl. 11a.) A broad band of pale buff shows forth on middle of wing in flight. Demeanor quiet; flight rather slow, faltering. *Voice:* Male has an elaborate song comparable in some respects with that of Black-headed Grosbeak; call note a mellow metallic *clink;* less often a harsh *chack.*

Occurrence.—Moderately common summer visitant in Canadian Zone (locally in Transition); more numerous on west slope of Sierra Nevada than on east side. Recorded from Hazel Green and Chinquapin eastward to Tenaya and Merced lakes; also near Mono Craters. Common during winter season in Transition Zone as in Yosemite Valley, about

El Portal, and on slopes above Coulterville. In fall recorded once at Tuolumne Meadows, and commonly at Glen Aulin, and, on eastern slope, on Tioga road near Warren Fork of Leevining Creek and on Williams Butte. During summer lives in forest, chiefly amid red firs, males singing at tops of trees, females nesting on ground. At other seasons frequents berry-producing trees and shrubs. Solitary or loosely gregarious.

Well rewarded are those nature lovers who upon visiting the Yosemite climb to the slopes far above the Valley floor to listen to the song of the Townsend Solitaire. The bird may be sought for with confidence in the deep fir forest just south of Glacier Point, or on the timbered slopes above Yosemite Point and along the Eagle Peak trail. The song season is not, as with many birds, restricted to the spring and early summer; but the autumn and even winter witnesses occasional outbursts of song, fully as melodious as those of the summer, and more impressive in the prevailing chill and silence.

The plain gray coloration and comparatively long tail of the Townsend Solitaire readily distinguish it from all other birds save perhaps the female or young of the California Pine Grosbeak. The solitaire has in addition a narrow white marking on the tail, a buff bar on the wing which shows clearly when the bird is in flight, and a small bill; any or all of these features will serve to distinguish it from the grosbeak. (See pl. 11a.) Furthermore, the solitaire keeps to the Canadian and Transition zones, whereas the pine grosbeak rarely strays from the higher Hudsonian Zone; the two will therefore not likely be seen in the same place. Young (juvenal) solitaires are heavily mottled on the breast, much in the manner of thrushes and young robins, thereby perhaps indicating their relationship; but this 'family' resemblance (in a systematic sense) disappears at the first fall molt, and the young then become indistinguishable from their parents.

The Townsend Solitaire as a species does not, in the Yosemite region, make much of a change in its haunts with the passage of the seasons. In summer the majority are to be found in and about the red fir forests of the Canadian Zone. At other times of year the birds forage and live in the western junipers which often grow close by on rocky slopes, or else they drop to the Transition Zone where mistletoe berries on the golden oaks afford bounteous forage. There are no solitaires in Yosemite Valley during the summer months, but with the coming of winter the oaks on the talus slopes become tenanted by numbers of the birds. We ourselves did not find the species at any station lower than El Portal (altitude 2000 feet) where it was seen but once, on March 1, 1916; but Mr. Donald D. McLean reports that solitaires are fairly common on the slopes above Coulterville (at 2000 feet altitude or higher) during some winters. The movements of the species during the winter are controlled chiefly by the food supply, in the form of berries.

As an indication of the numbers in which this bird occurs in the Yosemite region, we cite the following notebook censuses. Along the trail to Eagle Peak, on June 4, 1915, 8 were seen or heard between 12:30 and 4:10 P.M. Among the junipers on a south-facing slope near Glen Aulin, on September 30, 1915, 23 were seen in 3 hours. Three were seen and 8 heard in 20 minutes on the Big Oak Flat grade, at 4500 feet altitude, on December 28, 1914. These last two enumerations are maxima, the result of concentration where conditions were most favorable for the species.

The song of the Townsend Solitaire must be heard to be appreciated. No description can suffice. The notes are many of them clear, rich, and full, but of a sort which does not permit of rendition in syllables of human speech. In general effect the song resembles most closely that of the Black-headed Grosbeak, while certain notes or phrases recall the songs of the Western Mockingbird and California Thrasher. The song lacks set character, being much varied, and it is long sustained. 'Rests' of greater or less length are interpolated at irregular intervals. In summer much singing is done in the early morning and late afternoon hours; in colder weather some of the best songs are heard during the middle of the day. During the courting and nesting season the males do most of their singing while perched near the tops of lofty firs, but in the fall and early winter the birds sing in the low-growing junipers or oaks not many feet above the ground. A lofty circling flight accompanied by voluble singing is sometimes witnessed, again reminding the observer of the Black-headed Grosbeak.

The usual call given by the Townsend Solitaire is a single *clink*, not loud yet far-carrying, metallic yet mellow. It has been likened to the creaking of a wood-wagon coming down a cañon, or to the sound produced by an old windlass. The quality is such that it seems to echo, first from one direction, then from another. "Bell-like" has been used as a descriptive term, but fails to quite express the idea. To some hearers this note is so much like the whistle of the California Ground Squirrel that the observer is tempted to seek as the source of the note a mammal on the ground rather than a bird at the top of a tree. And, indeed, the peculiar ventriloquial quality serves to further this misdirection of attention. Less often, and, so far as our experience goes, only during the winter season, a solitaire when highly excited will utter a harsh *chack*, much like the note of a Red-winged Blackbird.

The bird student, to find the nest of the Townsend Solitaire, would search in vain the lofty trees where the male bird does his singing, for the female places her nest far below, on the ground. A steeply cut bank with protruding rootlets and niches left by dislodged stones, or the tangle of roots and earth at the base of some overturned forest tree makes a favored nesting place. The nest departs widely from the type constructed by robins and thrushes, not being composed of mud, and being so loosely put together that it can seldom be lifted intact from its placement.

A typical nest was found beside the Glacier Point road at about the 7000 foot level two miles above Chinquapin in June, 1915. (See pl. 55b.) It was in a cut bank, three feet above the road and two feet below the top of the bank, in a depression in the earth between rocks and at the base of a young fir tree the outstretching roots of which partially concealed the nest. As is usual with the solitaire, a straggling 'tail' or apron of material extended down the bank a foot or so from the nest proper. The constituent materials of the latter were slender dead fir twigs and old, brown needles of sugar and Jeffrey pines. Inside, the nest was about 3 inches (80 mm.) across and 2 inches (50 mm.) deep. On June 10 there were 2 eggs, by June 12, 4. On each visit to the nest the female bird was seen sitting, but she slipped off quietly and flew out of sight up the road. Once the male was heard singing from among the dense firs near by.

Solitaires at nesting time are notably unobtrusive birds. They haunt shady places. Their color tone is neutral. They can keep perfectly still, minutes at a time, and when they do move their motions are of a sort which do not catch the observer's eye quickly. Thus a female solitaire, whose nesting site is in plain view at the side of a well-traveled road, may come and go throughout the whole nesting period without ever giving any clear indication that her interests in the locality are more than casual. Her attitude, to outward appearances, is wholly the opposite of that of a robin or a junco.

During spring and summer the Townsend Solitaire subsists mainly upon insects, many of which it captures on the wing, flycatcher-fashion. The flight of the bird, however, is not swift; nor is it direct, as is that of the Olive-sided Flycatcher, for example; it reminds one rather of the Say Phoebe, in that the wings are widely spread and flapped rather slowly, and the flight course is irregularly circuitous. A solitaire watched July 1, 1915, at the head of the upper Yosemite Falls trail, was keeping close about the garbage cans maintained at the shaded lunch grounds there. The bird every now and then flew out past a can in pursuit of some foraging insect; then he sought another nearby perch, where he would sit quietly with only an occasional turn of the head. The light eye-ring gave the bird a large-eyed, passive expression, quite the opposite of that of the sharp-eyed, alert warblers. Sometimes a solitaire will perch on boulders or rocks on the ground, where it looks still more like a Say Phoebe.

Through the nesting season the solitaire, as we have said, is a rather reclusive species; but in fall and early winter its demeanor changes. Then, in suitable places, it is one of the most active and most conspicuous of the birds present. Near our camp in Glen Aulin during late September

c

a. Townsend Solitaire.   *b.* Russet-backed Thrush.   *c.* Sierra Hermit Thrush.

and early October of 1915, solitaires had congregated in considerable numbers to feast on the then abundant, ripening berries of the western juniper. The birds were busiest in the morning and along toward evening, but the middle of the day brought only slight diminution in their activity. Just as the sun came up over the rocky ridges to the east and touched the tips of the junipers, the solitaires would break forth in song nearly or quite as ecstatic as that of early summer, excelling in both quality and volume all other voices in the Glen. Sometimes during the mid-day hours one individual would give chase to another and occasionally a third bird joined the pursuit. Not infrequently one or another of the group would burst into song as it flew. No other bird of the Yosemite, except perhaps the American Dipper, seems to have quite such a revival of song in the fall as does the solitaire. The pleasant warmth of the mid-day sun and the melodious songs of the solitaires made it difficult to believe that the season was autumn. Only when one noted the dead dry herbage and the falling leaves was the near approach of winter manifest.

Examination of the ground beneath the trees where these birds were assembled revealed many berries of the season, still green, which had been pulled off, crushed in the bill, and then dropped. Not only were these numerous, but dried berries of previous crops were found with similar 'bill marks,' indicating that in years gone by the solitaires had resorted to these same trees during the fall months. A bird taken at this time was found to have nothing in its stomach and gizzard except the berries and seeds of the juniper.

At Gentrys, on December 28, 1914, with much snow on the ground there, Solitaires were plentiful, and were feeding on the dry berries of the Mariposa manzanita (*A. mariposa*), along with Western Robins and Varied Thrushes.

The stands of golden oaks, so heavily parasitized by mistletoe, which cover the warm sun-facing slopes on the north side of Yosemite Valley, are extensively patronized by solitaires during the winter time. At almost any hour of the day, from late September until the end of December and possibly even later, the birds may be sought there with assurance. There, as among the junipers, the diet is a monotonous one, consisting solely of mistletoe berries, which the birds swallow entire. The fleshy part of the berry is dissolved off, leaving a sticky-coated seed. Two of these were found adhering to the tail feathers of a captured solitaire, and the excrement of the birds contained many of the seeds. This suggests that the solitaire is quite likely an agent, along with the bluebirds, in distributing this parasite. This three-cornered arrangement between oaks, mistletoe, and solitaires has probably been in age-long existence, fluctuating in one direction or another according to the fortunes of the individual members.

RUSSET-BACKED THRUSH. **Hylocichla ustulata ustulata** (Nuttall)

Field characters.—Size nearly twice that of Junco; bill short and slender. Whole upper surface plain brown; wing with a concealed band of buffy which shows in flight; breast buffy with scattered triangular spots of brown; sides brownish, not streaked; belly white; eye surrounded by a narrow ring of buff. (See pl. 11b.) Movements deliberate. *Voice:* Song of male a set theme, 2 to 4 deep clear notes, then an equal number of slurred ones, ascending in pitch, the last one finely attenuated; call note a soft whistled *what* or *whoit;* less often a harsher *chee-ur-r.*

Occurrence.—Summer visitant in Transition Zone on west slope of Sierra Nevada. Recorded as nesting in Yosemite Valley and in vicinity of Bower Cave, and as a transient at Snelling and Pleasant Valley, and near Coulterville. Keeps to low growths near streams, males going up into trees to sing. Solitary.

The Russet-backed Thrush is extremely local in its occurrence in the Yosemite region. In fact we found it at nesting time only on the floor of Yosemite Valley and in the vicinity of Bower Cave. In the Valley it is usually present in some numbers and during the early part of the season may be heard in song about many of the camps.

This species resembles the Hermit Thrush in general appearance though it can be told easily from that bird. (See pl. 11.) The Russet-back is uniformly colored above, having no rufous tinge on the upper surface of the tail; it does not twitch its wings or raise and lower its tail in the manner of the Hermit Thrush. In point of size the present species is the larger, in the ratio of about 32 to 25, the average weight in grams for the two; but this difference in bulk is not enough for separating the two thrushes out of hand. The songs and calls are totally different and whenever heard are the most certain means of identifying their possessors.

In the month of May Russet-backed Thrushes are likely to be encountered as transients at almost any station in the foothill country. We noted the species at Snelling on May 26 to 29, 1915, and at Pleasant Valley on May 24 and 25 the same year. In 1919 it was observed near Coulterville on May 10 and 11. All the birds seen by us at these places acted as though they were merely resting and foraging while en route to more northern localities. Through much of May and on until some time in July Russet-backed Thrushes are much in evidence in Yosemite Valley, but they begin to disappear toward the end of the latter month and are seen but seldom thereafter. It is not known whether the bulk of the population migrates early or not; more likely their added reclusiveness at the season of molt tends to remove them from human view. Mr. C. W. Michael (MS) who kept continuous record of the birds in Yosemite Valley during the season of 1920 observed the Russet-backed Thrush almost daily until July 24. Thereafter it was noted upon but three occasions, namely, August 27, and September 1 and 11. And each of these records was for only a single bird.

The demeanor of this thrush is quiet and reserved. The bird inhabits by preference the rank growth of stream-side vegetation, departing from this only when the male happens to go up some distance in a nearby tree to sing. In migration time when passing through the lowlands the Russet-backs keep to the same sort of cover as is chosen by them for their summer haunts.

By early June, and sometimes sooner, the Russet-backed Thrushes in Yosemite Valley are in full song and may be heard during the day as well as in the morning and evening hours. The song is set in character and each individual thrush begins his song on about the same key—not changing from song to song as does the Hermit. The first syllables of any individual's song are always of the same pitch, and full, clear, and deep; the remainder are more wiry, ascending, and sometimes the last one goes up so high in pitch as to become almost a squeal: *wheer, wheer, wheer, whee-ia, whee-ia, whee-ia,* or *quer, quer, quer, quee-ia, quee-ia, quee-ia.* The call note oftenest heard is a soft liquid whistle, *what* or *whoit,* sounding much like the drip of water into a barrel. An imitation of this note by the observer will often bring a thrush into close range. Now and then a thrush will give an abrupt burred cry, *chee-ur-r;* and again there may be a single whistle, louder and higher than the usual call. The song season lasts until early July, after which the birds become quiet. By the end of the month not even the call note is to be heard.

The nest is located in some bush in the vicinity of a stream. One found in Yosemite Valley on June 24, 1915, may be described as typical in structure though it was placed a little higher than usual. This particular nest was at a height of 7 feet above the ground, settled firmly in the crotch of a willow where three branches about one-fourth of an inch in diameter gave ample support. The structure was bulky, 6 inches in height and about 4 in diameter on the outside, with the cavity about two and a half inches deep and the same in diameter. The material used was chiefly dry willow bark, with some grass stems and blades, a few pine needles, leaf 'skeletons' and weed stems. There was no moss on the outside, nor was there horsehair within, the lining being of loosely placed fine stems and roots. Just without the lining of the nest cup was a layer of dried sandy mud, "as firm as though cement were mixed with it," the notebook states (Mrs. Joseph Grinnell, MS). On the 24th the four young were nearly ready to leave and this they had done by the 26th, though they were still in the vicinity on the latter date, for the anxious calls of the parent birds were heard in adjacent trees.

Two nests of the Russet-backed Thrush were found in Yosemite Valley on June 28, 1915, by Miss Margaret W. Wythe (MS). One of these contained 3 young birds about half-grown. The other nest held 2 young birds just out of their shells, and 2 eggs which hatched on the 30th.

HERMIT THRUSHES.　**Hylocichla guttata** (Pallas)[39]

Field characters.—Decidedly larger than Junco, but not so large as Russet-backed Thrush; bill short and slender.　Upper surface plain brown, rufous tinged on tail; ring of buff around eye; wing with a concealed band of buffy, shown forth in flight; breast buffy with numerous triangular dark spots; sides grayish, not streaked; belly white. (See pl. 11c.)　Manner quiet; every few seconds, when bird is perched, the ends of the wings are spasmodically twitched and the tail is elevated and then slowly depressed. *Voice:* Song of male clear and musical, consisting of phrases uttered at varying intervals, each phrase of three to six 'words,' with the pitch of successive phrases now high, now low, etc.; usual call note a rather low soft *sup*.

Occurrence.—Common summer visitant on west slope of Sierra Nevada, chiefly in Canadian Zone; also spring transient near Mono Lake (subspecies *sequoiensis*).　Fall visitant at all altitudes on west slope, and winter visitant there below level of heavy snow (subspecies *guttata* and *nanus*).[39]　Keeps chiefly to wooded glades and ravine bottoms in summer; in winter affects sheltered situations generally, even chaparral.　Solitary.

The Hermit Thrush, as a species, exhibits in extreme degree the unobtrusiveness of manner which characterizes many other members of the thrush family.　It is garbed in plain colors of subdued tone, it has a sedate bearing, and save when singing its regular song is notably silent.　The bird does not restrict itself to thick foliage as does the Varied Thrush and yet it does not forage out far beyond the cover of the vegetation in the way of the robin, choosing, rather, territory of intermediate nature.　In summer the birds live in shaded glades amid coniferous trees or in sheltered cañon bottoms; in winter, when the species is more abundantly represented, the Hermits are found in similar places and also under the cover of chaparral on the hillsides.

Visitors in Yosemite Valley in some years have been fortunate in finding Hermit Thrushes settled fearlessly within the limits of one or more of the tent cities.　Here the birds are seen most often at dusk, or, if at

---

[39] Three closely similar subspecies of the Hermit Thrush have been found in the Yosemite region.　These are so much alike that they probably cannot be distinguished in life; the Sierran race is the only one present in summer.

SIERRA HERMIT THRUSH, *Hylocichla guttata sequoiensis* (Belding), a relatively large sized, pale-colored subspecies (pl. 11c) which summers from the Cascade Mountains to southern California, was found by us from Hazel Green and Chinquapin eastward through Yosemite Valley to Washburn Lake and Tuolumne Meadows.　It was already present at Hazel Green on May 13, 1919, and was recorded at Washburn Lake August 28, 1915; a single individual was collected at Ten Lakes, October 8, 1915.　One was noted at Mono Lake Post Office on May 23, 1916.

ALASKA HERMIT THRUSH, *Hylocichla guttata guttata* (Pallas), a smaller race of medium-brown tone of color found in summer in southwestern and interior Alaska, is a common winter visitant on the west slope of the Yosemite region from Yosemite Valley westward to Pleasant Valley and Lagrange.　The earliest definite record of arrival is for October 6, 1915, on Yosemite Creek at 7500 feet altitude.

DWARF HERMIT THRUSH, *Hylocichla guttata nanus* (Audubon), a smaller, dark-colored form whose summer range embraces the coast strip of southeastern Alaska, comes to the Yosemite region as a winter visitant in fair numbers.　It has been recorded from Glen Aulin (October 4, 1915) westward to Sweetwater Creek at 3800 feet altitude.

mid-day, where the shade is deepest, running along the narrow streets between the tents, just as they do, elsewhere, along the forest aisles.

In size the Hermit Thrush is about one-third the bulk of a robin. It is slightly smaller than the Russet-backed Thrush, but size alone will not serve readily to distinguish these two. (See pl. 11.) The Hermit has the upper side of the tail from its base strongly tinged with rufous, whereas the Russet-back is of the same brown color over the entire upper surface. Furthermore, the hermit thrush has a notable mannerism of twitching its wings spasmodically every few seconds, a movement often accompanied by a slow downward motion of the tail. These movements serve to identify the bird when it is in the shade where color features are of no avail.

The hermit thrush population of the Yosemite section is changed entirely each spring and fall. The birds which are present and nest in the region belong to a pale-toned subspecies designated as the Sierra Hermit Thrush. These arrive from the south and are already established by mid-May. Nesting begins soon afterward and the birds depart by the end of August. Then a short period ensues when there are few or no hermit thrushes in the region. By the latter part of September, birds which have nested in various parts of southern Alaska begin to arrive, to spend the winter here. In the fall the Dwarf and Alaska hermit thrushes, as the two races from the north are called, occur in considerable numbers at all altitudes below 9000 feet. The arrival of heavy snow forces most of those in the higher zones to below the 4000 or 3500 foot contour. Our records show the following examples of late tarrying at the higher altitudes. On the snowy morning of December 10, 1914, a hermit thrush was found in a dogwood thicket in Tenaya Cañon one-fourth of a mile above Mirror Lake; and on December 28 of the same year, 2 were seen at 5250 feet on the Big Oak Flat road near Gentrys. The latter were in thickets of the sticky-berried manzanita (*Arctostaphylos mariposa*).

The demeanor of the hermit thrush is quiet and deliberate. When foraging on the ground it acts in much the same manner as a robin, hopping several times in quick succession and then halting upright and immobile for a few seconds to scan the immediate vicinity before going forward again. There is this important difference, however: the hermit thrush seldom forages out in the open, and if it does it never goes far away from cover, to which it can flee in case of need. When foraging on shaded ground strewn with dead leaves its characteristic performance is to seize a leaf in its bill and throw it to one side with a very quick movement of the head, following this with an intent gaze at the spot uncovered. A thrush will flick over leaf after leaf in this manner, every now and then finding some insect which is swallowed, as is a berry, at one gulp. Hermit thrushes thus make use of a source of food not sought after by other birds;

fox sparrows may forage over the same ground, but they are after seeds, which they get at by scratching. The thrushes do not use their feet at all for uncovering food. The thrushes' legs are relatively long, so that the birds stand high, and have consequently an increased scope of vision.

If a hermit thrush is come upon while not busy foraging, the bird will often stand quietly on its perch and watch the passer-by seemingly with wide-eyed curiosity. Close approach is often permitted, especially on dull days, though there is no reason to suppose that the thrush is less able to see well then than in bright sunlight. In fact the reverse may be true, for hermit thrushes are most conspicuously active at dusk. In this connection attention may be called to the fact that thrushes in general are big-eyed as compared with finches of equal bulk. (See fig. 59.)

a   b

Fig. 59. Heads of (*a*) Sierra Hermit Thrush and (*b*) Cassin Purple Finch, natural size, showing the relatively large eye of a shade-inhabiting bird (Thrush) as contrasted with that of a species which lives chiefly in the open (Purple Finch). Also the difference in bill is shown between an insect- and berry-feeding bird as contrasted with bud- and seed-eater.

Every kind of bird has some feature of exceptional interest to the bird student. With some species it is brilliancy of plumage, with others peculiarity of nesting habits. With the plainly-garbed and retiringly-disposed hermit thrush it is the bird's song which attracts and holds our interest. Few if any among the birds of the region excel the hermit thrush in impressiveness of song. The utterance is clear, highly musical and agreeable to our ears, not especially joyful but inducing in the human listener a pleasant reverie. Structurally, the song is varied, not at all monotonous as is that of the robin. It consists of phrases separated by rests of one to two seconds duration, each phrase consisting of three to six syllables. Successive phrases are pitched on different keys, one low, another high, a third midway of the bird's scale. Each begins with a clear full-toned whistled or flute-like syllable and ends with a tinkle, in quality suggesting an overtone. The notes of one bird listened to at Chinquapin were written: *sur-wheel-yer-eel-yer; poor, aurelia-elia; seer, eetle-eetle; sir, wortle-ortle; per, wheetly-eetly*, etc. When singing a thrush will sit motionless near the top of a small tree and may maintain its perch there for a long period of time, though not continually in voice. The song season lasts from some time in spring until early July, our latest record being of a bird's singing at Tuolumne Meadows on July 8 (1915).

The common call note is a soft *chuck* or *sup*, often doubled. It is not likely to be confused with the call note of the Russet-back. On rarer occasions, the hermit thrush gives a quite different, hoarse, not loud squall, *tshee* or *kschee*, somewhat like one call note of the Spurred Towhee but more metallic.

The hermit thrush usually places its nest not far above the ground in a small coniferous tree standing in some shaded spot. At Tuolumne Meadows on July 4, 1915, we found and visited repeatedly a nest which was 4½ feet above the ground in one of a clump of young alpine hemlocks. There were three plain blue eggs. The bird which was doing the work of incubation was fairly tame, not quitting the nest until the observer was close at hand. She would fly a short distance away and then hop about on the ground. On July 13 the eggs were still unhatched, and as the nest was tilted and one egg had rolled out on the ground it was assumed that the parents had been frightened into deserting their home.

As already intimated, the hermit thrush does much of its foraging on the ground where during the summer it gets a variety of food including many insects. But in the winter season, like most members of the thrush family, it partakes to a large extent of berries. At El Portal in December one of these birds was seen feeding upon toyon berries, as was another at Pleasant Valley. Other individuals were seen to take the sticky sweet berries of the manzanita (*A. mariposa*), and remains of several of these small fruits were found in the crop of a bird collected on Sweetwater Creek November 1, 1915.

WESTERN ROBIN. **Planesticus migratorius propinquus** (Ridgway)

Field characters.—Size medium (length 10 inches); bill slender; tail nearly as long as body. Lower surface of body bright reddish brown; upper surface plain dark slate gray, blackish on head and tail; chin white; area under base of tail white. Young birds have under surface of body pale reddish and conspicuously marked with rounded black spots (fig. 60). When on ground moves rapidly, either walking or hopping; stops abruptly and fixedly in upright posture for a few seconds after each advance. Flight steady, not undulating. *Voice:* Of male, a loud caroling song. Both sexes utter short calls, some of them sounding like squeals; these given singly or in various combinations.

Occurrence.—Common summer visitant to forested portions of the Yosemite region from near Bullion Mountain, El Portal, and 3 miles east of Coulterville, eastward across the Sierra Nevada to Mono Lake Post Office; most abundant in Transition Zone on west slope, less numerous at the higher altitudes and on the east side of the mountains. Also common as a winter visitant in foothills of the west slope from El Portal and 6 miles east of Coulterville west to Pleasant Valley. A few remain in Transition Zone, as in Yosemite Valley, in certain winters. Forages chiefly on open grasslands in summer and generally in berry-producing trees and bushes in winter. Seeks open branches of trees for singing and roosting. In pairs or family groups during nesting season; in loose flocks up to 50 or more at other times of year.

The robin, of all our birds, least needs an introduction. For this reason we have used it as the standard of comparison for most medium sized birds of the region. Summer travelers in the Sierra Nevada recognize the Western Robin at once as characteristic of the mountains, inhabiting the small meadows which floor the openings in the coniferous forests; people who live in the foothills and valleys of California know the bird as a winter visitor to their orchards, fields, and gardens. Upon the establishment of towns within either its winter or summer range the robin quickly becomes a dooryard bird, regardless of whether the dooryards are those of permanent houses or those of the ephemeral tent cities which, as in Yosemite Valley, grow and vanish with the passage of each summer.

The robin population varies greatly according to place and season. In nesting time the birds are found only in the Transition, Canadian, and Hudsonian zones, in other words, in the boreal parts of the country; and even within this territory their numbers are not uniform, being greatest in the Transition Zone, as exemplified by Yosemite Valley, and smallest about the relatively sparse forests of the Hudsonian Zone, as about Tuolumne Meadows. On the east slope of the Sierras their numbers at best are small.

With the cessation of nesting activities the ties which hold the robins to their summer haunts are broken and the birds begin to range more widely. Food then seems to be the controlling factor in their distribution and continues to be so until they return to their breeding grounds the following spring. An abundance of easily obtained berries may bring about a local concentration of robins in one of the upper zones, and conversely a dearth of forage in the mountains may result in an early departure to the foothills, where adequate forage happens to be obtainable. In 1915 Western Robins were present in the high mountains until late, being seen at Ten Lakes on October 10 and at Aspen Valley on October 15; in Yosemite Valley they were present in numbers up until November 8, when there was a good fall of snow. The next day few robins were to be seen, nor were more than single individuals encountered thereafter, although we remained in the Valley that year until November 22.

Only a few venturesome robins continue in the mountains above the 3000-foot level during the Sierran winter. Two were noted near Clark Bridge in Yosemite Valley on December 10, 1914, and 10 at Gentrys on the Big Oak Flat road on December 30, 1914. On December 28, 1915, about 150 robins were reported at Crane Flat by one of the Park rangers, although no reason was suggested for such a concentration of the birds at that elevation on the date mentioned. In the foothills during the winter months robins are abundant. At Pleasant Valley, 117 were noted in a 3-hour census on December 4, 1915. The return to the higher mountains is accomplished by the birds as early as food conditions permit, irrespective of weather. Only 5 were seen at Pleasant Valley in a 3½-hour census on February 27, 1916; yet the population had not moved much higher into the mountains since none was noted in Yosemite Valley the following day. By the end of April (1916), however, robins had appeared in usual numbers in Yosemite Valley. East of the mountains, the robin population is doubtless altogether absent during the winter months.

In late spring and throughout the summer the robins go about in pairs when one or the other bird is not in attendance at the nest. After the young are grown, family parties are to be seen for a while. As soon as the young are capable of getting their living independently they gather into flocks. Meanwhile the adults go off by themselves and remain sequestered until completion of their annual molt. Then, in late September, the robins, without regard to sex or age, gather into mixed flocks and, for the most part, spend the winter in such gatherings. These flocks include anywhere from 4 or 6 up to half a hundred

Fig. 60. Western Robin in juvenal plumage. Photographed on a porch in Yosemite village, July 31, 1915.

individuals. We observed flocks of 10 to 20 in many places in the mountains during September and October, 1915. The flock formation is always loose, and individuals leave and rejoin it at will. For a species like the Western Robin, which subsists largely on crops which fluctuate greatly from year to year as well as from place to place, the flocking habit must be of decided advantage as an aid in locating an adequate supply of food.

The two sexes are very much alike in the robin. Male birds are slightly the larger, their breasts are on the average darker colored, and their bills in summer are nearly clear yellow. Some females are as dark colored on the breast as the lighter males, but their bills are always more or less tinged with dusky. Specimens of robins collected in the late summer show that the plumage of the female is more worn than is that of the male. This may be taken to indicate that to the female falls the greater proportion of the engrossing duties of incubation and caring for the brood. The young, in juvenile plumage, have many rounded black spots which are sharply defined against the whitish or buffy under surface of the body, and the feathers of the back have whitish shaft streaks and black tips.

(See fig. 60.) At the post-juvenal molt, in August and early September, the young assume a plumage much like that of their parents; birds of different ages cannot thereafter be distinguished readily in the field. The molt of the adults is not completed until about the first of October. The new feathers of the back have an olive tinge, and those of the lower surface are tipped with white; but these markings are lost by wear as the winter progresses, and give way to the clear slate back and red breast.

The niche occupied by the robin changes with the season. In nesting time the birds live near or upon the ground, save that the males perch high for singing in the morning and evening. They keep to the vicinity of openings in the forest, where there are small trees in which to place their nests and where there is, at the same time, grassland adjacent in which they may forage for worms and insects. The rest of the year they hunt their provender, then largely of a vegetable nature, in trees and bushes, and, for the most part, they fly and perch high above the ground.

The demeanor of a foraging robin depends upon the sort of food the bird is seeking. When hunting insects or worms on the ground, as in a meadow, it will run or hop several paces rapidly and directly, and then stop abruptly ('freeze') in an erect posture and remain very quiet for several seconds before making another advance. Now and then, a robin so engaged will be seen, at the end of an advance, to thrust its bill down into the turf and get something which is swallowed in a demonstrative manner. Presumably hearing as well as sight plays a part in this kind of foraging, and the short periods of quiet and immobility may be for the purpose both of listening and watching for prey which is moving.

The ground foraging habits of the robin are quite distinctive, and, to our way of thinking, effective. After a brief but intent survey of its immediate surroundings, if nothing be discovered, the bird moves speedily on to another location, a few paces distant, and there begins anew its close scrutiny. Only a minimum of time is used in changing position. In this way the Robin covers a large amount of territory rapidly, yet with a high degree of thoroughness. It thus combines the habits of two groups of birds which forage in entirely different ways, those which wait passively in one place and watch for *moving* prey, and those which hunt actively after food which is *stationary*. The erect posture assumed by the robin obviously gives the bird a wider field of vision from any one spot, and enables it to see better down into the bases of the grass clumps. The worms and insect larvae which form the bulk of the food obtained in this manner of foraging live, not on the exposed parts of the meadow vegetation, but about the bases of the grass tussocks. The bird probably locates many of these worms by seeing the upper parts of the grass blades move as the worms crawl among or feed upon the roots, just as we sometimes detect the presence of a pocket-gopher by seeing a plant shake violently when the animal is gnawing at the root. The periods of quiet between the changes of position by the robin probably subserve another function, namely, that of permitting the worms to become active again after their initial alarm. Any person who has dug angleworms for fishing will recall how sensitive the worms are to ground vibrations, even of a very slight nature, and how the worms will withdraw into their burrows and remain there until the disturbance has ceased. It may well be that these quiet poses by the robin give the worms time for reassurance, time to become active again, and thereby to betray their locations to the foraging bird.

The robin never digs with its bill as does a thrasher, nor does it scratch out food with its claws as does a fox sparrow. Structurally it is not adapted for either of these methods of foraging, for it is a 'soft-billed' bird, the sign of an eater of insects, worms, and berries.

In winter, when seeking chiefly vegetable food, the behavior of the robins is quite different. Then, caution as regards noise or movement seems to be almost entirely lacking, and the birds jump and flutter about actively, meanwhile uttering many short notes. They seem excitable at this season, at least when busily foraging, and are often ill content to stay long in one place. But when gorged with food they are likely to remain quietly perched in some leafless tree until the process of digestion has so far advanced that they can begin feeding again. In this latter respect their behavior recalls that of waxwings.

The song of the Western Robin is a conspicuous feature in the daily chorus of mountain bird voices. It is usually the first real song of the morning. Even before the coming of the faintest streaks of dawn the robins have begun their caroling, and in places where they are at all numerous, as in the Yosemite Valley, the forest and the granite cañon walls resound with their voices. For song perches, they seek the tips of exposed branches such as are reached by the first direct rays of the morning sun. The song consists of a long series of full rounded reverberant notes, grouped into bars with definite rests between. The notes are pretty much all on the same key, yet there is a distinct and alternate rising and falling of inflection. The songs of the Western Robin and Black-headed Grosbeak are sometimes confounded, but that of the latter bird is more varied, is given in quicker time, and it contains many little trills or shrill warbles not to be heard at all in the robin's song. To our ears the song of the robin does not compare in quality with that of many other birds of the mountains, as, for example, that of the Sierra Hermit Thrush and the Townsend Solitaire. After a time the robin's song becomes actually wearisome because of its monotony.

As the heat of the day increases, the robins become less voluble and take to foraging in the meadows, or resting silently on the lower branches of the trees. With the approach of early evening they become tuneful again. But as dusk comes on, the full songs are less frequently heard, and these are much interspersed with the loud unmusical cries and 'squeals.' At late dusk, when the birds are arranging and rearranging themselves for the night on their favorite perches high in the tall trees, they accompany the many short flights and changes of position with a multitude of the short calls. Sometimes these evening exercises of the robin become accentuated to an extreme degree. A bird will dash about wildly, resting on one perch for an instant, to sing a few bars of song, then darting to some other tree, and singing again, or else uttering a series of the loud cries. In early summer, robins in the Yosemite Valley have been heard singing as late in the evening as eight o'clock, long after the dusk of twilight had filled all but the most open portions of the Valley floor.

With the passage of the nesting season the full song is less often heard; our latest record of a song given fully is for July 3 (1915) at El Portal. Thereafter there are only a few occasional snatches of the song, as well as the usual shorter calls. During the period of molt the birds are practically quiet. As they gather in flocks for the winter their voices are heard again, but not in regular song. Their vocal disturbances while feeding and when going to roost of evenings become louder and louder so that in places where there is a large number of robins their calls rise into a veritable babel of voices. Not until February or March are the real songs again given with full strength.

The call notes of the Western Robin, as already intimated, are various. An attempt at expressing some of them in syllables, such as might be uttered by the human voice, is as follows: *tŭk, tŭk; tche'-ah* or *wi'eh* (a sort of squeal); *wēē', kŭk-kŭk-kŭk.*

Robins nest abundantly in the Yosemite region and their activities while engaged in the construction of their nests and the rearing of their broods are open to easy observation. Nest construction in the Transition Zone as exemplified by Yosemite Valley was in progress on April 30, 1916; and in mid-May, 1919, nests with eggs were fairly common. A nest with 4 fresh eggs, in which the parent was sitting, was seen at Hazel Green on May 14, 1919, and on the same day other birds were seen carrying building materials. On May 25, 1919, a nest with young was seen in Yosemite Valley. At the McCarthy ranch, 3 miles east of Coulterville, spotted-breasted young, out of the nest, were seen on June 4, 1915. Nesting continues well into summer, for on June 14, 1915, in Yosemite Valley, a female robin was seen gathering nest material. A parent bird was observed feeding young in the nest in Yosemite Valley on July 15, 1915.

This last date is the latest for nesting known to us at the time of writing, although it seems likely that still later instances of young in the nest are to be found. In any event, visitors to the Yosemite Valley are likely to see robins engaged in one phase or another of the nesting program from the first of May until toward the end of July, a range in nesting time probably not exceeded by that of any other bird in the Valley. Higher in the mountains the season is somewhat later. Adults were seen carrying food at Tuolumne Meadows on July 7, 1915, but no young were noted out of the nest at that station by the date mentioned. East of the mountains, at the Farrington ranch, near Williams Butte, on April 29, 1916, a robin was seen brooding on a nest; on May 9 another bird was found, near Walker Lake, on a nest containing 3 eggs; and adults were carrying food to young at Mono Lake Post Office on June 30, 1916.

The nest of the Western Robin is a stoutly constructed affair, composed of grasses and weed stems, pine needles, or similar material, and well plastered with mud. (See pl. 55a.) The site chosen for the nest varies with circumstances, as does the height at which it is placed above the ground. Probably a majority of the nests are placed in small trees at the edges of clearings; but there are many exceptions. We have noted nests in good-sized sugar, yellow, and lodgepole pines, in firs, black oaks, willows, and cottonwoods, and one was seen on a shelf in a farm shed. The height of nests above the ground ranges from 4 to 75 feet in observed instances, although a majority are probably at a height of less than 12 feet. A nest in a young coniferous tree is usually placed near the top, against the trunk, and supported by one or more small horizontal branches. A nest in a black oak or a willow, especially if the tree be a large one, is apt to be located in a slanting or upright crotch; in the biggest pines, a large outswaying branch is a favorite site. Several were noted amid unusual surroundings. In Yosemite Valley in 1919 there was a nest in a remarkably exposed situation, in a willow which grew at the side of the main traveled road between the village and Camp Curry, where the road borders directly on the Merced River. Many people, both walking and in automobiles, passed the spot daily, but the parent bird stayed persistently on the nest. In June, 1920, a robin was sitting in her nest on a beam just above the office entrance at Camp Curry. Many hundreds of persons passed daily just beneath her. In a willow tree beside the river above Stoneman Bridge another robin had built her nest early in May, 1919. With the rise of the water at flood time the tree was entirely surrounded by the swirling current 3 or more feet deep; but undaunted, the parent stayed at her post, incubating her eggs.

A typical nest measures outside about 4 inches in height by 6 or 7 inches in maximum breadth. The cavity is about 3½ inches across by

2½ in depth. In some, the mud used is located only in the basal portion; in others there is a smooth rim of mud at the top. The outside height of a nest depends somewhat on its location. Those nests saddled on large horizontal branches are least in volume.

The method of construction and the industry of the robin in carrying on the work of nest building may well be shown by direct quotation from one of our field notebooks.

Yosemite Valley, April 30, 1916. Found a robin engaged in building a nest 12 feet above the ground on a 3-inch horizontal branch of a big (4-foot) yellow pine. Very exposed situation, without any sheltering foliage. I watched the bird for over half an hour. Its schedule was as follows:

8:7:25 A.M. Flew to mud at small drainage ditch about 150 yards away.

8:7:50. Returned with small ball of mud in bill; placed this in bottom of nest, then got in latter (which was deep enough to shelter bird from chin to base of tail), threw its breast forward, tilted up its tail, held its wings well up (but not extended) on back, and 'tamped' mud into place by forcing breast against wall of nest; after several thrusts in one direction the bird rotated itself slightly and tamped again. This was kept up until more than one complete revolution had been made. This rounds the nest, and forces the mud into the interstices so that it holds together the grasses, string, etc., which form basis of nest. Mud was noted on breast feathers of bird when it emerged.

8:13:25. Bird left nest and went toward Yosemite Creek, a different direction from where other mud was obtained.

8:15:55. Returned with stringy mud; tamped.

8:17:50. Left nest and went to first source of mud.

8:19:00. Returned with moderate sized ball; tamped; lit on nest edge and not on usual twig.

8:21:00. Off to Yosemite Creek.

8:23:45. Returned with mud evidently containing leaves; tamped.

8:26:10. Off to Yosemite Creek again.

8:30:05. Returned with mass of stringy mud; tamped.

8:35:45. Off to Yosemite Creek again.

Several trips were made before I began timing the bird. Often, as it was tamping it would catch a free end of grass at the nest edge and tuck it down in. The tamping and circling serves to make the nest strong, regular, and smooth, so that it can shelter the eggs and young securely. The mud is very wet when gathered, as I found by visiting the place where the first lot was obtained. The bird always came directly to the nest, even when, as it approached, I was on the ground and in plain sight between it and the nest.

This particular robin, as we see, was bringing a fresh lot of material every five to ten minutes, and during the period when it was under observation it worked without a rest. After the nest is completed there is usually an interval of a few days before egg laying commences. This affords time for the mud to dry thoroughly.

The eggs of the robin are of a uniform deep blue color, with a slight greenish tinge, but without spots of any sort. The shells have a dull surface appearance which is characteristic of the eggs of this species. Four eggs are commonly to be found in the nest of the robin; yet we did not see more than 3 young robins in any one brood, within the nest, or out

with the parent birds. Whether any one pair of robins in the central
Sierra Nevada rears more than a single brood in a season is not known to us.

Not until all the eggs in a set are laid does the work of incubation begin;
thenceforth it is carried on without cessation. Often the sitting bird can
be approached very closely before it will leave the nest. The cup-like shape
of the nest is such that the bird can sink its whole body down into the
cavity, until only its head and tail project at steep angles above the rim.
Once one of our party came upon a robin as the bird sat on its nest in the
top of a small fir tree. The bird seemed startled by the observer's sudden
appearance and left the nest immediately, flying to another tree fifty feet
away where it began to squall loudly, making such a noise that it attracted
to the spot a Sierra Red-breasted Sapsucker and a Mariposa Fox Sparrow.

Ranger Forest Townsley has told us that in Yosemite Valley he has
seen one member of a pair of Robins (the male?) feed the other (the
female?) while the latter sat upon the eggs. It is our impression that most
of the robins which we saw abroad during the middle of the day in the
early part of the nesting season possessed richly colored breasts and clear
yellow bills, and hence were probably males. This fact would tend to
substantiate Mr. Townsley's observation.

The general nature of the robin's food has been alluded to in several
of the preceding paragraphs. Further remarks are in order. In the nesting season the birds feed largely on worms and insects, but in other parts
of the year their subsistence is gained mainly from berry-producing trees
and shrubs. At Walker Lake, in mid-September, 1915, robins were feeding
on berries of the red elder, and at Glen Aulin, later the same month,
in company with Townsend Solitaires, the robins were eating the berries
of the western juniper. In Yosemite Valley in early November, 1915,
they were taking chokecherries and coffee berries, while at Gentrys on
December 30, 1914, the few robins seen were eating the dry sticky-coated
berries of the manzanita (*Arctostaphylos mariposa*). Robins are quick
to take advantage of easily obtained food of a sort to their liking. Many
persons who sojourn in the Yosemite region during the summer months
find the robins ready visitors to their "bird feeding tables." The picture
of a spotted-breasted young shown herewith (fig. 60) was obtained at one
of these feeding places on a porch in the Yosemite village.

The robin's adaptability in the matter of food, and also its instinctive
haste to cleanse its nest of any débris, were both illustrated by an incident
which transpired on June 20, 1915, at Chinquapin. A robin was seen
to fly away from its nest nearby carrying in its bill something which looked
like a mouse dangling by the tail. The bird happened to drop the object
within the camp precincts and it proved to be a juvenile robin (with
feathers still in the sheaths). The old robin had obtained a large piece of

liver from a pile of discarded mammal bodies and had carried this material to the youngster as food. When the young bird had swallowed as much of the liver as it could hold, a portion still protruding from its mouth. The parent, in haste to clean the nest, had picked up the free end of the piece of liver, not appreciating the fact that the youngster had swallowed the other end, and had carried both the liver and the young robin out of the nest.

Mr. Donald D. McLean has recorded (1919, p. 160) the finding of remains of six Western Robins in the stomach of one female California Wildcat killed by him March 10, 1919, near Coulterville. At Chinquapin on May 20, 1919, a robin was seen flying at a Sierra Chickaree, snapping its beak loudly, until it forced the squirrel to descend the tree. The evidence is only circumstantial, but might indicate that the squirrel had invaded the robin's nesting precincts. Much further and careful observation must be made before the enemies of the robin are well known.

Toward the latter part of June, 1920, in Yosemite Valley, at least four young robins were picked up in which the plumage was oil-soaked, evidently as a result of the birds having bathed in pools of water upon which oil had been sprayed to kill mosquito larvae. One of these birds was nearly dead; the others were obviously not in normal condition. Here, then, is another way in which man's activities interfere with the course of events in nature.

Partial albinism is not an uncommon phenomenon in the Western Robin. Two instances came to our attention in the Yosemite region, in both of which the birds in question had some white feathers on the head. Complete albinos are much rarer, as are melanos (abnormally dark colored individuals). In a bird of the size and habits of the robin, abnormalities in coloration are much more likely to be observed and commented upon than are similar occurrences among the smaller and more retiring species. In any event, albinism is merely the outward physical manifestation of some defect, local or general, in the tissues or body processes of the animal in which it occurs, and does not warrant the attention which has been directed to the subject by some scientific as well as many lay students.

NORTHERN VARIED THRUSH.   **Ixoreus naevius meruloides** (Swainson)

Field characters.—Size of Robin and somewhat similar in coloration, but with a black, or (in female) slaty, band across chest, and a shorter tail. Upper surface slate-colored; under surface bright rusty brown (more orange than in Robin); conspicuous stripe of same color behind eye; also bars and spots of same on wing. In flight like Robin, but with a pale band showing lengthwise of each spread wing. *Voice:* Call note a single, not loud, deep, staccato *chuck;* song a slowly uttered series of weird syllables, successively on different pitches, now low, now high; each note intoned from one to three seconds: *zurrrrr.*

Occurrence.—A winter visitant to the western slope of the Sierras below the level of heavy snows. Common locally, reaching Yosemite Valley in late autumn (for example, October 28, 1915), and present in midwinter from south-facing slopes as high as 5000 feet (on Big Oak Flat road below Gentrys) down to the river-bottom thickets in vicinity of Snelling (January 7, 1915). Highest station: 7300 feet on ridge two miles north of Yosemite Point, three seen high in red firs October 30, 1915. Other stations of observation not mentioned beyond: Feliciana Mountain, October 28 to November 1, 1915; Gentrys, October 23, 1915 (earliest date); El Portal, December 9 and 17, 1914. Forages in scattered companies in chaparral or dense growths of small trees; seldom seen in the open.

Only the autumn or winter visitor to the Yosemite region will be likely to meet with the Northern Varied Thrush. Even when present, this bird is of such retiring disposition and quiet demeanor that it easily escapes detection. The writers have repeatedly approached within a few yards of birds on the ground or perched in bushes or trees, without realizing their presence until the birds took flight. One might think the bright markings of these birds would render them conspicuous; but, in fact, the broken pattern serves to obliterate their outlines against the leafy background.

Like its not distant relative, the Western Robin, the Varied Thrush (sometimes called Oregon Robin) feeds in the winter season chiefly on berries of various sorts, and its local occurrence and relative abundance is governed by the season's crop of these. Two or three of these birds seen among golden oaks near Camp Lost Arrow, November 13, seemed to be feeding on mistletoe berries. On the Big Oak Flat road, about 3 miles out of Yosemite Valley, on December 28, 1914, 8 or more Varied Thrushes were seen feeding on the sweetish berries of a manzanita (*Arctostaphylos mariposa*). On the Wawona road at Grouse Creek, November 26, 1914, two were apparently feeding on berries of the creek dogwood. In the Upper Sonoran foothill region, the Christmas berry or toyon (*Heteromeles arbutifolia*) furnishes a favorite food as long as the crop lasts.

In 1920 the species was first seen on October 24, and thereafter "large flocks" were observed on various dates throughout November and December (C. W. Michael, MS).

WESTERN BLUEBIRD. **Sialia mexicana occidentalis** Townsend

Field characters.—Size half again that of Junco; wings relatively long, reaching nearly to end of tail. Male: Upper surface of body mainly intense dark blue; chin and throat the same; middle of back and breast, and sides of body, chestnut brown. Female: Upper surface and throat dull grayish blue; breast and sides pale chestnut brown. Young: Breast mottled with dusky. Of quiet demeanor; movements deliberate. *Voice:* Song of male (seldom heard) a monotonous repetition of the call notes; call note a single soft *kew*, or else a harsh though not loud *che-check*.

Occurrence.—Common at all seasons in Upper Sonoran Zone on western foothills of Sierra Nevada. Recorded at nesting time from near Lagrange and at Snelling eastward to Smith Creek (6 miles east of Coulterville) and to near Bullion Mountain. In autumn and early winter appears at higher altitudes eastward as far as Colby Mountain (near Ten Lakes) and commonly in Yosemite Valley; present also in winter season in San Joaquin Valley at Snelling and below Lagrange. In nesting season lives chiefly about blue oaks; but at other seasons of year frequents berry-producing plants especially the mistletoe on oaks. Flocks (openly) through most of year, breaking into attentive pairs at nesting time.

The Western Bluebird is a species that is likely to be recognized at first sight, even by a beginning student. Nature has produced blue in but a very small number of animals and the species possessing any blue are usually conspicuous because of this color. There are only eight species of really *blue* birds in the Yosemite section and among all of these the Western Bluebird may be distinguished easily on the basis of other features.

The jays, including the California, Woodhouse, Blue-fronted, and Piñon, are all of much larger size, and none of them has any chestnut in its plumage. The California Blue Grosbeak is of about the same size as the Western Bluebird and has both blue and chestnut in its scheme of coloration, but its breast is never solidly chestnut and its bill is stout and conical, whereas that of the bluebird is quite slender; furthermore, the grosbeak is a bird of the stream-side thickets, whereas the bluebird lives as a rule in the more open upland country. The Lazuli Bunting is little more than half the bulk of the bluebird, and the male, who has a buff breast, is white on the belly and of 'lapis lazuli' blue on his back and throat. Both sexes of this bunting have a light wing bar, and the birds keep chiefly to brushy situations. The Western Bluebird may be distinguished from the Mountain Bluebird by its darker tone of blue and by the presence of areas of chestnut brown in its plumage.

In the spring and summer months the local Western Bluebird population is confined almost entirely to the blue oak belt of the western foothills and hence within the Upper Sonoran Zone. The species does nest in small numbers at Snelling, a short distance within the Lower Sonoran Zone, and it also occurs in that season within the margin of the Transition Zone, for example, at Smith Creek east of Coulterville. Although elsewhere this bluebird is known to nest abundantly in the Transition Zone, here at nesting time it avoids that zone almost entirely. Yosemite Valley would seem a very favorable place for the species to nest, but it has never been known to occur there in the summer season.

In the fall months, however, Western Bluebirds appear at many *up*-mountain localities not previously tenanted by the species. Several individuals were heard at Glacier Point on September 25, 1915, and flocks were seen on a ridge (Colby Mountain) above Ten Lakes on October 8 and 9, 1915. In Yosemite Valley the species appears regularly during October. It was seen, for example, first on the 7th in 1914, on the 15th in 1915, and on the 23d in 1920. In 1917 Mr. Joseph Mailliard (MS) saw Western Bluebirds in the Valley on September 17 and 27. The birds continue in the Valley, especially in the mistletoe-laden golden oaks along the sunny north wall (pl. 16*a*) through November and into December. In 1914, they were present even as late as December 28. How much longer they may remain is not known, but on a visit to the Valley at the end of February, in 1916, none was noted. The attraction for these birds at these higher altitudes is the abundant supply of food in the form of mistletoe berries. This food supply, rather than weather, short of extremely severe storms, seems to be the factor regulating the stay of the bluebirds in the mountains. That snow alone is no particular deterrent to the birds' stay is shown by our observations made on the stormy morning of December 10, 1914, at Mirror Lake, when bluebirds were flying about actively, now and again alighting on the snow-weighted mistletoe clumps. Masses of the snow would be dislodged and shower the observer beneath, but the birds themselves seemed in nowise discommoded.

Like other species such as the Golden-crowned Sparrow and Alaska Hermit Thrush which come into the higher zones in the fall, the Western Bluebirds, when once driven out of the higher mountains, do not return again until the following autumn. It has not been possible to ascertain whether this invasion of the mountains is the result of arrival of winter visitants from the Northwest (Oregon, Washington, and British Columbia) or due to temporary expansion of range by birds reared in the nearby foothills. The appearance of bluebirds in the higher country here agrees with the time given for departure of the species from the northwestern states. Furthermore, both adults and young are to be found among the birds occurring in Yosemite Valley.

With foothill species such as the wren-tit, bush-tit, and Bewick wren, which invade the higher mountains, this movement occurs in late summer, in July or early August, and is indulged in chiefly if not exclusively by birds-of-the-year. On the other hand, the bluebird is like the robin and varied thrush in that its autumnal movements about the country are governed by food supply, and this food supply is of a nature (berries) which fluctuates in quantity from year to year and place to place. The reason that the bluebirds appear with regularity in Yosemite Valley during October might well be in the fact that the crop of mistletoe berries there normally begins to ripen about that time. In such case the birds might come, in part at least, from the adjacent Upper Sonoran districts, returning there when the food source has been exhausted.

Western Bluebirds winter along Smith Creek east of Coulterville, according to Mr. Donald D. McLean. We found the birds in moderate numbers in the San Joaquin Valley below Lagrange and at Snelling, in December and January.

Some censuses will now be given which will serve to show how the numbers of the birds vary as to locality and season. At Pleasant Valley a 5-hour census on May 24, 1915, yielded 20 Western Bluebirds, practically all of them being in pairs. On February 27, 1916, a 3½ hour trip over the same territory gave count of 42 birds, most of which were in flocks. Twenty-three were noted in 3 hours spent north of Pleasant Valley on December 4, 1915, and 15 in 2 hours near Lagrange on December 12, 1915. On November 26, 1914, 20 or more were noted at Fort Monroe; fully 125 were congregated in oaks near the lower (Yosemite) end of the Big Oak Flat road on December 28, 1914; 75 of these were flushed at one time. In December, 1914, the aggregate population of Western Bluebirds in Yosemite Valley was believed to outnumber that of all other birds combined. The birds at Pleasant Valley in December were in groups of 7, 5, 5, 2, 2, and 2.

In the nesting season the two bluebirds of a pair stay close together, usually within a few yards of one another. Then in late May or early June the young are led abroad and the family group stays together for some time. The manner of association during the season of molt has not been observed, but by September flocks have formed which include both adult and immature birds, and in this fashion they spend the winter. The flocks, in observed instances, included from 6 to 25 members. Sometimes other birds are associated. In Yosemite Valley we saw Western Bluebirds in company with Audubon Warblers on one or more occasions, and Mr. C. W. Michael (MS) reports Western and Mountain bluebirds together there during November of 1920. Western Bluebirds and Robins are frequently seen together during the winter months though the two do not flock with each other in the usual sense of the word.

In general demeanor the Western Bluebird is much like other members of the thrush family, being of deliberate or even phlegmatic temperament. When perched it sits quietly, not hopping about as do many small birds such as sparrows and warblers. It ordinarily seeks a perch which will command a wide field of view, as on some upper or outer branch of a deciduous tree. Some time is spent, especially during the summer months, in catching insects, either by darting after such as pass in the air or by pouncing down from a fence post or low branch onto grasshoppers and other ground-dwelling species. Upon taking to flight bluebirds make off in the open, high in the air, uttering their soft call notes now and then as they fly. The high course of flight and the repeated flight calls are suggestive of the behavior of linnets under similar circumstances. Sometimes the flight is so far above the earth that the birds are quite beyond the range of vision of an observer stationed on the ground, only the mellow call notes giving indication of the passage of the birds overhead. When bluebirds are in flocks the formation is never compact or coherent; individuals move here and there among their companions and single birds or groups join and depart at intervals.

The Western Bluebird has two common calls which are used more or less throughout the year, and generally speaking these are the only notes which the bird utters. One of these is a soft *kew,* the other a harsh but not loud *che-check*. These two notes are used by solitary birds or by members of a flock and although given when the birds are at rest they are heard more often when flocks are moving from place to place. On occasion, during the nesting season, the male can be heard giving voice to extended series of notes similar to the above 'flock' or 'location' calls. At Pleasant Valley on May 24, 1915, and near Coulterville on May 11, 1919, this 'song' was heard. In the latter case there was repetition of the soft *kew* about as fast as a person could pronounce the syllable distinctly, though the bird did not maintain perfectly uniform intervals. Interpolated after every ten or so of the soft notes the harsher *che-check* would be given. In other words, the Western Bluebird's song is a very simple affair, just the common call notes uttered over and over again with monotonous persistence.

With the arrival of the warm days of early spring the bluebirds commence their nesting activities. Much time is spent in prospecting for a site, so that it is not until late April or early May that the nest is completed and eggs are laid. Our earliest data are for May 8 (1919) near Lagrange when one pair was seen carrying food to a nest in an old woodpecker hole while another pair had a nest with 4 fresh eggs. On May 9, near Hayward, adults were carrying food for young. In 1915, near Pleasant Valley, adults were seen carrying food on May 16, and young out of the nest were observed there on May 24 and 30. At Smith Creek a brood of 5 young was seen to leave the nest on June 5, 1915.

In spring after the pairs separate off they turn their attention to the oak trees and search for nest holes; for these birds, unlike the thrushes and robin, rear their broods in cavities. Old woodpecker holes are occupied when available, but failing to find one of these the birds will use some naturally formed opening in a tree. The decay of stubs of medium-sized branches often results in the formation of cavities in the heart wood of an oak which are appropriate in form and size for use by the bluebirds. It is not improbable that the mistletoe, which is of such direct service to the birds in winter by way of furnishing them with food, may render additional help in promoting, by its parasitic growth, the death of branches which with ensuing decay eventually afford nesting places for the birds.

The nest found near Lagrange was in a blue oak on a hill top. It was in a naturally rotted-out cavity at a height of 9 feet from the ground. Distant but 17 inches in the same stub was the nest of a Plain Titmouse. The bluebird's nest was 6½ inches below the rim of the opening and the sparse lining upon which the 4 eggs lay consisted chiefly of dry foxtail grass. Another nest seen at Smith Creek, east of Coulterville, was 14 feet above the ground in a black oak. A natural cavity about 11 inches deep by 5 inches in diameter had been filled for a depth of 4 to 5 inches with soft materials. Entrance was afforded to the nest on two sides; on the one was a hole about 2½ inches in diameter, while there was a much larger opening on the other side, so that the nest was easily visible from without.

The food of the Western Bluebird, as with most members of the thrush tribe, changes markedly with the season. In summer the birds live chiefly upon insects; and the young, at least while in the nest, are fed exclusively on this sort of food. But in the colder months of the year, when insects are relatively scarce, the bluebirds, both adult and immature, give their attention to berries. Insects are captured when found, but for the most part the winter food is vegetable in nature.

The most important single item of food for the bluebirds in the Yosemite region during the winter season is the berry of the mistletoe. (See pl. 13*b*.) Unfortunate as it may be from the standpoint of the trees parasitized and therefore from the standpoint of foresters and of nature lovers interested in trees, the oaks and certain conifers of the region are rather generally infested with the mistletoe. By reason of the abundance of the berries of the mistletoe, the Yosemite region is capable of, and does, support in winter a bluebird population in excess of that present in summer. This food supply lasts at the higher altitudes until well into the middle of winter, and the birds remain there as an apparent consequence, despite the inclemency of the weather.

In November and December a large part of the bluebird population of the Valley practically lives in the mistletoe-laden golden oaks along the north wall of the Yosemite. The birds may be found there at any hour of the day and if the observer has the patience to watch an individual or flock of the birds for some time the manner of feeding will be found to be somewhat as follows.

The birds individually will seek perches about clumps of mistletoe, either on adjacent parts of the tree or on the twigs of the parasite itself. Berries will be picked off and swallowed in rapid succession. Each bird, as it gets its fill of berries, flies to some nearby perch and sits there quietly. The process of digestion is a rapid one, and before many minutes have elapsed enough of the berries will have gone from the bluebird's gullet into its stomach to permit of further feeding. Thus the day is spent, alternately in feeding and digesting.

The mistletoe berry consists of three parts, a central hard coated 'seed' containing the plant embryo, a soft sticky pulp surrounding this seed, and a thin enclosing 'shell.' It is the middle part, the mucilage-like pulp, which the bluebirds seek as food. The berries which are eaten are not entirely consumed; were that the case the bluebird could be commended highly for aiding in the control of an obnoxious parasite. But when the berries pass through the bird's alimentary tract the digestive juices merely dissolve off the soft outermost layers. The central, harder part of the berry is voided without its germinative powers being harmed in the least; it also still retains a film of mucilaginous material and this causes it to adhere to whatever it happens to touch.

A means is thus afforded, and often operates, whereby the bluebird, incidentally of course, acts as an agency for the dissemination of mistletoe seeds. It is easily conceivable that should the bird chance to perch in a tree not previously parasitized by mistletoe the dropping of one or more seeds on the branches would afford opportunity for the plant to gain a start in that tree, providing the seed of the oak-tree mistletoe fell on an oak, or that from a conifer fell on another of its own kind of host. Not all the seeds by any means germinate and start a growth; for the conditions of germination must be just right in a number of concurrent respects. But by the very abundance of the berries and the continued patronizing of them by the birds it is likely that some new growths are started each year.

The mistletoe not only interferes immediately with the thrifty growth of the host tree, but it opens the way for early decay of the affected branches so that the wind and heavy snow of winter break them down— a calamity from many standpoints. It is fair to inquire here whether repressive measures should not be taken against the bluebird in an effort to save the trees. To this we would say decidedly *no,* and for the following reasons.

The relation between trees, mistletoe, and bluebirds is an ancient one, arrived at during eons of adjustment; a state of approximate equilibrium has been reached between the three. The fortunes of individual members of the trio may vary from time to time, but no great change is likely to occur, with general conditions of climate as they are. Furthermore, it is doubtful if any intervention by man could be of lasting effect. The Western Bluebird is but one of a number of birds which stand in practically the same relation to mistletoe, and if the former were to be eliminated some other species, such as the Cedar Waxwing or the Townsend Solitaire, would likely take its place. It would be impractical—indeed, we believe,

impossible—to exterminate the bluebirds. Even were all the locally
wintering individuals in the Yosemite region killed off—and that in itself
would be extremely difficult to accomplish—subsequent years would witness
a gradual infiltration of individuals and reëstablishment of a normal population. Nor would cutting out mistletoe be economical except in the case
of individual trees which it might be desirable to save. Interference by
man with the 'natural balance,' save where direct and rather complete
control is possible locally, as with ground-dwelling rodents, is never productive of the favorable results which some persons hope for.

MOUNTAIN BLUEBIRD. **Sialia currucoides** (Bechstein)

Field characters.—Size half again that of Junco; wings relatively long, reaching
nearly to end of tail. No chestnut color anywhere. Male: Clear light blue above, the
same but paler on breast; belly white. Female: Upper surface pale grayish blue; rump
and tail clearer blue; under surface pale grayish buff; belly whitish (pl. 56*b*). Young:
Breast mottled. Perches stolidly or else engages in flycatching; often hovers over open
ground on rapidly beating wings. *Voice:* No song heard by us; call note a weak *chirp.*

Occurrence.—Summer visitant to higher altitudes of Sierra Nevada (chiefly in Hudsonian Zone); also in valleys along east base of mountains. Recorded at Mono Meadow,
at Tenaya Lake, on Mount Hoffmann and Mount Clark, and thence eastward to Mono
Lake Post Office, near Williams Butte, and Mono Craters. Also winter visitant to San
Joaquin Valley, as below Lagrange; transient in Yosemite Valley and at Smith Creek,
east of Coulterville. Forages on grasslands; nests in cavities in trees, occasionally about
buildings. In pairs at nesting time and in small scattering companies at other seasons.

The Mountain Bluebird, sometimes called Arctic Bluebird, is, during
the summer season, chiefly a bird of the Hudsonian Zone. An exception
to this statement is found in the occurrence of the species regularly east
of the mountains in the neighborhood of Mono Lake, in territory which
lies below 7000 feet altitude and is in the arid part of the Transition Zone.
The greater part of the population, however, is found at altitudes above
8000 feet and from there it ranges up to the highest meadows found in our
mountains short of timber line. The highest points at which we saw the
species were near the head of Lyell Cañon, on the slopes of Mount Florence, and on Warren Peak, in each case at close to 10,500 feet altitude.
Mountain Bluebirds were observed once (June 21, 1915) at Mono Meadow,
which is a few miles southward from Glacier Point and at an altitude of
only 7400 feet; but these individuals were probably nesting at some higher
locality adjacent to the eastward.

There need be no difficulty in recognizing the Mountain Bluebird in its
summer haunts, as there is no other bird of similar size with conspicuously
blue coloration in the high mountains or on the east slope. In fall and
winter this species and the Western Bluebird sometimes occur on common
ground, but then the paleness of the blue and the total lack of chestnut

will readily distinguish the Mountain Bluebird. The Mountain Bluebird has a hesitating mode of flight, as with the Western, and the wings appear large and broad in proportion to the size of body. In general behavior the Mountain Bluebird is much like the Western Bluebird. In the matter of forage territory the present species displays greater preference for meadowlands, in large measure avoiding forested areas.

The numbers of these birds present locally at any season of the year are less than the numbers of the Western Bluebird. On Tuolumne Meadows one or two birds per hour of observation was a maximum. On Mount Hoffmann, June 29, 1915, 4 adults were seen near the top of the peak and a few others lower down, scarcity of available forage grounds and nest sites elsewhere in the vicinity having served, perhaps, to concentrate the birds. In the fall months small flocks are formed, 8 having been noted together on one occasion. These loose companies wander about with seeming aimlessness. There is no directness of movement in the fall such as characterizes many migrating birds.

The Mountain Bluebirds had apparently left the territory east of the Sierras before mid-September of 1915; yet they were noted in much higher country on two occasions in the latter part of that same month. On September 26 a flock was observed on the slopes of Warren Peak, and on September 28, 4 were observed in Tioga Pass and a like number on Tuolumne Meadows. Mr. C. W. Michael (MS) reports small numbers in Yosemite Valley on October 30, and November 2, 10, and 13, 1920, the only instances of occurrence we know of there. The species is reported as a transient at Smith Creek, 6 miles east of Coulterville, by Mr. Donald D. McLean, who took a specimen there October 8, 1916. In the winter season Mountain Bluebirds make their appearance in the San Joaquin Valley. Two birds noted along the road below Lagrange on December 16, 1915, constitute our only definite lowland record for the Yosemite section, but there are many reports of the winter occurrence of these birds in numbers on the San Joaquin plains.

The Mountain Bluebird nests in cavities, making use, for the most part, of deserted woodpecker holes. At Tuolumne Meadows one pair was nesting in such a hole, whose orifice was two inches in diameter, and which was situated 7 feet above the ground in a live lodgepole pine. At the Farrington ranch near Williams Butte a Flicker hole in a willow stump was utilized. At Mono Lake Post Office a pair of Mountain Bluebirds had appropriated to their uses a ledge in a woodshed, entrance to which was gained through a hole in the wall. Here at a height of 10 feet from the ground a loosely woven nest had been constructed. This nest was made of shreds of bark many of which showed evidence of having been freshly pulled from the trees for the purpose. There were included also numerous chicken feathers from the nearby farmyard. The dimensions outside were roughly 6 or 7 inches in diameter and 2½ inches in height. The depression for receiving the eggs was 3¼ inches wide and 1½ inches deep. After one brood had been reared this nest was re-lined to receive a second set of eggs.

In 1916, nesting activities with the Mountain Bluebirds (pl. 56b) in the neighborhood of Mono Lake were instituted early in May, which makes it readily possible for some at least of the pairs there to rear two broods. Thus the pair observed at Mono Lake Post Office had on May 20, 1916, a nest with 6 fresh eggs. The 5 young reared from this lot were abroad and being cared for by the male on June 30, and by July 3 there was a second set of 5 eggs which the female had commenced to incubate. A pair of birds which arrived at the Farrington ranch about May 1 took possession of an old Flicker hole almost at once. By May 10 the nest lining had been finished and by May 16, 5 eggs had been laid; incubation commenced the next day.

The several Mountain Bluebirds encountered on Mount Hoffmann on June 29 and 30, 1915, fluttered about as though anxious over the security of nests. They probably had eggs or small young in cavities left by the rotting out of branches in the stunted white-barked pines which abounded on the upper slopes of the peak. When we reached Tuolumne Meadows early in July of 1915 the bluebirds were already well started on their nesting program, as by July 8 one nest there had 3 young nearly ready to fly and other pairs were busily engaged in getting food for young. Presumably these high-mountain birds are one-brooded, for we did not see young abroad until well along in July and there would not have been time for them to rear another brood that season.

When the eggs have hatched both parents attend to feeding the young, and if a person approaches a nest at this season the bluebirds will hover in the air before the site and utter remonstrant chirps. After the broods were out, the relative numbers of the species almost reached the status of 'abundant.' The young Mountain Bluebirds have a spotted pattern of markings in the juvenile plumage—a 'family' resemblance to the robins, thrushes, and solitaires. In the bluebird this is due to white center streaks on the feathers of the breast and back. This plumage is worn but a short time, being replaced in early fall by one which is practically identical with that of the adults.

In the nesting season and indeed through most of the year the Mountain Bluebird subsists upon insects. These are captured in two totally different ways, according to the habits of the insects sought. For beetles and others which fly through the air a bluebird will take position on a boulder in a meadow or on the low outswaying branch of some tree and dart after the insects which pass by. For insects which live on the ground, such as grasshoppers, the bird mounts 10 to 20 feet into the air over the grassland and then by fluttering its wings rapidly, hovers in one place for several seconds and intently scans the surface below, like a Sparrow Hawk when similarly engaged. If something is sighted the bird drops quickly to the ground and seizes it; otherwise the bluebird moves a short distance to a new location which is given similar scrutiny. It thus examines the ground in a manner recalling that employed by the robin though from an aerial location where its scope of view is much greater though less thorough. The Mountain Bluebird elsewhere in its range is known to eat berries though not to the extent of its lowland relative; none of the birds which we saw or collected in the Yosemite section gave any indication of having eaten food other than insects.

THE REPTILES

BLUE-BELLIED LIZARDS. **Sceloporus occidentalis** Baird and Girard[40]

Field characters.—Of typical lizard form. Tail (when not injured) slightly more than length of head and body. (See pl. 57b.) Scales on upper surface, and sides of body and tail, with conspicuous ridges or 'keels'; 51 or fewer scales in longitudinal row from back of head to line across back of thighs; scales on back of thigh keeled. General coloration above dark brownish or blackish, patterned with lengthwise rows of spots of blackish brown; under surface of body (especially in males) with more or less deep blue. Head and body 3 to 3¾ inches; tail 3½ to 5 inches in adult males.

Occurrence.—Common almost throughout the region. Forage on trunks of trees, ou fences, or on rocks.[40]

The Blue-bellied Lizard is perhaps the best known of the typical lizards here in the west, being common throughout the settled districts of California, where it is known as the fence lizard. The two common names of the reptile just given refer respectively to the blue color on the under surface of the body in the male and to the animal's habit of coming out on rail fences and on similar above-ground structures upon which it can climb about and hunt for insects.

---

[40] Three subspecies of Blue-bellied Lizard live in different parts of the Yosemite region. Their general appearance is much the same, especially as compared with other lizards in the region, and but little is known concerning their life histories. For these reasons the three are treated together. The characters given below apply particularly to adult males, which sex may be distinguished by the presence of two enlarged plates on the under side of the tail behind the anal opening.

WESTERN FENCE LIZARD, *Sceloporus occidentalis occidentalis* Baird and Girard, the form which inhabits the northwestern half of California, is to be found in the western part of the Yosemite section, where it occurs from Snelling and Pleasant Valley eastward to, and including, Yosemite Valley. It may be distinguished by the greater amount of light color on the under surface of the hind limbs, on the chest, and between the dark patches on the belly. Also the blue patch on the throat is divided, as a rule, not solid. This and the following subspecies are ordinarily to be seen on tree trunks, fences, logs, and boulders.

PACIFIC BLUE-BELLIED LIZARD, *Sceloporus occidentalis bi-seriatus* Hallowell, the subspecies common in southern California, reaches the eastern end of the Yosemite section around Mono Lake. Our party took specimens at Mono Lake Post Office. It is characterized by somewhat larger size than the preceding and by darker coloration on the under surface. The thighs, middle of belly, and chest are gray or blackish, and the blue patch of the chin is never divided in the mid-line.

TENAYA BLUE-BELLIED LIZARD, *Sceloporus occidentalis taylori* Camp, is a subspecies known at present only from the high country about Merced and Washburn lakes, Tenaya Lake, and Glen Aulin, and from Little Yosemite Valley. It is recognizable at once by its solidly bluish black under surface and dark back (without conspicuous spotting). The highest station of observation, on the ridges above Merced Lake toward Mount Clark, was 8800 feet in altitude. This subspecies is to be seen chiefly on sunlit granite boulders.

Under original conditions the Blue-bellied Lizards lived chiefly upon and around rocks and trees, and this is still true in most of the Yosemite region. The Tenaya Blue-bellied Lizards of the higher altitudes are almost exclusively rock dwellers, whereas the Fence Lizards at the lower levels on the west slope inhabit tree trunks, downed logs and, of course, rail fences where these are available. Only seldom are these animals to be found on the ground. There is thus with lizards, as with other vertebrates, an ecologic segregation. The present species inhabits places above ground, while skinks, whip-tails, and alligator lizards live on the ground. In the high mountains the Tenaya Lizard when active resorts to the granite boulders, while the Mountain Lizard (*Sceloporus graciosus*) is chiefly terrestrial, and the Mountain Alligator Lizard strictly so.

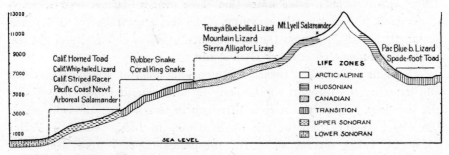

Fig. 61. Cross-section of the Sierra Nevada through the Yosemite region showing the distribution of some reptiles and amphibians which are either restricted to or find their maximum abundance in single life-zones.

The fences built about pastures in the forest belt, especially those made of split rails, are often occupied by numbers of these lizards. On one occasion a member of our field party, while working in the neighborhood of the McCarthy ranch east of Coulterville, estimated that there was one lizard to every 50 feet of a given fence.

In the territory occupied jointly by the Mountain Lizard (*Sceloporus graciosus*) and representatives of the present group, the Blue-bellied Lizards outnumber the smaller species. On the upper parts of the boulder talus along the north side of Yosemite Valley beneath Eagle Peak the proportion was about 25 of *occidentalis* to 10 of *graciosus*. On a trip to Clouds Rest, from 6 to 12 Tenaya Blue-bellied Lizards were noted to each Mountain Lizard.

Fence Lizards are abroad and active during all the warmer months of the year, but they spend the winter season, even at the lowest altitudes, in hibernation. On January 8, 1915, two were found in a damp place beneath a log at Snelling, "stiff in hibernation," as the collector says in his notes. As soon as the days of spring come, with the sunlight and warmth which induces growth in plants and activity in insects, these lizards begin to venture forth from their winter retreats. At first they are abroad only for a short time during the warmest of the mid-day hours, but by the middle of summer in the foothill country they are active at, or shortly after, sun-up and thenceforth throughout the day, even until well after sundown. In Yosemite Valley in 1916 several were abroad at the end of April, and at El Portal they were out in numbers on May 2 the same year. The latest seasonal record is of several abroad at Sweetwater Creek on October 28 (1915).

With the Tenaya Blue-bellied Lizard in the higher altitudes the season is shorter. Our earliest record for the species is May 16 (1919), when one was seen at Sierra Point. On May 18 that year numbers of males were in evidence in Little Yosemite Valley. A note made on August 28, 1915, near Washburn Lake states that these lizards had not become active until about 9 o'clock in the morning. The last appearance of the species seasonally, in 1915, was on October 1, when one was obtained at 7300 feet in the Tuolumne Cañon below Glen Aulin.

The male Blue-bellied Lizard has a curious habit of alternately raising and lowering the forepart of the body by straightening and then flexing the fore legs. When the body is lifted up in this manner the coloring on the under surface may be glimpsed. Once, in Little Yosemite Valley (May 18, 1919) several males (of subspecies *taylori*) were seen going through an even more elaborate performance than that just described. These particular lizards had puffed out their bodies and throats to about twice their natural size. Then they worked up and down several times on all four legs. Thereafter they deflated somewhat and continued the exercise, on the front legs alone. Although this movement is common, its purpose is as yet without a satisfactory explanation. From the momentary display of the bright color on the under surface of the body one might infer it to be a courting antic, comparable to the spreading of wings and tail, with consequent exhibition of bright markings, which is to be seen in many species of birds in the mating season.

MOUNTAIN LIZARD. **Sceloporus graciosus graciosus** Baird and Girard

Field characters.—Size small, total length 5 inches or less; scales everywhere very small, less than $\frac{1}{16}$ inch across; those of back, sides and tail ridged or 'keeled'; 42 or more scales in lengthwise row between back of head and line across back of thighs. (See pl. 57a.) General coloration of body above greenish or brownish gray, with 6 lengthwise rows of irregular dark blotches along back and sides; middle of under surface of body and whole under side of tail pale yellow; chin region and sides of belly deep blue in males, light bluish in females, but never with two separate blue patches on throat.

Occurrence.—Common resident in Canadian Zone on west side of Sierra Nevada. Recorded from Pilot Peak ridge and from Chinquapin eastward to Porcupine Flat and to Merced Lake. Also present east of mountains in Canadian and Transition from Walker Lake to Mono Craters. Lives chiefly on ground beneath brush plants, but to some extent around logs and rocks. Active in the warmer parts of summer days.

The Mountain Lizard is common in and about the thickets of snowbush, chinquapin, huckleberry oak, and other brush plants in the Canadian Zone, hence, chiefly above the level of Yosemite Valley. It stays mostly about and beneath the cover of this high mountain chaparral, though it is sometimes to be seen on rocks and on logs. Its habitat is thus rather different from that of the Tenaya Lizard; the latter is more of a climber, to be found on large granite boulders out in the open.

Although we did not find them on the floor of Yosemite Valley, some Mountain Lizards did come to our notice (June 8, 1915) on the uppermost parts of the steep taluses on the north side of the Valley beneath Eagle Peak. The altitude here is about 5000 feet, the lowermost station of ascertained occurrence for the species anywhere in the whole region. In our several trips up the Yosemite Falls Trail the first individuals were met with at the 5750-foot contour. The highest station of occurrence in the region was the summit of Ostrander Rocks, east of Glacier Point, at 8250 feet.

These lizards, like all the other high mountain reptiles, must spend fully half the year in dormancy, hidden away in crevices deep down among rocks or in spaces among the stems of bushes or at the bases of stumps. An early date, seasonally, for noting them is May 27 (1911), when several were seen at noon and shortly after on the bare sunlit surfaces of the rocks at the very summit of Eagle Peak (7700 feet) ; at that time there was deep snow all about. Our earliest date, at a lower altitude, 6700 feet, near the brink of Nevada Falls, is for May 18 (1919). Our latest record is for October 11 (1914) near Yosemite Point.

The Mountain Lizard is, when fully adult, only about 5 inches in length. The head and body is about 2½ inches long. It is decidedly smaller than any of the other local species, though it might be confused with young of the Fence Lizard. The body of the present species is covered, on the back and sides, with keeled or ridged scales which are of small size. Between the last of the large plates of the head and a line drawn across the back of the thighs there are usually 45 *or more* scales in a lengthwise row, whereas in the other 'swifts' (races of *Sceloporus occidentalis*) the scales usually number *less* than 45 (except in *S. o. taylori*). (See pl. 57*a*, *b*.) An additional character for distinguishing the two is found in the condition of the scales on the back of the thigh; in the present species these are smooth, whereas in the other local Scelopori they are keeled.

An individual of this swift comes to attention usually by reason of the rustling noises it makes as it scurries about in the dry leafy débris beneath the brush plants. Most of its time is spent within this type of surroundings, and it is often difficult to discover or to capture when it takes to the shelter immediately afforded. The food of the species seems to be gathered mostly on the ground; sometimes one of the lizards may be seen running about on the surface of a fallen tree trunk in search of flies and other insects which may be sunning themselves on the rough bark.

CALIFORNIA HORNED TOAD.   **Phrynosoma blainvillii frontale** Van Denburgh

Field characters.—Body broad and flattened, more than twice as broad as thick, and decidedly oval in outline as seen from above; a row of long slender spines (the 'horns') across back of head; other rows of shorter blunt spines on sides of head, and a double row of short spines along each side of body and tail; back with scattered short pointed spines of various sizes. Under surface of body with smooth scales. Coloration variable, but above usually dusky yellow with a double row of large black patches on back; under surface yellowish, sometimes with small dusky spots.

Occurrence.—Sparse resident in lower western portions of Yosemite section. Known to occur on plains of San Joaquin Valley and found by us near Smith Creek, east of Coulterville. Reported at Kinsley. Inhabits open sandy ground.

The California Horned Toad, which is, of course, *not a toad* (an amphibian), is so distinctive in appearance that it cannot be confused with any other animal in the region. It is, perhaps, the best known of all the western lizards, and is present in small numbers in the western part of the Yosemite region. The general scarcity of suitable surroundings is undoubtedly the factor which limits the numbers of this animal here. The plains of the San Joaquin Valley where not entirely taken over for agriculture are tenanted by horned toads, and a few dry sandy spots in the foothills also harbor a small population.

Occasional adults of the present species reach a total length of 5 inches, though most of the individuals met with are somewhat smaller. The one specimen obtained by our field party was found near Smith Creek, at about 3000 feet altitude, on June 2, 1915. It measured only 2½ inches in length and was probably a young of the previous year's brood. Its stomach upon examination was found to contain 15 ground beetles measuring about ⅓ inch (7–10 mm.) in length, 2 ants, an unidentified larval insect, and a small pebble, the latter doubtless taken by accident.

ALLIGATOR LIZARDS.   Genus **Gerrhonotus**[41]

Field characters.—Size large for a lizard, up to 12 inches, legs small; head large and diamond shaped; iris light yellow; body covered above and on sides with keeled scales in 14 or 16 lengthwise rows (pl. 58*b, c, d*); a flexible fold of skin, covered with granules, along each side of body; scales on under surface smooth and in rows length-

---

[41] Two distinct species of Alligator Lizards live in the Yosemite region. They are similar to one another in general appearance, and little or nothing concerning possible differences in their habits is known. For these reasons they are here treated together.

SAN DIEGO ALLIGATOR LIZARD, *Gerrhonotus scincicauda webbii* Baird, a southern form which ranges north along the western flank of the Sierra Nevada, is found in the western

a

a. Coral King Snake.   *b.* Western Skink, immature or ''blue-tailed.''
c. Western Skink, adult or ''red-headed.''

wise and crosswise. Coloration above, dark grayish, greenish, or brownish, with or without dark cross-bands. Under surface bluish gray. Movements slow; wriggles along clumsily, with much sidewise bending of body.

Occurrence.—Moderately common on west slope of Sierra Nevada from Upper Sonoran Zone (*webbii*) to lower part of Hudsonian Zone (*palmeri*). Recorded from Pleasant Valley eastward to Tuolumne Meadows.[41] Lives on ground under chaparral and forest cover.

People often mistakenly attribute poisonous qualities to any unusual or formidable-looking animal, particularly if it be a reptile, and this is eminently true in the case of the Alligator Lizards. These lizards often attain considerable size, their heads are of the diamond shape popularly thought to be indicative of poisonous properties, and the temper of the animals is such that when handled they usually make an effort to bite. But the damage which one of these lizards can inflict on a person is usually limited to a sharp pinch from the strongly muscled jaws, without drawing blood. There are no poison glands whatever in this or any other of our California lizards.

The Alligator Lizard gains its popular name from the resemblance which the animal bears to the alligator, both in appearance and supposed temperament. The head is a prominent feature (pl. 58*b*) and gains in prominence as the individual increases in age, being no wider than the body in young animals but decidedly wider in old adults. The tail is long and slender and when unbroken is nearly twice the length of the head and body. This member is easily broken off, as it is in the cases of swifts and whip-tailed lizards; in the present species it readily grows out again, sometimes to nearly its original form and size, its regeneration here being, as a rule, more nearly perfect than it is in some of the other species of lizards. (See pl. 58*b, d.*) The fold of skin along the side of the body serves as a sort of expansion joint which can be opened out when the animal is puffed up, when it is excited, or when it is filled with food.

Both in the foothill country and in the high mountains the Alligator Lizards live on the ground, on chaparral- and tree-covered hillsides. Sometimes an individual is to be found in the edge of grassland, but the species does not go far out into the open. The legs and feet are small and weak.

---

part of the Yosemite region from Pleasant Valley eastward to Smith Creek (6 miles east of Coulterville) and to the western part of the floor of Yosemite Valley, at the foot of Rocky Point. It is characterized by having the scales on the back in 14 lengthwise rows and the scales on the side of the head behind the eye (temporal region) smooth. The general tone of color is brown or grayish brown, with about 10 well marked dark bands across the back. (See pl. 58*b.*)

SIERRA ALLIGATOR LIZARD, *Gerrhonotus palmeri* Stejneger, the species which is found in the higher portions of the Sierra Nevada (Canadian Zone chiefly), was recorded locally from Chinquapin, Merced Grove Big Trees, and the eastern part of the floor of Yosemite Valley (from the village) eastward to Tuolumne Meadows, and near Merced Lake. The scales on the back and sides are in 16 longitudinal rows and those of the temporal region are faintly keeled. The general tone of color is olive, not banded, but with ill-defined dark markings, and with sharp points of white along the sides. (See pl. 58*c, d.*)

When traveling, even when undisturbed, an Alligator Lizard progresses slowly and rather clumsily, wriggling its body from side to side. Some of the relatives of this lizard in other parts of the world have entirely lost their legs, and their locomotion is accomplished in much the same manner as in snakes. Perhaps this relative handicap on the part of the Alligator Lizard when making its escape or when cornered is compensated for by the formidable appearance and 'vicious' temper of the animal. The tongue is rapidly protruded, in the fashion of some snakes, and this, with the further feature of yellow iris, adds to the menacing 'front' put up by the animal.

The Alligator Lizards (both species) are insect feeders.

CALIFORNIA WHIP-TAILED LIZARD.   **Cnemidophorus tigris mundus** Camp

Field characters.—Body and especially tail long and slender; legs stout, the hinder pair much the larger; toes long; a well marked fold of skin across throat; back and sides of body covered with minute rounded bead-like scales; under surface of body with flat rhomboid scales arranged in eight lengthwise rows; tail with ridged or keeled scales. (See pl. 57c.) Coloration varying with age, striped in young, becoming spotted in adults. Ground color of body blackish, with lengthwise stripes (young) or with scattered small spots of buff, yellow or white (adults); sides of head and legs blotched with dusky; under surface white, with scale edgings of black; tail dark brown above, yellowish beneath. Head and body measuring to 4 inches; tail to 10 inches.

Occurrence.—Resident in small to moderate numbers on west side of Yosemite region, chiefly in Upper Sonoran Zone. Recorded from Pleasant Valley eastward to Smith Creek, 6 miles east of Coulterville, and to foot of Big Oak Flat road in western part of Yosemite Valley. To be seen on surface of ground in open gravelly or sandy places.

The swiftest of all the lizards in the Yosemite region is the California Whip-tailed Lizard which occurs at certain locations in the western part of the section. This reptile is ordinarily thought of as an inhabitant of desert regions, and in truth it is; but it also occurs, or did occur formerly, on much of the floor of the San Joaquin Valley, and it penetrates into the foothills wherever there are conditions suitable for its existence. Its distribution in the Yosemite section is not continuous. We found it at Pleasant Valley, about Coulterville, at Smith Creek, in the neighborhood of Kinsley, and at two locations in the lower end of Yosemite Valley, namely, at the foot of the Coulterville grade and at the foot of the Big Oak Flat grade.

The whip-tailed lizard is specialized in somewhat the same manner as the kangaroo rat, and to achieve the same result. Its whole organization is modified for the attainment of speed in running on the surface of the ground. The body is slender and the tail is fully twice the length of head and body together, and finely and evenly tapered to the end. (See pl. 57c.) The legs are stout, especially the hinder pair, and the toes are long, particularly those of the hind feet. When frightened, one of these animals appears to get over the ground, for a short distance at least, faster than a man can run. Its usual procedure is to start up suddenly, make a rapid dash of 50 to 100 feet or so, then stop abruptly, often dodging around behind a bush at the instant of stopping. The long tail serves as a counterpoise and perhaps also as a rudder, in movement. The sudden start, extremely swift run and quick stop are, to the human eye, confusing, and may have the same effect on any animal, such as the Road-runner, which might attempt to prey on the lizards. When undisturbed the Whip-tail forages about with jerky movements of the body. The tail is then usually dragged on the ground and leaves a characteristic trail between the marks of the feet. When pursued, one of these lizards will often take shelter in some hole in the ground, usually at the base of a bush. One was seen to enter a ground squirrel burrow. In places where there are no open rodent burrows, and where the soil is sufficiently loose, Whip-tails dig their own burrows.

At Smith Creek a small whip-tailed lizard was seen in a pool of water, where it had evidently jumped when frightened by the approach of the observer. The animal was obviously unadapted to this element, for after a few strokes it sank to the bottom and was drowned.

The Whip-tail subsists upon insects. Some of these, such as grasshoppers, are obtained by stalking, just as a carnivorous mammal such as a coyote stalks a ground squirrel. Other prey, such as cutworms (moth larvae) and beetle larvae, are picked up by the Whip-tail from the surface of the ground about the bases of plants. This lizard does not climb at all, even over rocks.

WESTERN SKINK. **Plestiodon skiltonianus** Baird and Girard

Field characters.—Scales flat, thin, and not ridged or beaded, overlapping (shingled) and forming a very smooth body covering; body and tail evenly tapered to slender tip of tail; both pairs of legs short, scarcely longer than diameter of body (pl. 58a). Adults: Head coppery red; body olive brown above, bluish green on sides, pale beneath; tail pinkish red (pl. 12c). Young: Head and body dark brown, with two sharply defined yellowish stripes along back; under surface pale blue; tail brilliant blue (pl. 12b). Total length of adults: Head and body up to 4⅛ inches, tail to 6⅜ inches.

Occurrence.—Common resident throughout western part of Yosemite section, from Lagrange and Pleasant Valley eastward to Yosemite Valley. Forages in shaded places, in leafy débris in thickets and under trees; has retreats under stones, logs, boards, etc., and down rodent burrows.

Most interesting among the several species of lizards in the Yosemite region is the Western Skink, a peculiarly smooth-bodied reptile, notable for its brilliant coloration and for the great difference in color pattern between young and old individuals. (See pl. 12b, c.)

The young are commonly referred to by naturalists as "blue-tailed skinks," since the tail is bright blue. The back of the young is dark brown, relieved by two long stripes of golden yellow. The adults, on the other hand, show no trace of blue on the tail and seldom any indication of striping on the body. The tail in the older animals is salmon pink, the head coppery red, while the body is plain greenish olive. A greater age contrast in one species could scarcely be imagined. This sharp difference in coloration led to the description of the "red-headed skink" of the Yosemite Valley as a distinct species, *Eumeces gilberti* (Van Denburgh, 1896, pp. 350–352). The entire absence of small (that is, young) individuals of the "red-headed"'skink and of very large "blue-tailed" skinks, the capture of several individuals of intermediate size and coloration (green-bodied yet with indications of striping), and the fact that in a related species of skink inhabiting eastern North America a parallel change in coloration is known to occur, lead now to the conclusion that the two 'forms' found in the Yosemite region are but different phases of growth in one and the same species. In the northwestern part of California only the striped-backed, blue-tailed phase of the skink is known to occur.

The Western Skink is conspicuously smooth-bodied. The head merges imperceptibly into the 'shoulder' region, and the body and tail are evenly and finely tapered to the slender tip of the latter. The scales everywhere are thin and lie so closely against the body that the animal can slip through a person's fingers as if oiled. It can also slip through the piles of dead leaves, in which it often seeks its insect food, with the greatest ease. The legs are small and short, particularly in the adult, where they scarcely exceed in length the greatest diameter of the body. Locomotion is accomplished more by wriggling or squirming movements of the body than by use of these diminutive legs. The tail of the skink, as in most other local lizards, will break off if the animal be handled roughly, and will wriggle interestingly for some time. Individuals are sometimes met with in nature in which the tail has been broken off and later partly regenerated. Such animals can be recognized by the stubby form of the tail.

The local range of the Western Skink extends from the westernmost rocky outcrops on the foothills near Lagrange and Pleasant Valley eastward to Yosemite Valley. In the latter place the skink has been found as high as 4500 feet, at Inspiration Point (Van Denburgh, *loc. cit.*). A dried skin of this species was picked up at Snelling by one of our party, but otherwise no evidence of its existence out on the plains of the San Joaquin was forthcoming.

Skinks are in the main cover-seeking reptiles. They do not often forage in the open; they may come out, however, toward twilight of warm summer days. The rock fences built in many parts of the foothill country afford admirable shelter and forage grounds for many of these lizards, as does likewise the boulder talus along the north wall of Yosemite Valley. In the latter place, however, the skinks live on the ground *between* the rocks, in the débris consisting of accumulated oak leaves and pine needles; they do not go out on the surfaces of the rocks as do the swifts (*Sceloporus occidentalis*). Skinks are also to be found beneath fallen tree trunks or in slight excavations (burrows of other animals probably) under rocks lying on open ground. Logs or rocks in pastures or on grassy hillsides quite often afford retreats for one or two of these lizards. In the 'mother lode' district some individuals take shelter in the heaps of shale at old prospect holes.

Several skinks were obtained in mouse traps set on the ground under bushes for the capture of small mammals. These particular individuals either stumbled into the traps or else were attracted secondarily by ants and other insects which had gathered to feed on the bait (rolled oats). Still other individuals were obtained when we tore open dead and rotting tree trunks lying on the ground.

Western Skinks, particularly the blue-tailed youngsters, are able to run with considerable speed when frightened and upon open ground. But the normal movements, especially of adults, are rather slow and heavy. On several occasions we had chances to watch individuals which were undisturbed and engaged in foraging. The animals moved in a hesitating manner, proceeding this way and that, advancing and then remaining quiet for a second or two, usually going around rather than over small rocks and other obstacles, even if of less than an inch in height. These particular lizards kept their heads close to or even upon the ground, and one in the course of its meanderings was seen to snap up small insects from time to time. One red-headed skink was seen gliding over the surface of a black-oak log in strong sunlight, one afternoon in June. As the animal breathed a shimmering play of light was reflected from its smooth scales.

RUBBER SNAKE. **Charina bottae** (Blainville)

Field characters.—Size small for a snake, length usually under 24 inches; body stout and of about same diameter throughout; tail short, blunt ended, much like head in shape; whole surface of body very smooth, skin loose fitting. Coloration plain greenish brown above, uniform yellowish white beneath. A small spine (rudimentary leg) projects, slightly, on each side of vent (at base of tail). Movements sluggish.

Occurrence.—Recorded only from floor of Yosemite Valley. Lives on moist shaded ground.

The Rubber Snake is a northern species belonging to the same family as the boas and pythons of the tropical portions of the New and Old Worlds. It never attains to anywhere near the size of those better known 'constrictors.' The individual mentioned below is the largest Rubber Snake we have ever seen. When fully relaxed this example measured 645 milli-meters (25½ inches) from tip of nose to tip of tail, and its greatest girth was 65 millimeters (2½ inches). Most of the representatives of this species which we have seen have been less than 20 inches long.

The one individual noted by us in the Yosemite region was found October 7, 1914, in a road near Sentinel Bridge. It had been killed by some workmen who had passed along just previously. It is deplorable that people should persist in destroying non-poisonous snakes. The deep-rooted tendency in some human beings for this kind of reaction toward *all* snakes seems to operate entirely without reason. The Rubber Snake is not only harmless, but, for a reptile, it makes an admirable pet. We have never known of a snake of this species attempting to bite or to resent handling in any way.

GARTER SNAKES. Genus **Thamnophis**[42]

Field characters.—Body long, slender and tapering; tail pointed; scales of back all ridged (keeled), never in more than 23 rows. (See fig. 62*b*.) Coloration of upper sur-face black or grayish, with a light line along each side of body and another line down middle of back, or else many small light spots on back; pattern never in large blotches or cross-bands; under surface bluish green. Emit a foul-smelling liquid when handled.

Occurrence.—Common along streams, about margins of ponds, and in wet meadows throughout the Yosemite region up at least to 8600 feet altitude.[42] Live on damp ground and in water. Several individuals often found together.

---

[42] The identification of the species and subspecies of Garter Snakes is often a difficult matter even for a trained herpetologist. There is much variation among individuals, especially in the numbers of scales; consequently series of specimens are usually required to properly identify the snakes from any one locality. Difficulty may be experienced in attempting to name certain individual specimens. The latest comprehensive study of the Garter Snakes of western North America is that by Van Denburgh and Slevin (Proc. Calif. Acad. Sci., ser. 4, vol. 8, 1918, pp. 181–270, pls. 7–17) who have identified our specimens from the Yosemite region as belonging to two species, one of which is represented by three subspecies. These forms, with their principal characters (as exhibited by the most typical specimens), and the localities at which they were found, are as follows:

PACIFIC GARTER SNAKE, *Thamnophis sirtalis infernalis* (Blainville), has (usually) 7 scales on upper lip (supralabials), not more than 19 lengthwise rows of scales on back, and upper surface black with three distinct light stripes, one down middle of back and another low on each side of body. It is a lowland species, common at Snelling and Lagrange and ranging eastward as far as floor of Yosemite Valley.

GIANT GARTER SNAKE, *Thamnophis ordinoides couchii* (Kennicott), has usually 8 scales on upper lip, usually 21 rows of scales on forepart of body, and upper surface of body black but with no light line down middle of back, the upper surface being marked with small scattered light spots. (See fig. 62*b*.) It is a central California race, found on meadows in Yosemite Valley.

MOUNTAIN GARTER SNAKE, *Thamnophis ordinoides elegans* (Baird and Girard), has (usually) 8 scales on upper lip, not often more than 19 rows of scales on back, and a dark body coloration with 3 distinct light stripes, one down middle of back and one on each side of body. It is a high mountain subspecies, reported from floor of Yosemite Valley, but more common in the higher altitudes as at Merced Lake (7500 feet) and Tuolumne Meadows (8600 feet).

WANDERING GARTER SNAKE, *Thamnophis ordinoides vagrans* (Baird and Girard), has (usually) 8 scales on upper lip, 21 rows of scales on forepart of body, and a dull (often grayish or greenish) body coloration, but with a distinct line down middle of back; large scales on under surface often with black markings. This snake is a Great Basin form, taken at Walker Lake and near Mono Lake.

The Garter Snakes are often called Water Snakes in recognition of their association with streams, ponds, and wet meadows, and through most of the Yosemite region they may be looked for confidently in such surroundings. They occur the most widely of all the snakes in the region. Moreover, they are often found in considerable numbers in a single locality; hence, the Garter Snake population, as a whole, is far above that of any of the other snakes, or, perhaps, of all other snakes put together.

In hand or at close range the Garter Snakes may be readily distinguished from all other snakes of the Yosemite region by the fact that they possess keels or ridges on the scales of the back, in combination with a

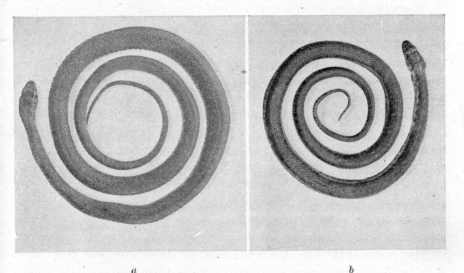

a   *b*

Fig. 62. (*a*) Western Yellow-bellied Racer; Yosemite Valley, June 4, 1915. (*b*) Giant Garter Snake; Yosemite Valley, May 22, 1919. Both photographed from freshly taken specimens, about ⅖ natural size.

pattern of coloration which never consists of large blotches. The most usual color pattern among the Garter Snakes is a dark upper surface with a light stripe down the middle of the back and another similar stripe low on each side of the body. The Giant Garter Snake is an exception, as it has only a short stripe on the neck region and the rest of its body is flecked with small spots of light color. The California Striped Racer of the foothill oaks and chaparral has a long slender body and a dark upper surface with a stripe along each side but not in the middle. This snake looks at first glance somewhat like a garter snake, but all of its scales are smooth and it has no light line down the middle of the back. The rattlesnake and gopher snake both have keeled scales, but the patterns of coloration and bodily form in these species are entirely different from those of the garter snakes.

The favorite haunt of the garter snakes is the margin of a shallow pool with gently sloping shores and bottom, a pool bordered closely by a dense stand of grass or other low plants. In such places these snakes often abound. Five were noted close together on the shore of one small pond near Tuolumne Meadows on July 6, 1915, and greater numbers have been seen in other localities. Such a place gives the snakes an easy retreat into the grass on one side and into the water on the other, while food in the form of frogs, tadpoles, or small fishes is usually to be obtained close by. When undisturbed the snakes will spend much of the day in sunning themselves on the shores of such a pool.

When it takes to water a garter snake swims readily, with only its head above the surface, making progress by whipping the body from side to side in broad loops. At best its speed is slow, not to be compared with that of any of the fishes, and after going a short distance it will usually rest momentarily before resuming its course. When resting in shallow water it will allow its body to sink to the bottom and will hold only its head above the surface; but in a deeper stream or pool it will glide up to the margin and rest its chin on a projecting ledge or log. On land as well as in water these snakes are slow movers, that is, for snakes. The form of the scales on the under surface of their bodies, and the musculature by which the free edges of these scales are lifted, do not seem to be adapted for rapid travel such as is exhibited by the racers. The garter snakes make their best progress when in a meadow, for there the scales get more of a purchase on the irregularities of the grass and sod.

The garter snakes are not belligerent, rarely if ever will they 'show fight' as do gopher snakes or rattlers. Even when harried they usually try to slip quietly off into the grass or swim away in the water. If captured, a garter snake will as a rule pour out a malodorous liquid that is effective in procuring its release, especially if its captor be a human being. How much of a protection from wild enemies this odor affords, is not known.

Garter snakes have large litters of young. Rarely are there less than 10 or a dozen, and litters of 20 and more are not uncommon. The rapidity of its reproduction probably reflects the degree of danger to which these reptiles are exposed. The eggs of Garter Snakes are not deposited on land and left to hatch unattended, as are those of many snakes, but are retained in the body of the female and developed there, and the young are born alive.

These snakes do not usually have to go far from their favorite haunts to find food, as they feed to a large extent on frogs, toads, tadpoles, and small fishes. The relative scarcity of frogs in certain meadows and along some of the slower moving streams, and their unusual abundance in some of the highest mountain lakes and along the swifter creeks, may perhaps be related to the presence or absence of garter snakes in these respective localities. Although 'cold-blooded' animals form the greater portion of the food of these snakes, they are not averse to taking birds or mammals when occasion offers. At Mono Lake Post Office on May 30, 1916, a Wandering Garter Snake was found trying to swallow a barely fledged young Modoc Song Sparrow. Both of the parent birds were highly excited and flew at the snake repeatedly.

The garter snakes, even in the lowlands, are seen but little during the colder portions of the year, while at the higher altitudes they spend several months in continuous hibernation. At Walker Lake a Wandering Garter Snake was picked up at 9 o'clock on the morning of September 13, 1915. It was some distance from water and so cold and torpid that it made practically no effort to escape. It would probably soon have gone into winter quarters in some sheltered crevice in the rocks. Tracks of a garter snake were seen near Snow Flat on October 5, 1915, but no evidence of activity was obtained after that date anywhere in the Yosemite region. By the third week of May, 1919, garter snakes were becoming active in Yosemite Valley. One seen wriggling across a road, May 21, near the Valley wall and going toward the river meadows, may have only just emerged from hibernation.

WESTERN RING-NECKED SNAKE

Diadophis amabilis amabilis Baird and Girard

Field characters.—Size small, body diameter usually not larger than a lead pencil, total length usually under 15 inches (380 mm.). Upper surface plain slaty olive; a whitish or reddish collar around neck; under surface of body red (of varying hue in different specimens), marked with numerous fine dots of black. Scales on back smooth, in 15 (rarely 17) crosswise rows.

Occurrence.—Sparse resident at middle altitudes. Recorded at Pleasant Valley (Mus. Vert. Zool.) and in Yosemite Valley (Stejneger, North American Fauna, no. 7, 1893, p. 204). Inhabits shaded ground, keeping usually under leafy débris, logs, or boulders.

The Western Ring-necked Snake was not found by our party, but its presence in the Yosemite region is established by the two records of it given above. This is the smallest of all the snakes which occur in the Yosemite section; the usual run of individuals found measure 15 inches or less in total length, while the body diameter is usually less than $\frac{5}{16}$ inch. The Western Ring-necked Snake is a quiet, inoffensive species, and feeds chiefly upon insects. An individual when suddenly uncovered, as when a stone or log is turned over, will sometimes lie with its brilliant undersurface uppermost and feign death. Under such circumstances, too, the tail of the snake is often curled in a tight spiral with the bright red under surface exposed.

CORAL KING SNAKE. **Lampropeltis multicincta** (Yarrow)

Field characters.—Of small to moderate size; total length usually under 30 inches; tail short; head rather blunt. Coloration conspicuously bright, consisting of crosswise rings or bands of black, red and yellow, each yellow band being bordered on either side by one of black. (See pl. 12a.)

Occurrence.—Resident in moderate numbers in Yosemite Valley. Reported from Smith Creek, 6 miles east of Coulterville. Inhabits chiefly shaded slopes beneath golden oaks.

The most beautiful reptile in the fauna of the Yosemite region is the Coral King Snake, which lives in and about the heaps of talus rock at the bases of the walls of Yosemite Valley, especially where shaded by golden oaks. The pattern of the reptile is composed of crosswise bands or 'zones' of black, red, and yellow. (See pl. 12a.) These vary in width on different individuals, but the sequence of the bands is the same on all. The arrangement is red, black, yellow, black, red, etc., each yellow band being bordered on either side by black. This arrangement is of little significance here in California, but in Arizona, where the Coral King Snake occurs there is also a venomous snake marked with the same colors, but with a different sequence that is useful to remember. No poisonous snake, save the Rattlesnake, occurs in the Yosemite region, so that no fear need be entertained concerning any brightly colored snake of the sort here described.

Our Coral King Snake is of quiet, sluggish behavior, so that it is likely to excite interest only by reason of its brilliant coloration. If a person happens to come upon one of these snakes while the latter is resting on the soft dust of a trail, the reptile is prone to remain motionless, with its body in a series of rounded loops. If disturbed it will glide away slowly into the cover of nearby rocks or leafy litter. If picked up, its demeanor is docile; in other words, it can be handled, according to our experience, with absolute impunity.

This quiet-appearing snake has the reputation of being highly predatory and is said to attack other reptiles, even including, according to some persons, rattlesnakes. A Coral King Snake taken by us in Yosemite Valley June 1, 1915, was found to have fed upon an adult Western Skink, the smooth-bodied lizard which lives in the same talus slopes.

BOYLE KING SNAKE. **Lampropeltis getulus boylii** (Baird and Girard)

Field characters.—Size medium; total length up to 42 inches, body diameter 1 inch or less; scales on back smooth, in 23 (or 25) rows. Coloration in alternate broad bands of brownish black and creamy white, which, brokenly, encircle the body. (See fig. 63a.)

Occurrence.—Moderately common in Upper Sonoran Zone on west slope of Sierra Nevada. Recorded at Pleasant Valley and at Smith Creek (6 miles east of Coulterville). Inhabits shaded ground with mixed vegetational cover.

The Boyle King Snake or "milk snake" is a strikingly colored animal with broad alternate bands of black and white crossing the back from the head to the end of the tail; these markings extend down the sides and onto the under surface, but do not meet evenly on the belly.

This species is a terrestrial snake and is usually to be found in the vicinity of thickets or other close vegetational cover. It does not affect the pure chaparral on the drier slopes, nor does it ordinarily occur in open grasslands. In general demeanor the Boyle King Snake is a quiet reptile, its ordinary movements being slow and deliberate. However, it bears the same reputation as the Coral King Snake, namely, that of using other snakes for food when chance offers.

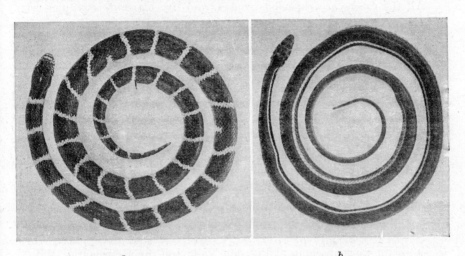

a   *b*

Fig. 63. (*a*) Boyle King Snake; Pleasant Valley, May 24, 1915. (*b*) California Striped Racer; Pleasant Valley, May 27, 1915. Both photographed from freshly taken specimens; about ⅓ natural size.

CALIFORNIA STRIPED RACER. **Coluber lateralis** (Hallowell)

Field characters.—Body long and very slender; tail long, tapering to fine point; scales of back all smooth (without ridges or keels), in 17 rows. General coloration above dark brown; a sharply defined light line along each side the whole length of the body. (See fig. 63*b*.) Under surface of body plain yellow.

Occurrence.—Common resident in Upper Sonoran Zone where recorded from Pleasant Valley east to Smith Creek, 6 miles east of Coulterville. Lives in chaparral country. Climbs into bushes and often into trees.

The California Striped Racer is a long, slender, smooth-bodied snake remarkable for its speed and for its skill in climbing. Superficially it bears somewhat of a resemblance to a garter snake, but the two differ in several important ways. The racer has fewer scales; these, counted in a transverse or diagonal line across the body, never number more than 17 rows, whereas a garter snake always has more than 17 and may have as many as 21 rows. The racer's scales are all smooth, whereas those of the garter snake are ridged or keeled. Both species have a single stripe along each side of body, but that of the racer involves the third and fourth rows of scales, while that on the garter snake is on the second and third rows. The racer never has a light stripe down the middle of the back, whereas this is a frequent (though not invariable) mark in the garter snake. Finally, the habitats of the two are different. The racer prefers dry chaparral and tree-covered areas, whereas the garter snake usually lives about water or in damp meadows.

All the racers are rapacious snakes, and live more or less upon vertebrates; the present species, at the appropriate season, takes toll of nestling birds. The long slender form of body seems to be a correlative of climbing ability, as 'tree' snakes in all parts of the world are of this general form.

In a dry grassy cañon bottom near Coulterville, May 12, 1919, one of these snakes was come upon while it was on the ground; its body rested in a long U-shape and its head was slightly raised. The snake was perfectly motionless, not even running its tongue out and in, as would a garter or gopher snake under similar circumstances. The snake was watched for a minute or more and a photograph was taken. During this time it could not be seen that the animal had moved at all. Then one of the observers changed position and advanced slightly in the direction of the snake, whereupon the latter abruptly vanished down a small hole in the ground, previously unnoticed by us.

While at work in camp at Pleasant Valley on the afternoon of May 27, 1915, our attention was attracted by a disturbance among some Western Chipping Sparrows and Green-backed Goldfinches in the top of a small blue oak. The cause for excitement was found to be a California Striped Racer about 10 feet above the ground in the oak. The snake was at the site of a nest and apparently just about to seize a young bird. The snake was shot by one of our party and then removed from the tree, but the excited birds did not cease their loud chippings for some time afterward.

Among some scattered manzanita bushes on a hillside near the McCarthy ranch, a California Striped Racer was found on June 5, 1915, while it was raiding the brood of a pair of Black-throated Gray Warblers. The snake appeared to have already swallowed one of the nestlings, and another lay on the ground. The female parent was flying about distractedly, uttering notes of concern. At our approach the snake attempted to make off into the brush but was shot.

738

WESTERN YELLOW-BELLIED RACER. **Coluber constrictor flaviventris** (Say)

Field characters.—Body long and slender; tail tapering to a fine point (fig. 62a); scales of back all smooth (without keels) and placed in 17 rows. General coloration above uniform olive brown, becoming greenish or bluish on sides of body and plain yellow on whole of under surface.

Occurrence.—Resident at lower levels in western part of Yosemite region. Recorded from 3 to 6 miles east of Coulterville and from floor of Yosemite Valley. Lives chiefly in grassland.

The Yellow-bellied Racer, often known as Blue Racer, is less common in the Yosemite section than is its striped relative. The present species is essentially an inhabitant of grasslands or meadows and the scarcity of this sort of habitat in the region is no doubt the factor which limits its numbers. Our local specimens, three in number, were all obtained in grassy places.

The Yellow-bellied Racer is closely related to the Black Snake of the eastern United States, and like that species has a rather aggressive disposition. When come upon, a Yellow-bellied Racer will first endeavor to escape, and it is able to travel at surprising speed. But if cornered or if pinned down under a stick or a person's shoe it will usually turn upon, and endeavor to bite, its captor. This action though somewhat terrifying to the average person is without serious consequences. The Racer has no venom, and the most it can do is to puncture the skin on a person's finger and perhaps cause a little bleeding.

VALLEY GOPHER SNAKE. **Pituophis catenifer heermanni** (Hallowell)

Field characters.—Size variable, often large; body always relatively stout, but tail tapering slenderly to a point. Scales on back ridged or keeled, and in 29 or more rows. Ground color of body ocher yellow, marked along back with many 'saddle-marks' of dark brown, and with smaller dark spots along sides. (See pl. 59a.) When first approached often lies motionless on ground; then glides off to nearest safety refuge; if cornered, is likely to 'show fight' by hissing and striking.

Occurrence.—Fairly common in the Lower and Upper Sonoran zones and lower part of Transition Zone on west side of Sierra Nevada. Recorded from Snelling and Pleasant Valley eastward to floor of Yosemite Valley. Lives in grasslands and along road margins; rarely or never goes into water or up into bushes or trees. Usually solitary.

The Valley Gopher Snake, sometimes called "bull snake," is fairly common in the western foothill district of the Yosemite region, and is likely to be seen in any of the grasslands or along any of the dusty roadways up to 4000 feet altitude.

The general run of gopher snakes to be found in the Yosemite region will probably exceed in average size the rattlesnakes now found there.

This is due in part to the fact that the gopher snake tends to grow to a large size and also to the fact that the rattlers are killed whenever found, while some at least of the gopher snakes are protected by the farmers of the country and so reach greater age. Gopher snakes elsewhere often grow to a length of 5 feet or even more and have a normal body girth in the neighborhood of 6 inches; but the largest individual which we chanced to encounter within the Yosemite region was 1025 millimeters (40½ inches) long. The average length of all those handled by us was 32 inches.

The Valley Gopher Snake is a distinctive species as regards its coloration (pl. 59a), being approached as to pattern only by the rattlesnake and by very young racers. The ground color is ocher yellow. Down the middle of the back there is a row of hexagonal or squarish blotches of dark brown which toward the end of the tail become black. Along each side of the body are rows of smaller spots usually blackish in color. The rattlesnake's pattern consists usually of very large blotches, each with a light margin, and it does not have so many side spots. The young racers are more spotted than the gopher snakes and of course they may be told from young gopher snakes at once by their smooth scales, those of the latter species, no matter what the age, always being ridged or keeled.

Generally speaking, the gopher snake is a rather quiet, even a lethargic species. When come upon on the ground in a field it will often lie perfectly quiet and thereby escape detection; there is no movement to catch the eye. Its usual color pattern is very close to that of the dry grassland in which it lives so much of the time. If aroused it can, and if unhindered will, make off with fair rapidity. But if cornered a gopher snake will show fight, coiling its body up and drawing back and spreading its head until the latter has the triangular outline often considered (though erroneously so) the mark of a poisonous species. Then it will usually fill its lungs with air, swell its body out considerably and suddenly lunge at its enemy, expelling the air with a hissing sound as it does so. This 'bluff' is often effective and gives the snake a chance to make good its escape. A curious habit of some individual gopher snakes is to vibrate rapidly the slender tip of the tail, whereby if the animal happens to be in dry grass or weeds a rattling sound is produced, suggestive of the rattle of a rattlesnake. This might, on occasion, serve the purpose of warning a potential enemy. But, of course, the Gopher Snake is not at all venomous.

Gopher snakes may often be seen around the burrows of earth-dwelling rodents such as the ground squirrels and pocket gophers, and the snakes subsist to a considerable extent upon these animals. The snakes are able to pursue the rodents underground and thus have an advantage over the large carnivorous mammals and birds which must either catch the squirrels and gophers above ground or else, as do most of the mammals except the weasel, dig them out.

The ability of a gopher snake, or, for that matter, of any other snake, to swallow prey much larger than itself is consequent upon the peculiar structure of the snake's mouth. Its lower jaw is loosely attached, there being a flexible connection between the two halves at the chin, while at the back on each side there is a bone (quadrate) which can be swung out so as to make the diameter of the mouth orifice much greater. Then, as there is no breast bone attaching to the ribs, the digestive tract can stretch to a much greater extent than is possible in birds and mammals. When engaged in swallowing a rodent, one of these snakes is relatively helpless and can easily be captured. Once the act of swallowing is commenced (the prey is practically always taken in head first), the squirrel or gopher cannot be quickly disgorged.

Near Stage Station (on the Coulterville road), on June 14, 1915, a rotten log, upon being broken apart in a search for a lizard, yielded a small Valley Gopher Snake which had in it a nearly full-sized White-footed Mouse (*Peromyscus,* probably *californicus*). The girth of the mouse was about twice that of the snake; consequently the snake's skin was so stretched opposite the place where the mouse lay in the digestive tract that the scales on the sides were widely separated, and the soft skin showed between them. The strong digestive juices had already begun to act, and the fore part of the mouse's skull was almost completely dissolved.

In Yosemite Valley near Pohono Bridge an active young gopher snake was seen at the roadside May 1, 1916. This happened to be our only record for the Valley proper.

During the winter, gopher snakes are practically never seen abroad. They spend this part of the year somewhere underground, coming out if at all only on the warmest days. At Snelling, on January 6, 1915, while Mr. Camp was excavating the burrow of a kangaroo rat he found a snake of this species in one of the rodent's tunnels. The snake was quite lively, showing none of the torpidity ordinarily to be expected of a hibernating animal.

PACIFIC RATTLESNAKE. **Crotalus oreganus** Holbrook

Field characters.—A segmented horny 'rattle' at end of tail (fig. 64). Body stout; tail (vent to rattles) short, usually less than $\frac{1}{10}$ length of body (to vent). Head bluntly triangular; a definite constriction at neck. (See pl. 59*b*.) Scales on back relatively large, keeled, and in 23 to 27 rows. Total length (snout to end of rattles) up to 4 feet (possibly more); girth of body up to 5 inches. General coloration yellowish brown or grayish brown, with a series of large saddle-marks of dark brown or black along middle of back; also two rows of smaller dark spots along each side of body, these alternating in position with the large blotches. *Track:* Broad, much curved; on soft roadways shows much earth pushed up at sides of curves (pl. 40*b*).

Occurrence.—Resident in numbers on west slope of Yosemite region where recorded from Snelling eastward to altitude of 8100 feet near junction of Sunrise and Merced Lake trails. Lives chiefly near rocks and in brushy places, but also in open country of lowlands.

The Pacific Rattlesnake is the only poisonous animal to be found among the vertebrates in the Yosemite section, and the experience of the great numbers of visitors to the region has shown that there is little real danger from even this animal. 'Rattlers' are to be found from the plains of the San Joaquin Valley eastward into the mountains to an altitude of 8100 feet, though they are more common in the foothill country than at the higher levels. Yosemite Valley originally had a fairly large population of rattlesnakes, but these reptiles have been pretty well eliminated there, by the hand of man, within the past two decades. On the east slope of the Sierras, between the Yosemite region and the neighborhood of Lake Tahoe, rattlesnakes appear to be wanting entirely, though they are present farther east in the Great Basin territory.

The danger from rattlesnakes is often exaggerated. This is not to say that their bite is not poisonous, for that has been proved beyond doubt. But the rattlesnake is ordinarily not an aggressive animal and when met with will usually try to escape if not cornered. Very few persons are actually bitten and of those who are bitten but a small percentage succumb, as in most cases prompt application of proper treatment counteracts the effect of the poison.

The extreme size attained by the Pacific Rattlesnake in the Yosemite region is not known with certainty. Exact measurements of freshly killed individuals are scarce. Occasionally rattlers measuring as much as 5 feet from tip to tip are killed in the foothill country, according to Mr. Donald D. McLean. The largest example obtained by our party measured 36 inches (915 mm.) in length. The average length of the rattlers in the region is probably slightly under this. Measurements from skins, either fresh or dried, are of but little service save to indicate the general size of the snakes from which they were taken. Such skins may be, and often are, stretched from 10 to 25 per cent beyond the dimensions of the reptile 'in the flesh.'

The head of the rattlesnake is bluntly triangular in outline and sharply set off by the relatively slender neck (pl. 59*b*). This shape of head, though always to be found in the rattler, is not a reliable character for distinguishing poisonous snakes generally from harmless ones. The garter and gopher snakes, both harmless species, are able to assume this form of head temporarily. The head of the rattlesnake shows other distinctive features: the upper surface is devoid of large plates, being covered with small scales; there is a distinct pit between the nostril and the eye; and the pupil of the eye is vertically elliptical. The body of the rattlesnake is usually thick, perhaps 5 inches in circumference in a large example. The scales on the body of the snake are large and coarse and each scale is surmounted by a conspicuous lengthwise ridge or keel. The tail is quite short and bears at the end the dry resonant rattle which has given rise to the common name of the reptile. The coloration of rattlesnakes is apt to be quite variable, even in a single locality. Some individuals may be dark, even nearly black, while others are extensively gray, reddish, or yellowish.

The rattle of the rattlesnake is a structure which is formed incidentally to the general molt of the outer skin. (See fig. 64). Snakes of all species cast off the outer, worn layer of the skin one or more times each year. In the garter or gopher snakes, in which the tail is tapered to the end, the 'slough' usually comes away in a single piece, being turned inside out as the snake glides out of it, and such cast skins are to be found from

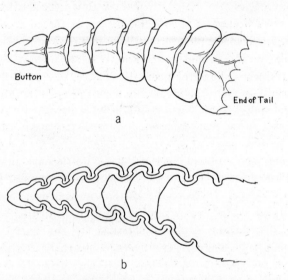

Fig. 64. Rattle of Pacific Rattlesnake (*a*) and diagrammatic section of same (*b*), showing manner in which parts of rattle are held together and yet remain loose enough to permit of movement when tail is vibrated.

time to time in the field. The molt of the rattlesnake, so far as the body is concerned, is the same as in other snakes. But the tip of the tail in this species is blunt and bears a thickened horny covering with one (later two) constrictions. When the molt occurs, this horny tip is held by the new tip growing beneath it. Successive molts result in a series of these dry segments being formed, each of which is caught over or under the two adjacent ones. The number of segments in a rattle (provided the first small segment or 'button' is still adhering) thus indicates merely the number of times the snake has molted. Large snakes have been found in which only a few segments of the rattle remained, the balance having been worn or broken off. The largest number of rattles which we know definitely to have been found on a rattlesnake was 22. Most individuals have 8 to 10.

When excited the rattlesnake vibrates the tip of the tail rapidly, causing the horny rattle to give forth an insistent cicada-like buzz that is usually recognizable at once. If danger threatens, the snake places its body in a series of S-shaped curves, the tip of the tail being held vertically. To "strike," the reptile straightens out suddenly, lunging at its prey or enemy, dropping the lower jaw and erecting the hollow teeth or 'fangs' in the roof of the mouth so that they point almost straight forward. (See fig. 65.) At best, the rattler cannot strike more than two-thirds its total length; one-third is probably the average distance struck. Stories of snakes "jumping" at their enemies are gross exaggerations. If the snake hits the object of its attack the two hollow fangs are buried in the flesh, the lower jaw is brought up and the poison is forced into the wounds. Leather tramping boots or puttees are likely to afford full protection against the rattlesnake, as the animal is not known to strike to a height of much if any over 12 inches above the ground.

If a person chances to be struck by a rattler certain things should be done promptly, but with as little flurry as possible.

1. If bitten on the leg or arm, apply a tourniquet above the wound, that is, toward the heart from the bite. This is done in order to stop the flow of blood toward the heart and prevent the poison from getting into the general circulation. A bandana handkerchief with two opposite corners knotted together, slipped over the limb and twisted tight by means of a stick makes a good tourniquet.

2. Cut open the site of the punctures with a pocketknife so as to promote a flow of blood and thus tend to wash out the poison. If available, inject potassium permanganate solution into the area immediately surrounding the bite. If the solution cannot be made or injected apply a few crystals of permanganate directly at the place of the bite.

3. After about half an hour loosen the tourniquet slightly for a fraction of a minute and then tighten it down again. Thereafter, loosening and tightening should be done every fifteen minutes or so. This is to allow the poison remaining in the wound to be absorbed by the system gradually and also to prevent gangrene setting in about the bite because of impeded circulation.

4. The patient should be placed in a comfortable position as soon as possible, and kept quiet. A mild stimulant such as coffee may be administered. Do *not* give whiskey or brandy. A doctor should be summoned as soon as possible.

For the rattlesnake the venom serves a twofold purpose, to kill animals which the snake uses for food, and to protect the reptile against its enemies. The food of the rattlesnake consists largely of small rodents of which, locally, chipmunks form a considerable part. These are killed by the snake's poison and then swallowed. A rattler killed on Smith Creek, 6 miles east of Coulterville, July 21, 1920, had the remains of a Mariposa Chipmunk in its alimentary canal, only the hind legs and tail remaining undigested. Another snake found on the Snow Creek zigzags of the trail to Tenaya Lake on September 29, 1915, had an adult Long-eared Chipmunk in its throat, with the tail protruding from the reptile's mouth. In both of these instances the snake had swallowed its prey head foremost. But a case has been reported by Dr. Barton W. Evermann (1915*b*) in which a rattlesnake killed near Cascade Falls (west of the lower end of Yosemite Valley) on July 15, 1914, contained an adult Mariposa Chipmunk which it had swallowed *tail first!* "The head of the chipmunk was toward the snake's head, and its legs, tail and fur all lay back toward the snake's tail, smooth and in perfect order."

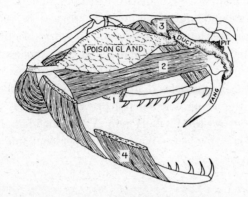

Fig. 65. Sketch of head of Pacific Rattlesnake, showing important parts of the anatomy which function in the bite and poisoning by this snake. The action of the poison apparatus is as follows. As the snake moves its head forward to strike a victim, be it man or animal, Muscle 1 (spheno-pterygoid) is contracted. This pushes forward the tooth-bearing bone preceding it and this in turn rocks forward the bone which carries the fang and causes the fang to come in line with the strike of the head. After the fang has entered the body of the victim, Muscle 1 relaxes and Muscles 2 and 3 (external pterygoid and spheno-palatine) contract, drawing the fang more deeply into the flesh. Then Muscle 4 (anterior temporal) contracts, bringing up the lower jaw and at the same time compressing the poison gland so that the poison is forced along the duct, through the fang, and into the flesh of the victim. Then the whole musculature of the head and neck relaxes, the head and fangs are drawn away from the victim and the fang is depressed again. This whole series of actions occupies but an instant.

The fang is shown partly elevated. Normally it lies close to the roof of the mouth and is covered by a membrane not shown in the drawing. When the fang is erected, preparatory to biting, this membrane is folded down at the base of the fang and directs the poison as it leaves the end of the duct of the gland into the base of the fang. (Adapted from Noguchi.)

A strong belief in many places is that the rattlesnakes "go blind" in late summer and are then very dangerous and likely to strike without warning. The basis of fact underlying this notion is that many of these snakes molt in that season, and that for a time just before the molt the skin overlying the eyes, which is likewise sloughed off, is clouded by the secretion which loosens the outer skin preparatory to its removal. Another widespread notion is that rattlers go about in pairs; we have never been able to find any conclusive evidence on this point.

The temperament of the rattlesnake is quite different from that of the racers, and reflects in a way the differences in form between the two types. The rattlesnake is generally quiet and slow, even lethargic, and is wont to spend much of its time in some warm sunny spot, as on a rocky out-crop. In such a place, too, it waits for prey. The cleared area of a trail is often made use of as a sunning place and this accounts for the number of rattlers encountered by hikers. If come upon, on trail or rocks, a rattle-snake may remain quiet, or again it may endeavor to glide away. Only when it is cornered, or when it 'thinks' itself cornered, is the rattler likely to prepare for striking.

In the winter months rattlesnakes "den up," that is, go into dormancy in holes in the ground and sometimes in crevices in rocks. In certain places, ground squirrel burrows are used. In a few localities regular dens have been reported where large numbers of these snakes are said to con-gregate together for the winter season. One such den is reported to have been found in the neighborhood of Horseshoe Bend when the Yosemite Valley Railroad was being constructed previous to 1908. Another is said to have been blown up in Hetch Hetchy Valley incidental to work on the San Francisco water project. We have no personal knowledge of occur-rences of this nature.

Pacific Mud Turtle. Clemmys marmorata (Baird and Girard)

Field characters.—Body protected by a firm "shell," arched above, flat on under surface; this shell consists of an outer horny integument, divided into numerous plates, and a supporting structure beneath composed of bone. Total length of shell up to 5½ inches. Upper surface olive brown; under surface yellow, irregularly marked with black or brown.

Occurrence.—Resident in Lower and Upper Sonoran zones on west side of Sierra Nevada. Recorded at Lagrange, Pleasant Valley, and Smith Creek, 6 miles east of Coulterville. Lives in ponds and in the quieter and deeper portions of streams.

The Pacific Mud Turtle, the only species of native fresh-water turtle to be found in central California, is resident in suitable places in the lower western portion of the Yosemite section. This turtle lives in ponds and in the parts of creeks and rivers which are deep and in which the current is very slow. The site selected for a resting place is usually some rock or log projecting above the surface of the water and at the same time some distance from the shore where there is no danger of surprise by enemies which prowl along the bank. In addition to these precautions against attack, turtles are gifted with rather keen sight, and they can detect an object moving along the shore when it is still some distance away. If a person comes rapidly up to the side of a pool where some turtles are out on their resting places the animals drop at once into the water and seek safety on the bottom; usually they do not return to the surface for some time. In the fall, the turtles disappear and do not come to notice again until the return of warm weather the following spring.

THE AMPHIBIANS

PACIFIC COAST NEWT. **Notophthalmus torosus** (Rathke)

Field characters.—Lizard-like in form, but without scales; skin soft and moist. Total length of adults about 6½ inches. Coloration reddish brown to blackish brown above, orange or pale yellow beneath; skin rough, with many low, black-tipped points when animal is on land, becoming smoother when in water, especially in males. Movements slow and deliberate.

Occurrence.—Resident chiefly in Upper Sonoran Zone on west slope of Sierra Nevada. Recorded at Pleasant Valley and near Coulterville, and reported from Smith Creek (6 miles east of Coulterville in Transition Zone). Gathers in pools of quiet water during spring months; usually on land at other times of year, and then solitary.

We found the Pacific Coast Newt or "water dog" at a few localities in the western foothills of the Yosemite region. It may be expected to occur in any of the cañons there which have pools of water lasting through the summer months; for the newt is the only one of our local species of salamanders which, like the toads and frogs, repairs to the water to deposit its eggs.

At Pleasant Valley in mid-May of 1915 we were told that, a month previous, "red salamanders" had been common in the creeks. On May 11, 1919, two of these animals were seen floating lazily with legs outstretched in a pool in Blacks Creek. When pursued they laid their feet close against their sides and wriggled, fish-like, to safety in the deeper parts of the pool.

Elsewhere it has been learned that the adults of this species enter the water in late winter, lay their eggs there in the spring, and then all but a few of the adults leave the pools. Thenceforth, until the following winter, the adults live on land, spending much of the time in damp places under logs. The egg masses are fastened to grass blades or stems in the water. Each mass includes one to twenty or more eggs, each in a small capsule. The capsules are massed into a firm, transparent, globular body about an inch in diameter. The tadpoles, after hatching out, live in the water for a number of weeks. In late summer they lose their gills and go through other transformations fitting them for terrestrial life and then quit the pools, save for the return each season at breeding time.

[651]

Mount Lyell Salamander.   **Eurycea platycephala** (Camp)

Field characters.—Length under five inches. Head broad and flat, wider than body at any point; tail shorter than body; small half-webs present between toes. (See pl. 60*f.*) Coloration dark chocolate with numerous lichen-like gray markings on upper surface and sides of body.

Occurrence.—One record; two specimens taken in head of Lyell Cañon at 10,800 feet altitude, July 18, 1915. Found in heather among rocks close to streams of water which issued from beneath snowbanks.

From a scientific standpoint the greatest event of the entire Yosemite survey was the discovery of a salamander new to science and belonging to a group (the genus *Eurycea,* earlier called *Spelerpes*) previously not known to occur in the Pacific coast region of North America.

In the middle of July, 1915, we established a collecting station near the head of Lyell Cañon, and lines of traps were run in various situations in order to ascertain the species of mammals occurring in the vicinity. We were particularly anxious to capture the Mountain Lemming Mouse and many traps were placed in patches of Sierran heather (*Bryanthus breweri*) where that mammal was believed to live. One mouse trap was placed by Mr. Charles L. Camp at the entrance of a small hole in the moist soil beside a large rock outcrop, under a patch of heather about one hundred feet in diameter. This location was on an east-facing slope at 10,800 feet altitude near the Donohue Pass trail and about one mile below the Lyell Glacier.

On the morning of July 18, as we were en route to ascend Mount Lyell, *two* of these remarkable salamanders were found in this one trap. The animals had evidently walked out of the hole simultaneously and directly into the trap. A stream of water issued from the snowbanks close by and disappeared in rock slides below. The patch of heather was in direct sunshine most of the day. No other specimens were obtained. (See Camp, 1916*a*, pp. 11–14, figs. 1–5.)

Other species of this group of salamanders, which occur in eastern North America, are known to be nocturnal in habits and to spend part of the larval (tadpole) stage of life in water. Whether or not the Mount Lyell Salamander conforms to these habits is unknown. Mountaineers visiting the alpine portions of the Yosemite region have the opportunity to discover many facts of great interest from a natural history standpoint relating to this novel species.

ARBOREAL SALAMANDER. **Aneides lugubris lugubris** (Hallowell)

Field characters.—Total length 6 inches or less. Head wedge-shaped, with bulging muscles above and behind eye; teeth on margin of upper jaw prominent; thirteen cross-wise furrows (costal grooves) in skin on side of body between fore and hind leg; skin everywhere smooth and soft. Upper surface dark brown, usually with small round spots of yellow; under surface plain yellow.

Occurrence.—Recorded commonly in Transition Zone near McCarthy ranch, 3 miles east of Coulterville. Lives near or on damp ground within or under logs, under stones, and in old wood rats' nests. Usually solitary.

The Arboreal Salamander, in the Yosemite region, was found by us only on or close to the surface of the ground. Elsewhere in its range the species is known to inhabit damp cavities in oak trees. In the Sierras we found it at but the one locality mentioned above, chiefly beneath logs and stones in pastures and woodlands. Two adults were found in the interior of a charred and slightly decayed yellow pine log which was lying on a sun-baked manzanita-covered hillside at the margin of the yellow pine forest; one of the animals was found in the nest of a wood rat; and another was discovered in a gopher burrow in the ground beneath a wood rat's house.

This species, like the Mount Lyell and Slender salamanders, is without either lungs or gills in the adult condition. The animal is provided with a moist skin which serves importantly for the interchange of oxygen and carbon dioxide in respiration. Hence the animal keeps to humid situations, where its soft skin can be kept from drying out.

So far as known the Arboreal Salamander is active only at night and spends the day hidden in some retreat of the sort mentioned above. During the night the atmosphere is more humid; hence the animals can venture abroad then without danger of desiccation.

The breeding season of this species is in late July and August. A female salamander collected on June 3 contained eggs which were well formed.

The stomach contents of such of these animals as were examined contained remains of terrestrial beetles and large ants—the sort of food materials which a ground-dwelling, night-foraging amphibian might be expected to take.

SLENDER SALAMANDER. **Batrachoseps attenuatus** (Eschscholtz)

Field characters.—Body slender and worm-like, ¼ inch or less in diameter; legs and feet very small and weak; but four toes on each foot; side of body with 19 (18 to 20) crosswise grooves. Middle of back dark brown; sides and under surface blackish, with many minute freckles of silvery white.

Occurrence.—Recorded definitely only at Snelling; to be expected in western foothills of Sierra Nevada, below 3500 feet altitude. Lives in moist places such as the interior of decayed logs, beneath rocks, and in the burrows of small rodents.

The Slender Salamander gains a place in the Yosemite fauna on the basis of one record. At Snelling, on January 8, 1915, an old rotted log half buried in river-washed débris was broken open by one of our party, and 3 of these salamanders were found inside. Two others were discovered in slight depressions in the ground beneath the log. In the interior of this same log was found a group of about 15 small eggs, each of which was in a gelatinous capsule to which was attached a slender thread of similar material. The size and form of the eggs, their situation and the time of year at which they were found, all suggest that they were eggs of this salamander. Unfortunately the eggs were not preserved, nor was their identity established with certainty at the time.

The presence of the Slender Salamander at so low a station as Snelling, in the Lower Sonoran Zone, while not an unique occurrence, is decidedly unusual. The possibility suggests itself that the animals found there had been transported while in the log, from some up-river locality, during a period of high water.

WESTERN SPADE-FOOT TOAD. **Scaphiopus hammondii hammondii** Baird

Field characters.—Total length 2½ inches or less; hind foot with a black sharp-edged, cutting ''spade'' on inner margin of the smooth sole (pl. 60*c.*); pupil of eye vertically elliptical in outline. Coloration above light gray with irregular small markings of dark gray or black; under surface of body plain yellowish.

Occurrence.—Moderately common east of Sierra Nevada in vicinity of Mono Lake. Lives below ground in sandy situations, coming forth at night and during rainstorms.

The Western Spade-foot Toad occurs in some numbers in the vicinity of Mono Lake, but as no especial search was made for it we have only a few specimens to record. On July 22, 1915, near the southwestern shore of Mono Lake, one individual was captured as it hopped out of a hole in the sand during a thunder storm. In the season of 1916 the species came first to attention on May 5 when two individuals were captured in ''auto-baited'' mouse traps set in a meadow near Williams Butte. The traps were so placed that the toads could not have blundered into them, so it seems likely that they were attracted by the special scent on the traps. On May 8 another individual was obtained at the same locality. Two more were obtained in traps set toward the lake from Mono Mills, on June 20, 1916.

The Western Spade-foot Toad is even more reclusive than the ordinary toads (*Bufo*) and frequently escapes observation entirely, even by naturalists, in a country where it occurs in some numbers. The animals are strictly nocturnal save when rains during the summer months bring them out to spawn. They are to a considerable degree opportunists, and make use of the ephemeral rain pools as places in which to deposit their eggs. Female Spade-foots captured on May 5 and 8, and June 20, 1916, contained numbers of eggs which would have been ready to lay in the near future.

CALIFORNIA TOAD. **Bufo boreas halophilus** Baird and Girard[43]

Field characters.—Size large, adult females being 4–5 inches long (males 3½ inches or less); skin rough with numerous large 'warts' (pl. 60a); a large raised gland (parotoid) on each shoulder behind ear region; space between the two glands broader than width of one gland; pupil round. Upper surface grayish green, with numerous large irregular spots or streaks of black; a conspicuous streak of white extends along middle of head and back; under surface dull yellow, sometimes with numerous small black spots. *Voice:* A rather deep-toned prolonged trilling, with rhythm slow.

Occurrence.—Common resident in western part of Yosemite region, below 4500 feet altitude. Recorded from Yosemite Valley westward to Snelling and Lagrange. Lives in sheltered situations on or below ground, coming forth at dusk of evening. Solitary except at spawning time.

The California Toad is common in the lowland and foothill territory in the western part of the Yosemite region, and upon two occasions it was found on the floor of Yosemite Valley. Its range is separated from that of the Yosemite Toad by a considerable altitudinal interval, involving the upper two-thirds of the Transition Zone. East of the mountains is found a close relative, the Northwestern Toad.

The California Toad, and toads in general (of the genus *Bufo*), may be distinguished from other tail-less amphibians of the Yosemite region by the presence of a large raised area, the parotoid gland, on each 'shoulder' behind the ear membrane (pl. 60a). The Spade-foot (*Scaphiopus*) may show a slight elevation in the same region, but that animal may be recognized otherwise by its cutting 'spade' on the hind foot and by the elliptical pupil in the eye. True toads (*Bufo*) have the pupil circular. The California and Northwestern toads have the parotoid glands rather long and widely separated, whereas the Yosemite Toad has these

---

[43] A closely related subspecies, the Northwestern Toad, *Bufo boreas boreas* Baird and Girard, occurs at Walker Lake and near Williams Butte. It is distinguished from the California Toad by darker coloration and by having the spread of the hind foot (from tip of first toe to tip of fifth toe) more than 36 per cent of body length. The habits of the two subspecies are alike, so far as known.

glands but little longer than broad and separated by about the width of one of the glands. Locality will serve to distinguish the California and Northwestern toads, the former occurring only on the west slope of the mountains and the latter, so far as the Yosemite section is concerned, exclusively on the east side.

At most localities in the western foothills we found the California Toad exceedingly abundant, probably in about the same numbers as were present before the country was settled by the white man. In most settled districts toads have suffered great decrease from one cause or another incident to man's activities. Early in the morning the soft dust of roadways was often closely patterned with tracks where the toads had been traveling about during the preceding evening. At Pleasant Valley count was kept on the evening of May 28, 1915, of the toads seen along a certain quarter-mile of dusty road which passed between a hayfield and an open pasture. At 7:40 P.M., in early twilight, nine were counted; upon returning at 8:00 P.M., when the light of day was practically gone, thirteen toads were checked off.

The California Toad is such a heavy-bodied animal that it seldom hops in the conventional manner in which toads are supposed to move. When not frightened it walks in slow fashion, dragging the hind feet so that the toes are continually in contact with the ground. The 'track' consists of a series of distinct little pits, 5 in number, indicating the positions of the toes when the foot is against the ground, and the successive series of dots are connected by faint grooves where the toes have been dragged along in the dust.

The difference in size between females and males is marked in this species. Females are decidedly larger and more heavily built, and during the breeding season their skin remains rough, whereas that of the males then becomes quite smooth. The males, during the breeding season at least, have developed on the 'thumb' and inner sides of two adjacent 'fingers' areas of rough dark-colored skin, which in combination with their smaller size makes possible easy distinguishment of the sexes.

In the late spring months the toads betake themselves to pools of water for the purpose of laying eggs. The spawning season had practically passed when our field party arrived at Pleasant Valley in May, 1915. One animal was noted croaking in the water of Piney Creek on May 22, and on May 23 the small black tadpoles of this species were noticed in a small creek near Forty-nine Gap. A majority of the toads taken on these dates had already deposited their eggs. A few of the females—and they were the largest of all, measuring 4 inches or more in length—had not laid their complement of eggs. Whether there is a differential laying, with the smaller animals coming first, is not known. Males were encountered in smaller numbers than females, and some at least of the former had already lost the dark horny patches on their 'fingers.'

On several occasions during the hot days of early summer, California Toads were observed at the entrances to burrows of meadow mice and ground squirrels. The toads probably make pretty general use of such burrows as daytime retreats, going greater or less distances below the surface as may be necessary to escape the heat and dryness of the midday hours.

YOSEMITE TOAD. **Bufo canorus** Camp

Field characters.—Size medium; total length 3 inches or less. A short broad raised gland (parotoid) on each shoulder behind ear membrane; space between parotoid glands not more than width of one of them; muzzle rounded in side view; pupil round. Male: Skin quite smooth, with few 'warts'; ground color above olive green with dots of black; under surface grayish white with scattered small spots of black. Female: Upper surface with irregular patches of black (pl. 60*d, e*), each outlined with white and marking the position of a low rounded wart; ground color light brownish; under surface chiefly clear white. *Voice:* Spring song a sustained melodious trilling, with rapid rhythm.

Occurrence.—Common resident in Canadian and Hudsonian zones from near Chinquapin and Tamarack Flat eastward to Tioga Pass. Lives in or about wet meadows. Solitary except at spawning season.

The Yosemite Toad was a second notable discovery among the amphibians found by our party in the Yosemite region. This species is quite different in appearance from the California and Northwestern toads, which live along the west and east flanks of the mountains, and its range is separated by some miles on either hand from those of the other two. The range of the present species includes most of the Canadian Zone and all of the Hudsonian, extending from near Chinquapin and Tamarack Flat eastward to Tioga Lake, and ranging altitudinally from about 6700 feet to as high as 10,350 feet (at Vogelsang Lake).

This species may be separated easily from other toads and frogs of the region by the shape and position of the two large parotoid glands which are located on each 'shoulder' immediately behind the ear membrane (pl. 60*d, e*). These glands are but little longer than they are broad and the space between them does not exceed the width of one gland. In the other two toads of the region the parotoid glands are proportionately longer and are more widely separated. Neither the tree-toads (*Hyla*) nor the frogs (*Rana*) possess these glands at all.

There are marked differences between the two sexes in the Yosemite Toad. Indeed they are so great that to a casual observer the male and female might be taken as belonging to distinct species. As with other kinds of toads, the females are somewhat larger than the males; but the greatest difference is in coloration. The male has very few obvious 'warts' and the skin on its upper surface is plain olive green marked with minute scattered dots of black, each of which is rimmed with white. The female, on the other hand, has the back and sides thickly marbled with irregular but clearly defined patches of black outlined by white. Low rounded warts of dark color are centered in these areas of black. The ground color between the spots varies from dull brown to white. Whether these marked differences in coloration and markings are maintained at other times of the year is not known definitely, though the few animals collected in early spring and in autumn would indicate that such is the case. In some species of amphibians such as the California Toad the male takes on a green-colored smoother-skinned appearance in the breeding season and then reverts to a condition more like the female for the remainder of the year. The males of the Yosemite Toad, as is true of all other true toads (genus *Bufo*), develop on the upper side of the 'thumb' and two adjacent digits of the fore limb an area of roughened brown skin during the breeding season.

The Yosemite Toad undoubtedly hibernates for a considerable period of time during the winter months, when snow covers the higher country and the temperature goes below the freezing point. Our observations were not continued in the higher altitudes long enough to determine the actual dates of spring emergence and fall disappearance. On May 20, 1919, we visited Peregoy Meadow and found the males there already out and trilling loudly; on September 3, 1915, at Vogelsang Lake, a single individual was collected. In all probability some of these toads emerge toward the end of April and a few may be out until early October. The hardihood of the species is indicated by the way in which the adults jubilate in the melting snow water during the spring and early summer months.

The winter season is spent in some retreat in the ground, presumably below the frost line; any individual toad which chances to seek a shelter above that level will in all probability be killed when the cold of winter freezes the upper ground. During that part of the summer not devoted to egg laying the toads spend the day solitarily in damp situations at the surface of the ground under logs or stones. A toad seen abroad during the day near Porcupine Flat quickly betook itself to a pool of water beneath a log. Several small individuals were observed on a hot, dry, sandy flat near Ragged Peak in July, and near Vogelsang Lake one individual was found beneath a rock in a damp heather patch 20 feet from a stream.

Immediately or very soon after emerging from their winter hibernation these toads repair to pools and small streams in the wet meadows, and continue there until the eggs are deposited or even longer. The males precede the females, as at Peregoy Meadow there were many males present on May 20, 1919, while the only females found were small non-breeding individuals. At Tamarack Flat, May 25, 1919, an adult female was found at the base of a rotted tree stump fully 200 yards from the edge of the nearest meadow and 200 feet above it in altitude, while males were heard trilling in the meadow that same evening. On June 15, 1915, a chorus of these toads was heard near Peregoy Meadow, although egg laying had been accomplished some time previously. At Snow Flat on June 28, 1915, and near Ragged Peak on July 9, 1915, other toads were heard in song. At the head of Lyell Cañon on July 16, 1915, numbers of Yosemite Toads were found in a small pond, and some at least of the females were engaged in laying their eggs.

On May 20, 1919, numbers of male Yosemite Toads were congregated in the wet meadows on either side of the ridge east of Chinquapin. During the preceding winter gophers from the adjacent slopes had moved down and occupied the grassy meadows, but with the spring break-up and melting of the snow the place had become untenable for the gophers, who had moved up onto the hillsides once more. Their tunnel systems were left as subterranean 'pipes' which carried off much of the water from the melting snow banks to the creek in the bottom of the cañon. These gopher tunnels served also as shelters for the toads. The latter when partially hidden in the entrances to the tunnels or even when they sat quietly on the open grassland were quite invisible to our eyes, so well did their pattern of coloration match the greens and browns of the meadow.

The mating song of the Yosemite Toad is a sustained series of ten to twenty or more rapidly uttered notes, constituting a 'trill,' and the whole song is repeated at frequent intervals. The notes, though mellow in character, carry well considering the size of the animal and have a ventriloquial quality which makes it difficult to locate any one animal by sound alone. When a number of males are giving their songs in the same place the songs overlap one another so that the general chorus is continuous. There is some difference in the pitch at which the several members of a group sing, varying perhaps with the size of the individual toad. The general effect of a chorus is rendered more pleasing to our ears by these variations, while the ensemble is even sleep-inducing in effect, as we can testify from experience. The notes recall the courting song of the Texas Nighthawk.

If a person walks out onto a meadow where toads (*Bufo*) and tree-toads (*Hyla*) are both 'singing,' the chorus soon comes to an abrupt termination. If he stands stock still for a while the Hylas will resume, but the Bufos do not ordinarily begin again until the intruder has quitted the vicinity. The animals probably get first knowledge of the approach of a person by the vibrations which his footfalls produce in the ground, and, as the water-logged ground in a meadow readily transmits such vibrations, the toads are on their guard long before the observer can get within sight of them.

As intimated above, the toad chorus, at different levels, may begin at least as early as May 20 and last until July 9; and, according to our experience, singing is carried on quite through the daylight hours and into early evening at least.

The Yosemite Toad spawns in late spring or in summer, depending somewhat upon the local climate. Specimens collected on May 24 to 26, 1919, at Tamarack Flat showed no signs of breeding. On June 22, 1915, numerous tadpoles and one recently metamorphosed young toad were seen at Mono Meadow. One female taken near Porcupine Flat June 28, 1915, had already laid most of her eggs. On July 16, 1915, at the head of Lyell Cañon several individuals were depositing eggs.

Our collection of Yosemite Toads includes 20 males and 28 females. Upon the basis of total length the representatives of each sex fall into several size groups which are quite probably age groups as well. These groups indicate that about four years is required for a toad to reach adult size, that males are always somewhat smaller than females of the same age, and that the females do not begin to spawn until more than 2 inches (50 mm.) in length, when they are presumably three years old.

Among the females taken are three which measure less than one inch (20, 22, and 23 mm.) in length. When it is recalled that toads are small at the time they transform from the tadpole stage, it seems highly probable that these three individuals came from eggs of the preceding season and so represented animals one year old or thereabout. Another group of 12 ranges from about 1½ to 2 inches (33 to 49 mm.) in length; in neither of these two size groups did any of the individuals show that eggs were being, or had been, developed. The third group, of 9 animals, measures about 2½ inches (57–62 mm.) in length; and the fourth of four individuals about 3 inches (70 to 74 mm.). In both the latter groups the animals were in breeding condition and contained eggs.

Male toads in the collection fall into two groups: 2 to 2¼ inches (50 to 55 mm.), and around 2½ inches (58 to 64 mm.) in length. These specimens were practically all collected in meadow ponds or streams and were breeding animals, for they have roughened brown areas on the inner digits of the fore limb. They are thought to represent animals three and four (or more) years of age. No males were obtained which could be called younger than these. Such individuals would probably be found by careful search on the upper slopes some distance from the breeding ponds.

The food of the Yosemite Toad includes a wide variety of insects and the like. One individual captured at Porcupine Flat, June 29, 1915, contained 2 Tenebrionid beetles, several weevils of different species, numerous large ants and one centipede, besides some red fir needles probably taken incidentally.

Pacific Tree-toad. **Hyla regilla** Baird and Girard

Field characters.—Size small; total length 2 inches or less; ends of toes with small rounded discs. Coloration extremely variable, ranging from pale light gray through vivid green and brown to nearly black; a dark streak is always evident on side of head extending from tip of nose at level of eye to behind ear membrane; under surface white, unspotted, blackish on throat in males; back may or may not be marked with dark streaks or spots. *Voice:* Song note a loud, raucous *krĕck-ĕk,* repeated at frequent intervals; call note a single low prolonged, guttural *kr-r-r-ĕck.*

Occurrence.—Distributed throughout the Yosemite section without regard to life zone. Recorded from Snelling eastward across Sierra Nevada to Walker Lake and up to 10,600 feet altitude on Conness Mountain. Lives chiefly in damp situations and on the ground, seldom being found in trees or even in bushes. Essentially solitary except when spawning.

The Pacific Tree-toad is one of the very few species of animals in the Yosemite section which ranges uninterruptedly from the San Joaquin plains to the highest passes of the Sierra Nevada. Of other land vertebrates only the Gambel White-footed Mouse, the Red-shafted Flicker, and the Western Chipping Sparrow can be said to do the same. The range of the Pacific Tree-toad is most remarkable when we remember that it is a 'cold-blooded' animal which has a body temperature always close to that of its environment, while each of the other species mentioned has a heatregulating mechanism which maintains its body at practically constant temperature irrespective of that of the surroundings.

At Snelling the air temperature at different seasons of the year varies from slightly below freezing to above 110° F., while on Tuolumne Meadows it undoubtedly goes below 0 F°. in winter and may reach above 85° F. in summer; yet tree-toads are found in both of these places. The animals keep to moist situations near the surface of the earth, where the temperature fluctuations are somewhat less than those given, and in freezing weather must of necessity seek shelters below the frost line. Even so, the Tree-toads must be subject to considerable variation in the temperature of their surroundings. The hardihood of these diminutive creatures is indicated by the fact that in Yosemite Valley on February 28, 1916, when there was two feet or more of snow on the Valley floor, tree-toads were chorusing in open marshy ponds below the Royal Arches; and on Mount Hoffmann on June 29, 1915, their voices were heard coming from beneath deep snow banks on the north side of the mountain. On July 8, 1915, several were croaking in a small lake covered almost completely with ice on Conness Mountain at 10,600 feet altitude. By way of contrast it may be mentioned that on May 27, 1915, at Snelling, when the air was to us uncomfortably hot, tree-toads were heard in voice near the river margin.

Among all the toads and frogs of the Yosemite region the Pacific Tree-toad may be known at a glance by the expanded discs on the ends of all its toes and by the presence of a streak of dark color which extends along the side of its head, at the level of the eye, from the tip of the nose to behind the ear membrane. These features are evident at all ages, from the smallest individuals recently transformed from tadpoles to the largest adults.

Many amphibians use their voices almost exclusively during the spawning season, but the Pacific Tree-toad is likely to be heard at any time of year, being silent, if at all, only during the dry hot days of late summer. Thus, in Yosemite Valley, the notes have been heard by us in February, May, June, October, and December; at Snelling in January and May; at Chinquapin in May and June; about Tuolumne Meadows in July; at Vogelsang Lake on August 30; and at McGee Lake and Ten Lakes in October. During the fall months the single note is usually the only one heard, while from January to June the two-syllabled song note, as well as the call, is given commonly.

The call-note consists of a single prolonged guttural syllable, *kr-r-r-r-ĕck,* which it requires a second or two to pronounce. This note is uttered at irregular intervals, by isolated individuals when in their retreats and by members of a group in a pond or marsh when their song chorus has been interrupted.

The 'song' note is a two-syllabled *krĕck-ĕk* given in faster time than the call and repeated at short intervals. There is slightly less emphasis on the second note, which drops in pitch and ends abruptly. When a number of Hylas are in a marsh or pool together, their notes tend to be given in unison, so that there is a continued series of notes, every alternate note being slightly stressed. Such a chorus may continue for a long period, but more often it is interrupted, ceasing rather abruptly and then beginning again after a period of quiet. If a person walks out into a meadow where tree-toads are chorusing, the voices soon cease. One or more call notes with an interrogative inflection are given, and then there is silence. If the observer stands absolutely still, the animals will shortly resume their singing. The chorus begins as it ended, with a few call notes; then one individual commences his song, to be quickly followed by another, and in five seconds or so the place resounds with the chorus once more.

The tree-toad is quite the strongest voiced of any of our amphibians, though it is the smallest in point of body size among the tail-less forms. Only the males sing, although females may give the low call note. The males when held in the hand are seen to possess loose folds of black skin on the throat. When the animal is singing, this skin is inflated to form a pouch which swells out beyond the chin and is kept continuously inflated while the notes are being given. The pouch evidently acts as a resonator and helps to give volume to the sound.

The eggs of the tree-toad are laid during the spring months. No egg masses were seen anywhere in the region, but it seems likely that the individuals living in the higher altitudes spawn at much later dates than those in the lowlands. On August 20 and 23, 1915, at Merced Lake, small tree-toads, measuring between one-half and three-fourths of an inch in length, were found in numbers. These were animals which had but recently changed to the adult condition, and which had undoubtedly come from eggs laid during the same season.

Among the specimens of this species collected in the Yosemite region are two individuals taken at Merced Grove Big Trees and Porcupine Flat, respectively, which after being preserved are nearly 2 inches (1⅞ and 1¹⁵⁄₁₆) in total length and are fully as large if not larger than any we have seen from anywhere. The cup-like discs or pads at the ends of the toes on these animals are unusually large and conspicuous and in life must have been fully twice the diameter of the toes themselves.

In Yosemite Valley on October 13, 1915, scores of half-grown Hylas were seen in a saw grass swale. There were also many grasshoppers there and it was often difficult to distinguish a toad from a grasshopper until the individual was scrutinized closely. The tree-toads exhibited much variation in color, ranging from uniform bright greenish yellow to dark brown; some were coarsely mottled with dark and light brown.

YELLOW-LEGGED FROGS. **Rana boylii** Baird[44]

Field characters.—No conspicuous raised glands on hind neck or back; hind toes long and slender, fully webbed, without discs at tips. Total length 3 inches or less. Upper surface of body rough-surfaced, with scattered low points. (See pl. 60b.) Coloration above blackish, dark green or brown, with markings few and indistinct; lower surface yellow or whitish, sometimes mottled on throat. No light line along upper jaw; ear region not darker than rest of head.

Occurrence.—Common resident practically throughout the Yosemite region. Recorded from Pleasant Valley, eastward to near Mono Lake. In Transition Zone on both sides of mountains, and in Upper Sonoran on west side, is subspecies *boylii;* in Canadian and Hudsonian zones is subspecies *sierrae* (see footnote for details). Lives in, and on the banks of, ponds and streams.

---

44 Two subspecies of Yellow-legged Frog are found in the Yosemite region. These occupy separate parts of the region and also present characters which make possible identification in the field.

CALIFORNIA YELLOW-LEGGED FROG, *Rana boylii boylii* Baird, resident throughout the Upper Sonoran Zone of central California, was found at Pleasant Valley and thence eastward to near Feliciana Mountain and to Smith Creek, east of Coulterville; it recurs in vicinity of Mono Lake (Farrington Ranch). It is distinguished by having many small points or roughnesses on the ear membrane and by a relatively long hind leg (when leg is bent forward the bent 'instep' reaches to or beyond nostril).

SIERRA YELLOW-LEGGED FROG, *Rana boylii sierrae* Camp, resident in boreal portions of the Sierra Nevada, was found in the Canadian and Hudsonian zones from Peregoy Meadow and Porcupine Flat eastward to Tuolumne Meadows and the head of Lyell Cañon. It has a relatively smooth ear membrane, and when the hind leg is bent forward the bent 'instep' does not usually reach beyond the nostril.

The Yellow-legged Frog is the commonest amphibian in most parts of the Yosemite section. Its total range is slightly less than that of the Pacific Tree-toad; but its numbers, especially at the higher altitudes, far exceed those of the smaller species. This frog is the species most likely to come to the attention of fishermen and others who may walk along the banks of Sierran streams and lakes.

The Yellow-legged Frog may best be identified by the characters which it lacks when compared with other species of frogs and toads from the same region. (See pl. 60b.) It differs from the Spadefoot in having a round instead of an elliptical pupil, from the California and Yosemite toads in the absence of enlarged glands on its shoulders and of prominent 'warts' on the back, from the tree-toad in not having expanded adhesive discs on its fingers, and from the Red-legged Frog in having no dark spot on the ear region, no ridges along the back, and no red in its coloration (save in individuals afflicted with the disease known as "red-leg"). The characteristics of the two local subspecies of Yellow-legged Frog are set forth in footnote 44.

During the daytime these frogs are to be seen sitting quietly on rocks or other places close to the water. If a person is walking along the shore of a stream or pond his attention is usually first drawn to the animals when one of them 'plops' into the water and makes for the bottom. In the higher zones one's progress along the bank of a pool is announced by a series of splashes ten to twenty-five feet ahead, as the numerous frogs in quick succession take to the safety of the water. Once under the surface a few quick strokes of the hind legs with their broad foot-webs put the frog under some sheltering rock. The mottled pattern of the upper surface is quite protective in character when the animal comes to rest. When once on the bottom the frog is likely to remain there quietly unless further disturbed. When the frog is in motion, either jumping or swimming, the yellow color on the legs shows contrastingly against the dark upper surface of the body, but it is almost entirely masked when the frog is at rest.

Certain of the lakes in the higher parts of the Yosemite contain large numbers of Yellow-legged Frogs in both the tadpole and adult conditions. It is a commonly repeated observation that frogs, in tadpole form at least, do not occur in lakes which are stocked with trout. Adult frogs are sometimes found around the margins of such lakes and they occur in numbers along the shores of streams inhabited by trout, but the advent of fish in a lake sooner or later nearly or quite eliminates the frogs. It seems probable that the fish prey upon the tadpoles, so that few or none of the latter are able to reach the stage at which they transform. The frogs which live along the streams probably spawn in small temporary pools in the meadows which the trout cannot reach.

The spawning season of the Yellow-legged Frog varies with altitude, although in each locality the adults, as a rule, probably lay their eggs when the season is locally 'spring.' Thus tadpoles of considerable size were seen in Blacks Creek near Coulterville on May 10, 1919, and the one adult female of breeding age collected at Smith Creek on June 3, 1915, had finished laying. An exceptional case, perhaps, was that of an adult female taken near Feliciana Mountain on November 1, 1915, which contained well developed eggs. Most of the high mountain frogs (*sierrae*) collected at Peregoy and Mono meadows on June 22, 1915, had already laid, and tadpoles were seen in some of the creeks. Some females collected at and near Tuolumne Meadows during the first half of July, 1915, had already deposited their eggs; others contained eggs ready to lay.

In the foothill district, where there is a long spell of warm weather, the tadpoles (subspecies *boylii*) are able to grow to the size necessary for transforming into frogs in a single season. But with the high mountain animals (subspecies *sierrae*) the case is different. The eggs are not laid until June or July, and there is then but a short season, scarcely three months in length, before cold weather sets in again. Consequently the tadpoles which hatch from the eggs in any one season go through the winter still in the tadpole condition and do not transform into frogs until the following summer. Thus the numbers of tadpoles, 2 inches or more in length, found in Young Lake on July 8 and 9, 1915, came from eggs which had been laid in 1914. On the dates mentioned many of the tadpoles had the hind legs fully developed and in all probability would soon have completed their metamorphosis.

In such alpine lakes as are suited to occupancy by frogs (through the absence of fish) both adults and tadpoles are usually present. The frogs sit along the shore, on the ground or on rocks, whence they can reach the lake at one bound. When cakes of ice are floating in the water the frogs do not seem able to discriminate and in leaping lakeward they sometimes land on the ice instead of in the water. Where large numbers of frogs are present, a greater degree of safety is probably enjoyed by each individual, for *all*, of course, are on the alert, and thus the approach of any danger is the sooner realized from the action of a neighbor. In spite of this consideration, a person does not have much difficulty in capturing numbers of the frogs, and it seems likely that a coyote or other carnivore would be able to gather them in easily by prowling along the shore.

When undisturbed the tadpoles rest on the sandy bottom close to the shore, where the water is shallowest and warmed somewhat by the sun; but when frightened they wriggle off into the deeper parts of the lake.

CALIFORNIA RED-LEGGED FROG. **Rana aurora draytonii** Baird and Girard

Field characters.—See preceding species. Total length up to 4 inches. Ear region darker than rest of head; fold along upper lip often light colored; under surface of hind legs usually more or less red.

Occurrence.—Sparse resident at lower altitudes on west slope of Sierra Nevada. Recorded by us once (May 25, 1915) at Snelling; reported from Smith Creek, 6 miles east of Coulterville. Lives in damp situations near streams or ponds.

The Red-legged Frog, known locally as "French frog" because of its size and the edible quality of its flesh, was found to be uncommon in the Yosemite region. We recorded it definitely only once, although Mr. Donald D. McLean tells us that it occurs in small numbers along Smith Creek, east of Coulterville. This species is more wary than the Yellow-legged Frog and often escapes observation by reason of this fact.

BIBLIOGRAPHY

Articles Relating Chiefly or Importantly to the Vertebrate Animals of the
Yosemite Section and Published up to the End of 1920

BRYANT, H. C.

1916. A note on the food of the northern pileated woodpecker. Condor, vol. 18,
p. 32 (January, 1916).

1920. Does the Barrow golden-eye breed in the Sierras? Calif. Fish and Game,
vol. 6, pp. 37–38 (January, 1920).

CAMP, C. L.

1916a. *Spelerpes platycephalus*, a new alpine salamander from the Yosemite National
Park, California. Univ. Calif. Publ. Zool., vol. 17, pp. 11–14, 5 figs. in text
(September 18, 1916).

1916b. Description of *Bufo canorus*, a new toad from the Yosemite National Park.
Univ. Calif. Publ. Zool., vol. 17, pp. 59–62, 4 figs. in text (November 17,
1916).

1916c. The subspecies of *Sceloporus occidentalis* with description of a new form
from the Sierra Nevada and systematic notes on other California lizards.
Univ. Calif. Publ. Zool., vol. 17, pp. 63–74 (December 28, 1916).

1917. Notes on the systematic status of the toads and frogs of California. Univ.
Calif. Publ. Zool., vol. 17, pp. 115–125, 3 figs. in text (February 3, 1917).

1918. Excavations of burrows of the rodent *Aplodontia*, with observations on the
habits of the animal. Univ. Calif. Publ. Zool., vol. 17, pp. 517–536, 6 figs.
in text (June 22, 1918).

CECIL, LADY W.

1919. Notes on some of the North American woodpeckers. Avicultural Magazine,
ser. 3, vol. 10, pp. 48–56 (January, 1919).

DAWSON, W. L.

1916. A personal supplement to the distributional list of the birds of California.
Condor, vol. 18, pp. 22–30 (January, 1916).

DIXON, J.

1919. Notes on the natural history of the bushy-tailed wood rats of California.
Univ. Calif. Publ. Zool., vol. 21, pp. 49–74, pls. 1–3, 3 figs. in text (December 10, 1919).

EMERSON, W. O.

1893. Random bird-notes from Merced Big Trees and Yosemite Valley. Zoe, vol. 4,
pp. 176–182 (July, 1893).

EVERMANN, B. W.

1915a. Note on the feeding habits of the blue-fronted jay. Condor, vol. 17, p. 58
(January, 1915).

1915b. Do snakes swallow small mammals heads or tails first? Copeia, no. 14,
January 25, 1915 (pp. 1–2).

FISHER, W. K.

1902. A trip to Mono Lake, ornithological and otherwise. Condor, vol. 4, pp. 2–11,
11 figs. (January, 1902).

GRINNELL, HILDA W.

1916. A new bat of the genus *Myotis* from the high Sierra Nevada of California. Univ. Calif. Publ. Zool., vol. 17, pp. 9–10 (August 23, 1916).

1918. A synopsis of the bats of California. Univ. Calif. Publ. Zool., vol. 17, pp. 223–404, pls. 14–24, 24 figs. in text (January 31, 1918).

GRINNELL, J.

1911. Early summer birds in the Yosemite Valley. Sierra Club Bull., vol. 8, pp. 118–124 (June, 1911).

1913. The species of the mammalian genus *Sorex* of west-central California with a note on the vertebrate palustrine faunas of the region. Univ. Calif. Publ. Zool., vol. 10, pp. 179–195, 6 figs. (March 20, 1913).

1914. A new race of *Microtus montanus* from the central Sierra Nevada. Proc. Biol. Soc. Wash., vol. 27, pp. 207–208 (October 31, 1914).

1917. The subspecies of *Hesperiphona vespertina*. Condor, vol. 19, pp. 17–22, fig. 5 (January, 1917).

1919. Five new five-toed kangaroo rats from California. Univ. Calif. Publ. Zool., vol. 21, pp. 43–47 (March 29, 1919).

GRINNELL, J., BRYANT, H. C., and STORER, T. I.

1918. The game birds of California (University of California Press, Berkeley), x + 642 pp., 16 col. pls., 94 figs. in text. (Issued December 28, 1918.)

GRINNELL, J., and DIXON, J.

1919. Natural history of the ground squirrels of California. Monthly Bull. State Comm. Hort. Calif., vol. 7 (1918), pp. 597–708, 5 pls., 30 figs. in text. (Issued January 27, 1919.)

GRINNELL, J., and STORER, T. I.

1916. Diagnoses of seven new mammals from east-central California. Univ. Calif. Publ. Zool., vol. 17, pp. 1–8, 1 fig. (August 23, 1916).

1917a. The Yosemite cony—a chapter in the natural history of the Yosemite National Park. Sierra Club Bull., vol. 10, pp. 160–164, pl. CLXI, 3 figs. (February 21, 1917).

1917b. A new fox sparrow, from the vicinity of Mono Lake, California. Condor, vol. 19, pp. 165–166, fig. 54 (September, 1917).

1920. Mammals and summer birds of the [Yosemite National] Park. Rules and Regulations, Yosemite National Park, 1920 (Dept. Interior, Washington, Gov't Printing Office), pp. 47–54.

JACKSON, H. H. T.

1914. New moles of the genus *Scapanus*. Proc. Biol. Soc. Wash., vol. 27, pp. 55–56 (March 20, 1914).

KEELER, C.

1908. Bird life of Yosemite Park. Sierra Club Bull., vol. 5, pp. 245–254 (January, 1908).

MAILLIARD, J.

1918. Early autumn birds in Yosemite Valley. Condor, vol. 20, pp. 11–19 (January, 1918).

MCLEAN, D. D.

1916. Nesting habits of the Virginia rail in Mariposa County, California. Condor, vol. 18, p. 229 (November, 1916).

1917. The mountain lion an enemy of the skunk. Calif. Fish and Game, vol. 3, p. 39 (January, 1917).

1919. Wildcat eats birds. Calif. Fish and Game, vol. 5, p. 160 (July, 1919).

MERRIAM, C. H.

1902. Two new shrews of the *Sorex tenellus* group from California. Proc. Biol. Soc. Wash., vol. 15, pp. 75–76 (March 22, 1902).

1908. Four new rodents from California. Proc. Biol. Soc. Wash., vol. 21, pp. 145–148 (June 9, 1908).

MUIR, J.

1874. The wild sheep of California. Overland Monthly, vol. 12, pp. 358–363 (April, 1874).

1878. The humming-bird of the California water-falls. Scribner's Monthly, vol. 15, pp. 545–554, 5 illus. (February, 1878).

1894. The Douglas squirrel [Chapter IX], The water ouzel [Chapter XIII], and The wild sheep [Chapter XIV], *in* Mountains of California (New York, The Century Co.), pp. xv + 381, 53 illus.

1898a. Among the animals of the Yosemite. Atlantic Monthly, vol. 82, pp. 617–631 (November, 1898).

1898b. Among the birds of the Yosemite. Atlantic Monthly, vol. 82, pp. 751–760 (December, 1898).

1901. Among the animals of the Yosemite [Chapter VI], and Among the birds of the Yosemite [Chapter VII], *in* Our National Parks (Boston and New York, Houghton, Mifflin), pp. 10 + 370, frontispiece, map, 10 pls.

RAY, M. S.

1898. A summer trip to Yosemite. Osprey, vol. 3, p. 55 (December, 1898).

STORER, T. I.

1917. Bohemian waxwing in Mariposa County. Condor, vol. 19, p. 103 (May, 1917).

SWARTH, H. S.

1918. Three new subspecies of *Passerella iliaca*. Proc. Biol. Soc. Wash., vol. 31, pp. 161–164 (December 30, 1918).

1920. Revision of the avian genus *Passerella*, with special reference to the distribution and migration of the races in California. Univ. Calif. Publ. Zool., vol. 21, pp. 74–224, pls. 4–7, 30 figs. in text (September 11, 1920).

TORREY, B.

1910. The western winter wren (*Nannus hiemalis pacificus*) in the Yosemite. Condor, vol. 12, p. 79 (March, 1910).

VAN DENBURGH, J.

1896. Description of a new lizard (*Eumeces gilberti*) from the Sierra Nevada of California. Proc. Calif. Acad. Sci., ser. 2, vol. 6, pp. 350–352 (August 28, 1896).

WIDMANN, O.

1904. Yosemite valley birds. Auk, vol. 21, pp. 66–73 (January, 1904).

WYTHE, MARGARET W.

1916. Nesting of the Tolmie warbler in Yosemite Valley. Condor, vol. 18, p. 123 (May, 1916).

PLATE 13

a. Margin of San Joaquin Valley near Snelling, showing associations in Lower Sonoran Life Zone. View taken in winter from earth bluffs northeast of town looking south across cultivated and pastured river-bottom lands; a slough scatteringly bordered with willows in middle distance, and Fremont cottonwoods bordering Merced River in far distance.

b. The blue oak marks a conspicuous association several miles in width along the foothills bordering the San Joaquin Valley. The view here shown was taken in February in the Upper Sonoran Zone near Pleasant Valley. In winter the mistletoe clumps in these trees are patronized for berries by the Audubon Warbler, Western Robin and Western Bluebird; throughout the year these trees are inhabited by such birds as the California Woodpecker, Interior California Jay, Phainopepla, Plain Titmouse, and Slender-billed Nuthatch.

a

b

PLATE 14

a. Scene near Pleasant Valley in May showing mixed brush and open forest associations in the Upper Sonoran Zone. The principal tree is the digger pine. Here on the ground were caught the Streator Wood Rat, Common and Boyle white-footed mice, and Digger Pine Pocket Gopher; the trees were inhabited by such birds as the Interior California Jay, Pacific Black-headed Grosbeak, and Western Gnatcatcher; and in the greasewood brush (*Adenostoma*) topping the ridge were the Bell Sparrow, Northern Brown Towhee, California Thrasher, and Pallid Wren-tit.

b. View near the McCarthy ranch, three miles east of Coulterville; altitude 3200 feet, at the lower edge of the Transition Zone. Trees shown are yellow pines, and the brush plants are sticky manzanita (*Arctostaphylos mariposa*). Photographed in June, 1915.

a

b

PLATE 15

a. Detailed view near Rocky Point on base of talus slope on north side of Yosemite Valley; golden oak association, Transition Zone. Inhabited by the California Wildcat, Boyle White-footed Mouse, Streator Wood Rat, California Ground Squirrel, Mariposa Chipmunk, California Gray Squirrel, Band-tailed Pigeon, California Woodpecker, Western Skink and Coral King Snake; and, in summer, by the Cassin Vireo and Black-throated Gray Warbler.

b. Shaded south margin of Merced River near El Portal, as photographed in December; lower margin of Transition Zone. The habitat of the Adorned Shrew and Sierra Cantankerous Meadow Mouse, and in winter, of the American Dipper.

a

b

PLATE 16

a. General view of lower part of Yosemite Valley as taken looking east from the Big Oak Flat Road in winter. At the left a talus slope clothed with golden oak; below, the forest on the Valley floor, comprising yellow pine, sugar pine, and black oak, and, in streamside tracts, black cottonwood. These areas constitute markedly differing associations in the Transition Zone.

b. Meadow on floor of Yosemite Valley near Rocky Point, as seen in June; Transition Zone. Here were trapped the Yosemite Mole, Yosemite Shrew, Yosemite Meadow Mouse, and Yosemite Pocket Gopher. The trees at the right, black cottonwoods, harbored such birds as the Willow Woodpecker, Modoc Woodpecker, California Yellow Warbler, and Western Warbling Vireo.

a

b

PLATE 17

a. Ridge directly east of Half Dome; altitude 7500 feet, in the Canadian Zone. The trees are chiefly Jeffrey pine and in them are to be found the Sierra Grouse, Audubon Warbler, Short-tailed Mountain Chickadee, Sierra Creeper and Red-breasted Nuthatch. The low brush is huckleberry oak and this affords shelter to the Allen Chipmunk and Mountain Alligator Lizard. Photo by Ansel F. Hall.

b. Forest association in Canadian Zone one mile east of Chinquapin; altitude 7000 feet. The trees are lodgepole pine, white fir, and red fir. Birds noted here were Calliope Hummingbird, Hammond Flycatcher, Blue-fronted Jay, Cassin Purple Finch, Pine Siskin, Audubon Warbler, Short-tailed Mountain Chickadee, Red-breasted Nuthatch, and Golden-crowned and Ruby-crowned kinglets. Mammals included the Tahoe Chipmunk, Sierra Flying Squirrel and Sierra Chickaree.

[GRINNELL–STORER] PLATE 17

PLATE 18

a. Vogelsang Lake (altitude 10,300 feet) and Pass (10,700 feet), Hudsonian Zone; photographed August 31, 1915. Rock talus at left and beyond, inhabited by Sierra Pine Marten, Alpine Chipmunk, Gray Bushy-tailed Wood Rat, and Yosemite Cony; meadow inhabited by Yosemite Meadow Mouse; willow thicket frequented by Hudsonian White-crowned Sparrow. Stunted white-bark pines on distant slopes.

b. Looking eastward across Tuolumne Meadows; photographed July 13, 1915. Meadows and forest are in Hudsonian Zone, distant bare ridges in Alpine-Arctic Zone; forest chiefly lodgepole pine. On the meadows were recorded the Yosemite Meadow Mouse, Southern Sierra Marmot, Belding Ground Squirrel, Pacific Nighthawk, Spotted Sandpiper, Killdeer, Hudsonian White-crowned Sparrow, and Mountain Bluebird; at the forest margin were the Mountain Weasel, California Badger, Golden-mantled Ground Squirrel, Southern Sierra Marmot, Alpine Chipmunk, Sierra White-tailed Jack Rabbit, and Western Chipping Sparrow; in the main forest were the Tahoe Chipmunk, Sierra Chickaree, Yellow-haired Porcupine, Arctic Three-toed Woodpecker, and Sierra Hermit Thrush.

a

b

PLATE 19

a. Looking westward to Mounts Dana and Gibbs from meadow at Farrington Ranch, southwest of Mono Lake; photographed June 22, 1916. Meadow in foreground is in Transition Zone; low hills beyond, interruptedly clothed with Jeffrey pine, are in Canadian Zone; the forests, chiefly of lodgepole pine, on the slopes of the peaks represent the Hudsonian Zone, and the upper bare portions of the two mountains are in the Alpine-Arctic Zone. (This figure is reversed, left to right.)

b. Side of Williams Butte facing northeast toward Mono Lake; Transition Zone. Trees on the Butte are piñon pines, while in the foreground are bushes of *Kunzia* and sagebrush, with a strip of willows in the middle distance. Some birds characteristic of the piñon covered hill in September were Black-billed Magpie, Woodhouse Jay, Piñon Jay, and Short-tailed Mountain Chickadee, while in the sagebrush were Nevada Sage Sparrow, Brewer Sparrow, Green-tailed Towhee, and Sage Thrasher.

For discussion of the life zones in this vicinity, see text, pp. 8–10.

a

b

PLATE 20

Common Shrews of the Yosemite region.

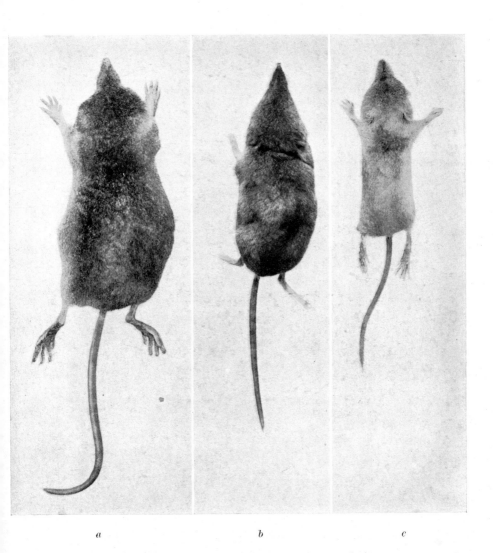

a   b   c

Common Shrews of the Yosemite region; $\frac{6}{7}$ natural size.

a. Navigator Shrew, east fork of Indian Cañon, June 23, 1915.
b. Yosemite Shrew, Yosemite Valley, December 29, 1914.
c. Dusky Shrew, same data as *a.*

The slender nose, inconspicuous eyes and ears, and plush-like pelage all indicate relationship with the moles. The expanded, fringed hind toes of the Navigator Shrew show correlation with its aquatic habits. For discussion of species, see text, pp. 47, 50.

[685]

PLATE 21

Bats of Yosemite Valley and the higher Sierra Nevada; all about $\%_{10}$ natural size; photographed from fresh specimens.

a. Hoary Bat, Merced Lake, August 21, 1915.

b. Merriam Bat, Pleasant Valley, May 23, 1915.

c. Little California Bat, Pleasant Valley, May 23, 1915.

d. Large Brown Bat, Merced Lake, August 23, 1915.

e. High Sierra Bat, Vogelsang Lake, August 31, 1915.

For accounts of these species, see text, pp. 51–60.

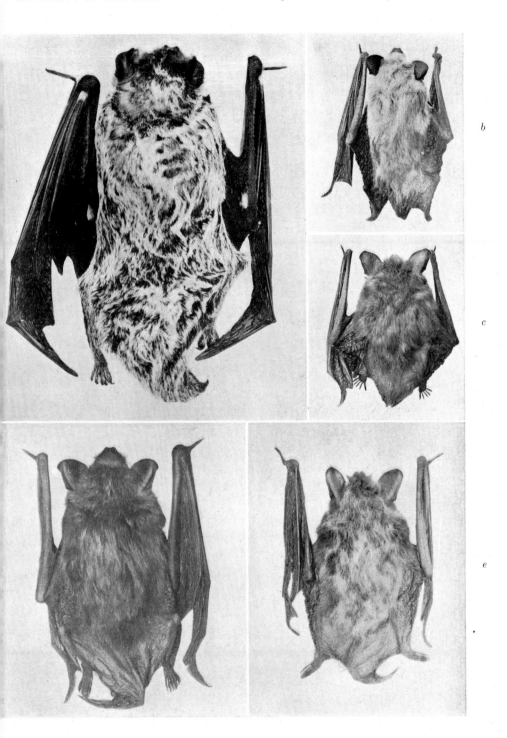

b

c

e

PLATE 22

a. Tracks of Black Bears in Yosemite Valley after a light snow fall, showing how a bear coming into another bear's trail at once treads "in the footsteps of its predecessor." Photographed below Cathedral Rocks, November 17, 1915.

b. Tracks of Black Bear in Yosemite Valley; photographed in road below Royal Arches, November 8, 1915. This bear was in haste; the print of the hind foot is ahead of that of the forefoot.

For general account of Black Bear, see text, pp. 63–68.

a

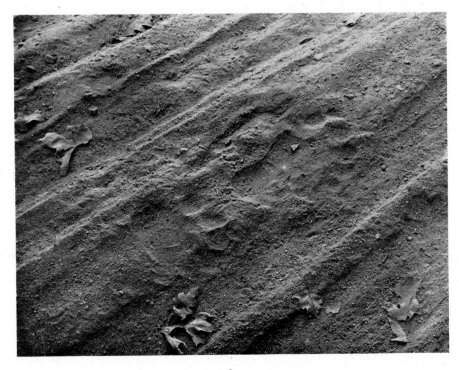

b

a

b

c

    a. Pacific Fisher, Chinquapin, December 21, 1915. Note rather slender body, long bushy tail, rather short legs, and short rounded ears.

    b. Sierra Pine Marten, Lyell Cañon, July 19, 1915. Note slender body, long neck, bushy tail, and rounded ears.

    c. Sierra Nevada Wolverine, head of Lyell Cañon, July 25, 1915. Note stout body, large head, short ears, big feet, and rather short tail.

    All the above about ⅛ natural size; photographs from animals fresh from the traps.

    For accounts of these mammals, see text, pp. 82–86.

a

b

c

The California Badger and its work.

a. Fresh burrow on the plains south of Lagrange, December 15, 1915.
b. Adult in trap, Tuolumne Meadows, July 11, 1915.
c. Young animal in burrow, near Mono Lake, June 25, 1916.

See text, p. 92.

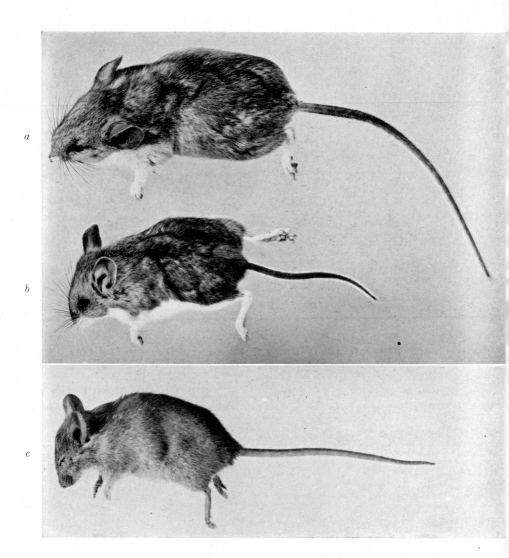

a. Boyle White-footed Mouse.

b. Common (Gambel) White-footed Mouse.

c. House Mouse. All about ⅘ natural size; photographed from specimens freshly trapped in Yosemite Valley, December 22, 1914. For discussion of diagnostic characters, see text, pp. 106, 107.

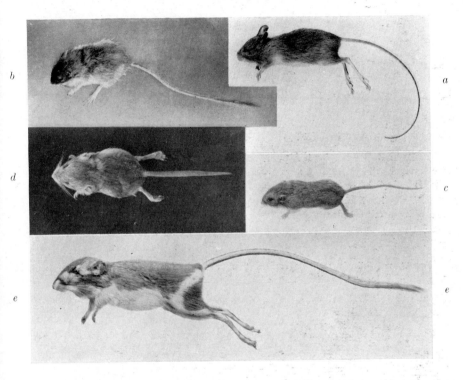

"Leaping" rodents of the Yosemite region. All close to ½ natural size; photographed from freshly trapped specimens.

a. Allen Jumping Mouse; Yosemite Valley near foot of Yosemite Falls, June 4, 1915.

b. California Pocket Mouse; El Portal, November 21, 1914.

c. San Joaquin Pocket Mouse; Snelling, May 28, 1915.

d. Mono Kangaroo Mouse; Mono Mills, June 21, 1916.

e. Merced Kangaroo Rat; Lagrange, December 21, 1915.

For descriptions of these species, see text, pp. 144, 146, 149.

PLATE 27

a. Yosemite Pocket Gopher, posed to show important external features, such as projecting incisor teeth, lack of any ''neck,'' short legs with heavily clawed fore feet, and short nearly hairless tail.

b. Yosemite Pocket Gopher, showing broadness of head, fur-lined cheek pouches, and white patches beneath.

c. Yosemite Mole, showing sharp snout, wedge-shaped head, laterally placed ''hands,'' and short hairy tail.

All $\frac{2}{3}$ natural size; photographed from animals freshly trapped on the floor of Yosemite Valley. For discussion of adaptive features of Pocket Gopher and Mole, see pp. 44, 134, 136.

a

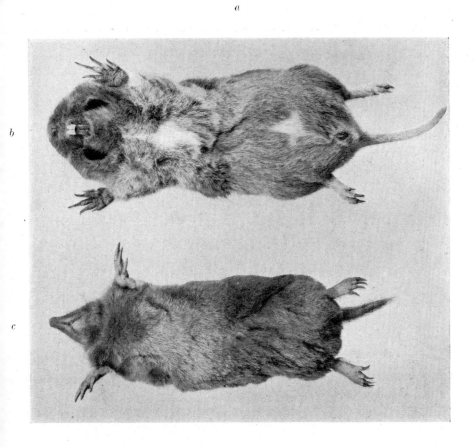

b

c

PLATE 28

Surface workings of Mole and Pocket Gopher as photographed in Yosemite Valley;
all about ⅓ natural size.

a. "Subsurface" forage run of Mole.
b. A Mole hill.
c. An earth mound made by a Pocket Gopher.

For comparative descriptions, see pp. 44, 137.

c

Yosemite Pocket Gopher in action, showing (*c*) method of digging with fore feet, (*b, d*) manner in which earth is pushed out from burrow, and (*a*) way in which gopher keeps part of its body in the burrow when alert to events above ground. The prominent forward-projecting vibrissae (''whiskers''), the small eyes placed on upper surface of head, and the small ears are shown to advantage. For discussion see text, p. 137.

PLATE 30

Winter earth cores made by Pocket Gophers.

a. Cores on surface of meadow three miles east of Chinquapin, May 20, 1919, as left after departure of winter snow.

b. Manner in which superimposed earth cores put up in snow during winter serve to bury rocks and thus develop a surface layer of soil. (Photo taken in Lyell Cañon, July 21, 1915.)

c. Fresh workings put up during an eight-inch fall of snow in Yosemite Valley. (Photo taken after a thaw, November 11, 1915.)

d. Rain-beaten cores covering up pine needles and branches on slopes near Tuolumne Meadows. (Photographed July 10, 1915.)

See text, p. 139.

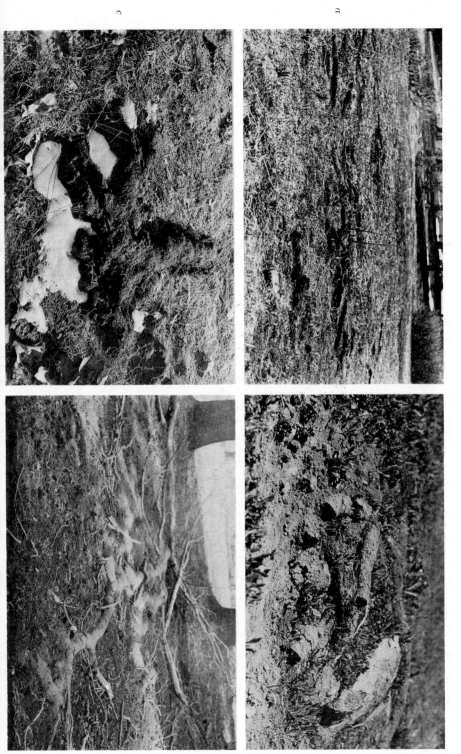

a

b

a. Living Sierra Mountain Beaver (*Aplodontia*) captured near head of Lyell Cañon, July 17, 1915. Note the small eye and ear, the apparent lack of tail, and the sluggish appearance of the animal. The matted condition of the pelage is due to its being wet.

b. Mouth of burrow of Sierra Mountain Beaver in boggy ground at Porcupine Flat. Photograph taken July 2, 1915. See text, p. 156.

a. Southern Sierra Marmot, photographed in rock slide in Lyell Cañon, July 20, 1915.

b. Typical perch of Marmot in glade near margin of Tuolumne Meadows, photographed July 8, 1915.

For account of the species, see text, p. 158.

a. Long-eared Chipmunk, at feeding place on Glacier Point. Photographed by Mr. Walter L. Huber. See text, p. 187.

b. California Gray Squirrel in characteristic pose when on the ground. Photographed by Mr. Charles D. Holliger on floor of Yosemite Valley, December 24, 1914. See text, p. 197.

California Gray Squirrel ascending the trunk of a black oak in Yosemite Valley. Photographed by Mr. Walter L. Huber. See description of climbing movements, in text, p. 197.

PLATE 35

a. Pile of 484 white fir cones gathered by the junior author from an area on the forest floor 50 by 50 feet, where they had been severally ''cached'' by a Sierra Chickaree. Photograph taken in Aspen Valley, October 18, 1915.

b. Twig-tips of lodgepole pine to the number of over 350 cut down by a Sierra Chickaree from a single tree. Photographed near Porcupine Flat, June 29, 1915. For general discussion, see text, pp. 206, 210.

a

b

PLATE 36

a. Granite talus in head of Lyell Cañon, altitude about 10,000 feet; Hudsonian Zone. The home of the Sierra Pine Marten, Gray Bushy-tailed Wood Rat, and Yosemite Cony.

b. Kitchen middens on a prostrate log where red fir cones had been customarily dissected by a Sierra Chickaree. Photograph taken on Porcupine Flat, July 1, 1915. See description in text, p. 208.

[GRINNELL-STORER] PLATE 36

PLATE 37

a. Work of Yellow-haired Porcupine on branches of prostrate lodgepole pine. Photographed at Porcupine Flat, 8100 feet altitude, July 1, 1915. See text, p. 153.

b. Dam made by Golden Beaver in slough formed by gold dredger in the Merced River bottom near Snelling. Photograph taken January 9, 1915. Although small, this dam shows typically the method of construction employed by this rodent. See text, p. 216.

a

b

a

b

a. Yosemite Cony, about ½ natural size; photographed from specimen freshly trapped at Ten Lakes, October 11, 1915. Note the small eye, large rounded ears, short legs, small feet, and the lack of tail. See text, p. 218.

b. Habitual ''lookout'' station of a Cony, with numerous droppings and stains on the granite; photographed in a talus at Ten Lakes, October 8, 1915. See text, p. 220.

a

b

a. Mountain Coyote captured at foot of Yosemite Falls trail, in Yosemite Valley, December 31, 1914. See text, p. 72.

b. Mule Deer, doe, in forest near Merced Lake. Photographed by Mr. W. H. Van Zwoll. See text, p. 231.

PLATE 40.

Records in the road:

a. Valley Quail, in dusty road near Coulterville, May 13, 1919. See text, p. 270.

b. Pacific Rattlesnake (which was traveling to left), on Wawona Road near Chinquapin, May 19, 1919. See text, p. 645.

c. Heermann Kangaroo Rat (prints of hind feet and tail as traveling to left), in road near Coulterville, May 13, 1919. See text, p. 146.

d. Mule Deer, probably old doe, in mud of Glacier Point Road east of Chinquapin, June 12, 1915. See text, p. 231.

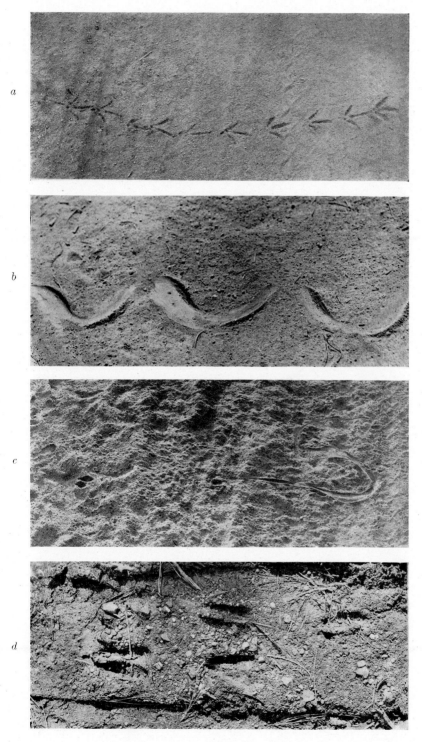

b

c

a

b

Long-eared Owls as photographed at the Farrington ranch, near Williams Butte.

a. Female sitting on eggs in depression on an old magpie's nest, May 4, 1916.

b. Young about eighteen days old, in another magpie's nest, May 19, 1916.

See text, p. 301.

a. Band-tailed Pigeons feeding on grain scattered in chickenyard in Yosemite Valley. Photographed May 1, 1916. See text, p. 276. *b*. Nuttall Poorwill resting on ground. Photograph taken near Williams Butte, June 22, 1916. See text, p. 344. *c*. Great Gray Owl (crippled). Photographed at Mono Meadow, June 19, 1915. See text, p. 306.

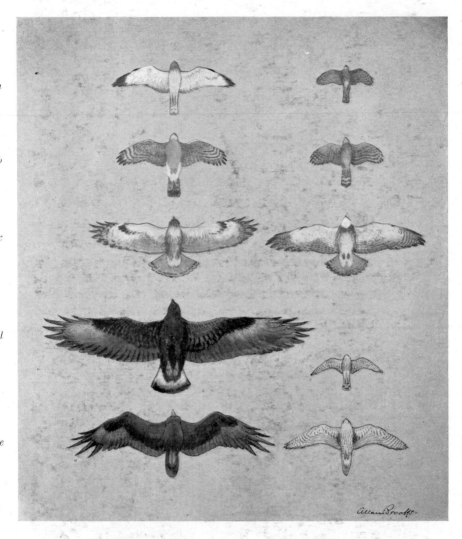

The principal diurnal birds of prey of the Yosemite region, as seen
overhead in flight:

a. Marsh Hawk, male adult.

b. Western Goshawk, male adult.

c. Western Red-tailed Hawk, male adult.

d. Golden Eagle, immature.

e. Turkey Vulture, adult.

f. Sharp-shinned Hawk, male adult.

g. Cooper Hawk, male adult.

h. Swainson Hawk, male adult.

i. American Sparrow Hawk, male adult.

j. Prairie Falcon, female adult.

For comparative descriptions and accounts, see text, pp. 279–296.

a. Nest and eggs of Swainson Hawk. Photographed near Lagrange, May 8, 1919. See text, p. 290.

b. ''Nest'' and eggs of Texas Nighthawk. Photographed near Lagrange, May 6, 1919. See text, p. 348.

PLATE 46

Hummingbirds which nest in the Yosemite region (see text, pp. 352, 353, 356); all about $\frac{9}{10}$ natural size.

a. Calliope Hummingbird, male adult; Yosemite Valley, June 8, 1915.

b. Anna Hummingbird, female adult; Pleasant Valley, May 23, 1915.

c. Black-chinned Hummingbird, male adult; El Portal, May 2, 1916.

Swallows and White-throated Swift compared (see text, p. 351); all about $\frac{1}{2}$ natural size.

d. Cliff Swallow; Pleasant Valley, May 27, 1915.

e. Barn Swallow; Pleasant Valley, May 24, 1915.

f. Northern Violet-green Swallow; Pleasant Valley, May 24, 1915.

g. White-throated Swift; Yosemite Point, June 25, 1915.

a   *b*   *c*

d   *e*   *f*   *g*

a

b

a. Nest of Cliff Swallow, one of a colony on rock wall of gully near Snelling. Photographed May 28, 1915.

b. Nest of California Linnet in old broken Cliff Swallow's nest, in same colony as above. See text, pp. 426, 498.

a. Mariposa Fox Sparrow; Yosemite Point, June 4, 1915.

b. Green-tailed Towhee; Yosemite Point, June 4, 1915.

c. Sacramento Spurred (Spotted) Towhee; El Portal, December 8, 1914.

All photographed, about ⅝ natural size, from freshly taken specimens, to show diagnostic features. All are ground dwellers; *a* and *c* are preëminently ''scratching'' sparrows. See text, pp. 473, 478, 482.

a. Nest of Green-tailed Towhee in snow bush at Tamarack Flat, May 26, 1919. See text, p. 483.

b. Nest of Northeastern Lincoln Sparrow near Porcupine Flat, June 29, 1915. See text, p. 471.

The Vireos of the Yosemite section. Photographed from freshly taken specimens, about ⅕ natural size.

a. Cassin Vireo; Pleasant Valley, May 23, 1915.
b. Western Warbling Vireo; Pleasant Valley, May 23, 1915.
c. Hutton Vireo; El Portal, December 8, 1914.
d. California Least Vireo; Snelling, May 29, 1915.

For discussions of comparative field characters, see pp. 509, 512, 513, 514.

a. Nest of California Least Vireo near Lagrange; photographed May 9, 1919. See text, p. 515.

b. Nest and eggs of Tolmie Warbler in Yosemite Valley; photographed June 24, 1915. See text, p. 536.

[GRINNELL–STORER] PLATE 52

PLATE 53

a. Western Mockingbird; Lagrange, December 10, 1915.

b. California Shrike; same data. Both from fresh specimens, about ⅓ natural size. See text, pp. 547, 506.

c. Dotted Cañon Wren; Yosemite Valley, December 29, 1914.

d. San Joaquin Bewick Wren; Snelling, May 29, 1915. Both from freshly taken specimens, about ¾ natural size. See text, pp. 552, 555.

a   *b*

PLATE 54

Western House Wrens; photographed by Joseph Dixon at the Farrington ranch near
Williams Butte.

a. Carrying stick to nest hole in dead tree; June 2, 1916.

b. Taking food to brood of young in nest in old oil can; June 23, 1916. See text,
p. 557.

a

b

a. Nest and eggs of Western Robin; photographed near Mono Lake Post Office, May 30, 1916. See text, p. 611.

b. Nest and eggs of Townsend Solitaire in cut bank at up-hill side of Glacier Point Road one mile east of Chinquapin; photographed June 12, 1915. See text, p. 598.

a. Young Black-billed Magpie; photographed near Williams Butte, June 21, 1916. See text, p. 378.

b. Female Mountain Bluebird perched near her nest in a building; photographed at Mono Lake Post Office, May 30, 1916. See text, p. 624.

a

b

c

a. Mountain Lizard; Merced Grove Big Trees, June 15, 1915. See text, p. 628.

b. Western Fence Lizard; Yosemite Valley, June 8, 1915. See text, p. 626.

c. California Whip-tailed Lizard; near Kinsley, at 2700 feet altitude, June 14, 1915. See text, p. 632.

All photographed, about ⅗ natural size, from freshly collected specimens.

a   b   c   d

a. Western Skink, adult; Pleasant Valley, May 28, 1915.

b. San Diego Alligator Lizard, tail regenerated; Yosemite Valley near the village, May 19, 1919.

c. Sierra Alligator Lizard, immature with tail complete; Yosemite Valley, May 19, 1919.

d. Sierra Alligator Lizard, adult with regenerated tail; Chinquapin, June 14, 1915.

All photographed, about ⅗ natural size, from freshly collected specimens. See text, pp. 630, 633.

PLATE 59

a. Valley Gopher Snake—harmless; Pleasant Valley, May 29, 1915. See text, p. 643. This and the lower figure, about ½ natural size.

b. Pacific Rattlesnake; Pleasant Valley, May 27, 1915. For full discussion of characteristics and of steps to be taken in case of being bitten, see text, pp. 645–650.

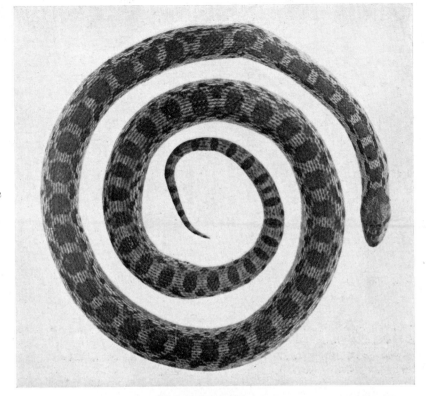

a

b

PLATE 60

Some amphibians of the Yosemite section:

a. California Toad; Pleasant Valley, May 25, 1915.
b. Sierra Yellow-legged Frog; Porcupine Flat, June 27, 1915.
c. Western Spade-foot Toad; Farrington ranch, near Williams Butte, May 5, 1916.
d. Yosemite Toad, young female; three miles east of Chinquapin, May 20, 1919.
e. Yosemite Toad, adult female; Porcupine Flat, June 27, 1915.
f. Mount Lyell Salamander; head of Lyell Cañon, July 19, 1915.

For text accounts, see pp. 652–665.

INDEX*

A

Accipiter cooperi, 17, *284-286*
  velox, 17, *282-284*
Actitis macularia, *263-265*
Aeronautes melanoleucus, *351-352*
Agelaius phoeniceus, *400-407*
  phoeniceus aciculatus, 19, *400*, 403
  phoeniceus californicus, 18, *400*, 404, 405
  phoeniceus nevadensis, 18, *400*, 404, 405
  tricolor, 19, *407-408*
Aimophila ruficeps ruficeps, 19, *467-468*
Ammodramus savannarum bimaculatus, 19, *443*
Amphispiza belli, 19, *464-466*
  nevadensis nevadensis, 19, *466*
Anas platyrhynchos, *253*
Aneides lugubris lugubris, 21, *653*
Antelope, American, 231, 242
  Pronghorn, 241, *242-243*
Anthus rubescens, *542-543*
Antilocapra americana americana, *242-243*
Antrozous pacificus, 15, *60-61*
Aphelocoma californica immanis, 18, *387-392*
  woodhousei, 18, *392*
Aplodontia, 155, 209, 702
Aplodontia rufa californica, 16, *155-158*
Aquila chrysaetos, 17, *292-294*
Archibuteo ferrugineus, *291-292*
Archilochus alexandri, 18, *352-353*
Ardea herodias, *256-258*
  herodias hyperonca, *256*
  herodias treganzai, *256*
Ash-throat, 360, 361
Asio wilsonianus, 17, *300-303*
Astragalinus lawrencei, 19, *437*
  psaltria hesperophilus, 19, *435-437*
  tristis salicamans, 19, *434-435*
Astur atricapillus striatulus, 17, *286-287*
Asyndesmus lewisi, *341-342*

B

Badger, California, 15, *92-95*, 680, 691
Baeolophus inornatus inornatus, 20, *572-574*
Baldpate, *253*
Bassariscus astutus raptor, 15, *81*
Bat, Free-tailed, 53, 58
  Fringed, 15, *57*
  High Sierra, 15, *55-56*, 686
  Hoary, 15, 53, 54, 58, *59-60*, 686
  Large Brown, 15, 51, 55, 56, 57, *58-59*, 60, 61, 62, 686
  Little California, 15, *51-55*, 56, 57, 58, 60, 61, 686
  Long-legged, 15, *56-57*
  Merriam, 15, 51, *57-58*, 60, 686
  Mexican Free-tailed, 15, *61-63*
  Pacific Pallid, 15, *60-61*
  Pallid, 53, 56, 59

Batrachoseps attenuatus, 21, *654*
Bear, American Black, 15, *63-68*
  Black, 69, 71, 688
  Grizzly, 63, 64, *68-71*
Beaver, Golden, 5, 17, *215-218*, 710
  Sierra Mountain, 16, 132, *155-158*, 702
Bibliography, 667
Bighorn, 243, 246
Bird, Cedar, 505
Bittern, American, *256*
  Least, *256*
Blackbird, Bi-colored Red-winged, 18, 26, *400*, 402, 406, 408
  Brewer, 19, 23, 26, 27, 29, 35, 286, 375, 401, *413-416*
  Kern Red-winged, 19, *400*
  Nevada Red-winged, 18, 35, *400*, 402
  Red-winged, 398, 399, 400, 401, 402, 403, 407, 597
  Tri-colored, 19, 401, *407-408*
  Yellow-headed, *399-400*
Blackbirds, Red-winged, *400-407*
Bluebird, Arctic, 622
  Mountain, 21, 34, 35, 616, 618, *622-625*, 680, 735
  Western, 7, 21, 25, 27, 28, 30, 31, 32, 283, 291, 490, 529, 573, *615-622*, 623, 670
Bob-cat, 98, 99
Bombycilla cedrorum, *504-505*
  garrula, *504*
Botaurus lentiginosus, *256*
Bubo virginianus pacificus, 17, *309-310*
Bufo boreas boreas, *655*
  boreas halophilus, 21, *655-657*
  canorus, 21, *657-660*
Bunting, Lazuli, 19, 26, 27, 28, 29, 35, 80, 467, 468, 490, *491-493*, 516
Bush-tit, 617
  California, 20, 26, 27, 28, *579-582*
  Lead-colored, 580, *582*
Buteo borealis calurus, 17, *287-289*
  lineatus elegans, 17, *289*
  swainsoni, 17, *290-291*
Butorides virescens anthonyi, *258-259*
Buzzard, 279
  Turkey, 279, 280, 281, 287, 288

C

Callospermophilus chrysodeirus chrysodeirus, 16, 163, *173-176*
Calypte anna, 18, *353-354*
Canis latrans lestes, 15, *71-76*
  ochropus ochropus, 71
Carpodacus cassini, 19, *423-424*
  mexicanus frontalis, 19, *425-427*
  purpureus californicus, 19, *420-422*
Castor canadensis subauratus, 17, *215-218*

* Italicized numbers refer to main account.

[743]

Cat, California Ring-tailed, *81*
Civet, 90
Ring-tailed, 5, 15
Cathartes aura septentrionalis, 17, *279-281*
Catherpes mexicanus punctulatus, 20, *552-555*
Centrocercus urophasianus, 17, *274-275*
Certhia familiaris zelotes, 20, *561-564*
Cervus nannodes, *241-243*
Ceryle alcyon caurina, 17, *313-315*
Chaetura vauxi, *350*
Chamaea fasciata henshawi, 20, *582-586*
Charina bottae, 21, *635-636*
Chat, Long-tailed, 20, 26, 27, 403, *539-540*
Chickadee, Mountain, 9, 23, 322, 323, 575, 576, 577, 579, 587
Short-tailed Mountain, 12, 20, 29, 30, 31, 32, 33, 34, 35, *574-579*, 678, 682, pl. 10
Chickaree, 196
Sierra, 17, 158, *203-211*, 367, 384, 614, 678, 680, 706, 708
Chipmunk, Allen, 5, 12, 16, 177, 178, *183-185*, 188, 194, 285, 286, 678, pl. 3
Alpine, 5, 16, 177, 178, 180, 184, *190-194*, 195, 680, pl. 3
Long-eared, 5, 16, 177, 178, 183, 184, 186, *187-190*, 648, 704, pl. 3
Mariposa, 16, 177, 178, 184, *185-187*, 188, 648, 649, 674, pl. 3
Mono, 5, 9, 16, 177, 178, 190, *194-195*, pl. 3
Sagebrush, 5, 16, 177, 178, *195-196*, pl. 3
Tahoe, 12, 16, 89, *176-183*, 188, 190, 191, 194, 678, 680, pl. 3
Yellow-headed, 174
Chondestes grammacus strigatus, 19, *444-446*
Chordeiles acutipennis texensis, 18, *347-348*
virginianus hesperis, 18, *346*
Cinclus mexicanus unicolor, 20, *543-546*
Circus hudsonius, *281-282*
Citellus beecheyi beecheyi, 16, 76, *162-168*
beldingi, 16, 163, *168-173*
mollis stephensi, 16, *173*
Clemmys marmorata, 21, *650*
Cnemidophorus tigris mundus, 21, *632-633*
Cock-of-the-woods, 334
Colaptes cafer collaris, 18, *342-343*
Coluber constrictor flaviventris, *643*
lateralis, 21, *641-642*
Columba fasciata fasciata, 17, *275-278*
Colymbus nigricollis californicus, *247*
Cony, Yosemite, 5, 17, 89, 161, *218-221*, 680, 708, 712
Coon, California, 15, *81-82*
Coot, 261
Copperhead, 169, 174
Cormorant, Farallon, *251-252*
Corvus brachyrhynchos hesperis, *392*
corax sinuatus, *392*
Cottontail, Sacramento, 17, *227-228*
Washington, 17, *227-228*
Cougar, 95
Cowbird, Dwarf, 7, 18, *398*, 399
Nevada, 18, 35, *398*, 399

Cowbirds, *398-399*
Coyote, California Valley, 72
Mountain, 15, 64, *71-76*, 86, 95, 176, 239, 713
Valley, 72, 73, 74, 75
Creeper, Sierra, 12, 20, 23, 28, 29, 30, 31, 33, 35, 305, *561-564*, 579, 587, 588, 678, pl. 10
Crossbill, Sierra, 31, 32, 423, *428-430*
Crotalus oreganus, 21, *645-650*
Crow, 393, 548
Clark, 393, 396
Fremont, 393
Western, 26, *392-393*
Cryptoglaux acadica, 17, *307-308*
Cyanocephalus cyanocephalus, 18, *397-398*
Cyanocitta stelleri frontalis, 18, *379-387*
Cypseloides niger borealis, 18, *349-350*

D

Dafila acuta, *254*
Deer, Mule, 17, 96, 97, 98, *231-240*, 246, 577, 713, 714
Rocky Mountain Mule, 76
Dendragapus obscurus sierrae, 17, *272-274*
Dendroica aestiva brewsteri, 20, *521-523*
auduboni auduboni, 20, *524-529*
coronata hooveri, *523-524*
nigrescens, 20, *529-531*
occidentalis, 20, *532-533*
townsendi, *531*
Diadophis amabilis amabilis, 21, *639*
Dipodomys, *146-149*
heermanni dixoni, 16, *146*, 147
heermanni heermanni, 16, *146*, 147, 149
leucogenys, 16, *146*, 147
Dipper, 544
American, 20, 30, 33, 34, *543-546*, 551, 599, 674, 729
Dog, Water, 651
Dove, Western Mourning, 17, 26, 27, 28, 33, 35, *278-279*
Dryobates nuttalli, 18, *319-320*
pubescens turati, 18, *317-319*
villosus orius, 17, *315-317*
Duck, Harlequin, 253, *255-256*

E

Eagle, Golden, 17, 31, 34, 279, 288, *292-294*, 720
Elanus leucurus, *281*
Elk, Dwarf, 231, *241-243*
Tule, 231, 241
Empidonax difficilis difficilis, 18, *372-373*
griseus, 18, *373-374*
hammondi, 18, *370-371*
trailli trailli, 18, *371-372*
wrighti, 18, *367-369*
Eptesicus fuscus, 15, *58-59*
Erethizon epixanthum epixanthum, 16, *151-154*
Eumeces gilberti, 634
Euphagus cyanocephalus, 19, *413-416*
Eurycea platycephala, 21, *652*

Eutamias alpinus, 16, 176, 177, 178, 180, 183, *190-194*
  amoenus monoensis, 16, 176, 177, 178, 191, *194-195*
  merriami mariposae, 16, 176, 177, 178, *185-187*
  pictus, 16, 176, 177, 178, 194, *195-196*
  quadrimaculatus, 16, 176, 177, 178, 180, 183, *187-190*
  senex, 16, 176, 177, 178, 180, *183-185*, 187, 285
  speciosus frater, 16, *176-183*, 194

F

Falco columbarius columbarius, *295-296*
  mexicanus, *294*
  peregrinus anatum, *294-295*
  sparverius sparverius, 17, *296-297*
Falcon, Prairie, 33, *294*, 720
Felis oregonensis hippolestes, 97
  oregonensis oregonensis, 15, *95-98*
Finch, California Purple, 7, 19, 28, 29, 30, 31, *420-422*, 423, 425, 429, pl. 7
  Cassin Purple, 7, 19, 32, 33, 34, 420, 421, *423-424*, 429, 431, 604, 678, pl. 7
  House, 425
  Purple, 420, 421, 422, 425, 426, 510
  Sierra Nevada Rosy, 7, 19, 34, *430-433*, pl. 1
Fisher, Pacific, 15, *83-85*, 274, 690
Flicker, 623, 624
  Red-shafted, 18, 23, 26, 27, 28, 29, 31, 32, 33, 34, 35, 61, 93, 286, 335, *342-343*, 557, 661, pl. 5
Flycatcher, Ash-throated, 18, 26, 27, 28, *360-361*
  Gray, 7, 18, *373-374*
  Hammond, 7, 9, 18, 31, 33, *370-371*, 373, 374, 678
  Olive-sided, 18, 27, 31, 32, 33, *364-365*, 366, 598
  Traill, 18, 26, 28, 29, 35, *371-372*, 373
  Western, 18, 29, 30, 31, 305, *372-373*
  Wright, 18, 27, 29, 31, 32, 34, 358, *367-369*, 370, 371, 372, 373, 374, 385, 477
Fox, California Gray, 5, 15, 77, *78-80*, 468
  Cascade Red, 5, 15, *77*
  Gray, 78, 100, 269, 271
  Red, 78, 79
  San Joaquin Kit, 15, *77-78*
Frog, California Red-legged, 21, *666*
  California Yellow-legged, 21, *663*
  Red-legged, 664, 666
  Sierra Yellow-legged, 21, *663*, 740
Frogs, Yellow-legged, *663-665*
Fulica americana, *261*

G

Gallinago delicata, *263*
Geococcyx californianus, 17, *313*
Geothlypis trichas, *538-539*
  trichas occidentalis, *538*, 539
  trichas scirpicola, 20, *538*
Gerrhonotus, *630-632*
  palmeri, 21, *631*
  scincicauda webbii, 21, *630*

Glaucidium gnoma californicum, 17, *311-312*
Glaucomys sabrinus lascivus, 17, 163, *211-215*
Gnatcatcher, Western, 21, 27, 28, 33, 391, 548, *593-595*, 672
Goldfinch, Green-backed, 19, 26, 27, 28, 352, *435-437*, 642
  Lawrence, 19, 435, 436, *437*
  Willow, 19, 26, 430, *434-435*, 436
Gopher, Digger Pine Pocket, 5, 16, *135*, 672
  Fisher Pocket, 16, *135*
  Fresno Pocket, 5, 16, *135*
  Sierra Nevada Pocket, 16, 44, 49, 76, *135*
  Yosemite Pocket, 5, 16, *135*, 303, 312, 676, 694, 698
Gophers, Pocket, *134-143*
Goshawk, 283, 284, 288
  Western, 7, 17, 274, *286-287*, 720
Grebe, American Eared, 35, *247*, 248
  Eared, 247, 295
  Pied-billed, 26, *248*
Grizzly, Henshaw, 69
Grosbeak, Black-headed, 23, 418, 419, 485, 486, 487, 488, 489, 595, 597, 609
  Blue, 490, 491
  California Blue, 7, 19, 26, *490-491*, 616
  California Evening, 19, 31, 32, *417-419*, 423, 429, 431
  California Pine, 7, 19, *419-420*, 596
  Evening, 417, 418, 419
  Pacific Black-headed, 19, 26, 27, 28, 29, 30, 31, 32, 35, *484-490*, 510, 672
  Pine, 419, 420
Grouse, Sierra, 7, 17, 31, 33, 34, 35, *272-274*, 286, 678
Guiraca caerulea salicarius, 19, *490-491*
Gull, California, 35, *248-250*, 716
Gulo luscus luteus, 15, *85-86*

H

Hare, Sierra, 224
Hawk, American Sparrow, 17, 26, 30, 35, *296-297*, 720
  California Squirrel, 292
  Cooper, 17, 27, 32, 38, 271, 283, *284-286*, 287, 288, 289, 300, 415, 720
  Duck, *294-295*
  Ferruginous Rough-legged, *291-292*
  Marsh, 35, *281-282*, 288, 720
  Northern Pigeon, *295-296*
  Red-bellied, 17, 26, 288, *289*
  Red-tailed, 279, 281, 282, 290, 291, 293, 294, 297, 358, 381, 392, 396
  Sharp-shinned, 17, 29, 32, *282-284*, 287, 288, 382, 720
  Sparrow, 50, 283, 288, 289, 294, 295, 296, 625
  Swainson, 17, 288, *290-291*, 573, 720, 721
  Western Red-tailed, 17, 22, 27, 32, *287-289*, 720
Heron, Anthony Green, *258-259*
  Black-crowned Night, 26, *259*
  California Great Blue, 26, *256*
  Great Blue, 256, 259
  Pallid Great Blue, *256*

Herons, Great Blue, *256-258*
Hesperiphona vespertina californica, 19, *417-419*
Hirundo erythrogaster erythrogaster, 20, *499-500*
Histrionicus histrionicus, *255-256*
Horned Toad, California, 630
Hummingbird, Allen, *355-356*
  Anna, 18, 27, 28, *353-354*, 356, 357, 722
  Black-chinned, 18, 35, *352-353*, 357, 722
  Calliope, 18, 29, 31, 32, *356-358*, 678, 722
  Rufous, *354-355*, 356, 357
Hydrochelidon nigra surinamensis, *251*
Hyla regilla, 21, *661-663*
Hylocichla guttata, *602-605*
  guttata guttata, *602*
  guttata nanus, *602*
  guttata sequoiensis, 21, *602*
  ustulata ustulata, 21, *600-601*

I

Icteria virens longicauda, 20, *539-540*
Icterus bullocki, 19, *411-413*
Iridoprocne bicolor, 20, *500-501*
Ixobrychus exilis exilis, *256*
Ixoreus naevius meruloides, *614-615*

J

Jay, Blue-fronted, 18, 23, 27, 28, 29, 30, 31, 32, 33, 35, 283, 286, 305, *379-387*, 396, 397, 570, 592, 616, 678
  California, 176, 305, 359, 379, 381, 384, *387-392*, 396, 397, 481, 548, 616
  Interior California, 7, 18, 26, 27, 28, *387-392*, 670, 672
  Mountain Blue, 379
  Piñon, 7, 18, 35, 379, 387, 394, *397-398*, 616, 682
  Steller, 379
  Woodhouse, 9, 18, 379, 387, 392, 397, 616, 682
Junco, Shufeldt, *459*, 461
  Sierra, 19, 23, 27, 28, 29, 30, 31, 32, 33, 34, 35, 291, 422, 454, 458, *459-464*
  Slate-colored, *458*, 460, 461
Junco hyemalis hyemalis, *458*
  oreganus shufeldti, *459*
  oreganus thurberi, 19, *459-464*

K

Killdeer, 26, 27, 34, 264, *265-267*, 680
Kingbird, Western, 18, 26, 27, 35, 286, *359-360*, 391, 415
Kingfisher, Belted, 23, 314
  Western Belted, 17, 29, 30, 33, *313-315*
Kinglet, Golden-crowned, 23, 305, 307, 518, 563, 581, 587, 588, 591, 595, 678
  Ruby-crowned, 23, 305, 306, 312, 354, 385, 513, 518, 587, 589, 590, 591, 592, 593, 595, 678
  Western Golden-crowned, 12, 21, 30, 31, 32, 33, *586-589*, pl. 10
  Western Ruby-crowned, 21, 26, 27, 29, 30, 31, 32, 33, 34, *589-593*, pl. 10
Kite, White-tailed, *281*

L

Lagurus curtatus, 16, *133*
Lampropeltis getulus boylii, 21, *640-641*
  multicincta, 21, *640*
Lanius ludovicianus, *506-508*
  ludovicianus excubitorides, 20, *506*, 507, 508
  ludovicianus gambeli, 20, *506*, 507, 508
Lanivireo solitarius cassini, 20, *511-513*
Lark, California Horned, 18, 27, *374*
  Dusky Horned, 35, *374*
Larks, Horned, *374-376*
Larus californicus, *248-250*
Lepus californicus, *221-224*
  californicus californicus, 17, *221*, 222
  californicus deserticola, 17, *221*, 222, 224
  townsendii sierrae, 17, *224-226*
Leucosticte, 431, 432, 433
Leucosticte tephrocotis dawsoni, 19, *430-433*
Linnet, 283, 420, 421, 422, 423, 426
  California, 19, 26, 27, 28, 35, 420, 423, *425-427*, 547, 618, 724, pl. 7
Lion, Mountain, 64, 74, 76, 99, 239, 240
  Northwestern Mountain, 15, *95-98*
  Rocky Mountain, 97
Lizard, Alligator, 631, 632
  California Whip-tailed, 21, 627, *632-633*, 736
  Fence, 627, 629
  Mountain, 21, 627, *628-630*, 736
  Mountain Alligator, 627, 678
  Pacific Blue-bellied, 21, *626*, 627
  San Diego Alligator, 21, *630*, 737
  Sierra Alligator, 21, 627, *631*, 737
  Tenaya, 627, 629
  Tenaya Blue-bellied, 21, *626*, 627, 628
  Western Fence, 21, *626*, 736
Lizards, Alligator, *630-632*
  Blue-bellied, *626-628*
Lobipes lobatus, *261-262*
Lophortyx californica vallicola, 17, *270-272*
Loxia curvirostra bendirei, *428-430*
Lynx eremicus californicus, 15, 98, *99-101*

M

Magpie, American, 376
  Black-billed, 18, 35, 301, *376-379*, 682, 735
  Yellow-billed, 376
Mallard, *253*, 254, 255
Mareca americana, *253*
Marmot, Sierra, 93, 151, 159, 220
  Southern Sierra, 5, 16, *158-162*, 680, 703, pl. 2
Marmota flaviventer sierrae, 16, *158-162*, 163
Marten, Pine, 84, 89
  Sierra Pine, 15, *82-83*, 220, 274, 680, 690, 708
Martes caurina sierrae, 15, *82-83*
  pennanti pacifica, 15, *83-85*
Martin, Bee, 359
  Western, *497*

Meadowlark, 409, 411
  Western, 19, 26, 27, 28, 35, *409-411*, 412, 547
Melanerpes formicivorus bairdi, 18, *337-341*
Melospiza lincolni, *470-472*
  lincolni gracilis, *470*, 471
  lincolni lincolni, 19, *470*, 471
  melodia, *468-470*
  melodia fisherella, 19, *468*, 469, 470
  melodia heermanni, *469*
  melodia merrilli, *469*
  melodia rufina, *469*
Mephitis occidentalis, 15, *91-92*
Merganser, American, *252*
  Red-breasted, 252
Mergus americanus, *252*
Mice, Big-eared, *111-112*
  California Meadow, *126-129*, 131
  Common White-footed, *104-109*
  Pocket, *144-146*
Microdipodops polionotus, 16, *149*
Microtus californicus, 123, *126-129*
  californicus aestuarinus, 16, *126*, 127,130
  californicus mariposae, 16, 123, *126*, 127, 130
  montanus yosemite, 16, *122-126*, 130, 300
  mordax sierrae, 16, *129-133*
Mimus polyglottos leucopterus, 20, *547-548*
Mink, Pacific, 15, 87, *89-90*
Mockingbird, Western, 7, 20, 26, *547-548*, 597, 730
Mole, Mono, 5, 15, *43*
  San Joaquin, 15, *43*
  Yosemite, 15, *43*, 44, 676, 694
Moles, *43-46*
Molothrus ater, *398-399*
  ater artemisiae, 18, *398*
  ater obscurus, 18, *398*
Mouse, Allen Jumping, 16, 49, *149-151*, 693
  Boyle, 107, 110, 113
  Boyle White-footed, 15, 100, 105, 106, *110-111*, 112, 672, 674, 692
  California Pocket, 5, 16, *144*, 145, 146, 147, 693
  Cantankerous Meadow, 122, 123, 134
  Common White-footed, 105, 106, 107, 108, 672, 692
  Gambel, 106, 107
  Gambel White-footed, 15, 76, 93, 102, *104*, 105, 112, 150, 661, 692
  Gilbert, 110, 111, 112, 113
  Gilbert White-footed, 5, 15, 105, 107, *111*
  Great Basin Pocket, 5, 16, 51, *144*, 145, 146
  Harvest, 102
  House, *101-103*, 106, 692
  Jumping, 149
  Long-tailed Harvest, 16, *114-115*
  Mariposa Meadow, 5, 16, 122, 124, *126*, 128
  Meadow, 49
  Mono Kangaroo, 5, 16, *149*, 693

Mountain Lemming, 5, 16, 131, *133-134*
  Parasitic, 112, 113
  Parasitic White-footed, 5, 16, 105, 107, *112-113*
  San Joaquin Pocket, 5, 16, *144*, 145, 146, 693
  Sierra Cantankerous Meadow, 16, 123, *129-133*, 674
  Short-tailed Grasshopper, 5, 16, *113*
  Short-tailed Meadow, 16, *133*
  Sonora, 106, 107
  Sonora White-footed, 15, *104*, 109, 113
  True, 111
  True White-footed, 9, 16, 107, *111*
  Tule Meadow, 5, 16, 122, *126*
  White-footed, 303, 305, 645
  Yosemite Meadow, 16, *122-126*, 127, 131, 132, 300, 303, 676, 680
Mud-hen, 26, 35, *261*
Mus musculus, *101-103*
Mustela arizonensis, 15, *86-89*
  muricus, 15, *89*
  vison energumenos, 15, *89-90*
  xanthogenys, 86
Myadestes townsendi, 21, *595-599*
Myiarchus cinerascens cinerascens, 18, *360-361*
Myiochanes richardsoni richardsoni, 18, *365-367*
Myotis californicus californicus, 15, *51-55*
  longicrus longicrus, 15, *56-57*
  lucifugus altipetens, 15, *55-56*
  thysanodes, 15, *57*

N

Nannus hiemalis pacificus, 20, *558-560*
Neosorex palustris navigator, 15, 48, *50-51*
Neotoma cinerea cinerea, 16, *120-122*
  fuscipes streatori, 16, *116-120*,305
Newt, Pacific Coast, 21, 627, *651*
Nighthawk, Pacific, 18, 34, *346*, 347, 680
  Texas, 7, 18, *347-348*, 659, 721
Notophthalmus torosus, 21, *651*
Nucifraga columbiana, 18, *393-396*
Nutcracker, Clark, 9, 18, 32, 33, 34, 35, 379, 380, *393-396*, 397
Nuthatch, Pigmy, 20, 31, 35 565, 567, 569, *571*, pl. 10
  Red-breasted, 20, 28, 29, 30, 31, 32, 33, 385, 562, 565, 567, *568-570*, 571, 678, pl. 10
  Slender-billed, 20, 27, 28, 32, 35, 323, *564-568*, 569, 571, 670, pl. 10
Nuttallornis borealis, 18, *364-365*
Nycteris cinerea, 15, *59-60*
Nycticorax nycticorax naevius, *259*
Nyctinomus mexicanus, 15, *61-63*

O

Oberholseria chlorura, 19, *482-484*
Ochotona schisticeps muiri, 17, *218-221*
Odocoileus hemionus hemionus, 17, 76, *231-240*
Onychomys leucogaster brevicaudus, 16, *113*

Oporornis tolmiei, 20, *534-538*
Oreortyx picta plumifera, 17, *267-269*
Oreoscoptes montanus, 20, *546-547*
Oriole, Bullock, 19, 26, 27, 28, *411-413*
Osprey, 288
  American, *297*
Otocoris alpestris, *374-376*
  alpestris actia, 18, *374*, 376
  alpestris merrilli, *374*, 376
Otus asio quercinus, 17, *308-309*
Ouzel, Water, 23, 544, 729
Ovis canadensis sierrae, *243-246*
Owl, Barn, 17, *298*, 299
  Billy, 310
  Burrowing, 17, 165, 299, *310-311*
  California Pigmy, 7, 17, 30, 299, *311-312*, 323, 592
  California Screech, 311
  California Spotted, 17, 299, *304-305*, 592
  Golden, 298
  Great Gray, 17, 38, 299, *305-307*, 309, 326, 592, 719
  Great Horned, 304, 309
  Ground, 310
  Horned, 271, 309
  Long-eared, 17, 35, 299, *300-303*, 377, 718
  Monkey-faced, 298
  Pacific Horned, 17, 299, 304, 307, *309-310*
  Pigmy, 307, 309, 312
  Saw-whet, 17, 299, *307-308*, 589
  Screech, 307, 348
  Southern California Screech, 17, 299, *308-309*
  Spotted, 38, 309
Oxyechus vociferus vociferus, *265-267*

P

Pandion haliaetus carolinensis, *297*
Panther, 95
Passer domesticus, *439-440*
Passerculus sandwichensis, *442-443*
  sandwichensis alaudinus, *442*
  sandwichensis nevadensis, 19, *442*
  sandwichensis sandwichensis, *442*
Passerella iliaca, *472-477*
  iliaca altivagans, 472, *473*
  iliaca insularis, *472*
  iliaca mariposae, 19, 472, *473*
  iliaca megarhyncha, *473*
  iliaca monoensis, 19, 472, *473*
  iliaca schistacea, 472, *473*
  iliaca sinuosa, 472, *473*
  iliaca unalaschcensis, *472*
Passerina amoena, 19, *491-493*
Pelecanus erythrorhynchos, *252*
Pelican, White, *252*
Penthestes gambeli abbreviatus, 20, *574-579*
Perognathus, *144-146*
  californicus californicus, 16, *144*
  inornatus inornatus, 16, *144*
  parvus olivaceus, 16, *144*

Peromyscus boylii boylii, 15, 106, 107, *110-111*
  californicus californicus, 16, 107, *112-113*, 645
  maniculatus, *104-109*
  maniculatus gambeli, 15, 76, *104*, 107
  maniculatus sonoriensis, 15, *104*, 107, 109
  truei, *111-112*
  truei gilberti, 15, 107, *111*
  truei truei, 16, 107, *111*
Petrochelidon lunifrons lunifrons, 19, *497-499*
Pewee, Western Wood, 18, 26, 27, 28, 29, 30, 31, 33, 34, 35, *365-367*
  Wood, 107, 209, 366, 367
Phainopepla, 20, 27, *505-506*, 670
Phainopepla nitens, 20, *505-506*
Phalacrocorax auritus albociliatus, *251-252*
Phalaenoptilus nuttalli, *343-345*
  nuttalli californicus, 18, *343*
  nuttalli nuttalli, 18, *343*
Phalarope, Northern, *261-262*
  Wilson, *262*
Phenacomys orophilus, 16, *133-134*
Phloeotomus pileatus abieticola, 18, *334-337*
Phoebe, Black, 18, 26, 27, 28, *362-363*, 499
  Say, 35, *362*, 598
Phrynosoma blainvillii frontale, 21, *630*
Pica nuttalli, 376
  pica hudsonia, 18, *376-379*
Picket-pin, 88
Picoides arcticus, 18, *326-327*
Pigeon, Band-tailed, 7, 17, 23, 29, 30, *275-278*, 301, 307, 382, 398, 674, 719, pl. 4
Pinicola enucleator californica, 19, *419-420*
Pintail, *254*
Pipilo crissalis carolae, 19, *480-481*
  maculatus, *477-479*
  maculatus curtatus, 19, *477*, 478
  maculatus falcinellus, 19, *477*, 478
Pipistrelle, Merriam, 52
Pipistrellus hesperus merriami, 15, *57-58*
Pipit, 375, 376, 441, 503, 543
  American, 34, *542-543*
Piranga ludoviciana, 19, *493-497*
Pisobia minutilla, *263*
Pituophis catenifer heermanni, 21, *643-645*
Planesticus migratorius propinquus, 21, *605-614*
Plestiodon skiltonianus, 21, *633-635*
Podilymbus podiceps, *248*
Polioptila caerulea obscura, 21, *593-595*
Pooecetes gramineus, *440-442*
  gramineus affinis, *440*
  gramineus confinis, 19, *440*
Poor-will, California, 344
  Dusky, 18, *343*, 344, 345
  Nuttall, 18, *343*, 345, 719
Poor-wills, *343-345*
Porcupine, Yellow-haired, 5, 16, *151-154*, 680, 710
Procyon lotor psora, 15, *81-82*

Progne subis hesperia, *497*
Pronghorn, 242
Psaltriparus minimus californicus, 20, *579-582*
  plumbeus, *582*
Puma, 95

Q

Quail, Mountain, 17, 28, 31, 32, 33, 35, 80, *267-269*, 271, 272, 273
  Valley, 17, 26, 27, 28, 80, 100, 267, *270-272*, 313, 714
Querquedula cyanoptera, *253-254*

R

Rabbit, California Jack, 17, *221*, 222, 223
  Desert Jack, 5, 9, 17, *221*
  Mariposa Brush, 5, 17, *228-231*
  Sacramento Cottontail, 5, 229
  Sierra White-tailed Jack, 17, *224-226*, 680
  Snowshoe, 224, 225
  Washington Cottontail, 5
  White-tailed Jack, 222, 225, 226
Rabbits, Black-tailed Jack, *221-224*
Racer, Blue, 643
  California Striped, 21, 531, 627, 637, *641-642*
  Western Yellow-bellied, 637, *643*
  Yellow-bellied, 643
Raccoon, 313
Rail, Virginia, *260-261*
Rallus virginianus, *260-261*
Rana aurora draytonii, 21, *666*
  boylii boylii, 21, *663*, 665
  boylii sierrae, 21, *663*, 665
Rat, Alexandrine, *103-104*
  Alexandrine Roof, 116
  Black, 103
  Brown, 103
  Bushy-tailed Wood, 83, 89, 117, 161, 220
  Gray Bushy-tailed Wood, 16, 116, *120-122*, 680, 708
  Heermann Kangaroo, 5, 16, 145, *146*, 147, 148, 714
  Kangaroo, 313
  Merced Kangaroo, 5, 16, 145, *146*, 147, 693
  Norway, 103
  Pale-faced Kangaroo, 5, 9, 16, 145, *146*, 147
  Roof, 103
  Streator Wood, 16, 100, 104, *116-120*, 122, 198, 672, 674
Rats, Kangaroo, *146-149*
Rattlesnake, 640, 643, 644
  Pacific, 21, 165, *645-650*, 714, 738
Rattus rattus alexandrinus, *103-104*
Raven, Western, *392*
Red-wing, 400-407, 408, 413, 415
  Bi-colored, 402
Regulus calendula cineraceus, 21, *589-593*
  satrapa olivaceus, 21, *586-589*
Reithrodontomys megalotis longicauda, 16, *114-115*
Road-runner, 17, *313*, 633

Robin, Oregon, 615
  Western, 21, 23, 27, 28, 29, 30, 31, 32, 33, 34, 35, 100, 167, 286, 358, 396, 598, *605-614*, 615, 670, 734
Rough-leg, Ferruginous, 288

S

Sable, American, 82
Sage-hen, 7, 9, 17, *274-275*
Salamander, Arboreal, 21, 627, *653*
  Mount Lyell, 21, 627, *652*, 653, 740
  Slender, 21, 653, *654*
Salpinctes obsoletus obsoletus, 20, *550-552*
Sandpiper, Least, 263
  Spotted, 34, *263-265*, 680
Sapsucker, Red-breasted, 329, 330, 333, 354, 591, 613
  Red-naped, *330*
  Sierra Red-breasted, 18, 31, *327-330*, 331, pl. 5
  Williamson, 7, 18, 33, 34, *331-334*, pl. 5
Sayornis nigricans, 18, *362-363*
  sayus, *362*
Scapanus latimanus, *43-46*
  latimanus campi, 15, *43*
  latimanus monoensis, 15, *43*
  latimanus sericatus, 15, *43*
Scaphiopus hammondii hammondii, 21, *654-655*
Sceloporus graciosus graciosus, 21, 627, *628-630*
  occidentalis, *626-628*, 629, 635
  occidentalis bi-seriatus, 21, *626*
  occidentalis occidentalis, 21, *626*, 627
  occidentalis taylori, 21, *626*, 628, 629
Sciurus douglasii albolimbatus, 17, 163, *203-211*
  griseus griseus, 17, 163, *196-203*
Scotiaptex nebulosa nebulosa, 17, *305-307*
Selasphorus alleni, *355-356*
  rufus, *354-355*, 356
Sheep, Domestic, 244, 245
  Mountain, 241, 243
  Sierra Mountain, 232
  Sierra Nevada Mountain, *243-246*
Shoveller, *254*
Shrew, Adorned, 5, 15, *47*, 48, 674
  Dusky, 15, *47*, 48, 49, 50, 685
  Lyell, *47*
  Navigator, 15, *50-51*, 685
  Sierra Nevada, 15, *47*, 50
  Yosemite, 5, 15, *47*, 50, 676, 685
Shrews, *47-50*
Shrike, California, 20, 26, 27, *506*, 507, 508, 730
  Loggerhead, 506
  White-rumped, 20, *506*
Shrikes, *506-508*
Sialia currucoides, 21, *622-625*
  mexicanus occidentalis, 21, *615-622*
Siskin, Pine, 19, 23, 29, 31, 32, 33, 34, 436, *438-439*, 678
Sitta canadensis, 20, *568-570*
  carolinensis aculeata, 20, *564-568*
  pygmaea pygmaea, 20, *571*

Skink, Western, 21, *633-635*, 640, 674, 737, pl. 12
Skunk, California Spotted, 15, *90-91*
  Hydrophobia, 90
  Little Spotted, 90, 91
  Spotted, 81
  Striped, 15, 90, *91-92*, 98
Snake, Black, 643
  Boyle King, 21, *640-641*
  Bull, 643
  Coral King, 21, 627, *640*, 641, 674, pl. 12
  Giant Garter, *636*, 637
  Milk, 641
  Mountain Garter, 21, *636*
  Pacific Garter, 21, *636*
  Rubber, 21, 627, *635-636*
  Valley Gopher, 21, *643-645*, 738
  Wandering Garter, *636*, 639
  Western Gopher, 165
  Western Ring-necked, 21, *639*
Snakes, Garter, *636-639*
  Water, 637
Snipe, Wilson, *263*
Solitaire, 420
  Townsend, 7, 21, 25, 30, 31, 32, 33, 419, *595-599*, 609, 613, 621, 734, pl. 11
Sorex, *47-50*
  lyelli, *47*, 48
  montereyensis mariposae, 15, *47*, 48
  obscurus obscurus, 15, *47*, 48
  ornatus, 15, *47*, 48
  vagrans amoenus, 15, *47*, 48
Sparrow, Alberta Fox, *473*
  Aleutian Savannah, *442*
  Bell, 7, 19, 80, *464-466*, 467, 468, 672, pl. 8
  Black-chinned, 453, *458*
  Brewer, 7, 19, 35, 453, *456-457*, 682, pl. 8
  Chipping, 454, 456, 458, 464, 494
  English, 27, *439-440*
  Forbush, 470, 471
  Fox, 448, 472, 477
  Gambel, 447
  Golden-crowned, 26, 27, 30, 32, 448, *450-452*, 474, 484, 617, pl. 8
  Heermann Song, *469*
  Hudsonian White-crowned, 7, 19, 33, 34, 35, 132, *446*, 447, 449, 680
  Intermediate, 27, 447, 448, 449, 450, 451, 474, pl. 8
  Intermediate White-crowned, 26, 35, *446*, 447, 450
  Kadiak Fox, 32, *472*
  Lark, 448, 451
  Lincoln, 469, 470, 471
  Mariposa Fox, 7, 19, 31, 32, 33, *473*, 477, 482, 483, 489, 613, 725
  Merrill Song, *469*
  Modoc Song, 19, 35, *468*, 469, 639
  Mono Fox, 7, 19, 35, *473*, 477
  Nevada Sage, 7, 19, 35, *466*, 467, 682, pl. 8
  Nevada Savannah, 19, 35, *442*, 443, pl. 8
  Northeastern Lincoln, 32, 33, *470*, 471, 726
  Northwestern Lincoln, 19, 26, *470*, 471

  Oregon Vesper, *440*, 441
  Rufous-crowned, 19, 80, *467-468*, pl. 8
  Rusty Song, *469*
  Savannah, 441
  Shumagin Fox, *472*
  Slate-colored Fox, *473*
  Thick-billed Fox, *473*
  Valdez Fox, *473*
  Western Chipping, 19, 22, 23, 26, 27, 28, 29, 30, 31, 32, 33, 34, *452-456*, 457, 460, 461, 579, 642, 661, 680, pl. 8
  Western Grasshopper, 19, *443*, pl. 8
  Western Lark, 19, 26, 27, 28, 35, *444-446*, 483
  Western Savannah, 441, *442*
  Western Vesper, 19, 35, *440*, 441, 444
  White-crowned, 88, 420, 430, 440, 446, 470, 474, 483, pl. 8
Sparrows, Fox, *472-477*
  Lincoln, *470-472*
  Savannah, *442-443*, 446
  Song, *468-470*, 473
  Vesper, *440-442*
  White-crowned, *446-450*, 451
Spatula clypeata, *254*
Speotyto cunicularia hypogaea, 17, *310-311*
Sphyrapicus thyroideus thyroideus, 18, *331-334*
  varius daggetti, 18, *327-330*
  varius nuchalis, *330*
Spilogale phenax phenax, 15, *90-91*
Spinus pinus pinus, 19, *438-439*
Spizella atrogularis, *458*
  breweri, 19, *456-457*
  passerina arizonae, 19, *452-456*
Spoonbill, 254
Sprig, 254
Squirrel, Belding, 169, 174
  Belding Ground, 5, 16, 88, 94, 162, 163, *168-173*, 174, 175, 176, 680, pl. 2
  Bummer, 204
  California Gray, 17, *196-203*, 204, 209, 305, 382, 384, 414, 674, 704, 705
  California Ground, 16, 76, 94, 159, *162-168*, 170, 171, 174, 176, 197, 577, 597, 674
  Douglas, 204
  Golden-mantled Ground, 76, 109, 163, 680
  Gray, 100, 101, 182, 196-203, 415
  Pine, 204
  Red, 88, 182, 184, 196, 198, 203, 213
  Sierra Flying, 17, *211-215*, 323, 678
  Sierra Nevada Golden-mantled Ground, 16, *173-176*, pl. 2
  Stephens Ground, 164
  Stephens Soft-haired Ground, 9, 16, *173*
Steganopus tricolor, *262*
Stelgidopteryx serripennis, 20, *503*
Stellula calliope, 18, *356-358*
Sterna forsteri, *251*
Strix occidentalis occidentalis, 17, *304-305*
Sturnella neglecta, 19, *409-411*
Swallow, Barn, 20, 26, 27, 498, *499-500*, 722

Cliff, 19, 27, 426, *497-499*, 500, 722, 724
Northern Violet-green, 20, 27, 28, 29, *501-503*, 722
Rough-winged, 20, 498, *503*
Tree, 20, 498, *500-501*
Violet-green, 291, 350, 352, 498, 501, 502
Swift, Black, 349
Northern Black, 18, *349-350*
Vaux, *350*
White-throated, 18, 28, 29, 31, *351-352*, 501, 722
Sylvilagus audubonii audubonii, 17, *227-228*
bachmani mariposae, 17, *228-231*
nuttallii nuttallii, 17, *227-228*

T

Tachycineta thalassina lepida, 20, *501-503*
Tanager Louisiana, 494
Western, 19, 27, 28, 29, 30, 31, 32, 35, 286, 385, 477, *493-497*, 510
Taxidea taxus neglecta, 15, *92-95*
Teal, Cinnamon, *253-254*
Telmatodytes palustris plesius, *560-561*
Tern, Black, *251*
Forster, *251*
Thamnophis, *636-639*
ordinoides couchii, *636*
ordinoides elegans, 21, *636*
ordinoides vagrans, *636*
sirtalis infernalis, 21, *636*
Thomomys, *134-143*
alpinus awahnee, 16, *135*, 139, 303
bottae mewa, 16, 134, *135*, 138, 139
bottae pascalis, 16, 134, *135*, 138, 139
monticola monticola, 16, 76, *135*, 138, 139
quadratus fisheri, 16, *135*, 139
Thrasher, California, 7, 20, 27, 78, 377, 545, *548-550*, 597, 672
Sage, 20, 35, *546-547*, 682
Thrush, Alaska Hermit, 30, 31, *602*, 603, 617
Dwarf Hermit, *602*, 603
Hermit, 473, 600
Northern Varied, 31, 32, *614-615*
Russet-backed, 21, 26, 27, 29, 31, 371, *600-601*, 602, 603, pl. 11
Sierra Hermit, 21, 29, 31, 32, 33, 34, *602*, 603, 604, 609, 680, pl. 11
Varied, 599, 602, 615
Thrushes, Hermit, *602-605*
Thryomanes bewicki drymoecus, 20, *555-556*
Titmouse, Plain, 7, 20, 27, 28, 291, 548, *572-574*, 575, 592, 620, 670
Toad, California, 21, 165, 313, *655-657*, 658, 664, 740
California Horned, 21, 627, *630*
Northwestern, 655, 656, 657
Spade-foot, 627, 655, 664
Western Spade-foot, 21, *654-655*, 740
Yosemite, 21, 655, *657-660*, 664, 740

Towhee, Brown, 422, 480, 481, 573
Green-tailed, 19, 31, 32, 33, 34, 35, 473, 476, *482-484*, 682, 725, 726
Nevada Spurred, 19, *477*
Northern Brown, 7, 19, 26, 27, 28, *480-481*, 672
Sacramento Spurred, 19, 26, 27, 28, 29, 30, 31, 32, 286, *477*, 725
Spurred, 88, 303, 384, 460, 478, 479, 481, 482, 605
Towhees, Spurred, *477-479*
Toxostoma redivivum redivivum, 20, *548-550*
Tree-toad, Pacific, 21, *661-663*, 664
Troglodytes aedon parkmani, 20, *556-558*
Turtle, Pacific Mud, 21, *650*
Tyrannus verticalis, 18, *359-360*
Tyto pratincola, 17, *298*

U

Urocyon cinereoargenteus californicus, 15, *78-80*
Ursus americanus, 15, *63-68*
henshawi, *68-71*

V

Vermivora celata, *519-520*
celata lutescens, 20, *519*
celata orestera, 20, *519*
ruficapilla gutturalis, 20, *516-519*
Vireo, California Least, 7, 20, 26, 27, 509, *514-516*, 727, 728
Cassin, 7, 20, 23, 27, 28, 29, 30, 31, 32, 33, 305, 373, 385, 509, *511-513*, 579, 674, 727
Hutton, 7, 20, 27, 28, 31, 305, 509, *513-514*, 590, 727
Least, 403, 513, 514, 515, 539
Warbling, 512, 513, 579
Western Warbling, 20, 23, 26, 28, 29, 30, 31, 32, 33, 305, 372, 385, *508-510*, 511, 518, 676, 727
Vireo belli pusillus, 20, *514-516*
huttoni huttoni, 20, *513-514*
Vireosylva gilva swainsoni, 20, *508-510*
Vole, Cantankerous, 130
Vulpes cascadensis, 15, *77*
macrotis mutica, 15, *77-78*
Vulture, Turkey, 17, 26, 27, *279-281*, 292, 293, 720

W

Warbler, Alaska Myrtle, *523-524*, 526, 527
Alaska Pileolated, 35, *540*, 541
Audubon, 20, 23, 27, 29, 30, 31, 32, 33, 34, 35, 60, 286, 385, 516, 517, 518, 523, *524-529*, 530, 533, 581, 591, 618, 670, 678, pl. 9
Black-throated Gray, 7, 20, 28, 29, 30, 31, 305, 516, 517, 518, *529-531*, 533, 579, 642, 674, pl. 9
Calaveras, 7, 20, 23, 29, 31, 32, 33, *516-519*, 520, 532, 534, pl. 9

California Yellow, 20, 23, 26, 27, 28, 29, 31, 35, 286, 492, *521-523*, 676, pl. 9
Eastern Orange-crowned, 519
Golden Pileolated, 20, 31, 32, 33, 516, *540*, 542, pl. 9
Hermit, 20, 23, 29, 31, 32, 516, 517, 518, 527, *532-533*, pl. 9
Lutescent, 20, 33, *519*, 520, 521, 528, pl. 9
Macgillivray, 534
Myrtle, 524, 526
Orange-crowned, 26, 520
Pileolated, 35, 517, 518, 534, 541
Rocky Mountain Orange-crowned, 20, 35, *519*, 520
Tolmie, 7, 20, 29, 32, 35, 516, 517, 518, *534-538*, 541, 728, pl. 9
Townsend, 27, 35, 530, *531*, 532
Yellow, 284, 403, 516, 517, 518, 520, 521, 522, 541, 549
Warblers, Orange-crowned, *519-520*
Pileolated, *540-542*
Waxwing, Bohemian, *504*
Cedar, *504-505*, 621
Weasel, California, 86
Least, 89, 192, 220
Mountain, 15, *86-89*, 93, 158, 173, 220, 680
Sierra Least, 5, 15, 87, *89*
Yellow-cheeked, 86
Widgeon, American, 253
Wildcat, 269, 271
California, 15, *99-101*, 614, 674
Wilsonia pusilla, *540-542*
pusilla chryseola, 20, *540*, 541
pusilla pileolata, *540*, 541
Wolverine, Sierra Nevada, 5, 15, *85-86*, 95, 690
Woodpecker, Arctic Three-toed, 7, 18, *326-327*, 680, pl. 5
California, 18, 26, 27, 28, 29, 30, 291, 305, 317, 329, 331, *337-341*, 354, 385, 670, 674, pl. 5
Downy, 317
Hairy, 327
Lewis, 26, 27, 35, 340, *341-342*, pl. 5
Modoc, 17, 28, 29, 30, 32, 33, 34, *315-317*, 318, 319, 321, 676, pl. 5

Northern Pileated, 18, 32, *334-337*
Northern White-headed, 18, 28, *320-326*, pl. 5
Nuttall, 7, 18, 27, 316, *319-320*
Pileated, 335, 337
White-headed, 38, 320-325, 331, 567, 577
Willow, 18, 23, 28, 30, 316, *317-319*, 320, 329, 385, 676, pl. 5
Wren, Bewick, 555, 556, 617
Cañon, 551, 552
Dotted Cañon, 20, 27, 28, 29, 30, 31, *552-555*, 730
House, 555, 557
Parkman, 23, 556
Rock, 20, 27, 34, *550-552*, 553
San Joaquin, 555, 557
San Joaquin Bewick, 7, 20, 26, 27, 28, 468, *555-556*, 557, 730
Vigors, 555
Western House, 20, 26, 28, 35, 470, 510, *556-558*, 732
Western Marsh, *560-561*
Western Winter, 7, 20, 31, *558-560*, 561
Winter, 117, 557, 559
Wren-tit, 363, 391, 467, 617
Pallid, 7, 20, 27, 28, 30, *582-586*, 672

X

Xanthocephalus xanthocephalus, *399-400*
Xenopicus albolarvatus albolarvatus, 18, *320-326*

Y

Yellowthroat, Tule, 20, 26, *538*, 539
Western, 35, *538*, pl. 9
Yellowthroats, 403, *538-539*

Z

Zamelodia melanocephala capitalis, 19, *484-490*
Zapus pacificus alleni, 16, *149-151*
Zenaidura macroura marginella, 17, *278-279*
Zonotrichia coronata, *450-452*
leucophrys, *446-450*
leucophrys gambeli, *446*, 447, 450
leucophrys leucophrys, 19, *446*, 447